GAR

C000024559

OF ENGLAND AND WALES
OPEN FOR CHARITY

St Paul's Walden Bury, Hertfordshire, the childhood home of Her Majesty Queen Elizabeth The Queen Mother

A guide to over 3,300 gardens, the majority of which are not normally open to the public

2000

© The National Gardens Scheme 2000
Illustrations © Val Biro 2000
The copyright in the photographs belongs to the individual photographers.

All rights reserved. No part of this publication may be transferred to any other medium by any means or in any form or be reproduced or transmitted in any form by any means electronic or mechanical including photocopying, recording or any other information storage and retrieval system without prior written permission from the Publisher.

Published by the National Gardens Scheme
Hatchlands Park, East Clandon, Guildford,
Surrey GU4 7RT

Editor: The Director, National Gardens Scheme

Front cover photograph by Clive Boursnell

The drawings by Val Biro that decorate this book are from *The Sunday Telegraph Gardening Book* by Fred Whitsey and *Garden Glory* by Ted Humphris. Val's work will be familiar to readers from the many *Yellow Book* covers he has designed since 1966. He is also a writer and illustrator of children's stories. The 37th title in his *Gumdrop* series, about his vintage car, will be published this year.

A catalogue record for this book is available from the British Library.

Data manipulation, image setting, printing and binding by Unwin Brothers Ltd, Old Woking, Surrey

Typeset in Linotype Bell Centennial

Trade Distributors: Portfolio, Unit 1C, West Ealing Business Centre, Alexandria Road, London W13 0NJ

ISBN 0-900558-32-6

ISSN 1365-0572

The National Gardens Scheme Charitable Trust
Hatchlands Park, East Clandon, Guildford,
Surrey GU4 7RT

Tel 01483 211535 Fax 01483 211537

Website www.ngs.org.uk

Registered Charity no. 279284

ENJOY THEM AT PARTICIPATING NGS GARDENS

There is no better way to enjoy the world's finest teas than in the beautiful surroundings of a National Gardens Scheme garden. Jacksons of Piccadilly supports the NGS, by offering gardens the opportunity to serve a selection of their teas to visitors during their garden open days. So during your visit, take time to relax with a cup of your favourite Jacksons speciality tea.

The full range of Jacksons of Piccadilly teas is available at independent grocers, delicatessens and fine food stores nationwide.

Contents

Photographic acknowledgements

Front cover, St Paul's Walden Bury, Hertfordshire	Clive Boursnell
Back cover, Newbiggin Hall and High Cleabarrow, both Cumbria	Val Corbett
Chairman's portrait	Derek St Romaine
Saltmarshe Hall, Yorkshire	Suzanne Shacklock
Misarden Park, Gloucestershire	Andrew Lawson
Chidmere, Sussex	Consie Dunn
Old Rectory, Sudborough, Northamptonshire	Andrew Lawson
Moleshill House, Surrey	Derek St Romaine
Croft House, Lincolnshire	Brian Chapple
Lady Elizabeth Bowes Lyon and the Hon. David Bowes Lyon	courtesy of Mr and Mrs Simon Bowes Lyon
Lady Elizabeth Bowes Lyon and her father, the Earl of Strathmore and Kinghorne	PA Photos
Lady Elizabeth Bowes Lyon and the Duke of York	Camera Press
Her Majesty Queen Elizabeth and the Women's Land Army	Camera Press
Her Majesty Queen Elizabeth The Queen Mother visits a rose walk in St James's Park	Ron Bell, PA Photos
Her Majesty Queen Elizabeth, a welcome garden visitor	PA Photos
Ash Tree House, Yorkshire	Brian Chapple
Mill House, Glandyfi	Alex Ramsay
Holt Farm, Somerset	Mark Bolton
Dalemain, Cumbria	Val Corbett
Hill House, Suffolk	Alan Munson
Sticky Wicket, Dorset	Andrew Lawson
Polgwynne, Cornwall	Brian Chapple
Stone House Cottage, Worcestershire	Marianne Majerus
North Court, Isle of Wight	Oliver Mathews
286 Handley Road, Derbyshire	Mike Vardy

Carr Sheppards Crosthwaite and the National Gardens Scheme

It is now seven years since we first became supporters of the National Gardens Scheme. As long established investment managers and stockbrokers, we decided to sponsor the 'Yellow Book' because we felt that the vision, patience and hard work which goes into these gardens have some parallels in the way we continue to advise our private clients in these turbulent and often inexplicable times.

Now we have extended our support by sponsoring the National Gardens Scheme's innovative and informative web site. We are proud to be associated with you and we hope our happy relationship will continue for many years.

Fred Carr

Fred Carr, Chief Executive

CARR SHEPPARDS CROSTHWAITE

2 Gresham Street, London EC2V 7QN

Carr Sheppards Crosthwaite is a member of the London Stock Exchange and regulated by the Securities and Futures Authority.

A member of the Investec Group.

A message from the Chairman

In this year of the millennium we pay special tribute to Her Majesty Queen Elizabeth The Queen Mother whose continuous support as our Patron has been an inspiration and encouragement to us all.

Whether we garden or not, all of us can enjoy some memorable visits to the wide range of fine gardens listed in this book. Some families have been opening for over 60 years and their gardens remain as fresh and inspiring as ever; others are listed for the first time. This is because they have attained the high standards of quality and interest that are the hallmarks of the National Gardens Scheme.

Our heartfelt thanks go to our Garden Owners who are both generous and dedicated. By visiting one of their gardens you will not only have a wonderful day out but you will also help to swell the amount of money which we can pass on to our charities.

Trevarno

ESTATE AND GARDENS

An historic and tranquil haven protected and unspoilt for 700 years. Experience the magical atmosphere of Trevarno, an original and fascinating Cornish Estate.

- ◆ Beautiful Victorian and Georgian Gardens.
- ◆ Extensive collection of rare shrubs and trees.
- ◆ Numerous garden features and follies.
- ◆ Fascinating Gardening Museum including an intriguing collection of tools and implements.
- ◆ Splendid Fountain Garden Conservatory - enjoy the plants and refreshments whatever the weather.
- ◆ Walled Gardens, Woodland Walks and abundant Wildlife.
- ◆ Follow the progress of major restoration and conservation projects.

Enquiries: 01326 574274
Trevarno Manor, Trevarno Estate, Helston, Cornwall, TR13 0RU
Open: all year round 10.30-17.00 hrs, except Christmas Day.
Admission: Adults £3.50. OAPs/Disabled £3.20. U14 £1.25. U5 free.
Group Visits: Welcome, prior booking helpful.
Facilities: Part Disabled Access, Indoor Fountain Garden, Plant Sales/Bee Centre/Handmade Soap, Refreshments, Toilets, Dogs on leads, Car & Coach Park.
Directions: OS Ref SW6423902. Leave Helston on Penzance road, signed from B3302 junction and north of Crowntown village.

Trevarno - the Renaissance of a surviving Cornish Estate

About the National Gardens Scheme

What precisely is the National Gardens Scheme?

To put it at its simplest, it's a very British way of having your cake and eating it – of having a good time while also doing good.

It began back in 1927 when Miss Elsie Wagg of the Queen's Nursing Institute had the bright idea of raising funds for that charity by persuading people to open their private gardens to the public for the grand sum of 'a shilling a head'. From those modest beginnings – with only a few mostly large-scale gardens opening for the benefit of a single charity – it has grown to become nothing less than a national institution, with almost three and a half thousand gardens, of every possible size and style, giving over a million pounds a year to nearly a dozen charities.

Do you need to be a devoted gardener to be interested in all of this?

No, you don't. The gardens which open for the NGS certainly include some of the most outstanding in the country (many of them offering Plant Sales frequently with rare plants at remarkably low prices) but you don't need to be expert, or even interested in the details of the plants or planting, to be able to enjoy an NGS garden simply as a beautiful and relaxing place in which to spend an afternoon. There are even people who visit particular gardens as much for the delicious home-made teas which are often on offer as for the gardens themselves!

And always, at the back of your mind when you visit an NGS garden, is the pleasant knowledge that your money (usually around £2 nowadays, rather than 5p or 'a shilling') is going to help a whole range of good causes from cancer care to nurses' welfare.

For thousands of people, each year's issue of the NGS Yellow Book, listing all of the gardens open under the scheme in England and Wales, has come to be as much a sign of the arrival of spring as the arrival of the first swallow. And while one swallow may not make a summer, one Yellow Book certainly does!

By Tim Longville
Writer and gardener

Roger Platts

Garden Design & Nurseries

Award winning design, inspirational advice, and an exciting selection of plants including large specimens.

The Spout Garden. RHS Gold Medal Chelsea Flower Show 1997

Craftsman built traditional pergolas and small buildings constructed in green oak - in complete harmony with formal and informal gardens.

Roger Platts Garden Design & Nurseries
Stick Hill Edenbridge Kent TN8 5NH
Tel/Fax: 01732 863318
Email: plattsgdn@aol.com

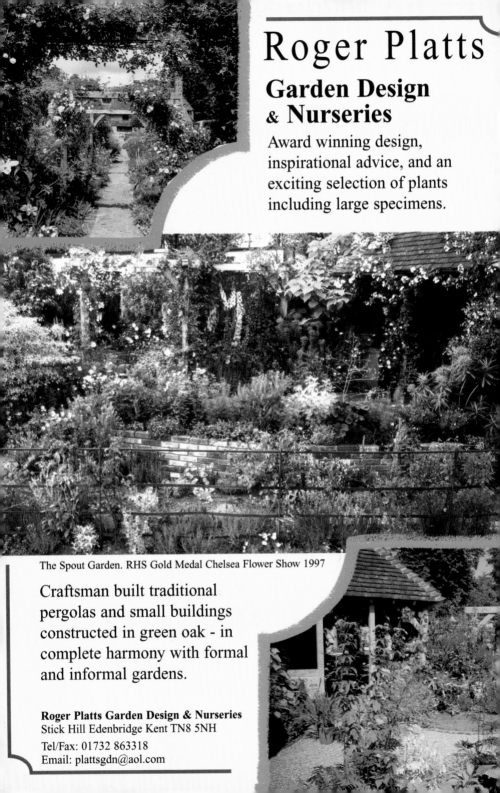

Patron, President and Council of the National Gardens Scheme Charitable Trust

Patron	Her Majesty Queen Elizabeth The Queen Mother
President	Her Royal Highness Princess Alice, Duchess of Gloucester
Vice-Presidents	Lady Heald CBE; Mrs Christopher Hussey; Mrs Alan Hardy OBE VMH; Mrs Charles Budden; Edmund de Rothschild CBE TD; Mrs Nigel Azis; Mrs Graeme Anton; Michael Toynbee JP, DL
Trustees	Mrs Maureen Acland OBE; Algernon Heber-Percy; Henry Boyd-Carpenter CVO
Chairman of Council	Mrs Daphne Foulsham
Vice-Chairman of Council	Mrs Ann Trevor-Jones

The Council (* County Team)

Mrs Maureen Acland OBE (The Queen's Nursing Institute)
Mrs Carol Lindsay*
Mrs Bridget Marshall*
Mrs Angela Baker*
Christopher Melluish (Hon Treasurer)
Henry Boyd-Carpenter CVO
John Paton OBE (GRBS & RGOF)
Mrs Jill Cowley*
Nicholas Payne*
Colin Ellis (The Royal Horticultural Society)
Julian Prideaux OBE (The National Trust)
Mrs Daphne Foulsham*
Mrs Sue Rathbone*
Algernon Heber-Percy
Mrs Jane Streatfeild*
Mrs Judy Johnson*
Mrs Ann Trevor-Jones*

The Director	Clive Barham Carter
Head Office	Hatchlands Park, East Clandon, Guildford, Surrey GU4 7RT Tel 01483 211535 Fax 01483 211537 Website www.ngs.org.uk
Auditor	Gilbert Allen & Co, Church Down, Bordyke, Tonbridge TN9 1NR
Solicitor	Radcliffes, 5 Great College Street, London SW1P 3SJ
Bankers	Royal Bank of Scotland Plc, 10 North St, Guildford, Surrey GU1 4AF

Save £5 · Save £5 · Save £5 · Save £5 · Save £5 · Save £5 · Save £

Step into a world of

Membership of the Royal Horticultural Society is the gardeners' guide to inspirational gardens and gardening knowledge. With free admission to 40 wonderful gardens, privileged tickets to the world's most famous flower shows, and a copy of *The Garden* magazine every month, RHS Membership offers you the inspiration and advice to achieve your gardening aspirations.

Membership normally costs £35 for 12 months, which includes a one-off £7 joining fee. But if you join today, you can take advantage of a special introductory saving of £5 – meaning you pay just £30.

Outstanding benefits for gardeners

To see if you would enjoy being a Member, simply take a look at the special Membership benefits listed opposite and tick all those which appeal to you.

If you have ticked more than two boxes, then we feel sure you will enjoy RHS Membership.

Joining couldn't be easier

Simply call us today on ☎ 020 7821 3000 (quoting code 1556) or complete and return the application form opposite. This offer is valid until 31 October 2000.

THE ROYAL HORTICULTURAL SOCIETY

inspirational gardens

Enjoy all these benefits with RHS Membership

- FREE monthly copy of *The Garden* magazine (worth £33). ❑
- FREE entry for you and a guest to RHS Gardens Wisley, Rosemoor and Hyde Hall. ❑
- FREE entry to a further 37 beautiful gardens. ❑
- Privileged tickets to Chelsea and Hampton Court Palace Flower Shows. ❑
- FREE gardening advice from the RHS experts. ❑
- Privileged admission to the RHS Flower Show at Tatton Park, the Spring Gardening Show Malvern, BBC Gardeners' World Live. ❑
- Discounted admission to hundreds of demonstrations, workshops, talks and garden tours throughout Britain. ❑
- FREE entry to the monthly RHS London Flower Shows. ❑
- FREE seeds from RHS Garden Wisley. ❑
- Access to the famous Lindley Library.

Join today ☎ 020 7821 3000

(Please quote code 1556)

The credit card hotline is open from 9.00am to 5.00pm, Monday to Friday.

RHS Membership Offer – Save £5

Title *Surname* *Initials*

Address

Postcode *Daytime Tel. No.*

☐ I enclose a cheque for £30 made payable to The Royal Horticultural Society

☐ Please debit my RHS Mastercard / Mastercard / Visa / Diners / AmEx

Card No. ☐☐☐☐ ☐☐☐☐ ☐☐☐☐ ☐☐☐☐

Expiry ☐ / ☐ Signature ☐ Code 1556

Please return this form to The Royal Horticultural Society, Membership Department, PO Box 313, London SW1P 2PE
This offer is valid until 31 October 2000.

Save £5 · Save £5 · Save £5 · Save £5 · Save £5 · Save £5 · Save £

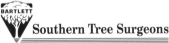

BARTLETT

Southern Tree Surgeons

The F.A. Bartlett Tree Expert Co. Limited

Visit us at our website at
www.southerntreesurgeons.com

For your nearest branch call our Head Office - (01342) 717171

Bedfordshire/Cambridgeshire	(01234) 354673
Cheshire/Staffordshire	(01625) 890150, (01619) 415921 or (01538) 384877
Gloucestershire/Oxfordshire	(01285) 652421, (01823) 252595, or (01722) 339811
London S./Surrey/Sussex	(01342) 712215
London W./Home Counties	(01494) 677889
London N./Hertfordshire	(01923) 850322

The F.A. Bartlett Tree Expert Co. Limited trading as Southern Tree Surgeons
Registered Off.: Bouverie Hse, 1st Fl., 154 Fleet St., London EC4A 2DQ. Registered in England under No 2850930

Charities supported by the National Gardens Scheme:

- **The Queen's Nursing Institute**
  for the welfare of elderly and needy district nurses
- **County Nursing Associations**
  for support to retired and needy nurses
- **The Nurses' Welfare Service**
  for assistance to nurses in personal difficulty
- **Macmillan Cancer Relief**
  for the provision and training of Macmillan cancer nurses
- **Marie Curie Cancer Care**
  for the care of people with cancer
- **Help the Hospices**
  for support to the hospice movement throughout the country
- **Crossroads**
  for practical support and respite care for carers
- **The National Trust**
  Careership Bursaries – for the education and training of gardeners
  Gardens Fund – for the restoration of historic gardens
- **The Gardeners' Royal Benevolent Society**
  for assistance to retired gardeners
- **The Royal Gardeners' Orphan Fund**
  for assistance to the orphans of gardeners
- **Additional charities nominated by owners (ACNO)**
  in total, about 1000 Registered Charities or charitable causes which are defined as 'for the relief of poverty, religion, education or other purposes beneficial to the community'
- **Other charities as decided from time to time by Council**

IN THE HEART OF ENGLAND'S GARDEN

Our three magnificent Elite Hotels enjoy spectacular settings in Southern England. For the serious horticulturist or the enthusiastic amateur, we have a wealth of famous gardens and historic mansions close by in addition to secret, sunken and classically designed gardens within our own grounds.

Each hotel displays individual charm and character and offers discerning guests spacious and exquisitely furnished accommodation and extensive leisure facilities.

Our award-winning restaurants all boast two rosettes and offer the finest cuisine and wine selections.

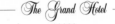

Ashdown Park Hotel and Country Club
★★★★
Wych Cross, Nr Forest Row
East Sussex, RH18 5JR
Telephone +44 (0)1342 824988
Facsimile +44 (0)1342 826206
E-mail reservations@ashdownpark.co.uk
Website www.ashdownpark.co.uk

Tylney Hall
★★★★
Rotherwick, Hook,
Hampshire RG27 9AZ
Telephone +44 (0)1256 764881
Facsimile +44 (0)1256 768141
E-mail reservations@tylneyhall.com
Website www.tylneyhall.com

The Grand Hotel
★★★★★
King Edwards Parade, Eastbourne
East Sussex BN21 4EQ
Telephone +44 (0)1323 412345
Facsimile +44 (0)1323 412233
E-mail reservations@grandeastbourne.co.uk
Website www.grandeastbourne.co.uk

Elite HOTELS
COUNTRY HOTELS OF DISTINCTION

SLH SMALL LUXURY HOTELS OF THE WORLD

For further information on weekend breaks and special promotions, please telephone the hotel of your choice and enjoy the ultimate in elegance and comfort.

How to use this book

The gardens, most of which are privately owned and open to the public just a few times in the year, are grouped alphabetically by county. Welsh gardens have their own section. Each entry gives: general location and directions (in italics); a brief description written by the owner with the advice of the county team; details of opening times and arrangements. The diary at the start of each county gives a summary of openings, with a map and contact details for the county team. There is a general map on page 20 and an index of gardens on page 437.

Visiting the gardens

Please remember that most of these gardens are private property. They may not be adapted for public visiting, since they are open only rarely through the generosity and enthusiasm of their owners. Please treat them sensibly, stay on the marked paths, avoid hazards and take care not to damage plants. Most garden owners are happy to share their knowledge and experience. Please be considerate – they will have put a very great deal of work into the opening and may be extremely busy.

Symbols, labels and notes

NEW	Opening this year for the first time
❀	Plants/produce usually for sale. If proceeds go elsewhere this will be shown
♿	Wheelchair access to at least the main features of the garden
(no dogs symbol)	No dogs except assistance dogs
TEA	Tea and biscuits normally available, at a charge.
TEAS	Tea and home-made cake normally available, at a charge.
TEAS in aid of	Part, or all, of the proceeds goes to the organisation named
Open by appointment	Please do not be put off by this. Some gardens can only accommodate small parties, some have limited parking space, some may only be able to cope with small numbers on particular days: all will be pleased to see visitors by prior arrangement, some may set a minimum number
ACNO	stands for 'Additional Charity Nominated by Owner'. The owners of these gardens contribute a proportion of the money collected to the charity named, which is their personal choice.

Some gardens, which open to the public on a regular or commercial basis also kindly contribute to the Scheme in various ways. They are distinguished as follows:

■	Regularly opening garden giving specific days to NGS
▲	As above, but for details of other, not NGS, openings please contact garden directly. Some have links to NGS website, www.ngs.org.uk
●	Regularly opening garden giving guaranteed contribution to NGS

All distances and sizes given are approximate. **Coach parties** – only by appointment, please, unless otherwise stated. **Photographs** – taken in a garden may not be used for sale or reproduction without prior permission of the owner. **Lavatories** – are not usually available. **Children** – must be accompanied by an adult. **Dogs** – where allowed, must be on leads unless otherwise stated. **Maps** – are designed to show approximate position. For precise directions see the individual garden entry. **Updates** – every effort is made to ensure that entries are accurate but with so many gardens there will inevitably be last minute changes. These will be advertised locally and recorded on the update line 01483 211535. They will also be found, with details of special events, on the NGS website: www.ngs.org.uk

THE WORLD'S MOST BEAUTIFUL GARDEN MAGAZINE

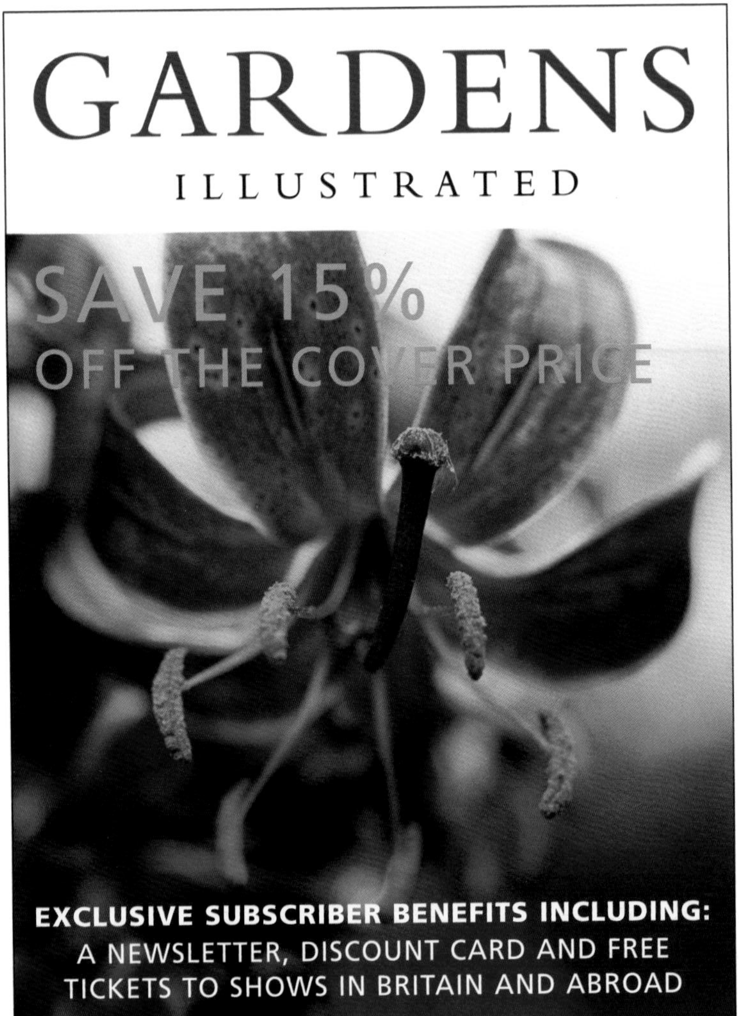

TO SUBSCRIBE FOR JUST £29.50
PLEASE CALL 01454 618905
OFFER AVAILABLE UNTIL DECEMBER 2000 (REF.R130)

MONEY BACK GUARANTEE

ADVANCE ORDER FORM

GARDENS OF ENGLAND AND WALES OPEN FOR CHARITY 2001

Price £5.75 including UK postage (subject to review)
Available internationally on the Internet via www.ngs.org.uk or by enquiry to NGS office (see below)

To: The National Gardens Scheme, Hatchlands Park,
East Clandon, Guildford GU4 7RT
Tel: 01483 211535
Fax: 01483 211537
Email: lhowlett@ngs.org.uk

Please send .... copies of Gardens of England and Wales 2001 for which I enclose PO/Cheque for ....

Name Mr/Mrs/Ms (Block Letters) ....

Address ....

....

....

The books will be posted on publication (Feb/Mar 2001).
If you wish to receive an acknowledgement of your order, please enclose s.a.e.

Trade Terms: Supplies of this book on sale or return can be obtained from our trade distributors; Portfolio, Unit 1c, West Ealing Business Centre, Alexandria Road, London W13 0NJ
Tel: 0208 579 7748
Fax: 0208 567 0904

The National Gardens Scheme is a Registered Charity No. 279284

Garden visiting around the world

Australia

Australia's Open Gardens Scheme, a non-profit organisation founded in 1987, promotes the knowledge and pleasure of gardens and gardening across Australia by opening inspiring private gardens to the public. 35% of the proceeds from entry fees are returned to the garden owner or the charity of their choice. 65% covers AOGS operating costs, with any surplus being returned to the community as grants for garden and horticulture-related projects. **Publication:** *Australia's Open Garden Scheme Guidebook*, published annually in August, available from major booksellers or from the Scheme's head office, lists over 770 gardens open in every state of Australia. **Contact:** Neil Robertson, Chief Executive Officer, National Office, PO Box 87, New Gisborne, Australia 3438

Tel +61 3 5428 4557 Fax +61 3 5428 4558

Email national@opengarden.org.au

Website www.opengarden.abc.net.au

Belgium

Jardins Ouverts-Open Tuinen is a non-profit organisation founded in 1990. Most of the proceeds from entry fees support charities chosen by garden owners. **Publication:** *Catalogue of Belgian Open Gardens*, published annually in March, may be obtained for a one-year membership (valid for two people) at 500 BEF (12,5 Euro, approximately £9) sent to: Post Account 000-1390451-53, 'Jardins Ouverts', Chaussee de Vleurgat, 108, 1000 Brussels. Please ensure your name and address are clearly printed. Around 200 private gardens are listed. **Contact:** Christine de Groote, Jardins Ouverts, 1000 Brussels

Fax +32 (0) 2 646 97 36

England & Wales

The National Gardens Scheme, a registered charity founded in 1927 with proceeds from entry fees support ten nursing, caring and educational charities. Owners may donate up to 25% of the funds they raise to a charity of their choice, and over 1,000 additional charities benefit from the proceeds every year. Over 3,300 gardens open for the Scheme annually. **Publication:** *Gardens of England and Wales Open For Charity* published annually in February, is available from all major booksellers in the UK for £4.50 or through amazon.com, or through the head office. Garden details are on Garden Finder on the Scheme's website www.ngs.org.uk. **Contact:** Clive Barham Carter, Director or Elizabeth Tagge, Public Relations Officer, The National Gardens Scheme, Hatchlands Park, East Clandon, Surrey GU4 7RT

Tel +44 (0) 1483 211535 Fax +44 (0) 1483 211537

Email ngs@ngs.co.uk Website www.ngs.org.uk

Netherlands

De Tuinspeigel is related to the Nederlandse Tuinenstichting (Dutch Gardens Foundation) founded in 1981 to promote the preservation of valuable parks and gardens. **Publication:** *het open tuinenboekje,* published annually, is available from the head office for a donation of Dfl.45 (approx. £13). Over 200 gardens open for the Foundation over one or two week-ends on a non-profit basis. Other gardens not regularly open to the public can only be visited on certain dates. Admission is usually around Dfl. 7,50 (approx. £2). Group arrangements should be made in advance. **Contact:** Karen de Keizer-Van der Lingen Hoflaan 38, 3062 JH Rotterdam, The Netherlands

Tel and fax +31 (0) 10 414 2029 Email info@tuinspiegel.com

Website www.tuinspiegel.com

Scotland

Scotland's Gardens Scheme is a registered charity founded in 1931. Garden owners donate entry fees and revenue from teas and plant sales to support the Scheme's beneficiaries, and charities of the owners' choice. **Publication:** *Gardens of Scotland*, published annually in February, lists over 350 gardens and is available through major booksellers in the UK for £3.50 or from the Scheme's head office. Over 350 gardens open for the Scheme. **Contact:** Robin St Clair-Ford, Director, Scotland's Garden Scheme, 31 Castle Terrace, Edinburgh, Scotland EH1 2EL

Tel +44 (0) 131 229 1870 Fax +44 (0) 131 229 0443

Email sgsoffice@aol.com Website (see Scotland's Gardens Scheme information on Garden Finder at www.ngs.org.uk)

United States of America

The Garden Conservancy, founded in 1989, is a national non-profit organisation dedicated to the preservation of America's finest gardens. Entry fees support the preservation of America's exceptional private gardens and facilitate their transition from private to independent not-for-profit ownership and operation. **Publication:** *Open Days Directory* published annually in February. US$10.95 members, $14.95 non-members. 400 gardens in 23 states are open in 2000. **Contact:** Antonia Adezio, Executive Director, The Gardens Conservancy, PO Box 219, Cold Spring, New York 10516

Tel +1 914 265 2029 Fax +1 914 265 9620

Email gardencons@aol.com

Website www.gardenconservancy.org

Royal support

In 1927, the National Gardens Scheme started almost by accident. It had been suggested that some of the great gardens of England might open to the public to raise money in memory of Queen Alexandra who had died in 1925. She was the wife of King Edward VII and had been Patron of Queen Victoria's Institute for District Nursing since her mother-in-law, Queen Victoria, had died. Among the gardens that opened in that first year was Sandringham, the Norfolk home of Queen Alexandra's son, King George V. The openings were such a success that the King wrote to suggest that garden opening should become a permanent way of raising money for district nurses.

The next member of the Royal Family to follow the King's example was his sister, Princess Mary, who with her husband the Earl of Harewood, started opening their garden, Harewood House in Yorkshire in 1928. Like Sandringham, it continues its openings today.

Then the next generation joined in. Just before the start of the war, the Duke and Duchess of Kent, the youngest brother of King George VI and his wife, opened their garden at Coppins, Iver in Buckinghamshire in 1939 and continued for 19 years until 1964. During the war the number of gardens opening for the Scheme was inevitably much reduced but another brother of the King, the Duke of Gloucester and his wife started to open their garden at Barnwell in Northamptonshire. This was particularly encouraging in difficult times. Barnwell continued to open for another 50 years. The then Duchess of Gloucester, now Princess Alice, maintains her link with the Gardens Scheme, as its President.

After the war there was much work to be done in rebuilding the number of gardens open. Here King George and Queen Elizabeth, an enthusiastic gardener, led the way. With the support of Queen Mary, they gave the Scheme a boost by allowing the family's private garden at Frogmore House, Windsor to open on one day in 1946. From 1948 to 1997, it opened on two days a year for the Gardens Scheme: reverting to one day in 1998. This year, Frogmore will have opened for 55 years. In 1948 and 1949, Windlesham Moor in Surrey, then the home of the present Queen and her husband joined the Scheme.

In 1980 the Gardens Scheme became a charity in its own right – the National Gardens Scheme Charitable Trust. Queen Elizabeth The Queen Mother, Patron of the renamed Queen's Nursing Institute, and Princess Alice, its President agreed to continue their long association with the Scheme by becoming respectively Patron and President of the new charity. Between them these two royal ladies have a combined record of 84 years of opening gardens for the Scheme.

Royal and National Trust gardens open in aid of the National Gardens Scheme

Royal gardens

Sandringham House and Grounds, Norfolk

By gracious permission of Her Majesty The Queen, the House and Grounds at Sandringham will be open on the following days: from April 15 to October 8 inclusive. Please note that the House only will be closed to the public from July 19 to August 2 inclusive and that the House and Grounds will be closed on Good Friday and from July 23 to August 2 inclusive. Coach drivers and visitors are advised to confirm these closing and opening dates nearer the time. Picnicking and dogs are not permitted inside the Grounds.

Hours

Sandringham House: 11.00am – 4.45pm; Museum: 11.00am – 5.00pm and Grounds: 10.30am – 5.00pm.

Admission charges

House, Grounds and Museum:
adults £5.50, OAPs £4.50, children £3.50.
Grounds and Museum only:
adults £4.50, OAPs £4.00; children £3.00.
Advance party bookings will be accepted. There are reductions in admission fees for pre-paid parties. Free car and coach parking.

Sandringham Church

Subject to weddings, funerals and special services, opening times will be 11.00am – 1.00pm April to October when the Grounds are open. At other times of the year the Church is open by appointment only.

Sandringham Flower Show

Wednesday 26 July.

Enquiries

The Public Enterprises Manager, Estate Office, Sandringham or by telephone 9.00am – 1.00pm, 2.00 – 4.30pm Monday to Friday inclusive on 01553 772675.

Frogmore Gardens, Berkshire

By gracious permission of Her Majesty The Queen, Frogmore Gardens, Windsor Castle, will be open from 10.00am – 7.00pm (last admission 6.00pm) on Tuesday 16 May. Entrance to Gardens and Mausoleum through Long Walk gate. Coaches by appointment only: apply to the National Gardens Scheme, Hatchlands Park, East Clandon, Guildford, Surrey GU4 7RT (Tel 01483 211535), stating whether you are interested in a morning or afternoon visit. Admission £2.50, accompanied children free of charge. Dogs, other than assistance dogs, not allowed. Visitors are requested kindly to refrain from entering the grounds of the Home Park. Light refreshments will be available. Also open:

Royal Mausoleum

Included in admission charge for gardens.

Frogmore House

Open in aid of the Royal Collection Trust. Entrance only from Frogmore Gardens. Admission £3.40 (adults), £2.40 (over 60s), £1.20 (8-16 year olds). Children under the age of 8 not admitted. Regrettably, the House is not suitable for wheelchairs.

National Trust gardens

Certain gardens opened by the National Trust are opened in aid of the National Gardens Scheme on the dates shown in this book. National Trust members are requested to note that where a National Trust property has allocated one of its normal opening days to the National Gardens Scheme, members can still gain entry on production of their National Trust membership card (although donations to the Scheme will be welcome). However, where the day allocated is one on which the property would not normally be open, payment of the National Gardens Scheme admission fee will be required.

The Counties of England and Wales

Note. The areas shown on this map are not necessarily precise geographic counties. Some are areas specific to the administration of the National Gardens Scheme

ENGLAND

Bedfordshire

Hon County Organiser and Treasurer: Mr & Mrs Chris Izzard, Broadfields, Keysoe Row East, Keysoe, Bedford MK44 2JD

DATES OF OPENING

Regular openings
For details see garden description
King's Arms Path Garden, Ampthill

By appointment only
For telephone numbers and other details see garden descriptions. Private visits welcomed
The Old Stables, Hockliffe
37 Rectory Lane, Houghton Conquest

February 20 Sunday
Manor Farm, Swineshead

March 18 Saturday
Swiss Garden, Biggleswade

March 26 Sunday
Howard's House, Cardington

April 2 Sunday
Broadfields, Keysoe Row East

April 9 Sunday
Broadfields, Keysoe Row East
Manor Farm, Swineshead

April 16 Sunday
The Manor House, Stevington
Woburn Abbey, Woburn

April 23 Sunday
King's Arms Path Garden, Ampthill

May 2 Tuesday
Seal Point, Luton

May 21 Sunday
Grove Lodge, Potton

May 27 Saturday
88 Castlehill Rd, Totternhoe

May 28 Sunday
88 Castlehill Rd, Totternhoe
Milton House, nr Bedford
The Old Rectory, Pertenhall
Valley Forge, Totternhoe

May 29 Monday
88 Castlehill Rd, Totternhoe

June 4 Sunday
Southill Park

June 6 Tuesday
Seal Point, Luton

June 11 Sunday
Manor Farm, Swineshead

June 18 Sunday
Yelden Gardens

June 25 Sunday
Grove Lodge, Potton

July 2 Sunday
Woburn Abbey, Woburn

July 4 Tuesday
Seal Point, Luton

August 1 Tuesday
Seal Point, Luton

September 5 Tuesday
Seal Point, Luton

September 17 Sunday
Manor Farm, Swineshead

September 23 Saturday
Swiss Garden, Biggleswade

DESCRIPTIONS OF GARDENS

Broadfields, Keysoe Row East ♿ (Mr & Mrs Chris Izzard) *Leave Bedford on Kimbolton rd B660 approx 8½m. Turn R at Keysoe Xrds by White Horse public house ½m on R.* 3 acres; herbaceous borders; spring bulbs, summer bedding, fuchsias; mature trees; shrubs and vegetable garden. TEAS. *Adm £2 Chd 50p. Suns April 2, 9 (2-6). Private visits (garden societies etc) welcome, please* **Tel 01234 376326**

88 Castlehill Rd, Totternhoe ✤❀ (Chris & Carole Jell) *Middle End. 2m W of Dunstable, turn R off B489 Aston to Clinton Rd. Fronting main rd approx ½m through village.* ¾ acre, S-sloping on limestone and clay, entirely created by owners. Interesting design of small gardens within a garden. Diverse planting managed in a natural and artistic way to create great peace and beauty. Old roses, clematis and herbaceous for scent and form. Aquilegias good in May. TEAS. *Adm £2 Chd £1. Sat, Sun, Bank Hol Mon May 27, 28, 29 (2-6). Also private visits of small groups June and July, please* **Tel 01525 220780**

Grove Lodge, Potton ❀ (Peter Wareing & Jean Venning) *6 Deepdale. 2m E of Sandy on B1042 towards Potton, past RSPB Reserve, downhill to Xrds. L at 'Locomotive' - lane to TV mast; first house on R.* 1½ acre, sandy hillside garden; conifers; heathers, shrubs, incl rhododendrons, climbing roses, herbaceous border, orchard with wild flowers, rockery banks with pond. *Adm £1.50 Chd 50p. Sun May 21 with plant sale, Sun June 25 TEAS and plant sale (2-6). Private visits welcome for parties of 12 and over, please* **Tel 01767 261298**

Howard's House, Cardington ♿ (Humphrey Whitbread Esq) *2m SE of Bedford.* Large walled flower and vegetable gardens; flowering cherries and clematis, mature trees. *Adm £1.50 Chd 50p. Sun March 26 (2-6)*

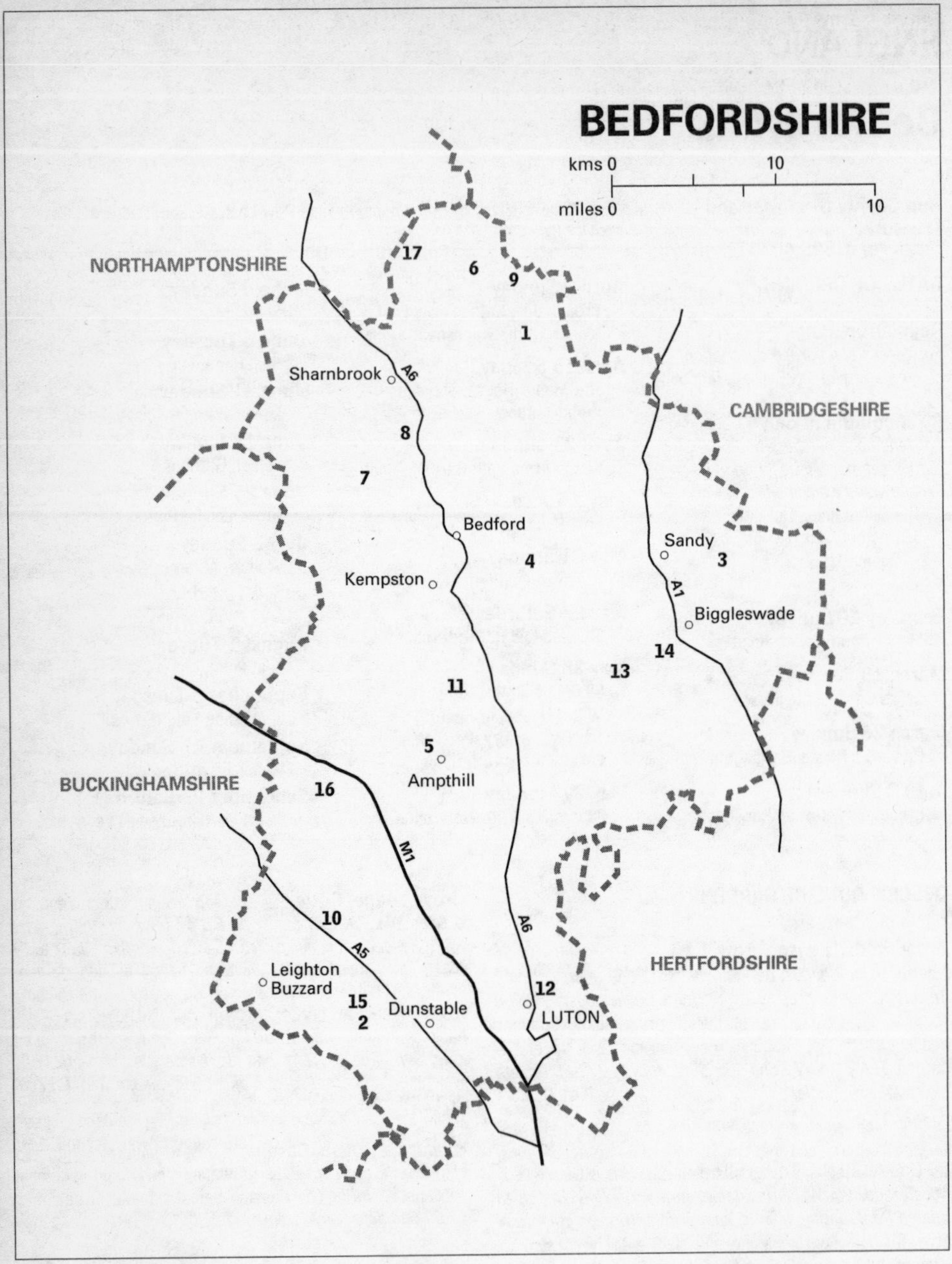

KEY

1 Broadfields
2 88 Castlehill Rd
3 Grove Lodge
4 Howard's House
5 King's Arms Path Garden
6 Manor Farm
7 The Manor House
8 Milton House
9 The Old Rectory
10 The Old Stables
11 37 Rectory Lane
12 Seal Point
13 Southill Park
14 Swiss Garden
15 Valley Forge
16 Woburn Abbey
17 Yelden Gardens

■ **King's Arms Path Garden, Ampthill** (Mrs N W Hudson) *Free parking in town centre. Entrance opp old Market Place, Ampthill, down Kings Arms Yard.* Small woodland garden of about 1½ acres created by plantsman the late William Nourish. Trees, shrubs, bulbs and many interesting collections. Maintained since 1987 by 'The Friends of the Garden' on behalf of Ampthill Town Council. Tea at adjacent Bowling Club or in the town. *Adm £1 Chd 25p. Suns Feb 13 (2-4); May 28, June 18, Aug 27, Oct 22 (2.30-5). For NGS Easter Sun April 23 (2.30-5). Private group visits welcome, please* **Tel 01525 402030/403945**

Manor Farm, Swineshead (Michael & Diana Marlow) *High St. 3m from Kimbolton between A6 and B660.* Developing and changing garden of 3 acres laid out around C16 farmhouse (not open). Yew hedges, herbaceous borders, pond garden, unusual plants and trees, large vegetable garden, soft fruits and old varieties of top fruits, paddock with geese and rare breeds of poultry, woodland walk. Feb - snowdrops and hellebores; April - spring bulbs and pulmonarias; June - herbaceous and roses; Sept - autumn colours. TEAS. *Adm £2 Chd free (ACNO to St Nicholas's Church Restoration and Village Hall Fabric Fund). Suns Feb 20 (11-4), April 9, June 11, Sept 17 (11-6)*

The Manor House, Stevington (Kathy Brown) *Church Rd. 5m NW Bedford off A428 through Bromham.* Home of garden writer and designer specialising in 'garden recipes'. Features unusual long-term and seasonal containers, formal French-style garden, wisteria walk, cottage garden, zig-zag pergola and summer xeriscape garden, ornamental grass parterre, spring bulbs a speciality, wild flowers in orchard and grasslands; old roses and herbaceous plants. No photography. TEAS in aid of St Mary's. *Adm £2.50 Chd free. Guided tours available. Sun July 9 (2-6).* **For NGS** *Sun April 16 (2-6). Private parties welcome, please* **Tel 01234 822064**

Milton House, nr Bedford (Mr & Mrs Clifton Ibbett) *N of Bedford on A6, S of village of Milton Ernest. Drive to house is on R,* Formal, terrace and sunken gardens set in large grounds with lakes and waterfall. Guide dogs only. TEAS in aid of All Saints Parish Church, Milton Ernest. *Adm £2.50 Chd free. Sun May 28 (2-6)*

The Old Rectory, Pertenhall (Mr & Mrs F R Finston) *Situated on B660 approx 10m from Bedford, 1½m from Kimbolton.* 4 acres of mature gardens approached through lime avenue. Walled garden with special features, ancient mulberry and medlar. Shrubberies and herbaceous borders; scented and kitchen gardens, views over large pond and paddocks. *Adm £2 Chd free. Sun May 28 (2-6)*

The Old Stables, Hockliffe (Mr & Mrs D X Victor) *3m N of Dunstable. From A5 in Hockliffe, proceed W on A4012. Turn R after ¼m (signposted Church End), then L at church. Follow lane for ½m and take field track on R.* 2 acres, incl walled garden, with panoramic views of countryside. Large collection of plants incl alpines, hardy geraniums and clematis, in formal and informal plantings. *Adm £2 Chd £1. Private visits, individual or groups, welcome please* **Tel 01525 210633**

37 Rectory Lane, Houghton Conquest (Keith & Lucyna Toms) *Small village 5m S of Bedford between A6 and B530.* Over 500 scented and aromatic plant species and cultivars share ½ acre with vegetables and small orchard. Created by partially sighted owner and husband. Regret not suitable for children. TEA and plants in aid of Mayhew Animal Home. *Adm £2. Individual and small groups welcome by appt June, July and September (2-8), not Suns, please* **Tel 01234 741346**

Seal Point, Luton (Mrs Danae Johnston) *7 Wendover Way. In NE Luton, turning N off Stockingstone Rd into Felstead Way.* Small, sloping, exciting town garden with unusual herbaceous plants, grasses and trees; water features, topiary cats and bonsai; beds representing yin and yang; original ornaments. Featured on Gardeners' World Sept 25 1998. Winner BBC Gardener of the Year 1999 for SE region. TEA by arrangement. *Adm £2.50 Acc chd under 14 free. Tues May 2, June 6, July 4, Aug 1, Sept 5 (2-6). Private visits welcome, also small groups, please* **Tel 01582 611567**

Southill Park (Mr & Mrs S C Whitbread) *3m W of Biggleswade.* Large garden, rhododendrons, conservatory. *Adm £2.50 Chd £1 (ACNO to Tradescant Trust). Sun June 4 (2-5)*

Swiss Garden, Biggleswade (Bedfordshire County Council) *Old Warden. Signposted from A1 and A600. 2m W Biggleswade, next door to the Shuttleworth Collection* 9-acre landscape garden set out in 1830s alongside a further 10 acres native woodland with lakeside picnic area. Garden includes many tiny buildings, footbridges, ironwork features and intertwining ponds. Romantic landscape design highlighted by daffodils, rhododendrons and old rambling roses in season. *Adm £3 Concessions and Chd £2 (ACNO to Friends of the Swiss Garden). Sats March 18, Sept 23 (1-6). Last admission 5.15*

Valley Forge, Totternhoe (Pat & Mike Sutcliffe) *2m W of Dunstable. Turn R off B489 Aston to Clinton Rd, ½m from Dunstable centre, signposted Totternhoe. Fronting main rd, corner of Chapel Lane, 1m through village.* Garden to rear of C17 grade II listed thatched cottage (not open), ½-acre sloping site, terraced on chalk, planted from scratch by owners during last 7yrs. Interestingly landscaped featuring pergolas and archways, shrubs, perennials and trees, including rare Aylesbury Prune. Site also houses Mike Sutcliffe's famous collection of early Leyland buses (1908-1934). TEA in aid of Totternhoe Lower School. *Adm £1.50 Chd 50p. Sun May 28 (2-6)*

Woburn Abbey, Woburn ✂ (The Marquess of Tavistock) *Woburn Abbey is situated 1½m from Woburn village, which is on A4012 almost mid-way from junctions 12 and 13 of M1.* 22 acres of private garden not generally open to public originally designed by Wyattville, with recent restoration of The Duchess's rose garden. Unique hornbeam maze with C18 temple by Chambers. TEAS. *Adm £2 Chd free (gardens only). Suns April 16, Sun July 2 (11-5)*

Yelden Gardens ✂ *Beds/Northants border, 14m N of Bedford, 4m S of Rushden. Adjacent to A6 and A45.* Teas and plants from gardens for sale in aid of St Mary's Church *Adm £2.50 Chd free. Sun June 18 (2-6)*

The Manor (Mr & Mrs P Laughton) 2.5 acres. Formal rose garden surrounding fish pond. Shrubberies, herbaceous borders, ornamental vegetable garden, natural pond, orchard

The Old Rectory (Mr & Mrs P Rushton) 2.5 acres of established gardens. Many fine trees, ornamental pond, herb garden, shrubberies, woodland walk

USUAL - & NOT SO USUAL PERENNIALS, SHRUBS AND TREES

Come and visit our nursery where you will find a wide range of perennials, many of them rather unusual, as well as some interesting shrubs, and trees.

- 70 varieties of Clematis, plus other climbers.
- Huge range of bedding plants in season.
- Please write or 'phone for our free catalogue.

ASTERBY & CHALKCROFT NURSERY
The Ridgeway, Blunham, Beds, MK44 3PH
01767 640148

Just off the A603, near the A1 at Sandy. We are easy to find.

Open six days a week, closed Mondays

Macmillan Cancer Relief

Macmillan's nurses and doctors help to increase expertise in cancer treatment and care by sharing their knowledge and skills with other professionals across the country, a process which is aided by formal education programmes.

Macmillan Cancer Relief
Information Line: 0845 601 6161
Macmillan Cancer Relief
Website: www.macmillan.org.uk

Gardeners' Royal Benevolent Society

Gardeners' Royal Benevolent Society has been helping retired gardeners, groundsmen, horticultural workers, nurserymen and seedsmen for 160 years.

Gardeners' Royal Benevolent Society
Bridge House, 139 Kingston Road, Leatherhead, Surrey KT22 7NT
Tel: 01372 373962

Berkshire

Hon County Organiser: Bob Avery Esq, Jingles, Derek Road, Maidenhead, Berkshire SL6 8NT Tel 01628 627580

Assistant Hon County Organisers:
North West Mrs C Povey, The Mill House, Boxford, Newbury RG20 8DP Tel 01488 657996
South West Christopher Verity Esq, Boundary House, Brimpton Common, Reading RG7 4RT Tel 0118 9814849
East Mrs Jackie Bewsher, Arcturus, Church Road, Bray, Berkshire SLl6 3QU Tel 01628 622824

Hon County Treasurer: Bob Avery Esq

DATES OF OPENING

Regular openings
For details see garden description
The Old Rectory, Burghfield
The Thatch, Littlewick Green
Waltham Place, White Waltham

By appointment only
For telephone numbers and other details see garden descriptions. Private visits welcomed
21 Berrys Road, Upper Bucklebury
Braywood House, Windsor Forest
Donnington Grove Country Club, Donnington
Whiteknights, Finchampstead

March 12 Sunday
Foxgrove, Enborne

March 26 Sunday
Stanford Dingley Village Gardens

April 16 Sunday
Blencathra, Finchampstead
Folly Farm, Sulhamstead
Foxgrove, Enborne
The Old Rectory, Farnborough

April 24 Monday
Swallowfield Park, nr Reading

April 26 Wednesday
The Old Rectory, Burghfield

April 30 Sunday
69 Albert Road, Caversham Heights
Bussock Wood, Snelsmore Common
Odney Club, Cookham
Simms Farm House, Mortimer

May 1 Monday
69 Albert Road, Caversham Heights
Simms Farm House, Mortimer

May 7 Sunday
The Harris Garden, Whiteknights, Reading
Scotlands, nr Wargrave

May 14 Sunday
Hurst Gardens
The Old Rectory, Farnborough

May 16 Tuesday
Frogmore Gardens, Windsor

May 18 Thursday
Meadow House, nr Newbury

May 21 Sunday
Blencathra, Finchampstead
Little Harwood, Pinkneys Green
Sunningdale Park, Ascot

May 28 Sunday
Little Bowden, Pangbourne
Waltham Place, White Waltham

June 1 Thursday
Meadow House, nr Newbury

June 3 Saturday
Sonning Village Gardens

June 4 Sunday
Blencathra, Finchampstead
Sonning Village Gardens
Trunkwell Park, Beech Hill
Welford Park, nr Newbury

June 11 Sunday
Kirby House, Inkpen
The Mill House, Donnington

June 15 Thursday
Meadow House, nr Newbury

June 17 Saturday
Eton College Gardens, Windsor

June 18 Sunday
Basildon Park, Reading
Blencathra, Finchampstead
Chieveley Manor, nr Newbury
Peasemore Gardens

June 25 Sunday
The Old Rectory, Farnborough
The Priory, Beech Hill
Sandleford Place, Newtown
Stone House, Brimpton
Woolley Park, nr Wantage

June 28 Wednesday
Rooksnest, Lambourn Woodlands

July 6 Thursday
Meadow House, nr Newbury

July 9 Sunday
Inkpen House, Inkpen

July 12 Wednesday
Swallowfield Park, nr Reading

July 16 Sunday
Priory House, Sunningdale

July 20 Thursday
Meadow House, nr Newbury

July 23 Sunday
Waltham Place, White Waltham

July 26 Wednesday
The Old Rectory, Burghfield

July 30 Sunday
Folly Farm, Sulhamstead

August 6 Sunday
Simms Farm House, Mortimer

August 27 Sunday
Hurst Lodge

September 3 Sunday
Trunkwell Park, Beech Hill

September 24 Sunday
The Harris Garden, Whiteknights, Reading

By Appointment Gardens. These owners do not have a fixed opening day, usually because they cannot accommodate large numbers or have insufficient parking space.

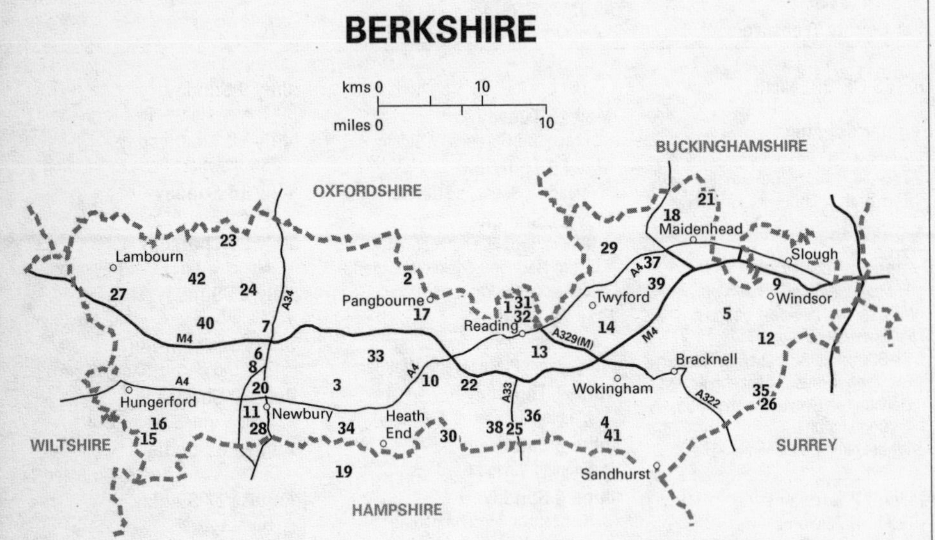

KEY

1 69 Albert Road
2 Basildon Park
3 21 Berrys Road
4 Blencathra
5 Braywood House
6 Bussock Wood
7 Chieveley Manor
8 Donnington Grove Country Club
9 Eton College Gardens
10 Folly Farm
11 Foxgrove
12 Frogmore Gardens
13 The Harris Garden
14 Hurst Gardens
15 Inkpen House
16 Kirby House
17 Little Bowden
18 Little Harwood
19 Meadow House
20 The Mill House
21 Odney Club
22 The Old Rectory, Burghfield
23 The Old Rectory, Farnborough
24 Peasemore Gardens
25 The Priory
26 Priory House
27 Rooksnest
28 Sandleford Place
29 Scotlands
30 Simms Farm House
31 Sonning Gardens
32 Stanford Dingley Village Gardens
33 Stone House
34 Sunningdale Park
35 Swallowfield Park
36 The Thatch
37 Trunkwell Park
38 Waltham Place
39 Welford Park
40 Whiteknights
41 Woolley Park

DESCRIPTIONS OF GARDENS

69 Albert Road, Caversham Heights ♿✂ (Mr & Mrs Clive Nichols) *From Reading town centre, follow signs for Caversham. Crossing river Thames over Caversham bridge. Take 1st L (A4074), 1st R (St Anne's Rd) 1st L (Clifton Park) and on into Albert Rd.* Garden photographer's small town garden (100′ × 30′) designed for family fun. Hundreds of tulips in borders and containers. Design features incl child-safe water feature, built-in sandpit and paddling pool, gazebo and covered seat. Bold use of colour in planting and hardscaping. Teas on Suns only at St Andrews Church Hall *Adm £2 Chd free Suns April 30, Mon May 1 (2-6)*

▲ **Basildon Park, Reading** ♿✂❀ (Lady Iliffe) *Lower Basildon. Between Pangbourne and Streatley, 7m NW of Reading on W of A329.* Private garden designed and planted by Lady Iliffe with help of Lanning Roper. Mainly old roses but other interesting plants constantly being added by owner. Lunches. TEAS in NT house. *Adm to Garden only NT members 50p non members £1 Chd free. For NGS Sun June 18 (1-5.30)*

NEW **21 Berrys Road, Upper Bucklebury** ❀ (Richard and Meri Mower) *From A4 to E of Thatcham take rd N signposted for Upper Bucklebury at antique shop. Once in village proceed past shops to Berrys Rd 500yds on R.* Small family garden. Designer Dan Pearson made a striking modern garden in an area backed my mature woodland. Interesting range of architectural, shade-loving and woodland plants. *Adm £2 Chd free. Private visits welcome, please* **Tel 01635 864975**

Blencathra, Finchampstead ♿❀ (Dr & Mrs F W Gifford) *Entrance from private drive at the NW end of the Ridges on B3348. Parking on joint private drive or The Ridges. Disabled passengers may alight near the house.* 11-acre garden which present owners started in 1964, laid out and maintained with minimum of help. Many varied mature trees; lawns, heather, rhododendrons, azaleas, wide range of conifers, three small lakes and stream; Spring bulbs. Interesting throughout year. TEAS. *Adm £2.50 Chd free (ACNO to other charities). Suns April 16, May 21, June 4, 18 (2-6); private visits welcome,* **Tel 0118 9734563**

Braywood House, Windsor Forest ✂ (Mr & Mrs M Pawson) *4 m SW of Windsor. B3022 past Legoland on R. Turn R at next roundabout. Turn R immed into Drift Rd. After 1½m Braywood House on R.* Young 7-acre garden. Planned, planted & maintained by Mrs Pawson. Small arboretum with specimen trees contrasting with several ancient oaks. A Victorian Churchyard C1866 with interesting historical associations; Spring walk, shady walk, mulberry garden, pond garden, woodland walk. TEA *Adm £2 Chd free Private visits welcome May 1 to Sept 30 please,* **Tel 01344 882670**

Bussock Wood, Snelsmore Common ❀ (Mr & Mrs W A Palmer) *3m N of Newbury. On B4494 Newbury-Wantage Rd.* Bluebells, fine trees and views; sunken garden with lily pond. Early Briton Camp. TEAS in aid of St James the Less, Winterbourne. Plants for sale *Adm £1 Chd 50p Sun April 30 (2-5.30)*

Chieveley Manor, nr Newbury ♿✂❀ (Mr & Mrs C J Spence) *5m N of Newbury. Take A34 N pass under M4, then L to Chieveley. After ½m L up Manor Lane.* Large garden with fine views over stud farm. Walled garden containing borders, shrubs & rose garden. Listed house (not open). TEAS. *Adm £1 Chd free (ACNO to St Mary's Church, Chieveley). Sun June 18 (2-6)*

Donnington Grove Country Club, Donnington (Shi-Tennoji Int Ltd) *Leave M4 at Junction 13; take A34 to Newbury. Leave A34 at 1st junction, turn R then L towards Donnington Castle for 2m. Cross 1st mini roundabout. At 2nd, turn R into Grove Rd. From Hungerford take the A4 Bath Rd, turn L at Oxford Rd B4494 and L into Grove Rd.* Buddhist Temple and water garden set within 25-acre walled English garden, being centrepiece of approx 80 acres of C18 country parkland. Lake, river and woodland walks. The temple garden contains fish ponds and wide selection of rhododendrons and azaleas. The remaining garden is laid out to herbaceous borders, shrubs and lawns. TEAS. *Adm £1.50 Chd free. By appt please,* **Tel 01635 552217** Head Gardener, Charles Robins

Eton College Gardens, Windsor ♿✂❀ (J N B Cook Esq) *Stations: Windsor ¾m Eton ½m. Bus: Green Line 704 & 705 London-Windsor 1m. Parking off B3022 Slough to Eton rd, signposted.* Luxmoore's Garden is an island garden created by a housemaster about 1880; reached by beautiful new bridge; views of college and river. Provost's and Fellows' Gardens adjoin the ancient buildings on N and E sides. TEAS in aid of Datchet PCC. *Combined adm £1 Chd 20p. Sat June 17 (2-6)*

Folly Farm, Sulhamstead ♿✂ (Sir Desmond & Lady Pitcher) *7m SW of Reading. A4 between Reading/Newbury (2m W of M4 exit 12); take rd marked Sulhamstead at Mulligans Restaurant.* One of the few remaining gardens where the Lutyens architecture remains intact. Garden, laid out by Gertrude Jekyll, has been planted to owners' taste, bearing in mind Jekyll and Lutyens original design. Raised white garden, sunken rose garden; spring bulbs; herbaceous borders; ilex walk; avenues of limes, yew hedges, formal pools. House (not open). TEAS. *Adm £2 Chd free. Suns April 16, July 30 (2-6)*

Foxgrove, Enborne ♿✂ (Miss Audrey D Vockins) *2½m SW of Newbury. From A343 turn R at 'The Gun' 2m from town centre. Bus: AV 126, 127, 128; alight Villiers Way PO 1m.* 1-acre garden with adjoining nursery (Foxgrove Plants); interesting foliage plants, troughs, raised beds, spring bulbs, naturalised in orchard; snowdrop species and varieties; peat bed. New 40yd ditch and bank garden. Collection of daphnes (30+). Cyclamen and colchicums in the autumn. TEAS. *Adm £2 Chd free. Suns March 12, April 16 (2-6). Groups by appt, please* **Tel 01635 40554**

Frogmore Gardens, Windsor ♿✂ (Her Majesty The Queen) *Windsor Castle; entrance via Park St gate into Long Walk (follow AA signs). Visitors are requested kindly to keep on the route to the garden and not stray into the Home Park. Station and bus stop; Windsor (20 mins walk from gardens); Green Line bus no 701, from London. Limited parking for cars only (free).* 30 acres of landscaped gardens rich in history and beauty. Large lake, fine trees, lawns, flowers and flowering shrubs. The Royal Mausoleum, within the grounds, will also be open free of charge. Refreshment tent adjoining Frogmore House. **Coaches by appointment only** (apply to NGS, Hatchlands Park, East Clandon, Guildford, Surrey GU4 7RT enc s.a.e. or **Tel 01483 211535** stating am or pm). *Adm £2.50 Chd free Tues May 16 (10-7; last adm 6)*

The Harris Garden, Whiteknights, Reading (The University of Reading, School of Plant Science) *Off A327, Shinfield Rd, 1½m S of Reading Town Centre. Turn R just inside Pepper Lane entrance to University campus.* 12-acre research and teaching garden. Rose gardens; herbaceous borders, winter garden, herb garden etc. Jungle garden new in 1996 and Gold garden started in 1997. Extensive glass-houses. Many plants labelled. TEAS in aid of Friends of The Harris Garden. *Adm £1.50 Chd free. Suns May 7, Sept 24 (2-6)*

Hurst Gardens ♿ *On the A321 between Twyford and Wokingham* Both gardens are in the village of Hurst but quite a distance apart. They offer an interesting contrast in age, size and approach. TEAS at Hurst Lodge only. *Combined adm £3 Chd free (ACNO Helen House Childrens Hospice). Suns May 14, Aug 27 (2.5.30) (Hurst Lodge Sun May 27 only adm £2)*

Hurst Lodge ❀ (Mr & Mrs Alan Peck) Large 5-acre old garden which has been cared for by members of the same family for over 75 yrs. It features lawns and mature trees, a rockery, pond and bog garden, a formal parterre, a walled garden with herbaceous borders, a large kitchen garden as well as camellias, azaleas, rhododendrons, magnolias, flowering cherries, a variety of Japanese maples and bulbs

Reynolds Farm (Mr & Mrs Christopher Wells) When this garden was devised, it was intended to provide pleasure for our old age. It is with some shock I realise that point has been reached and it is time to take stock. Yes we have bought the plants, shrubs and trees. No it is not a riot of flower power throughout the year. However in a small area it does take quite a while to get round and there is a lot that is quite unusual. In short it does show how much pleasure you can have with minimal effort and help. I can safely say the dog likes it.

Inkpen House, Inkpen ✇❀ (Mr & Mrs David Male) *Lower Green. Between Newbury and Hungerford; turn off A4 at sign marked Kintbury and Inkpen. Drive into Kintbury. Turn L by shop onto Inkpen Rd. After approx 1m turn R at Xrds. After red telephone kiosk on R take 2nd turn on L marked C13 Ch. Car park in field on L.* 4-acre garden laid out at beginning of C18 in the Versailles style with formal planting of avenues and bosquets. Pleached lime walk and walled kitchen garden. TEAS. *Adm £2 Chd free. Sun July 9 (2-6)*

Kirby House, Inkpen ✇❀ (Mr & Mrs R Astor) *Turn S off A4 to Kintbury; L at Xrds in Kintbury (by Corner Stores) towards Coombe. 2m out of Kintbury turn L immed beyond Crown & Garter PH, turn L at junction, house and garden at bottom of hill.* 6 acres in beautiful setting. Formal rose borders, replanted herbaceous border in kitchen garden, colour theme border between yew buttress hedges. Lily pond garden, lake. C18 Queen Anne house (not open). *Adm £2.50 Chd free (ACNO to St Swithins Church) Sun June 11 (2-6)*

Little Bowden, Pangbourne ♿❀ (Geoffrey Verey Esq) *1½m W of Pangbourne on Pangbourne-Yattendon Rd.* Large garden with fine views; woodland walk, azaleas, rhododendrons, bluebells. Heated swimming pool 50p extra. TEAS. *Adm £2 Chd free. Sun May 28 (2.30-6)*

Little Harwood, Pinkneys Green ❀ (Mr & Mrs D Harrold) *From Maidenhead take A308 towards Marlow. At Pinkneys Green turn R into Winter Hill Rd signposted to Winter Hill & Cookham Dean. Where rd forks continue on main rd towards Cookham Dean, now Choke Lane. 500yds along Choke Lane you reach a Z bend & SLOW sign. Little Harwood is on the L.* 2 acres of mature formal & informal terraced gardens, incl water garden, rock garden, herbaceous border, herb bed and contemporary garden building. Large specimen trees and clipped yew & hawthorn hedges. 13 acres of bluebell woodland walk. TEAS. *Adm £1.50 Chd free (ACNO to Compassion in World Farming). Sun May 21 (2-6)*

▲ **Meadow House, nr Newbury** ♿✇❀ (Mr & Mrs G A Jones) *Ashford Hill is on the B3051 8m SE of Newbury. Take turning at SW end of village signposted Wolverton Common and Wheathold. House on R approx 350yds down unmade track.* Approx 1¾-acre plantsman's garden in beautiful rural surroundings. Designed by owners to create a feeling of tranquillity and space. Pond with waterside planting; mixed shrub, rose and herbaceous borders. Trellis with wisteria roses and clematis. Many unusual plants. *Adm £2 Chd free. Open for NGS Thurs May 18, June 1, 15, July 6, 20, (11-4). Private visits welcome by appt from May to end of Aug, please* **Tel 0118 9816005**

The Mill House, Donnington ✇ (Mr & Mrs Stephen Kingsley) *On B4494, about 1m from Newbury, at edge of village, between Alms Houses. Please park considerately in village.* Enchanting 2¼ acre garden with river, small lake, mill stream, woodland, bog and decked area and mixed shrub borders. TEA. *Adm £2 Chd free (ACNO to St Mary's Church, Shaw-cum-Donnington) Sun June 11 (2-6)*

Odney Club, Cookham ♿❀ (John Lewis Partnership) *Car park in grounds.* 120 acres; lawns, garden and meadows on R Thames; specimen trees. Cream TEAS in River Room. *Adm £2.50 Chd free. Sun April 30 (2-6)*

■ **The Old Rectory, Burghfield** ♿✇❀ (Mr A R Merton) *5m SW of Reading. Turn S off A4 to Burghfield village; R after Hatch Gate Inn; entrance on R.* Medium-sized garden; herbaceous and shrub borders; roses, hellebores, lilies, many rare and unusual plants collected by owner from Japan and China; old-fashioned cottage plants; autumn colour. Georgian house (not open). TEAS. *Adm £2 Chd free. Open last Wed in month Feb to Oct incl (11-4). For NGS Weds April 26, July 26 (11-4)*

The Old Rectory, Farnborough ✇❀ (Mrs Michael Todhunter) *4m SE of Wantage. From B4494 Wantage-Newbury Rd, 4m from Wantage turn E at sign for Farnborough.* Outstanding garden with unusual plants: fine view;

old-fashioned roses, arboretum; collection of small flowered clematis; herbaceous borders. New boule garden with four big beds. Beautiful house (not open) built C1749. Near church with John Piper window in memory of John Betjeman who lived at The Old Rectory. Teas in village. *Adm £2 Chd free (ACNO to Farnborough PCC), Suns April 16, May 14, June 25 (2-6). Private visits by written appt*

Peasemore Gardens *7m N of Newbury on A34 to M4 junction 13. N towards Oxford then immed L signed Chievely. Through Chievely and onto Peasemore approx 3½m or B4494 from Newbury 6m R signposted Peasemore.* TEAS at The Old Rectory. *Combined adm £2 Chd free. Sun June 18 (2-6)*

The Old Rectory, Peasemore ♿❀ (Mr & Mrs I D Cameron) Georgian house with fine trees in lovely setting. Shrub roses, peonies, rose garden, herbaceous border & new double mixed borders, 3 acre wild flower meadow

Paxmere House ♿❀ (The Marchioness of Lansdowne) Opp The Old Rectory. 4-acre cottage garden. Roses, shrubs, etc

Peasmore House ♿ (Mr & Mrs W Brown) Past 3 thatched cottages on R entering Peasemore. Garden on R behind flint and brick wall. 2½ acres traditional garden with lovely trees, shrubs and roses with extensive views over arable downland

The Priory, Beech Hill ♿✿❀ (Mr & Mrs C Carter) *4m S of Reading, M4 junction 11. Follow signs to A33, then Beech Hill. When in village turn opp church into Wood Lane, house at end of drive.* Extensive gardens in grounds of former C12 Benedictine Priory (not open), rebuilt 1648 and renovated 1996 by present owners. Situated in the beautiful surroundings of the River Loddon the mature gardens are now being restored and re-developed. Large formal walled garden with espalier fruit trees, lawns, extensive mixed and herbaceous borders, vegetables and roses. Walk across river leads to woodland and lake. Many fine specimen trees. TEAS. *Adm £2. Sun June 25 (2-6)*

Priory House, Sunningdale ✿❀ (Mr & Mrs J Leigh) *Take turning opp Waitrose, Ridgemount Rd, Priory Rd 1st L Free parking at Sunningdale BR Station. Courtesy bus to garden at regular intervals. No parking at Priory House or in Priory Rd.* 2¼ acre garden designed in 1930s by Percy Cane planted for yr-round interest and colour. Ornamental pond, large lawn with shrub borders, yew hedges and rare trees. Perennial borders, heathers, vegetable garden, new rose garden; rhododendrons and azaleas with impressive hostas by stream. Mature camellias, fine shrubs and conifers. *Adm £2.50 Chd free (ACNO to Make-A-Wish Foundation UK). Sun July 16 (2-6)*

Rooksnest, Lambourn Woodlands ❀ (Dr & Mrs M D Sackler) *Earls Court Farm. Situated approx 3m from the A338 (Wantage) Rd along the B4000. Nearest village, Lambourn. Rooksnest signposted on the B400 in both directions, ie whether approaching from Lambourn or from the A338.* Approx 10-acre exceptionally fine traditional English garden. Recently restored with help from Arabella Lennox-Boyd. Incl terraces; rose garden, lilies, herbaceous border, herb garden, many specimen trees and fine shrubs. TEA. *Adm £1.50 Chd free. Wed June 28 (2-5)*

NEW **Sandleford Place, Newtown** ♿✿ (Mr & Mrs Alan Gatward) *House is on A339 1½m S of Newbury at W side of Swan roundabout. From Newbury go to roundabout and turn 180 degrees.* 4 acre garden with many unusual plants. Walled garden containing herb border, mixed borders and kitchen garden. Wild flowers along river. Other shrub and beautiful herbaceous borders. *Adm £2 Chd free. Sun June 25 (2-6)*

Scotlands, nr Wargrave ♿❀ (Mr Michael & The Hon Mrs Payne) *In centre of triangle formed by A4130 (was A423) E of Henley-on-Thames, the A321 to Wargrave and the A4 at Knowl Hill - midway between Warren Row Village and Cockpole Green.* 4 acres; clipped yews; shrub borders, grass paths through trees to woodland and pond-gardens with Repton design rustic summer house. Rocks with waterfall and gazebo. Featured in Good Gardens Guide & several garden books. TEAS. *Adm £2 Chd free. Sun May 7 (2-6). Private parties welcome, please* **Tel 01628 822648**

Simms Farm House, Mortimer ♿✿❀ (The Rev His Hon Christopher & Mrs Lea) *6m SW of Reading. At T-junction on edge of village, from Grazeley, turn R uphill approx 1m; L by church into West End Rd; at next Xrd L down Drury Lane; R at T-junction.* 1-acre garden with mixed shrub borders, small rockery; bog garden; formal pond; unusual plants. Lovely view. TEA. *Adm £1.50 Chd free Sun April 30 Mon May 1, Sun Aug 6 (2-6). Private visits welcome, please* **Tel 01189 332360**

Sonning Village Gardens ✿❀ *4m E of Reading in Sonning Lane off the A4 (9m W of Maidenhead of the A4) 400m heading N along Sonning Lane. School found on L. At least six village gardens will be open each day. Parking at Reading Blue Coat School by kind permission of the Headmaster.* Teas in Village Hall. *Combined adm £3 Chd free Sat, Sun June 3, 4 (11-5)*

Stanford Dingley Village Gardens ♿✿❀ *Village on the Pang River, 5m from M4 junction 12. Take A4 then A340 and turn to Bradfield. Go through Bradfield College junction and after the small bridge take the L turn. Follow Back Lane into Stanford Dingley arriving at the N end, turn L, S, to find church, bridge pub and gardens. Field parking at Bradfield Farm. Other gardens possibly open on the same dates.* Teas at the Old Boot Inn. *Combined adm £2 Chd free. Suns March 26 (2-6)*

Bradfield Farm ♿ (Mrs Christopher Newton) 1½-acre domestic gardens round restored farm buildings. Newly planted woodlands and 6 acre wild area being restored by river. Private visits by appt. Tel 01189 744113

Bridge Cottage (Mr & Mrs M Ranwell) ½ acre very pretty cottage garden with deep herbaceous borders, mixed shrubs and vegetable garden

Stone House, Brimpton (Mr & Mrs N Bingham) *6m E of Newbury. Turn S off A4 at junction by Coach & Horses, signed Brimpton & Aldermaston. ½m W of T-junction by War Memorial signed Newbury.* Medium-sized garden in attractive park; naturalised bulbs, rhododendrons, water garden, extensive collection plants and shrubs, walled kitchen garden; picnic area. Cream TEA. *Adm £1.50 Chd free. Sun June 25 (2-6)*

Sunningdale Park, Ascot ❀ (Civil Service College) *1½m E of Ascot off A329 at Cannon Inn or take Broomhall Lane off A30 at Sunningdale.* Over 20 acres of beautifully landscaped gardens reputedly designed by Capability Brown. Terrace garden and victorian rockery designed by Pulham incl cave and water features. Lake area with paved walks; extensive lawns with specimen trees and flower beds, impressive massed rhododendrons. Beautiful 1m woodland walk. Grade II listed building (not open). Limited access for wheelchairs. Cream TEAS. *Adm £3 Chd free. Sun May 21 (2-5)*

Swallowfield Park, nr Reading ♿❀ (Miss Fiona Dean) *5m S of Reading off B3349, entrance nr village hall.* Level grounds of 25 acres which incl a large walled garden and herbaceous borders, rose beds, massed rhododendrons and many specimen trees. There are wide lawns and gravel paths, with a small lake and a wooded walk to the R Loddon. Visit dogs' graves. The distinguished house (open) was built in 1689 for Lord Clarendon. Home-made TEAS *Adm £2.50 Chd free (ACNO to Country Houses Association) Weds, Thurs May 1 to Sept 30. Parties welcome, please* **Tel 01189 883815** For the NGS Mon April 24, Wed July 12 (2-5)

The Thatch, Littlewick Green ♿✿❀ (Lynn & David Penfold) *Turn S into Jubilee Rd in Littlewick Green, on A4, 2m W of Maidenhead. The Thatch is next to the cricket pitch.* ¾-acre exuberant cottage garden complements thatched cottage on village green. Waterfall, pool, bog garden and terraced beds in old chalkpit. Many plants, mostly scented planted for dry, chalky soil. Herbaceous beds, shrubs, mature trees, tiny woodland garden. Best late spring and early summer, especially for old roses. Organic allotment nearby. TEAS, plants in aid of village hall. *Adm £1.50 Chd 50p. Appt, incl groups, only,* **Tel 01628 825718**

Trunkwell Park, Beech Hill ♿❀ (Manager) *From Reading: M4 junction 11 follow Basingstoke sign approx ¼m at roundabout turn L and follow Three Mile Cross-Spencers Wood. Beech Hill Rd on R and follow into Village and follow signs. From Basingstoke follow A33 to Wellington roundabout turn L following Beech Hill signs. At village turn R. Located in grounds of Trunkwell House Hotel. Parking and toilets.* Conducted tours. 3-acre site with Victorian walled garden run by Thrive to give disabled and disadvantaged people the chance to use horticultural therapy and training programmes to improve their health, skill and quality of life. TEAS. *Adm £2 Chd free (ACNO to Horticultural Therapy). Suns June 4, Sept 3 (2-4.30)*

Waltham Place, White Waltham ♿❀ (Mr & Mrs N Oppenheimer) *3½m S of Maidenhead. Exit 8/9 on M4, the A423(M) or M40 exit 4 then A404 to A4 Maidenhead exit and follow signs to White Waltham. L at church (opp airfield), situated at top of hill. From the S B3024 to White Waltham* 20 acres of organic gardens with bluebell woods and lake. Special features incl splendid weeping beech and atlas cedar, herbaceous borders with planting immune to rabbits, traditional walled garden with hot border, japanese, butterfly and iris gardens. Part of a self sufficient organic farm with kitchen garden. Stalls inc pottery, turned wood, plants and home-made cream TEAS. *Adm £2.50 Chd 50p (ACNO to other charities). Open weekdays between May 30 to July 21, For NGS Suns May 28, July 23 (2-7)*

Welford Park, nr Newbury ♿❀ (Mrs J H Puxley) *6m NW of Newbury on Lambourn Valley Rd. Entrance on Newbury/Lambourn Rd (fine gates with boot on top).* Spacious grounds; new formal garden; spring flowers; walk by R. Lambourn. Queen Anne house (not open). TEAS. *Adm £2 Chd free (ACNO to Welford Church Council) Sun June 4 (2-5)*

Whiteknights, Finchampstead ♿✿❀ (Mrs Heather Bradly) *Midway along Finchampstead Ridges on B3348 between Finchampstead War Memorial and Crowthorne Station.* Large garden includes a Japanese garden, a Chinese garden and a Mediterranean garden. Two greenhouses with cacti, a lean-to and a conservatory, herbaceous border, gravel garden, dwarf conifers and an organic vegetable garden all add to the interest. There is also a 1/12th scale model Tudor Village. Open by appointment. Adm including TEA with home-made cakes. *£3.50 Chd £2.50p. Please* **Tel 0118 9733274**

Woolley Park, nr Wantage ♿✿ (Mrs P Wroughton) *5m S of Wantage on A338 turn L at sign to Woolley.* Large park, fine trees and views. Two linked walled gardens beautifully planted. Teas close to Old Rectory, Farnborough. *Adm £1.50. Sun June 25 (2-6)*

Chelsea Week – London Garden Tours

The National Gardens Scheme will be offering five exclusive tours of private London gardens during Chelsea Week. The tours include gardens not normally open to the public.

For more information please see the NGS website www.ngs.org.uk or contact Mrs Julia Hickman (44) (0) 181 339 0931.

Bristol & South Gloucestershire

Hon County Organiser: Mrs Mary Bailey, Quakers, Lower Hazel, Rudgeway, Bristol BS35 3QP Tel 01454 413205

Assistant Hon County Organisers: Dr Margaret Lush, Hazel Cottage, Lower Hazel, Rudgeway, Bristol BS35 3QP Tel 01454 412112

Mrs Amanda Osmond, Church Farm House, Hawkesbury, Badminton, South Gloucestershire GL9 1BN Tel 01454 238533

County Leaflet: Mrs Jean Damey, 2 Hawburn Close, Brislington, Bristol BS4 2PB Tel 0117 9775587

Hon County Treasurer: Mr J K Dutson, The Firs, Rockhampton, Berkeley, Gloucestershire GL13 9DY Tel 01454 413210

DATES OF OPENING

Regular openings
For details see garden description
Cold Ashton Gardens
Jasmine Cottage, Clevedon
10 Linden Road, Clevedon
Pearl's Garden, Coalpit Heath
Sherborne Garden, Litton

By appointment only
For telephone numbers and other details see garden descriptions. Private visits welcomed
The Urn Cottage, Charfield

April 1 Saturday
The Brake, Tockington
Old Down House, Tockington

April 2 Sunday
The Brake, Tockington
Old Down House, Tockington

April 10 Monday
Emmaus House, Clifton Hill, Bristol

April 15 Saturday
Camers, Old Sodbury

April 16 Sunday
Camers, Old Sodbury

April 23 Sunday
Algars Manor & Algars Mill, Iron Acton

April 24 Monday
Algars Manor & Algars Mill, Iron Acton

May 4 Thursday
Jasmine Cottage, Clevedon
The Manor House, Walton-in-Gordano

May 7 Sunday
Barum, Clevedon

May 8 Monday
Emmaus House, Clifton Hill, Bristol

May 11 Thursday
Jasmine Cottage, Clevedon
The Manor House, Walton-in-Gordano

May 14 Sunday
The Yews, Stoke Gifford

May 18 Thursday
Cold Ashton Gardens
Jasmine Cottage, Clevedon
The Manor House, Walton-in-Gordano

May 21 Sunday
Algars Manor & Algars Mill, Iron Acton

May 25 Thursday
Jasmine Cottage, Clevedon
The Manor House, Walton-in-Gordano

May 28 Sunday
Highview, Portishead
10 Linden Road, Clevedon
Pearl's Garden, Coalpit Heath
Rock House, Elberton

May 29 Monday
Church Farm House, Hawkesbury
Pearl's Garden, Coalpit Heath

June 1 Thursday
Jasmine Cottage, Clevedon
The Manor House, Walton-in-Gordano

June 4 Sunday
Canynge Road Gardens, Clifton, Bristol
Sherborne Garden, Litton
Whistlewind Cottage, Barrow Gurney

June 8 Thursday
Jasmine Cottage, Clevedon
The Manor House, Walton-in-Gordano

June 11 Sunday
Barum, Clevedon
Canok Garth, Clevedon
Hazel Cottage, Lower Hazel
Tranby House, Norton Lane, Whitchurch

June 12 Monday
Emmaus House, Clifton Hill, Bristol (evening)

June 14 Wednesday
Highview, Portishead

June 15 Thursday
Cold Ashton Gardens
Jasmine Cottage, Clevedon
The Manor House, Walton-in-Gordano

June 18 Sunday
Brooklands, Burnett
Doynton House, Doynton
The Old Vicarage, Hill, nr Berkeley

June 21 Wednesday
Brooklands, Burnett

June 22 Thursday
Jasmine Cottage, Clevedon
The Manor House, Walton-in-Gordano

June 25 Sunday
Highview, Portishead
10 Linden Road, Clevedon
University of Bristol Botanic Garden

June 27 Tuesday
Bristol Zoo Gardens (evening)

June 29 Thursday
Jasmine Cottage, Clevedon
The Manor House, Walton-in-Gordano

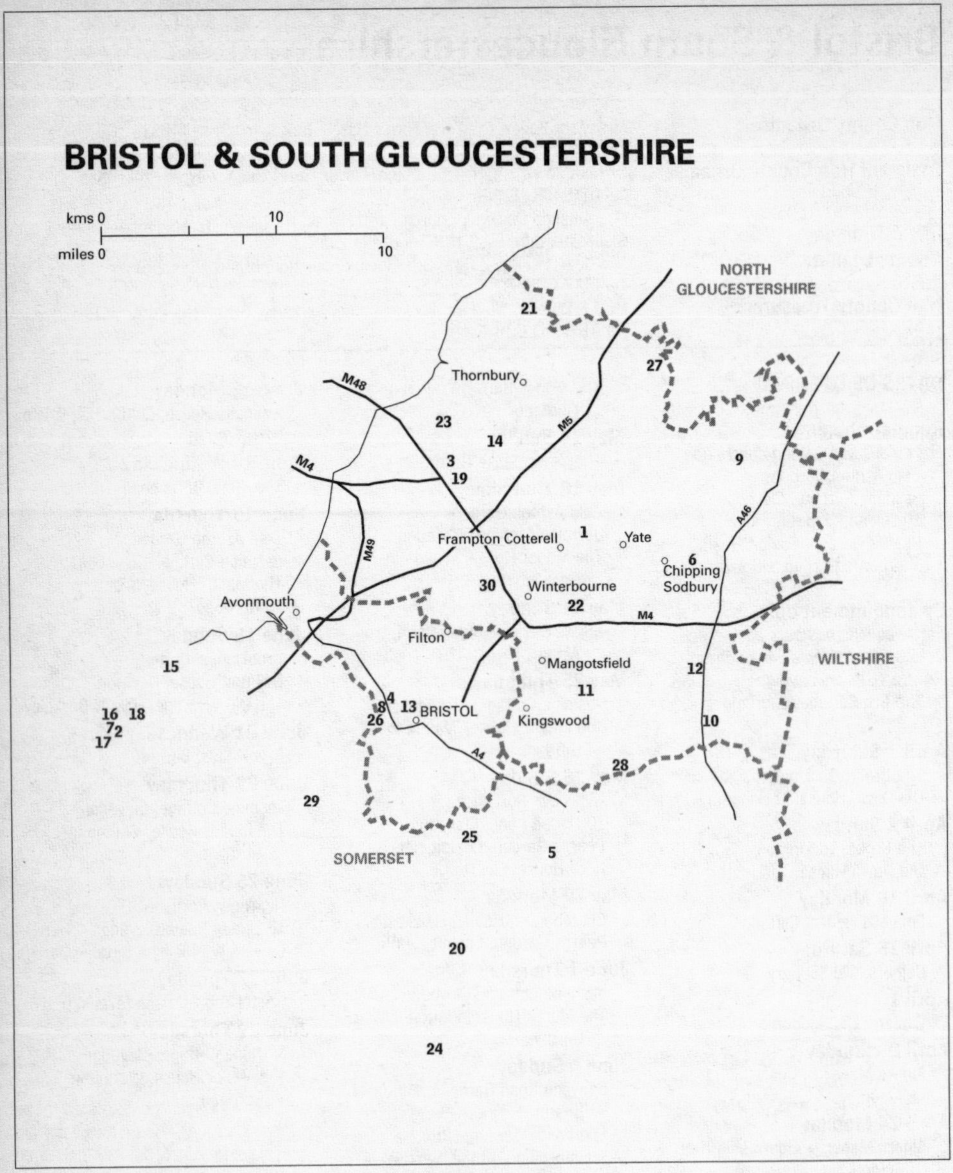

KEY

1 Algars Manor & Algars Mill
2 Barum
3 The Brake
4 Bristol Zoo Gardens
5 Brooklands
6 Camers
7 Canok Garth
8 Canynge Road Gardens
9 Church Farm House
10 Cold Ashton Gardens
11 Doynton House
12 Dyrham Park
13 Emmaus House
14 Hazel Cottage
15 Highview
16 Jasmine Cottage
17 10 Linden Road
18 The Manor House
19 Old Down House
20 2 Old Tarnwell
21 The Old Vicarage
22 Pearl's Garden
23 Rock House
24 Sherborne Garden
25 Tranby House
26 University of Bristol Botanic Garden
27 The Urn Cottage
28 West Tyning
29 Whistlewind Cottage
30 The Yews

July 2 Sunday
Barum, Clevedon
Dyrham Park, Chippenham
The Manor House, Walton-in-Gordano
Sherborne Garden, Litton

July 5 Wednesday
Highview, Portishead
2 Old Tarnwell, Upper Stanton Drew

July 6 Thursday
Jasmine Cottage, Clevedon

July 8 Saturday
West Tyning, Beach

July 9 Sunday
West Tyning, Beach

July 10 Monday
Emmaus House, Clifton Hill, Bristol

July 13 Thursday
Jasmine Cottage, Clevedon
2 Old Tarnwell, Upper Stanton Drew

July 16 Sunday
Tranby House, Norton Lane, Whitchurch

July 18 Tuesday
2 Old Tarnwell, Upper Stanton Drew

July 19 Wednesday
Highview, Portishead

July 20 Thursday
Cold Ashton Gardens
Jasmine Cottage, Clevedon

July 22 Saturday
Camers, Old Sodbury

July 23 Sunday
Camers, Old Sodbury

July 27 Thursday
Jasmine Cottage, Clevedon

July 29 Saturday
Jasmine Cottage, Clevedon

July 30 Sunday
Highview, Portishead
Jasmine Cottage, Clevedon

August 3 Thursday
Jasmine Cottage, Clevedon

August 6 Sunday
Sherborne Garden, Litton

August 10 Thursday
Jasmine Cottage, Clevedon

August 13 Sunday
Highview, Portishead

August 16 Wednesday
Highview, Portishead

August 17 Thursday
Cold Ashton Gardens
Jasmine Cottage, Clevedon

August 20 Sunday
Barum, Clevedon
Tranby House, Norton Lane, Whitchurch

August 24 Thursday
Jasmine Cottage, Clevedon

August 27 Sunday
Highview, Portishead

August 30 Wednesday
Highview, Portishead

August 31 Thursday
Jasmine Cottage, Clevedon

September 3 Sunday
University of Bristol Botanic Garden

September 10 Sunday
Highview, Portishead

September 11 Monday
Emmaus House, Clifton Hill, Bristol

September 13 Wednesday
Highview, Portishead

September 17 Sunday
Sherborne Garden, Litton

September 21 Thursday
Cold Ashton Gardens

DESCRIPTIONS OF GARDENS

Algars Manor & Algars Mill, Iron Acton *9m N of Bristol. 3m W of Yate/Chipping Sodbury. Turn S off Iron Acton bypass B4059, past village green, 200yds, then over level Xing (Station Rd).* TEAS outdoors at Algars Manor (weather permitting). *Combined adm £2 Chd free. Easter Sun, Mon April 23, 24, Sun May 21 (2-5)*

Algars Manor ❀ (Dr & Mrs J M Naish) 2 acres of woodland garden beside R Frome; mill stream; native plants mixed with azaleas, rhododendrons, camellias, magnolias, eucalyptus. Picnic areas. Early Jacobean house (not open) and old barn. *Private visits welcome* **Tel 01454 228372**

Algars Mill (Mr & Mrs John Wright) *Entrance via Algars Manor.* 2 acres woodland garden beside R Frome; spring bulbs, shrubs; early spring feature of wild Newent daffodils. 300-400 yr old mill house (not open) through which mill-race still runs

Barum, Clevedon ✤❀ (Marian & Roger Peacock) *50 Edward Rd. M5 junction 20 follow signs to pier, cont N, past Walton Park Hotel, turn R at St Mary's Church, then up Channel Rd, over Xrds, turn L into Edward Rd at top.* ⅓ acre plantsman's garden in sheltered coastal location on well-drained soil. Crammed with unusual plants giving yr-round interest. Specialities: southern hemisphere and half-hardies. Vegetable patch. Plants propagated from garden. Cold refreshments. *Adm £1.50 Chd free. (ACNO to League of Friends of Clevedon Cottage Hospital) Suns May 7, June 11, July 2, Aug 20 (2-5.30). Groups welcome by appt, please* **Tel 01275 341584** More info at www.50-barum.freeserve.co.uk

The Brake, Tockington (Mr & Mrs D C J Skinner) *Vicarage Lane. 10m N of Bristol. From A38 turn L signposted Tockington/Olveston after bridging M4. Turn R at triangle in Tockington, after 50yds turn L into Old Down Hill. Turn L at top of hill then immed R. Alternatively follow brown signs to Oldown.* Fine views of Severn Estuary and both bridges. Long mixed borders with emphasis on plants and shrubs that thrive on dry, exposed hillside; woodland walk with interesting ground cover, bulbs, cyclamen. *Combined adm with Old Down House £2 Chd free (ACNO to Fairbridge West). Sat, Sun April 1, 2 (2-6)*

Bristol Zoo Gardens ♿✤ (Bristol Zoo Gardens) *From M5, take A4018 via junction 17 or A4 via junction 18, then follow brown elephant signs. These signs can also be followed from city centre. Please use main entrance on A4176 (Clifton Down).* The Zoo has 12 acres of garden with something for everyone, from spectacular bedding and herbaceous borders to a rose garden, rock garden, large lake and numerous trees and shrubs. Gardens established in 1835. Sorry no guide dogs. TEAS in aid of Zoological Society. *Adm £2.50 OAPs £2 Chd £1.* **Evening Opening** *Tues June 27 (6-8)*

Brooklands, Burnett ♿✤❀ (Mr & Mrs P Stevens) *2m S Keynsham on B3116. Turn R into Burnett village.* 1½ acres; mature trees and variety of ornamental shrubs; rose garden; herbaceous border; extensive planting of shrub roses and clematis; fine views of distant Mendip Hills. TEAS (on Sun in aid of St Michael's Church, Burnett) *Adm £1.50 Chd free. Sun June 18, Wed June 21 (2-6)*

Camers, Old Sodbury ❀ (Mr & Mrs A G Denman) *Entrance in Chapel Lane off A432 at Dog Inn.* Over 2 acres set on hillside, with fine views across Severn Vale. Mature setting with recent planting, large expanding collection of shrubs and herbaceous plants. Good spring display of bulbs and flowering shrubs plus yr-round interest, incl parterre, walled herbaceous borders, waterfall, orchard, small wooded area, wild area and attractive Elizabethan house (not open). TEAS. *Adm £2. Sats, Suns April 15, 16 (No Teas), July 22, 23 (Plants for sale) (2-6). Private parties welcome weekdays only, min 10 people, please* **Tel 01454 322430**

Canok Garth, Clevedon ♿ (Mr & Mrs Peter Curtis) *9 Channel Rd. 12m W of Bristol (Junction 20 off M5). Follow signs to seafront and pier, continue N on B3124 past Walton Park Hotel, turn R at St Mary's Church.* ½ acre garden with a little of everything. Herbaceous border, shrubs and trees, annuals, lawns, fruit and vegetables. Fairly intensively cultivated, but with ample room for grandchildren. TEA. *Adm £1.50 Chd free. Sun June 11 (2-6)*

Canynge Road Gardens, Clifton, Bristol *Close to Clifton Suspension Bridge between The Mansion House and Christ Church. Combined adm £2. Sun June 4 (2-5.30)*

43 Canynge Road (Martin & Angela Appleby) Happy garden for children and birds. Organic vegetables. Lovely summer house. Half the plot newly planted in 98. Each separate lawn area has a different mood

45 Canynge Road ♿ (Professor & Mrs J F Nye) ⅓ acre mostly shrubs. Mulberry tree and pool backed by yew hedge

51 Canynge Road ♿ (Mr & Mrs Feneley) ¼ acre walled town garden

43 Canynge Square ✗ (Mr & Mrs Simon Moore) Small town garden on different levels, walled and mostly laid with gravel. Strong emphasis on plants, particularly climbers, that enhance its architectural qualities. Sculpture and Art Exhibition TEAS.

Norland House ♿ (Prof J L & Dr P A Burton) *33 Canynge Road.* Front garden of regency house (not open) with shrubs, geraniums, bonsai trees, gazebo, pergola and pond

NEW **11 Percival Road** ✗❀ (Mr & Mrs R L Bland) Small, enclosed urban garden, most plants in containers. Large variety of individual, interesting plants all grown from seeds and cutttings

Wellington House (Jan & Nigel Pickersgill) *21 Canynge Road.* Beautifully constructed (summer 1997) family garden covering approx ⅓ acre on 3 sides of the dwelling. Large lawn, shrub, herbaceous perennial and shade planting

Church Farm House, Hawkesbury ✗❀ (Mr & Mrs R N Osmond) *Turn off A46 to Hawkesbury Upton and drive through village. Turn L by pond and drive down hill, signed to St Mary's Church.* Idyllic country garden with pond and newly established formal garden in ancient hamlet opp historic church (open). TEAS in aid of St Mary's Church. *Adm 1.50 Chd free. Bank Hol Mon May 29 (2-6)*

Cold Ashton Gardens ♿✗ *6m N of Bath on A46. Turn R into village just before roundabout. Turn R into drive by telephone box. Park in Cold Ashton and transport will be provided to Special Plants. Combined adm £1.50 Chd 50p. Thurs May 18, June 15, July 20, Aug 17, Sept 21 (2-6). Private visits by appt see each garden.*

■ **The Chestnuts** (Carol and Dave Watts) 1 acre in the making. Enclosed areas of differing character. Lawns, ponds, mixed plantings, dried flowers. Visitors are invited to share our progress as we expand to incl a potager and herb garden. TEAS. *Open every weekend and Bank Hol Mons May to Sept (2-6).*
Tel 01225 892020

Special Plants ❀ (Derry Watkins) Architect-designed ½ acre hillside garden with stunning views. Started autumn '96. Exotic plants, many collected in S Africa. Gravel garden for borderline hardy plants. Grass garden. Spring-fed ponds. Bog garden. Woodland walk.
Tel 01225 891686

Doynton House, Doynton ♿❀ (Mrs C E Pitman) *8m E of Bristol 7m N of Bath, ¾m NE of A420 at E end of Wick.* Mature, old-fashioned 2 acre garden with herbaceous borders, roses and clematis, shrubs and lawns. TEAS. *Adm £1.50 Chd free. Sun June 18 (2-6)*

▲ **Dyrham Park, Chippenham** ♿✗❀ (The National Trust) *8m N of Bath. 12m E of Bristol. Approached from Bath to Stroud rd (A46), 2m S of Tormarton interchange with M4 exit 18.* Situated on W side of late C17 house. Herbaceous borders, yews clipped as buttresses, ponds and cascade, Parish Church set on terrace. Niches and carved urns. Long lawn to old West entrance. Deer Park and restored orangery. TEAS in aid of NT. *Adm incl Deer Park £2.60 Chd £1.20 Family group £6.50. For NGS Sun July 2 (11-5.30)*

Emmaus House, Clifton Hill, Bristol ✗❀ (Sisters of La Retraite) *From Clifton Downs down to Clifton Village to bottom of Regent St on R.* 1½ acres with Victorian walled kitchen garden, also fruit, formal herb and Zen gardens. Rose and herbaceous borders, lawns, secret garden, ponds with fountains and fine views towards Dundry. Bristol in Bloom winner 1997, 1999. TEAS. *Adm £1.50 OAPs £1 Chd free. Mons April 10, May 8, July 10, Sept 11 (10.30-4.30).* **Evening Opening** *Mon June 12 (5.30-8). Private visits welcome by prior arrangement, weekdays only April-Sept please,*
Tel 0117 9079950

Hazel Cottage, Lower Hazel ✗❀ (Dr & Mrs Brandon Lush) *700yds W of Rudgeway from A38; 10m N of Bristol.* ½ acre cottage garden in rural setting with wide variety of plants and shrubs incl alpines and some unusual varieties. TEAS in aid of BRACE. *Adm £1.50 Chd 50p. Sun June 11 (2-5)*

Highview, Portishead ✗ (Mr & Mrs M Clavey) *From Bristol take A369 (10m) M5 junction 19. At Portishead take Nore Rd (Coast Rd) for 1½m, pass garden centre, take 2nd L into Hill Crest Rd and L to bottom of private drive. Please park in Hillcrest Rd.* ¾ acre garden with over 400 mixed heathers. Herbaceous and rockery plants, rose bed, water features, alpine bed, pergolas. Outstanding Channel views. Approach to house (not open) and garden on slope. Home-made TEAS. Light lunches on Suns. *Adm £1.50 Chd free.*

Weds June 14, July 5, 19, Aug 16, 30, Sept 13, Suns May 28, June 25, July 30, Aug 13, 27, Sept 10 (11-5.30). Private visits welcome, please **Tel 01275 849873**

Jasmine Cottage, Clevedon ✇❀ (Mr & Mrs M Redgrave) *26 Channel Rd. 12m W of Bristol (M5 junction 20). Follow signs to seafront and pier, continue N on B3124, past Walton Park Hotel, turn R at St Mary's Church.* Medium-sized garden created by owners from wooded shelter belt for interest in all seasons. New features and plantings for new century with many clematis, tender perennials and unusual climbers. Toilet facilities. TEAS. *Adm £1.50 Chd free. Garden and nursery open every Weds, Thurs May 3 to Aug 31 (2-5), Sat, Sun July 29, 30. (2-5.30). Private visits and groups welcome May to Sept, please* **Tel 01275 871850**

10 Linden Road, Clevedon ❀ (Mr & Mrs W Salisbury) *Coming from seafront, head up Alexandra Rd opp the pier, cross roundabout. Linden Rd is between Midland and Barclays Banks. No 10 is 150yds on R.* Very small but richly planted seaside town garden. Over 400 different species of trees, shrubs and plants grow in 3 areas, the largest being 35′ × 40′. After 10 yrs this area has been redesigned and visitors are welcome to share the changes with owners as they develop the garden as featured on 'Gardeners World'. TEAS on open days. *Adm £1 Chd free. Suns May 28, June 25. (2 - 5.30). Open by appt Jan to Oct, please* **Tel 01275 874694**

The Manor House, Walton-in-Gordano ♿✇ (Mr & Mrs Caryl Wills & Mr & Mrs Simon Wills) *2m NE of Clevedon. Entrance on N side of B3124, Clevedon to Portishead Rd, just by houses on roadside nearest Clevedon. Clevedon-Portishead buses stop in village.* 4 acres; trees, shrubs, herbaceous and bulbs, mostly labelled. TEAS Suns only. *Adm £2, Acc chd under 14 free (ACNO to St Peter's Hospice, Bristol) Sun July 2 (2-6), Thurs May 4, 11, 18, 25, June 1, 8, 15, 22, 29 (10-4). Open by appt all year, please* **Tel 01275 872067**

Old Down House, Tockington ♿❀ (Mr & Mrs Robert Bernays) *10m N of Bristol. Follow brown Tourist Board signs to Oldown from A38 at Alveston.* 5 acres divided into small formal and informal gardens by hedges and walls; topiary, shrubs; extensive lawns; rock garden; fine trees (weeping beeches, etc). Herbaceous borders, semi-wild areas with spring and autumn cyclamen; fine views to Severn and Welsh hills. TEAS. *Combined adm with The Brake £2 Chd free (ACNO to Fairbridge West) Sat, Sun April 1, 2 (2-6). Private parties welcome, please* **Tel 01454 413605**

2 Old Tarnwell, Upper Stanton Drew ✇❀ (Mr & Mrs K Payne) *Lies 6m S of Bristol between B3130 and A368 just W of Pensford. Detailed directions given when appt. is made.* A quart of good plants poured into a quarter-pint sized plot featuring colour themed borders, ornamental grasses, clematis and a well stocked "puddle"! Possibly the smallest, most intensively planted garden in the Yellow Book (total 0.02 acres). Plenty of ideas for small gardeners! Regret not suitable for children. Featured on HTV's All Gardens Great and Small, and in The English Garden. *Adm £2 (incl plant list). Only by appt Wed July 5, Thur July 13, Tues July 18 (10-8), please* **Tel 01275 333146**

The Old Vicarage, Hill, nr Berkeley ♿✇❀ (Dr & Mrs A Longstaff) *2m N of Thornbury. At Whitfield on A38 take B4061. Turn R at Upper Morton and follow signposts to Rockhampton then Hill. Old Vicarage on R after entrances to Church and Hill Court.* Set against the backdrop of the small arboretum of Hill Court and charming tiny Church of St Michael, this Victorian vicarage garden has in recent yrs been largely redesigned and replanted. Features incl a part-walled brick-pathed potager, with moon gate. Unusual herbaceous plants and shrubs, 2 ponds and new bog garden. TEAS. *Adm £1.50 Chd free. Sun June 18 (2-5)*

■ **Pearl's Garden, Coalpit Heath** ♿✇❀ (Mr D Watts) *Take Downend (Westerleigh Rd) to Tormarton Rd past Folly public house over motorway and garden is 500yds on L. From junction 18 on M4, turn N on A46 and almost immed L signposted Pucklechurch. After 5½m garden is on R shortly before bridge over M4.* 2 acres mature trees; herb and terrace gardens; 100 different hollies. Designed and built by owners since 1966 with water features and peafowl. Seating. TEAS. *Adm £2 Chd free. Each Sun in May and June. For NGS Sun, Bank Hol Mon May 28, 29 (12-5). Ploughman's lunch available. Also private visits welcome May and June, please* **Tel 01179 562953**

Rock House, Elberton ✇❀ (Mr & Mrs John Gunnery) *From Old Severn Bridge on M48 take B4461 to Alveston. In Elberton, take 1st turning L to Littleton-on-Severn and turn immed R.* 1-acre walled garden undergoing improvement. Pond and old yew tree,mixed borders, cottage garden plants. *Adm £1.50 Chd free (ACNO to St John's Church, Elberton). Sun May 28 (2-6)*

■ **Sherborne Garden, Litton** ♿❀ (Mr & Mrs John Southwell) *15m S of Bristol, 15m W of Bath, 7m N of Wells. On B3114 Litton to Harptree rd, ½m past The Kings Arms.* 4½ acre gently sloping landscaped garden of considerable horticultural interest. There is a small coniferum, giant grasses area, a woodland garden and three linked ponds with bridges. The collections of hollies (100), ferns (250), Asian wild roses and their hybrids and climbing species are all well labelled, likewise hemerocallis, water lilies and unusual trees and shrubs. Picnic area, field car park. Coffee/TEA. *Adm £2 Chd free. Every Mon, June to end of Sept. For NGS Sun June 4, July 2, August 6, Sept 17 (11-6). Private visits and groups welcome throughout year, please* **Tel 01761 241220**

Tranby House, Norton Lane, Whitchurch ✇❀ (Jan Barkworth) *½m S of Whitchurch. Leave Bristol on A37 Wells Rd, through Whitchurch village 1st turning on R, signposted Norton Malreward.* 1¼ acre informal garden, designed and planted to encourage wildlife. Wide variety of trees, shrubs and flowers; ponds and wild flower meadow. Plants and pressed flower cards for sale in aid of The Wildlife Trust. Partly suitable for wheelchairs. TEA. *Adm £1.50 Chd free. Suns June 11, July 16, Aug 20 (2-5)*

University of Bristol Botanic Garden ♿✇❀ *Bracken Hill, North Rd, Leigh Woods, 1m W of Bristol via Clifton. Cross suspension bridge, North Rd is 1st R.* As featured on Gardeners' World and HTV Garden Calendar, Superintendent Nicholas Wray (Presenter). 5 acre garden supporting approx

4,500 species. Range of glasshouses and large Pulhams rock garden. Cream TEAS. *Adm £1.50 Chd free (ACNO to Friends of Bristol University Botanic Garden). For NGS Suns June 25, Sept 3 (10-5). NB Nursery for plant sales closed 1-2 for watering, tidying and restocking. Group visits welcome by appt all year, please* **Tel/Fax 01179 733682**

The Urn Cottage, Charfield (Mr A C & Dr L A Rosser) *19 Station Rd. 3m E of M5 exit 14. In Charfield turn off main road at The Railway Tavern, then 400yds on L: short walk from parking.* Family garden, created from scratch by owners since 1982 surrounding stone-built cottage (not open) with Cotswold views. Richly planted with schemes differing in character from sunbaked flagstones to stream-side shade. Experiments in plant association incl colour, foliage, grasses, groundcover, with always an emphasis on well behaved plants, continuity of interest and wildlife. TEAS in aid of Camphill Village Trust. *Adm £2. Parties by appt all year,* **Tel 01453 843156**

West Tyning, Beach (Mr & Mrs G S Alexander) *From Bath (6m) or Bristol (7m) on A43l. From Bitton turn N up Golden Valley Lane, signposted Beach. Continue 2m to Wick-Upton Cheyney Xrds, turn R towards Upton Cheyney for 200yds.* 1¼ acre garden; roses and clematis over pergolas which separate and join different areas; lawns with curved mixed borders in sun and shade; woodland with ferns, hellebores and other shade plants; rough grass with fruit and shrubs; rock garden and vegetable garden. Cream TEAS with home-made cakes in aid of Bitton WI. *Adm £1.50 Chd free. Sat, Sun July 8, 9 (2-6). Groups welcome by appt, please* **Tel 01179 322294**

Whistlewind Cottage, Barrow Gurney (Mr and Mrs K Clark) *Take A38 SW from Bristol. At t-lights by Barrow water tanks, turn R to Barrow Gurney on B3130. 50yds turn R into Hern Lane and R again into Wild Country Lane. Approx ½m on L.* Main gardens approx 1 acre, with pond/patio area, alpines, shade area as well as many other beds stocked with herbaceous and half-hardy perennials, many unusual or rare. Gardens developed over past 16yrs. Cream TEAS in aid of Cheddar Vale Lions Club. *Adm £1.50 Chd 50p Sun June 4 (2-5). Private visits and groups welcome, please* **Tel 01275 472873**

NEW **The Yews, Stoke Gifford** (Dr Barbara Laue) *Take A4174 ring road from Filton towards M32. Continue over roundabout by Sainsburys towards M32. After 200yds take L turn into Harry Stoke Rd. Entrance is first house on R, after 150yds. NB access to Harry Stoke Rd may be changed in spring 2000 due to roadworks.* Approx 1 acre in rural setting, extended and developed by present owners since 1990. Small formal area with pond surrounded by herbaceous borders and clipped box. Spring bulbs and blossom. Raised bed system in vegetable garden. TEAS in aid of St Peter's Hospice. *Adm £1.50 Chd free. Sun May 14 (2-5.30)*

Evening Opening (See also garden description)

Bristol Zoo Gardens	June 27
Emmaus House, Clifton Hill, Bristol	June 12

Association of Gardens Trusts

The Association of Gardens Trusts is the national organisation representing the growing number of County Gardens Trusts which are actively engaged in researching, documenting and caring for our heritage of parks, gardens and designed landscapes. The aims of the AGT are to provide support for the Trusts and to promote a proper understanding of the importance of parks and gardens at a local and national level.

The County Gardens Trusts have been established since 1984, as educational charities to promote the enjoyment and conservation of historic parks and gardens. They are active in many ways, including conservation, protection, education and community activities. The Trusts are always looking for new members who can help in numerous ways and will enjoy a host of activities e.g. recording, fund raising, publicity, checking planning applications, working with schools, or simply enjoying the stimulating programme of visits to gardens which are often of historic interest.

To find your local County Gardens Trust, please contact:

Sally Walker, The Administrator
Association of Gardens Trusts
70 Cowcross Street, London EC1M 6EJ
Telephone and Fax: 0207 251 2610
Email: gardenstrusts@btinternet.com
Website: www.btinternet.com/gardenstrusts

Buckinghamshire

Hon County Organiser: Mrs Sue Wright, Brudenell House, Church Street, Quainton, Aylesbury HP22 4AW Tel 01296 655250

Assistant Hon County Organisers: Mrs Angela Sanderson, Wellfield House, Cuddington, Aylesbury HP18 0BB (Supplies) Tel 01844 291626
Mrs Maggie Bateson, Fressingwood, Little Kingshill HP16 0EF Tel 01494 866265

Hon County Treasurer: Dr H Beric Wright

DATES OF OPENING

Regular openings
For details see garden description
Turn End, Haddenham

By appointment only
For telephone numbers and other details see garden descriptions. Private visits welcomed
Blossoms, Cobblers Hill
Court Farm, Worminghall
Hall Barn, Beaconsfield
Old Farm, Brill
Springlea, Seymour Plain
Watercroft, Penn
Wichert, Ford

February 20 Sunday
Great Barfield, Bradenham

March 5 Sunday
Campden Cottage, Chesham Bois

April 2 Sunday
Turn End, Haddenham

April 9 Sunday
Campden Cottage, Chesham Bois
Great Barfield, Bradenham
6 Oldfield Close, Little Chalfont

April 16 Sunday
Long Crendon Gardens
The Old Vicarage, Padbury
6 Oldfield Close, Little Chalfont
Whitchurch Gardens
The White House, Denham Village

April 23 Sunday
Overstroud Cottage, Frith Hill
Whitewalls, Marlow

April 30 Sunday
The Manor House, Bledlow
Nether Winchendon House

May 1 Monday
Ascott, Wing
Gracefield, Lacey Green
Turn End, Haddenham
Winslow Hall, Winslow

May 3 Wednesday
Waddesdon Dairy Water Garden

May 7 Sunday
Campden Cottage, Chesham Bois
Cliveden, Taplow
Waddesdon Dairy Water Garden

May 10 Wednesday
Cublington Gardens

May 14 Sunday
Favershams Meadow, Gerrards Cross
Fressingwood, Little Kingshill
Peppers, Gt Missenden

May 17 Wednesday
Gipsy House, Gt Missenden

May 21 Sunday
Brill Gardens

May 28 Sunday
63 Highbridge Road, Aylesbury
Cuddington Gardens, nr Thame
The Lee Gardens, Great Missenden
Overstroud Cottage, Frith Hill

May 29 Monday
The Manor Farm, Little Horwood

May 31 Wednesday
Cuddington Gardens, nr Thame

June 4 Sunday
Campden Cottage, Chesham Bois
Chalfont St Giles Gardens

June 7 Wednesday
Gipsy House, Gt Missenden
Waddesdon Dairy Water Garden

June 10 Saturday
Olney Gardens

June 11 Sunday
Cublington Gardens
Olney Gardens
Quainton Gardens
Waddesdon Dairy Water Garden

June 18 Sunday
Abbotts House, Winslow
Favershams Meadow, Gerrards Cross
Hillesden House, Hillesden
Long Crendon Gardens
The Manor House, Bledlow
Nether Winchendon House
Weir Lodge, Chesham

June 21 Wednesday
Old Manor Farm, Cublington

June 25 Sunday
Askett Gardens
Aylesbury Gardens
East & Botolph Claydon Gardens
The Manor House, Hambleden
Tythrop Park, Kingsey
Woolleys, Hambleden

June 28 Wednesday
Dorneywood Garden, Burnham

June 29 to 30 Thursday to Friday
The Old Vicarage, Padbury (evening)

July 2 Sunday
Cheddington Gardens
Overstroud Cottage, Frith Hill

July 5 Wednesday
14 The Square, Brill
Stowe Landscape Gardens, Buckingham

July 7 Friday
Stowe Landscape Gardens, Buckingham

July 9 Sunday
Campden Cottage, Chesham Bois
The White House, Denham Village

July 12 Wednesday
Gipsy House, Gt Missenden
14 The Square, Brill

July 16 Sunday
Quainton Gardens
Whitewalls, Marlow

July 19 Wednesday
Dorneywood Garden, Burnham
14 The Square, Brill

July 23 Sunday
63 Highbridge Road, Aylesbury
Hughenden Manor, High Wycombe

July 26 Wednesday
14 The Square, Brill

August 2 Wednesday
14 The Square, Brill

August 5 Saturday
Dorneywood Garden, Burnham

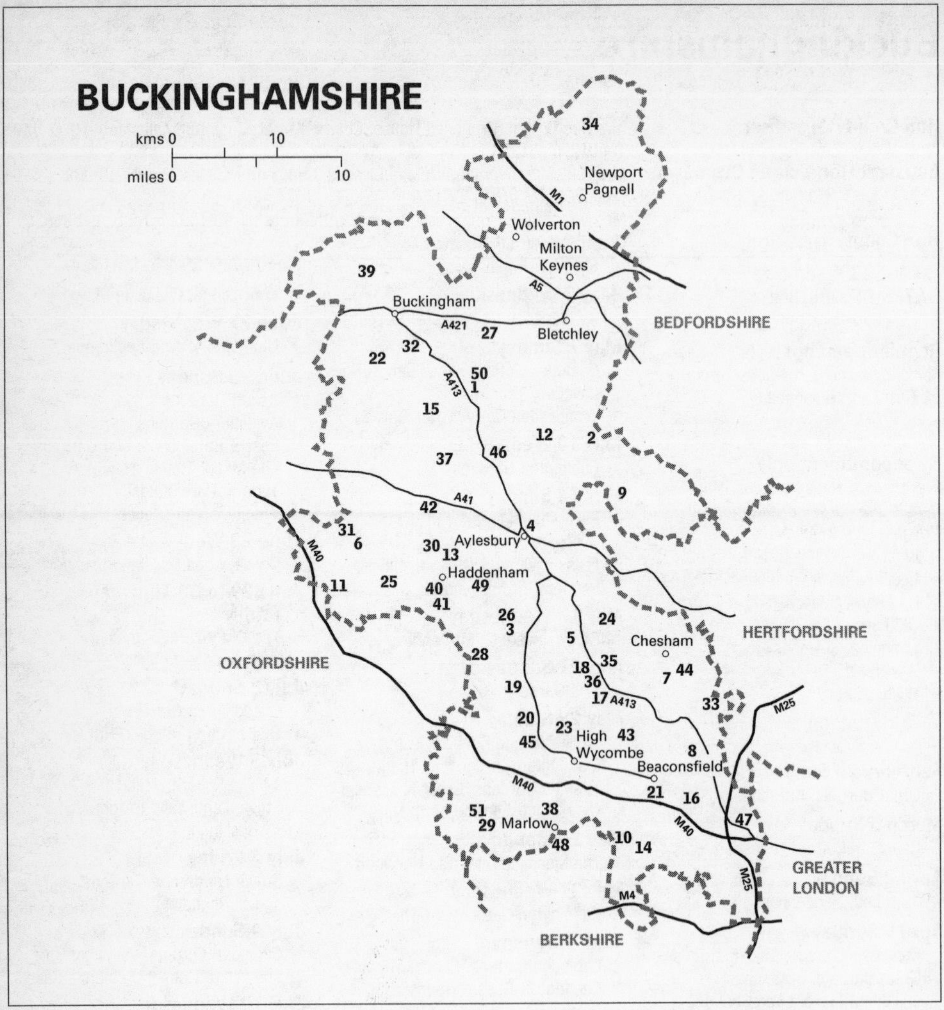

KEY

1 Abbotts House
2 Ascott
3 Askett Gardens
4 Aylesbury Gardens
5 Blossoms
6 Brill Gardens
7 Campden Cottage
8 Chalfont St Giles Gardens
9 Cheddington Gardens
10 Cliveden
11 Court Farm
12 Cublington Gardens
13 Cuddington Gardens
14 Dorneywood Garden
15 East & Botolph Claydon Gardens
16 Favershams Meadow
17 Fressingwood
18 Gipsy House
19 Gracefield
20 Great Barfield
21 Hall Barn
22 Hillesden House
23 Hughenden Manor
24 The Lee Gardens
25 Long Crendon Gardens
26 Lower Icknield Farm
27 The Manor Farm
28 The Manor House, Bledlow
29 The Manor House, Hambleden
30 Nether Winchendon House
31 Old Farm
32 The Old Vicarage
33 6 Oldfield Close
34 Olney Gardens
35 Overstroud Cottage
36 Peppers
37 Quainton Gardens
38 Springlea
39 Stowe Landscape Gardens
40 Turn End
41 Tythrop Park
42 Waddesdon Dairy Water Garden
43 Watercroft
44 Weir Lodge
45 West Wycombe Park
46 Whitchurch Gardens
47 The White House
48 Whitewalls
49 Wichert
50 Winslow Hall
51 Woolleys

August 6 Sunday
Campden Cottage, Chesham Bois

August 9 Wednesday
14 The Square, Brill

August 16 Wednesday
14 The Square, Brill

August 19 Saturday
Lower Icknield Farm, Kimble

August 20 Sunday
Lower Icknield Farm, Kimble

August 23 Wednesday
14 The Square, Brill

August 27 Sunday
Peppers, Gt Missenden

August 28 Monday
Ascott, Wing

August 30 Wednesday
14 The Square, Brill

September 3 Sunday
Campden Cottage, Chesham Bois
West Wycombe Park, West Wycombe

September 10 Sunday
Cliveden, Taplow

September 17 Sunday
Turn End, Haddenham
Whitewalls, Marlow

September 24 Sunday
Gipsy House, Gt Missenden

October 8 Sunday
Campden Cottage, Chesham Bois

October 28 Saturday
Great Barfield, Bradenham

October 29 Sunday
Great Barfield, Bradenham

November 29 Wednesday
Waddesdon Dairy Water Garden

December 3 Sunday
Waddesdon Dairy Water Garden

DESCRIPTIONS OF GARDENS

Abbotts House, Winslow ♿⚘❀ (Mrs Jane Rennie) *9m N of Aylesbury on A413, into Winslow. Town centre parking. Pedestrian access off Church Walk, opp W door of St Laurence's Church.* ¼ acre, walled Victorian kitchen garden. Renovated and replanted in 1989. Herbaceous borders, herb and vegetable beds, fruit pergola, wall fruit and shrubs, greenhouse. Pond, pergola and numerous tubs. TEAS (% tea and plant sales to NGS). *Adm £1.20 Chd free. Sun June 18 (2-5). Private visits welcome, please* **Tel 01296 712326**

▲ **Ascott, Wing** ♿⚘ (Sir Evelyn & Lady de Rothschild) *2m SW of Leighton Buzzard, 8m NE of Aylesbury via A418. Bus: 141 Aylesbury-Leighton Buzzard.* Combining Victorian formality with early C20 natural style and recent plantings to lead it into the C21. Terraced lawns with specimen and ornamental trees; panoramic views to Chilterns. Naturalised bulbs, mirror image herbaceous borders. Impressive topiary incl box and yew sundial and Planet garden. *Adm (incl NT members) £4 Chd £2 under 5 free. For NGS Bank Hol Mons May 1, Aug 28 (2-6). Last adm 5pm*

Askett Gardens ♿⚘❀ *1m from Princes Risborough on A4010 to Aylesbury. At Black House roundabout, turn into Askett village. Plant stall on green.* TEAS. *Combined adm £3 Chd free (ACNO to Lymphoma Association). Sun June 25 (2-6)*

The Bell House (Mr & Mrs I Pearce)

The Bell House Barn (Mrs Christine Ramsay) 1 acre cottage garden with stream. Hardy perennials, shrubs and roses with backcloth of mature trees in parkland setting

Meadowcroft Farmhouse (Mr & Mrs N Murtagh) Walled garden with stream. Mixed shrub border

Old Rose Cottage (Mr & Mrs G A Davies) 1 acre with N-facing walled border. Collection of hardy geraniums and old roses. Herb garden and specimen trees. TEAS.

NEW **Penn Cottage** (Mr & Mrs A Brett) Cottage garden with views of Chiltern Hills. Landscaped pond and water feature

Three Ways Cottage (Dr & Mrs P N J Appleton) 1 acre former orchard. Mixed herbaceous plants and shrubs, kitchen garden. TEAS.

Aylesbury Gardens ⚘❀ *¾m SE of Aylesbury centre. Four well designed interesting town gardens off A413.* TEAS. *Combined adm £3 Chd free. Sun June 25 (11-5)*

63 Highbridge Road, Aylesbury ❀ (Mr & Mrs H.A. Goodair) 8yr-old cottage garden with fine collection of unusual and rare plants, many variegated. Young trees and over 100 clematis. Paved patio with raised pond and containerised plants. Teas. *Also open Suns May 28, July 23. Adm £1 Chd free.*

2 Spenser Road (Mr & Mrs G.A. Brown) Well stocked with large Victorian greenhouses. Collection of pelargoniums, ornamental pond and numerous trees, many raised from seed

90 Walton Way (Mr & Mrs R Lewis-Smith) Established garden with wide variety of hardy and tender perennials. Winding paths past informal borders lead to wildlife pond with marginal and bog areas; larger pond with koi carp

7 Westminster Drive (Mr & Mrs B J Ferguson) Formal town garden with interesting features incl mixed borders, shrubs and annuals. Pergola with hanging baskets, also vegetable parterre and recently established pond. Winner 1999 Aylesbury Vale in Bloom for best large garden. TEAS.

Blossoms, Cobblers Hill ♿⚘ (Dr & Mrs F Hytten) *2½m NW of Great Missenden by Rignall Rd, signed Butler's Cross, to Kings Lane 1½m on R, then to top of Cobblers Hill. Turn R at yellow stone marker and after 50yds turn R again at stone, marked Blossoms.* 4 acres begun as hill-top fields, plus 1-acre beechwood. Lawns, old apple orchard, small lake, water, troughs, scree and patio gardens. Large areas of bluebells, wild daffodils, fritillaria and other spring bulbs. Flowering cherries, large climbing roses and many other interesting trees incl acers, eucalyptus and salix; foliage effects throughout year. TEAS. *Adm £1.50. Private visits only, please* **Tel 01494 863140**

Brill Gardens ♿⚘❀ *7m N of Thame. Turn off B4011, or turn off A41 at Kingswood, both signed Brill.* C17 windmill open. TEAS. *Combined adm £3 Chd free. Adm to windmill 50p Chd 30p (2-5) Sun May 21(2-6)*

Leap Hill (Mr & Mrs R Morris-Adams) *Thame Rd. Approx 1m from Brill centre.* 2 acres; roses, shrubs, hedges and herbaceous borders; pond, bog area and rockery, vegetable garden and woodland. Windy garden with outstanding views over Vale of Aylesbury

The Old Vicarage (Mr & Mrs Peter Toynbee) 3/4 acre, partly walled garden. Mature trees; 2 small ponds with wildlife; formal potager; many shady areas; unusual features. Children especially welcome

NEW **11 The Square, Brill** (Mr & Mrs W B Downing) Small cottage garden with patio. Herbaceous plants in borders. Assorted pots on patio. Climbing plants, roses, clematis and golden hop

NEW **12 The Square, Brill** (Mrs Heather Howes) Very small, triangular garden. With more vertical than horizontal space there are clematis, roses and other climbing plants. Owner's sculptures amongst foliage. Circular pond with water jet

14 The Square, Brill (Mrs Audrey Dyer) *Near War Memorial.* Small, secret paved garden behind terraced cottage packed with plants for yr-round interest, many scented, some in pots handbuilt by owner. Small wildlife pond. *Also open Weds July and August (2-5). Teas. Adm £1 Chd free. Small parties welcome, please* **Tel 01844 237148**

NEW **Temple House** (Mr & Mrs W Underwood) *Temple St.* Brambles and ground elder were main features until recently. Now original paths revealed and on-going planting schemes have created a garden more in keeping with house and surrounding walls.

Campden Cottage, Chesham Bois ✗✿ (Mrs P Liechti) *51 Clifton Rd, signed from A416 mid-way between Amersham-on-the-Hill and Chesham nr pedestrian lights. Car park signed on main rd.* ½-acre plantsman's garden of yr-round interest; fine collection of unusual and rare plants. Hellebores in March. Featured in The Good Gardens Guide 2000. Regret no pushchairs. Teas in Old Amersham. *Adm £1.50 Acc chd free. Suns March 5, April 9, May 7, June 4, July 9, Aug 6, Sept 3, Oct 8 (2-6). Also by appt for parties with TEAS. No coaches. Please* **Tel 01494 726818**

Chalfont St Giles Gardens ✗✿ *From London take A413 signed Amersham.* TEAS at Halfpenny Furze in aid of Iain Rennie Hospice at Home. *Combined adm £3 for 2 or 3 gardens or £1.50 per garden Chd free. Sun June 4 (2-6)*

 Concordia (Mrs L E Cobb) *76 Deanway. Parking in Deanway.* Small challenging garden on difficult sloping site. Herbaceous and shrub borders; rock garden with waterfall; fruit trees; collection of epiphytic orchids; Japanese garden

 Halfpenny Furze (Mr & Mrs Richard Sadler) *Mill Lane. About* ¼m *past mini roundabouts at Chalfont St Giles. Limited parking.* 1 acre plantsman's garden; ⅓ woodland (rhododendrons, azaleas, hydrangeas, magnolias and unusual trees), ⅔ formal, with lawns, many unusual shrubs, roses, mixed borders and Mediterranean garden. Featured in the Good Gardens Guide. TEAS. *Parties welcome by arrangement, please* **Tel 01494 872509**

 North Down (Mr & Mrs J Saunders) *From Halfpenny Furze, short uphill walk L into Dodds Lane. Garden is 250yds on R. Limited parking in Dodds Lane.* Approx ¾-acre sloping, N-facing rather exposed garden planned for scenic effect with interest throughout yr. Mixed beds of perennials, unusual plants, shrubs, incl rhododendrons,

azaleas, acers; spring bulbs; many clematis and other climbers; sempervivums; patio with water feature

Cheddington Gardens ✗✿ *11m E of Aylesbury; turn off B489 at Pitstone. 7m S of Leighton Buzzard; turn off B488 at Cheddington Station.* Teas in Methodist's Chapel or on the green. *Combined adm £3 Chd free (ACNO to Methodist Chapel and St Giles Church, Cheddington). Sun July 2 (2-6)*

 Chasea (Mr & Mrs A G Seabrook) Medium-sized garden; 100+ assorted tubs and baskets; 2 pools backing onto rockeries; water feature; conifers; perennials and bedding. 1998 2nd prize winner in Hillier's Best Bedding Competition. Winner of Bucks Herald 1999 Small Garden competition and Best Overall Garden. First prize Best Hanging Basket in 1999 AVDC competition

 34 Gooseacre (Mrs Barbara Smith) Well-designed partly paved small garden with magnificent views over Chilterns. Delightful water feature, patio, mixed shrubs and climbers for yr-round interest

 Rose Cottage (Mr & Mrs D G Jones) ¼ acre for all seasons featuring series of small rooms viewed from conservatory incorporating wildlife pond and vegetable parterre

 21 Station Rd (Mr & Mrs P Jay) ½ acre informal garden with wildflower conservation area; herbaceous and shrub borders; herbs and kitchen garden

 Woodstock Cottage (Mr & Mrs D Bradford) *42 High Street.* Front garden laid to gravel with assorted shrubs. Back courtyard and patio with small fountain at base of ancient elder tree

▲ **Cliveden, Taplow** ♿✗ (The National Trust) *2m N of Taplow.* Separate gardens within extensive grounds, first laid out in C18 incl water garden, rose garden; topiary; herbaceous borders; woodland walks and views of R Thames. New timber steps, generously funded by NGS, lead down yew tree walk to river. Suitable for wheelchairs only in part. Cream TEAS. *Adm grounds only £5 Parties £4.50 Chd £2.50. For NGS Suns May 7, Sept 10 (2-6)*

NEW **Court Farm, Worminghall** ♿✗ (Mr & Mrs Hector Sants) *8m NE of Oxford. Approx 2m. from M40 junction 8, proceed via Wheatley, follow signs to Waterperry Gardens, then Worminghall. Entrance behind church at end of The Avenue.* Approx 2-acre, organic garden. Hedges, pergola and mixed borders with herbaceous perennials and roses; wild garden. Well stocked and maintained walled garden containing vegetables, soft fruit and apple arches. Many recently planted shrubs and trees. *Adm £2 Chd free. Private visits welcome by written application to owners at: Court Farm, Worminghall, Aylesbury HP18 9LD*

Cublington Gardens ♿✗✿ *From Aylesbury take Buckingham rd (A413). After 4m at Whitchurch turn R to Cublington.* TEAS. *Combined adm £2.50 Chd free. Wed May 10, Sun June 11 (2-5)*

 Old Manor Farm, Cublington (Mr & Mrs N R Wilson) *Reads Lane.* Large country garden divided into knot and yellow gardens, ¼-acre 'old' roses, herbaceous borders; ha-ha, walled vegetable garden and gravel garden. TEAS. *Also open Wed June 21. TEAS in aid of Royal National Rose Society 2000. Private visits and parties welcome, please* **Tel 01296 681279**

The Old Rectory (Mr & Mrs J Naylor) 2-acre country garden with herbaceous border, rosebeds, shrubs and mature trees; vegetables; ponds, climbing plants

Cuddington Gardens, nr Thame *3½m NE of Thame or 5m SW Aylesbury off A418. Park at The Old Rectory.* TEAS in aid of Sunshine Club and Village Hall Restoration Fund. *Combined adm £3 Acc chd free. Sun, Wed May 28, 31 (2-6)*

NEW **Old Forge Cottage** (Mr & Mrs M Pegge) Enlarged and totally re-designed 3 yrs ago as relatively small but picturesque cottage garden. Built on two levels and divided into 'rooms' each reached by way of circuitous gravel or paved paths. Great variety of plants, unusual flowering shrubs, trees, climbing plants and roses; central water feature.

The Old Rectory (Mr & Mrs R J Frost) 2-acre garden bounded by mature trees with stunning views over Winchendon valley. Laid out as country garden of borders, island beds, paved garden with fish pond and pavillion. Interest and continuity of colour throughtout yr. Not suitable for wheelchairs. Plant stall

NEW **The Old Stables** (Mr & Mrs R Bates) Walled, flower arranger's garden providing peaceful setting with wide variety of plants in mixed beds and containers. New arched walkway planted with roses, wisteria and other climbers. Small vegetable plot and well stocked conservatory

Tyringham Hall (Mr & Mrs Ray Scott) Water and bog garden, patios and lawns surround mediaeval house. Dell with well and waterfall TEAS.

Wellfield House (Mr & Mrs C S Sanderson) ½ acre garden with mixed borders for all-yr colour; shaded areas; terrace with rockery and small water feature. Newly planted area for flowering trees and wildlife. Vegetable garden

▲ **Dorneywood Garden, Burnham** (The National Trust) *From Burnham village take Dropmore Rd, and at end of 30mph limit take R fork into Dorneywood Rd. Entrance is 1m on R. From M40 junction 2, take A355 to Slough then 1st R to Burnham, 2m then 2nd L after Jolly Woodman, signed Dorneywood Rd. Dorneywood is about 1m on L.* 6 acres, country house garden on several levels with herbaceous borders, greenhouse, rose, cottage and kitchen gardens. TEAS. *Adm £2.80 Chd under 15 free. Open by written appt only Weds June 28, July 19, Sat Aug 5 (2-5). Apply to: The Secretary, Dorneywood Trust, Dorneywood, Burnham, Bucks SL1 8PY*

East & Botolph Claydon Gardens *2 and 3m SE of Winslow. Follow signs to Claydons.* Teas in village hall in aid of WI and Marie Curie Cancer Care. *Combined adm £3 Chd free. Sun June 25 (2-6)*

Ashton (Mr & Mrs G Wylie) *Botyl Rd, Botolph Claydon.* ⅓ acre plot on clay with superb views on site of former barnyard. Mixed beds of shrubs and herbaceous plants

The Emerald (Mr & Mrs J P Elder) *St Mary's Rd, East Claydon.* 3/4 acre garden with mature trees, shrubs, perennial beds and rockery banks using sleepers and brickwork. Gravelled and paved area in front of house with pond and planting. Vegetable garden with beds bounded by sleepers

1 Emerald Close (Mr & Mrs L B Woodhouse) *East Claydon.* Small garden with collection of deciduous and coniferous bonsai

Inglenooks (Mr & Mrs D. Polhill) *St Mary's Rd, East Claydon.* ½ acre garden under development since 1994

Littleworth Farm (Mrs M O'Halloran) *Verney junction.* ½ acre with walled herbaceous and formal kitchen gardens

The Old Vicarage (Mr & Mrs N Turnbull) *Church Way, E Claydon.* 3/4 acre on clay, started in 1991 and aiming at yr-round interest. Shrub roses, herbaceous and secret dell garden

Rosamund Cottage (Mr & Mrs M Gould) *Botolph Claydon.* ¼ acre, interesting garden with some unusual plants, raised vegetable beds, fruit and mulberry tree

The Pump House (Mr & Mrs PM Piddington) *St Mary's Rd, East Claydon.* 3/4 acre, garden with mature trees, shrubs, borders, herbs and fishpond

Favershams Meadow, Gerrards Cross (Mr & Mrs H W Try) *1½m W Gerrards Cross on A40. Turn N into Mumfords Lane opp lay-by with BT box. Garden ¼m on R.* 1½ acres with views over Bulstrode Park. Mixed herbaceous, knot, parterre and separate blue and white garden. Roses on part C16 house and in David Austin rose garden. Very productive enclosed brick-paved vegetable garden. All maintained to very high standard. TEAS in aid of Uxbridge Open Door Christian Fellowship. *Adm £2 Chd free. Suns May 14, June 18 (2-6). Group visits welcome, May, June, July, please* **Tel 01753 882733**

Fressingwood, Little Kingshill (Mr & Mrs J & M Bateson) *From A413 Amersham to Aylesbury rd, turn L at Chiltern Hospital, signed Gt and Little Kingshill. Take 1st L into Nags Head Lane, then turn R under railway bridge and 1st L into New Rd, continue to top, turn into Hare Lane, 1st house on R.* ½-acre garden with yr-round colour. Shrubbery, small formal garden, pergolas with wisteria, roses and clematis. Landscaped terrace. Formal lily pond and bonsai collection. Many interesting features. TEAS in aid of Children in Distress. *Adm £1 Chd free. Sun May 14 (12-6)*

Gipsy House, Gt Missenden (Mrs Felicity Dahl) *Take A413 to Gt Missenden. From High St turn into Whitefield Lane, continue under railway bridge. Large Georgian house on R.* York stone terrace, pleached lime walk to writing hut; shrubs, roses, herbs, small walled vegetable garden, orchard, sunken garden, gipsy caravan and maze for children. Limited access for wheelchairs. Teas locally. *Adm £2 Chd 50p (ACNO to Roald Dahl Foundation) Weds May 17, June 7, July 12, Sun Sept 24 (2-5)*

Gracefield, Lacey Green (Mr & Mrs Brian Wicks) *Take A4010 High Wycombe to Aylesbury Rd. Turn R by Red Lion at Bradenham, up hill to Walters Ash; L at T-junction for Lacey Green. Brick and flint house on main rd beyond church facing Kiln Lane.* 1½-acre mature garden; unusual plants, orchard, soft fruit, shrub borders, rockery; sink gardens. Two ponds. Most plants well labelled. Ploughman's lunches, TEAS and plants in aid of local Macmillan Nurses Group. *Adm £2 Chd free. Bank Hol Mon May 1 (11.30-5). Parties welcome by written appt May to Aug*

Great Barfield, Bradenham ♿✂❀ (Richard Nutt Esq) *A4010 4m NW of High Wycombe. Turn at Red Lion, park on The Green.* 1½ acres, designed as informal background for unusual plants. Feb snowdrops, hellebores, drifts of crocuses; April pulmonarias and bergenias, naturalised red trilliums chloropetalum. Autumn colour, sorbus in fruit and colchicum. TEAS. *Adm £1.50 Chd free (ACNO to NCCPG). Suns Feb 20 (2-5), April 9 (2-5.30), Sat, Sun Oct 28, 29 (2-4). Private visits welcome, please* **Tel 01494 563741**

Hall Barn, Beaconsfield (The Hon Mrs Farncombe) *Lodge gate 300yds S of Beaconsfield Church in town centre.* One of the original gardens opening in 1927, still owned by member of Burnham family. Unique landscaped garden of great historical interest, laid out in the 1680s. Vast 300-yr-old curving yew hedge. Formal lake. Long avenues through the Grove to temple, classical ornament or statue. Obelisk with fine carvings in memory of Edmund Waller's grandson who completed the garden about 1730. *Open by written application only to: The Hon Mrs Farncombe, Hall Barn, Beaconsfield, Buckinghamshire HP9 2SG*

Hillesden House, Hillesden ♿✂❀ (Mr and Mrs R M Faccenda) *3m S of Buckingham.* By superb perpendicular church 'Cathedral in the Fields'; lawns, shrubberies; rose, alpine and foliage gardens; interesting clipped hedges; conservatory; surrounded by park with red deer and highland cattle. Large lakes with ornamental duck and carp. Views over countryside. TEAS in aid of Hillesden Church. *Adm £2 Chd under 12 free. Sun June 18 (2-5)*

▲ **Hughenden Manor, High Wycombe** ♿✂❀ (The National Trust) *1½m N of High Wycombe on W side of Great Missenden Rd A4128.* Mary Anne Disraeli's colour schemes inspire spring and summer bedding. Unusual conifers, planted from photographs taken at time of Disraeli's death. Walled garden (not usually open) with herbs and Victorian fruit varieties. Old English apple orchard with picnic area. Beech woodland walks. Sub-tropical border. Restaurant. *Adm House & Garden £4.20 Chd £2.10 Family £10.50. Adm garden only £1.50 Chd 75p For NGS Sun July 23, Garden (12-5), House (1-5). Last adm 4.30. Timed tickets for entry to Manor*

The Lee Gardens, Great Missenden ♿✂❀ *Follow A413 Great Missenden to Wendover. Turn 3rd R up Rocky Lane. After 2m turn L at 1st Xrds. 200yds turn R down drive. Combined adm £2.50 Chd free. Sun May 28 (2-6)*

2 Kingswood Cottages (Mr & Mrs J Swain) 2-acre garden started approx 7yrs ago. Path through large indigenous woodland and old orchard. Informal gardens with mixed beds, specimen trees, wildlife pond

Kingswood House (Mr & Mrs T Hart) 4-acre mature garden being constantly developed by owners. Wildlife pond, formal pond, croquet lawn, hot colour borders, scented sundial garden and fruit and vegetable areas. Cream TEAS in aid of Lee Church

Long Crendon Gardens ♿ *2m N of Thame B4011 to Bicester.* TEAS. *Combined adm £3 Chd free (ACNO to Long Crendon Parish Church Fund). Suns April 16, June 18 (2-6). Please see individual gardens for dates.*

Baker's Close (Mr & Mrs Peter Vaines) 2 acres on SW slope. Partly walled with courtyard, terraced lawns, rockery with pond, roses, shrubs, herbaceous plantings and wild area. *Sun June 18*

Barry's Close (Mr & Mrs Richard Salmon) 2-acre, sloping garden with interesting collection of trees and shrubs. Herbaceous border, spring-fed pools and water garden. *Sun April 16*

Braddens Yard ❀ (Mr & Mrs P Simpson) ½ acre walled garden, largely created over past 8 yrs. Collection of roses, herbaceous and climbing plants. Arched walk with clematis, honeysuckle and roses; pond; small bothy garden. Cake stall. *Sun June 18*

Croft House ❀ (Cdr & Mrs Peter Everett) *Thame Rd. In Square.* White wrought iron railings. ½-acre walled garden; plants and shrubs of botanical interest especially to flower arrangers. Pond, conservatory and greenhouse. TEAS. *Sun June 18*

NEW **48 High Street** ♿ (Mr and Mrs John Allerton) Cottage garden of ¼ acre hidden from High St. Extensive lawn, paving and variety of shrubs and roses. Small, formal vegetable garden. *Sun June 18*

8 Ketchmere Close (Mr & Mrs A Heley) Colourful, split-level garden with extensive views. Wide range of shrubs and conifers; rockery and water feature. *Sun June 18*

Manor House (Sir William & Lady Shelton) *Turn R by church, entrance through wrought iron gates.* 6 acres; lawns sweep down to 2 ornamental lakes, each with small island; walk along lower lake with over 20 varieties of willow; fine views towards Chilterns. *Suns April 16, June 18*

The Old Crown (Mr & Mrs R H Bradbury) *100yds past Chandos Inn.* 1 acre on SW slope with lawns looking over unspoiled countryside towards Oxford. More than 250 assorted roses with colourful annual and perennial plants including clematis, flowering shrubs; assorted colorful pots and containers, 2 sizeable vegetable patches. Spring bulbs *Suns April 16, June 18*

Old Post House (Mr and Mrs Nigel Viney) *In picturesque High St.* Attractive cottage garden with interesting spring and summer shrubs. *Sun April 16*

Windacre ❀ (Mr and Mrs K Urch) *62 Chilton Rd, next to primary school.* 1 acre; roses, interesting shrubs, herbaceous plants and lenten roses. Sunken lawns with fish pond, conifer and trees. Cream TEAS. *Sun April 16*

Lower Icknield Farm, Kimble ✂❀ (Mr & Mrs J Baldwin) *2m N of Princes Risborough on B4009 between Longwick and Kimble, opp Askett turn.* 5½ acres with 2 acres of well maintained garden planted for late summer colour. Display borders with over 85 varieties of argyranthemums: holders of National Collection. Natural stream and pond, newly planted ornamental grassland walk. Picnic area. Adjoining nursery. *Adm £1.50 Chd 50p Sat, Sun Aug 19, 20 (11-5)*

The Manor Farm, Little Horwood ♿❀ (Mr and Mrs Peter Thorogood) *2m NE Winslow, signed from A413. 5m E Buckingham and 5m W Bletchley S of A421.* Hill-top garden on acid clay. Wide range of alpines and plantsman's plants for yr-round interest in colour, form and foliage; good roses, pergola, 100′ hosta border, herbaceous, damp garden, lovely views. TEAS by Milton Keynes Soroptimists. *Adm £2. Bank*

Hol Mon May 29 (2-6). Parties and private visits welcome May to Sept, please **Tel 01296 714758**

The Manor House, Bledlow (The Lord & Lady Carrington) *½m off B4009 in middle of Bledlow village. Station: Princes Risborough, 2½m.* Paved garden, parterres, shrub borders, old roses and walled kitchen garden. Water and species garden with paths, bridges and walkways, fed by 14 chalk springs. Also 2 acres with sculptures and landscaped planting. Partly suitable for wheelchairs. TEA in aid of Bledlow Church April. TEAS June. *Adm £3 Chd free. Suns April 30, June 18 (2-6); also group visits welcome by appt in writing*

The Manor House, Hambleden (Maria Carmela, Viscountess Hambleden) *NE of Henley-on-Thames, 1m N of A4155.* Conservatory; shrubs and rose garden with more than 100 scented specimens. Strictly no dogs. TEA at Hambleden Church. *Adm £2 Chd 25p (ACNO to Rose 2000 Appeal). Sun June 25 (2-6)*

▲ **Nether Winchendon House** (Mr & Mrs R Spencer Bernard) *5m SW of Aylesbury; 7m from Thame.* 5 acres; fine trees, variety of hedges, naturalised spring bulbs, shrubs and herbaceous borders. Tudor manor house in picturesque village with beautiful church. TEA weather permitting. *Adm £2 Chd under 15 free. For NGS Suns April 30, June 18 (2-5.30). Private visits welcome by written application*

Old Farm, Brill (Raymond & Judy Brown) *South Hills, off Windmill St. 7m N of Thame. Turn off B4011, Thame to Bicester rd, or turn off A41 at Kingswood, both signed to Brill.* ½ acre established garden around 3 terraces in secluded position with open views over Otmoor; old shrub roses, trees, patio pots, vegetables and soft fruit; most plants grown from seed, incl S African annuals and rarer species. *C17 windmill open Suns 2.30-5.30. Private visits welcome, June, July and August; please* **Tel 01844 238232**

The Old Vicarage, Padbury (Mr & Mrs H Morley-Fletcher) *2m S of Buckingham on A413 follow signs in village.* 2½ acres on 3 levels; flowering shrubs and trees. Display collection of hebes, geometric vegetable garden; pond and sunken garden; parterre and millennium arch. TEAS in aid of League of Friends of Buckingham Hospital. *Adm £1.50 Chd free. Sun April 16 (2-6).* **Evening Openings** *Thurs, Fri June 29, 30 (6.30-8.30) Wine. Private visits and groups welcome, please* **Tel 01280 813045**

6 Oldfield Close, Little Chalfont (Jolyon & Phyllis Lea) *3m E of Amersham. Take A404 E through Little Chalfont, turn 1st R after railway bridge, then R again into Oakington Ave.* Mature sixth-acre garden of shrub borders, peat beds, rock plants, troughs and alpine house. Over 2,000 species and varieties of rare and interesting plants, incl spring bulbs, cyclamen and dwarf rhododendrons. Plants and TEA in aid of Bethany Village Leprosy Society, India. *Adm £1 Chd free. Suns April 9, 16 (2-5). Private visits welcome all yr, please* **Tel 01494 762384**

Olney Gardens *On A509 5m N of Newport Pagnell and 12m S of Wellingborough. Please park in Market Place, Cattle Market car park or High St.* Flower Festival. Teas at, and in aid, of Parish Church. *Combined adm £2 Chd free Sat, Sun June 10, 11 (2-6)*

Cowper & Newton Museum (Cowper and Newton Museum) *Market Place.* Walled flower garden being restored to incl only plants up to 1800, many of which were mentioned by poet William Cowper. Adjacent Summerhouse Garden, maintained by Mr & Mrs Charles Knight, in style of Victorian kitchen garden with organic new and old unusual vegetables. Border of herbs and medicinal plants

The Old Vicarage (Dr & Mrs J F Wallace) *Church St.* Walled C17 town garden recreated since 1993 with long, wide herbaceous border. Trimmed yew hedge separates gravel sun area with wall fruits and vines from lawn and specimen Cedrus libani. Pyrus calleryana 'Chanticleer' underplanted with iris and lily; extensive pergola with climbing roses and clematis. S front has raised bed of old shrub roses and cistus. Grade II vicarage was home of Revd John Newton, co-writer with Cowper of the Olney Hymns (Amazing Grace)

Overstroud Cottage, Frith Hill (Mr & Mrs Jonathan Brooke) *The Dell. Turn E off A413 at Gt Missenden onto B485 Frith Hill to Chesham rd. White Gothic cottage set back in layby 100yds up hill on L. Parking on R at Church.* Artistic chalk garden on 2 levels. Potager featured in Joy Larkcom's Creative Vegetable Gardening; snowdrops, narcissi, hellebores, primulas, pulmonarias, geraniums, species roses, clematis and lily pond. Not suitable for children or pushchairs. Teas at Parish Church. *Adm £1.50 Chd 50p. Suns April 23 (Easter), May 28, July 2 (2-6). Parties welcome by appt, please* **Tel 01494 862701**

Peppers, Gt Missenden (Mr & Mrs J Ledger) *4 Sylvia Close. A413 Amersham to Aylesbury Rd. At Great Missenden by-pass turn at sign Great & Little Kingshill (Chiltern Hospital). After 400yds turn L, Nags Head Lane. After 300yds turn R under railway bridge. Sylvia Close 50yds on R.* Approx 1 acre. Wide variety of plants, shrubs, trees, incl uncommon conifers, collection of acers, unusual containers, herbaceous borders all-yr colour. Large ornamental fish pond. TEAS. Donation from plant sale and teas to Workaid. *Adm £1 Chd free. Suns May 14, Aug 27 (10-5). Private visits welcome, please* **Tel 01494 864419**

Quainton Gardens *7m NW of Aylesbury. Nr Waddesdon turn off A41.* TEAS. *Combined adm £3 Chd free. Suns June 11, July 16 (2-6).*

Brudenell House (Dr and Mrs H Beric Wright) *Opp Church.* 2½ productive acres, reflecting 'his and hers' interests, sweet peas, dahlias, soft fruit and vegetables; wide range of perennials in herbaceous and mixed shrub borders, set against backdrop of fine mature trees. Large pond for reflections, unusual sculptures. Teas in aid of Quainton Sports Club/NGS.

Capricorner (Mrs G Davis) Small garden planted for yr-round interest with many scented plants; semi-wild area with trees

Hatherways (Mr & Mrs D Moreton) Cottage garden as featured in 'The Garden' with old-fashioned roses and clematis; interesting and unusual shrubs, herbaceous plants and ditch garden

Thorngumbald (Mr & Mrs J Lydall) Lots of garden in small space incl old-fashioned plants, organically grown; small pond, conservatory; attempts to encourage wildlife

Springlea, Seymour Plain ♿✗❀ (Mr & Mrs Michael Dean) *1m from Marlow, $2\frac{1}{2}$m from Lane End off B482. From Lane End pass Booker airfield; in 1m L at pillar-box on grass triangle.* $\frac{1}{2}$ acre, flower arrangers' garden for colour and foliage. Spring bulbs, azaleas, rhododendrons, unusual trees, shrubs. Rockery, pond, waterfall, bog garden, hostas. Arched walkway with over 240 clematis. 60′ herbaceous border against brick wall with many climbers; plants labelled throughout garden. Great collection of rare and unusual plants. *Adm £1.50 Chd free. Private visits only April to September, please* **Tel 01628 473366/0780 8512815**

▲ **Stowe Landscape Gardens, Buckingham** (The National Trust) *3m NW of Buckingham via Stowe Ave. Follow brown NT signs.* Supreme creation of Georgian era; first, formal layout was adorned with buildings by Vanbrugh, Kent and Gibbs; in 1730s Kent designed the Elysian Fields in more naturalistic style, one of earliest examples of the reaction against formality leading to evolution of the landscape garden; miraculously, this beautiful garden survives; its sheer scale must make it Britain's largest work of art. Light refreshments. *For NGS Wed, Fri July 5, 7 (10-5). Guided tours in aid of NGS. £5 Chd free to incl entry,* **to be booked in advance** *through Stowe NT office*
Tel 01280 822850

■ **Turn End, Haddenham** ❀ (Peter Aldington Esq OBE) *Townside. Haddenham turn off A418. At Rising Sun take Townside.* Architect's own post-war listed house. Garden less than 1 acre but space used to create illusion of size. Series of enclosed gardens, sunken or raised, sunny or shady, each different yet harmonious, contrast with lawns, borders and glades. Spring bulbs, iris, old roses and climbers. Courtyard with fish pool. Featured internationally. TEAS in aid of Haddenham 3rd World Link. *Adm £2 Chd 50p. Weds in June (10-4). For NGS Sun April 2, Bank Hol Mon May 1, Sun Sept 17 (2-6). Groups by appt at other times, please*
Tel 01844 291383/291817

Tythrop Park, Kingsey ♿❀ (Jonathan & Medina Marks) *2m E of Thame, via A4129; lodge gates just before Kingsey.* 7 acres. Formal gardens with many fine specimen trees and shrubs. Intricate dwarf box parterre with fountains. Large walled garden with wide variety of fruit trees, soft fruits and vegetables, divided by rows of roses and flowers. Magnificent greenhouse containing muscat and black muscat d'Hamburg vines propagated from vine at Hampton Court 150 years ago. Secluded water garden with attractive walks, old roses etc. Nut grove. Wilderness area. Arboretum. TEAS. *Adm £2 Chd free (ACNO to NCH Action for Children). Sun June 25 (2-6)*

▲ **Waddesdon Dairy Water Garden** ✗❀ (The Alice Trust) *Off A41 between Aylesbury and Bicester on Waddesdon Estate.* Private garden restored by Lord Rothschild, with naturalistic outcrops of Pulham rock, cascading water, still ponds and intricate planting which provide overwhelming drama. Refreshments at NT restaurant. *Adm £1 Chd 50p. For NGS Weds, Suns May 3, 7, June 7, 11, Nov 29, Dec 3 (2-5). Guided walks Weds; brief introduction but unacc walks Suns*

Watercroft, Penn (Mr & Mrs Paul Hunnings) *3m N of Beaconsfield on B474, 600yds on L past Holy Trinity Church.* Medium-sized garden on clay; unusual spring bulbs and hellebores, white flowers, decorative herb garden, rose walk, weeping ash; topiary and interesting summer pots in courtyard. Kitchen garden with new box hedging. Large mature pond, wildflower meadow. Italianate garden with yew hedges and fine views. TEAS (afternoons), wine and smoked salmon (evenings). *Adm £1.50. Private visits and parties welcome by appt April to Aug. please* **Tel 01494 813113**

Weir Lodge, Chesham ♿✗❀ (Mr & Mrs Mungo Aldridge) *Latimer Rd. 1m SE of Chesham. Turn L from A416 along Waterside at junction of Red Lion St and Amersham Rd. From A404 Rickmansworth to Amersham rd turn R at signpost for Chenies and proceed for 4m. Parking at Weir House Mill (McMinns).* $\frac{3}{4}$ acre on bank of R Chess. Natural stream and ponds with planted banks. Gravelled terrace with sun-loving plants. Assorted containers; mixed beds, wood carvings. Mature trees, incl fine beeches in adjoining paddock with Jacob sheep. TEAS. *Adm £1.50 Chd free. Sun June 18 (2-5.30)*

▲ **West Wycombe Park, West Wycombe** ♿ (The National Trust) *3m W of High Wycombe on A40. Bus: from High Wycombe and Victoria.* Landscape park; numerous C18 temples and follies incl Temple of the Winds, Temple of Venus, Temple of Music. Swan-shaped lake with flint bridges and cascade. *Adm (grounds only) £2.50 Chd £1.25 (incl NT members) For NGS Sun Sept 3 (2-5)*

Whitchurch Gardens ✗❀ *4m N of Aylesbury on A413.* TEAS. *Combined adm £3 Chd free. Sun April 16 (2-6)*

Badgers (Mr & Mrs J E Bellamy) Secluded, peaceful garden with many trees, shrubs and garden seats. Fishpond under weeping willow

Mullions (Dr & Mrs L I Holmes-Smith) $\frac{1}{3}$ acre picturesque cottage garden with 2 ponds and garden on 3 terraces

The Old Cottage (Roger Gwynne-Jones) $\frac{3}{4}$ acre cottage garden with herbaceous border, herb garden and wild area. Views over Vale of Aylesbury

Priory Court (Mr & Mrs Ian Durrell) Approx $\frac{2}{3}$ acre, split-level garden with rose beds, shrubbery and herbaceous borders. Water feature, decking and new planting. Entrance and stableyard re-designed with new shrubbery

Yew Tree Cottage ✗ (Mr & Mrs B S Foulger) 3-tier garden with fish pond, patios and small wooded area, the whole offering sanctuary for wildlife. Panoramic views over Vale of Aylesbury. Strictly no dogs

The White House, Denham Village ♿❀ (Mr & Mrs P G Courtenay-Luck) *Approx 3m NW of Uxbridge, signed from A40 or A412; nearest station Denham Green. Underground Uxbridge. Parking in village rd. The White House is in centre of village.* Well established 6-acre, formal garden in picturesque setting. Mature trees and hedges, with R Misbourne meandering through lawns. Shrubberies, flower beds, rockery, rose garden and orchard. Large walled garden with Italian garden and developing laburnum walk; herb garden, vegetable plot and Victorian greenhouses. Cream TEAS in aid of Buckinghamshire Association of Youth Clubs *Adm £2 Acc chd free. Suns April 16, July 9 (2-5)*

Whitewalls, Marlow ♿🚫 (Mr W H Williams) *Quarry Wood Rd. From Marlow cross over bridge. 1st L, 3rd house on L, white garden wall.* Thames-side garden approx ½ acre with spectacular view of weir. Large lily pond, interesting planting of trees, shrubs and herbaceous perennials. Many colourful containers. Sight of large conservatory with exotic plants. Teas available in Marlow. *Adm £1.50 Chd free. Suns April 23 (Easter), July 16, Sept 17 (2-5). Private visits and parties welcome, please* **Tel 01628 482573**

Wichert, Ford ♿🚫 (Mr & Mrs C Siggers) *5m SW of Aylesbury. From Aylesbury take A418 towards Thame. Turn L at Bugle Horn into Portway. After 3m turn L into Ford. Approx 100yds beyond Xrds turn L into drive immed after Old Bakehouse.* Approx 1½ acres developed into separate gardens: silver and pearl, shade, fern, kitchen and pavement; two mazes, orchard, willow arbour, ponds and wild garden with copse; garden which blends into rural surroundings. TEA. *Adm £2 Chd free. Individuals and groups very welcome, please* **Tel 01296 748431**

Winslow Hall, Winslow ♿ (Sir Edward & Lady Tomkins) *On A413 10m N of Aylesbury, 6m S of Buckingham. Free public car park.* Winslow Hall (also open), built in 1700, designed by Christopher Wren, stands in beautiful garden with distant perspectives, planted with many interesting trees and shrubs. In spring, blossom, daffodils and contrasting foliage of trees combine to make garden particularly attractive. TEAS. *Adm house & garden £3 garden only £1.50 Chd free. Bank Hol Mon May 1 (2-6)*

NEW **Woolleys, Hambleden** ♿ (Mr & Mrs A Guthrie) *NE of Henley-on-Thames, 1m N of A4155. Garden is ¼m N of village.* 6½ acres. Elegant garden with views across valley. Pleached lime avenue, paeony and delphinium beds and herbaceous border. Conifer bed and assortment of specimen trees. Rose borders, climbing roses and shrubs. Orchard. *Adm £2 Chd 25p. Sun June 25 (2-6)*

Evening Opening (See also garden description)

The Old Vicarage, Padbury	June 29 & 30

Macmillan Cancer Relief

In recent research, Macmillan discovered that only a third of all cancer patients are offered any written information during the course of their treatment. The charity has addressed this by launching *The Cancer Guide*, a 40 page booklet which gives patients the information they need to play a full part in their treatment and care. *The Cancer Guide* is available free from the Macmillan Information Line on 0845 601 6161, a telephone information service for people with cancer and their families. *The Cancer Guide* is also being distributed via the health services in the UK.

Macmillan Cancer Relief Information Line: 0845 601 6161
Macmillan Cancer Relief Website: www.macmillan.org.uk

Cambridgeshire

Hon County Organisers:
South: Lady Nourse, Dullingham House, Dullingham, Newmarket, Suffolk CB8 9UP Tel 01638 508186
North: Mr George Stevenson, 1a The Village, Orton Longueville, Peterborough, Cambridgeshire PE2 7DN Tel 01733 391506
Assistant County Organisers:
South: Mrs Alison Gould, The Grange, Church Road, Easton, Nr Huntingdon, Cambridgeshire PE18 0TU Tel 01480 891043
North: Mrs P Bullivant, Rosewell House, 60 Prickwillow Road, Ely, Cambridgeshire CB7 4TX Tel 01353 667355
Hon County Treasurers:
South: Mr John Drake, Hardwicke House, Highditch Road, Fen Ditton, Cambridgeshire CB5 8TF Tel 01223 292246
North: Mrs Christine Stevenson, 1a The Village, Orton Longueville, Peterborough, Cambridgeshire PE2 7DN Tel 01733 391506

DATES OF OPENING

Regular openings
For details see garden description
The Crossing House, Shepreth
Docwra's Manor, Shepreth
Elgood's Brewery Gardens, Wisbech
The Manor, Hemingford Grey
Northborough Manor

By appointment only
For telephone numbers and other details see garden descriptions. Private visits welcomed
Childerley Hall, Dry Drayton
Hardwicke Farm, Gt Gransden
Mill House, North End, Bassingbourn
7 Pelham Close, South Bretton
Scarlett's Farm, West Wratting

March 25 Saturday
The Manor, Balsham

March 26 Sunday
Bainton House, nr Stamford
Chippenham Park, Chippenham
The Manor, Balsham

April 2 Sunday
Barton Gardens, Cambridge
Netherhall Manor, Soham
Tadlow House, Tadlow

April 9 Sunday
Trinity College, Fellows' Garden, Cambridge

April 14 Friday
Wimpole Hall, Arrington

April 16 Sunday
Docwra's Manor, Shepreth

April 23 Sunday
Orton Longueville & Alwalton Gardens, Peterborough

April 24 Monday
Weaver's Cottage, Streetly End, West Wickham

April 30 Sunday
Cambridge University Botanic Garden, Cambridge

May 1 Monday
Ely Gardens

May 7 Sunday
Florence House, Fridaybridge
Leckhampton, Cambridge
Netherhall Manor, Soham
Tadlow House, Tadlow

May 14 Sunday
Docwra's Manor, Shepreth
Tetworth Hall, Sandy

May 27 Saturday
Hyset, Cardinals Green
Padlock Croft, West Wratting
Weaver's Cottage, Streetly End, West Wickham

May 28 Sunday
Fen Ditton Gardens
Island Hall, Godmanchester

May 29 Monday
Hyset, Cardinals Green
Padlock Croft, West Wratting
Weaver's Cottage, Streetly End, West Wickham

June 4 Sunday
Crowden House, March
Ely Gardens
Florence House, Fridaybridge

June 10 Saturday
Hyset, Cardinals Green
Padlock Croft, West Wratting
Weaver's Cottage, Streetly End, West Wickham

June 11 Sunday
Madingley Hall, Cambridge
Maxey & Northborough Gardens
Upton Gardens

June 15 Thursday
Fen Ditton Gardens (evening)

June 18 Sunday
Catworth & Brington Gardens
Comberton Gardens
Shingay Gardens
Whittlesford Gardens

June 24 Saturday
21 Lode Road, Lode
Padlock Croft, West Wratting

June 25 Sunday
Anglesey Abbey, Cambridge
1 Chapel Hill, Haslingfield
Easton Gardens
83 High Street, Harlton
Horningsea & Waterbeach Gardens
21 Lode Road, Lode
Melbourn Gardens

June 29 Thursday
Newnham College, Cambridge (evening)

July 1 Saturday
The Manor, Balsham

July 2 Sunday
Chippenham Park, Chippenham
Clare College, Fellows' Garden, Cambridge (evening)
Dullingham Gardens
Florence House, Fridaybridge
Nuns Manor, Shepreth
Ramsey Gardens, nr Huntingdon.
Sawston Gardens
Shingay Gardens

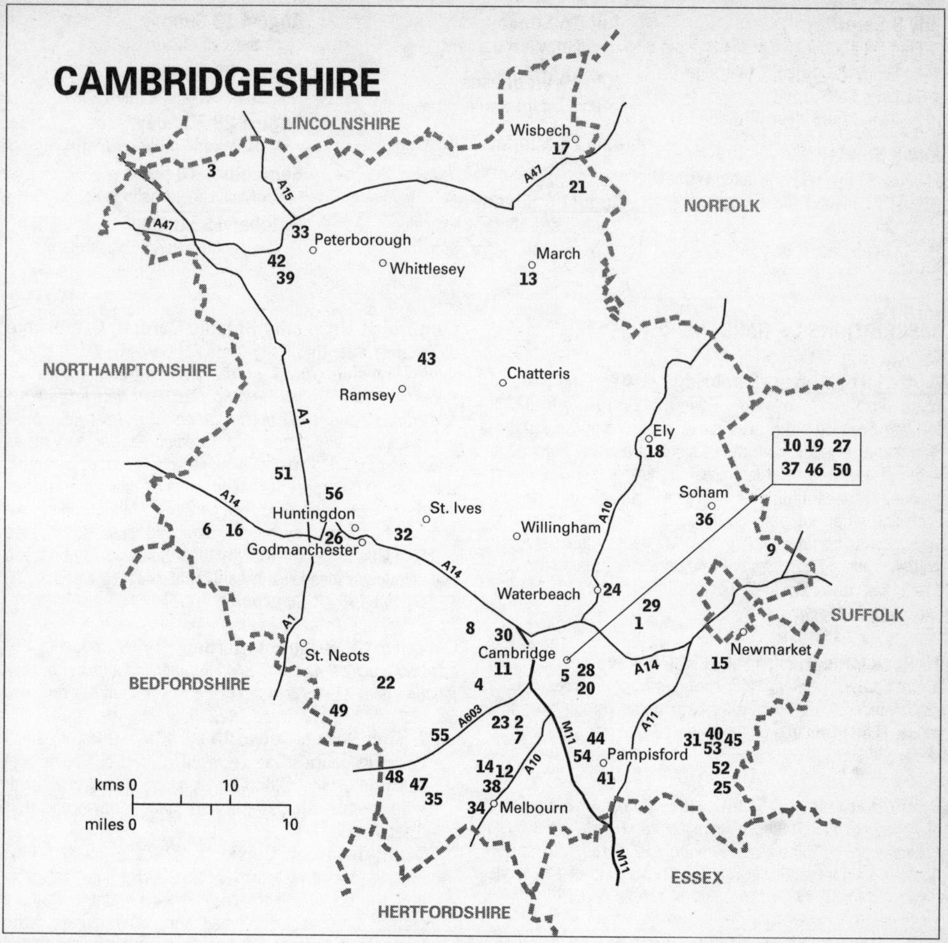

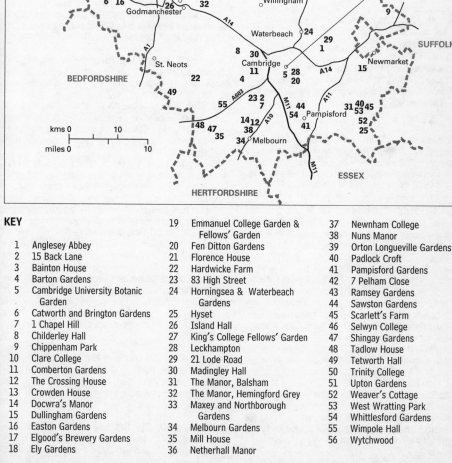

KEY

1 Anglesey Abbey
2 15 Back Lane
3 Bainton House
4 Barton Gardens
5 Cambridge University Botanic Garden
6 Catworth and Brington Gardens
7 1 Chapel Hill
8 Childerley Hall
9 Chippenham Park
10 Clare College
11 Comberton Gardens
12 The Crossing House
13 Crowden House
14 Docwra's Manor
15 Dullingham Gardens
16 Easton Gardens
17 Elgood's Brewery Gardens
18 Ely Gardens
19 Emmanuel College Garden & Fellows' Garden
20 Fen Ditton Gardens
21 Florence House
22 Hardwicke Farm
23 83 High Street
24 Horningsea & Waterbeach Gardens
25 Hyset
26 Island Hall
27 King's College Fellows' Garden
28 Leckhampton
29 21 Lode Road
30 Madingley Hall
31 The Manor, Balsham
32 The Manor, Hemingford Grey
33 Maxey and Northborough Gardens
34 Melbourn Gardens
35 Mill House
36 Netherhall Manor
37 Newnham College
38 Nuns Manor
39 Orton Longueville Gardens
40 Padlock Croft
41 Pampisford Gardens
42 7 Pelham Close
43 Ramsey Gardens
44 Sawston Gardens
45 Scarlett's Farm
46 Selwyn College
47 Shingay Gardens
48 Tadlow House
49 Tetworth Hall
50 Trinity College
51 Upton Gardens
52 Weaver's Cottage
53 West Wratting Park
54 Whittlesford Gardens
55 Wimpole Hall
56 Wytchwood

July 8 Saturday
Emmanuel College Garden & Fellows' Garden, Cambridge
21 Lode Road, Lode
Padlock Croft, West Wratting

July 9 Sunday
Elgood's Brewery Gardens, Wisbech
King's College Fellows' Garden, Cambridge
21 Lode Road, Lode

July 16 Sunday
Whittlesford Gardens

July 19 Wednesday
Pampisford Gardens (evening)

July 23 Sunday
Wytchwood, Owl End

August 6 Sunday
Anglesey Abbey, Cambridge
Netherhall Manor, Soham

August 13 Sunday
Netherhall Manor, Soham

August 20 Sunday
Selwyn College, Cambridge

August 28 Monday
West Wratting Park, West Wratting

September 10 Sunday
15 Back Lane, Haslingfield

October 15 Sunday
Chippenham Park, Chippenham

DESCRIPTIONS OF GARDENS

▲ **Anglesey Abbey, Cambridge** ♿✇❀ (The National Trust) *6m NE of Cambridge. From A14 turn N on to B1102 through Stow-cum-Quy.* 100 acres surrounding an Elizabethan manor created from the remains of a priory founded in reign of Henry I. Garden created during last 70 years; avenues of beautiful trees; groups of statuary; hedges enclosing small intimate gardens; daffodils and hyacinths; herbaceous border (June); dahlia beds (July-October); Winter Walk. *Adm house, mill and garden £7.10; garden only £3.75 Chd over 5 £1.85. For NGS Suns June 25, Aug 6 (11-5.30). Last adm 4.30*

15 Back Lane, Haslingfield ✇ (Mr & Mrs Wiseman) *5m SW of Cambridge along A10. Turn R in Harston.* ⅔ acre, on a slight slope. A mixed garden with paths through a small copse. TEAS in aid of a charity. *Adm £1 Chd free. Sun Sept 10 (2-6)*

Bainton House, nr Stamford ♿ (Major W & Hon Mrs Birkbeck) *B1443 Stamford-Helpston rd. Turn N at Bainton Church into Tallington rd. ¼m on L.* 2 acres with spring flowers, spinney and wild garden. TEA in aid of St Mary's Church. *Adm £1.50 Chd 50p. Sun March 26 (2-5.30)*

Barton Gardens, Cambridge ♿✇❀ *3½m SW of Cambridge. Take A603, in village turn R for Comberton Rd.* Delightful group of gardens of wide appeal and expertise. Gift stalls. Teas in village hall. *Combined adm £1.50 Chd 50p (ACNO to GRBS). Sun April 2 (2-5)*

Farm Cottage (Dr R M Belbin) *18 High St.* Cottage garden with water feature. Courtyard garden. Newly opened orchard, woodland and walled garden extension

The Gables (P L Harris Esq) *11 Comberton Rd.* 2-acre old garden, mature trees, ha-ha, spring flowers

14 Haslingfield Road (J M Nairn Esq) Orchard, lawns, mixed domestic garden

King's Tythe (Major C H Thorne) *Comberton Road.* Small domestic garden. Good through way to larger gardens of Town's End and The Gables

31 New Road (Dr D Macdonald) Cottage garden

The Seven Houses ❀ (GRBS) Small bungalow estate on L of Comberton Rd. 1½ acre spring garden. Bulbs naturalised in orchard. Colourful summer borders

Town's End (B Overton Esq) *15a Comberton Rd.* 1 acre. Lawns, trees, pond and extensive views. Raised vegetable beds

Cambridge University Botanic Garden, Cambridge ✇ (Cambridge University Botanic Garden) *Cory Lodge. Approx 3/4m to the S of the city centre. Entrance via Bateman St, off Trumpington Rd (A10) and Hills Rd (604). 5 min from station. Walk down Station Rd to Hills Rd, turn R and within 20 yds turn L into Bateman St. Car parking on adjacent rds.* 40 acres with plant collections of scientific value in a landscape of mature trees and wild flower meadows. Winter garden; rock gardens; Alpine House; lake and stream garden; systematic beds and glasshouses. Late spring bulbs, flowering trees and shrubs, woodland garden and wildflower meadows in April. TEAS. *Adm £2 OAPs & Chd £1.50 from 5 to 17. Sun April 30 (10-6)*

Catworth & Brington Gardens *Nr Huntingdon. For Catworth turn off A14 onto B660 Southbound approx 7m W of junction with A1.* TEAS in aid of Catworth Church. *Combined adm £2 Chd 50p. Sun June 18 (2-6)*

1 High Street, Catworth (Mr & Mrs G Reffin) Small haven of peace in an enclosed garden behind an old house in village. Old and new planting and new landscaping, mixed borders, a herb garden, lawn and fruit trees

32 High Street, Catworth ❀ (Colin Small) A long narrow garden of approx ¼ acre. Large informal patio and pergola with herbaceous borders and containers planted with unusual foliage plants; a lawned area with herbaceous borders either side and a native woodland area. Many rare plants and a collection of salvias

The Old Post Office, Brington ❀ (The Hon Mrs Sue Roe) *nr Huntingdon. Turn off A14 onto B660 northbound approx 7m W of junction with A1. Then follow signs to Brington. In Brington go towards Old Weston. Last house on L.* Cottage garden with unusual plants. Approx ¾ acre. The boundary between garden and countryside is deliberately left blurred to encourage wildlife. Pond, and many native plants. TEA. *Private visits at weekends welcome April to Sept by appt, please* **Tel 01832 710223**

1 Chapel Hill, Haslingfield ✇❀ (Mr & Mrs A R King) *5m SW of Cambridge, 2m from A10 (Harston), 2m from A603 (Barton).* A garden with mature trees, shrubs and roses. Also many herbaceous perennials, a large patio and 2 ponds. *Adm £1 Chd free. Sun June 25 (2-6)*

Childerley Hall, Dry Drayton ✇ (Mr & Mrs John Jenkins) *6m W of Cambridge on A428 opp Caldecote turn.* 4 acres of mixed planting with special emphasis on shrub roses. *Adm £2 Chd free. Private visits welcome May 16 to June 30, please* **Tel 01954 210271**

Chippenham Park, Chippenham (Mr & Mrs Eustace Crawley) *5m NE of Newmarket, 1m off A11.* 3½m of walled park landscaped by Mr Eames and Mr Lapidge to incl "a beautiful sheet of water ¾m long, small stretches of canal existing from the old formal garden, 2 lines of lime trees to represent the Anglo-Dutch and French fleets at the Battle of La Hogue in 1692". C18 dovecote. 7-acre garden with rare shrubs, trees and perennials. Daffodils by the lake in spring, summer borders and dramatic autumn colour. Specialist Plant Stalls. Refreshments. *Adm £2.50 Chd free (ACNO to St Margaret's Church). Suns March 26, July 2, Oct 15 (11-5)*

Clare College, Fellows' Garden, Cambridge (Clare College) *The Master and Fellows are owners of the Fellows' Garden which is open. The Master's garden (nearby) is not open to the public. Approach from Queen's Rd or from city centre via Senate House Passage, Old Court and Clare Bridge.* 2 acres. One of the most famous gardens on the Cambridge Backs. *Adm £3 Chd under 13 free. Sun July 2 (5.30-7.30)* **Evening Opening**. *Wine. Private visits welcome, please* **Tel 01223 333 222**

Comberton Gardens *5m SW of Cambridge. From M11, junction 12, take A603 away from Cambridge then 1st R on to B1046 to Comberton. 2½m.* Diverse garden styles. *Combined adm £3 Chd 50p. Sun June 18 (2-5.30)*

Greystones, Swaynes Lane (Dr & Mrs L Davies) Plantswoman's garden of approx ½ acre planted with a wide range of flowering plants framed by foliage and shrubs with gravel beds, troughs and water feature. Plant stall. *Private visits welcome, please* **Tel 01223 264159**

NEW **Hawthorn House, 60 Green End** (Dr & Mrs Anthony Hosking) A country garden of about 1 acre with lawns and borders, old orchard land, and mixed hedgerows. Many native trees and shrubs and mini arboretum of less familiar trees.

Meadow Croft, 72 West Street (Mr & Mrs D Gordon) 3 acres of lawns and herbaceous borders around the house with 2-acre hay meadow and a 10-yr-old native woodland plantation to the rear. Architect designed potager garden created last yr adjoining restored farm building. TEAS

The Crossing House, Shepreth (Mr & Mrs Douglas Fuller) *Meldreth Rd. 8m SW of Cambridge. ½m W of A10.* Internationally famous as King's Cross-Cambridge railway runs alongside garden. Small cottage garden with many old-fashioned plants grown in mixed beds in company with modern varieties. Shrubs, bulbs and many alpines in rock beds and alpine house. *Collecting box. Open daily, dawn till dusk. Parties by appt, no coaches, please* **Tel 01763 261071**

NEW **Crowden House, March** (Claire Lewis) *Park in March town centre (free). At traffic lights turn L into Dartford Road. 2ndR onto Prince's Walk. At the end use the public footpath adjacent to the gravel drive. 1st gate on R.* Designer's ¼ acre garden with different informal areas and styles, flamboyantly planted with unusual combinations of colour and type of plant. A work in progress. TEA. *Adm £1 Chd 50p. Sun June 4 (2-6).*

■ **Docwra's Manor, Shepreth** (Mrs John Raven) *8m SW of Cambridge. ½m W of A10. Cambridge-Royston bus stops at gate opp the War Memorial in Shepreth.* 2½ acres of choice plants in series of enclosed gardens. TEA April 16, May 14 only, in aid of Shepreth Church Funds. *Adm £2 Chd free. All yr, Weds, Fris (10-4), Suns April 2, May 7, June 4, July 2, Aug 6, Sept 3, Oct 1 (2-5). Proceeds for garden upkeep. For NGS Suns April 16, May 14 (2-6). Also private visits welcome by appt, please* **Tel 01763 261473**

Dullingham Gardens *4m S of Newmarket off A1304.* Classic and vintage vehicles. TEAS. Craft fair incl plant stalls. *(ACNO to Parish Church). Sun July 2 (2-5.30)*

7 Bakehouse Hill (Dr N H Chamberlain) Small suburban garden, flowers, pots, baskets, tubs, fish pond, glass house and vegetable patch.

NEW **Clare Farm** (Kim & Beth Waterhouse) 2-acre country garden with mature trees and flowering shrubs and walled garden for fruit. Home made TEAS.

Dullingham House (Sir Martin & Lady Nourse) Repton garden in course of restoration. Bowling green and herbaceous borders enclosed by substantial walls. CRAFT FAIR incl plant stalls

Hill House (Mrs P B Taylor) *200yds W of Dullingham station.* 2-acre landscaped garden and vegetable garden

The Old School (Mrs Gill Andrews) *1st turn L at Xrds. 3rd house on L.* 3-yr-old ½-acre garden with small gravel and paving area planted with evergreen shrubs, leading to colourful cottage garden style planting and children's play area

Easton Gardens *7m W of Huntingdon on A14.* Teas in village. *Adm £2 Chd free. Sun June 25 (1-5)*

NEW **Brook House** (Beth & Brian Davis) Garden of 1 acre created from farmyard. Mature trees, herbaceous borders, rock garden and potager. Wild garden in old orchard with mown paths.

NEW **The Grange** (Alison Gould) Walled garden with herbaceous borders: fruit and vegetable beds being made and restored.

NEW **2 Grange Croft** (Mr & Mrs Farren) Small walled garden with a variety of planting schemes and water features.

NEW **Oversland** (Mr & Mrs F G Tomline) Plantswoman's ¼ acre garden with pergola and natural pond. Wide range of flowering plants overlooked by tall elms.

■ **Elgood's Brewery Gardens, Wisbech** (Elgood's Brewery Gardens Ltd) *In the town of Wisbech on the N Brink of the R Nene approx 1m W of the town centre.* Approx 4 acres, established in the Georgian, restored around many of the original 200-yr-old specimen trees. Lawns, lake, rockery, rose, herb gardens and maze. TEAS, licensed bar. *Adm £2 OAPS/Chd £1.50. May 1 to Oct, Wed to Sun and Bank Hols. For NGS Sun July 9 (1-5)*

Ely Gardens *14m N of Cambridge on A10. Combined adm £1 Chd 50p May 1. Combined adm £3, Single*

garden £1, Chd 50p. June 4. (ACNO to Old Palace Sue Ryder Home). Bank Hol Mon May 1 (2-5), Sun June 4 (2-5.30)

Belmont House, 43 Prickwillow Rd ❀ (Mr & Mrs P J Stanning) Designed ½ acre garden with interesting and unusual plants. *Sun June 4*

31 Egremont Street (Mr & Mrs J N Friend-Smith) *A10 Lynn Rd out of Ely. 2nd L.* Approx 1 acre. Lovely views of cathedral, mixed borders, cottage garden. Ginkgo, tulip and many other fine trees. *Sun June 4*

The Old Fire Engine House (Mr & Mrs M R Jarman) Delightful walled country garden with mixed herbaceous borders and wild flowers. Situated just W of the Cathedral. TEAS. *Mon May 1*

The Old Palace (Sue Ryder Home) 1½ acres with duck pond in fine setting next to Cathedral. 2 borders planted with C17 plants and other interesting mixed borders. Superb trees, oldest and largest oriental plane tree in the country. TEAS on June 4. *Mon May 1, Sun June 4*

NEW **50A Prickwillow Rd** (Mr & Mrs J Hunter) Enthusiast's small walled garden with variety of plants. *Sun 4 June*

Queen's Hall (Mr & Mrs R H Youdale) *In Cathedral Close.* Re-created in theme of 'mediaeval garden', using plants available pre 1600 where possible. *Sun June 4*

Rosewell House, 60 Prickwillow Road (Mr & Mrs A Bullivant) Well stocked garden with emphasis on perennial planting and splendid view of cathedral and surrounding fenland. *Sun June 4*

NEW **35 St Mary's Street** (Dr G Parry) Walled garden with variety of planting, incl some borders in dry shade *Sun June 4*

48 St Mary's Street (Mr J Hardiment) Formal walled garden with a wide variety of unusual plants. *Sun June 4*

Emmanuel College Garden & Fellows' Garden, Cambridge ♿✄ (Emmanuel College) *In centre of Cambridge. Car parks at Parker's Piece and Lion Yard, within 5 mins walk.* One of the most beautiful gardens in Cambridge. Buildings of C17 to C20 surrounding 3 large gardens with pools, herb garden, herbaceous borders, fine trees incl Metasequoia glyptostroboides. On this date access allowed to Fellows' Garden with magnificent oriental plane and more herbaceous borders. Teashops in Cambridge. *Adm £1 Chd free. Sat July 8 (2.30-5.30). Private visits welcome, please* **Tel 01223 334200**

Fen Ditton Gardens ✄❀ *3½m NE of Cambridge. From A14 Cambridge-Newmarket rd turn N by Borough Cemetery into Ditton Lane; or follow Airport sign from by-pass.* Teas in church hall. *Combined adm £3 Chd 50p (ACNO to Children's Ward Addenbrooke's). Sun May 28 (2-5.30), Thurs June 15 (6-8)* **Evening opening**. *Wine*

NEW **16 Church St** ♿❀ (Mr & Mrs Dan Jackson) Hidden garden with shrubs grown for variety of foliage and alpines

Hardwicke House ❀ (Mr J Drake) *Please park in rd opp.* 2 acres designed to provide shelter for plants on exposed site, divided by variety of hedges. Species roses and rare herbaceous plants. National collection of aquilegias and collection of plants grown in this country prior to 1650. Sculpture exhibition Sun May 26. Rare plant sale. *Private visits welcome by appt, please* **Tel 01223 292246**

NEW **The Old Rectory** (Mr & Dr McCann) 1¼ acres of lawns, paths and mature shrubs and trees overlooking R Cam, with views down long reach and to Cambridge beyond. *Sun May 28 only*

The Old Stables (Mr C Zavros) Large informal garden; old trees, shrubs and roses; many interesting plants, herbs and shrubs have been introduced. House (not open) converted by owners in 1973 from C17 stables

The Rectory (Reverend Lawrence & Mrs L Marsh) Small rectory garden. Largely mediterranean flowers, extensive range of climbers and trompe l'oeil. Intensive organic vegetable garden which supplies household, incl 34' long decorative arch support for beans, sugar peas, spaghetti marrows, cucumbers and tomatoes

NEW **Florence House, Fridaybridge** ♿✄❀ (Mr & Mrs A Stevenson) *3.5m S of Wisbech on B1101. In Fridaybridge centre turn R in front of Chequers PH on to Back Rd. Parking, toilet.* Plant collectors' 3/4 acre garden with colourful herbaceous borders. Hellebores in Feb. Collections of grasses, bamboos and ferns. Trees include cercis, liquidambar, catalpa and ginko. Sales of plants propagated from garden. TEAS. *Adm £2 Chd 50p. Suns May 7, June 4, July 2 (12-5.30). Private visits or parties welcome, please* **Tel 01945 860268**

Hardwicke Farm, Gt Gransden ♿✄ (Mr & Mrs N H M Chancellor) *Situated mid way between the villages of Gt Gransden and Caxton (A1198) 12m W of Cambridge, 8m S of Huntingdon, 12m N of Royston. House on R travelling towards Gt Gransden.* 4-acre garden, herbaceous border, shrubs and recently planted courtyard incorporating 1830 red brick barn. Decorative pond and conservatory. *By appt only, summer garden May-Aug* **Tel 01954 719483**

83 High Street, Harlton ♿✄❀ (Dr Ruth Chippindale) *7m SW of Cambridge. A603 (toward Sandy). After 6m turn L (S) for Harlton.* ⅓ acre interesting design which includes many different features, colours and a wide diversity of plants. As seen on TV. TEAS. *Adm £1 Chd free (ACNO to Harlton Church Restoration Fund). Sun June 25 (2-5.30). Private visits welcome, please* **Tel 01223 262170**

Horningsea & Waterbeach Gardens ✄ *Combined adm £2 Chd 50p (ACNO to Village Church). Sun June 25 (2-5.30)*

15 Abbots Way, Horningsea (Mr & Mrs D Edwards) *4m NE of Cambridge from A1307 Cambridge Newmarket Rd. Turn N at borough cemetery to Horningsea or take B1047 N from A14. Entrance to car park and garden signposted nr village hall. No access to garden via Abbots Way.* 1-acre developing plantswoman's garden on old flood bank of R Cam, overlooking river and water meadows. Spring and natural pond. Pergola. Clematis and solomon's seal amongst fine collection of rare and unusual plants, shrubs and trees. TEAS in aid of Church.

92 Bannold Road, Waterbeach (Mr & Mrs R L Guy) Plantsman's tiny garden. Over 300 plants in 150 varieties. Clematis, shrubs, grasses

Muffs Cottage, 7 Greenside, Waterbeach (John & Julie Runham) Plantsman's cottage garden, with new pond feature, surrounding lovely thatched cottage (not open) on village green

Hyset, Cardinals Green (Mr & Mrs S Agnew) *A1307 between Linton and Haverhill. On opp side of bypass A1307 to Horseheath Village. Take turning signed 'The Camps'. Hyset is 2nd on R.* ⅓ acre garden being developed by professional plantsman/horticulturist. Interesting range of herbaceous, shrubs and climbers. Water feature displaying plants and insect life. Poly tunnel growing range of salads. *Combined adm £2.50 Chd 50p with* **Padlock Croft**, *and* **Weaver's Cottage**. *Sat May 27, Mon May 29, Sat June 10 (2-6). Private visits welcome, please* **Tel 01223 892982**

Island Hall, Godmanchester ⊘❀ (Mr Christopher & the Hon Mrs Vane Percy) *In centre of Godmanchester next to free car park. 1m S of Huntingdon (A1) 15m NW of Cambridge (A14).* 3-acre grounds. Mid C18 mansion (not open). Tranquil riverside setting with mature trees in an area of Best Landscape. Chinese bridge over Saxon mill race to an embowered island with wild flowers. Garden restored over the last 15yrs to a mid C18 formal design, with box hedging, clipped hornbeams, parterres, topiary and good vistas over borrowed landscape, punctuated with C18 wrought iron and stone urns. TEAS. *Adm £2 Chd free. Sun May 28 (1-5)*

King's College Fellows' Garden, Cambridge ♿⊘ Fine example of a Victorian garden with rare specimen trees. Colour booklet available £1.50, free leaflet describing numbered trees. Cream TEAS. *Adm £1.50 Chd free. Sun July 9 (2-6)*

Leckhampton, Cambridge ♿⊘ (Corpus Christi College) *37 Grange Rd. On W side of Cambridge and runs N to S between Madingley Rd (A1303) and A603. Drive entrance opp Selwyn College.* 10 acres. Originally laid out by William Robinson as garden of Leckhampton (Civic Trust Award). Formal lawns, rose garden, small herbaceous beds, extensive wild garden with bulbs, cowslips, prunus and fine specimen trees. TEAS. *Adm £1.50 Chd free. Sun May 7 (2-6)*

21 Lode Road, Lode ⊘ (Mr Richard P Ayres) *Take B1102 from Stow-cum-Quy roundabout NE of Cambridge at junction with A14. Lode is 2m from roundabout.* Small garden adjoining C15 thatched cottage (not open) designed by the owner (head gardener at Anglesey Abbey NT). Planted with bold groups of herbaceous plants complimenting a fine lawn and creating an element of mystery and delight. TEAS. *Adm £1 Chd 50p (ACNO to Lode Church). Sats, Suns June 24, 25, July 8, 9 (11-5)*

Madingley Hall, Cambridge ⊘ (University of Cambridge) *4m W, 1m from M11 Exit 13.* C16 Hall (not open) set in 7½ acres of attractive grounds. Features incl landscaped walled garden with hazel walk, borders in individual colours and rose pergola. Meadow, topiary and mature trees. Cream TEAS. *Adm £1.50 Chd free (ACNO to Madingley Church Restoration Fund). Sun June 11 (2.30-5.30)*

NEW **The Manor, Balsham** ⊘ (Mr & Mrs J Potter) *3m E of A11, 10m SE of Cambridge, 10m S of Newmarket. Opp village green at 42 High St.* 3 acres of formal and wild garden full of spring bulbs. Large pond and musical maze. TEA. *Adm £2 Chd £1. Sat, Sun March 25, 26 (12-4), Sat July 1 (12-6)*

● **The Manor, Hemingford Grey** ❀ (Mrs P S Boston) *4m E of Huntingdon off A14. Entrance to garden by small gate off river towpath. No parking at house except disabled by arrangement with owners. Park in village.* Garden designed and planted by author Lucy Boston, surrounds C12 manor house on which her Green Knowe Books were based (House only open by prior appt). 4 acres with topiary; over 200 old roses and large herbaceous borders with mainly scented plants. Enclosed by river, moat and wilderness. *Adm to garden £1 Chd 50p. Open daily (10-6 sunset in winter) 10 per cent takings to NGS, rest to preservation of garden*
Tel 01480 463134

Maxey & Northborough Gardens ♿ *Turn off A15, 1m S of Market Deeping, W into Maxey, then 1st R.* TEAS at **Northborough Gardens.** *Combined adm £2 Chd free. Sun June11 (2-6)*

8A Castle End Road, Maxey ⊘❀ (John & Sue Dinenage) ½ acre plant lover's garden on heavy clay. Herbaceous perennials, mixed shrubs, climbers especially clematis, and interesting trees. Planted since 1978

NEW **Northborough Manor** ♿ (Mr & Mrs John Trevor) *R to Northborough then 1st R.* 2 acre garden being designed to compliment mediaeval manor house (not open). Garden writer Roy Gender's parterre. Ha ha. Use of willow. *(ACNO to MCR)*

Melbourn Gardens ⊘❀ *3½m N of Royston, 8m S of Cambridge.* TEAS at **Melbourn Bury**. *Combined adm £3 Chd free. Sun June 25 (2-6)*

2 Garden End, Melbourn (Michael & Krystyna Aldridge) Plantman's garden which is well stocked with perennials and shrubs incl some unusual plants, all yr interest. Private visits by appt, please Tel 01763 260263

Melbourn Bury, Royston ♿ (Mr & Mrs Anthony Hopkinson) 5 acres; small ornamental lake and river with wildfowl; large herbaceous border; fine mature trees with wide lawns. TEAS.

Melbourn Lodge, Royston ♿ (Mr J R M Keatley) 2-acre garden maintained on 9 hrs work per week in season. C19 grade II listed house (not open)

Mill House, North End, Bassingbourn ♿⊘❀ (Mr & Mrs A Jackson) *Fen Road. On the NW outskirts of Bassingbourn 1m from Church, on the rd to Shingay. Take North End at the war memorial in the centre of Bassingbourn which is just W of the A1198, 2m N of Royston. (Do not take Mill Lane).* Garden created out of open countryside by garden designer owners. Clever use of walls, pergolas, water and varying land levels provide a backdrop for many very fascinating plants notably viticella clematis, giving interest and colour throughout the year. *Private and group visits welcome by appt in June and July, please* **Tel 01763 243491**

Netherhall Manor, Soham ⊘ (Timothy Clark Esq) *Enter Soham from Newmarket, Tanners Lane is 2nd R 100yds after cemetery. Enter Soham from Ely, Tanners Lane is 2nd L after War Memorial.* 1-acre walled garden incl courtyard featured on Geoffrey Smiths 'World of Flowers' and 'Gardeners World'. April-Crown Imperials, Victorian hyacinths and old primroses. May-florists ranunculus (picotee and bizarre), and tulips (rose, bizarre, byblomen). Aug-formal beds of Victorian pelargoniums, calceolarias, fuchsia, lobelias and heliotropes, an organic seasonal kitchen garden. TEAS in aid of The Fordham Society. *Adm £2 Chd 50p. Suns April 2, May 7, Aug 6, 13 (2-5)*

Newnham College, Cambridge ♿✇❀ (Newnham College) *Entrance from Newnham Walk. Can be approached from Sidgwick Ave or Newnham Walk, Cambridge. From City Centre via Queen's Rd or Silver St. Parking on street or College car parks.* Unsuspected haven in busy city. 18 acres of Victorian and Edwardian gardens, encircled by Basil Champney's buildings. Herbaceous borders, nut walk, summer house and memorial mound. Sunken rose garden with lily pond and fountain; observatory. *Adm £3 Chd free. (ACNO to Newnham College Development Trust). Thurs June 29 (6-8)***Evening Opening** *Wine*

Nuns Manor, Shepreth ♿✇❀ (Mr & Mrs J R L Brashaw) *Frog End. 8m SW of Cambridge 300yds from A10 Melbourn-Shepreth Xrds.* C16 farmhouse (not open) surrounded by delightful 2-acre garden, designed, created and maintained by owners. A plantsman's garden with interesting plants in mixed and herbaceous borders and large pond. Featured in The English Garden. Owners unusual homegrown plants for sale. TEA in aid of Shepreth Church. *Adm £2 Chd free. Sun July 2 (2-5.30); also group visits by appt April to July, please* **Tel 01763 260313**

Orton Longueville & Alwalton Gardens, Peterborough ♿✇❀ *Off 605 Oundle Rd, 2½m E of intersection with A1 before junction with Nene Parkway. Combined adm £2 Chd 50p. Sun April 23 (12-4)*

The Forge ♿✇❀ (Mr & Mrs M Watson) *4m W of Peterborough between E of E Showground and A1.* Organic cottage garden. TEAS

Hemingdale (Mr & Mrs John Wilkinson) A cottage garden, incl material for flower arranging and herbs

The Old School (Mr & Mrs J Colman) A converted 1853 village school, playground, school master's house and garden. Formal layout with informal planting of ⅓ acre gardens in picturesque village

9 Oundle Road (Mr & Mrs C Leary) *Approx 5m from Peterborough W along Oundle Rd. After passing the roundabout to the E of E Showground take 1st turn on RH-side into Alwalton. 1st house on L.* Small to medium garden of mixed trees, shrubs and flowers, featuring an informal pond. *(ACNO to Alwalton Church)*

1a The Village, The Village (Mr & Mrs G Stevenson) Garden developed during the past 6 yrs, featuring shrubs, herbaceous beds and arches supporting varieties of rose, honeysuckle and clematis.

Padlock Croft, West Wratting ♿✇❀ (Mr & Mrs P E Lewis) *From dual carriageway on B1207 between Linton and Horseheath take turning N (Balsham W Wratting). Padlock Road is at entry to village.* Plantsman's organic garden of ⅔ acre, home of the National Campanula Collection. Mixed borders, troughs and alpine house incl rare plants. Rock and scree gardens, succulents and potager with raised beds. *Adm £1 Combined adm £2.50 Chd 50p with* **Hyset**, *and* **Weaver's Cottage**. *Sat, Mon May 27, 29, Sat June 10 with* **Hyset**, *and* **Weaver's Cottage** *and alone on Sats June 24, July 8 (2-6). Private visits also welcome, weekdays, please* **Tel 01223 290383**

Pampisford Gardens ♿✇ *8m S of Cambridge on A505. Combined adm £3 Wed July 19 (6-8)* **Evening Opening**. *Wine*

Beech Corner (Dr and Mrs B E Bridgland) *22 Church Lane.* Part of the garden has been planned as a courtyard with raised borders.

The Dower House (Dr and Mrs O M Edwards) *7 High Street.* C16 house (not open) surrounded by pretty nature garden with small pond

The Old Vicarage (Mr and Mrs T Nixon) 3-acre garden next to well-kept churchyard. Mature trees, shrubs and herbaceous borders. A large clump of Romneya coulteri thrives. Interesting conservatory. Wine

NEW **7 Pelham Close, South Bretton** ♿ (Mr & Mrs K G Brown) *Easily accessed from A1, A47 and A15 on W outskirts of Peterborough. Off Bretton Way opp Fitzwilliam Hospital.* Small garden with flowers for all seasons, the romantic blending with the unusual. Hellebores, clematis, new English roses, alpines, foliage effects and alpines. TEA. *Adm £1 Chd 50p. Private or group visits welcome. Please Tel* **01733 264157**

Ramsey Gardens, nr Huntingdon. *Combined adm £2 Chd free. Sun July 2 (2-6)*

The Elms, Ramsey Forty Foot (Mr & Mrs K C Shotbolt) *From Ramsey travel through Ramsey Forty Foot, just before bridge over drain, turn R, 300yds on R.* Large water garden beautifully landscaped with shrubs, water lilies, ferns and large tank koi carp. Mirror carp, golden orfe in lakes. 2 acres full of unusual plants. Spring flowers. *Also by appt, please* **Tel 01487 812601**

77 Great Whyte (Mr & Mrs H Holden) Cottage garden 55′ × 45′ well stocked with trees, shrubs, flowers and many interesting plants and features. *At other times by appt, please* **Tel 01487 812529**

NEW **Sawston Gardens** ✇❀ *7m SE of Cambridge. 3m from junction 10 M11. A505 follow signs to Sawston. Combined adm £2 Chd 50p. Sun July 2 (2-6)*

NEW **The Brook** (Mr & Mrs B J Butler) Nature garden surrounding C17 house (not open) including ancient mulberry tree

NEW **The Grove** (Bob & Sue Hodgson) Long established garden with mature trees. Raised pond, terrace and pergolas. Beds by the House currently being planted in the Arts and Crafts style of the property.

NEW **Poppy Cottage** (Paul Dracott) Long narrow cottage garden. Herbaceous perennials planted in a naturalistic N European style in rear garden. Front garden has native annuals.

NEW **Vine Cottage** (Dr & Mrs T Wreghitt) C17 house (not open) surrounded by nature garden. Contemporary garden featuring Japanese courtyard adjacent to recent extension.

Scarlett's Farm, West Wratting ♿✇❀ (Mr & Mrs M Hicks) *Padlock Rd. From dual carriageway on A1307 between Linton and Horseheath take turning N (W Wratting 3½). Padlock Road is at entry to village. Scarlett's Farm at end of Padlock Road.* ⅓ acre mixed country garden, incl formal but irregular parterre, full of colourful ornamentals. *Adm £1, Chd 50p. Visitors welcome by appt.* **Tel 01223 290812**

Selwyn College, Cambridge ♿✂❀ (Selwyn College) *Grange Road. Situated ½m W of the city centre. Selwyn College can be entered from Grange Rd which runs parallel with Queens Rd, known locally as 'The Backs'.* Unusual, exotic and an original approach to the use of plants in the recreation of this Victorian garden make this an exciting garden to visit, particularly in late summer when the circular border is stunning. Many unusual plants. Renovated over the past 4 yrs. TEAS and plant sales. *Adm £2 Chd free under 14. Sun Aug 20 (2-5)*

Shingay Gardens ✂ *12m W of Cambridge, 3m beyond A603 junction with A1198.* TEAS and parking at **South Farm**. *Combined adm £2.50 (ACNO to CAMVET). Suns June 18, July 2 (2-6)*

Brook Cottage (Mr & Mrs Charvil) *4 mins walk from* **South Farm.** A countryman's cottage garden. Abundant yr long mixed colour, spilling over boundary stream, inter-mixed with traditional vegetables and poultry

Private Nature Reserve (Herr Wentzel) *8 mins walk from* **South Farm** *(or drive).* Centred on 3 acre lake with remarkable naturally established wild flowers, aquatic birds, dragonflies and butterflies

South Farm ✂❀ (Mr P Paxman) Grounds of 10 acres, ringed by shelter planting surround farm house of Tudor origins (not open) and courtyard of listed farm buildings, home to rare breed poultry collection. Woodland, wild meadow, bog and water gardens contrast with more formal plantings, an exotic conservatory and large kitchen garden with more than 100 unusual varieties and species. New features incl borehole, irrigation and reed bed for domestic effluent draining to new bog and pond

Tadlow House, Tadlow ♿✂ (Mr & Mrs Andrew Parkinson) *3½m W of Arrington on N side of B1042 adjacent to church.* 4-acre garden with spring flower walks and blossom incl tulips, narcissi, anemone blanda and fritillaria. Plantings incl recently designed water garden, parterre and circle gardens; interesting shrubs and trees. Adjacent C13 church with William Butterfield's C19 restoration. TEAS in aid of Tadlow Church. *Adm £2 Chd free. Suns April 2, May 7 (2-5)*

Tetworth Hall, Sandy ❀ (Lady Crossman) *4m NE of Sandy. 6m SE of St Neots off Everton-Waresley Rd.* Large woodland and bog garden; rhododendrons; azaleas, unusual shrubs and plants; fine trees. Queen Anne house (not open). TEA. *Adm £2 Chd free (ACNO to Waresley Church). Sun May 14 (2-5.30). Open by appt April 15 to June 15, please* **Tel 01767 650212**

Trinity College, Fellows' Garden, Cambridge ♿✂ *Queen's Road.* Garden of 8 acres, originally laid out in the 1870s by W B Thomas. Lawns with mixed borders, shrubs and specimen trees. Drifts of spring bulbs. Recent extension of landscaped area among new college buildings to W of main garden. *Adm £1.50 Chd free. Sun April 9 (2-6)*

Upton Gardens ❀ *8m NW of Huntingdon. From A1 from N, and A14 from Cambridge, take B1043 and follow signs to Upton. From A1(M) from S take A14 (Cambridge) then 1st exit, B1043 (The Alconburys) and follow signs to Upton.* Teas in the Village Hall. Flowers in Church. *Combined adm £2. Sun June11 (1-5)*

NEW **Manor Farm** ♿ (Coralie & Richard Sandilands) Walled garden with mature trees. Adjoining field left to grow wild. Conservatory and large greenhouse

NEW **Meadow Heights** ♿✂ (Mr & Mrs A G Wood) Well stocked large garden with emphasis on perennial planting overlooking paddock and stables. Mature conifers and shrubs. Fruit cage

NEW **Rivendell** ♿ (Mr & Mrs D Stewart) Lawn, vegetable plot, flower borders, roses, fruit trees and display of containers and hanging baskets

NEW **School House** ♿❀ (Lyn & Bill Gibson) ⅓ acre country garden with arbours, retreats and glasshouses specialising in unusual, scented and climbing plants. Collections of datura, hibiscus, hoya, hedychium, jasmine, lonicera, passiflora and plumeria. Plants for sale

NEW **Southfields** (Mr & Mrs Abayawickrema) Domestic garden with pots, grapevine, vegetable and herb area, small pond and sitting areas framing open views

NEW **Stangate House** ✂ (Mr & Mrs M Alder) Front overlooks village pond and church and the back has a peaceful country view. A small selection of alpine plants

NEW **1 Upton Park** ✂ (Mr & Mrs L Weller) Family garden with rockeries, conifers, fish pond with waterfall and fountain.

Weaver's Cottage, Streetly End, West Wickham ✂ (Miss Sylvia Norton) *On A1307 between Linton and Haverhill turn N at Horseheath towards W Wickham. Weaver's Cottage is 8th on R after 40 sign.* ½-acre garden exuberantly planted for fragrance with spring bulbs; shrubs; herbaceous; climbers; old roses. Newly created scree garden. NCCPG Lathyrus Collection. TEA. *Adm £1 Chd 50p. Mon April 24. Combined adm £2.50 Chd 50p. Sat, Sun May 27, 29, Sat June 10 with* **Hyset** *&* **Padlock Croft** *(2-6). Private visits welcome, please* **Tel 01223 892399**

West Wratting Park, West Wratting ♿✂❀ (Mr & Mrs Henry D'Abo) *8m S of Newmarket. From A11, between Worsted Lodge and Six Mile Bottom, turn E to Balsham; then N along B1052 to West Wratting; Park is at E end of village.* Georgian house (only orangery shown), beautifully situated in rolling country, with fine tree. Rose and herbaceous gardens. TEA. *Adm £2 Chd free. Mon Aug 28 (2-6)*

Whittlesford Gardens ❀ *7m S of Cambridge. 1m NE of Junction 10 of the M11 and A505.* TEAS. Flowers in Parish church. *Combined adm £2 (ACNO to village hall). Suns June 18, July 16 (2-6)*

Brook Cottage (Mr R Marshall & Ms J Lewis) *Newton Road.* Small untidy peaceful cottage garden bordered by stream. *July 16 only*

Cherrytree Cottage ❀ (Mr & Mrs J Eastwood) Easy maintenance, organic garden, fishpond. Pretty places to sit. *June 18, July 16*

The Guildhall (Dr P & Prof M Spufford) *North Road.* Mediaeval building (not open) with small knot garden. *June 16 only*

Moonrakers (Mr & Mrs K Price) 1½ acre wildlife garden, espalier apple trees, shrubs and pond. *June 18, July 16*

23 Newton Rd ♿ (Mr F Winter) Cottage garden, herbaceous plants, shrubs, fish pond. Allotment consisting of all veg, fruit, flowers and bird aviary. *July 16 only*

41 North Road (Mr & Mrs R Proud) Cottage garden. Pond with waterfall. Rockery. Ancient C12 moat. *June 18, July 16*

5 Parsonage Court ♿✂ (Mrs L Button) *Please park on main rd.* Trees, shrubs and large pond. *June 18 only*

30 Royston Road (Mr & Mrs R Halls) Large garden with 2 fish ponds. TEAS. *June 18 only*

11 Scotts Garden ✂❀ (Mr & Mrs M Walker) Shady walled garden with shrub borders. *June 18, July 16*

Tudor Cottage, 4 West End (Mrs Patricia Downes) Cottage garden with pond and secret wild garden. *June 18 only*

21 West End (Mr & Mrs George Jezierski) Cottage garden with herbaceous beds, shrubs, pond and vegetable area. *Sun June 18 only*

NEW **Woodlands** (Mr & Mrs P Smail) Formal garden and woodland with wildlife pond. *Sun July 16 only*

▲ **Wimpole Hall, Arrington** ♿✂❀ (The National Trust) *5m N of Royston signed off A603 to Sandy 7m from Cambridge or off A1198.* Part of 350-acre park. Restored Dutch garden and Victorian parterres on N lawns. Rose garden and fine trees, marked walks in park. National Collection of walnuts. Massed plantings of daffodil. Lunches & TEAS. *Adm £2 Chd £1 For NGS Fri April 14 (10.30-5)*

Wytchwood, Owl End ❀ (Mr & Mrs David Cox) *2m N of Huntingdon on B1043. Parking at village hall, Owl End.* 2-acre brightly planted borders of perennials, annuals and shrubs, lawns and ponds leading to 1 acre of wild plants and grasses set among rowan and birch trees. TEAS. *Adm £2 Chd 50p. Sun July 23 (1.30-5.30)*

Evening Opening (See also garden description)

Clare College, Fellows' Garden, Cambridge	July 2
Fen Ditton Gardens	June 15
Newnham College, Cambridge	June 29
Pampisford Gardens	July 19

Carmarthenshire & Pembrokeshire

See separate Welsh section on page 397

Ceredigion/Cardiganshire

See separate Welsh section on page 401

HELP THE HOSPICES

Help the Hospice care is based on the simple idea that a dying patient is a living person – someone who deserves peace, love and calm until the very end of their life. Hospices seek to add life to days, even when days cannot be added to life, and restore dignity, quality and a sense of fulfilment to the closing days of a patient's life. They also work to ensure that the needs of each patient, their family and their friends, are met according to their wants and wishes.

For further information on this charity, please contact: Help the Hospices, 34–44 Britannia Street, London WC1X 9JG.

Information is also available on the NGS website (www.ngs.org.uk)

Cheshire & Wirral

Hon County Organiser: Mr Nicholas Payne, The Mount, Whirley, Macclesfield SK11 9PB
Tel 01625 426 730
Assistant Hon County Organisers: Mrs T R Hill, Salterswell House, Tarporley CW6 0ED Tel 01829 732 804
Mrs N Whitbread, Lower Huxley Hall, Hargrave, Chester CH3 7RQ
Tel 01829 781481
Mrs P M Mahon, Rectory Cottage, Eaton, Congleton CW12 2ND
Tel 01260 274 777

DATES OF OPENING

Regular openings
For details see garden description
Arley Hall & Gardens, Northwich
Norton Priory, Runcorn
Peover Hall, Knutsford
Rode Hall, Scholar Green

By appointment only
For telephone numbers and other details see garden descriptions. Private visits welcomed
Ness Cottage, Mollington
Rosewood, Puddington
2 Stanley Road, Heaton Moor

March 5 Sunday
Tulip Tree Cottage, Coppenhall

April 2 Sunday
37 Bakewell Road, Hazel Grove
Cherry Hill, Malpas
Poulton Hall, Poulton Lancelyn
The Well House, Tilston

April 9 Sunday
Orchard Villa, Alsager

April 16 Sunday
Briarfield, Burton
Cranberry Cottage, Smallwood, nr Sandbach
Tulip Tree Cottage, Coppenhall

April 23 Sunday
37 Bakewell Road, Hazel Grove

May 1 Monday
Willaston Village Gardens

May 7 Sunday
Lyme Park, Disley
Tushingham Hall, Whitchurch

May 12 Friday
Bolesworth Castle, Tattenhall (evening)

May 14 Sunday
Hare Hill Gardens, Over Alderley
Haughton Hall, Bunbury
Rode Hall, Scholar Green
Willaston Grange, Willaston

May 20 Saturday
Peover Hall, Knutsford

May 21 Sunday
Bolesworth Castle, Tattenhall
Fir Tree Cottage, Henbury
Little Moreton Hall, Congleton
Peover Hall, Knutsford
St Davids House, Noctorum
Withinlee Ridge, Prestbury

May 24 Wednesday
Reaseheath College, Nantwich

May 28 Sunday
Henbury Hall, nr Macclesfield
The Stray, Neston

May 29 Monday
Ashton Hayes, Chester

May 31 Wednesday
Reaseheath College, Nantwich

June 3 Saturday
Arley Hall & Gardens, Northwich
Bank House, Bickerton

June 4 Sunday
Bank House, Bickerton
Ollerton Lodge, nr Knutsford
Orchard Villa, Alsager

June 7 Wednesday
Reaseheath College, Nantwich

June 10 Saturday
The Old Parsonage, Arley Green

June 11 Sunday
Free Green Farm, Lower Peover
Norton Priory, Runcorn
The Old Parsonage, Arley Green
Tulip Tree Cottage, Coppenhall

June 17 Saturday
17 Poplar Grove, Sale

June 18 Sunday
35 Heyes Lane, Timperley
Mere Hall, Oxton, nr Birkenhead
3 Over Hall Drive, Winsford
17 Poplar Grove, Sale
Stonyford Cottage, Cuddington
13 Yew Tree Cottages, Compstall

June 19 Monday
Tatton Park, Knutsford

June 21 Wednesday
35 Heyes Lane, Timperley

June 25 Sunday
Burton Village Gardens
Long Acre, Bunbury
The Mount, Higher Kinnerton
The Old Hough, Warmingham

July 1 Saturday
36 Woodhouse Lane, Sale

July 2 Sunday
12 Burnham Close, Cheadle Hulme
73 Hill Top Avenue, Cheadle Hulme
Lower Huxley Hall, Hargrave
Sandymere, Cotebrook
Tulip Tree Cottage, Coppenhall
36 Woodhouse Lane, Sale
13 Yew Tree Cottages, Compstall

July 9 Sunday
Dorfold Hall, Nantwich
Rhodewood House, Macclesfield
Wood End Cottage, Whitegate

July 12 Wednesday
Cholmondeley Castle, Malpas

July 15 Saturday
Bridgemere Garden World, Bridgemere

July 16 Sunday
Edith Terrace, Compstall
Henbury Gardens
Poulton Hall, Poulton Lancelyn
Warrington Gardens
13 Yew Tree Cottages, Compstall

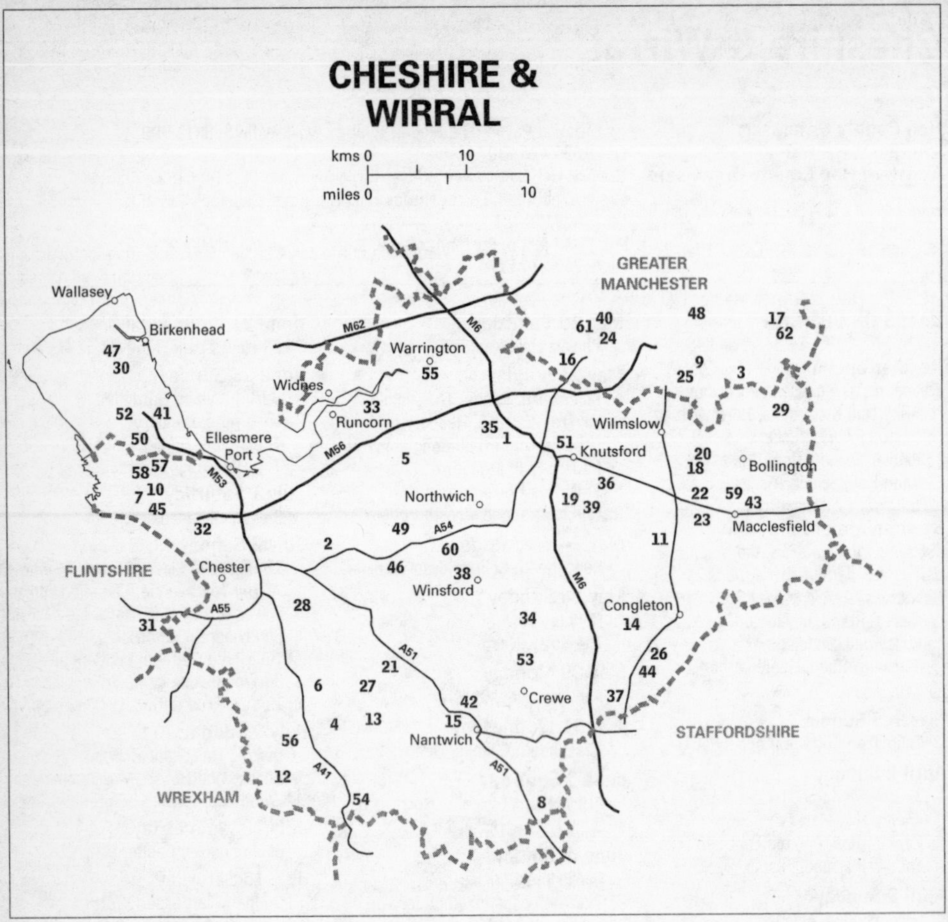

KEY

1 Arley Hall & Gardens
2 Ashton Hayes
3 37 Bakewell Road
4 Bank House
5 Bluebell Cottage
6 Bolesworth Castle
7 Briarfield
8 Bridgemere Garden World
9 12 Burnham Close
10 Burton Village Gardens
11 Capesthorne Hall
12 Cherry Hill
13 Cholmondeley Castle
14 Cranberry Cottage
15 Dorfold Hall
16 Dunham Massey
17 Edith Terrace
18 Fir Tree Cottage
19 Free Green Farm
20 Hare Hill Gardens
21 Haughton Hall
22 Henbury Gardens
23 Henbury Hall
24 35 Heyes Lane
25 73 Hill Top Avenue
26 Little Moreton Hall
27 Long Acre
28 Lower Huxley Hall
29 Lyme Park
30 Mere Hall
31 The Mount
32 Ness Cottage
33 Norton Priory
34 The Old Hough
35 The Old Parsonage
36 Ollerton Lodge
37 Orchard Villa
38 3 Over Hall Drive
39 Peover Hall
40 17 Poplar Grove
41 Poulton Hall
42 Reaseheath College
43 Rhodewood House
44 Rode Hall
45 Rosewood
46 Sandymere
47 St Davids House
48 2 Stanley Road
49 Stonyford Cottage
50 The Stray
51 Tatton Park
52 Thornton Manor
53 Tulip Tree Cottage
54 Tushingham Hall
55 Warrington Gardens
56 The Well House
57 Willaston Grange
58 Willaston Village Gardens
59 Withinlee Ridge
60 Wood End Cottage
61 36 Woodhouse Lane
62 13 Yew Tree Cottages

July 23 Sunday
Cranberry Cottage, Smallwood, nr Sandbach

August 2 Wednesday
Capesthorne Hall, Macclesfield

August 6 Sunday
Bluebell Cottage, Dutton
13 Yew Tree Cottages, Compstall

August 13 Sunday
Dunham Massey, Altrincham

August 20 Sunday
Lyme Park, Disley

August 28 Monday
Thornton Manor, Thornton Hough

2001

March 4 Sunday
Tulip Tree Cottage, Coppenhall

DESCRIPTIONS OF GARDENS

■ **Arley Hall & Gardens, Northwich** ♿❀ (The Viscount Ashbrook) *Well signed from M6 junctions 19 & 20 & M56 junctions 9 & 10.* 12 acres; twin herbaceous borders, avenue of Quercus Ilex, walled gardens; azaleas, shrub roses, rhododendrons; woodland garden. Lunches. Gift shop. Specialist plant nursery. TEA. *Adm Gardens & Grounds only £4.40 OAP £3.80 under 16 £2.20; Hall £2.50 Extra Chd £1.50 (ACNO to Boys & Girls Welfare Society). April 9 to Oct 1 incl (11-5) Tues to Sun & Bank Hols. Hall open days vary throughout season, last adm to gardens 4.30. For NGS Sat June 3 (11-4.30)* **Tel 01565 777353** Arley Garden Festival Sat, Sun June 24, 25 (10-5)

Ashton Hayes, Chester ✗ (Mrs J Searle) *Midway between Tarvin and Kelsall on A54, take B5393 N to Ashton and Mouldsworth. Approach to Ashton Hayes can be seen halfway between Ashton and Mouldsworth.* The ¾m drive is beside former lodge. About 12 acres, incl arboretum and ponds. Predominantly a valley garden of mature trees and flowering shrubs; great variety of azaleas and rhododendrons; notable embothrium. TEAS. *Adm £2 OAPs £1.50 Chd 50p (ACNO to Church of St John the Evangelist, Ashton Hayes). Mon May 29 (2-6)*

37 Bakewell Road, Hazel Grove ✗ (Mr & Mrs H Williams) *From Manchester on A6 following signs to Buxton, bear R at Rising Sun Public House, Hazel Grove. Taking the Macclesfield Rd (A523) take 1st R (Haddon Rd) then 1st L into Bakewell Rd.* Small suburban garden 17 yds × 6½ yds heavily planted with azaleas, rhododendrons (several rare and unusual varieties), hydrangeas; woodland dell and fountain. Excellent example of how much can be planted in a small area. TEA. *Adm £1.50 Chd free. Suns April 2, 23 (11-6). Private visits by appt, please* **Tel 01625 260592**

Bank House, Bickerton ❀ (Dr & Mrs M A Voisey) *11m S of Chester on A41 turn L at Broxton roundabout to Nantwich on A534. Take 5th R (1.8m) to Bickerton. Take 2nd R into Goldford Lane. Bank House is then 0.9m on L.* 1½-acre garden situated at the foot of Bickerton Hill, below the Sandstone Trail. Sheltered, terraced borders stocked with a wide range of shrubs, trees and herbaceous plants, and a productive vegetable garden. Field parking. TEAS. *Adm £2 Chd 50p (ACNO to Age Concern & The Multiple Sclerosis Support Centre). Sat, Sun June 3, 4 (2-6)*

Bluebell Cottage, Dutton ♿✗❀ (R L & D Casey) *Lodge Lane. From M56 (junction 10) take A49 (Whitchurch) turn R at T-lights towards Runcorn. Then 1st turning L.* A cottage garden featuring herbaceous borders stocked with unusual perennials. Large pond; scree; bog area; ornamental grasses bed in this 1½-acre garden, situated within picturesque, environmentally friendly scenery. Adjacent nursery; meadow and woodland. TEAS. *Adm £2 Chd 50p Sun Aug 6 (1-5). Private visits welcome, please* **Tel 01928 713718**

Bolesworth Castle, Tattenhall ♿❀ (Mr & Mrs A G Barbour) *Enter by lodge on A41 8m S of Chester.* Landscape with rhododendrons, shrubs and borders. Woodland walk replanted 1993/9. TEAS only on Sun. *Adm £2.50 Chd free (ACNO to Harthill & Burwardsley Churches).* **Evening Opening** *Fri May 12 (5.30-8); Sun May 21 (2-5.30)*

Briarfield, Burton ✗❀ (Mrs E Carter) *9m NW of Chester. Turn off A540 at Willaston-Burton Xrds (traffic lights) and follow rd for 1m to Burton Village centre. Free car parking.* 1½-acres of rare trees and shrubs, many spring flowering. Mixed borders with spring bulbs, erythroniums a speciality. Set against National Trust woodland background. TEA. *Adm £2 Chd free. Sun April 16 (2-5). Open by appt all year, please* **Tel 0151 336 2304**

▲ **Bridgemere Garden World, Bridgemere** ♿✗ (Bridgemere Nurseries Ltd) *On A51 7m S of Nantwich, 1m N of Woore. Follow brown tourist signs from Nantwich.* The Bridgemere Gardens, over 22 gardens showing many different styles of plant grouping. Plus the recreated Bridgemere Garden World prize winning exhibition gardens from Garden Festivals, Chelsea Flower Show Gold Medal gardens and the garden where the Gardeners' Diary television programme is filmed. Coffee shop and restaurant on site. *Adm £1.50 OAPs and Chd over 8yrs £1. For NGS Sat July 15 (10-6)*

NEW **12 Burnham Close, Cheadle Hulme** ✗❀ (Mr & Mrs Tim Saville) *Leave A34 at Cheadle on B5358 towards Heald Green. Turn L at 1st Lights to Cheadle Hulme and L at Conway Public House down Conway Rd. Park nr school or opp on Henley Ave. Burnham is 3rd R on Henley.* Plantspersons suburban garden of two halves. Colour combinations on one side from the flowers of Austin roses, violas and clematis etc; on the other side from the variegated foliage of perennials and shrubs. The borders, gravel scree and patios in particular feature over 100 hostas, incl many new American introductions. TEA. *Adm £1.50 Chd 50p. Sun July 2 (2-6)*

Burton Village Gardens ✗❀ *9m NW of Chester. Turn off A540 at Willaston-Burton Xrds (traffic lights) and follow rd for 1m to Burton. Free parking.* Teas at Village Hall in aid of Clare House Children's Hospice. *Combined adm £3 Chd free Sun June 25 (2-6).*

Bank Cottage (Mr & Mrs J R Beecroft) Small, very colourful, mixed, cottage garden with old roses backing on to cricket ground

Briarfield ❀ (Mrs E Carter) 1½ acres of rare trees and shrubs, colourful mixed borders together with fruit and vegetable garden in woodland setting. Woodland trail to

Lynwood ❀ (Mr & Mrs P M Wright) *On the fringe of the village on the Neston Road.* ½-acre garden with shrub border, rockery, pond with waterfall, pergola and arbour with climbers

▲ Capesthorne Hall, Macclesfield ♿ (Mr & Mrs WA Bromley-Davenport) *5m W of Macclesfield. 7m S of Wilmslow on A34. Free car park.* Varied garden; daffodil lawn; azaleas, rhododendrons; herbaceous border, arboretum and lake. Georgian chapel and memorial garden. TEAS Butler's Pantry serving coffee, teas, soup, sandwiches, cakes, ices etc. *Adm garden £3.50 OAPs £3 Chd £1.50. For NGS Wed Aug 2 (12-6)* **Tel 01625 861221**

Cherry Hill, Malpas ♿ (Mr & Mrs Miles Clarke) *2m W of Malpas signed from B5069 to Chorlton.* Massed bulbs in spring; walks through pine woods and rhododendrons to trout lake; walled garden, herbaceous borders, shrub roses. Ornamental vegetable garden. TEAS in attractive house overlooking Welsh mountains. Cricket ground. *Adm £2 Chd 50p. Sun April 2 (2-5.30). Open by appt please* **Tel 01948 860355**

▲ Cholmondeley Castle, Malpas ♿❀ (The Marchioness of Cholmondeley) *Situated off A41 Chester/Whitchurch rd and A49 Whitchurch/Tarporley rd.* Romantically landscaped gardens full of variety. Azaleas, rhododendrons, flowering shrubs, rare trees, herbaceous borders and water garden. Lakeside picnic area; rare breeds of farm animals, incl llamas; gift shop. Ancient private Chapel in the park. TEAS, Tearoom offering light lunches etc. *Adm gardens only £3 OAPs £2.50 Chd £1 For NGS Wed July 12 (11.30-5)* **Tel 01829 720383 or 720203**

Cranberry Cottage, Smallwood, nr Sandbach ♿✗ (Paula & Malcolm Bright) *From A50 at public house 'Legs of Man' turn into Back Lane. From A34 turn to Smallwood to public house 'Blue Bell'; thereafter signed.* ¾-acre country cottage garden planted with rare bulbs. Spring flowering shrubs; clematis, azaleas, rhododendrons and viburnums. Magnolias and a variety of blossom trees. TEA. *Adm £2 Chd 50p. Suns April 16, July 23 (1-5). Also by appt, please* **Tel 01477 500239**

▲ Dorfold Hall, Nantwich ✗❀ (Mr & Mrs Richard Roundell) *1m W of Nantwich on A534 between Nantwich and Acton.* 18-acre garden surrounding C17 house (not open) with formal approach; lawns and herbaceous borders; spectacular spring woodland garden with rhododendrons, azaleas, magnolias and bulbs. TEAS in aid of Acton Parish Church. *Adm £2 Chd 75p. For NGS Sun July 9 (2-5.30)*

▲ Dunham Massey, Altrincham ♿✗❀ (The National Trust) *3m SW of Altrincham off A56. Well signed.* Garden over 20 acres, on ancient site with moat lake, mount and orangery. Mature trees and fine lawns with extensive range of shrubs and herbaceous perennials suited to acid sand, many planted at waterside. Set in 350 acres of deer park. TEAS. *Adm £3 Chd free NGS day only (car entry £3). For NGS Sun Aug 13 (11-5)*

NEW **Edith Terrace, Compstall** ✗ (The Edith Terrace Group) *6m E of Stockport. Take Bredbury junction off M60. Follow Romiley/Marple Bridge sign on B6104. Turn into Compstall at Etherow Country Park sign. Take 1st R, situated at the end of Montagu Street. Parking in village public car parks - short walk to Edith Terrace.* A series of gardens in mixed style from cottage to formal, situated to front and rear of Victorian terrace. Mixed herbaceous perennials, ornamental backyards and back alleyway. In lakeside setting in the conserved mill village of Compstall, adjacent to Etherow Country Park. TEAS. *Adm £2 combined with* **Yew Tree Cottage** *£3 Chd £1 (ACNO to BLISS). Sun July 16 (2-5)*

Fir Tree Cottage, Henbury ✗ (Mrs Peter Smith) *On A537 Whirley Lane is 2nd L after Monks Heath t-lights towards Macclesfield.* Cottage garden with topiary and adjoining 3 -acre arboretum with rhododendrons. Picnics welcome. *Adm £2 Chd 50p. Sun May 21 (1-5)*

Free Green Farm, Lower Peover ♿✗ (Sir Philip & Lady Haworth) *Free Green Lane connects the A50 with the B5081. From Holmes Chapel take A50 past the Drovers Arms. L into Free Green Lane, farm is on R. From Knutsford take A50, turn R into Middlewich Lane (B5081), turn L into Broom Lane, turn L into Free Green Lane, farm is on L.* 2-acre garden with pleached limes, herbaceous borders, ponds, parterre; new garden of the senses and British woodland. Parking in field behind house (sign posted) not in lane. TEAS in aid of Cancer Research Campaign. *Adm £2.50 Chd free. Sun June 11 (2-6)*

▲ Hare Hill Gardens, Over Alderley ♿✗ (The National Trust) *Between Alderley Edge and Prestbury, turn off N at B5087 at Greyhound Rd [118:SJ85765].* Attractive spring garden featuring a fine display of rhododendrons and azaleas; a good collection of hollies and other specimen trees and shrubs. The 10-acre garden incls a walled garden which hosts many wall shrubs incl clematis and vines; the borders are planted with agapanthus and geraniums. Partially suitable for wheelchairs. *Adm £2.50 Chd £1.25. For NGS Sun May 14 (10-5.30)*

Haughton Hall, Bunbury ❀ (Mr & Mrs R J Posnett) *Tarporley. 5m NW of Nantwich off A534 Nantwich/Wrexham Rd, 6m SE of Tarporley via A49.* Medium-sized garden; species rhododendrons, azaleas, shrubs, rock garden; lake with temple; waterfall. Collection of ornamental trees. Home-made TEAS. *Adm £2.50 Chd 50p. Sun May 14 (2-6)*

Henbury Gardens *Approx 2m due W of Macclesfield along A537 opp Blacksmiths Arms. At Henbury go up Peppar St. Turn L into Church Lane then Andertons Lane in 100 yds.* TEAS at The Mount. *Combined adm £3 Chd 50p. Sun July 16 (2-5.30)*

NEW **Far Hills** ✗ (Mr & Mrs Ian Warburton) Mixed ½-acre garden; planted for yr-round interest with regard for wildlife. Trees; shrubs; herbaceous perennials; small pond; fruit & vegetable area; native copse

The Mount, Whirley, Henbury ♿✗❀ (Mr & Mrs Nicholas Payne) The garden is approx 2 acres and has interesting trees including eucryphia nymansensis, fern leaved beech and sciadopitys. Shrubberies; herbaceous border; swimming pool and short vista of Irish Yews. TEAS in aid of East Cheshire Hospice *Parties welcome, please* **Tel 01625 426730**

Henbury Hall, nr Macclesfield ♿✂ (Mr & Mrs Sebastian de Ferranti) *2m W of Macclesfield on A537 rd. Turn down School Lane, Henbury at Blacksmiths Arms: East Lodge on R.* Large garden with lake, beautifully landscaped and full of variety. Azaleas, rhododendrons, flowering shrubs, rare trees, herbaceous borders. TEAS in aid of East Cheshire Hospice. *Adm £3 Chd £1 (ACNO to Drugwatch). Sun May 28 (2-5)*

35 Heyes Lane, Timperley ❀ (Mr & Mrs David Eastwood) *Heyes Lane is a turning off Park Rd (B5165) 1m from the junction with the A56 Altrincham-Manchester rd 1½m N of Altrincham. Or from A560 turn W in Timperley Village for ¼m. Newsagents shop on corner.* A small suburban garden 30′ × 90′ on sandy soil maintained by a keen plantswoman member of the Organic Movement (HDRA). A yr-round garden; trees; small pond; greenhouses; 16 kinds of fruit with a good collection of interesting and unusual plants. *Adm £2 incl TEA Chd free. Sun June 18, Wed June 21 (2-5)*

73 Hill Top Avenue, Cheadle Hulme ✂ (Mr & Mrs Martin Land) *Turn off A34 (new by-pass) at roundabout signed Cheadle Hulme (B5094). Take 2nd turn L into Gillbent Rd, signposted Cheadle Hulme Sports Centre. Go to end, small roundabout, turn R into Church Rd. 2nd rd on L is Hill Top Ave. From Stockport or Bramhall turn R/L into Church Rd by The Church Inn. Hill Top Ave is first rd on R.* A sixth of an acre plantswoman's garden. Plantings of herbaceous, shrub and climbing roses, clematis, pond and damp area, shrubs and small trees. TEAS. *Adm £2 Chd free (ACNO to Arthritis Research Campaign). Sun July 2 (2-6) also by appt, please* **Tel 0161 486 0055**

▲ Little Moreton Hall, Congleton ♿✂❀ (The National Trust) *On A34, 4m S of Congleton.* 1½-acre garden surrounded by a moat, next to finest example of timber-framed architecture in England. Herb and historic vegetable garden, orchard and borders. Knot garden. Adm includes entry to the Hall with optional free guided tours. Wheelchairs and electric mobility vehicle available. Picnic lawns. Shop and restaurant serving coffee, lunches and teas. TEAS. *Adm £4.30 Chd £2.10. For NGS Sun May 21 (11.30-5 last admission 4.30)*

NEW **Long Acre, Bunbury** ✂❀ (Mr & Mrs M Bourne) *3½m SE of Tarpoley on the A49. Follow the signs for Bunbury, turn 2nd L after Wild Boar Hotel. L at 1st rd junction then 1st R by Nags Head Public House 400yds on L. From A51 follow signs for Bunbury until Nags Head. Turn into Wyche Lane before Public House car park. 400yds to garden.* A plantswomans country garden of approx ½-acre with rare and unusual plants. Roses, fruit and vegetable gardens; pool garden; small vineyard. Sub-tropical conservatory; herbaceous; specialise in orchids, fuschias, proteas. TEAS. *Adm £2 Chd £1 (ACNO to St Boniface Church, Millennium Fund & Horses & Ponies Protection Association). Sun June 25 (2-5.30)*

NEW **Lower Huxley Hall, Hargrave** ♿✂ (Neville & Juliet Whitbread) *Between Huxley & Hargrave 7m SW of Chester. Huxley is 4m from Tarporley, 2m from Tattenahll & 4m from Tarvin. A good road map is advisable.* 4-acre garden with follies; pergolas; arches; a moat; herbaceous, shrub and rose beds; within a picturesque and romantic setting. TEAS in aid of Tarporley Hospital. *Adm £2 Chd £1. Sun July 2 (2-5.30)*

▲ Lyme Park, Disley ♿✂ (The National Trust) *6m SE of Stockport just W of Disley on A6 rd.* 17-acre garden retaining many original features from Tudor and Jacobean times; high Victorian style bedding; a Dutch garden; a Gertrude Jekyll style herbaceous border; an Edwardian rose garden, a Wyatt orangery and many other features. Also rare trees, a wild flower area and lake. TEAS. Donations to NGS. *Adm £3.50 per car to estate, £2 Chd £1 to gardens. For NGS Suns May 7, Aug 20 (11-4.45)*

NEW **Mere Hall, Oxton, nr Birkenhead** ✂ (Mere Hall Conservation Association) *1m NW of Oxton Village, L off B5151 into Wexford Rd (turning after St Saviour's Church), L into Mere Farm Rd, drive to Mere Hall on L.* Victorian garden of 6 acres currently being restored. Woodland walks; mixed borders; terraces; pond and walled garden. TEAS. *Adm £2 Chd 50p. Sun June 18 (2-6)*

The Mount, Higher Kinnerton ♿✂❀ (Mr & Mrs J Major) *6m W of Chester, L off A5104 just after it crosses A55* Approx 2½-acre garden with mature trees; shrubs, lawns; kitchen garden; variety of perennial plants. A lot of reorganising and planting has taken place over the last 12 months. TEAS, Bric-a-Brac Stall in aid of All Saints Church. *Adm £2.50 Chd free. Sun June 25 (2-6) private parties welcome, please* **Tel 01244 660275** Best months June and July

Ness Cottage, Mollington ♿✂❀ (Mrs S Harris) *Coalpit Lane. Off the A540, 5m N of Chester and ¼m S of A5117 (Little Chef roundabout).* ½-acre garden of all-round interest. Front planted to attract wildlife, incl pond and camomile lawn. Back designed for all-yr colour, with sitting areas, herbaceous borders, ponds, heather, rhododendrons and water arrangements. *Adm £2 Chd free. Private visits (for NGS) welcome, please* **Tel 01244 880122**

■ Norton Priory, Runcorn ♿❀ (Mrs Margaret Warhurst) *Tudor Road, Manor Park. From M56 Junction 11 turn for Warrington and follow signs. From Warrington take A56 for Runcorn and follow signs.* 16 acres of gardens; Georgian summerhouses; rock garden and stream glade; 3-acre walled garden of similar date (1760s) recently restored. Fruit training; rosewalk; colour borders; herb garden, cottage garden. Priory remains also open. TEA. *Combined adm £3.30 Chd £2 Family ticket £8.80. Daily April to October (12-5) weekends and bank hols (12-6) Nov to March (12-4) (Walled garden closed Nov-Feb). For NGS Sun June 11 (12-6)* **Tel 01928 569895**

The Old Hough, Warmingham ♿✂ (Mr & Mrs D S Varey) *2m from Middlewich on A530 to Nantwich, turn L to*

Warmingham and L again T-junction or L on A533 from Sandbach to Middlewich and R at T-junction. 2½-acres owner-designed and maintained garden, enhancing period house and farm buildings (not open). Architectural in character, with much use of old materials. Choice planting. Wildlife pond, interesting young trees. Lily pond, rill, lawns, borders. Ample parking and WCs. TEAS in aid of Warmingham Church. *Adm £2.50 Chd 50p (ACNO to Warmingham Church). Sun June 25 (2-6)*

The Old Parsonage, Arley Green ♿❀ (The Viscount & Viscountess Ashbrook) *5m NNE of Northwich and 3m Great Budworth; M6 junctions 19, 20 and M56 junction 10. Follow signposts to Arley Hall and Gardens and notices to Old Parsonage which lies across park at Arley Green.* 2-acre garden yew hedges, herbaceous and mixed borders, shrub roses, climbers; woodland garden and pond, with unusual young trees and foliage shrubs. Waterplants, rhododendrons, azaleas, meconopsis. TEAS. *Adm £2.50 Chd under 5 free (ACNO to Save the Children). Sat, Sun June 10, 11 (2-6)*

NEW **Ollerton Lodge, nr Knutsford** ♿✇ (Mr & Mrs D Charlesworth) *E from Knutsford, take the A537 (Macclesfield rd). School lane is the 2nd turn on the R after the 'Dun Cow'. Approx 2m from Knutsford and 1m before reaching Chelford. Ollerton Lodge approx 200yds on the R.* Approx 1-acre garden. Shrubs, herbaceous border; new yew walk; small parterre and secret garden. Pond and waterfall. TEAS. *Adm £2 Chd 50p. Sun June 4 (2-5.30)*

Orchard Villa, Alsager ♿❀ (Mr & Mrs J Trinder) *72 Audley Rd. At traffic lights in Alsager town centre turn S towards Audley, house is 300yds on R beyond level Xing* Long and narrow, this ⅓-acre has been planted by enthusiastic plant collectors and features spring bulbs, hellebores, alpines, irises, grasses and other herbaceous perennials. TEAS *Adm £2 Chd free Suns April 9, June 4 (12-5) also private visits welcome, please* **Tel 01270 874833**

3 Over Hall Drive, Winsford ✇❀ (Mr & Mrs P Banks) *From the W side of Winsford take the B5074 from roundabout at top of dual carriageway, signposted Nantwich. Turn 1st R into Beeston Drive then 1st L into The Loont, and immed L again into Over Hall Drive.* Meandering informal ¼ acre garden. Young trees, shrubs, small pond, clematis, rhododendrons, azaleas, perennials and self-seeded annuals, all collected for their contrasting shapes, textures and colour. TEAS. *Adm £2 Chd free (ACNO to Christies Against Cancer). Sun June 18 (1-6)*

■ **Peover Hall, Knutsford** ♿✇ (Randle Brooks Esq) *Over Peover. 3m S of Knutsford on A50, L at Whipping Stocks down Stocks Lane. Lodge gates off Goostrey Lane signed to Church.* 15 acres. 5 walled gardens: lily pond, rose, herb, white and pink gardens; C18 landscaped park, moat, C19 dell, rhododendron walks, large walled kitchen garden, Church walk, purple border, blue and white border, pleached lime avenues, fine topiary work. TEAS. *Adm £2 (ACNO Over Peover Church). Mons & Thurs (2-5) May to Oct. NOT Bank Hols. Other days by appt for parties. For NGS Sat, Sun May 20, 21 (2-6)*

17 Poplar Grove, Sale ✇❀ (Gordon Cooke Esq) *From the A6144 at Brooklands Station turn down Hope Rd. Poplar Grove 3rd on R.* This town garden has been created by the owner who is a potter and landscape designer. It has a special collection of unusual plants in an artistic setting with many interesting design features and details. Incl a pebble mosaic 'cave'. TEAS. *Adm £2 Chd 50p (ACNO to North Manchester General Hospital). Sat, Sun June 17, 18 (2-5)*

Poulton Hall, Poulton Lancelyn ❀ (The Lancelyn Green Family) *2m from Bebington. From M53, exit 4 towards Bebington; at traffic lights (½m) R along Poulton Rd; house 1m on R.* 2½ acres; lawns, ha-ha, wild flower meadow, shrubbery, walled gardens with sculptures relating to the books of Roger Lancelyn Green. Cream TEAS. *Adm £2 Chd 20p. Suns April 2, July 16 (2-6)*

Reaseheath College, Nantwich ♿✇❀ (Mrs A Harrison) *1 1/2m N of Nantwich on the A51.* The Gardens of 12 acres, used as a teaching resource, are based on a Victorian Garden containing many mature trees of horticultural interest. Glass houses; model fruit, rose, woodland lakeside and bog gardens; extensive shrub borders and lawns. New garden centre now open to the public 7 days per week. *Adm £2.50. Weds May 24, 31, June 7 (2-4.30). Parties welcome, Guided Tours by arrangement, contact Anne Harrison please* **Tel 01270 625131; Fax 01270 625665 steved@reaseheath.ac.uk** Report to College Reception

Rhodewood House, Macclesfield ✇❀ (Mr & Mrs Roger Gorvin) *Prestbury Road. On the B5087 1½m NW of centre of Macclesfield.* 3-acre well-stocked undulating garden with yr-round interest incl rose garden, herbaceous borders, woodland walk, wildlife pond, bridge over natural stream and a good selection of rhododendrons (over 200 recently planted species and cultivars); shrubs, conifers, clematis and hydrangeas. TEAS in aid of East Cheshire Hospice. *Adm £2 Chd 50p. Sun July 9 (11-5)*

■ **Rode Hall, Scholar Green** ❀ (Sir Richard & Lady Baker Wilbraham) *[Grid SJ8157] 5m SW of Congleton between Scholar Green (A34) and Rode Heath (A50).* Nesfield's terrace and rose garden with view over Humphrey Repton's landscape is a feature of Rode gardens, as is the woodland garden with a terraced rock garden and grotto. Other attractions incl the walk to the lake, a restored ice house and working walled kitchen garden. TEAS. *Adm £2.50 Chd £1 (ACNO to All Saints Odd Rode Parish Church). Tues, Weds, Thurs & Bank Hols April 4 to Sept 28 (2-5). For NGS Sun May 14 (1.30-5)*

Rosewood, Puddington ❀ (Mr & Mrs C E J Brabin) *6m N of Chester turn L (W) off Chester to Hoylake A540 to Puddington. Telephone for precise directions.* 1-acre garden incl small wood, pond with bogside species, rhododendron, magnolia and azalea species and hybrids; many unusual trees. Most of the new plantings are grown from seed by owner. TEAS by arrangement. *Adm £2 Chd free. Open by appt only to groups or individuals, please* **Tel 0151 353 1193**

St Davids House, Noctorum ❀ (Ian Mitchell Esq) *3.2m S from Birkenhead Town Hall. From there A553 then A502 through Claughton village. After 2 sets of lights, 1st L*

(Noctorum Lane). After Xrds, St Davids Lane is 1st on R. Victorian garden of 1½ acres currently being restored. Azaleas, camellias, rhododendrons, herbaceous borders, rock garden and pool. TEAS. *Adm £2 Chd free. Sun May 21 (2-6)*

Sandymere, Cotebrook ♿✂❀ (John & Alex Timpson) *On A54 about 300yds W of traffic lights at Xrds of A49/A54.* A large, beautifully landscaped garden with lakes, woodland walks, terraces, undulating lawns and mixed borders. The wide variety of hostas are of particular interest. TEAS. *Adm £2.50 OAPs £1.50 Chd free. Sun July 2 (2-5.30)*

2 Stanley Road, Heaton Moor ✂❀ (Mr G Leatherbarrow) *Approx 1½m N of Stockport. Follow Heaton Moor Rd off A6. Stanley Rd on L. 1st house on R.* Tiny town garden with all year interest, cultivated with wildlife in mind, packed with interesting plants, creating a secret cottage garden atmosphere. Old species and English roses, clematis, hardy geraniums, ivies, varied evergreens, daphnes, hellebores, delphiniums, penstemons, mixed herbaceous; ponds. Max no. of visitors 2 - no room for more. Not suitable for less agile. TEA. *Adm £2 Chd 75p. Private visits welcome Feb to end Sept, please* **Tel 0161 442 3828** www.maigold.co.uk

▲ **Stonyford Cottage, Cuddington** ♿✂❀ (Mr & Mrs Anthony Overland) *6m W of Northwich. Turn R off A556 (Northwich to Chester). At Xrds ¾m past A49 junction (signpost Norley-Kingsley NB not Cuddington signs). Entrance in ½m on L.* This informal natural grden with many unusual waterside plants, has been developed around a 'Monet' style pool with bridges to an island, woodland walk and damp garden. Shown on BBC Gardeners World. Adjacent nursery. Cream TEAS in aid of Special Olympics (Cheshire). *Adm £2 Chd 50p. For NGS Sun June 18 (1.30-5.30). Private visits and parties welcome, please* **Tel 01606 888128**

The Stray, Neston ♿✂❀ (Mr & Mrs Anthony Hannay) *Approx 10m NW of Chester ½m NW of Hinderton Arms (t-lights). Turn off A540 into Upper Raby Rd. After 3/10m turn into unmade lane and The Stray is immed on L.* 1½-acre garden which is establishing itself after replanting commenced in 1991. Many unusual and interesting shrubs and plants have been planted in the mixed and herbaceous borders, and round small pond. TEAS in aid of RNLI. *Adm £2 Chd 50p. Sun May 28 (2-5)*

▲ **Tatton Park, Knutsford** ♿✂❀ (The National Trust) *Well sign-posted on M56 junction 7 and from M6 junction 19. 2½m N of Knutsford.* Features incl orangery by Wyatt; fernery by Paxton; Japanese, Italian and rose gardens. Greek monument and African hut. Hybrid azaleas and rhododendrons, swamp cypresses, tree ferns, tall redwoods, bamboos and pines. TEAS. *Adm £3 Group £2.40 Chd £2. For NGS Mon June 19 (10.30-3)*

Thornton Manor, Thornton Hough ❀ (The Viscount Leverhulme) *From Chester A540 to Fiveway Garage; turn R on to B5136 to Thornton Hough village. From Birkenhead B5151 then on to B5136. From M53, exit 4 to Heswall; turn L after 1m. Bus: Woodside-Parkgate; alight Thornton Hough village.* Large garden of yr-round interest. TEAS. Free car park. *Adm £2 OAPs £1 Chd 50p. Bank Hol Mon Aug 28 (12-7)*

Tulip Tree Cottage, Coppenhall ✂❀ (Mr & Mrs A Mann) *85 Warmingham Road, Crewe. Approx 3m N of Crewe town centre on the road between Leighton Hospital and Warmingham Village. Close by White Lion Inn, Coppenhall.* ⅔-acre plantsman's garden, with shrubs, new perennial borders, raised beds, troughs, rock garden, peat garden, pond and greenhouse with cacti and succulents. Speciality alpines. TEAS. *Adm £2 Chd free. Suns March 5 (11-3), April 16, June 11, July 2 (1-5). Sun March 4 (11-3) 2001. Private visits welcome March to Sept (to see snowdrops, hellebores and spring bulbs in March), please* **Tel 01270 582030**

Tushingham Hall, Whitchurch (Mr & Mrs P Moore Dutton) *3m N of Whitchurch. Signed off A41 Chester-Whitchurch Rd.* Medium-sized garden in beautiful surroundings; bluebell wood alongside pool; ancient oak, girth 26ft. TEAS. *Adm £2 Chd 50p (ACNO to St Chad's Church, Tushingham). Sun May 7 (2-5.30)*

Warrington Gardens *Gardens 5 minutes walk from each other. Combined adm £2.50 Chd free. Sun July 16 (11-6)* Plants, Garden Crafts.

68 Cranborne Avenue ✂❀ (Mr & Mrs J Carter) *From Stockton Heath N on A49 over swing bridge. L at 2nd set of lights into Gainsborough Rd. 4th L into Cranbourne Ave.* A small garden of elegant design approx 235 sq yds. Soft hues, water and statuary combine to bring a sensual calm to a town garden

62 Irwell Road ✂ (Mr & Mrs D Griffiths) *From Stockton Heath, N on A49 over swing bridge on to Wilderspool Causeway. L at 2nd set of lights into Gainsborough Rd. 2nd R into Irwell Rd. No 62 approx halfway down on R. Approx 1m from Warrington town centre.* A small cottage garden approx 150 sq yds divided into several 'rooms'. The garden has been redesigned to celebrate the millennium. Emphasis is placed on the 5 elements of Earth, Air, Metal, Fire and Water which combine with lush planting to create a tranquil oasis. The garden has featured on TV and in several gardening magazines.

The Well House, Tilston ✂ (Mrs S H French-Greenslade) *Nr Malpas. 12m S of Chester on A41, 1st turn R after Broxton roundabout, L on Malpas Rd through Tilston. House and antique shop on L. Field parking signed.* 1-acre cottage garden, bridge over natural stream, many bulbs, herbs and shrubs. TEAS. *Adm £2 Chd 50p (ACNO to Cystic Fibrosis Trust). Sun April 2 (2-5.30). Private visits by appt March-July, please* **Tel 01829 250332**

Willaston Grange, Willaston ♿ (Sir Derek & Lady Bibby) *A540 Chester to West Kirby until opposite the Elf Garage. Proceed down B5151 Hadlow Rd, towards Willaston.* Approx 3 acres. Borders; rock garden; vegetable garden; orchard. Special feature - woodland walk. TEAS. *Adm £1.50 OAPs £1 Chd free. Sun May 14 (2-5)*

Willaston Village Gardens *Take A540 Chester to West Kirby Rd; turn R on B5151 to Willaston; at village centre turn R into Hooton Rd. Overdale Rd is ¼m on L Change Lane is a further 400yds on R opp garage and horseshoe store.* These two gardens are about 400yds from each other *Combined adm £3 Chd free Mon May 1 (2-5.30)*

Change Hey, Change Lane (Mr & Mrs Keith Butcher) A 2-acre garden with mature trees, developing woodland area underplanted with rhododendrons and azaleas. Good parking facilities. TEAS in aid of Willaston School Grounds Project

Wickham Orchard, Overdale Rd (Dr & Mrs M W W Wood) 2½ years ago, the owners moved from The Old Hall, Willaston with a lot of plants, to a small garden with mature trees, a pond and waterfall. They have found it interesting putting quarts into pint pots and trying to retain the flavour. ¼-acre may be transformed into a landscaped estate! *(ACNO to Neuromuscular Centre)*

NEW **Withinlee Ridge, Prestbury** (Mr & Mrs M G Rusbridge) *Take A538 from Wilmslow towards Prestbury; pass Bull's Head on R then after 1m turn into Withinlee Rd. From Prestbury, follow A538 towards Wilmslow, turn L after top of Castle Hill, then ¼m on R.* Approx 1-acre with mature trees, displays of rhododendrons, unusual shrubs incl Embothrium lanceolatum (in flower), Cornus kousa, Eucryphia nymansensis, Berberis temolaica; rockery with 'silver' saxifrages, dwarf rhododendons, other ericaceous shrubs; small alpine house; mixed borders and a small pond. *Adm £2 Chd 50p (ACNO John Muir Trust). Sun May 21 (2-5)*

Wood End Cottage, Whitegate (Mr & Mrs M R Everett) *Turn S off A556 (Northwich by-pass) at Sandiway P/O lights; after 1.7m, turn L to Whitegate village; opp. school follow Grange Lane for 300yds.* ½-acre plantsman's garden sloping to a natural stream. Mature trees; many clematis; herbaceous; raised beds; shade and moisture loving plants. Large plant stall. TEAS. *Adm £2 Chd 50p (ACNO to David Lewis Centre for Epilepsy). Sun July 9 (2-6); also by appt, please* **Tel 01606 888236**

36 Woodhouse Lane, Sale (Mr & Mrs Peter Nightingale) *Off the A56 (Washway Rd) half way between Sale and Altrincham from Altrincham direction turn L at t-lights after Pelican Hotel. Then 100yds on R.* Lush tropical planting in suburban Sale. Many exotic and unusual species grown in different habitats in a semi-detached garden. *Adm £1.50 Chd 75p. Sat, Sun July 1, 2 (2-5)*

13 Yew Tree Cottages, Compstall (Mr & Mrs M Murphy) *6m E of Stockport. Take Bredbury junction off M60 (M63). Follow Romiley, Marple Bridge sign on B6104. Turn into Compstall village at Etherow Country Park sign, take 2nd L after 'Andrew Arms' public house. Parking restricted but within walking distance of village car parks.* ⅓-acre cottage garden set in an elevated position. Large collection of hardy perennials, roses, old and new, clematis, penstemons, hardy geraniums, shrubs and more. TEA. *Adm £2 Chd £1. Suns June 18; July 2, 16 combined ticket with* **Edith Terrace** *£3. Sun Aug 6 (1-5). Private visits also welcome, please* **Tel 0161 427 7142**

Evening Opening (See also garden description)

Bolesworth Castle, Tattenhall	May 12

Gardeners' Royal Benevolent Society

Today the GBRS gives assistance to nearly 600 retired gardeners, and youger disabled gardeners and their partners, in the form of sheltered accommodation, quarterly payments, and special needs grants. Anyone who has earned his or her living in horticulture or gardening is eligible to apply for help from the GBRS

The Society also gives birthday and Christmas gifts, organises holidays and offers advice and support through the Casework Department.

The Society owns a range of properties in England and one in Scotland, from modern flats and bungalows to homes in rural setting. Between them they offer a variety of accommodation from residential/nursing care to indepenent self contained homes.

The Gardeners' Royal Benevolent Society
Bridge House, 139 Kingston Road, Leatherhead, Surrey KT22 7NT
Tel: 01372 373962

Cornwall

Hon County Organiser: Mr W Croggon, Creed House, Grampound, Nr Truro, Cornwall TR2 4SL 01872 530372

Assistant County Organisers: Mrs D Morison, Boskenna, St Martin, Manaccon, Helston, Cornwall TR12 6BS Tel 01326 231 210
Mrs Richard Jerram, Trehane, Trevanson, Wadebridge, Cornwall PL27 7HP Tel 01208 812 523
Mrs Michael Latham, Trebartha Lodge, North Hill, Launceston, Cornwall PL15 7PD 01566 782 373
Mrs R Vyvyan-Robinson, Mellingey Mill House, St Issey, Wadebridge, Cornwall PL27 7QU Tel 01841 540 511
Mr G J Holborow, Ladock House, Ladock, Truro, Cornwall TR2 4PL Tel 01726 882 274

Leaflet/Yellow Books: Mr & Mrs Michael Cole, Nansawsan House, Ladock, Truro, Cornwall TR2 4PW Tel 01726 882 392
Mrs E A Waldron Yeo, Penbre, Trelill Bodmin, Cornwall PL30 3HZ 01208 850 793

Hon County Treasurer: Mr Nigel Rimmer, 11 Melvill Road, Falmouth, Cornwall TR11 4AS Tel 01326 313 429

DATES OF OPENING

Regular openings
For details see garden description
Carwinion, Mawnan Smith
Flambards Victorian Village Garden, Helston
Headland, Polruan
Heligan Gardens, Pentewan
The Japanese Garden & Bonsai Nursery, St Mawgan
Ken Caro, Bicton, nr Liskeard
Lamorran House, St Mawes
Paradise Park, Hayle
Prideaux Place, Padstow
Trebah, Mawnan Smith
Tregenna Castle Hotel, St Ives
Tregrehan, Par
Trevarno Gardens, Helston
Trewithen, Truro

March 12 Sunday
Trengwainton, Penzance

March 19 Sunday
Ince Castle, Saltash

April 2 Sunday
Penjerrick Garden, Budock

April 5 Wednesday
Nansawsan House, Ladock

April 8 Saturday
Glendurgan, Mawnan Smith

April 9 Sunday
Bodwannick, Nanstallon
Trelissick, Feock

April 12 Wednesday
Nansawsan House, Ladock

April 16 Sunday
Ince Castle, Saltash
Ladock House, Ladock
St Michael's Mount, Marazion

April 19 Wednesday
Nansawsan House, Ladock

April 26 Wednesday
Nansawsan House, Ladock

April 30 Sunday
Carclew Gardens, Perran-ar-Worthal
Drannack Mill, Gwinear Hayle
Estray Parc, Penjerrick
Ladock House, Ladock
Polgwynne, Feock

May 1 Monday
The Japanese Garden & Bonsai Nursery, St Mawgan
Moyclare, Liskeard

May 4 Thursday
Headland, Polruan

May 7 Sunday
Estray Parc, Penjerrick
Pencarrow, Bodmin
Tregrehan, Par

May 13 Saturday
Cotehele, Saltash
Trenance, Launceston

May 14 Sunday
Boconnoc, Lostwithiel
Bodwannick, Nanstallon
Creed House, Creed
The Hollies, Grampound, nr Truro
Ince Castle, Saltash
Lanhydrock, Bodmin
Nansawsan House, Ladock
Trenance, Launceston

May 18 Thursday
Headland, Polruan

May 21 Sunday
Braggs Wood Gardens, Boyton
Drannack Mill, Gwinear Hayle

May 23 Tuesday
Hallowarren, Carne

May 25 Thursday
Headland, Polruan

May 28 Sunday
Roseland House, Chacewater

June 3 Saturday
Lamorran House, St Mawes

June 4 Sunday
Tregenna Castle Hotel, St Ives
Treviades Gardens, Constantine

June 10 Saturday
East Down Barn, Menheniot
Scawns House, Menheniot

June 11 Sunday
East Down Barn, Menheniot
Ince Castle, Saltash
Scawns House, Menheniot

June 18 Sunday
Long Cross Victorian Gardens, Trelights, St Endellion

June 25 Sunday
Bodwannick, Nanstallon
Braggs Wood Gardens, Boyton
Drannack Mill, Gwinear Hayle
Scawn Mill, nr Liskeard
Water Meadow, Luxulyan

July 2 Sunday
Kingberry, Bodmin
The Ranch House, St Issey

July 9 Sunday
Caervallack, St Martin

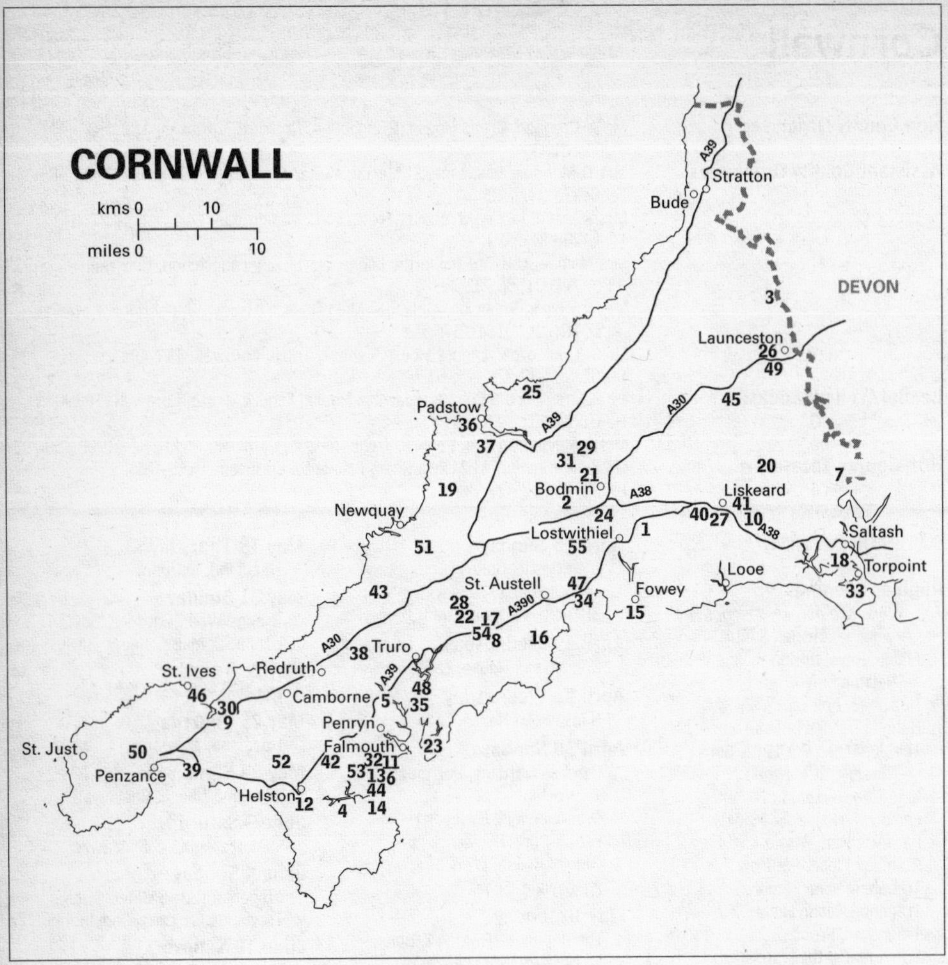

KEY

1 Boconnoc
2 Bodwannick
3 Braggs Wood Gardens
4 Caervallack
5 Carclew Gardens
6 Carwinion
7 Cotehele
8 Creed House
9 Drannack Mill
10 East Down Barn
11 Estray Parc
12 Flambards Victorian Village Garden
13 Glendurgan
14 Hallowarren
15 Headland
16 Heligan Gardens
17 The Hollies
18 Ince Castle
19 The Japanese Garden & Bonsai Nursery
20 Ken Caro
21 Kingberry
22 Ladock House
23 Lamorran House
24 Lanhydrock
25 Long Cross Victorian Gardens
26 Manaton
27 Moyclare
28 Nansawsan House
29 The Old Mill Herbary
30 Paradise Park
31 Pencarrow
32 Penjerrick Garden
33 Peterdale
34 Pine Lodge Gardens
35 Polgwynne
36 Prideaux Place
37 The Ranch House
38 Roseland House
39 St Michael's Mount
40 Scawn Mill
41 Scawns House
42 Seworgan Gardens
43 Talisonny House
44 Trebah
45 Trebartha
46 Tregenna Castle Hotel
47 Tregrehan
48 Trelissick
49 Trenance
50 Trengwainton
51 Trerice
52 Trevarno Gardens
53 Treviades Gardens
54 Trewithen
55 Water Meadow

The Japanese Garden & Bonsai Nursery, St Mawgan
The Ranch House, St Issey
Seworgan Gardens

July 16 Sunday
Kingberry, Bodmin
The Ranch House, St Issey
Scawn Mill, nr Liskeard

July 23 Sunday
Ince Castle, Saltash
The Ranch House, St Issey
Talisonny House, Goonhavern, Truro

July 29 Saturday
Pine Lodge Gardens, Cuddra, St Austell

August 6 Sunday
Peterdale, Millbrook

August 16 Wednesday
Trerice, nr Newquay

August 27 Sunday
The Old Mill Herbary, Helland Bridge
Roseland House, Chacewater

August 28 Monday
The Japanese Garden & Bonsai Nursery, St Mawgan

September 3 Sunday
Manaton, Launceston

September 24 Sunday
Paradise Park, Hayle
Trebartha, nr Launceston

DESCRIPTIONS OF GARDENS

Boconnoc, Lostwithiel ♿❀ (Mr & Mrs J D G Fortescue) *2m S of A390. On main rd between middle Taphouse and Downend garage, follow signs.* Privately owned gardens covering some 20 acres, surrounded by parkland and woods. Magnificent old trees, flowering shrubs and views. TEAS. *Adm £2 Chd free (ACNO to Boconnoc Church Window Fund). Sun May 14 (2-5)*

Bodwannick, Nanstallon (Mr P M & Mrs W M Appleton) *2½m W Bodmin. Turn at Bodmin Trailer Centre (A30) signposted Nanstallon, L at Xrds signposted Hoopers Bridge then sharp R.* Approx 1-acre compact garden incl water garden, herbaceous, granite Cornish cross, roses, shade garden and shrubs. Over 50 varieties of daffodils and narcissi. Large stone circle. Plantsman's garden. TEAS. *Adm £2 Chd free (ACNO to F.L.E.E.T.). Suns April 9, May 14, June 25 (2-6). Private visits welcome, please* **Tel 01208 831427**

NEW **Braggs Wood Gardens, Boyton** ♿❀ (Peter Horrell) *Take Bude Rd from Launceston signed to Boyton at Ladycross or take Holsworthy to Launceston Rd signed to Boyton at Chapmanswell, go over R Tamar up hill for 100 yds on R.* Braggs Wood Gardens is a new garden under construction during the last 3 yrs and has at present large water features almost completed. Herbaceous borders, ornamental ponds, walks and also a lake within the grounds stocked with trout. Many new features and planting are planned. TEAS. *Adm £1.50 Chd 50p. Suns May 21; June 25 (2-6)*

Caervallack, St Martin ❀ (Louise & Mathew Robinson) *5 m SE of Helston. Between Mawgan and St Martin villages [OSSW727245].* Whimsical garden arranged into rooms with courtyard, pergola, herbaceous borders, walled pond and secret garden leading to orchard. New cob walls; emerging fruit and vegetable garden. *Adm £1.50 Chd under 16 free (ACNO to Meningitis Trust). Sun July 9 (1.30-4.30)*

Carclew Gardens, Perran-ar-Worthal (Mrs R Chope) *Nr Truro. From A39 turn E at Perran-ar-Worthal. Bus: alight Perran-ar-Worthal 1m.* One of the original NGS gardens 1st opened in 1927 and home to the 'Sir Charles Lemon' rhododendron. 200 years of history are reflected in this large private garden with rare and mature specimen trees and shrubs 'listed' walls; fine terraces and ornamental water. TEAS. *Adm £2.50 Chd 50p (ACNO to British Heart Foundation) Sun April 30 (2-5.30)*

● **Carwinion, Mawnan Smith** ❀ (Mr H A E & Mrs J E Rogers) *Via Carwinion Rd.* A luxuriant, traditional, 12-acre Cornish Valley Garden with delightful walks running down to the Helford River. Home of the UK's premier collection of Bamboos, now assimilating Towan Nurseries and their specialist collection of Camellias and Hydrangeas. Ferns and wildflowers abound. A garden of yesterday, today and tomorrow. Cream TEAS April - end of Sept (2-5.30). *Adm £2.50 Chd free. Open daily through the year (10-5.30). Private visits welcome, please* **Tel 01326 250258**

▲ **Cotehele, Saltash** ♿❀ (The National Trust) *2m E of St Dominick, 4m from Gunnislake (turn at St Ann's Chapel); 8m SW of Tavistock; 14m from Plymouth via Tamar Bridge.* Terrace garden falling to sheltered valley with ponds, stream and unusual shrubs. Fine medieval house (one of the least altered in the country); armour, tapestries, furniture. Dogs in wood only and on leads. Lunches and TEAS. *Adm garden, grounds & mill £3.20 Chd £1.60. For NGS Sat May 13 (11-dusk)*

▲ **Creed House, Creed** ❀ (Mr & Mrs W R Croggon) *From the centre of Grampound on A390. Take rd signposted to Creed. After 1m turn L opp Creed Church and the garden is on L. Parking in lane* 5-acre landscaped Georgian Rectory garden; tranquil rural setting; spacious lawns. Tree collection; rhododendrons; sunken cobbled yard and formal walled herbaceous gardens. Trickle stream to ponds and bog. Natural woodland walk. Restoration began 1974 - continues and incl recent planting. TEAS. *Adm £2 Chd free. For NGS Sun May 14 (2-5.30)* **Tel 01872 530372**

NEW **Drannack Mill, Gwinear Hayle** ❀ (Mr & Mrs Colin Douglas) *2.7m out of Hayle on B3302 turn L into Wheal Alfred Rd. 0.7m R down Bridleway. [Grid ref: 367588]. Parking signposted.* Mill dating back to 1786 (not open) with 12 acres in beautiful wooded valley; formal garden well stocked with mature unusual shrubs and trees. Stream, 1 acre lake with island and wildlife; pathways and lakeland walk. TEAS. *Adm £2 Chd free (ACNO to Cornwall Blind Association). Suns April 30; May 21; June 25 (2-5)*

NEW **East Down Barn, Menheniot** (Julian & Valerie Sturdy) *4m on A38 from Liskeard to Plymouth; take Menheniot turning NE. 1m turn sharp R at Cricket Club sign, House* *is end of track.* Approx 3/4-acre garden in a peaceful country setting. The steep slope is overflowing with sun loving shrubs; ground cover plants intermingle and cascade over the wall (and some of the gravel paths!) There is a pergola; herbaceous border; ornamental grass area and small bridge over the stream. A plantsman's dream. Teas by W.I at Scawns House in aid of Parish Church. *Combined adm with Scawns House £2.50 Chd free. Sat, Sun June 10, 11 (2-5.30)*

Estray Parc, Penjerrick (Mr & Mrs J M Williams) *Leave Penjerrick main entrance on R follow the rd towards Mawnan Smith until entrance to The Home Hotel on L. Directly opp turn R and follow the signs.* In 1983 most of this 3-acre garden was a bramble, thistle-infested field. A considerable variety of plants have been introduced and continuous grass cutting has produced passable sloping lawns interspersed by a large collection of trees and shrubs. *Adm £1.50 Chd over 13 50p (ACNO to Paediatric Appeal). Suns April 30, May 7 (2-6)*

● **Flambards Victorian Village Garden, Helston** ♿✂❀ (Mr & Mrs Douglas Kingsford Hale) *From A394 follow official brown and white signs to Flambards, located on A3083.* A well designed and maintained 20-acre site providing an excellent family day out. Interesting sections of very colourful award winning bedding displays and hanging baskets. Mature trees, named shrubs of varied and striking foliage. Many exciting activities. Re-creation of a Victorian village and several exhibitions illustrating wartime Britain, Cornwall at war and the history of Aviation. Wheelchairs available. Cafeteria *Open most days Easter to end Oct (10.30-5). Please* **Tel 24hr info 01326 564093**

▲ **Glendurgan, Mawnan Smith** ✂❀ (The National Trust) *Take rd to Helford Passage, 5m SW of Falmouth. Follow NT signposts.* Walled garden, laurel maze, giants stride, valley with specimen trees, bluebells and primulas running down to Durgan fishing village on R Helford. Large car park. Lunches and TEAS. *Adm £3.50 Chd £1.75. For NGS Sat April 8 (10.30-5.30). Last admission 4.30*

Hallowarren, Carne ✂ (Mr & Mrs Mark Osman) *1m out of the centre of Manaccan village. Down hill past Inn on R, follow signpost to Carne. House on R. Parking nearby or signposted.* Approx 1½ acres set in a beautiful wooded valley bordering a gentle stream. Happy mixture of wilderness and cultivation, bog and cottage garden with primulas, old roses, lilies and kitchen herbs, unusual shrubs and trees. TEAS in aid of St Anthony Church. *Adm £1.50 Chd free. Sun May 23 (2-5.30)*

■ **Headland, Polruan** ✂ (Mr & Mrs J R Hill) *Battery Lane. Passenger ferry from Fowey and 10min walk up the hill. Or follow signs to Polruan (on East of Fowey Estuary) ignore first car park, turn L for second car park (overlooking harbour) turn L (on foot) down St Saviour's Hill.* 1¼-acre cliff garden with sea on 3 sides; mainly plants which withstand salty gales but incl sub-tropical. Cove for swimming. *Adm £2 Chd £1. Open every Thurs May 4 to Sept 7. For NGS Thurs May 4, 18, 25 (2-6)*

● **Heligan Gardens, Pentewan** ♿❀ *From St Austell take B3273 signposted Mevagissey, follow signs.* Heligan Gardens is the scene of the largest garden restoration project undertaken since the war. Of special interest in this romantic Victorian garden are; the fern ravine, 4 walled gardens with peach houses, vineries, melon grounds, sundial garden, northern summerhouse garden, a splendid collection of Bee boles, crystal grotto, Italian garden with a pool, an Elizabethan beacon 'Mount', a large tropical 'Jungle' garden and 30 acre 'Lost Valley'. Tea room serving a wide selection of food and drinks. *Adm £5.50 OAPs £5 Chd £2.50. Open every day (10-6). Groups welcome,* **Tel 01726 845100**

The Hollies, Grampound, nr Truro ♿✂❀ (Mr J & Mrs N B Croggon) *In centre of village on Truro-St Austell rd.* 2-acre garden of unusual design; unusual mixed planting of trees, shrubs and alpines. TEAS. *Adm £1 Chd free. Sun May 14 (2.30-5). Coach and private parties welcome by appt* **Tel 01726 882474**

Ince Castle, Saltash ♿ (Viscount & Viscountess Boyd of Merton) *3m SW of Saltash. From A38 at Stoketon Cross take turn signed Trematon, then Elmgate.* 5 acre garden, woodlands, borders, orchard, bulbs, shell house and lovely views of River Lynher. TEAS. *Adm £2.50 Chd free. Suns March 19; June 11 (ACNO to Cornwall Garden Society), April 16; July 23 (ACNO to Cornwall Historic Churches Trust), May 14 (ACNO to Red Cross) (2-5)*

■ **The Japanese Garden & Bonsai Nursery, St Mawgan** ♿✂❀ (Mr Robert & Mrs Stella Hore) *6m E of Newquay, 1.5m from North coast. 'Japanese Garden'. Rd signs from A3059 and B3276.* Authentic Japanese Garden set in 1 acre: water garden, stroll garden, zen garden, bamboo grove. Japanese Maples, azaleas, rhododendrons and ornamental grasses in abundance etc. Bonsai nursery adjacent to garden - entrance free. *Adm £2.50 Chd £1 Group rate for ten or more £2 (ACNO to St Mawgan School 1 May). Open 7 days a week (not 25-27 Dec to 1 Jan). For NGS Mon May 1; Sun July 9; Mon Aug 28 (10-6 Last entry to garden 5)*

● **Ken Caro, Bicton, nr Liskeard** ✂❀ (K R Willcock Esq JP & Mrs Willcock) *Pensilva 5m NE of Liskeard. From A390 to Callington turn off N at Butchers Arms, St Ive; take Pensilva Rd; at next Xrds take rd signed Bicton.* 2 acres mostly planted in 1970, with a further 2-acre extension in 1993; well-designed and labelled plantsman's garden; rhododendrons, flowering shrubs, conifers and other trees; herbaceous. Panoramic views. Collection of aviary birds. *Adm £2 Chd 50p. April 16 to June 28 every Sun, Mon, Tues, Wed; Tues & Weds only July & Aug (2-6)* **Tel 01579 362446**

Kingberry, Bodmin ❀ (Dr & Mrs M S Stead) *N-side of town, 100yds uphill from East Cornwall Hospital. Ltd parking on hill, otherwise car parks in town centre.* Approx 1-acre garden. Herbaceous borders, formal lawns, gravel terrace, ornamental pond, original stone walls, orchard and conservatory, some interesting perennials. A surprising haven in centre of Bodmin. TEAS. *Adm £1.50 Chd free. Suns July 2, 16 (2-6)*

Ladock House, Ladock ♿ (G J & Lady Mary Holborow) *7m E of Truro on B3275. Car park and entrance by church.* Georgian Old Rectory with 4 acres of lawns, rhododendrons, camellias and azaleas with woodland garden. All planted during last 30yrs. TEAS in aid of NSPCC April 16, Ladock Church April 30. *Adm £2 Chd free. Suns April 16, 30 (2-5.30)*

■ **Lamorran House, St Mawes** (Mr & Mrs Dudley-Cooke) *Upper Castle Rd. First turning R after garage; signposted to St Mawes Castle. House ½m on L. Parking in rd.* 4-acre sub-tropical hillside garden with beautiful views to St Anthonys Head. Extensive water gardens in Mediterranean and Japanese settings. Large collection of rhododendrons, azaleas, palm trees, cycads, agaves and many S hemisphere plants and trees. *Adm £2.50 Chd free Open Weds and Fri April through Sept. For NGS Sat June 3 (10-5)* **Tel 01326 270800**

▲ **Lanhydrock, Bodmin** (The National Trust) *2½m on B3268. Station: Bodmin Parkway 1¾m.* Large-sized garden; formal garden laid out 1857; shrub garden with good specimens of rhododendrons and magnolias and fine views. Lunches and TEAS. House closed Mondays. *Adm garden only £3.60 Chd £1.80. For NGS Sun May 14 (11-5.30; last adm to house 5)*

▲ **Long Cross Victorian Gardens, Trelights, St Endellion** (Mr & Mrs Crawford) *7m N of Wadebridge on B3314.* Charm of this garden is mazelike effect due to protecting hedges against sea winds; views of countryside and sea scapes (Port Isaac and Port Quin Bays) Garden specially designed to cope with environment of Cornwall's N Coast. Lunches and cream TEAS, coffee, evening meal. *Adm £1.50 Chd 25p. For NGS Sun June 18 (10.30-6.30). Open all year.* **Tel 01208 880243**

NEW **Manaton, Launceston** (Mr & Mrs Peter Hodgson) *Follow signs for the Leisure Centre along Dunheved Rd. At college end of rd take sharp L bend and immed after this take another L turning into Windmill Hill. Entrance to car parking is approx 400 yds on L.* Hilltop garden, 4 acres created over last 40 yrs, stunning views; formal areas around the house featuring yew hedging; sweeping lawns leading to woodland areas with mature and specimen trees. Large kitchen garden; 100ft herbaceous border. TEAS. *Adm £2 Chd 50p. Sun Sept 3 (2-5.30)*

Moyclare, Liskeard (Major & Mrs Henslowe) *Lodge Hill. ½m S from Liskeard centre on St Keyne/Duloe Rd (B3254) 200yds past station on L.* Started in 1927, extended 1936, this 1-acre garden contains many rare and unusual plants, shrubs and trees; many variegated. *Adm £2 Acc chd free. For NGS Mon May 1 (2-5)* **Tel 01579 343 114**

Nansawsan House, Ladock (Mr & Mrs Michael Cole) *7m E of Truro on B3275(A39). Parking at Falmouth Arms or Parish Hall* 1½ acres, part of a once larger Victorian garden. Rhododendrons, camellias, shrubs, trees and borders. Teas in aid of Ladock Parish Church. *Adm £2 Chd free. Weds April 5, 12, 19, 26 (Teas in aid of FSID) Sun May 14 (Teas in aid of Ladock Parish Church) (2-5)*
Tel 01726 882392

■ **The Old Mill Herbary, Helland Bridge** (Mr & Mrs R Drew Whurr) *[Map ref: 065715]. Access from A30 1m N of Bodmin and from B3266 Bodmin to Camelford Rd.* Unique 5-acre semi-wild herb/water garden set in an oasis of tranquility alongside R Camel and C14 Helland Bridge. Now SAC/SSSI of historical/Botanical interest to Aromatherapists, Gardeners, Research Chemists, Pharmacists, Conservationist, Entomologists, Herbalists, Universities, Wildlife Enthusiasts, Artists. Restored clapper bridge; mature woodland; secret island walks. 1½-acre mini-arboretum with 50 unusual named trees; terraced 3 level garden set around Greek fertility theme, with planted identified displays. Many herbs and other plants, chamomile lawn, fish pond. Hard parking, Toilet. TEAS. *Adm £2 Chd £1. Open April - Sept incl (10-5) (closed Weds). For NGS Sun Aug 27 (2-5)*
Tel 01208 841206

■ **Paradise Park, Hayle** (Mr Michael Reynolds) *Follow the A30 to Hayle, go to St Ives/St Erth roundabout then follow official brown and white signs to Paradise Park* The 2-acre walled garden is part of the 14 acres opened in 1973 as 'The rare and endangered birds breeding centre'. Much effort has been expended to make the gardens a suitable setting for a bird breeding collection of international importance. The World Parrot Trust is based here. Walled garden with pergolas, trellis and gazebos; roses, clematis, 'Parrot Jungle' and 'Australian themes'. TEAS. Café in park. *Open throughout the yr from 10am to 5pm. Adm £5.99 Chd £3.99 (ACNO to World Parrot Trust). For NGS Sun Sept 24 (10-5)*

Pencarrow, Bodmin (Iona Lady Molesworth-St Aubyn) *4 miles N.W. Bodmin, signed off the A389 and B3266.* 50 acres of formal and woodland gardens laid out in the 1840's. Marked walks past the Victorian Rockery, Italian and American Gardens, Lake and Ice House. Over 650 different varieties of rhododendrons, also an internationally known specimen conifer collection. TEAS. *Adm £2.50 Chd free. Historic Georgian family lived in house open April 2 - mid Oct, Sun to Thurs. Sun May 7 (1.30-5)*

▲ **Penjerrick Garden, Budock** (Mrs Rachel Morin) *3m SW of Falmouth between Budock/Mawnan Smith, opp. Penmorvah Manor Hotel. Parking along drive verge. Coaches outside gate.* 15-acre subtropical garden, home to important rhododendron hybrids Penjerrick/Barclayi, and the C19 Quaker Fox family. The upper garden with sea view contains rhododendrons, camellias, magnolias, bamboos, tree ferns and magnificent trees. Across a bridge a luxuriant valley features ponds in a wild primaeval setting. *Adm £2 Chd £1 (ACNO to C.G.S.). For NGS Sun April 2 (11.30-4) Tours*
Tel 01872 870105

Peterdale, Millbrook (Mrs Ann Mountfield) *St John's Rd. From Skinners Garage follow rd to mini roundabout and turn L. Straight ahead up St John's Rd Peterdale sign next to gate on wall. Last house on L.* A plantsperson's garden featured on TV and Practical Garden, also Gardener's World magazine. Special feature a full monty japanese tea garden incl japanese tea-house and pagoda with views right across Dartmoor, completed Oct 1997. Featured Spring 2000 on BBC2 Gardeners World with Gay Search. *Adm £2 Chd free. Sun Aug 6 (2-5.30). Groups of 20 or less by written application* **Tel 01752 823364**

Pine Lodge Gardens, Cuddra, St Austell (Mr & Mrs R H J Clemo) *On A390 E of St Austell between*

Holmbush and Tregrehan. Follow signs. 30-acre estate comprises gardens within a garden. The wide range of some 6,000 plants all of which are labelled, have been thoughtfully laid out using original designs and colour combinations to provide maximum interest for the garden lover. In addition to rhododendrons, magnolias, camellias, herbaceous borders with many rare and tender plants, marsh gardens, tranquil fish ponds, lake with black swans within the park, pinetum. Japanese garden under construction. TEAS. *Adm £3.50 Chd £1.75. April-Sept, Weds to Suns and Bank Hols (2-5). Sat July 29 (2-5). groups by appt all year*
Tel and Fax 01726 73500

Polgwynne, Feock ♿❀ (Mrs P Davey) *5m S of Truro via A39 (Truro-Falmouth rd) and then B3289 to 1st Xrds: straight on ½m short of Feock village* 3½-acre garden and grounds. Fruit and vegetable garden, woodlands extending to shore of Carrick Roads; magnificent Ginkgo Biloba (female, 12′ girth) probably the largest female ginkgo in Britain; other beautiful trees; many rare and unusual shrubs. Lovely setting and view of Carrick Roads. Cream TEAS. *Adm £2.50 Chd free. Sun April 30 (2-5)* **Tel 01872 862612**

● **Prideaux Place, Padstow** ♿ (Mr & Mrs Peter Prideaux-Brune) *On the edge of Padstow follow brown signs for Prideaux Place, from ring rd (A389).* Surrounding Elizabethan house the present main grounds were laid out in the early C18 by Edmund Prideaux. Ancient deer park with stunning views over Camel estuary; Victorian woodland walks currently under restoration. Restored sunken formal garden. A garden of vistas. Cream TEAS *Adm £2 Chd £1. Easter Sun to April 27; Suns to Thurs May 28 to Oct 5 (1.30-5)*

NEW **The Ranch House, St Issey** ♿✗ (Mr & Mrs W E Corley) *In St Issey on A389 to Padstow, turn L opp Ring of Bells PH (Some car parking available in car park belonging to PH). After 15 yds, drive on Rh-side. No available parking.* 1½ acres of sheltered gardens, full of interesting shrubs and features, developed over 30 yrs to incl the kitchen garden and chickens. *Adm £1.50 Chd free. Suns July 2, 9, 16, 23 (2-5)*

■ **Roseland House, Chacewater** ❀ (Mr & Mrs Pridham) *4m W of Truro, at Truro end of main st. Parking in village car park (100yds) or surrounding rds.* 1-acre garden subdivided by walls and trellises hosting a wide range of climbers. Mixed borders of unusual plants, Victorian conservatory and greenhouse extend the gardening yr. TEAS. *Adm £1.50 Chd free. All Tues April to July & Sept. For NGS Suns May 28; Aug 27 (2-5)* **Tel 01872 560451**

▲ **St Michael's Mount, Marazion** ✗❀ (The Rt Hon Lord St Levan DL DSC) *½m from shore at Marazion by Causeway; otherwise by ferry.* Flowering shrubs; rock plants, castle walls; fine sea views. TEAS *Adm Castle & gardens £4.40, Chd £2.20 (under 16) For NGS Sun April 16 (10.30-5.30) last entrance 4.45*

Scawn Mill, nr Liskeard ✗❀ (Mrs A Ball & Dr Julian Ball) *From the A38 at the E end of Dobwalls take the signpost to Duloe, Herodsfoot and Looe for 1½ m. Turn R at sign for Scawn and continue for 1m down to the river.* Water lily lake lying beside the West Looe River terraced with azaleas, black pines and Japanese maples. Walks beside primulas, herbaceous border and Japanese garden. ½m walk through newly planted woodland with spectacular wild flowers. Public footpath following West Looe River to Herodsfoot. TEAS. *Adm £2 Chd free (ACNO to Red Cross). Suns June 25; July 16 (2-5.30)*

Scawns House, Menheniot ❀ (Richard & Elaine Bateman) *Approx 3m from the Liskeard by-pass on the A38 signed Menheniot. Scawns House is adjacent to the Parish Church. Parking available in village.* Mature 5-acre landscaped garden, rhododendrons, camellias and azaleas, many mature trees; terraces leading to large tree-lined lawn. Cream TEAS in aid of Menheniot Church. *Combined adm with East Down Barn £2.50 Chd free. Sat, Sun June 10, 11 (2-5.30)*

NEW **Seworgan Gardens** ❀ *3m NE Helston off A394 R to village or 1½m S off Edgcumbe to Gweek Rd R to village.* TEAS. *Combined adm £2 Chd under 16 free. Sun July 9 (1.30-5)*

NEW **Dewlands** (John & Dorothy Maud) Sloping garden approx 3/4-acre divided into rooms; screen hedges; walk through shubbery; steps; rose arches; mixed borders; lawns; greenhouses; conservatory and patio.

Windmill Cottage (David & Carol Pearce) ⅓-acre, large variety of shrubs; perennials; ornamental grasses massed in cottage garden style. Hoheria tree smothered in blossom in July

Talisonny House, Goonhavern, Truro ♿❀ (Diana & Michael Craig) *5m S of Newquay situated 1m off A30 on B3285 for Goonhavern and Perranporth between Goonhavern and A30.* A young colourful and interesting 2-acre garden, started 1994. Many unusual shrubs and herbaceous plants, climbers and roses, garden edged by stream planted with wate-loving plants. Cream TEAS. *Adm £2 Chd 50p Sun July 23 (2-5.30)*

● **Trebah, Mawnan Smith** ❀ (Trebah Garden Trust) *4m from Falmouth. Follow tourism signs from Hillhead Roundabout on A39 approach to Falmouth. Parking (free)/access for coaches.* 25-acre S facing ravine garden, planted in 1830's. Extensive collection rare/mature trees/shrubs incl glades, huge tree ferns 100 yrs old, and sub-tropical exotics. Hydrangea collection covers 2½ acres. Water garden, waterfalls, rock pool stocked with mature Koi Carp. Magical garden for plantsman/artist/family. Play area/trails for children. Use private beach. Coffee Shop. *Adm £3.50 OAPs £3.20 Chd and disabled £1.75. Special group and winter prices. RHS members free Open every day throughout year (10.30-5 last admission)* **Tel 01326 250448 Fax 01326 250781.** Website: www.trebah-garden.co.uk

Trebartha, nr Launceston (The Latham Family) *North Hill, SW of Launceston. Nr junction of B3254 & B3257.* Wooded area with lake surrounded by walks of flowering shrubs; woodland trail through fine woods with cascades and waterfalls; American glade with fine trees. No coaches. TEAS. *Adm £2 Chd 50p. Sun Sept 24 (2-5.30)*

■ **Tregenna Castle Hotel, St Ives** ♿❀ *Leave A30 West Hayle, A3074 to St Ives. After Carbis Bay entrance signs to Tregenna Castle L-hand side.* Magnificent setting overlooking

St Ives Bay. A garden mix within 72 acre estate incl a rediscovered Woodland Garden and a newly created Subtropical Walled Garden. Cream TEAS. *Adm £1.50 Chd 50p (ACNO to RNLI). Open all year round to public. For NGS Sun June 4 (10-dusk)*

■ **Tregrehan, Par** ♿✿❀ (T Hudson Esq) *Entrance on A390 opp Britannia Inn 1m W of St Blazey. Access for cars and coaches.* Garden largely created since early C19. Woodland of 20 acres containing fine trees, award winning camellias raised by late owner and many interesting plants from warm temperate climes. Show greenhouses a feature containing softer species. TEA. *Adm £3 Chd free.. Mid March to mid June Wed to Sun & Bank Hols Mons. Not open Easter Sunday. For NGS May 7 (10.30-5)*

▲ **Trelissick, Feock** ♿✿ (The National Trust) *4m S of Truro, nr King Harry Ferry. On B3289.* Planted with tender shrubs; magnolias, camellias and rhododendrons with many named species characteristic of Cornish gardens. Fine woodlands encircle the gardens through which a varied circular walk can be enjoyed. Superb view over Falmouth harbour. Georgian house (not open). Lunches and TEAS. *Adm £4.30 Chd £2.15. Car park £1.50 refundable. For NGS Sun April 9 (12.30-5.30)*

Trenance, Launceston ✿❀ (Mr & Mrs John Dingle) *Follow signs for Leisure Centre along Dunheved Rd. At College end of rd take sharp L bend and immed after this take another L turning into Windmill Hill. Trenance is approx 200yds on L* A 2-acre garden for all seasons. A wide variety of trees and shrubs incl rhododendrons, camellias, azaleas, acers and magnolias; heathers and conifers, Ballard hellebores, 60 varieties hardy geraniums, primulas, herbaceous borders, roses and clematis; several smaller gardens within the main garden. Cream TEAS. *Adm £2 Chd 50p. Sat, Sun May 13, 14 (2-5.30)*

▲ **Trengwainton, Penzance** ♿✿❀ (The National Trust) *2m N W of Penzance, ½m West of Heamoor on Penzance-Morvah rd (B3312), ½m off St Just rd (A3071).* The garden of mainland Britain perhaps most favoured for the cultivation of exotic shrubs and trees. Plantsman's delight. *Adm £3.50 Chd £1.75. For NGS Sun March 12 (10.30-5.30)*

▲ **Trerice, nr Newquay** ♿✿❀ (The National Trust) *Newlyn East 3m SE of Newquay. From Newquay via A392 and A3058; turn R at Kestle Mill (NT signposts).* The summer-flowering garden is unusual in content and layout and there is an orchard planted with old varieties of fruit trees. A small museum traces the history of the lawn mower. Lunches & TEAS. *Adm house & garden £4.20 Chd £2. For NGS Wed Aug 16 (11-5.30)*

● **Trevarno Gardens, Helston** ♿❀ (Messrs M Sagin & N Helsby) *Sithney Helston. Signed from Crowntown on the B3303, 3m NW of Helston.* Set within beautiful and historic Trevarno Estate dating back to 1296, one of Cornwall's most romantic and secret woodland gardens covering 40 acres. Extensive collection of rare shrubs, specimen trees, walled gardens, mysterious rockeries, grotto, enchanting lake, cascade and fountains and abundant wildlife; now subject of major restoration and replanting programme. TEAS. *Adm £3.50 OAPs/Disabled £3.20 Chd under 14 £1.25, under 5 free. Open daily (10.30-5) Jan 1 to Dec 31 (excl Xmas Day). Guided tours and evening functions by arrangement* **Tel 01326 574274**

Treviades Gardens, Constantine ♿ *Off the Falmouth to Constantine R at High Cross - 1m on the Falmouth side of Constantine and N of Port Navas. The gardens are on the L going down hill. Travelling from Turo area follow the A39. Use the Penryn by pass. At Hillhead Roundabout, follow the signs to Constantine.* Cream TEAS. *Combined adm £2 Chd free (ACNO to Cornwall Children's Hospital Appeal). Sun June 4 (2-5.30)*

Treviades Barton (Mr & Mrs M J Ford) Series of walled gardens, each one with own character (ie roses in one); vegetable garden and small arboretum

Treviades Wollas (Mrs P Watson) S facing medium sized garden in two parts - leading down to small water garden fed by two springs

● **Trewithen, Truro** ♿❀ (A M J Galsworthy Esq DL) *½m E Probus. Entrance on A390 Truro-St Austell Rd. Sign-posted. Large car park.* Internationally renowned garden of 30 acres laid out by Maj G Johnstone between 1912 & 1960 with much of original seed and plant material collected by Ward and Forrest. Famed for towering magnolias and rhododendrons; wide range of own hybrids. Flatish ground amidst original woodland park. Walled Garden only open Mon & Tues, in June & July 5,6. TEAS. *Adm £3.50 Chd £2 Group £3.20. Mon to Sat March 1 to Sept 30, Suns April-May only (10-4.30). Special arrangements for coaches* **Tel 01726 883647**

Water Meadow, Luxulyan ✿ (Mr Philip & Mrs Rose Lamb) *5m NW of St Austell, 6m S of Bodmin. [map ref SX 052582.] Park in village street between church and school. Turn by church, garden 200yds downhill on L.* 1½-acre garden on sloping site with Grade II listed grotto. Large pond with streamside and waterside planting and bog garden with extensive primula, astilbe, gunnera, arum lilies etc. Gravel garden surrounded by roses & herbaceous planting. Specimen trees and shrubs with mixed borders. Cream TEAS in aid of WI. *Adm £2 Chd free. Sun June 25 (2-5) also by appt please* **Tel 01726 851399**

Duchy of Cornwall Nursery

Cott Road, Lostwithiel, Cornwall PL22 0HW

e-mail: nursery@duchyofcornwall.gov.uk

Old favourites and rarities, hardy and tropical, our range will astound you.

We are now happy to offer our full range of nursery stock to mail order customers.

Send £2.00 (stamps or cheque) for our catalogue, or we can e-mail our price list to you.

Better still, why not pay us a visit. It'll be worth it!

Tel: 01208 872668 Fax: 01208 872835

Plants grown by plant lovers for plant lovers

Marie Curie Cancer Care

Cancer is the UK's single biggest killer – one in three people will get it and one in four will die from it. The National Gardens Scheme supports Marie Curie Cancer Care, a comprehensive cancer care charity, helping people with cancer and their families throughout the UK

- **Marie Curie Nurses help ease the burdens on patients' families and friends and help cancer patients remain at home. Last year, Marie Curie Nurses cared for more than half the people who died of cancer at home**

  Marie Curie Nurse Eleanor Pountain says: "We're there to provide skilled nursing care and take action where necessary, but there's more to it than that. We're also there to talk to patients into the small hours if that's what they want, to listen to the concerns of their loved ones or simply be there for them while their carers rest".

- **Marie Curie Centres provide the largest number of hospice beds outside the NHS. Patients are supported by professional teams including consultants, nurses, physiotherapists, social workers and chaplains.**

- **Marie Curie Centres help patients to remain at home as long as possible. Expanded out-patient, day care and home care services enable people to remain well for longer. More than 40 per cent of in-patients return home**

- **Marie Curie Research Institute stands at the forefront of molecular biological research into the causes of cancer.**

  Marie Curie's Director of Research Dr Graham Currie says: "We're trying to understand cancer by trying to understand how normal cells work. Only then have we got a chance of understanding what's going wrong when cancer develops".

For more information about Marie Curie Cancer Care, ring 0800 716 146 or visit our web site at www.mariecurie.org.uk

Cumbria

Hon County Organiser:
(South) Mrs Reginald Tongue, Paddock Barn, Winster, Windermere, Cumbria LA23 3NW
Assistant County Organisers:
(North West) Mrs E C Hicks, Scarthwaite, Grange-in-Borrowdale, Keswick, Cumbria CA12 5UQ
(North East) Mrs Lavinia Howard, Deer Park Lodge, Johnby, Penrith, Cumbria CA11 0UU
Hon County Treasurer: Mr Derek Farman, Mill House, Winster, Windermere, Cumbria LA23 3NW

DATES OF OPENING

Regular openings
For details see garden description
Brockhole, Windermere
Dalemain, Penrith
Holker Hall Gardens, Cark-in-Cartmel
Hutton-in-the-Forest, Penrith
Levens Hall, Kendal
Winderwath, nr Penrith

By appointment only
For telephone numbers and other details see garden descriptions. Private visits welcomed
The Mill House, Sebergham
The Old Smithy, Occupation Lane, Broughton-in-Furness
Scarthwaite, Grange-in-Borrowdale
Wood Hall, Cockermouth

April 17 Monday
Levens Hall, Kendal

April 22 Saturday
Copt Howe, Chapel Stile

April 23 Sunday
Copt Howe, Chapel Stile

April 24 Monday
Copt Howe, Chapel Stile

April 30 Sunday
Dallam Tower, Milnthorpe
Rydal Mount, Eskdale
Stagshaw, nr Ambleside

May 1 Monday
High Dixon Ground, Coniston
Rydal Mount, Eskdale

May 3 Wednesday
Chapelside, Mungrisdale, Penrith

May 6 Saturday
Acorn Bank, Temple Sowerby

May 7 Sunday
The Nook, Helton

May 10 to 11 Wednesday to Thursday
Browfoot, Skelwith

May 10 Wednesday
Chapelside, Mungrisdale, Penrith

May 13 Saturday
Hollace, Torver

May 14 Sunday
Brockhole, Windermere
Lindeth Fell Country House Hotel, Bowness-on-Windermere

May 17 Wednesday
Chapelside, Mungrisdale, Penrith
Matthew How, Troutbeck

May 17 to 18 Wednesday to Thursday
St Annes, Great Langdale

May 21 Sunday
Blakeholme Wray, Newby Bridge
Browfoot, Skelwith
40 Fairfield Lane, Barrow-in-Furness
Matson Ground, Windermere
Matthew How, Troutbeck
Palace How, Loweswater
Stagshaw, nr Ambleside
Townfoot, Troutbeck
Winderwath, nr Penrith

May 24 Wednesday
Brackenburn, Manesty

May 24 to 25 Wednesday to Thursday
Browfoot, Skelwith

May 24 Wednesday
Chapelside, Mungrisdale, Penrith
High Rigg, Grange-in-Borrowdale
Matthew How, Troutbeck
Townfoot, Troutbeck

May 27 Saturday
Copt Howe, Chapel Stile

May 28 Sunday
Copt Howe, Chapel Stile
Fell Yeat, Casterton, nr Kirkby Lonsdale
Halecat, Witherslack
Hazel Mount, Thwaites, Millom

May 29 Monday
Copt Howe, Chapel Stile

May 31 Wednesday
Chapelside, Mungrisdale, Penrith
Windy Hall, Windermere

June 4 Sunday
Beck Head, Witherslack
Hutton-in-the-Forest, Penrith
Newbiggin Hall, Temple Sowerby
Station House, Lamplugh

June 7 Wednesday
Chapelside, Mungrisdale, Penrith

June 10 Saturday
Acorn Bank, Temple Sowerby
Bush Green Cottage, Broughton-in-Furness
Tomarobandy, Blitterlees

June 11 Sunday
Bush Green Cottage, Broughton-in-Furness
Dacre Lodge, Dacre
Dalemain, Penrith
40 Fairfield Lane, Barrow-in-Furness
Tomarobandy, Blitterlees

June 14 Wednesday
Chapelside, Mungrisdale, Penrith

June 17 Saturday
Rannerdale Cottage, Buttermere

June 18 Sunday
Brockhole, Windermere
Dallam Tower, Milnthorpe
Fell Yeat, Casterton, nr Kirkby Lonsdale
Rannerdale Cottage, Buttermere

June 21 Wednesday
Chapelside, Mungrisdale, Penrith
Fell Yeat, Casterton, nr Kirkby Lonsdale

June 24 Saturday
Sizergh Castle, nr Kendal

June 25 Sunday
Beck Head, Witherslack
Beckfoot Mill, Duddon Bridge
High Beckside Farm, Cartmel
Windy Hall, Windermere

June 28 Wednesday
Chapelside, Mungrisdale, Penrith

July 2 Sunday
Askham Hall, Penrith
Whitbysteads, Askham

July 5 Wednesday
Chapelside, Mungrisdale, Penrith
1 Sycamore Close, Whitehaven

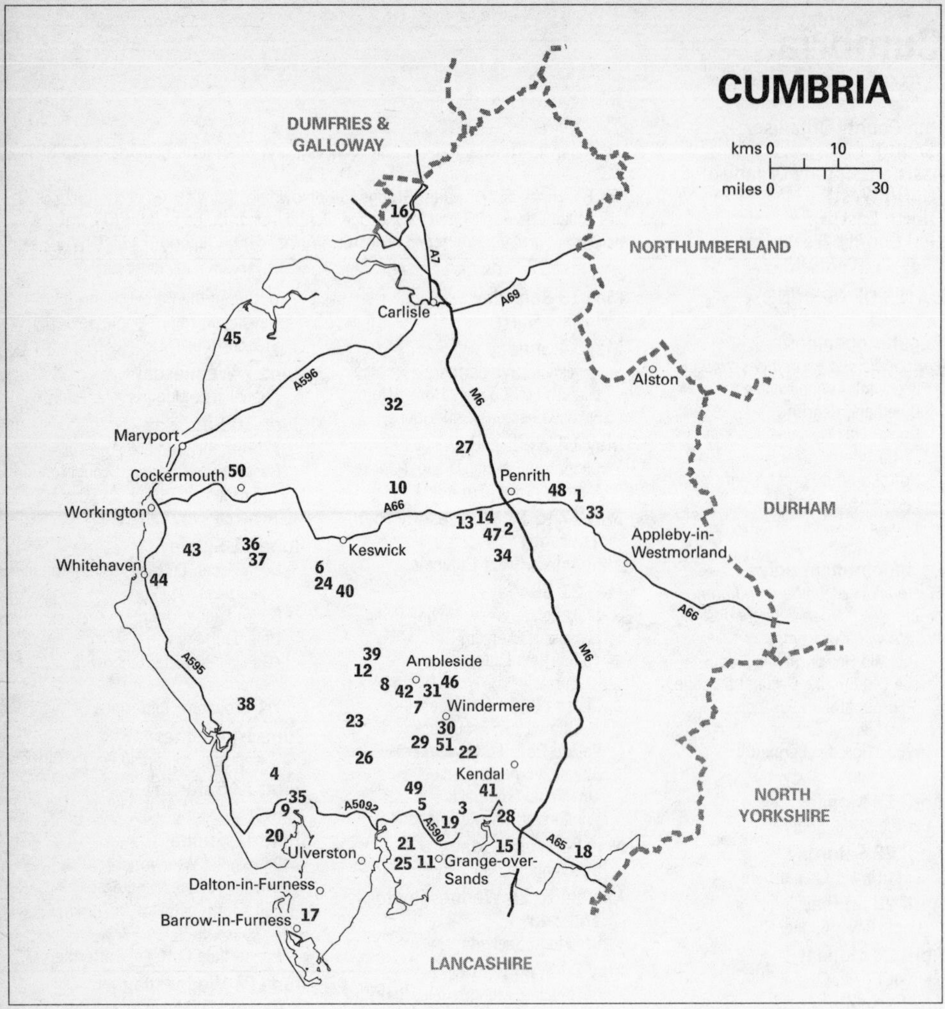

KEY

1 Acorn Bank
2 Askham Hall
3 Beck Head
4 Beckfoot Mill
5 Blakeholme Wray
6 Brackenburn
7 Brockhole
8 Browfoot
9 Bush Green Cottage
10 Chapelside
11 Charney Well
12 Copt Howe
13 Dacre Lodge
14 Dalemain
15 Dallam Tower
16 38 English Street
17 40 Fairfield Lane
18 Fell Yeat
19 Halecat
20 Hazel Mount
21 High Beckside Farm
22 High Cleabarrow
23 High Dixon Ground
24 High Rigg
25 Holker Hall & Gardens
26 Hollace
27 Hutton-in-the-Forest
28 Levens Hall
29 Lindeth Fell Country House Hotel
30 Matson Ground
31 Matthew How
32 The Mill House
33 Newbiggin Hall
34 The Nook
35 The Old Smithy
36 Palace How
37 Rannerdale Cottage
38 Rydal Mount
39 St Annes
40 Scarthwaite
41 Sizergh Castle
42 Stagshaw
43 Station House
44 1 Sycamore Close
45 Tomarobandy
46 Townfoot
47 Whitbysteads
48 Winderwath
49 Windy Hall
50 Wood Hall
51 Yews

July 8 Saturday
Acorn Bank, Temple Sowerby
Bush Green Cottage, Broughton-in-Furness

July 9 Sunday
Bush Green Cottage, Broughton-in-Furness
38 English Street, Longtown
High Cleabarrow, Windermere
Yews, Bowness-on-Windermere

July 12 Wednesday
Chapelside, Mungrisdale, Penrith
Holker Hall Gardens, Cark-in-Cartmel (evening)

July 16 Sunday
Dallam Tower, Milnthorpe
Hutton-in-the-Forest, Penrith

July 19 Wednesday
Chapelside, Mungrisdale, Penrith

July 23 Sunday
Halecat, Witherslack
High Dixon Ground, Coniston

August 12 Saturday
Charney Well, Grange over Sands

August 13 Sunday
Charney Well, Grange over Sands

August 27 Sunday
Rydal Mount, Eskdale

August 28 Monday
Rydal Mount, Eskdale

September 10 Sunday
1 Sycamore Close, Whitehaven

September 18 Monday
Levens Hall, Kendal

DESCRIPTIONS OF GARDENS

▲ **Acorn Bank, Temple Sowerby** ♿✂❀ (The National Trust) *6m E of Penrith on A66; ½m N of Temple Sowerby. Bus: Penrith-Appleby or Carlisle-Darlington; alight Culgaith Rd end.* Medium-sized walled garden; fine herb garden; orchard and mixed borders; wild garden with woodland/riverside walk leading to a partly restored watermill open to the public. Dogs on leads only woodland walk. Refreshments. *Adm £2.30 Chd £1.20 Family £5.80. For NGS Sats May 6 June 10, July 8 (10-5)*

Askham Hall, Penrith ✂❀ (The Earl & Countess of Lonsdale) *5m S of Penrith. Turn off A6 for Lowther and Askham.* Askham Hall is a pele tower, incorporating C14, C16 and early C18 elements in courtyard plan. Formal outlines of garden with terraces of herbaceous borders and original topiary, probably from late C17. Plants propagated by ourselves will be on sale. Shrub roses and recently created herb garden. Kitchen garden. TEAS. *Adm £1.50 Chd free (ACNO Askham & Lowther Churches). Sun July 2 (2-5)*

NEW **Beck Head, Witherslack** (Mr & Mrs J & B Kinnear) *From the M6, junction 36 travel W on Kendal by pass then turn 1st L onto the A590 Barrow rd. After approx 3m turn R signed Beck Head and Millside. Proceed approx ½m to Beck Head.* Mature 2-acre garden, in the shelter of Whitbarrow Scar, comprising of lawns, herbaceous borders, planted rocky outcrops, small stream and bog garden; good collection of trees, especially acers. Field walk from the garden through trees and round a small lake. Partially suitable for wheelchairs. Dogs on leads. TEA. *Adm £2 Chd under 12 free. Suns June 4, 25 (1-5)*

Beckfoot Mill, Duddon Bridge ✂❀ (Mr & Mrs J M Atkinson) *Broughton in Furmess.* ⅔-acre woodland garden in dell with beck flowing through into R Duddon. Believed to be on site of an Elizabethan bloomery. Choice plantings of shrubs and perennials on steep banks. Surrounds converted mill (not open). Paths steep in places. TEAS. *Adm £1.50 Chd 50p. Sun June 25 (1.30-5)*

Blakeholme Wray, Newby Bridge ✂ (Mr & Mrs Rooney) *[Grid Ref GR 384 895] Blakeholme Wray is 2m N of Newby Bridge on A592* Limited disabled parking. 4 acres garden, 22 acres woodland. An outstanding position with lawns sweeping down to the shore of Windermere. Informal planting is ongoing under present owners: massed rhododendrons and azaleas, damson orchard, wild orchids, bluebell carpets, ancient woodland walk, abundant wildlife. Partially suitable for wheelchairs. TEA. *Adm £2 Chd free. Sun May 21 (12-5)*

Brackenburn, Manesty (Prof & Mrs D C Ellwood) *Take rd signed Portinscale and Grange off A66. Follow all signs for Grange Garden is 1½ acres on the mountainside on RH-side of rd 3½m from A66.* The Garden has wonderful views of Lake Derwentwater. Several water features planted for damp, acid conditions with many rhododendrons, azaleas, ferns and primulas. Brackenburn is the former home of author Sir Hugh Walpole. *Adm £1.50 Acc chd free (ACNO to Scottish terrier emergency care scheme). Wed May 24 (11-5)*

■ **Brockhole, Windermere** ♿ (Lake District National Park) *2m NW of Windermere on A591 between Windermere and Ambleside.* 10 acres formal gardens, designed by Thomas Mawson. Acid soils and mild aspect, many unusual or slightly tender plants, shrub roses, herbaceous borders, scented garden. 20 acres informal grounds, wide variety of trees and shrubs. Picnic area, adventure playground, boat trips on Lake Windermere. Dogs on leads. Restaurant and tea rooms. *Adm free (Pay and display car parking available). Daily April to Nov. For NGS Suns May 14, June 18 (10-5)* **Tel 015394 46601**

Browfoot, Skelwith ❀ (Mr Trevor Woodburn) *Ambleside on A593 2½m from Ambleside.* Re-vamped woodland garden approx 2 acres; collection of rhododendrons, azaleas, conifers, natural rockery, many other shrubs; delightful views of Loughrigg and the Brathay Valley. Unsuitable for wheelchairs, dogs on leads. *Adm £2 Chd free. Wed, Thurs May 10, 11, 24, 25, Sun May 21 (11-5)*

Bush Green Cottage, Broughton-in-Furness ♿✂❀ (Mr & Mrs James Haunch) *On A595 on edge of Broughton. ½m from Foxfield on RH-side.* Approx 1-acre cottage garden. Streams and pool. Originally Crossing Keepers Cottage on Furness Railway; large collection geraniums. Wide variety hardy plants; new areas under development. Well stocked adjacent nursery *Adm £1.50 Acc chd under 12 free. Sats, Suns June 10, 11; July 8, 9 (11-5). Private visits welcome from June onwards, please* **Tel after 8pm (except Mons) 01229 716 724**

NEW **Chapelside, Mungrisdale, Penrith** (Mrs & Mr R Acland) *Roughly halfway between Penrith and Keswick on A66 take unclassified rd N, signed Mungrisdale Village. House is far end of scattered village on L immediately after tiny church on R. Some parking by parish church room at foot of short drive, not up drive.* 1-acre informal garden having fun with local stone, mixed plantings (often unruly), small pond, art contructions in and out. Fine views, so unkind winds. *Adm £1.50 Chd free. Weds May 3 to July 19 (2-6.30)*

Charney Well, Grange over Sands (Christopher Holliday & Richard Roberts) *Follow signs at Crown Hill roundabout in centre Grange. Turn R at Midland Bank then 1st L, garden 100yds on L.* Garden designer and writer's Mediterranean garden with panoramic views across Morecambe Bay. S facing ½-acre steep hillside site replanted over 12yrs to create connoisseur's plant paradise. 'A jewel in the crown of Lakeland gardens'. Great interest for flower arrangers/plantsmen. Still developing it has excited much media interest incl BBC, Country Life (2000). Only NCCPG collection of Phormiums on UK mainland. Sheltered walled garden with micro climate. Cream TEAS. *Adm £2 Chd free (ACNO Kendal Mountain Rescue). Sat, Sun August 12, 13 (10-5) Private visits (min 10) always welcome, please* **Tel 015 395 34526**

Copt Howe, Chapel Stile (Professor R N Haszeldine) *Chapel Stile. Great Langdale.* 2-acre plantsman's garden. Superb views Langdale Pikes. Extensive collections of acers (especially Japanese), camellias, azaleas, rhododendrons, quercus, fagus, rare shrubs, trees, unusual perennials; herbaceous and bulbous species; alpines, trough gardens; rare dwarf and large conifers; Expedition plants from many mountanous regions especially Far East.Outstanding spring colour. Wild life sanctuary. Featured by the media, BBC 2, gardening magazines. *Adm £2 OAP £1.50 Chd free. Sats, Suns, Mons April 22, 23, 24, May 27, 28, 29 (11-5). Open many other days mid April-Sept* **Tel 015394 37685** for recorded weekly information, please

Dacre Lodge, Dacre (Lt Col & Mrs T Washington) *About 4½m from exit 40 of the M6. Turn W onto A66 to Keswick and then L onto A562 signed Ullswater and Dalemain R to Dacre. After ½m green entrance gate with white top on L.* Approx 1-acre with herbaceous border and beds of perennial plants, roses and shrubs. Interesting trees and delightful riverside walk. Dacre Lodge is a 20-30 minute walk from Dalemain along an extremely pretty route. TEAS. *Adm £2 Chd free (ACNO to Dacre Village Hall & Childrens Playground). Sun June 11 (10.30-4.30)*

■ **Dalemain, Penrith** (Mr & Mrs R B Hasell-McCosh) *3m SW of Penrith on A592 to Ullswater.* 5-acre plantsman's gardens in parkland, set against the grandeur of the Lakeland Fells. Herbaceous borders; rose walk with old-fashioned roses and named ancient apple trees; Abies Cephalonica; tulip tree and Tudor knott garden. Wild garden with blue himalayan poppies. Woodland walks. **Dacre Lodge** also open June 11. Free electric scooters. Gift shop. TEA Room. *Adm £3 Chd free gardens only. Garden tours arranged. Open Sun-Thurs April 2 to Oct 8. For NGS Sun June 11, Sept 3 (10.30-5)*

Dallam Tower, Milnthorpe (Brig & Mrs C E Tryon-Wilson) *7m S of Kendal. 7m N of Carnforth, nr junction of A6 and B5282. Station: Arnside, 4m; Lancaster, 15m.* Medium-sized garden; natural rock garden, waterfalls, rambler roses and rose beds; wood walks, lawns, shrubs. C19 cast iron orangery. Dogs on leads. *Adm £1.50 Chd free. Suns April 30, June 18, July 16 (2-5)*

38 English Street, Longtown (Mr & Mrs C Thomson) *Carlisle. M6 junction 44, A7 for 6m into Longtown. 300yds on L next door to Annes Hairdressers. Entrance through open archway.* Terraced house garden. Red sandstone and water features; containers and troughs, pergola and herbaceous. TEA. *Adm £1.50 Acc chd free (ACNO to Cat Protection League). Sun July 9 (11-4). Private visits and parties welcome, please* **Tel 01228 791364**

40 Fairfield Lane, Barrow-in-Furness (Mr & Mrs Malcolm Needham) *Approach Barrow on A590 and turn L at sign to Furness General Hospital. Turn R at mini roundabout, L at first lights, and then R opp public house. House L at top of the hill.* ½ acre garden with good mixture of unusual shrubs, perennials and alpines. Collection of cacti and succulents in greenhouse, small pond and fruit/vegetable garden. *Adm £1.50 Chd under 12 free (ACNO to Marie Curie Nurses). Suns May 21, June 11 (11-4). Also open by appt, please* **Tel 01229 834859**

Fell Yeat, Casterton, nr Kirkby Lonsdale (Mr & Mrs O S Benson) *Approx 1m E of Casterton Village on the rd to Bull Pot. Leave A65 at Devils Bridge, follow A683 for a mile, take the R fork to High Casterton at the golf course, straight across at two sets of Xrds, the house is immediately on the L about ¼m from no through rd sign.* 1-acre informal country garden with many unusual plants. Divided into garden 'rooms'. 2 small ponds, herbaceous borders, old roses and ferns. National Collection of Ligularia. TEAS Suns in aid of Holy Trinity Church, Casterton and TEA on Wed in aid of NGS. *Adm £2 Chd free. Suns May 28, June 18, Wed June 21 (1.30-5)*

▲ **Halecat, Witherslack** (Mrs Michael Stanley) *10m SW of Kendal. From A590 turn into Witherslack following the Halecat brown signs. L in township at another brown sign and L again, signpost 'Cartmel Fell'; gates on L ⅓ [map ref. 434.834].* Medium-sized garden; mixed shrub and herbaceous borders, terrace, sunken garden; gazebo; daffodils and cherries in Spring; over 70 different varieties of hydrangea; beautiful view over Kent estuary to Arnside. Nursery garden attached. TEA. *Adm £1.50 Chd free. For NGS Suns May 28, July 23 (2-5). Also private parties welcome, please* **Tel 015395 52229**

Hazel Mount, Thwaites, Millom (Mrs Timothy Barratt) *2m from Broughton-in-Furness off A595 up hill after crossing Duddon River Bridge.* 5-acre woodland garden; small lake with stream and water garden; spring display of species rhododendrons, azaleas and flowering shrubs. Mature trees and exceptional views of Duddon Estuary and sea. Dogs on lead. Cream TEAS. *Adm £2 Chd free. Sun May 28 (2-5.30)*

High Beckside Farm, Cartmel ✂❀ (Mr & Mrs P J McCabe) *1¼m N of Cartmel. Take the Haverthwaite Rd, R at the village shop in the square.* Newly created conservation area; wild garden with ponds, waterfalls, waterfowl; flowering bushes and a number of rare trees. Arboretum in the very early stages of formation. 11 acres of wild flowers on a hillside with fine views. Small house garden and scree garden. Approx ¼m from house to conservation area. Stout shoes. TEA. *Adm £2 Chd free. Sun June 25 (1-5). Private visits welcome, please* **Tel 015395 36528**

High Cleabarrow, Windermere ♿✂❀ (Mr & Mrs R T Brown) *3m SE of Windermere off B5284 Crook to Kendal Rd (nr Windermere Golf Course).* 2-acre plantswoman's garden. Owner designed. Featured in 'The English Garden' and 'Cumbria Life'. A garden for all seasons comprising mixed borders, traditional rose garden, rocky outcrop, alpines, pond and waterside planting. Many unusual plants with a keen eye for plant association. Favoured plant groups, hydrangeas, hardy geraniums, hostas, hellebores and roses. Exciting new plantings and features always in progress. TEAS. *Adm £2 Chd under 12 free. Sun July 9 (11-5.30). Also private groups by appt, please* **Tel 015394 42808**

NEW **High Dixon Ground, Coniston** ✂❀ (Mr & Mrs David J Walmsley) *From Coniston centre going towards Ulverston/Torver over bridge, past garage, 1st R up Station Rd, 2nd turning on R-handside.* Approx 1½ acres of hillside (with splendid views over Coniston Fells and Yewdale Valley). Developed over 10yrs. Small arboretum, pond, streams, waterfowl, pergola and herbaceous borders. Use of natural features integrates and merges garden into the wilder landscape, using organic methods where possible. TEAS. *Adm £2 Chd under 12 free. Mon May 1, Sun July 23 (10-6)*

High Rigg, Grange-in-Borrowdale (Miss Barbara Newton) *From Keswick take B5289 to Grange; cross rd bridge, suitable for mini-buses. House ½m on L.* ¾-acre fellside garden with mixed shrub/herbaceous border, rock and bog gardens. Rhododendrons, azaleas and many other shrubs and trees. *Adm £1.50 Acc chd free. Wed May 24 (11-5)*

■ **Holker Hall Gardens, Cark-in-Cartmel** ♿✂❀ (Lord & Lady Cavendish) *4m W of Grange-over-Sands. 12m W of M6 (junction 36).* Magnificent formal and woodland gardens world-class. Exotic trees, shrubs, ancient oaks, beech walk with a stunning display of rhododendrons, azaleas, magnolias and camellias. Summer garden, rose garden, elliptical garden. A limestone cascade. National Collection of styracaceae. Wildflower meadow. Largest slate sundial in world. Deer park, adventure playground, gift shop, cafe. Holker Garden Festival June 2, 3, 4. *Adm £3.50 Chd £2 gardens only. Garden tours arranged. House & garden £6.25 Chd £3.95. Open Sun-Fri April 2 to Oct 31 (10-6) last admission 4.30pm. For NGS Adm* **Evening Opening** *£2.50 Chd £1.75. Wed July 12 (6.30-9)*

NEW **Hollace, Torver** ❀ (Mr & Mrs R Prickett) *SW from Coniston A593 2½m, N from Greenodd on A5092-A5084 8m, NE from Boughton-in-Furness on A593 6m. Follow signs in Torver Village. Limited Parking.* Approx 1-acre garden. Lawns, herbaceous, heather borders and fruit and vegetables. Emphasis will be on the sale of plants (no bedding plants). Main sale day will be on NGS open day. Open on other days when signs are displayed for 6 weeks. Dogs on leads. *By Donation. (ACNO to MCR). Sat May 13 (1-5.30). Private visits welcome, please* **Tel 015394 41416**

■ **Hutton-in-the-Forest, Penrith** (Lord Inglewood) *On B5305 6m NW of Penrith, 3m from exit 41 of M6.* Magnificent grounds with C18 walled flower garden, terraces and lake. C19 Low garden, specimen trees and topiary; woodland walk and dovecote. Mediaeval House with C17, C18 and C19 additions. TEAS. *Adm £2.50 gardens, and woodland walk, £4 house, gardens and woodland walk. Chd free gardens, grounds, £2 house, garden and woodland walk. Gardens open daily all year except Sats (11-5). House open (12.30-4). Tearoom (12-4.30). Thurs, Fris, Suns and Bank Hols April 20 to Oct 1. For NGS Suns June 4, July 16 (11-5)*

■ **Levens Hall, Kendal** ♿✂❀ (C H Bagot Esq) *5m S of Kendal on A6; exit 36 from M6.* 10 acres incl topiary garden and 1st ha-ha laid out by M Beaumont in 1694. Magnificent beech circle; formal bedding; herbaceous borders. Superb panelling, plasterwork in Elizabethan mansion, added to C13 pele tower. Steam collection. Wheelchairs garden, shop and tea room only. Gift shop, tea-room, children's play and picnic areas. *Adm House & Garden £5.50 Chd £2.80 Garden only £4 Chd £2.10. Reduction for groups April 2 to Oct 12. Sun, Mon, Tues, Wed, Thurs house (12-5) grounds (10-5) last adm 4.30, Steam collection (2-5). Closed Fri & Sat. For NGS Mons April 17, Sept 18 (10-5)*

Lindeth Fell Country House Hotel, Bowness-on-Windermere ♿ (Air Cdr & Mrs P A Kennedy) *1m S of Bowness on A5074.* 6-acres of lawns and landscaped grounds on the hills above Lake Windermere, probably designed by Mawson around 1907; conifers and specimen trees best in spring and early summer with a colourful display of rhododendrons, azaleas and Japanese maples; grounds offer splendid views to Coniston mountains. Top terrace suitable for wheelchairs. TEAS in hotel £1. *Adm £2 Chd free. Sun May 14 (1-5). Also private parties welcome, please* **Tel 01539 443 286**

Matson Ground, Windermere ♿❀ (Matson Ground Trust) *From Kendal turn R off B5284 signposted Heathwaite, 100yds after Windermere Golf Club. Garden is on L after ½m. From Bowness turn L onto B5284 from A5074. After ¾m turn L at Xrds. Garden on L ¾m along lane.* Stream flows through ornamental garden to large pond in the wild garden of spring bulbs, later wild flowers. Azaleas, rhododendrons, large mixed shrub/herbaceous borders, topiary work. New white garden, spring/summer border, camomile lawn on terrace. ½-acre walled organic kitchen garden, greenhouses and dovecote. 2-acre woodland. Dogs on leads. TEAS. *Adm £1.50 Chd 50p. Sun May 21 (1-5)*

Matthew How, Troutbeck ✂ (Mr & Mrs John Griffiths) *2½m equidistant from Windermere and Ambleside. From Windermere after Lakes school turn R up Bridges Lane off A591. From Ambleside L up Holbeck Lane between Town End (NT) and PO. Parking in village and Town End car park.* Delightful 1-acre fellside garden full of surprises with accent on shapes around C17 cottage (not open), overlooking the beautiful Troutbeck valley, High Street Range. Wide variety of plants incl clipped box and yew, tree ferns, magnolias, camellias, rhododendron and azaleas. A haven for birds incl pied fly catchers, nuthatches and woodpeckers. Red squirrels visit garden. Tea when possible next door. *Adm £2 Chd free. Wed May 17 (12-5) Combined adm with* **Town Foot Garden** *£2.50 (ACNO Troutbeck Village Hall). Sun, Wed May 21, 24 (12-5) Private visits and groups welcome May/June, please* **Tel 015394 33276**

The Mill House, Sebergham (Mr & Mrs R L Jefferson) *Take junction 41 off M6 A5305 Penrith to Wigton Rd into Sebergham turning to L into an easily missed lane just before bridge over river Caldew. 200 yds up lane, after bungalow take L fork in drive.* Available parking. 2-acre garden set in secluded valley around the water mill (not open); features millstream and pond, a large herbaceous border and a gravel garden; ornamental vegetable garden. Wildflower meadow walks to river. *Adm £2 Chd free. Open May16 to July 18, Tues only (1.30-8.30). Private visits welcome by appt, please* **Tel 01697 476472**

Newbiggin Hall, Temple Sowerby (Major & Mrs J H C Sawrey-Cookson) *In village of Newbiggin, 2½m from A66 at Temple Sowerby or Kirkby Thore, and 7-8m SE of Penrith. Entrance to garden signed from Xrds in village.* Approx 7 acres of mature garden under gradual restoration. Formal garden; yews, lawns, old roses, herbaceous border, avenues of trees (incl C18 Sycamore Avenue). Informal garden; specimen and ancient trees, shrubs (especially rhododendron), rustic bridge. Woodland and beckside walk. Exhibition of history of garden. *Adm £2 Chd under 12 free (ACNO to St Edmund's Church, Fabric Fund, Newbiggin). Sun June 4 (1.30-5)*

The Nook, Helton (Mr & Mrs P Freedman) *Penrith N 5m from B5320, take signs to Askham-Haweswater. Turn R into Helton.* ½-acre terraced rock garden, beds and tubs, alpines, ornamental pool, goldfish, bog plants, fruit and herb garden; magnificent views over R Lowther and parkland. Homemade provisions and cakes for sale. TEAS. *Adm £1.50 Chd free. Sun May 7 (11-4)*

The Old Smithy, Occupation Lane, Broughton-in-Furness (Mrs Carol Coleman) *From A595 turn R as indicated and on entering Broughton 1st L at bottom of hill (Foxfield Rd). Then R into Broughton Park follow rd round behind white houses, house on RHS. From Coniston through square downhill and 3rd R onto Foxfield Rd as before.* Starting from plantation of conifers 6yrs ago owner has created large new informal 1-acre garden of which ⅓ still under development. Rhododendrons, camellias and azaleas. Herbaceous borders and species roses on damp, alluvial soil. Bog garden, pool and stream envisaged. *Adm £1.50 Chd free. By appt from Mid May- end Sept write or* **Tel 01229 716864 after 7**

Palace How, Loweswater (Mr & Mrs A R Johnson) *6m SE Cockermouth on B5292 and B5289, from Keswick 10m over Whinlatter Pass, through Lorton Village, follow signs for Loweswater.* 1-acre damp garden set in lovely situation amongst mountains, fine views. Unusual trees and shrubs, especially rhododendrons and acers. Pond with bog plants, candelabra primulas, Himalayan poppies, roses and alpines. TEAS. *Adm £2 Chd free (ACNO to Pets Lifeline-Keswick). Sun May 21 (11-5)*

Rannerdale Cottage, Buttermere (The McElney Family) *8m S of Cockermouth, 10m W of Keswick.* ½-acre cottage garden with beck and woodland walk overlooking Crummock Water, splendid mountain views. Herbaceous, shrubs, roses, perennial geraniums, tree peonies, pond with fish. TEAS *Adm £1.50 Chd free (ACNO to The Museum of East Asian Art) Sat, Sun June 17, 18 (11-5)*

Rydal Mount, Eskdale (Mr & Mrs Don Richards) *Nr Gosforth. Turn off A595 where signed 6m to Eskdale Green. Turn sharp R opp Eskdale Stores. 2nd house on R.* 1½ acre garden on natural rock facing SW. Heathers and tree heaths with shrubs and small trees favouring acid soil; eucalyptus and American blueberrys; water garden. *Adm £2 Chd free (Acno to West Cumbria Hospice at Home). Suns, Mons April 30, May 1, Aug 27, 28 (2-5) Also private visits welcome, please* **Tel 019467 23267**

St Annes, Great Langdale (Mr & Mrs R D Furness) *5m from Ambleside on B5343. Follow signs for Langdale/Old Dungeon Ghyll. At Skelwith Bridge take R hand fork and at Elterwater take R hand. Through Chapel Stile, ¾m on L hand side travelling W.* 3-acre partial woodland with established variety of conifers and trees, azaleas and rhododendrons. Establishing wild flower area. Natural rock faces with alpines, streams and rocky paths. Magnificent views Langdales. Partially suitable for wheelchairs. TEAS. *Adm £1.50 Chd free. Wed, Thurs May 17, 18 (11-4.30). Open for groups by appt, please* **Tel 015394 37271**

Scarthwaite, Grange-in-Borrowdale (Mr & Mrs E C Hicks) *From Keswick take B5289 to Grange. Cross road bridge, into village, house 1/4m on L. Bridge NOT suitable for coaches but mini buses may cross. (1/4m walk from far side of bridge for coach parties).* Ferns, cottage garden plants and many others packed into ⅓ acre. *Adm £2 Acc chd free. Open May until end August (not Suns) by appt. Private visits and parties welcome, please* **Tel 017687 77233**

▲ Sizergh Castle, nr Kendal (The National Trust) *3m S of Kendal. Approach rd leaves A590 close to and S of A590/A591 interchange.* ⅔ acre Limestone Rock Garden, largest owned by the National Trust; collection of Japanese maples, dwarf conifers, hardy ferns, primulas, gentians, perennials and bulbs; water garden, aquatic plants; on castle walls shrubs and climbers, many half-hardy; south garden with specimen roses, lilies, shrubs and ground cover. Wild flower areas, herbaceous border, crab apple orchard with spring bulbs, 'Dutch' garden. *Castle & garden adm £4.60 Chd £2.30; Garden adm £2.30 Chd £1.20. For NGS Sat June 24 (12.30-4.30)*

▲ Stagshaw, nr Ambleside (The National Trust) *½m S of Ambleside. Turn E off A 591, Ambleside to Windermere rd. Bus 555 Kendal-Keswick alight Waterhead.* Woodland gdn incl fine collection of rhododendrons and azaleas. Ericaceous trees & shrubs incl magnolias, camellias, embothriums. Views over Windermere. *Adm £1.50 Chd 75p For NGS Suns April 30, May 21 (10-5.30)*

Station House, Lamplugh ♿❀ (Mr & Mrs G H Simons) *Wright Green. Lamplugh approx 6m from Workington, Whitehaven and Cockermouth signposted off A5086 Lilyhall-Workington from Cockermouth-Egremont Rd ½m under disused railway line. From Workington-Whitehaven A595 at Leyland roundabout take rd signposted Branthwaite-Loweswater.* 2-acre garden created over site of disused railway line and station. Features shrubs and trees; vegetable and fruit garden. Morning coffee/TEAS. *Adm £1 Chd 50p. Sun June 4 (10.30-4.30)*

NEW **1 Sycamore Close, Whitehaven** ✿❀ (Mrs Jean Purkiss) *Travelling S on the A595 (The Loop Rd) take 1st L opposite BP Garage into Aikbank Rd. Keep going up hill, Sycamore Close is 3rd on R. House 1st on L.* Small established cottage garden with water feature. Large collection of hardy plants specialising in corydalis, dicentra, meconopsis, polemonium (incl the new 'Elworthy Amethyst'), and large collection of hardy geraniums. *Adm £1.50 Acc chd free. Wed July 5, Sun Sept 10 (2-5)*

Tomarobandy, Blitterlees ✿❀ (Mr & Mrs Tom Wrathall) *Nr Silloth. On Silloth-Maryport Rd, B5300, centre of village on W side of rd. (Parking behind Tom Wrathall's service station).* 1½-acre coastal garden, compartmented by windbreaks to form a series of thirteen themed gardens. Wide variety of plants for yr-round interest. *Adm £2 Acc chd free. Sat, Sun June 10, 11 (10-4)*

NEW **Townfoot, Troutbeck** ✿ (Mr & Mrs Peter Renison) *2½m equal distance from Windermere and Ambleside. From Windermere after Lakes School turn R up Bridge Lane off A591. 1m 1st house on L. Parking in village and NT Townend car park* Recently acquired and newly planted 3/4-acre fellside garden surounding grade II C17 farmhouse (not open). Lovely views of the Troutbeck fells and Garburn Pass. Terraces comprising rhododendrons, azaleas, acers, rockery, herbaceous perennials and bulbs, Many varieties of birds and occasional red squirrels, rare breed hens in field. TEAS. *Combined adm with* **Matthew How** *£2.50 Chd free (ACNO Troutbeck Village Institute). Sun, Wed May 21, 24 (12-5)*

Whitbysteads, Askham ✿❀ (The Hon Mrs Anthony Lowther) *8m from Penrith. Turn R at Eamont Bridge off the A6. Turn L at Y fork after railway bridge signed Askham. Through village, turn R at Queen's Head.* 1-acre garden on several levels surrounding farmhouse on edge of fells, featuring wide variety of shrub roses, unusual herbaceous plants and geraniums. Pergola; fountain. Magnificent views over Eden Valley. *Adm £1.50 Chd free (ACNO to Killingbeck Heart Hospital, Leeds). Sun July 2 (2-5)*

■ **Winderwath, nr Penrith** ✿❀ (Miss Jane Pollock) *5m E of Penrith N of A66.* Mature garden laid out at end of C19 with interesting trees and borders. Recently established rock garden; many specialist alpines. Surplus plants and second-hand garden tools for sale. Picnic area. TEA. *Adm £2 Acc chd free. 1 March to 31 Oct Mon-Fri (10-4). For NGS Sun May 21 (1-5)*

Windy Hall, Windermere ✿ (Diane & David Kinsman) *Crook Road. 8m from Kendal on B5284 up Linthwaite Country House Hotel driveway.* 3 to 4-acre garden maintained by owners and developed from wilderness in 17yrs. Woodland, herbaceous, alpine, and kitchen gardens. Wide variety of plants, especially rhododendrons, camellias, magnolias, sorbus, hydrangeas and many climbers. NCCPG collections of Aconitum, Aruncus and Filipendula. Waterfowl gardens and rarebreed sheep. TEAS. *Adm £2 Chd 25p. Wed May 31, Sun June 25 (10-6). Private visits and parties by appt, please* **Tel 015394 46238**

Wood Hall, Cockermouth ❀ (Mr & Mrs W Jackson) *Entrance to drive in large lay-by ¼m N (towards Carlisle) from the A595/A594 roundabout nr Cockermouth.* A 5½ acre Thomas Mawson garden, with terraces, walls, small feature gardens, lawns, woods and paths. Venerable trees and newer planting with extensive rock bank newly cleared and replanted. Alpines, shrubs and herbaceous plants. Partially suitable for wheelchairs. *Adm £2 and Acc chd free. Private visits and parties welcome, please* **Tel 01900 823585**

Yews, Bowness-on-Windermere ✿❀ (Sir Oliver & Lady Scott) *A5074 1m out of Bowness-on-Windermere. Middle Entrance Drive, 50yds.* Medium-sized formal Edwardian garden; fine trees, ha-ha, herbaceous borders; greenhouses. Bog area being developed, Bamboo, Primula, Hosta. Young yew maze. TEAS. *Adm £2 Chd free (ACNO to Marie Curie Cancer Care). Sun July 9 (2-5.30)*

Evening Opening (See also garden description)

Holker Hall Gardens, Cark-in-Cartmel	July 12

Denbighshire & Colwyn

See separate Welsh section on page 406

Nurses Welfare Service

How much does it cost to train a new nurse or midwife? Over £35,000. Your donation to the Nurses Welfare Service can help sick nurses and midwives get back to work. Tel 0171 222 1563.

Derbyshire

Hon County Organisers: Mr & Mrs R Brown, 210 Nottingham Road, Woodlinkin, Langley Mill, Nottingham NG16 4HG Tel 01773 714903

Hon County Treasurer: Mrs Judy Nutland, 4 Sadler Close, Adel, Leeds LS16 8NN

DATES OF OPENING

Regular openings
For details see garden description
Lea Gardens
Renishaw Hall, Renishaw

By appointment only
For telephone numbers and other details see garden descriptions. Private visits welcomed
Birchfield, Ashford in the Water
Birchwood Farm, Coxbench
Cherry Tree Cottage, Hilton
57 Portland Close, Mickleover

April 9 Sunday
Crossways, 32 Heanor Rd, Codnor

April 15 Saturday
Castle Farm, Melbourne

April 16 Sunday
Castle Farm, Melbourne
Meynell Langley, Kirk Langley

April 19 Wednesday
Bluebell Nursery & Woodland Garden, Smisby

April 23 Sunday
Bluebell Nursery & Woodland Garden, Smisby
The Riddings Farm, Kirk Ireton

April 30 Sunday
Pabryella, Wingerworth
Radburne Hall, Radburne
35 Wyver Lane, Belper

May 1 Monday
Oaks Lane Farm, Brockhurst

May 7 Sunday
Bath House Farm, Ashover
Broomfield College, Morley
Fir Croft, Calver

May 8 Monday
Oaks Lane Farm, Brockhurst

May 14 Sunday
Crossways, 32 Heanor Rd, Codnor

May 21 Sunday
Dam Farm House, Ednaston
Fir Croft, Calver
The Limes, Apperknowle
100 Wellington Street, Matlock

May 24 Wednesday
Bluebell Nursery & Woodland Garden, Smisby

May 28 Sunday
Bluebell Nursery & Woodland Garden, Smisby
Corner Cottage, Osmaston-by-Ashbourne
Dove Cottage, Clifton
286 Handley Road, New Whittington
Monksway, Tideswell
Thatched Farm, Radbourne

May 29 Monday
Corner Cottage, Osmaston-by-Ashbourne
Monksway, Tideswell
Shatton Hall Farm, Bamford

June 1 Thursday
Gamesley Fold Cottage, Glossop
Kedleston Hall, Kedleston

June 3 Saturday
Castle Farm, Melbourne

June 4 Sunday
Castle Farm, Melbourne
Fir Croft, Calver
Gamesley Fold Cottage, Glossop
26 Wheeldon Avenue, Derby
35 Wyver Lane, Belper
Yew Tree Bungalow, Tansley

June 5 Monday
Oaks Lane Farm, Brockhurst

June 8 Thursday
Gamesley Fold Cottage, Glossop

June 11 Sunday
334 Belper Road, Stanley Common
10 Chestnut Way, Repton
The Cottage, Findern
Crossways, 32 Heanor Rd, Codnor
210 Nottingham Road, Woodlinkin
11 Stanley Close, Ilkeston

June 12 Monday
Oaks Lane Farm, Brockhurst

June 15 Thursday
Gamesley Fold Cottage, Glossop

June 17 Saturday
Rock House, Nether Heage, nr Belper

June 18 Sunday
10 Chestnut Way, Repton
Corner Cottage, Osmaston-by-Ashbourne
Fields Farm, Codnor
Fir Croft, Calver
The Gardens at Dobholme Fishery, Troway
Laurel Bank, Ilkeston
11 St Helen's Avenue, Pinxton
Thatched Farm, Radbourne

June 21 Wednesday
Bluebell Nursery & Woodland Garden, Smisby

June 22 Thursday
Gamesley Fold Cottage, Glossop

June 25 Sunday
Bluebell Nursery & Woodland Garden, Smisby
Cashel, Kirk Ireton
Dove Cottage, Clifton
Gamesley Fold Cottage, Glossop
Monksway, Tideswell
Otterbrook, Chinley
Rivendell, Mickleover
100 Wellington Street, Matlock
White Gate, Arleston Meadows
Yew Tree Bungalow, Tansley

June 28 Wednesday
Wharfedale, Duffield (evening)

June 29 Thursday
Gamesley Fold Cottage, Glossop

July 2 Sunday
Churchside Cottage, Ashover
Fanshawe Gate Hall, Holmesfield
Monksway, Tideswell

July 3 Monday
Oaks Lane Farm, Brockhurst

July 5 Wednesday
Field Farm, Kirk Ireton

July 8 Saturday
Spindlewood, Darley Dale
Tissington Hall, nr Ashbourne

July 9 Sunday
334 Belper Road, Stanley Common
Crossways, 32 Heanor Rd, Codnor
Fanshawe Gate Hall, Holmesfield
274 Heanor Road, Ilkeston
Locko Park, Spondon
46 Long Meadow Road, Alfreton
Longarth Piece, 159 Longfield Lane, Ilkeston
Mill Lane Gardens, Codnor
Monksway, Tideswell

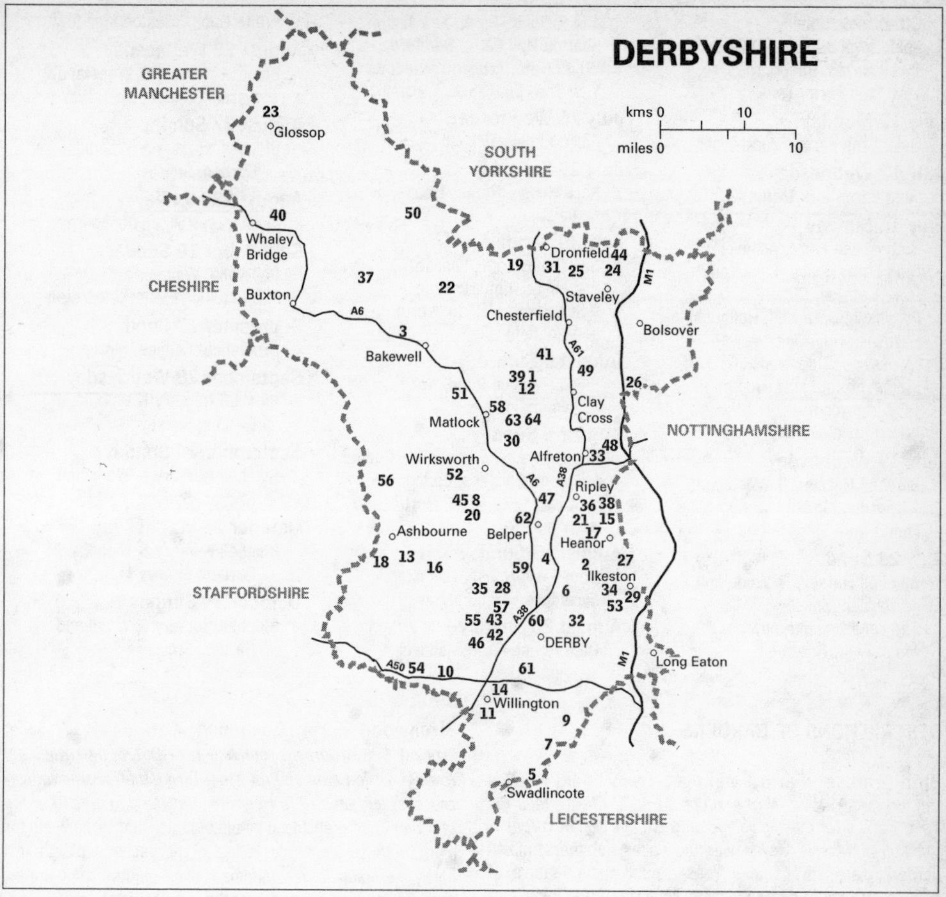

KEY

1 Bath House Farm
2 334 Belper Road
3 Birchfield
4 Birchwood Farm
5 Bluebell Nursery & Woodland Garden
6 Broomfield College
7 Calke Abbey
8 Cashel
9 Castle Farm
10 Cherry Tree Cottage
11 10 Chestnut Way
12 Churchside Cottage
13 Corner Cottage
14 The Cottage
15 Crossways
16 Dam Farm House
17 62A Denby Lane
18 Dove Cottage
19 Fanshawe Gate Hall
20 Field Farm, Kirk Ireton
21 Fields Farm, Codnor
22 Fir Croft
23 Gamesley Fold Cottage
24 The Gardens at Dobholme Fishery
25 286 Handley Road
26 Hardwick Hall
27 274 Heanor Road
28 Kedleston Hall
29 Laurel Bank
30 Lea Gardens
31 The Limes
32 Locko Park
33 46 Long Meadow Road
34 Longarth Piece
35 Meynell Langley
36 Mill Lane Gardens
37 Monksway
38 210 Nottingham Road
39 Oaks Lane Farm
40 Otterbrook
41 Pabryella
42 57 Portland Close
43 Radburne Hall
44 Renishaw Hall
45 The Riddings Farm
46 Rivendell
47 Rock House
48 11 St Helen's Avenue
49 9 St Lawrence Road
50 Shatton Hall Farm
51 Spindlewood
52 Stainsborough Hall
53 11 Stanley Close
54 Sycamore Farm
55 Thatched Farm
56 Tissington Hall
57 Tyrell Hayes
58 100 Wellington Street
59 Wharfedale
60 26 Wheeldon Avenue
61 White Gate
62 35 Wyver Lane
63 Yew Tree Bungalow
64 Yew Tree Farm

Otterbrook, Chinley
Spindlewood, Darley Dale
Tyrell Hayes, Radbourne
Yew Tree Farm, Tansley

July 10 Monday
Oaks Lane Farm, Brockhurst

July 12 Wednesday
Field Farm, Kirk Ireton

July 16 Sunday
Bath House Farm, Ashover
Dam Farm House, Ednaston
Dove Cottage, Clifton
Fanshawe Gate Hall, Holmesfield
Hardwick Hall, Doe Lea
Monksway, Tideswell
Stainsborough Hall, Hopton nr Wirksworth
Wharfedale, Duffield

July 19 Wednesday
Bluebell Nursery & Woodland Garden, Smisby
Field Farm, Kirk Ireton

July 23 Sunday
Bluebell Nursery & Woodland Garden, Smisby
The Limes, Apperknowle
Monksway, Tideswell
The Riddings Farm, Kirk Ireton
Shatton Hall Farm, Bamford
White Gate, Arleston Meadows
Yew Tree Bungalow, Tansley

July 26 Wednesday
Calke Abbey, Ticknall

July 29 Saturday
Rock House, Nether Heage, nr Belper

July 30 Sunday
62A Denby Lane, Loscoe
The Limes, Apperknowle
9 St Lawrence Road, North Wingfield

August 5 Saturday
9 St Lawrence Road, North Wingfield

August 6 Sunday
Crossways, 32 Heanor Rd, Codnor
Mill Lane Gardens, Codnor
9 St Lawrence Road, North Wingfield

August 13 Sunday
Dam Farm House, Ednaston
Sycamore Farm, Foston

August 20 Sunday
Bath House Farm, Ashover
White Gate, Arleston Meadows

August 23 Wednesday
Bluebell Nursery & Woodland Garden, Smisby

August 27 Sunday
Bluebell Nursery & Woodland Garden, Smisby

August 28 Monday
Tissington Hall, nr Ashbourne

September 10 Sunday
Pabryella, Wingerworth
The Riddings Farm, Kirk Ireton

September 17 Sunday
Broomfield College, Morley

September 20 Wednesday
Bluebell Nursery & Woodland Garden, Smisby

September 24 Sunday
Bluebell Nursery & Woodland Garden, Smisby

October 25 Wednesday
Bluebell Nursery & Woodland Garden, Smisby

October 29 Sunday
Bluebell Nursery & Woodland Garden, Smisby

DESCRIPTIONS OF GARDENS

Bath House Farm, Ashover ♿✂ (Mr & Mrs Hetherington) *4½m N of Matlock on A632 Chesterfield Rd. Take 1st R after leaving village of Kelstedge and next R at T-junction.* Extensive views over the valley; heathers, mixed borders, rare shrubs and trees around main feature of ponds, streams and waterfalls. New features include a pergola, woodland stream and rhododendrons:indoor display of airplants. TEA. *Adm £2. Suns May 7, July 16, Aug 20 (12-4.30). For private appointments* **Tel 01246 590562**

334 Belper Road, Stanley Common ♿✂❀ (Gill and Colin Hancock) *7m N of Derby, 3m W of Ilkeston on the A609, ¾m from the Rose and Crown Xrds (A608). Please park in rear of Working Mens Club car park.* ¾ acre garden. Large herbaceous island bed, shrub borders, pergolas, kitchen. Small water features, a natural wildlife pond and a conservatory with streptocarpus. TEAS. *Adm £1.50 Chd free. Suns June 11, July 9 (2.30-5.30). Private visits welcome, please* **Tel 0115 930 1061**

Birchfield, Ashford in the Water ✂ (Brian Parker) *Dukes Drive. 2m NW of Bakewell on A6 to Buxton.* Beautifully situated terraced garden of approx ¾ acre. Designed for all-yr-round colour, it contains a wide variety of shrubs and perennials, bulbs, water and scree gardens. Areas of copse with wild flowers are being developed in adjacent field. TEA. *Adm £1.50 Chd free (ACNO to Derbyshire Red Cross). Private visits welcome from individuals as well as groups April to Sept, please* **Tel 01629 813800**

Birchwood Farm, Coxbench ✂❀ (Stuart & Janet Crooks) *5m N Derby. From A38 take B6179 by Little Chef through Little Eaton till first Xrds. Turn L then R over railway crossing and take rd to Holbrook. Car parking in field at top of drive.* ⅓-acre enclosed within old brick and stone walls for plant enthusiasts. Wide range of herbaceous plants incl hardy geraniums, penstemons, silver plants, campanulas, delphiniums, English roses and pond. Private nursery adjacent. *Adm £2 Chd free. Coach parties and private visits welcome, please* **Tel 01332 880685**

Bluebell Nursery & Woodland Garden, Smisby ♿✂❀ (Robert & Suzette Vernon) *From the A511 Burton on Trent to Ashby-de-la-Zouch Rd, turn for Smisby by the Mother Hubbard Inn, 1m NW of Ashby. Arboretum is on L after ½m Annwell Lane.* 5-acre arboretum planted in the last 7 yrs incl many specimens of rare trees and shrubs. Bring wellingtons in wet weather. TEA. *Adm £1 Chd 50p (ACNO to MENCAP). Suns April 23, May 28, June 25, July 23, Aug 27, Sept 24, Oct 29; Weds April 19, May 24, June 21, July 19, Aug 23, Sept 20, Oct 25 (10.30-5). Private visits welcome, please* **Tel 01530 413700**

Broomfield College, Morley ♿✂❀ *On A608, 4m N of Derby and 6m S of Heanor.* Landscaped garden of 10 ha; shrubs, trees, rose collection, herbaceous borders; glasshouses; walled garden; garden tour guides; demonstrations of seasonal garden tasks, hanging baskets. Carvery lunches, refreshments. *Adm £1 Chd free. Suns May 7, Sept 17 (10-4)*

▲ **Calke Abbey, Ticknall** ♿✂ (The National Trust) *9m S of Derby on A514 between Swadlincote and Melbourne.* Extensive walled gardens constructed in 1773. Divided into flower garden, kitchen garden and physic garden. Restoration commenced in 1987. Replanted informal pleasure grounds. Glass domed C18 orangery under restoration. Plant and produce sales. Lunches and TEAS. *Adm £2.30 Chd £1.10. For NGS Wed July 26 (11-5)*

Cashel, Kirk Ireton ❀ (Anita & Jeremy Butt) *Turn off B5023 (Duffield-Wirksworth rd). 2m S of Wirksworth. Follow rd to Kirk Ireton take sharp R turn at church corner. Follow lane for 200 metres. Garden on R, car parking 50 metres beyond the house.* 2½ acres situated on a sloping site featuring a terraced ravine and view of the Ecclesbourne Valley. Many interesting trees, plants and shrubs. TEAS in aid of local church. *Adm £1.50 Chd free. Sun June 25 (2-5). Private visits welcome, please* **Tel 01335 370495**

Castle Farm, Melbourne ♿❀ (Mr & Mrs John Blunt) *From Melbourne Market Place turn into Potter St (side of Melbourne Hotel) continue down into Castle Square. Castle Farm faces across the square.* 1-acre farmhouse garden on site of Melbourne Castle with some ruins remaining. Herbaceous borders. Herb garden and old roses garden. Ornamental pond and bog garden. Large orchard. Vegetable garden with greenhouses and tree nursery. TEAS. *Adm £1.50 Chd free (ACNO to St John's Ambulance Brigade). Sats, Suns April 15, 16, June 3, 4 (2-5)*

Cherry Tree Cottage, Hilton ✂❀ (Mrs A Hamblin) *7m W of Derby, turn off A516 opp the Old Talbot Inn in village centre.* A plant lover's C18 cottage garden. Approx ⅓ acre with herbaceous borders, herb and scree garden, gravel garden with small pond. Many unusual and interesting plants. Species aquilegias, geraniums, iris, campanula, pulmonaria etc. Partially suitable for wheelchairs. Featured on Gardeners' World and in several gardening magazines. *Adm £1.50 Chd free. Groups by appt, please* **Tel 01283 733778**

10 Chestnut Way, Repton ♿❀ (Robert and Pauline Little) *From the A38, S of Derby, follow signs to Willington, then Repton. In Repton turn R at the roundabout to Burton. Chestnut Way is ¼m up hill, on L.* Close to the centre of historic Repton, this ⅓-acre informal garden is overflowing with unusual herbaceous perennials and shrubs. Many varieties of clematis and 2 ponds. Run on organic lines, there is an emphasis on labour-saving techniques in both the ornamental and kitchen gardens. A garden to relax in. TEAS. *Adm £1.50 Chd free. Suns June 11, 18 (2-6)*

NEW **Churchside Cottage, Ashover** ❀ (R H Broomhead) *4½m N of Matlock on A632 Chesterfield Rd. Ashover church spire leads you to Church St, Churchside Cottage is 50yds S of church.* Small walled-in garden with an interesting and varied collection of shrubs, roses and clematis. A pebble water feature and gravel bed with alpines and grasses. Sadly no access for wheelchairs due to the many steps. TEA. *Adm £1.50 Chd free (ACNO to M S Therapy Centre, Sheffield). Sun July 2 (2-5). Private visits welcome, please* **Tel 01246 590422**

Corner Cottage, Osmaston-by-Ashbourne ✂❀ (Alan & Lynn Poulter) *2½m SE of Ashbourne in centre of village ½m off A52.* Well-loved garden of over ½ acre, created by present owners, providing seclusion, tranquillity and colour with many hidden corners and pleasant walkways. Various settings incl formal walled garden, pond, quiet spot etc. Some unusual specimens. Cream TEAS. *Adm £1.50 Chd free (ACNO to Kwale Eye Hospital, Kenya). Sun May 28, Mon May 29, Sun June 18 (1-5). Group visits by appointment, please* **Tel 01335 346112**

The Cottage, Findern ✂❀ (Mrs M N Eccles) *Approx 6m between Derby and Burton-on-Trent. Accessible via A38. Take sign for Findern, into and through village, over flyover of A50. 1st L sign leading to Heath Lane. Follow rd over railway bridge, beyond primary school.* Well established garden of ¾-acre. Species trees and shrubs. Large herbaceous border, 3 natural ponds. Large area of roses, climbing roses and clematis. TEAS. *Adm £1.50 Chd under 16 free. Sun June 11 (1-5)*

Crossways, 32 Heanor Rd, Codnor ♿✂❀ (Janet and Ross Eyre) *300yds from Codnor Market Place on A6007 towards Heanor. Parking in field. Down lane at side of shop.* 1½ acre with variety of trees, shrubs, mixed borders with unusual plants, pergola and water feature with waterfalls and rockery. New large Japanese style garden with tea house, bridge over stream leading to pond, trees, camellias, azaleas, bamboos. Winner of the Amber Valley 'Best Kept' large garden competition, 1999 and featured in the 'Water Gardener'. TEA. *Adm £1.50 Chd free. Suns April 9, May 14, June 11, July 9, Aug 6 (2-5). Coach parties and private visits welcome, please* **Tel 01773 746626**

■ **Dam Farm House, Ednaston** ♿✂❀ (Mrs J M Player) *Yeldersley Lane, Ednaston, 5m SE of Ashbourne on A52, opp Ednaston Village turn, gate on R 500yds.* 3 acres extended to incl a young arboretum. Beautifully situated. Contains mixed borders, scree. Unusual plants have been collected many are propagated for sale. TEAS (some Suns). *Adm £2.50 Chd free. For NGS Suns May 21, July 16, Aug 13 (2-4.30). Private visits and groups welcome April 1 to Oct 31 by appt, please* **Tel 01335 360291**

NEW **62A Denby Lane, Loscoe** ❀ (Mrs J Charlesworth) *Halfway between Codnor and Heanor on A 6007. Follow Denby sign.* Interesting garden with heathers, ferns, grasses, conifers and shrubs. 2 small water features. Japanese features. Chrysanthemums and dahlias, bedding plants. Small bog garden. TEAS. *Adm £1 Chd free. Sun July 30 (2-5)*

Dove Cottage, Clifton ✂❀ (Mr and Mrs S G Liverman) *1½m SW of Ashbourne.* ¾-acre garden by R Dove extensively replanted and developed since 1979. Emphasis on establishing collections of hardy plants and shrubs incl alchemillas, alliums, berberis, geraniums, euphorbias, hostas, lilies, variegated and silver foliage plants inc astrantias. Plantsman's garden featured in magazines and on TV. TEA. *Adm £2 Chd free (ACNO to British Heart Foundation). Suns May 28, June 25, July 16 (1-5). Private visits welcome, please* **Tel 01335 343545**

Fanshawe Gate Hall, Holmesfield ✂❀ (Mr & Mrs John Ramsden) *Situated on the edge of the Peak National Park. Follow B6054 towards Owler Bar. 1st R turn after Robin Hood Inn.* C13 seat of the Fanshawe family. Old-fashioned cottage-style garden. Many stone features, fine C16 dovecote. Upper walled garden with herbaceous, variegated and fern plantings, water features, climbers, rose beds, terracing and lawns. Lower courtyard with knot garden and herb border. TEAS. *Adm £1.50 Chd free (ACNO to Oesophageal Patients Association). Suns July 2, 9, 16 (11-5). Private visits welcome by appt, please* **Tel 0114 2890391**

Field Farm, Kirk Ireton ❀ (Graham & Irene Dougan) *At top of Main St, Kirk Ireton turn L signed Blackwall, on sharp RH bend find Field Lane (unmade road), Field Farm 400 metres.* A tranquil 1½ acres with glorious views. Informal planting of trees and shrubs blends garden with countryside. Roses, clematis and fuchsias in abundance. Alpines and herbaceous borders. Gravelled courtyard holds plants and trees in containers. Three water features. Garden designed and planted by present owners since 1981 and featured on TV. TEAS. *Adm £1.50 Chd free. Weds July 5, 12, 19 (11-5) or by appt April to Oct, please* **Tel 01335 370958** http:/website.lineone.net/~field.farm

Fields Farm, Codnor ♿✂❀ (Mr & Mrs Graham Woolley) *300yds from Codnor Market Place on A6007. Towards Heanor.* Approx 1-acre garden with mixed herbaceous borders, shrubs, climbers, hostas, small pond, separate water feature, pergola, small Mediterranean garden. TEAS in aid of 3rd Codnor Scout Group. *Adm £1.50 Chd free. Sun June 18 (1-5)*

■ **Fir Croft, Calver** ✂❀ (Dr S B Furness) *Froggatt Rd, via Sheffield. 4m N of Bakewell; at the junction of B6001 with A625 (formerly B6054) adjacent to the 'power' garage.* Plantsman's garden; rockeries; water garden and nursery; extensive collection (over 2000 varieties) of alpines; conifers; over 600 sempervivums, 500 saxifrages and 350 primulas. Tufa and scree beds. *Collection box. Nursery opens every Sun (1-5) and Sat, Mon (10-5) March to Dec. Adjacent garden for NGS Suns May 7, 21, June 4, 18 (2-5)*

Gamesley Fold Cottage, Glossop ✂❀ (Mrs G Carr) *Off Glossop-Marple Rd nr Charlesworth, turn down the lane directly opp St Margaret's School, Gamesley. White cottage at the bottom.* Old-fashioned cottage garden down a country lane with lovely views of surrounding countryside. Spring garden planted with herbaceous borders, wild flowers and herbs in profusion to attract butterflies and wildlife. Featured in Good Housekeeping and Derbyshire Life. TEAS. *Adm £1.50 Chd free. Suns June 4, 25, Thurs June 1, 8, 15, 22, 29 (11-4). Groups welcome May and June, please* **Tel 014578 67856**

The Gardens at Dobholme Fishery, Troway ❀ (Paul & Pauline Calvert) *Halfway along B6056, Dronfield to Eckington, 2½m from each. Coming from Dronfield turn L at Blackamoor Head Inn for Troway. Follow signs in village.* Situated in beautiful conservation area of Moss Valley. Developed on sloping site of approx 2 acres around fishing ponds only 7yrs ago. Designed to encourage wildlife; planted in a wild, natural look. Heavy clay with many springs; stone quarried from the site is widely used to pave the pond sides. Sloping uneven terrain. Additional new garden area for 2000. *Adm £1.50 Chd free. Sun June 18 (12-4.30)*

286 Handley Road, New Whittington ❀ (E.J. Lee) *From A6135, take B6052 through Eckington and Marsh Lane 3m. Turn L at Xrds signed Whittington, then 1m. From Coal Aston (Sheffield), take B6056 towards Chesterfield to give way sign, then 1m. From Chesterfield, take B6052.* ⅓-acre sloping site. Herbaceous borders, rock garden, alpines, streams, pools, bog gardens, alpine house. Acers, bamboos, ferns, eucalyptus, euphorbias, grasses, conifers, Himalayan bed. 1500 plants permanently labelled. TEA. *Adm £1.50 Chd free (ACNO to Sheffield Botanical Gardens Trust). Sun May 28 (2-5). Private parties by appt, written application please*

▲ **Hardwick Hall, Doe Lea** ♿✂❀ (The National Trust) *8m SE of Chesterfield. S of A617.* Grass walks between yew and hornbeam hedges; cedar trees; herb garden; herbaceous and rose borders. Finest example of Elizabethan house in the country. Restaurant in Old Kitchens. TEAS on days the Hall is open. *Adm hall and garden £6 Chd £3.20 garden only £3 Chd £1.50. For NGS Sun July 16 (12-5.30 last entry 4.30)*

274 Heanor Road, Ilkeston ❀ (Mr & Mrs G Seagrave) *On A6007, 2m from Heanor towards Ilkeston, opp Ilkeston Hospital* Large all yr-round garden, with over 40 different varieties of conifers, 70 different shrubs, ornamental trees, rockery, pergola, greenhouse. Varieties of soft, top and stone fruit, vegetables. 'Beautiful Erewash' mixed gardens 1999 2nd place. TEA and biscuits. *Adm £1.50 Chd free. Sun July 9 (2-5.30)*

High Park see Nottinghamshire

▲ **Kedleston Hall, Kedleston** ♿✂ (The National Trust) *3m NW of Derby. Signed from junction of A38/A52.* 12 acres. A broad open lawn, bounded by a ha-ha, marks the C18 informal garden. Formal layout to the W was introduced early this century when the summerhouse and orangery, both designed by George Richardson late C18, were moved to their present position. Gardens at their best during May and June when the azaleas and rhododendrons are one mass of colour. The Long Walk, a woodland walk of some 3m, is bright with spring flowers. Guided walk of gardens and Long Walk at 2pm. TEA. *Adm £2 Chd £1. For NGS Thurs June 1 (11-6)*

NEW **Laurel Bank, Ilkeston** ❀ (Bob & Sydney Boaden) *S of Ilkeston, Quarry Hill Rd leads from the A6096 (Bull's Head) to Stanton and Sandiacre. Garden is just after junction with Longfield Lane. Parking Longfield Lane or lay-by at foot of hill.* ⅓-acre S sloping site. Continually developing enthusiasts' garden with open views and yr-round interest. Very wide range of hardy perennials, shrubs and heathers in terraced beds exploit the gradient (average 1 in 6) to offer varying perspectives. Landscaped pond, dry stone walls and terraced patio. TEAS. *Adm £1 Chd free. Sun June 18 (1-6). Private visits welcome, please* **Tel 01159 307024**

● **Lea Gardens** ♿❀ (Mr & Mrs J Tye) *Lea, 5m SE of Matlock off A6.* Rare collection of rhododendrons, azaleas, kalmias, alpines and conifers in delightful woodland setting. Light lunches, homemade TEAS. *Adm £3 Chd 50p daily,* *season ticket £4. Daily March 20 to June 30 (10-5.30). Coaches by appt*

The Limes, Apperknowle ♿❀ (Mr Roy Belton) *6m N of Chesterfield; on A61 taking the Dronfield, Unstone turn off to Unstone, turn R at Unstone school for 1m to Apperknowle; 1st house past Unstone Grange. Bus; Chesterfield or Sheffield to Unstone.* 2½-acre garden with herbaceous borders, lily ponds, roses and flowering shrubs; hundreds of naturalised daffodils. Massed bedding of pansies and polyanthus in the spring; geraniums and bedding plants in the summer. Large natural pond with ducks and geese. Nature trail over 5 acres. TEAS. *Adm £1 Chd 25p. Suns May 21, July 23, 30 (2-6)* **Tel 01246 412338**

Locko Park, Spondon ❀ *6m NE of Derby. From A52 Borrowash bypass, 2m N via B6001, turn to Spondon.* Large garden; pleasure gardens; rose gardens. House (not open) by Smith of Warwick with Victorian additions. Chapel (open) Charles II, with original ceiling. TEA. *Adm £1.50 Chd 50p. Sun July 9 (2-5)*

46 Long Meadow Road, Alfreton ♿✂❀ (Rosemary Townsend) *A38 Derby/M1. Take A61 Chesterfield and Matlock exit. At roundabout towards Alfreton through traffic light, past Swan and Salmon public house on R. Take next R, just before the church into Long Meadow Rd.* Walled garden, jointly managed between 2 houses. Mainly cottage garden type with vegetable and fruit area and 2 ponds. Approx ¼-acre. TEAS. *Adm £1.50 Chd free (ACNO to Avema Trust). Sun July 9 (2-5). For other dates,* **Tel 01773 521612/836521**

Longarth Piece, 159 Longfield Lane, Ilkeston ✂❀ (Diane & David Bennett) *(Stanton side) off Quarry Hill, opp Hallam Fields Junior School.* Described by visitors as an artist's garden; a large, informal, over-flowing with fruit, shrubs, flowers; two small fish ponds and a conservatory. A strong emphasis on texture, colour and lots of unexpected corners. Home-made TEAS. *Adm £1 Chd free. Sun July 9 (2-5.30). Private visits of 6 and under welcome, May to July, please* **Tel 01159 325238**

Meynell Langley, Kirk Langley ♿❀ (Godfrey Meynell Esq & the Rev Honor Meynell) *Enter by Green Iron Gate and Grey Lodge to N of Derby-Ashbourne Rd (A52) between Mackworth and Kirk Langley. About 4m WNW of Derby.* Lawns, trees, daffodils, rural views, access to park, lake and Regency house. TEAS in house. *Adm £2 Chd 50p (ACNO to St Michael's Church, Kirk Langley). Sun April 16 (2-5.30)*

Mill Lane Gardens, Codnor *12m NW Nottingham. 10m N of Derby. Mill Lane situated opp Codnor Market Place (Clock Tower) on the A610. 2 car parks nearby. Suns July 9, Aug 6 (11-6)*

NEW **Ash House, 45 Mill Lane** ❀ (Mrs Joyce Parke) New garden developed on various levels with herbaceous border, rockery, pond, water features, tubs and gravel garden. TEAS. *Adm £1.50 Chd free.*

23 Mill Lane ♿✂❀ (Mrs S Jackson) Lawn, herbaceous borders, small pond, waterfall; fruit trees; clematis and Mediterranean garden. TEA. *Adm £1.50 Chd free. Private visits also welcome June to Sept, please* **Tel 01773 745707**

Monksway, Tideswell (Mr & Mrs R Porter) *Summer Cross. Tideswell is situated 9m N of Buxton on the B6049. Turn up Parke Rd, between newsagent and greengrocer, off Queen St. Take a L turn at the top and then 1st R onto Summer Cross. Monksway is 4th semi-detached house on L. Limited parking.* Well stocked, gently sloping garden 1000′ above sea level containing perennial and shrub borders, rose, conifer, alpine scree beds and aviary. *Adm £1.50 Chd free. Suns May 28, June 25, July 2, 9, 16, 23, Mon May 29 (1-5). Private visits welcome, please* **Tel 01298 871687**

210 Nottingham Road, Woodlinkin (Mr & Mrs Ray Brown) *Nr Codnor; A610.* ½-acre; collections of old, modern, shrub and climbing roses; shrubs; trees. TEA. *Adm £1.50 Chd free. Sun June 11 (2-5)*

Oaks Lane Farm, Brockhurst ✂❀ (Mr & Mrs J R Hunter) *Ashover nr Chesterfield. At Kelstedge 4m from Matlock on A632 Chesterfield Rd, just above Kelstedge Inn, turn L up Kelstedge Lane, in ½m take 1st R, garden and car park 100yds on R.* Large cottage style garden with mixed borders, spring bulbs and hellebores, old fashioned roses, euphorbias, hostas and many rare plants, shrubs and trees. Natural streams and small bog garden. TEA. *Adm £1.50 Chd free. Mons May 1, 8, June 5, 12, July 3, 10 (2-5). Also open by appt May to Aug, please* **Tel 01246 590324**

NEW **Otterbrook, Chinley** ✂❀ (Mary & Dennis Sharp) *Otterbrook is reached by a 300yd walk up Alders Lane which is on outskirts of village off Buxton Rd (B6062) between Chinley and Chapel-en-le-Frith. Parking is very limited at house so please park on Buxton Rd.* Approx 1-acre informal plantspersons' garden evolved since 1968 and maintained by owners. Trees, island beds and borders with wide variety of herbaceous perennials and shrubs. Paths meander to various structures incl pergolas supporting climbing roses and shrubs; 2 ponds, one with bridge, folly etc. Kitchen garden, greenhouses. Views. TEAS in aid of Chinley and Boxworth Mobile Physiotherapy Committee. *Adm £1.50 Chd free. Suns June 25, July 9 (2-5)*

NEW **Pabryella, Wingerworth** ✂ (Arthur & Jean Tindle) *2m S of Chesterfield. Take A61 S (Derby Rd). After passing the Esso garage take next R on to Langer Lane. Follow rd for approx 1m, take 1st R after fields into Chartwell Rise leading to Chartwell Ave.* Featured in BBC Gardeners' World magazine 98 and in Practical Fishkeeping magazine 98. Main features incl Japanese themed area with koi pond and waterfall, 'Shangri-la' (a quiet peaceful retreat) and a patio garden with many interesting pots. The garden was developed from scratch in 1994 to provide all-yr-interest and minimum maintenance. Use the garden benches to enjoy the tranquil atmosphere. Something different every year! TEAS. *Adm £1.50 Chd 50p. Suns April 30, Sept 10 (2-5).*

57 Portland Close, Mickleover ✂❀ (Mr & Mrs A L Ritchie) *Approx 3m W of Derby, turn R off B5020 Cavendish Way then 2nd L into Portland Close.* Small plantsman's garden, wide variety of unusual bulbs, alpines and herbaceous plants. Special interest in sink gardens, hostas, named varieties of primulas (single and double), violas and hardy geraniums. *Adm £1 Chd free under 16. Private visits welcome of 10 and over, please* **Tel 01332 515450**

Radburne Hall, Radburne ✿ (Mrs J W Chandos-Pole) *5m W of Derby. W of A52 Derby-Ashbourne rd; off Radburne Lane.* Large landscape garden; large display of daffodils; shrubs; formal rose terraces; fine trees and view. Hall (not open) is 7-bay Palladian mansion built c1734 by Smith of Warwick. Ice-house in garden. *Adm £1 Chd 50p. Sun April 30 (2.30-5)*

● **Renishaw Hall, Renishaw** ♿❀ (Sir Reresby & Lady Sitwell) *Renishaw Hall is situated equidistant 6m from both Sheffield and Old Chesterfield on A616 2m from its junction with M1 at exit 30.* Italian style garden with terraces, old ponds, yew hedges and pyramids laid out by Sir George Sitwell c1900. Interesting collection of herbaceous plants and shrubs; nature trail; museum; lakeside walk. Shop provides wine, souvenirs, antiques; also Art Galleries. TEAS. *Adm £3 OAPs £2.50 Chd £1. Every Fri, Sat, Sun and Bank Hol Mons April 21 to Sept 24 (10.30-4.30). Private parties of 20 and over welcome, please* **Tel 01777 860755**

The Riddings Farm, Kirk Ireton ✿❀ (Mr & Mrs P R Spencer) *Between Ashbourne and Wirksworth. Leave Kirk Ireton via Gorsey Lane (close to Barley Mow). Turn L at T-junction onto Broom Lane. 1st R into Hays Lane.* Informal hillside garden about ¾ acre, overlooking Carsington Water. A garden for romantics, with winding woodland paths, bridges and pergolas. Fragrant carpets of primulas in spring. A peaceful paradise. Unusual plants propagated for adjacent nursery. TEAS in aid of Ashbourne Animal Welfare. *Adm £1.50 Chd free. Suns April 23, July 23, Sept 10 (2-5). Private visits welcome, please* **Tel 01335 370331**

NEW **Rivendell, Mickleover** ✿❀ (Mr & Mrs M J Maughan) *Approx 3m W of Derby. Turn into Ladybank Rd at Mickleover Court Hotel roundabout. Take 3rd R into Glenfield Crescent and 2nd R into Parkstone Court.* Small plantsman's garden with herbaceous borders, pond and rockery. Wide variety of perennials and shrubs, some unusual. TEAS. *Adm £1 Chd free. Sun June 25 (1-5)*

Rock House, Nether Heage, nr Belper ♿✿❀ (Ann Taylor) *[Map ref. SK 363506.] 11m N of Derby. From the A38 at Ripley W to Heage 3m. From the A6 at Belper N to Heage 3m. From Heage to Nether Heage W on Ambergate Rd ½m. From A6 at Ambergate E to Nether Heage 1½m.* Award winning medium sized informally planted garden, with hundreds of varieties of perennials, shrubs and climbers, and a few trees. New extension this year is an 'enchanted garden'. The whole reflects the owner's artistic skill and passion for plants! *Adm £1 Chd free. Sats June 17, July 29 (2-5). Private visits welcome afternoons and evenings June to Sept incl, please* **Tel 01773 852804**

11 St Helen's Avenue, Pinxton ❀ (Mr & Mrs J Froggatt) *From J28 off the M1. N-bound 2nd exit, S-bound 4th exit. Follow signs for Pinxton, 1st R off the main rd (Westend) very narrow. Then 1st L (Hilltop Rd) St Helen's Avenue is on the R.* Unusual shaped garden. Slight slope. Mixed overflowing herbaceous borders. Pergola, pond, conservatory and a small 'wild' bit. Waterfall. TEAS. *Adm £1.50 Chd free. Sun June 18 (2-6)*

NEW **9 St Lawrence Road, North Wingfield** ❀ (Julian & Judith Waring) *On A6175 at junction with B6039. Between Clay Cross 1½m and junction 29 M1.* Approx 15yds x 80yds. Small urban garden split into secret areas established over 10yrs by current owners. Large fuchsia collection in lots of pots, colourful perennial borders. Low maintenance garden to the front of the house made up of gravel beds. Small formal pond. Limited access for wheelchairs. TEA. *Adm £1 Chd free. Suns July 30, Aug 6, Sat Aug 5 (2-5.30)*

Shatton Hall Farm, Bamford (Mr & Mrs J Kellie) *3m W of Hathersage, take A6187 from Hathersage, turn L to Shatton, after 2m (opp High Peak Garden Centre). After ½m turn R through ford, drive ½m and house is on L over cattle grids.* Informal plantings and large water garden merge into the picturesque landscape surrounding the C16 farmhouse (not open). The gardens now extend to an acre with many new and unusual plants and shrubs; extensive woodland and streamside walks remain a feature. TEAS. *Adm £1.50 Chd 50p. Mon May 29, Sun July 23 (1.30-5). Private visits welcome April to September, please* **Tel 01433 620635**

NEW **Spindlewood, Darley Dale** ♿❀ (Mr & Mrs J G Ball) *3m N of Matlock. After 'The Grouse' Inn, turn R up Whitworth Rd. Park on L by signs. Elderly/disabled may continue to private parking areas.* 3/4-acre setting, bordering a wild area. A S facing garden with patio plantings. Mixed and herbaceous borders with stream, cascades, wildlife pond and bog garden. 3rd yr of planting, features being added regularly. *Adm £2 (ACNO to Dale Road Church Re-Development Fund, Darley Dale). Sat, Sun July 8, 9 (2-5)*

Stainsborough Hall, Hopton nr Wirksworth ♿❀ (Mr & Mrs Twogood) *On B5035 Wirksworth to Ashbourne Rd. 1½m W of Wirksworth take L turning to Kirk Ireton, house ¼m.* The stone house (not open) and buildings merge delightfully with lawns, shrubs, roses and flower beds designed informally on different levels to provide meandering walks. Covering some 2 acres, the garden incl many young trees, shrubs, herbaceous borders and rose beds. Duck pond with a variety of domestic ducks adds to the tranquillity of the scene. Cream TEAS. *Adm £1.50 Chd free. Sun July 16 (2-6)*

NEW **11 Stanley Close, Ilkeston** ✿❀ (Mr & Mrs F W Rice) *Nr Ilkeston town centre. Take A609, then shortly turn L into Belper St, between 'Three Horseshoes' and 'Miners' Arms'. 1st R into Union Rd, 1st R into Stanley Close.* Informal cottage-type garden in suburban setting. Shrubs, climbers, herbaceous plants, waterfall and pond. Natural bank makes interesting feature. TEAS. *Adm £1 Chd free. Sun June 11 (2-5)*

NEW **Sycamore Farm, Foston** ♿✿❀ (A J Robinson) *10m SW of Derby. From Derby take A516 to Hilton. Continue through to Hatton. Straight on through traffic lights and take 1st R then 2nd L.* ⅓ acre garden planted for late summer colour. Large collection (300 + varieties) of tender perennials particularly argyranthemums (90 varieties), salvias, dahlias and penstemons. Traditional herbaceous border, old roses and vegetable garden. TEAS. *Adm £1 Chd free. Sun Aug 13 (2-5.30)*

Thatched Farm, Radbourne ♿✂❀ (Mr & Mrs R A Pegram) *Exit A52 Derby-Ashbourne rd. 2m N of Derby Ring Road.* A 2-acre plant lover's garden. The garden surrounds a C17 listed farmhouse (not open). Mediterranean and island beds, troughs and alpines in raised beds, wild garden. Trees, shrubs and herbaceous perennials, bulbs, extensive collection of tender perennials. 2 ponds and bog garden. Featured in the The English Garden, and Derbyshire Life. Home-made cream TEAS. *Adm £2 Chd free (ACNO to RELATE May 28 & Parkinson's Disease Society June 18). Suns May 28, June 18 (2-5.30). Private parties, min 12, also welcome, please* **Tel 01332 824507**

Tissington Hall, nr Ashbourne ✂❀ (Sir Richard & Lady FitzHerbert) *N of Ashbourne. E of A515.* Large garden; roses, herbaceous borders. Tea available in village at The Old Coach House (party bookings on 01335 352200 with tour of gardens possible). Please park considerately. *Adm £2 Chd free. Sat July 8, Mon Aug 28 (2-5). Parties by written appt only on other days, consult The Estate Office, Tissington, Ashbourne, Derbyshire DE6 1RA*

NEW **Tyrell Hayes, Radbourne** ♿✂ (Guy & Jean Magnus) *[OS 2704 3501 'Terrel Hays']. Take A52 from Derby towards Ashbourne. In 1m turn L signposted Radbourne, 4th L still signposted Radbourne. At X-rds in 3m 1st property on R.* A delightful Georgian farmhouse (not open) surrounded on all 4 sides by 3 acres of formal and mature gardens. Fish pond with fountains and a fine collection of fir trees and conifers. Extensive shrubs and perennial borders, also rockeries and innovative hard landscaping. The whole garden surrounded by mature hedges. TEAS. *Adm £2 Chd free. Sun July 9 (2-5.30)*

100 Wellington Street, Matlock ❀ (Mrs Denise Marriott) *½m from Matlock town centre, take Bank Rd bear R at top, in 200yds car park on R.* This semi-walled, award winning, secret garden of approx 300sq yds overflows with many unusual plants and shrubs. Water features and subtle colour combinations are all designed to give a feeling of peace and tranquility. TEAS. *Adm £1.50 Chd free (ACNO to Waifs and Strays, Animal Rescue, Matlock). Suns May 21, June 25 (1-5). Private visits and group visits welcome, please* **Tel 01629 57290**

Wharfedale, Duffield ✂❀ (Mr & Mrs R D Roberts) *Turn on to B5023 Wirksworth Rd (Broadway) off A6 midway between Belper and Derby. No.34 350yds on R.* ⅓-acre plant enthusiasts' garden featuring over 500 varieties of choice and unusual shrubs, trees, perennials and bulbs. Themed borders incl hot, late summer tropical, Japanese, woodland and single colour schemes. Cottage garden to front. 5-yrs-old with new projects every year. TEAS. *Adm £1.50 Chd free. Sun July 16 (11-6).* **Evening Opening** *Wed June 28 (6-9.30) £4 Chd £1. Wine and cheese. Private visits from individuals and groups welcome from April 15 to October 15, please* **Tel 01332 841905**

NEW **26 Wheeldon Avenue, Derby** ♿ (Ian Griffiths) *1m from city centre and is approached directly off the Kedleston Rd or from A6 Duffield Rd via West Bank Ave.* Tiny Victorian walled garden near to the city centre. Lawn and herbaceous borders with old roses, lupins, delphiniums, foxgloves etc. Small terrace with topiary and herb garden. Limited on-street parking and possible timed tickets if unable to accommodate numbers due to limited size of garden. TEAS. *Adm £1 Chd 50p. Sun June 4 (2-5)*

White Gate, Arleston Meadows ✂❀ (Mrs Judy Beba-Thompson) *S of Derby. From A5132 at Barrow-upon-Trent take 'Sinfin' turn, 1m, L into Wragley Way, garden signed through cutting.* A delightful little romantic garden, colour-themed and scented, brimful with over 70 varieties of old and English rose and clematis, lilies, hardy geraniums, crocosmias, unusual perennials, climbers, foliage plants; lily pools and fountains; rose arch leads to serene white garden. Home made cream TEAS. *Adm £1.50 Acc chd free. Suns June 25, July 23, Aug 20 (1.30-5.30). Private visits and groups welcome by appt, please* **Tel 01332 763653**

NEW **35 Wyver Lane, Belper** ❀ (Jim & Brenda Stannering) *A6 from Derby through Belper to traffic lights at triangle. Turn L A517 to Ashbourne, over river bridge 1st R onto Wyver Lane. Parking in River Gardens, entrance on A6.* Cottage garden of approx 500 sq m on the side of the R Derwent opp to Belper River Gardens. Full of hardy perennial plants with pergola, troughs, greenhouse, small pond. TEAS. *Adm £1 Chd free. Suns April 30, June 4 (2-5). Private visits welcome April to Sept, please* **Tel 01773 824280**

Yew Tree Bungalow, Tansley ✂❀ (Jayne Conquest) *Thatchers Lane. 2m E of Matlock on A615, 2nd R after Tavern at Tansley.* ½-acre informal plantswoman's garden, with a wide range of herbaceous plants and shrubs, many rare and unusual incl hardy geraniums, penstemons, campanulas and variegated foliage plants. Vegetable and herb gardens. TEA. *Adm £1 Chd free (ACNO to Friends of Whitworth Hospital). Suns June 4, 25, July 23 (2-5.30)*

Yew Tree Farm, Tansley ✂❀ (Mrs Avril Buckley) *2m E of Matlock on A615, 2nd R after 'Tavern at Tansley'.* 1-acre country garden with stream-fed pond and terrace area. Stocked with hostas, ferns, astilbes, roses, topiary. Ornamental and productive kitchen garden. Orchard with free-range poultry. Garden 'rooms' of herbaceous perennials, dappled shady area with a woodland feel, and gold and purple themed shrubbery. TEAS. *Adm £1.50 Chd free. Sun July 9 (1.30-5). Group private visits by appt, please* **Tel 01629 57493**

Evening Opening (See also garden description)

Wharfedale, Duffield	June 28

Devon

Hon County Organisers: Michael & Sarah Stone, The Cider House, Buckland Abbey, Yelverton PL20 6EZ Tel 01822 853285

Assistant County Organisers:

North Devon Mr Mervyn T Feesey, Woodside, Higher Raleigh Road, Barnstaple EX31 4JA Tel 01271 343095

East Devon Mrs Ruth Charter, Ravenhill, Long Dogs Lane, Ottery St Mary EX11 1HX Tel 01404 814798

North-East Devon Mrs Diane Rowe, Little Southey, Northcott, Cullompton EX15 3LT Tel 01884 840545

Central Devon Mrs Miranda Allhusen, Sutton Mead, Moretonhampstead, Newton Abbot TQ13 8PW Tel 01647 440296

Torbay and Dartmouth Mrs Juliet Sutton-Scott-Tucker, Riversbridge, Dartmouth TQ6 0LG Tel 01803 770372

South Devon Mrs Sheila Blake, Higher Homefield, Sherford, Kingsbridge TQ7 2AT Tel 01548 531229

South-West Devon Mrs Shirin Court, Westpark, Yealmpton, Plymouth PL8 2HP Tel 01752 880236

Exeter Dr & Mrs John Lloyd, Little Cumbre, 145 Pennsylvania Road, Exeter EX4 6OZ Tel 01392 258315

Hon Treasurer: Mrs Julia Tremlett, Bickham House, Kenn, Nr Exeter EX6 7XL Tel 01392 832671

DATES OF OPENING

Regular openings

For details see garden description

Avenue Cottage, Ashprington
Bickham House, Kenn
Broad Oak Nurseries, Kenton
Burrow Farm Garden, Dalwood
Docton Mill and Garden, Lymebridge
The Downes, Monkleigh
Fast Rabbit Farm, Ash Cross
The Garden House, Buckland Monachorum
Hill House Nursery & Garden, Lanscove
Lewtrenchard Manor, Lewdown
Lukesland, Ivybridge
Marwood Hill, Marwood
Plant World, Newton Abbot
Rosemoor Garden, Great Torrington
Rowden Gardens, Brentor
Sherwood, Newton St Cyres
Tapeley Park, Instow
The Water Garden, Wembworthy
Yonder Hill, Colaton Raleigh

By appointment only

For telephone numbers and other details see garden descriptions. Private visits welcomed

Barton House, Nymet Rowland
Emmerford Cottage, Tiverton
The Gate House, Lee
Lee Ford, Budleigh Salterton
Longham, Coryton
The Moorings, Rocombe
The Old Rectory, Woodleigh
Orchard Cottage, Exmouth
Southcombe House, Widecombe-in-the-Moor
Spillifords, Lower Washfield

February 27 Sunday
Fast Rabbit Farm, Ash Cross
Yonder Hill, Colaton Raleigh

March 5 Sunday
Fast Rabbit Farm, Ash Cross
The Pines, Salcombe

March 6 Monday
Dippers, Shaugh Prior
Docton Mill and Garden, Lymebridge

March 12 Sunday
Fast Rabbit Farm, Ash Cross
Greenlands
Yonder Hill, Colaton Raleigh

March 13 Monday
Dippers, Shaugh Prior
Yonder Hill, Colaton Raleigh

March 19 Sunday
Bickham House, Kenn
Fast Rabbit Farm, Ash Cross
The Pines, Salcombe
Wood Barton, Kentisbeare

March 20 Monday
Dippers, Shaugh Prior

March 21 to 22 Tuesday to Wednesday
Bickham House, Kenn

March 23 Thursday
Greenway Gardens, Churston Ferrers

March 26 Sunday
Broad Oak Nurseries, Kenton
Fast Rabbit Farm, Ash Cross
Gorwell House, Barnstaple
Higher Knowle, Lustleigh
Westpark, Yealmpton
Yonder Hill, Colaton Raleigh

March 27 Monday
Dippers, Shaugh Prior
Yonder Hill, Colaton Raleigh

March 29 Wednesday
38 Phillipps Avenue, Exmouth
Westpark, Yealmpton

March 30 Thursday
Greenway Gardens, Churston Ferrers

April 2 Sunday
Bicton College of Agriculture, East Budleigh
Fast Rabbit Farm, Ash Cross
Higher Knowle, Lustleigh
The Pines, Salcombe

April 3 Monday
Docton Mill and Garden, Lymebridge

April 5 Wednesday
38 Phillipps Avenue, Exmouth

April 9 Sunday
Fast Rabbit Farm, Ash Cross
Higher Knowle, Lustleigh
Meadowcroft, Plympton
Saltram House, Plympton

Yonder Hill, Colaton Raleigh

April 10 Monday
Yonder Hill, Colaton Raleigh

April 12 Wednesday
Greenlands
38 Phillipps Avenue, Exmouth

April 15 Saturday
Shobrooke Park Gardens, Crediton

April 16 Sunday
Bickham House, Kenn
Coleton Fishacre, nr Kingswear
Dippers, Shaugh Prior
Fast Rabbit Farm, Ash Cross
Gorwell House, Barnstaple
Greenlands
Hartland Abbey, Hartland
Higher Knowle, Lustleigh
Killerton Garden, Broadclyst
Rock House Garden, Chudleigh
Wrangaton House, Wrangaton

April 18 to 19 Tuesday to Wednesday
Bickham House, Kenn

April 21 Friday
Membland Villa, Newton Ferrers (evening)
Yonder Hill, Colaton Raleigh

April 22 Saturday
Yonder Hill, Colaton Raleigh

April 23 Sunday
Andrew's Corner, Belstone
Fast Rabbit Farm, Ash Cross
Higher Knowle, Lustleigh
Yonder Hill, Colaton Raleigh

April 24 Monday
1 Feebers Cottage, Westwood
Higher Knowle, Lustleigh
Lower Coombe Farm, Brithem Bottom
Yonder Hill, Colaton Raleigh

April 26 Wednesday
38 Phillipps Avenue, Exmouth
St Olaves, Murchington

April 29 Saturday
Cleave House, Sticklepath
Haldon Grange, Dunchideock
Mothecombe House, Holbeton
The Old Rectory, East Portlemouth

April 30 Sunday
Andrew's Corner, Belstone
Bundels, Sidbury
Castle Drogo, Drewsteignton
Cleave House, Sticklepath
Fast Rabbit Farm, Ash Cross
Haldon Grange, Dunchideock
Hamblyn's Coombe, Dittisham
Hartland Abbey, Hartland
Higher Knowle, Lustleigh
Knightshayes Gardens, Tiverton
Meadowcroft, Plympton
Membland Villa, Newton Ferrers
Mothecombe House, Holbeton
The Old Rectory, East Portlemouth
Starveacre, Dalwood
Westcott Barton, Barnstaple
Wrangaton House, Wrangaton
Yonder Hill, Colaton Raleigh

May 1 Monday
Docton Mill and Garden, Lymebridge
Haldon Grange, Dunchideock
Hamblyn's Coombe, Dittisham
Higher Knowle, Lustleigh
The Old Rectory, East Portlemouth
Westcott Barton, Barnstaple
Wrangaton House, Wrangaton
Yonder Hill, Colaton Raleigh

May 3 Wednesday
Greenlands
Lukesland, Ivybridge
38 Phillipps Avenue, Exmouth
Pleasant View Nursery, Two Mile Oak

May 4 Thursday
Little Cumbre, Exeter

May 5 Friday
Pleasant View Nursery, Two Mile Oak

May 6 Saturday
Dicot, Chardstock
The Water Garden, Wembworthy

May 7 Sunday
Arlington Court, Arlington
Broad Oak Nurseries, Kenton
Broadhembury House, Broadhembury
Dicot, Chardstock
Fast Rabbit Farm, Ash Cross
Greenlands
Half Moon House, Manaton
Higher Knowle, Lustleigh
Honeyway Farm, Dunsford
The Lodge, Mannamead
Lukesland, Ivybridge
Manaton Gate, Newton Abbot
Saltram House, Plympton
Sowton Mill, Dunsford
The Water Garden, Wembworthy

May 10 Wednesday
38 Phillipps Avenue, Exmouth
St Olaves, Murchington

May 11 Thursday
Meadowcroft, Plympton

May 13 Saturday
Bicton College of Agriculture, East Budleigh
Dartington Hall Gardens, Dartington
The Old Glebe, Eggesford
Shobrooke Park Gardens, Crediton
Withleigh Farm, Withleigh Village
Wolford Lodge, Dunkeswell

May 14 Sunday
Andrew's Corner, Belstone
Broadhembury House, Broadhembury
Coleton Fishacre, nr Kingswear
Dartington Hall Gardens, Dartington
Fast Rabbit Farm, Ash Cross
1 Feebers Cottage, Westwood
Gorwell House, Barnstaple
Higher Knowle, Lustleigh
Moretonhampstead Gardens
The Old Glebe, Eggesford
Sunnybrook Cottage, Luffincott
Withleigh Farm, Withleigh Village
Wolford Lodge, Dunkeswell
Wood Barton, Kentisbeare
Wylmington Hayes, Wilmington
Yonder Hill, Colaton Raleigh

May 15 Monday
Yonder Hill, Colaton Raleigh

May 17 Wednesday
38 Phillipps Avenue, Exmouth

May 20 Saturday
Pikes Cottage, Madford, Hemyock
Wolford Lodge, Dunkeswell

May 21 Sunday
Bickham House, Kenn
Broadhembury House, Broadhembury
The Cider House, Buckland Abbey
Dippers, Shaugh Prior
Fast Rabbit Farm, Ash Cross
Higher Knowle, Lustleigh
Inglewood, Newton Ferrers
The Old Mill, Blakewell
Overbecks, Sharpitor
Penrose, Crediton
Pikes Cottage, Madford, Hemyock
Wylmington Hayes, Wilmington

May 22 Monday
Fardel Manor, Ivybridge

May 23 to 24 Tuesday to Wednesday
Bickham House, Kenn

May 24 Wednesday
38 Phillipps Avenue, Exmouth

May 26 Friday
Sidmouth Gardens

May 27 Saturday
Monks Aish, South Brent
Sidmouth Gardens
The Water Garden, Wembworthy

May 28 Sunday
Andrew's Corner, Belstone
Bundels, Sidbury
Fast Rabbit Farm, Ash Cross
1 Feebers Cottage, Westwood
Higher Knowle, Lustleigh
Higher Watertown, Nr South Molton

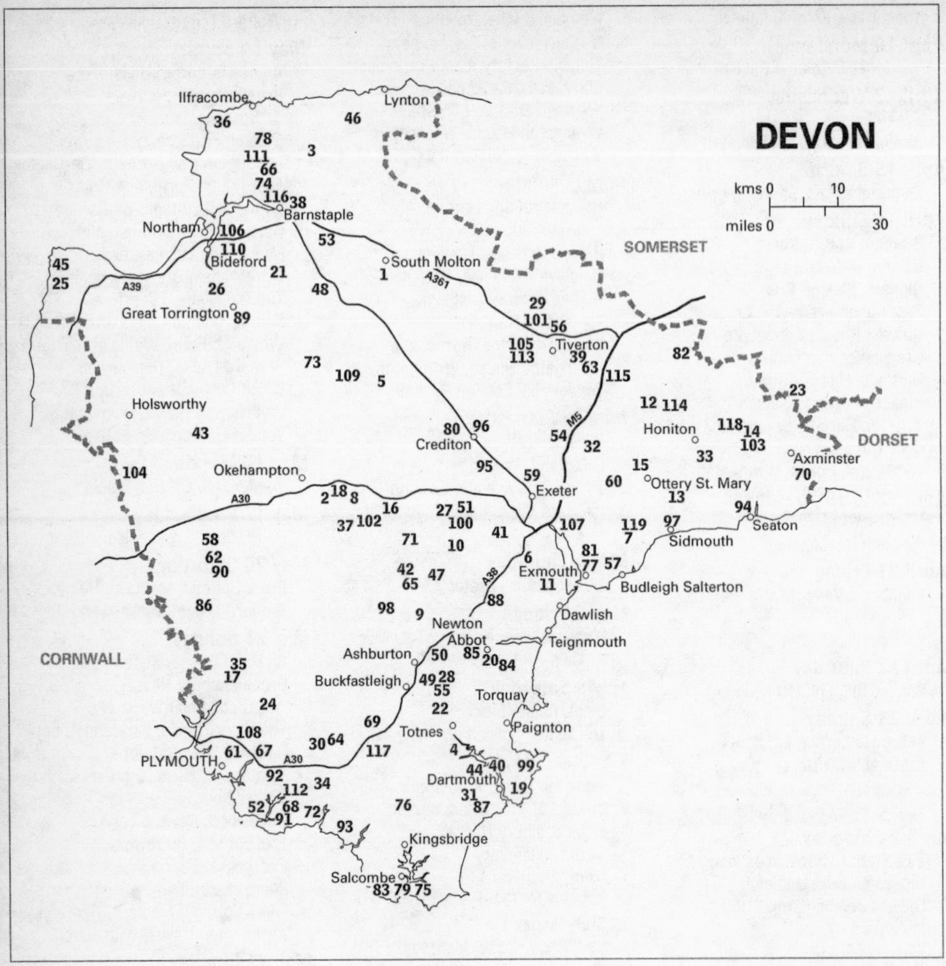

KEY

1 Alswood
2 Andrew's Corner
3 Arlington Court
4 Avenue Cottage
5 Barton House
6 Bickham House
7 Bicton College of Agriculture
8 Blackhall Manor
9 Bovey Tracey Gardens
10 Bridford Gardens
11 Broad Oak Nurseries
12 Broadhembury House
13 Bundels
14 Burrow Farm Garden
15 Cadhay
16 Castle Drogo
17 The Cider House
18 Cleave House
19 Coleton Fishacre
20 Collepardo
21 The Croft
22 Dartington Hall Gardens
23 Dicot
24 Dippers
25 Docton Mill and Garden
26 The Downes
27 Dunsford Gardens
28 Elmpark
29 Emmerford Cottage
30 Fardel Manor
31 Fast Rabbit Farm
32 1 Feebers Cottage
33 Feniton & Fenny Bridges Gardens
34 Flete
35 The Garden House
36 The Gate House
37 Gidleigh Gardens
38 Gorwell House
39 Greenlands
40 Greenway Gardens
41 Haldon Grange
42 Half Moon House
43 Halwill Gardens
44 Hamblyn's Coombe
45 Hartland Abbey
46 Heddon Hall
47 Higher Knowle
48 Higher Watertown
49 Hill House Nursery & Garden
50 Hole Farm
51 Honeyway Farm
52 Inglewood
53 Kerscott House
54 Killerton Garden
55 Kingston House
56 Knightshayes Gardens

57 Lee Ford
58 Lewtrenchard Manor
59 Little Cumbre
60 Little Upcott Gardens
61 The Lodge
62 Longham
63 Lower Coombe Farm
64 Lukesland
65 Manaton Gate
66 Marwood Hill
67 Meadowcroft
68 Membland Villa
69 Monks Aish
70 The Moorings
71 Moretonhampstead Gardens
72 Mothecombe House
73 The Old Glebe, Eggesford
74 The Old Mill, Blakewell
75 The Old Rectory, East Portlemouth
76 The Old Rectory, Woodleigh
77 Orchard Cottage
78 Outer Narracott
79 Overbecks
80 Penrose
81 38 Phillipps Avenue
82 Pikes Cottage
83 The Pines
84 Plant World
85 Pleasant View Nursery
86 Portington
87 Riversbridge
88 Rock House Garden
89 Rosemoor Garden
90 Rowden Gardens
91 Rowden House
92 Saltram House
93 Scypen
94 Seaton & Colyford Gardens
95 Sherwood
96 Shobrooke Park Gardens
97 Sidmouth Gardens
98 Southcombe House
99 Southdown Farm
100 Sowton Mill
101 Spillifords
102 St Olaves
103 Starveacre
104 Sunnybrook Cottage
105 Sunrise Hill
106 Tapeley Park
107 Topsham Gardens
108 96 Wasdale Gardens
109 The Water Garden
110 Webbery Gardens
111 Westcott Barton
112 Westpark
113 Withleigh Farm
114 Wolford Lodge
115 Wood Barton
116 Woodside
117 Wrangaton House
118 Wylmington Hayes
119 Yonder Hill

Lower Coombe Farm, Brithem Bottom
Membland Villa, Newton Ferrers
Monks Aish, South Brent
Moretonhampstead Gardens
The Old Glebe, Eggesford
The Pines, Salcombe
Rock House Garden, Chudleigh
Starveacre, Dalwood
Sunnybrook Cottage, Luffincott
Topsham Gardens
The Water Garden, Wembworthy
Westcott Barton, Barnstaple
Wylmington Hayes, Wilmington
Yonder Hill, Colaton Raleigh

May 29 Monday
Alswood, George Nympton
Bicton College of Agriculture, East Budleigh
Higher Knowle, Lustleigh
Higher Watertown, Nr South Molton
Moretonhampstead Gardens
The Old Glebe, Eggesford
The Old Rectory, East Portlemouth
Topsham Gardens
Westcott Barton, Barnstaple
Yonder Hill, Colaton Raleigh

May 31 Wednesday
Greenlands

June 3 Saturday
Bovey Tracey Gardens
The Water Garden, Wembworthy

June 4 Sunday
Andrew's Corner, Belstone
Bovey Tracey Gardens
Bridford Gardens
Fast Rabbit Farm, Ash Cross
Greenlands
Kingston House, Staverton
Little Upcott Gardens, Marsh Green
Meadowcroft, Plympton
Rowden House, Noss Mayo
The Water Garden, Wembworthy
Wylmington Hayes, Wilmington

June 5 Monday
Docton Mill and Garden, Lymebridge

June 7 Wednesday
Bicton College of Agriculture, East Budleigh
Pleasant View Nursery, Two Mile Oak

June 8 Thursday
Little Cumbre, Exeter

June 9 Friday
Pleasant View Nursery, Two Mile Oak

June 10 Saturday
Shobrooke Park Gardens, Crediton

June 11 Sunday
Andrew's Corner, Belstone
Castle Drogo, Drewsteignton
The Croft, Yarnscombe
Fast Rabbit Farm, Ash Cross
Gorwell House, Barnstaple
The Lodge, Mannamead
Rowden Gardens, Brentor
Sunnybrook Cottage, Luffincott
Yonder Hill, Colaton Raleigh

June 12 Monday
Rowden Gardens, Brentor
Yonder Hill, Colaton Raleigh

June 14 Wednesday
Scypen, Ringmore

June 17 Saturday
Bicton College of Agriculture, East Budleigh
Bundels, Sidbury
Collepardo, 3, Keyberry Park, Newton Abbot
Flete, Ermington, Ivybridge
Southdown Farm, Brixham
Webbery Gardens, Alverdiscott

June 18 Sunday
Bickham House, Kenn
Bundels, Sidbury
Collepardo, 3, Keyberry Park, Newton Abbot
Dippers, Shaugh Prior
Fast Rabbit Farm, Ash Cross
1 Feebers Cottage, Westwood
Membland Villa, Newton Ferrers
Mothecombe House, Holbeton
Overbecks, Sharpitor
Penrose, Crediton
Riversbridge, Dartmouth
Scypen, Ringmore
Southdown Farm, Brixham
Webbery Gardens, Alverdiscott
Yonder Hill, Colaton Raleigh

June 19 Monday
Yonder Hill, Colaton Raleigh

June 20 to 21 Tuesday to Wednesday
Bickham House, Kenn

June 21 Wednesday
Bundels, Sidbury
Cleave House, Sticklepath
Collepardo, 3, Keyberry Park, Newton Abbot
Greenlands (evening)
38 Phillipps Avenue, Exmouth

June 24 Saturday
Bundels, Sidbury
Cleave House, Sticklepath
Collepardo, 3, Keyberry Park, Newton Abbot
Dunsford Gardens, Dunsford
Elmpark, Broadhempston
Higher Watertown, Nr South Molton
The Water Garden, Wembworthy

June 25 Sunday
Alswood, George Nympton
Bundels, Sidbury
Cadhay, Ottery St Mary
The Cider House, Buckland Abbey
Cleave House, Sticklepath
Collepardo, 3, Keyberry Park, Newton Abbot
The Croft, Yarnscombe
Dunsford Gardens, Dunsford
Elmpark, Broadhempston
Fast Rabbit Farm, Ash Cross
1 Feebers Cottage, Westwood
Greenlands
Half Moon House, Manaton
Higher Watertown, Nr South Molton
Kerscott House, Swimbridge
Kingston House, Staverton
Knightshayes Gardens, Tiverton
Lower Coombe Farm, Brithem Bottom
Riversbridge, Dartmouth
Rock House Garden, Chudleigh
Rowden Gardens, Brentor
Sunnybrook Cottage, Luffincott
The Water Garden, Wembworthy
Westcott Barton, Barnstaple

June 26 Monday
Rowden Gardens, Brentor
Westcott Barton, Barnstaple

June 28 Wednesday
Bicton College of Agriculture, East Budleigh
Sunrise Hill, Withleigh

July 2 Sunday
Arlington Court, Arlington
Blackhall Manor, South Tawton
Cadhay, Ottery St Mary
Killerton Garden, Broadclyst
Rowden Gardens, Brentor

July 3 Monday
Docton Mill and Garden, Lymebridge
Rowden Gardens, Brentor

July 5 Wednesday
Pleasant View Nursery, Two Mile Oak

July 7 Friday
Pleasant View Nursery, Two Mile Oak

July 8 Saturday
Gidleigh Gardens

July 9 Sunday
The Croft, Yarnscombe
Fast Rabbit Farm, Ash Cross
Gidleigh Gardens
Heddon Hall, Parracombe
Honeyway Farm, Dunsford
Portington, Lamerton
Seaton & Colyford Gardens
Sowton Mill, Dunsford
Woodside, Barnstaple
Yonder Hill, Colaton Raleigh

July 10 Monday
Yonder Hill, Colaton Raleigh

July 12 Wednesday
The Garden House, Buckland Monachorum

July 15 Saturday
Bicton College of Agriculture, East Budleigh

July 16 Sunday
Bickham House, Kenn
Blackhall Manor, South Tawton
Feniton & Fenny Bridges Gardens, Honiton
Gorwell House, Barnstaple
Greenlands
Kingston House, Staverton
The Lodge, Mannamead
Membland Villa, Newton Ferrers
Outer Narracott, Bittadon
Portington, Lamerton
Seaton & Colyford Gardens

July 18 to 19 Tuesday to Wednesday
Bickham House, Kenn

July 19 Wednesday
Greenlands
The Old Mill, Blakewell
Sunrise Hill, Withleigh

July 23 Sunday
The Croft, Yarnscombe
Fast Rabbit Farm, Ash Cross
The Old Mill, Blakewell
Rock House Garden, Chudleigh
Yonder Hill, Colaton Raleigh

July 24 Monday
Fardel Manor, Ivybridge
Yonder Hill, Colaton Raleigh

July 29 Saturday
Dicot, Chardstock
Halwill Gardens, Beaworthy
Higher Watertown, Nr South Molton

July 30 Sunday
Alswood, George Nympton
Broad Oak Nurseries, Kenton
Dicot, Chardstock
Halwill Gardens, Beaworthy
Higher Watertown, Nr South Molton
Hole Farm, Farlacombe
Kerscott House, Swimbridge
Sunnybrook Cottage, Luffincott
96 Wasdale Gardens, Estover, Plymouth
Westcott Barton, Barnstaple
Yonder Hill, Colaton Raleigh

July 31 Monday
Westcott Barton, Barnstaple
Yonder Hill, Colaton Raleigh

August 2 Wednesday
Pleasant View Nursery, Two Mile Oak
96 Wasdale Gardens, Estover, Plymouth

August 4 Friday
Pleasant View Nursery, Two Mile Oak

August 6 Sunday
Bridford Gardens
Outer Narracott, Bittadon
Rowden House, Noss Mayo
96 Wasdale Gardens, Estover, Plymouth

August 7 Monday
Docton Mill and Garden, Lymebridge

August 9 Wednesday
Greenlands

August 13 Sunday
Greenlands
Rowden Gardens, Brentor
Yonder Hill, Colaton Raleigh

August 14 Monday
Rowden Gardens, Brentor
Yonder Hill, Colaton Raleigh

August 16 Wednesday
The Garden House, Buckland Monachorum
Sunrise Hill, Withleigh

August 19 Saturday
Flete, Ermington, Ivybridge

August 20 Sunday
Bickham House, Kenn
Fast Rabbit Farm, Ash Cross
Penrose, Crediton

August 22 to 23 Tuesday to Wednesday
Bickham House, Kenn

August 27 Sunday
Alswood, George Nympton
Higher Watertown, Nr South Molton
Kerscott House, Swimbridge

Membland Villa, Newton Ferrers
Sunnybrook Cottage, Luffincott
Westcott Barton, Barnstaple
Yonder Hill, Colaton Raleigh

August 28 Monday
Higher Watertown, Nr South Molton
Westcott Barton, Barnstaple
Yonder Hill, Colaton Raleigh

September 4 Monday
Docton Mill and Garden, Lymebridge

September 6 Wednesday
Pleasant View Nursery, Two Mile Oak

September 8 Friday
Pleasant View Nursery, Two Mile Oak

September 10 Sunday
Bickham House, Kenn
1 Feebers Cottage, Westwood
Gorwell House, Barnstaple
Greenlands
Lower Coombe Farm, Brithem Bottom
Rock House Garden, Chudleigh
Yonder Hill, Colaton Raleigh

September 11 Monday
Yonder Hill, Colaton Raleigh

September 12 to 13 Tuesday to Wednesday
Bickham House, Kenn

September 17 Sunday
Inglewood, Newton Ferrers
Rock House Garden, Chudleigh

September 24 Sunday
Fast Rabbit Farm, Ash Cross
1 Feebers Cottage, Westwood
Westcott Barton, Barnstaple
Yonder Hill, Colaton Raleigh

September 25 Monday
Westcott Barton, Barnstaple
Yonder Hill, Colaton Raleigh

October 1 Sunday
Yonder Hill, Colaton Raleigh

October 2 Monday
Docton Mill and Garden, Lymebridge
Yonder Hill, Colaton Raleigh

October 8 Sunday
Fast Rabbit Farm, Ash Cross
1 Feebers Cottage, Westwood
Gorwell House, Barnstaple

October 15 Sunday
Starveacre, Dalwood
Yonder Hill, Colaton Raleigh

October 16 Monday
Yonder Hill, Colaton Raleigh

October 22 Sunday
Fast Rabbit Farm, Ash Cross

October 29 Sunday
Rock House Garden, Chudleigh

2001

February 7 Wednesday
Little Cumbre, Exeter

February 14 Wednesday
Little Cumbre, Exeter

DESCRIPTIONS OF GARDENS

Alswood, George Nympton ♿✗❀ (Bob & Marjorie Radford) *2m S of S Molton, halfway between the villages of George Nympton and Alswear. Ample parking.* 2-acre developing garden, enthusiastically designed and maintained by owners; set in rural area, views of the Crooked Oak and Mole valleys are more than enough to merit a visit. Vast collection of unusual trees and shrubs. Well established spectacular herbaceous, erica and aquatic areas; pond and stream; unique architectural follies as featured in 'Devon Life' 1999. Plants and cream TEAS in aid of George Nympton Parish Church. *Adm £1.50 Chd free. Bank Hol Mon May 29, Suns June 25, July 30, Aug 27 (2-5.30)*

Andrew's Corner, Belstone ♿✗❀ (Robin and Edwina Hill) *3m E of Okehampton signed to Belstone. Parking restricted but cars may be left on nearby common.* Plantsman's garden 1,000' up on Dartmoor, overlooking Taw Valley; wide range of unusual trees, shrubs, herbaceous plants for yr-round effect incl alpines, rhododendrons, bulbs, dwarf conifers; well labelled. TEAS. *Adm £1.50 Chd free. Suns April 23 (Easter), 30, May 14, 28, June 4, 11 (2.30-6); also private visits welcome, please* **Tel 01837 840332**

▲ Arlington Court, Arlington ♿✗ (The National Trust) *Nr Barnstaple. 7m NE of Barnstaple on A39.* Rolling parkland and woods with lake. Rhododendrons and azaleas; fine specimen trees; small terraced Victorian garden with herbaceous borders and conservatory. Regency house containing fascinating collections of objets d'art. Carriage collection in the stables, carriage rides. Restaurant. *Adm garden only £3.30 Chd £1.65. For NGS Suns May 7, July 2 (11-5.30)*

Avenue Cottage, Ashprington ♿ (Mr R J Pitts & Mr C H Soans) *A381 from Totnes to Kingsbridge. 3m SE Totnes, from centre of village uphill past church for 400yds, drive on R.* 11 acres of garden with woodland. Part of listed C18 landscape. Secluded valley site undergoing re-creation. Large collection of young and mature plants. Guided tours and tea by prior arrangement. *Adm £2 Chd 25p. Collecting box. Tues to Sats April 4 to Sept 30 (11-5). Private visits also welcome, please* **Tel 01803 732769** No coaches

Barton House, Nymet Rowland ✗ (Mr & Mrs A T Littlewood) *9m NW of Crediton. Follow signs to Nymet Rowland from A377 at Lapford or B3220 at Aller Bridge. Garden opposite Norman and C15 church.* 1-acre garden designed and maintained by owners. Beautiful views to Dartmoor. Individual areas developed with varied character. Herbs, pond, herbaceous, yew garden, ferns, grotto, roses and fountain pool. *Adm £2 Chd 50p. By appointment only June and July, please* **Tel 01363 83534**

Bickham House, Kenn ♿✗❀ (Mr & Mrs John Tremlett) *6m W of Exeter, 1m off A38. Leave dual carriageway at Kennford Services, follow signs to Kenn. 1st R in village, follow lane for ¾m to end of no-through rd.* 5 acres in peaceful wooded valley. Lawns, mature trees and shrubs; naturalised bulbs, mixed borders. Conservatory, small parterre, pond garden; 1-acre walled kitchen garden; lake. Cream TEAS. *Adm £2 Chd 50p. Suns, Tues, Weds March 19, 21, 22, April 16, 18, 19, May 21, 23, 24, June 18, 20, 21, July 16, 18, 19, Aug 20, 22, 23, Sept 10, 12, 13 (11-5). Private visits welcome by appt, please* **Tel 01392 832671**

● Bicton College of Agriculture, East Budleigh ♿✗❀ *Use Sidmouth Lodge entrance, ½ way between Budleigh Salterton and Newton Poppleford on B3178.* Renowned monkey puzzle avenue; walled garden; glasshouses. Rich variety of plants in beds and borders, laid out for teaching and effect. National Collections of agapanthus and pittosporum; ½m arboretum with magnolias, cherries and camellias. TEAS. *Adm £2 Chd free (ACNO to Bicton Overseas Agricultural Trust). Sun April 2 (Mothering Sun), Sats May 13, June 17, July 15; Bank Hol Mon May 29; Weds June 7, 28 (10-4.30). Gardens also open daily throughout year, except Christmas Day and Good Friday. Closed weekends Nov-March. Groups welcome, please* **Tel 01395 562400**

Blackhall Manor, South Tawton ✂❀ (Roger & Jacqueline Yeates) *6m E of Okehampton. Leave A30 at either Whiddon Down or Okehampton signed Sticklepath for 4m. South Tawton 2m N of Sticklepath. Parking in village square. Walk through churchyard into garden.* Small cottage garden around C16 thatched listed former farmhouse (not open). *Adm £1.50 Chd 50p. Suns July 2, 16 (2-6). Private visits welcome, please* **Tel 01837 840171**

Bovey Tracey Gardens *Gateway to Dartmoor. On A382 midway between Newton Abbot and Moretonhampstead.* TEAS. *Combined adm £2.50 Sat, Sun June 3, 4 (2-6)*

Bibbery ❀ (The Misses E & A Hebditch) *Higher Bibbery. B3344 to Chudleigh Knighton. Cul-de-sac behind Coombe Cross Hotel.* Plantspersons' small garden, sheltered corners harbouring interesting shrubs and tender plants. TEAS. *Also private visits April-June welcome, please* **Tel 01626 833344**

Church View ❀ (Mr & Mrs L Humphreys) *East Street. B3344 opp St Peter & St Paul's Church.* Small garden, but many unusual plants, incl secluded vegetable area. Disabled parking

2 Devon House Drive ❀ (Mr & Mrs L Miskin) *Near entrance to Coombe Cross Hotel, few yds beyond Higher Bibbery.* Interesting variety of roses. Herbaceous borders with contrasting colours and shapes. Interested in organic and companion planting. Fruit trees, herbs and vegetable areas

Pineholm ❀ (Dr & Mrs A A Baker) *High Close. B3344 to Chudleigh Knighton, 1st L past Coombe Cross Hotel.* Terraced garden on sloping site. Wide variety of fruit incl many figs, grapes and citrus. Greenhouses and polytunnel.

Sunnyside (Mr & Mrs J D Green) *Hind Street. Nr town centre off A382. Opp Baptist Church. Parking nearby.* Well established enclosed garden; trees and shrubs; herbaceous and colourful conservatory; productive vegetable area

Thuja ❀ (Mr & Mrs J F Bowman) *Hind Street.* Small enclosed garden with spot planting in chippings

Towns End Cottage (Mr & Mrs S Penney) *Newton Road opp The Dartmoor Inn. Large public car park nearby.* C18 cottage (not open) and gardens completely derelict 7yrs ago. Front garden and developing rear garden. Herbaceous border, pond, shrubs and mature fruit trees

Bridford Gardens ✂❀ *11m from Exeter on Moretonhampstead rd. L at Nogsland Farm then L over bridge into Teign Valley Road; R after Venn Park Garage; up Bridford Hill to village; L beside chapel, down hill 100yds; R at fork, signed Hennock. Garden 1m on R. Access and car park at Middle Hole Farm. Footpath (not suitable for disabled persons) leading to Lower Hole Farm.* Cream TEAS. *£3 Chd free. Sun June 4, Aug 6(2-6)*

Lower Hole Farm ❀ (Ted & Annette Clapton) 6 acres sloping land facing N with views across Bridford and Teign Valley

Middle Hole Farm ❀ (Mr & Mrs B C McMillan) 2½ acre cottage garden with variety of old and new herbaceous plants, many unusual varieties, ornamental grasses. Bog garden with stream and 3 ponds. Laburnum walk. Rhododendron bank with pieris and acers. Rockery, orchard with bulbs. Walled garden, raised patios, heather bank, vegetable garden. Nursery garden

NEW **Broad Oak Nurseries, Kenton** ♿✂❀ (Eileen Bevington Smith) *From Exeter go W on A38/380 towards Torquay. At top of Haldon Hill turn L, signed Mamhead. Proceed 3¾m towards Starcross. Turn R into Mowlish Lane, nursery 100yds.* 10 acres of grounds with 2 acres under development for showing and trials. Unusual trees and shrubs, grasses, spring bulbs, eucalyptus copse, iris garden, water garden, rockery. TEAS. *£1.50 Chd free. Open all year Wed-Sun (10-4) Donations. For NGS Suns March 26, May 7, July 30 (2-5).*

Broadhembury House, Broadhembury ❀ (Mr & Mrs W Drewe) *5m equidistant on A373 Honiton to Cullompton rd, signed, Broadhembury.* 2-acre informal garden in C16 picturesque thatched village. Spring garden with rhododendrons and azaleas, daffodils and bluebells. Ample parking in village square. TEAS. *Adm £1.50 Chd 50p. Suns May 7, 14, 21 (2-5)*

Bundels, Sidbury ♿❀ (Alan & Barbara Softly) *Ridgway. From Sidmouth B3175 turn L at free car park in Sidbury. From Honiton A375, turn R. Garden 100yds up Ridgway on L.* 1½ acre organic garden incl small wood and ponds set round C16 thatched cottage (not open); over 100 varieties of old-fashioned and other shrub roses. Typical cottage garden with accent on preservation of wildlife. Dogs on lead. Gift stall. As seen on TV. *Adm £1.50 Acc chd free. Suns April 30, May 28, Sats, Suns June 17, 18, 24, 25, Weds June 21 (2-5.30)* **Tel 01395 597312**

● **Burrow Farm Garden, Dalwood** ♿❀ (Mary & John Benger) *Between Axminster and Honiton. From A35 3½m W of Axminster turn N at Taunton X then keep L towards Stockland, garden ½m on R.* Secluded 6-acre garden of informal design with many unusual shrubs and herbaceous plants. Pergola walk with shrub roses. Woodland with rhododendrons and azaleas, ponds and large bog garden. Terraced courtyard featuring later flowering plants. New for 2000, rill garden with water feature. Traditional stone summerhouse and informal planting all with wonderful views. Coffee, light lunches, cream TEAS. *Adm £3 Chd 50p. April 1 to Sept 30 daily (10-7)*

Cadhay, Ottery St Mary ♿❀ (Oliver William-Powlett) *1m NW of Ottery St. Mary on B3176. Ample parking.* Tranquil 2-acre garden in lovely setting between the Elizabethan Manor House (not open) and ancient stew ponds. Carefully planned double herbaceous borders particularly colourful in summer. Small part-walled water garden, roses and clematis. *Adm £1.50 Chd 50p Suns June 25, July 2 (2-5)*

▲ Castle Drogo, Drewsteignton ♿✂❀ (The National Trust) *W of Exeter, S of A30.* Medium-sized garden with formal beds and herbaceous borders; shrubs, woodland walk overlooking Fingle Gorge. Wheelchair available. Plant centre. Restaurant. Tea room. *Adm gardens only £2.60 Chd £1.30. For NGS Suns April 30, June 11 (10.30-5.30)*

The Cider House, Buckland Abbey ♿✂❀ (Mr & Mrs M J Stone) *Yelverton. From A386 Plymouth to Tavistock rd, follow NT signs to Buckland Abbey. At Xrds before Abbey entrance turn N signed Buckland Monachorum. Drive 200yds on L, or short walk for visitors to Abbey.* 3 acre garden in very peaceful surroundings looking down to Tavy valley, part of former Cistercian monastery. Terrace gardens complement the mediaeval house (not open), herb garden, woodland and herbaceous borders, wild garden with rhododendrons, camellias and other shrubs. Former walled kitchen garden productively maintained to give abundance of fruit, vegetables and flowers. Cream TEAS. *Adm £2 Chd 50p. Suns May 21, June 25 (2-6). Parties, incl evening visits, welcomed by prior arrangement*

Cleave House, Sticklepath ♿✂❀ (Ann & Roger Bowden) *3½m E of Okehampton on old A30 towards Exeter. Cleave House on L in village, on main rd just past R turn for Skaigh.* ½ acre garden with mixed planting for all season interest. National Collection of hostas with 750 varieties, 300 of these are for sale. Partially suitable for wheelchairs. *Adm £1.50 Chd free (ACNO to NCCPG). Sat, Sun April 29, 30, June 24, 25, Wed June 21(10.30-5). Private visits also welcome April to Oct, please* **Tel 01837 840481**

▲ Coleton Fishacre, nr Kingswear ✂❀ (The National Trust) *2m NE of Kingswear.* 8-ha garden created by Rupert and Lady Dorothy D'Oyly Carte between 1925 and 1948. Re-established and developed by NT since 1983. Wide range of tender and uncommon trees and shrubs in spectacular coastal setting. Refreshments and light lunches. *Adm £3.70 Chd £1.85. For NGS Suns April 16, May 14 (10.30-5.30)*

Collepardo, 3, Keyberry Park, Newton Abbot ✂ (Betty & Don Frampton) *Take A380 for Newton Abbot. From Penn Inn roundabout follow sign for town centre. Take 1st L, 1st R, 2nd L. (½m from Newton Abbot railway stn).* ¼ acre town garden completely redesigned as a grass-free garden for the plantsperson. The garden is laid out in series of interlinked small areas to give emphasis on colour and form. Includes 60′ semi-circular rockery, many unusual herbaceous perennials, pond and walkway. TEAS. *Adm £1.50 Chd free. Sats, Suns June 17, 18, 24, 25, Wed June 21 (2-6)*

The Croft, Yarnscombe ♿✂❀ (Sam & Margaret Jewell) *From A377, 5m S of Barnstaple turning W opp Chapelton railway stn. After 3m drive on L at village sign. From B3232, ¼m N of Hunshaw TV mast Xrds, turn E for 2m.* 1-acre plantswoman's garden on edge of village with unspoilt distant views. Creating Japanese garden area. Also wide selection of unusual plants and shrubs. Island beds, much herbaceous material, ponds and bog area. No toilets. Cream TEAS (Suns if fine). *Adm £1.50 Chd free. Jun 11-25, July 9-23 (2-6)*

▲ Dartington Hall Gardens, Dartington ♿✂ (Dartington Hall Trust) *Approx 1½m NW of Totnes. From Totnes take A384, turn R at Dartington Parish Church.* 28-acre modern garden, created since 1925 around C14 mediaeval hall (not open). Courtyard and tournament ground. Recent additions incl dry landscape Japanese garden. Extensive wildflower meadows and new mixed shrub and herbaceous border. *Adm (donation) £2 per person. For NGS Sat, Sun May 13, 14 (dawn to dusk)*

Dicot, Chardstock ✂❀ (Mr & Mrs F Clarkson) *Axminster to Chard A358 at Tytherleigh to Chardstock. R at George Inn, L fork to Hook, R to Burridge, 2nd house on L.* 3-acre enthusiasts' garden, trees, unusual shrubs and conifers, bog orchids in June. Stream, mixed borders, fish pool, features. TEAS. *Adm £1.50 Chd 75p. Sats, Suns May 6, 7 July 29, 30 (2-5.30). Private visits also welcome, please* **Tel 01460 220364**

Dippers, Shaugh Prior ✂❀ (Mr & Mrs R J Hubble) *8m NE of Plymouth. Garden 100yds down lane opp church near top of village. Park in village. No parking in lane.* ¾ acre informal garden. Emphasis on foliage contrast with collection of dwarf rhododendrons, dwarf conifer, shrubs and herbaceous. Extensive collection of alpines, in raised beds, troughs and tufa under glass. NCCPG National Collection of Dianthus (pinks). Hellebores for sale in March. *Adm £1.50 Chd free (ACNO to St Edward's Church, Shaugh Prior) Mons March 6, 13, 20, 27 (2-4); Suns April 16; May 21, June 18 (1-5)*

■ Docton Mill and Garden, Lymebridge ❀ (Mr & Mrs M G Bourcier) *Nr Hartland. Follow brown flower signs from Hartland or West Country Inn on A39.* Less than 1m from the sea, nestling in one of Devon's outstanding beauty spots. A garden for all seasons (depicted on BBC, ITV and Channel 4's Garden Party). Restored mill (not open) surrounded by 8 acres of gardens, created around original mill streams, encompassing an exceptional bog garden, orchard and natural woodland. Devon cream TEAS at Mill. *Adm £3.25 OAPs £3 Chd under 14 £1. Daily March 1 to Oct 31 (10-6). For NGS 1st Monday each month. Parties by arrangement*
Tel 01237 441369

The Downes, Monkleigh ✂❀ (Mr & Mrs R C Stanley-Baker) *4½m S of Bideford; 3m NW of Torrington. On A386 to Bideford turn L (W) up drive, ¼m beyond layby.* 15 acres with landscaped lawns; fine views overlooking fields and woodlands in Torridge Valley; many unusual trees and shrubs; small arboretum; woodland walks. TEA Sats, Suns only. *Adm £2 Chd 20p. Daily April 22 to June 11 (all day). Private visits also welcome by appt June to Sept, please* **Tel 01805 622244**

Dunsford Gardens, Dunsford ✂ *Approx 1m from Dunsford village on Tedburn St Mary rd. Take B3212 from Exeter, take 1st turning R, signed Dunsford and Cheriton Bishop, then follow signs. Limited disabled parking. Remainder 400yds flat walk (in field). Combined adm £1.50 Chd 50p Sat, Sun June 24, 25 (2-6)*

Lockhouse, Dunsford (Mr E Ruiz & Mr T Griffin) 1 acre wild rambling garden with stream surrounded by woods. Gently sloping over grass paths. Flowers, shrubs and vegetables TEAS in aid of local charity.

Pencuit, Dunsford (J & I Bryant) ⅓ acre on hillside. Perrenials, shrubs, vegetables and trees. Steep steps and paths. Informal layout

Elmpark, Broadhempston ♿✂❀ (Mr & Mrs J James) *From Newton Abbot take A381 to Totnes. After 2m R turn through Ipplepen village on to Broadhempston. From thence directed. From Totnes take A384 to Buckfastleigh. After 3m turn R at brow of hill to Staverton, through village on to Broadhempston directed from there. Elmpark 50yds S of church. 5m from Totnes. 6m from Newton Abbot.* Approx 2 acres. Old country house garden. Small walled vegetable and fruit garden with beeboles. Herbaceous borders. Specimen trees and shrubs. Old orchard and ¼ acre young tree plantation. Cream TEAS. *Adm £2 Chd 50p under 10 free. Sat, Sun June 24, 25 (2-5)*

Emmerford Cottage, Tiverton (Mr & Mrs M J Bassano) *N of Tiverton take A396, from roundabout L in 2½m signed Stoodleigh, over bridge, R in ½m at 'Weak Bridge' sign, signposted Cove. House ¼m on L just before farm.* 3½ acres, begun in 1989, lie in their own woodland setting in Exe Valley. Wide variety of plants and trees set in various situations where plants 'get on together'. Shrub and herbaceous borders around house, shrub roses on terrace, sloping azalea and rhododendron woodland with stream and pond features. A new arboretum is taking shape. TEA. *Adm £1.50 Chd free (ACNO to CHICKS). Private visits welcome, please* **Tel 01398 351287** in advance

Fardel Manor, Ivybridge ♿✂❀ (Dr A G Stevens) *1¼m NW of Ivybridge; 2m SE of Cornwood; 200yds S of railway bridge.* 5-acre, all organic, garden maintained with conservation and wildlife in mind. 2½ acres developed over past 16 yrs with stream, pond and lake. Also, small courts and walled gardens around C14 manor (not open), with orangery, herbaceous borders, formal pond and shrub garden. Also fruit and vegetable area. TEAS. *Adm £1.50 Chd 50p (ACNO to Frame) Mon May 22, July 24 (11-4.30)*

Fast Rabbit Farm, Ash Cross ♿❀ (Mr A S Mort) *1½m from Dartmouth off A3122 Dartmouth to Totnes rd, pass park and ride. Turn L at Rose Cottage. From Totnes or Kingsbridge, pass Woodland Park on R, drive past Norton Park on L turn R at Rose Cottage.* Garden created in sheltered valley with natural stream. Several ponds and lake; partially wooded; rockery; extensively planted; extends 12 acres plus new woodland planting and walks created through woodland at head of valley. Small specialist nursery open daily. Car park. Some level walks. 'Invalids' please phone prior to visit. TEAS. *Adm £2.50 Chd 50p. Suns Feb 27, March 5, 12, 19, 26, April 2, 9, 16, 23, 30, May 7, 14, 21, 28, June 4, 11, 18, 25, July 9, 23, Aug 20, Sept 24, Oct 8, 22 (11-5). Parties welcome by appt, please* **Tel 01803 712437**

1 Feebers Cottage, Westwood ♿✂❀ (Mr & Mrs M S Squires) *2m NE of Broadclyst from B3181 (formerly A38) Exeter to Taunton rd, at Dog Village bear E to Whimple, after 1½m fork L for Westwood.* Modern cottage garden, a little of everything set in ¾ acre, with a maze of pathways; specialising in plants which tolerate heavy clay soil (alpines in raised beds). Also section of plants introduced by Amos Perry. Nursery. Cream TEAS June 25 only, TEA other days. *Adm £1 Chd free. Easter Mon April 24, Suns May 14, 28, June 18, 25, Sept 10, 24, Oct 8 (2-6). Private visits welcome, please* **Tel 01404 822118**

Feniton & Fenny Bridges Gardens, Honiton ✂❀ *Approx 4m W of Honiton, leave new A30 at Feniton/Fenny Bridges exits and follow NGS signs.* TEAS. *Combined adm £2.50 Chd 50p. Sat, Sun July 15, 16.*

Little Ash Farm, Fenny Bridges ♿ (Sadie & Robert Reid) Peaceful ¾ acre garden, immaculate lawns, trees, shrubs, large pond with unique water feature, integrated vegetables. Panoramic views. *(2-6)*

Monteverde, Old Feniton ✂❀ (Mr & Mrs D C Harvey) Enthusiasts' large garden developing from old pasture, around modern bungalow. Varied shrubs, herbaceous perennials and bulbs. Perfume, colour-coordination and mini nature reserve. Stream, waterfalls, large pool, bog garden and potager. *(ACNO to Friends of Kew) (2-5)*

■ **Flete, Ermington, Ivybridge** ✂ (Country Houses Association) *Ermington, 2m W of Modbury on A379 Plymouth to Kingsbridge rd. Entrance adjacent to Sequers Bridge.* 15 acres overlooking R Erme and valley. Landscaped in 1920s by Russell Page, Italian garden and water garden which Lawrence of Arabia helped to construct. Many fine trees and shrubs. Interesting cobbled terrace to W face of original Tudor manor (not open). *House and gardens open every Wed, Thurs, May to Sept (2-5). Adm £3.50 Chd £1. Gardens open for NGS Sats June 17, Aug 19. Adm £2 Chd £1 (2-5)* **Tel 01752 830308**

■ **The Garden House, Buckland Monachorum** ✂❀ (The Fortescue Garden Trust) *Yelverton. W of A386, 10m N of Plymouth.* 8 acres, incl romantic, terraced walled garden surrounding the ruins of C16 vicarage (not open). Acer glade, spring garden, rhododendron walk, herbaceous glade, cottage garden and quarry garden. TEAS. *Adm £4 Chd £1. March 1 to Oct 31 daily. For NGS Weds July 12, Aug 16 (10.30-5) Coaches and parties by appt only*

The Gate House, Lee ✂ (Mr & Mrs D Booker) *Lee Coastal Village 3m W of Ilfracombe. Park in village car park. Take lane alongside The Grampus public house. Garden is 50yds past inn buildings.* 2¼ acres, where no chemicals are used, only few minutes walk from the sea and dramatic coastal scenery. Peaceful streamside garden with range of habitats; bog garden, National Collection of Rodgersia, woodland, herbaceous borders, patio garden with semi-hardy 'exotics'. Good food at The Grampus. *Collecting box. Open most days (9-12 and 2-4). Please* **Tel 01271 862409** to check especially in Aug

Gidleigh Gardens ✂ *From A30 take A382 for Mortonhampstead via Whiddon Down. After 100yds, turn R to Gidleigh. proceed for 4m. Entrances adjacent C15 church.* Cream TEAS at Castle Farm. *Combined adm £2 Chd £1. Sat, Sun July 8, 9 (2-5.30)*

Castle Farm, Gidleigh ✂ (Mr & Mrs M Bell) A natural garden in one of Dartmoor's sheltered combes;

stream, waterfalls and pools. Streamside walk in 6-acre wild valley. Views to deer forest and Castle Drogo

Castle House, Gidleigh ✂ (Mr & Mrs M Hardy) Hillside gardens around remains of mediaeval castle. Plantings amongst granite stones and water cascades link the gardens to the Dartmoor landscape

Gorwell House, Barnstaple ♿❀ (Dr & The Hon Mrs J A Marston) *1m E of Barnstaple centre, on Bratton Fleming rd, drive entrance between two lodges on left.* 4 acres of trees and shrubs, rare and tender; walled garden, mostly created since 1982; grotto; small temple; summerhouse with views across estuary to Hartland Point. TEAS (except March 26, April 16, Oct 8). *Adm £1.50 Acc Chd free. Suns March 26, April 16, May 14, June 11, July 16, Sept 10, Oct 8 (2-6)*

Greenlands ✂❀ (Dr & Mrs J P Anderson) *From Tiverton town centre follow signs for Halberton. After 3m at Halberton, turn R onto minor rd signposted Ash Thomas. After 1¼m turn R at Crow Green Xrds. Garden immed on L. Garden also signposted from junction 27 of M5 on open days.* ⅓ acre rural garden divided into several smaller rooms with yr-round interest. Roses, clematis, penstemons, herbaceous borders, rock garden and ponds. Early spring bulbs. Circular fruit garden, raised bed vegetable garden. Parking. TEAS. *Adm £1.50 Chd 50p (ACNO to Mencap and St Francis Hospital, Katete, Zambia). Suns March 12, April 16, May 7, June 4, 25, July 16, Aug 13, Sept 10; Wed April 12, May 3, 31, July 19, Aug 9 (2-5.30).* **Evening opening** *Wed June 21 (2-9). Also by appt, please* **Tel 01884 821257**

Greenway Gardens, Churston Ferrers ❀ (Mr & Mrs A A Hicks) *4m W of Brixham. From B3203, Paignton-Brixham, take rd to Galmpton, thence towards Greenway Ferry.* 30 acres; old-established garden with mature trees; shrubs; rhododendrons, magnolias and camellias. Recent plantings; commercial shrub nursery. Woodland walks by R Dart. Limited parking, partly suitable for wheelchairs. Plants in adjacent nursery not sold in aid of NGS. TEA. *Adm £2 Chd 50p. Thurs March 23, 30 (11-5)* **Tel 01803 842382**

NEW **Haldon Grange, Dunchideock** ✂❀ (Ted & Mary Phythian) *In centre of Dunchideock follow sign to Lord Haldon Hotel, then L again.* 8-acre well established garden with camellias, azaleas and rhododendrons, rare and mature trees. Small lake and ponds with river and water cascade as a feature. TEAS (if fine). *Adm £1.50 Chd 50p. Sat, Sun, Bank Hol Mon April 29, 30, May 1(9-5). Also by appt, please* **Tel 01392 832349**

▲ **Half Moon House, Manaton** ✂ (Noel Welch & The National Trust) *From Bovey Tracey take B3387 (passing entrance to park on R) for ¼m then bear R to Manaton (signed) for approx 4m. Car park at church with donation box and Half Moon House (not open), a thatched Devon longhouse, at far end of village green.* Formal enclosed garden, a recreation of the old mediaeval Marian garden, surrounded by woodland with extensive views over Dartmoor National Park and magnificent granite outcrops throughout (approx 25 acres). The woodland leads to Manaton Rocks viewpoint and is carpeted with bluebells in spring. TEAS. *Adm £1.50 Chd 50p Suns May 7, June 25 (2-5.30)*

NEW **Halwill Gardens, Beaworthy** ♿✂❀ *On A3079 between Okehampton (12m) and Holsworthy (9m).* TEAS. *Combined adm £3 Chd £1. Sat, Sun July 29, 30 (10-5)*

Amberley, Beaworthy (Don & Doreen Parsons) *Next door to Winsford Walled Garden.* Authentic Japanese garden, 45' by 45' with pond, tea house and ornaments of stone. TEAS. *(ACNO to Devon Air Ambulance)*

Chapel Farm House, Beaworthy (Robin & Toshie Hull) *At W end of village on main A3079 rd.* Approx ½ acre created 8 yrs ago by present owners, landscaped with shrub borders, heathers, rhododendrons and azalea and alpine bed. Kitchen garden. 2 small greenhouses for mixed use; small bonsai collection. *(ACNO Missions to Seamen). Private visits welcome May to Oct. Closed Mons except bank hols.*

Winsford Walled Garden, Beaworthy (Aileen Birks & Mike Gilmore) *Take Black Torrington rd in Halwill Junction, after ½m turn R at red painted bungalow. Follow lane for ½m then turn L at sign.* 1-acre Victorian walled garden undergoing extensive restoration. Greenhouse ranges in original materials. New and varied plantings; large fuchsia collection. Present owners moved 10 tonnes of plants from previous NGS garden. *(ACNO to Devon Air Ambulance). Private visits welcome May to October, not Mons except bank hols.*

Hamblyn's Coombe, Dittisham (Robert & Bridget McCrum) *From Red Lion Inn follow The Level until it forks R up steep private road. Car park at top.* 10 min pretty walk to 7-acre garden with stunning views, sloping steeply to R Dart. Extensive planting with unusual design features accompanying Bridget McCrum's stone carvings and bronzes. Wildflower meadow and woods. TEAS. *Adm £2 Chd free. Sun, Mon April 30, May 1 (2-6). Private visits also welcome by appt, please* **Tel/Fax 01803 722228/722521**

▲ **Hartland Abbey, Hartland** ♿❀ (Sir Hugh & Lady Stucley) *Turn off A39 W of Clovelly Cross. Follow signs to Hartland through town on rd to Stoke and Quay. Abbey 1m from town on R.* Woodland gardens of camellias, rhododendrons, azaleas, hydrangeas and rare plants lead to bog garden and Victorian fernery by Jekyll, unearthed in 1998 and replanted. Secret C18 walled gardens of herbaceous borders, tender plants and vegetables are being replanted. Glasshouses. Wildflower walk to remote Atlantic cove. Wheelchairs only on lawns around Abbey. Cream TEAS. *Adm £3 Chd 50p (ACNO to St Necton's Church, Hartland). For NGS Sun April 16, 30 (2-5.30)* **Tel/Fax 01237 441264** (The Administrator)

Heddon Hall, Parracombe ❀ (Mr & Mrs W H Keatley) *10m NE of Barnstaple off A39. 400yds N up hill from village centre. Entrance to drive on R. Ample parking.* Garden of former rectory on edge of Exmoor extending to 4 acres. Walled garden with formal layout, vegetables and herbaceous beds; sheltered flower garden; semi-shaded, S sloping shrubbery with paths leading down to natural stream and water garden; recently planted arboretum. Cream TEAS. *Adm £1.50 Chd 50p. Sun July 9 (2-5.30)*

Higher Knowle, Lustleigh (Mr and Mrs D R A Quicke) *3m NW of Bovey Tracey. Take A382 towards Moretonhampstead. In 2½m turn L for Lustleigh; in ¼m L/R; in ¼m steep drive*

L. 3-acre woodland garden around 1914 house (not open) with Lutyens style features. Spectacular views to Dartmoor, sheltered hillside garden usually avoids late frosts. Old oak wood with primroses and bluebells among giant boulders, mature Asiatic magnolias in late March, camellias, new hybrid magnolias, rhododendrons, azaleas and embothriums. *Adm £2.50 Chd free. Suns March 26; April 2, 9, 16, 23 (Easter), 30; May 7, 14, 21, 28; Easter Mon April 24, Bank hol Mons May 1, 29 (2-6). Private visits welcome, please* **Tel 01647 277275**

Higher Watertown, Nr South Molton ♿✂❀ (Mr & Mrs R A Abell) *4m SW of S Molton on B3226.* Small intimate rural garden surrounding C16 farmhouse (not open) in picturesque Mole Valley. Expanding collection of the very best in flower and foliage herbaceous perennials, grasses and climbers. Borders planned for complementary association of colour and form. Plants well labelled. Guaranteed colour, rain or shine! TEAS *Adm £1.50 Chd 50p. Sun, Bank hol Mon May 28, 29, Sats, Suns June 24, 25, July 29, 30, Sun, Bank Hol Mon Aug 27, 28 (2-6)* **Tel 01769 540 470**

Hill House Nursery & Garden, Lanscove ♿❀ (Ray & Matthew Hubbard) *Follow brown signs from A384 Buckfastleigh to Totnes rd.* Old vicarage (not open) beside church, both designed by John Loughborough Pearson, architect of Truro Cathedral. This 3-acre garden was the subject of 'An Englishman's Garden' by Edward Hyams, a previous owner. Also featured in 'English Vicarages and Their Gardens' and on TV. Fine collection of plants in adjacent nursery. *Adm collection box. Open all year. Tea Room open March 1 to end September (11-5)*

Hole Farm, Farlacombe ♿ (Rev Ian Graham-Orlebar) *A383 Ashburton to Newton Abbot rd 3m NE from Ashburton signed Gale, Burne, Woodland. Follow signs to Farlacombe, after 1m, at top of hill, lane on R to Hole Farm.* 1½ acre valley garden, with woodland, wild garden, 2 ponds, herbaceous borders and bog areas. Old farm and buildings (not open). Cream TEAS. *Adm £2 Chd 50p. Sun July 30 (2-5)*

Honeyway Farm, Dunsford ♿❀ (B S & G E Hearson) *From Exeter take B3212 (Moretonhampstead) W for 6m reaching Two Crosses Xrds at top of steep hill, turn R, garden ½m on L.* 2 acres subject to winds from SE and SW. Extensive rocks, views, paths winding to new outlooks. Shrubs and herbaceous perennials, island beds being established. Ponds with goldfish and lilies. Yr-round interest. Woodland walks around new plantations (deciduous and conifer), dogs off leash here at owners risk. *Adm £2 Chd free, Combined adm with Sowton Mill £3. (ACNO Devon Air Ambulance). Suns May 7, July 9 (2-6)*

Inglewood, Newton Ferrers ✂❀ (Major & Mrs Stevenson) *10m E of Plymouth. Take A374 Plymouth to Kingsbridge rd. At Yealmpton, turn S to Newton Ferrers. At Green Xrds (signed), turn R into Parsonage Rd then along Court Rd for ¾m. Entrance on L.* Unusual situation overlooking R Yealm. Steep garden with many terraces packed with plants and shrubs. Ever-changing and hopefully improving! TEAS. *Adm £1.50 Chd free. Suns May 21, Sept 17 (2-5)*

Kerscott House, Swimbridge ♿✂❀ (Jessica & Peter Duncan) *1m E of Swimbridge on Barnstaple-South Molton rd, turn R at top of hill, immed fork L, 100yds on L, 1st gate past house.* 6 acres surrounding C16 farmhouse (not open) in peaceful rural setting. Ornamental trees, wide selection of shrubs, herbaceous and tender perennials, ponds and bog garden. Mediterranean garden within roofless barn. Living willow constructions and natural sculptures. 2½ acres woodland planted 1995. *Adm £1.50 Chd free. Suns June 25, July 30, Aug 27 (2-6). Groups welcome for private visits during June and July, please* **Tel 01271 830943**

▲ Killerton Garden, Broadclyst ♿✂❀ (The National Trust) *8m N of Exeter. Take B3181 rd to Cullompton (formerly A38), after 7m fork left and follow NT signs.* 8ha of spectacular hillside gardens with naturalised bulbs sweeping down to large open lawns. Delightful walks through fine collection of rare trees and shrubs; herbaceous borders. Wheelchair and 'golf' buggy with driver available. Restaurant. Tea room, plant centre. *Adm gardens only £3.60 Chd £1.80. For NGS Suns April 16, July 2 (10.30-5.30)*

Kingston House, Staverton ♿✂ (Mr & Mrs M R Corfield) *4m NE of Totnes. A384 Totnes to Buckfastleigh, from Staverton, 1m due N of Sea Trout Inn, follow signs to Kingston.* George II 1735 house grade II (not open). Gardens being restored in keeping with the period. Walled garden, rose garden, herbaceous borders, pleached limes and hornbeams, vegetable garden. Unusual formal garden with santolinas, lavender and camomile. Cream TEAS. *Adm £1.50 Chd 50p (ACNO to Animals in Distress, Ipplepen) Suns June 4, June 25, July 16 (2-6). Private parties over 20 welcome by arrangement, please* **Tel 01803 762235** No coaches

▲ Knightshayes Gardens, Tiverton ♿✂❀ (The National Trust) *2m N of Tiverton. Via A396 Tiverton to Bampton rd; turn E in Bolham, signed Knightshayes; entrance ½m on L.* Large 'Garden in the Wood', 20ha of landscaped gardens with pleasant walks and views over Exe valley. Choice collections of unusual plants, incl acers, birches, rhododendrons, azaleas, camellias, magnolias, roses, spring bulbs, alpines and herbaceous borders; formal gardens; Wheelchair available. Restaurant, plant centre. *Adm garden only £3.70 Chd £1.85. For NGS Suns April 30, June 25 (11-5.30)*

Lee Ford, Budleigh Salterton ♿❀ (Mr and Mrs N Lindsay-Fynn) *Knowle.* Extensive, formal and woodland garden, largely developed in the 1950s, but recently much extended with mass displays of camellias, rhododendrons and azaleas, incl many rare varieties. Traditional walled garden, herb garden, bog garden. Ornamental conservatory and Adam pavilion. Light refreshments. *Adm £2 by prior appt for parties of 20 or more. Open Sun June 4, by ticket application only, for lunch and conducted tour £20, cream teas and afternoon tour £10. For reservations*
Tel 01395 445894 (office hours)

Lewtrenchard Manor, Lewdown ✂❀ (Mr & Mrs J S Murray) *From Lewdown on old A30 take signs to Lewtrenchard, house well signed.* Approx 6 acres designed by Walter Sorel with Gertrude Jekyll influences. Parkland garden with stream and water gardens. Parts of garden still being restored, but very peaceful situation round attractive C17 house (not open). TEA. *Adm £2 Chd free (ACNO to Devon Air Ambulance). Mon to Fri May 1 to Sept 29 (10-4.30)*

Little Cumbre, Exeter ✿❀ (Dr & Mrs John Lloyd) *145, Pennsylvania Road. Near top of hill, 50yds below telephone kiosk on same side. Ample parking in rd.* Extensive views to Dartmoor and Exe Estuary. ½ acre formal garden with shrubs and bulbs plus ½ acre of woodland. Winter opening especially for snowdrops and hellebores, while summer is for clematis, interesting bark and lovely general effect. *Adm £1.50 Chd free. Thurs May 4, June 8 (2-5), Suns Feb 7, 14, 2001 (1-4)*

Little Upcott Gardens, Marsh Green ❀ (Mike & Maureen Jones) *2m W of Ottery St Mary, signposted from B3180 and from village.* Scented, informal 2 acre garden with sensitive combinations of styles and colour and unusual plant varieties. Water features with ducks and original cottage garden. Plenty of seating and assistance for the disabled. TEAS. *Adm £2 Chd 50p. Sun June 4 (10.30-5). Parties, incl evening visits, welcomed, by prior arrangement. Descriptive brochure with opening times available on request, please* **Tel 01404 822797**

The Lodge, Mannamead ♿❀ (Mr & Mrs M H Tregaskis) *Hartley Ave, Plymouth. 1½m from city centre via Mutley Plain. Turn R at Henders Corner into Eggbuckland Rd, 3rd R at tel kiosk to end of cul de sac.* ½ acre, S-sloping aspect with variety of citrus fruits, olives, unusual shrubs, conifers, camellias and ground cover plants. Large vegetable area. Former L.A. nursery with range of lean-to glasshouses for fruit and tender subjects. TEA. *Adm £1.50 Acc chd free (ACNO to St. Luke's Hospice) Suns May 7, June 11, July 16 (2-5). Private visits also welcome, please* **Tel 01752 220849**

Longham, Coryton ✿❀ (Jennie Hale & Andrew Osborne) *From A30, take A386 to Tavistock. Proceed 5m to Dartmoor Inn, signed Lydford, past Lydford Gorge (NT). After 3m, turn R for Chillaton, after 500yds, turn R to Liddaton, then downhill to Liddaton Cross, turn sharp R, 400yds over railway bridge, immed R into T sign(dead end) rd, ½m downhill, L over small bridge, signed Longham Farm. Follow short track to cottage.* Small ⅓ acre garden in beautiful wooded valley. Colourful mass plantings, herbaceous perennials, ornamental grasses, bamboos, cannas, large collection of tender perennials. Many unusual plants, large range of salvias, interesting climbers with exotic plants grown in containers. Vegetable garden with raised beds and polytunnel. TEAS. *Adm £1.50 Chd 50p. Private visits and groups welcome from 1st May to end Sept, by appt only, please* **Tel 01822 860287**

Lower Coombe Farm, Brithem Bottom ✿ (Mr & Mrs M Weekes) *From junction 28 of M5, 2m NW of Cullompton on B3181 to Willand. Take L turn after 1m.* 3/4 acre informal garden, including a ditch garden, behind farmhouse (not open) and yard. Planted slowly for 18 yrs for yr-round interest with special emphasis on old roses, clematis, Barnhaven primulas, bulbs, hellebores and asters. Trees and shrubs for autumn colour. Parking in farmyard. *Adm £1.50 Chd free. Easter Mon April 24, Suns May 28, June 25, Sept 10 (12-5)*

■ **Lukesland, Ivybridge** (Mr & Mrs B N Howell) *1½m N of Ivybridge on Harford Rd, E side of Erme valley.* 15 acres of flowering shrubs, wild flowers and rare trees with pinetum in Dartmoor National Park. Beautiful setting of small valley around Addicombe Brook with lakes, numerous waterfalls and pools. Extensive and unusual collection of large and small leaved rhododendrons and one of the largest Magnolia campbellii in country. Partially suitable for wheelchairs. TEAS. *Adm £2.90 Chd free. Suns, Weds, April 16 to June 11. Easter Mon April 24, Bank Hol Mons May 1, 29. For NGS Wed May 3, Sun May 7 (2-6). Coaches on application only,* **Tel 01752 893390**

NEW **Manaton Gate, Newton Abbot** ♿ (Dr Roger Mules) *From Bovey Tracey take B3387 for 4m. Follow sign to Manaton past Becky Falls and turn R in village to church and village green. Entrance through granite archway to R of green.* Recently restored old rectory (not open) garden in 4½ acres with mature trees, rhododendrons, azaleas and much new planting. Old walled garden. Typical Dartmoor woodland carpeted with ferns and bluebells. Massive granite outcrops and extensive views over National Park to Hay Tor. Cream TEAS. *Adm £1.50 Chd 50p. Sun May 7 (2-5.30)*

● **Marwood Hill, Marwood** ❀ (Dr J A Smart) *4m N of Barnstaple. Signed from A361 Barnstaple to Braunton rd and B3230 Barnstaple to Ilfracombe rd. Outside Guineaford village, opp Marwood church.* 20 acres with 3 small lakes. Extensive collection of camellias under glass and in open; daffodils, rhododendrons, rare flowering shrubs, rock and alpine scree; waterside planting; bog garden; many clematis; Australian native plants and many eucalyptus. National Collections of astilbe, Iris ensata, tulbaghia. Partially suitable for wheelchairs. Plants for sale between 11-5. Teas in Church Room (Suns & Bank Hols or by prior arrangement for parties). *Adm £3 Acc chd under 12 free. Daily except Christmas Day (dawn-dusk)*

Meadowcroft, Plympton ♿❀ (Mrs G M Thompson) *1 Downfield Way. From Plymouth, turn L at St Mary's Church roundabout, along Glen Rd, 3rd R into Downfield Drive; garden on immed R. From A38, Plympton turn-off L at 1st roundabout, turn R at 2nd roundabout, proceed down Hillcrest Drive and Glen Rd, turn L at bottom of hill before Dillons and into Downfield Drive, garden on immed R.* 2-acre country garden in urban area, rhododendrons, azaleas, fruit, bog garden, mixed borders, spring bulbs, interesting trees. TEAS. *Adm £1.50 Chd under 14 free - must be accompanied. Suns April 9, 30, Thurs May 11, Sun June 4 (2-5)*

Membland Villa, Newton Ferrers ✿❀ (Mr & Mrs Jack Hockaday) *10m E of Plymouth. Take A374 Plymouth to Kingsbridge rd. At Yealmpton, turn S to Newton Ferrers. Follow signs.* Late C19 house (not open), part of Revelstoke Estate, built by Edward Baring. Charming country garden with varied and unusual plants incl old roses and climbers. Organic kitchen garden. Small exhibition of wildlife paintings. Extensive bluebell wood, spectacular in season. TEAS served in conservatory. *Adm £2 (ACNO to RNLI). Suns April 30, May 28, June 18, July 16, Aug 27 (2-5).* **Evening Bluebell Opening** *Fri April 21 (4-8). Groups of 20+ welcome, please write or* **Tel 01752 872626**

Monks Aish, South Brent (Captain & Mrs M J Garnett) *1m W of South Brent, near hamlet of Aish, off B3372 W of village. Follow signposts to Aish. After going under Aish railway bridge up hill, 3rd house on L next to Great Aish. [Grid Ref 688603]* Very attractive 1-acre garden with stream, a little different from most with varieties of shrubs, trees incl Embothrium coccineum (Chilean Fire Tree), flowers, fruit and vegetables. TEAS. *Adm £2 Chd under 12 50p (ACNO to Missions to Seamen) Sat, Sun May 27, 28 (2-5). Private visits welcome, please* **Tel 01364 73102**

The Moorings, Rocombe (Mr and Mrs A Marriage) *Uplyme, 2m NW of Lyme Regis. From Lyme Regis, about 1m on A3070, turn R signposted Rocombe, over Xrds, take narrow lane signposted Rocombe 4th house on R, drive beyond house. From Axminster, straight at Hunters Lodge then fork R twice, straight at Xrds and R again. ¾m on L.* 3 acres of peaceful woodland garden, developed since 1965, on hillside with terraced paths, overlooking unspoilt countryside. Fine trees incl many species eucalyptus, unusual pines, nothofagus; flowering shrubs; daffodils and other spring flowers, ground cover, many ferns, autumn colour. *Adm £1 Chd free. Private visits welcome, please* **Tel 01297 443295**

Moretonhampstead Gardens *12m from Exeter and Newton Abbot on eastern fringes of Dartmoor.* TEAS. *Combined adm £3 Chd free. Suns May 14, 28, Bank Hol Mon May 29 (2-6)*

NEW **Mardon** (Graham & Mary Wilson) *From centre of village head towards church, turn L into Lime St. Bottom of hill on R.* 2 acres with lawns and terraces, wildflower meadow, trout pond, stream, water meadow, roses and rhododendrons, large herbaceous border. Fine views TEAS.

Sutton Mead (Edward & Miranda Allhusen) *½m N of village towards Chagford on A382. Turn R beside speed derestriction sign.* 3-acre garden with views of Dartmoor. Rhododendrons and azaleas, bog garden, ponds, blubell woodland, spring bulbs and primroses, mixed borders, vegetable garden. TEAS in conservatory.

Mothecombe House, Holbeton (Mr and Mrs A Mildmay-White) *SE of Plymouth 10m. From A379, between Yealmpton and Modbury, turn S for Holbeton. Continue 2m to Mothecombe.* Walled gardens, herbaceous borders. Orchard with spring bulbs; camellia walk and flowering shrubs. Bog garden; streams and pond; bluebell woods leading to private beach. Queen Anne house (not open). Strictly no dogs. Teas at beach car park, Old School tea house. *Adm garden £2 Chd free. Sat, Sun April 29. 30 Sun June 18 (2-5). Parties welcome by appt, please* **Tel 01752 830444**

The Old Glebe, Eggesford (Mr & Mrs Nigel Wright) *4m SW of Chulmleigh. Turn S off A377 at Eggesford Station (½-way between Exeter & Barnstaple), cross railway and River Taw, drive straight uphill (signed Brushford) for ¾m; turn R into bridleway.* 7-acre garden of former Georgian rectory (not open) with mature trees and several lawns, courtyard, walled herbaceous borders, bog garden and small lake; emphasis on species and hybrid rhododendrons and azaleas, 750 varieties. Rhododendrons for sale. TEAS. *Adm £2 Chd £1 (ACNO to The Abbeyfield, Chulmleigh) Sat, Sun May 13, 14, Sun, Bank Hol Mon May 28, 29 (2-6)*
Tel 01769 580632

The Old Mill, Blakewell (Les & Barbara Shapland) *Muddiford, nr Barnstaple. ½m past hospital off B3230 to Ilfracombe at Blakewell Fisheries. Follow signs to Mill (grade II) at end of lane. Ample parking in field.* 4-acre, S-sloping garden started in 1989 set in beautiful countryside. Unusual trees, conifers and shrubs. A lavender walk, vegetable plot, orchard and ponds. Lime tree avenue leading to folly and secret Japanese-style garden. Lower garden, rockpool, with large waterfall. *Adm £1.50 Chd free Suns May 21, July 23 (11-5), Wed July 19 (2-8). Private visits also welcome, please*
Tel 01271 375002

The Old Rectory, East Portlemouth (Mr & Mrs Charles Barwell) *Opp Salcombe. From A379 Kingsbridge to Dartmouth rd, turn R at Frogmore over bridge towards E Portlemouth for 5m. Through village to estuary, turn R, entrance on L after 200yds. Or from Salcombe, passenger ferry to E Portlemouth, turn L proceed for ½m.* Former rectory (not open) in 3 acres on Salcombe estuary with lovely views of Southpool Creek. Landscaped and walled gardens with camellias, magnolias, viburnums. Herbaceous and mixed borders with roses and tender plants in walled garden. Home-grown plants for sale. TEAS. *Adm £2 Chd free. Sat, Sun, April 29, 30 Bank Hol Mons May 1, 29 (11-5)*
Tel 01548 842670

The Old Rectory, Woodleigh (H E Morton Esq) *Nr Loddiswell. 3½m N of Kingsbridge, E off Kingsbridge to Wrangaton rd at Rake Cross (1m S of Loddiswell). 1½m to Woodleigh.* Secret garden of trees, shrubs and naturalised bulbs with emphasis on rhododendrons, camellias and magnolias in spring and hydrangeas in Autumn. Chemical free. Maintained by owner. *Adm £2 Chd 50p. Private visits usually welcome at any time, please* **Tel 01548 550387**

Orchard Cottage, Exmouth (Mr & Mrs W K Bradridge) *30, Hulham Rd. From Exeter A376, turn L into Hulham Road, just before 1st set of t-lights. Entrance lane between Nos 26 and 32 Hulham Rd, opp lower end of Phillipps Avenue. Parking in Hulham Road or Phillipps Avenue.* ¼ acre, typical cottage garden. *Adm £1 Chd free. (2.30-5.30) By appt only, please* **Tel 01395 278605**

Outer Narracott, Bittadon (Mr & Mrs Ralph Burge) *3m SE of Ilfracombe. A3123 Lynton to Woolacombe rd, ½m W of Berrydown Cross or ½m E of Lynton Cross Garage.* ½ acre, mostly herbaceous garden in elevated position with stream, small pond, varied ornamental shrubs and trees. Vegetable garden. Some parts of garden recently developed; interesting informative leaflet. TEA. *Adm £1.50 Chd 50p. Suns July 16, Aug 6 (2-5.30)*

▲ **Overbecks, Sharpitor** (The National Trust) *1½m SW of Salcombe. From Salcombe or Malborough follow NT signs.* 2.4ha garden with rare plants and shrubs; spectacular views over Salcombe estuary. Tea room same days as museum (12-4.15). *Adm garden only £2.80 Chd £1.40. For NGS Suns May 21, June 18 (10-8 sunset if earlier)*

Penrose, Crediton (Mr & Mrs A Jewell) *On A377 main Exeter to Barnstaple rd, turn into Park Rd by Hillbrow Residential Home. Garden opp third turning on L.* ⅓ acre town garden with lawns, shrubs and herbaceous borders, pond with waterfall and wishing well, areas for fruit and vegetable and for growing produce for exhibition. Spring bulbs and summer annuals. TEA. *Adm £1 Chd free. Suns May 21, June 18, Aug 20 (2-5). Private visits of 10 or over welcome, please* **Tel 01363 773587**

38 Phillipps Avenue, Exmouth (Mr and Mrs R G Stuckey) *From Exeter, turn L into Hulham rd just before 1st set of t-lights, 1st L into Phillipps Avenue (ample parking).* Very small highly specialised and extensive collection of alpine and rock garden plants in scree bed and troughs. Many rare and unusual specimens. NCCPG Helichrysum collection. Small alpine nursery. Teashops Exmouth. *Adm £1 Chd free (ACNO to NCCPG, Helichrysum Day - June 21). Weds March 29, April 5, 12, 26, May 3, 10, 17, 24, June 21 (2-5.30). Private visits also welcome, please* **Tel 01395 273636**

NEW **Pikes Cottage, Madford, Hemyock** (Christine & Brian Carver) *7m N of Honiton off A30 towards Wolford Chapel through Dunkeswell to Hemyock, then follow signs . Or 7m S of Wellington off M5 at junction 26 to Hemyock. Then follow signs to Madford. Turn in at gates opp Madford Farm and up farm track.* Set in 19 acres of bluebell woods, some with hilly access. 6 acres of cultivated garden incl herb garden, scree, shrubs, antipodean area and sensory garden are more level. Most features accessible or visible from a wheelchair. 1½ acre lawn slopes down to large pond. Steps up to newly planted arboretum. Plenty of seating. Send s.a.e. for map. TEAS. *Adm £1.50 Chd free. Sat, Sun May 20, 21 (10-6). Also open by appt June to Oct, please* **Tel 01823 680345**

The Pines, Salcombe (Mrs F J Bitmead) *Main Rd. At junction of Devon and Sandhills rds; lower entrance and parking Sandhills Rd.* All seasons ¾ acre S-facing garden; fine coastal views to Sharpitor Headland and N Sands Valley. Informal garden of surprises; many interesting and unusual shrubs, trees; water gardens; bulbs, camellias, azaleas, heathers. *Adm £2 Chd free. Suns March 5, 19, April 2, May 28 (11-5). Private visits also welcome all year, please* **Tel 01548 842198**

Plant World, Newton Abbot (Raymond Brown) *St. Mary Church Rd. Follow brown signs from A380 Penn Inn Roundabout. Car park on L past aquatic centre.* 4-acre hillside garden, laid out as a map of the world with native plants. Alpines, especially primulas and gentians, shrubs, herbaceous. Himalayan and Japanese gardens. Comprehensive cottage garden with hardy geraniums, campanulas. 3 National Primula Collections. Rare and unusual plants sold in adjacent nursery. Picnic area, viewpoint over Dartmoor and Lyme Bay. Collecting box. *Adm £1 Chd under 12 free. Easter to end of Sept every day incl Suns (9.30-5)*

■ **Pleasant View Nursery, Two Mile Oak** (Mr & Mrs B D Yeo) *Nr Denbury. 2m from Newton Abbot on A381 to Totnes. R at Two Mile Oak public house signed Denbury. ¾m on L.* 2-acre plantsman's garden with wide range of choice and uncommon shrubs giving colour all season. Additional 2-acre field planted as an arboretum with individual specimen shrubs. National Collections of Abelia and Salvia. Plants for sale in adjoining nursery. *Adm £2 Chd 25p. Every Wed and Fri, May to Sept incl (2-5). For NGS first Wed and Fri of each month. Parties welcome by appt at any time, please* **Tel 01803 813388**

Portington, Lamerton (Mr & Mrs I A Dingle) *From Tavistock B3362 to Launceston. ¼m beyond Blacksmiths Arms, Lamerton, fork L (signed Chipshop). Over Xrds (signed Horsebridge) first L then L again (signed Portington). From Launceston turn R at Carrs Garage and R again (signed Horsebridge), then as above.* Garden in peaceful rural setting with fine views over surrounding countryside. Mixed planting with shrubs and borders; woodland walk to small lake. TEAS. *Adm £1.50 Chd free (ACNO to St Luke's Hospice). Suns July 9, 16 (2-5.30)*

Riversbridge, Dartmouth (Mr & Mrs Sutton-Scott-Tucker) *½m inland from Blackpool sands and signed from A3122.* Small walled gardens adjoining farmyard in lovely unspoilt valley with ponds and stream; herbaceous plants, roses and some unusual shrubs. TEAS. *Adm £2 Chd free. Sun June 18, 25 (2-6)*

Rock House Garden, Chudleigh (Mrs D B & B Boulton) *Station Hill. A38 Exeter to Plymouth signed Chudleigh. S edge of town. Entrance at Rock Nursery.* Garden in ancient bishop's palace quarry with massive limestone rock. Delights for all seasons. Rare and unusual trees and shrubs. Massed daffodils in spring. Autumn brings one of the finest displays of cyclamen. Cave and ponds with Koi and Orfe. Walk with spectacular views of Dartmoor and access to Chudleigh rock, glen and waterfall. *Adm £2 Chd £1. Suns April 16, May 28, June 25, July 23, Sept 10, 17, Oct 29 (9.30-5.0)*

● **Rosemoor Garden, Great Torrington** (The Royal Horticultural Society) *1m SE of Great Torrington on A3124 to Exeter.* 40-acre plantsman's garden; rhododendrons (species and hybrid), ornamental trees and shrubs, woodland garden, species and old-fashioned roses, scree and raised beds with alpine plants, arboretum. 2000 roses in 200 varieties, two colour theme gardens, herb garden, potager, 200 metres of herbaceous border, a large stream and bog garden, cottage garden, foliage and plantsman's garden and a fruit and vegetable garden. Facilities for the disabled. *Adm £4 Chd £1 Groups £3.25 per person Open daily all year except Christmas Day (10-6 April to Sept. 10-5 Oct to March) (Share to NGS)* **Tel 01805 624067**

■ **Rowden Gardens, Brentor** (Mr & Mrs John Carter) *4m N of Tavistock on Lydford to Tavistock rd. Take sign to Liddaton between Mucky Duck and Brentor inns. Garden 300yds on R.* 1-acre garden begun in 1986 by author/lecturer John Carter. Featured in many TV programmes. 13 ponds displaying huge collection of aquatics and waterlilies. Herbaceous and bog gardens with dierama, grasses, iris, ligularias and rheums. Numerous rare and unusual plants incl new water iris. 2 NCCPG National Collections. Plants for sale in adjoining nursery. *Adm £2 Chd free. For NGS Suns, Mons June 11, 12, 25, 26, July 2, 3, Aug 13, 14 (10-5). Private visits welcome, please* **Tel 01822 810275**

Rowden House, Noss Mayo ❀ (Mr & Mrs T Hill) *10m E of Plymouth. A374 Plymouth to Kingsbridge rd. At Yealmpton, turn S to Noss Mayo. At church follow signs to Stoke Beach for 1m. Entrance on R.* Grade II listed farmhouse (not open) with ½ acre garden in rural setting. Developed over past 12 yrs. Exposed to salt-laden winds. Spring-fed pond. Interesting collection of plants. *Adm £2 Chd free. Suns June 4, Aug 6 (2-5.30)*

▲ **Saltram House, Plympton** ♿✀ (The National Trust) *3m E of Plymouth, S of A38, 2m W of Plympton.* 4ha with fine specimen trees; spring garden; rhododendrons and azaleas. C18 orangery and octagonal garden house. George II mansion with magnificent plasterwork and decorations, incl 2 rooms designed by Robert Adam. Wheelchair available. Restaurant. *Adm gardens only £2.90 Chd £1.40. For NGS Suns April 9, May 7 (10.30-5.30)*

Scypen, Ringmore ✀❀ (Mr & Mrs John Bracey) *From A379 Plymouth to Kingsbridge rd, turn S at Harraton Cross on B3392. R at Pickwick Inn. Park in Journey's End car park on L opp church.* ½ acre coastal garden, integrating design, landscaping and mixed planting for yr-round effect and to take advantage of lovely views. Salt and wind tolerant plants; silver garden. Imaginative sculptural walls and structures. Featured on BBC and Westcountry TV and in 'The Garden' and 'The English Garden'. TEAS. *Adm £1.50 Chd 25p. Wed, Sun June 14, 18 (2-5)*

Seaton & Colyford Gardens *Far E of Devon off A3052, midway between Sidmouth and Lyme Regis.* Cream TEAS at Paddocks *Combined adm £2 Chd 50p. Suns July 9, 16 (2-6)*

Blue Firs ❀ (Mr & Mrs E Reynolds) *Wessiters, Seaton. From A3052, turn at Water Tower Service Station, proceed down hill, turning R at two bollards into Marlpit Lane. At Beer Rd junction turn R and R again. Park in rd.* Small interesting garden with mixed borders. NCCPG National Collection holder of Penstemon cultivars.

Paddocks (Alan & Wendy Davies) *Stafford Lane, Colyford. At W end of Colyford, turn N following signs to Colyton Grammar School. Parking in school following signs (disabled at house).* Developing 2 acres on gentle slope, views over Axe valley. Lawns with mixed shrub planting, herbaceous border, good vegetables and a Bear! TEAS. *(ACNO to Cancer Research Fund)*

The Vinyard (Mollie & Michael Pickup) *Seaton Rd, Colyford. At Colyford PO turn S. House 200yds on L. Parking.* 1¼ acres, scree bed, ponds, mature trees, shrubs, borders, vegetables, small orchard

Sherwood, Newton St Cyres (John & Prue Quicke) *Off A377 Exeter to Barnstaple rd, ¾m Crediton side of Newton St Cyres, signed Sherwood, entrance to drive in 1¾m.* 14 acres comprising 2 steep valleys. Mature trees, wild daffodils, primroses, bluebells and other wild flowers; extensive collections of magnolias, camellias, rhododendrons, azaleas (mainly deciduous), heathers, acers, prostrate cotoneasters, hostas, hydrangeas, rodgersias and other ornamental trees and shrubs. Limited access for wheelchairs. *Adm £2 (ACNO to UNICEF) Every Sun March 12 to Nov 12 (2-5)*

Shobrooke Park Gardens, Crediton ♿✀ (Dr & Mrs J R Shelley) *1m NE Crediton on A3072.* 15-acre woodland garden with daffodils, rhododendrons and roses. Laid out in mid C19 with extensive Portland Stone terraces with views over the park and ponds. Restoration in an early stage with help from The Countryside Commission. TEAS. *Adm £2 Chd free. Sats April 15, May 13, June 10 (2-5)*

Sidmouth Gardens ✀❀ *From Sidford take A3052 E, turn R after Blue Ball public house, signposted Sidmouth/Fortescue. Approx 1m, both gardens are very close. Combined adm £2 Chd 50p Fri, Sat May 26, 27 (2-5.30)*

The Anchorage (Mr & Mrs Horton) Large garden on steep slope. Many steps with viewing points overlooking river Sid and lush planting. Park in rd.

Clevedon Lodge (Mr R W Webb) Artist's garden on gentle slope with lovely views. ⅓-acre with great variety of trees, shrubs, climbers and urns. Parking

Southcombe House, Widecombe-in-the-Moor (Dr & Mrs JR Seale) *6m W of Bovey Tracey, house marked on Landranger OS map 191. After village church take rd SW for 200yds then sharp R, signposted Southcombe, up steep hill. House is 200yds on L. Pass house and park on L.* 5 acres, SE-facing garden, recently planted arboretum, developing wild flower meadow on steep slope at 900' above sea level with fine views to nearby tors. Primarily of interest to wild flower enthusiasts. *Adm £2 Chd free By appt only, please* **Tel 01364 621365**

Southdown Farm, Brixham (Mrs Etessami) *Southdown Hill Rd. From Brixham town centre take Bolton St to Kingswear past St Mary's Church, then in ¼m L up Southdown Hill Rd. Farm is at end of rd.* 1 acre of shrubs, roses and herbaceous perennials. Magnificent country views to sea. Not suitable for wheelchairs. *Adm £2 Chd free. Sat, Sun June 17, 18 (11-6)*

Sowton Mill, Dunsford ❀ (A Cooke & S Newton) *From Dunsford take B3193 S for ½m. Entrance straight ahead off sharp R bend by bridge. From A38 N along Teign Valley for 8m. Sharp R after humpback bridge.* 4 acres laid out around former mill (not open), leat and river. Part woodland with multitudes of wildflowers in spring, ornamental trees and shrubs, mixed borders and scree. Yr-round interest. TEAS. *Adm £2 Chd free (ACNO to Cygnet Training Theatre). Combined adm with Honeyway Farm £3. Suns May 7, July 9 (2-6). Private visits also welcome, please* **Tel 01647 252347/252263**

Spillifords, Lower Washfield (Dr Gavin Haig) *Tiverton. Take A396 Tiverton to Bampton rd, turn L over iron bridge signposted Stoodleigh.Turn L again after crossing bridge marked Washfield and L again on hill following Washfield sign. Bridge is approx 2m from link rd roundabout. Spillifords is 1st house on L after Hatswell. Parking in field.* Wildllife garden of 4 acres on sloping bank of R Exe (unsuitable for disabled) wild flowers, butterflies, birds and other wildlife abound in an ideal arboreal and riverside environment. Dogs welcome. TEAS. *Adm £2 Chd £1. Guided tours by appt only. Weds and some selected weekends, April to Aug (3-6). Please check by phone first,* **Tel 01884 255353** weekdays only (9-6.30)

St Olaves, Murchington ✂ (Mr & Mrs R Padley) *1m W of Chagford. On A382 1m S of Whiddon Down signposted Throwleigh and Gidleigh, then follow signs to Murchington and to garden.* Garden converted, restored and replanted since 1971. On S-facing slope down which a cascade falls to river. Romantic landscape views over Upper Teign Valley. Fine old trees and many younger ones, incl collection of modern magnolia hybrids. Massive granite retaining walls. *Adm £2 Chd 50p (ACNO to Devon Gardens Trust®) Weds April 26, May 10 (2-5.30). Also private visits always welcome (for magnolias and camellias mid-March to May, please* **Tel 01647 433415**

Starveacre, Dalwood ❀ (Mr & Mrs Bruce Archibold) *Leave Axminster on A35 travelling W. After 3m (Shute Xrds) turn R. At staggered Xrds follow signs to Dalwood and go through village, over stream, round sharp L bend. Follow road, ignoring L turn, up steep hill and at top turn L. Under pylons and up hill. Car park on L.* Plantsman's garden of 5 acres on hillside facing S and W with superb views. Mixed plantings of rhododendrons, camellias, conifers, acers, magnolias and much more. TEAS. *Adm £2 Chd free. Suns April 30, May 28, Oct 15 (2-5)*

Sunnybrook Cottage, Luffincott ❀ (Bill & Jean Wonnacott) *A388 halfway between Holsworthy and Launceston signed Luffincott at lay-by, cottage 1m on L. Ample parking.* Walking from something organised, through changing areas with pond, streams, bogs, wood, yr-round interest. Not so much a garden as a safari! Children welcomed and free. Cream TEAS. Plants for sale in aid of Save the Children Fund. *Adm £1.50. Suns May 14, 28, June 11, 25, July 30, Aug 27 (2-6). Private visits also welcome, please* **Tel 01409 271380**

Sunrise Hill, Withleigh ✂❀ (Chris & Sharon Britton) *3m W of Tiverton on B3137 to Witheridge and South Molton. Garden reached through Withleigh Nurseries, situated at E end of village.* 1½ acres of colourful garden incl 40m 'rainbow' border, unusual plants, shrubs, lawns and new plantings. Plants for sale at adjacent nursery (on open days 10% of sales to Meningitis Research Trust). TEAS in aid of Meningitis Research Trust. *Adm £1.50 Chd free. Weds June 28, July 19, Aug 16 (2-5.30). Parties welcome by appt, please* **Tel 01884 253351**

■ **Tapeley Park, Instow** ♿ (Hector Christie) *A39 Barnstaple-Bideford drive entrance and lodge 1m S of Instow.* Italianate garden with stunning coastal views to Atlantic and Lundy Island. Terraces with long wall borders shelter many herbaceous and tender plants, replanted under the infuence of Mary Keen and Carol Klein. Walled kitchen and vegetable garden with long greenhouse for tender plants and grapes. Ice and shell houses. Organic permaculture garden; clematis specialist. Lunches and cream TEAS. *Adm £3.50 OAP £3 Chd £2. Sun 19 March to Tues Oct 31 daily except Sats (10-5)*

Topsham Gardens ♿❀ *4m from Exeter. Free parking at Holman Way car park and Grove Hill.* Teas at 20 Monmouth Ave. *Adm £1 each garden Chd free. Sun, Mon May 28, 29 (2-6)*

4 Grove Hill (Mr & Mrs A J Boyce) *Off Elm Grove Rd, opp junction with Station Rd.* Small town garden with rare plants, troughs and screes with alpine plants and unusual bulbs

20 Monmouth Avenue (Anne & Harold Lock) *Access to Monmouth Ave by footpath on L after leaving Holman Way car park.* ⅓ acre level garden, wide range of unusual plants and shrubs giving yr-round effect, mixed curved borders, herbaceous, shrubs and bulbs incl collection of hardy geraniums, alliums, pulmonarias and ferns. Featured on TV 'Gardens For All'. TEAS. *Private visits also welcome, please* **Tel 01392 873734**

96 Wasdale Gardens, Estover, Plymouth ✂❀ (Mr & Mrs D Fenwick) *From A38 Forder Valley Junction, follow signs for Estover, turn L at ASDA sign. Turn L at 2nd mini roundabount past ASDA (Keswick Crescent) 1st L into Wasdale Gardens. Car park RH-side of 102. 96 is beyond 95 and 94 at W end of car park.* Small garden totally dedicated to South African plants, complete re-design winter 1999. NCCPG Plant Collections of Crocosmia and Chasmanthe. *Adm £2 Chd £1. Suns July 30, Aug 6, Wed Aug 2 (10-4). Visits welcome by appt June 1 to Sept 1, please* **Tel 01752 785147**

NEW **The Water Garden, Wembworthy** ♿✂❀ (J M Smith Esq) *From A377 at Eggesford Stn follow signs to Wembworthy (2m W). From Winkleigh take Wembworthy to Eggesford rd (2m E). Turn at Xrd sign at Lymington Arms.* 1 acre with 8 water features; hot stony slopes, shade and bog plantings, wild area surrounding clay pond, irises, shrubs, trees, ferns, clematis and unusual plants; conservatory. Plant sales available from stock propagation. Toilet. TEAS. *Adm £2 Chd 50p. Fris, Suns, Mons, April to September. For NGS Sats, Suns May 6, 7, 27, 28, June 3, 4, 24, 25 (10-5). Private visits welcome by appt, please* **Tel 01837 83566**

Webbery Gardens, Alverdiscott ✂❀ *Approx 2½m E of Bideford. Either from Bideford (East the Water) along Alverdiscott rd, or from Barnstaple to Torrington rd B3232, take rd to Bideford at Alverdiscott and pass through Stoney Cross.* TEA. *Combined adm £2 Chd free. Sat, Sun June 17, 18 (2-6)*

Little Webbery, Alverdiscott (Mr & Mrs J A Yewdall) *Parking in next door field.* Approx 3 acres with two large borders and lawns running down a valley; pond, mature trees on either side and fields below, separated by 2 ha-has. Lake beyond. Walled garden with box hedging partly used for fruit and vegetables, greenhouse; rose garden and trellises; shrubs and climbing plants.

Little Webbery Cottage (Mr & Mrs J A Yewdall) *Parking and entrance as for Little Webbery.* Self contained cottage garden with wide selection of flowering plants and shrubs incl pergolas with roses, clematis and jasmine

NEW **Westcott Barton, Barnstaple** ♿✂❀ (Ann Burnham) *From Barnstaple 4m N to Guineaford, continue N for 1m. Turn L, signed Middle Marwood, 2nd L at Westcott Barton sign.* 2-acre developing valley garden with stream and bridge. Bluebell walk through woods. Garden surrounds C12 farmhouse (not open) with cobbled courtyard and range of outbuildings with water wheel. Mediaeval tithe barn. Collection of farm implements. Cream TEAS. *Adm £1.50 Chd 50p. Suns, Mons April 30, May 1, 28, 29 (Bank Hol), June 25, 26,*

July 30, 31, Aug 27, 28 (Bank Hol), Sept 24, 25 (2-6). Also open by appt, please **Tel 01271 814825**

Westpark, Yealmpton (Mr and Mrs David Court) *7m E of Plymouth. On A379 Kingsbridge rd, at Xrds at centre of village, turn S on B3186 Newton Ferrers rd; park at end of Torr Lane.* Rambling cherished garden set in quiet countryside created in 1900s, retaining many original features. Woodland walk, rocky outcrop, mulberry (1907) var magnolia. In spring esp interesting variety of exciting old bulbs species. Vegetable garden. Family album of original owners on view. TEAS. *Adm £2 Chd free (ACNO to St Bartholomew's Church). Sun, Wed March 26, 29 (2-5). Private visits welcome, please* **Tel 01752 880236**

Withleigh Farm, Withleigh Village (T Matheson) *3m W of Tiverton on B3137, 10yds W of 1st small 30mph sign, entrance to drive at white gate.* Peaceful undisturbed rural setting with valley garden, 17 years in making; stream, pond and waterside plantings; bluebell wood walk under canopy of mature oak and beech; wild flower meadow, primroses and daffodils in spring: wild orchids in June. TEA. *Adm £1.50 Chd 50p (ACNO to Cancer & Arthritis Research) Sat, Sun May 13, 14 (2-5). Private visits also welcome, please* **Tel 01884 253853**

Wolford Lodge, Dunkeswell (The Very Rev & Mrs Patrick Mitchell) *Take Honiton to Dunkeswell rd. After 3m up hill go L at Limer's Cross. Drive ½m down small hill. Enter drive on L at white railings then entrance gate and lodge.* 4 acres semi-woodland with massed rhododendrons, azaleas, magnolias and camellias. Distant views to S over unspoilt Devon countryside. Woodland walks. *Adm £1.50 OAP/Chd £1 (ACNO to Research Trust for Metabolic Diseases in Children). Sats May 13, 20, Sun May 14 (2-6)*

Wood Barton, Kentisbeare (Mr & Mrs Richard Horton) *3m from M5 exit 28. Take A373 Cullompton to Honiton rd. After 2m turn L, signed Goodiford, for 1m and turn L again at White Cottages. Farm drive, 100yds on R. Bull on sign. [Landranger 192. Lat 09 Long 05/06].* 2 acres woodland garden planted 50yrs ago with species trees on S-facing slope. Magnolias, azaleas, camellias, rhododendrons, acers; several ponds and water feature. Autumn colour. TEAS. *Adm £1.50 Chd free (ACNO to Action Research). Sun March 19, Sun May 14 (2-6). Also private visits by appt, please* **Tel 01884 266285**

Woodside, Barnstaple (Mr & Mrs Mervyn Feesey) *Higher Raleigh Rd. A39 to Hospital and Lynton, turn R 300yds above fire station.* Semi-woodland, S sloping with intensive shrub and tree planting. Ornamental grasses, sedges, bamboos and monocots (Author of RHS Handbook on Ornamental Grasses). Parts of garden are shaded and peaceful, offering protection to unusual and tender shrubs, many variegated and acid-loving. Special interest in New Zealand flora. Emphasis on form and colour of foliage. *Adm £1.50 Chd 50p. Sun July 9 (2-5.30)*

Wrangaton House, Wrangaton (Surgeon Captain & Mrs R L Travis) *Midway between Ivybridge and S Brent. ½m N of A38. From Exeter leave A38 at Wrangaton Cross, cross over to N of A38 and proceed westward ½m. From Plymouth leave A38 at Ivybridge and take Exeter rd for 3m. Both directions turn N up Blacksmith Lane. Wrangaton House is ¼m on L past thatched cottage.* 3 acres mature garden to mellow manor house (not open) on southern slopes of Dartmoor. Large pool; water plants; streams; rhododendrons; azaleas; camellias and bulbs. Adjacent bluebell wood of 1½ acres. Beautiful situation. TEAS. *Adm £2 Chd under 14 free. Sun April 16, Sun, Mon April 30, May 1 (2-5)*

Wylmington Hayes, Wilmington (Mr & Mrs P Saunders) *5½m NE of Honiton on A30, turn R signposted Stockland 3m, Axminster 10m. After 3½m entrance gates on R (before Stockland TV Station). Or from A35, 3½m W of Axminster turn N nr Shute Garage on to Stockland rd, proceed for 3m, entrance on L nr TV mast.* 83 acres of reclaimed gardens created in 1911. Woodlands with spectacular hybrid rhododendrons, azaleas, magnolias, camellias and acers. Lakes, ponds, topiary, arboretum, woodland walks with wildlife. Collection of ornamental and domestic waterfowl including black swans. Scottish Country Dancing June 4. Open peak rhododendron/azalea time. TEAS. *Adm £3 Chd £1. Suns May 14, 21, 28, June 4 (2-5). Coaches & parties by appt please* **Tel 01404 831751**

Yonder Hill, Colaton Raleigh (Mrs M H Herbert) *On B3178 Newton Poppleford to Colaton Raleigh rd, take turning signed to Dotton, then immed R into small lane. ¼m, 1st house on R.* 2 acres peaceful gardeners' paradise in magical setting. Surprises everywhere, trees, shrubs, pebble and letter beds, rare grasses, ponds, loggeries, bamboos, eucalyptus, alpines, herbaceous and more. Wheelchair available, toilet, DIY TEA. *Adm £1 Chd 50p. Suns, Mons, Tues, Fris, Sats Feb 27, March 12, 13, 26, 27, April 9, 10, 21, 22, 23, 24, 30, May 1, 14, 15, 28, 29 June 11, 12, 18, 19, July 9, 10, 23, 24, 30, 31, Aug 13, 14, 27, 28, Sept 10, 11, 24, 25, Oct 1, 2, 15, 16 (11-4.30). Visitors welcome on other days between Feb 27 and Oct 16, but please* **Tel 01395 567541** in advance

Evening Opening (See also garden description)

Greenlands	June 21
Membland Villa, Newton Ferrers	April 21

HOSTAS
ANN & ROGER BOWDEN
specialise in HOSTA PLANTS
National Collection of 750 plants in 1 acre ornamental garden, open for viewing. Send 3 x 1st class stamps for illustrated catalogue of 350 varieties. Mail order.
Visitors by arrangement only
Tel: 0183 784 0481
Sticklepath, Okehampton, Devon EX20 2NL
Collecting box

The Edgemoor - Hotel and Restaurant

Romantically styled Country House set in two acres of grounds literally adjacent to Dartmoor National Park. A wonderful position from which to tour the area, which has many National Trust properties and gardens within easy reach.

All rooms en-suite
AA 2 Rosettes for Food   Elegance without Pretension
*AA***RAC   Johansens   Which? Hotel Guide*

Haytor Road, Bovey Tracey, Devon TQ13 9LE Tel: (01626) 832466 www.edgemoor.co.uk

The National Gardens Scheme Year 2001 Calendar

The perfect gift for garden-lovers, this calendar, produced by the Medici Society Ltd., is available from Medici retailers or by mail or telephone (priced £4.95 plus p&p) from the Gardeners Royal Benevolent Society, Bridge House, 139 Kingston Road, Leatherhead, Surrey KT22 7NW.

Telephone orders with debit or credit card on (44) (0) 1372 373962

HILL HOUSE NURSERY & GARDENS

A nursery growing majority of own plants (not a garden centre). Three acres of garden. Range of glass houses displaying many thousands of high quality garden-worthy plants, from the most common to the rare and exotic. Our Nemesia 'Bluebird' was released for sale 1999 worldwide.

Nursery open all year from 11 am - 5 pm
Tea room for cream teas and light lunches
open 1st March to 1st October

Landscove, Nr Ashburton, Devon

Tel. 01803 762273

Edge of Exmoor

Small and attractive country hotel offers tranquility in eight acres of gardens, woodland, paddocks and pond. Superb long scenic views.

Near Arlington, Marwood, Rosemoor and Exmoor's magnificent coastline.

Accommodation includes two ground-floor rooms and 2-person self catering cottage.

Well-trained dog-owners welcome.

Please ring for full brochure

(01598) 710320

AA ♦♦♦♦♦ ETC Gold Award
The Good Hotel Guide 2000

Prue & Lawrie Scott
Bracken House
Bratton Fleming.

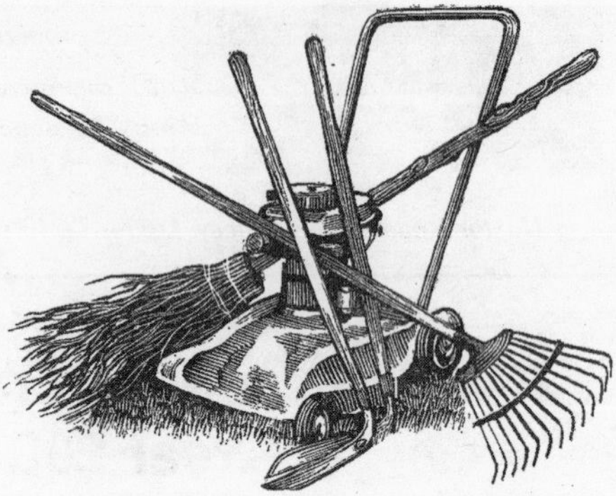

The Quiet Garden Trust

The Quiet Garden Trust was founded to initiate and resource a network of local opportunities for prayer, silence, reflection, and the appreciation of beauty; for learning about Christian life and spirituality; and for experiencing creativity and healing in the context of God's love. The Quiet Garden Trust encourages provision of local venues where there is an opportunity to set time aside to rest and to pray. These quiet spaces allow those caught up in the stress of work and domestic chores the opportunity, however short, to take time to stop and simply "be".

For more information about the Quiet Garden Trust, please contact:

The Quiet Garden Trust
Stoke Park Farm, Park Road
Stoke Poges, Buckinghamshire SL2 4PG
Tel: **01753 643050**
Fax: **01753 643081**
Email: **quiet.garden@ukonline.co.uk**

Dorset

Hon County Organiser: Mrs Hugh Lindsay, The Old Rectory, Litton Cheney, Dorchester DT2 9AH
Tel 01308 482383 Fax 01308 482261

Assistant Hon County Organisers: Miss Jane Bennett, The Maples, Fontmell Magna, Shaftesbury SP7 0PF
Tel 01747 811766
Mrs Boileau, Rampisham Manor, Dorchester DT2 0PT Tel 01935 83612
Stanley Cherry Esq, Highbury, Woodside Road, West Moors, Ferndown BH22 0LY
Tel 01202 874372 Fax 01202 874370
Walter Ninniss Esq, 52 Rossmore Road, Parkstone, Poole BH12 3NL
Tel 01202 740913

Publicity: Mrs Susan Henwood, The Old Rectory, West Compton, Dorchester DT2 0EY
Tel & Fax 01300 320007

Hon County Treasurer: Michael Gallagher Esq, 6 West Street, Chickerell, Weymouth DT3 4DY

DATES OF OPENING

Regular openings

For details see garden description

- Abbotsbury Gardens, nr Weymouth
- Athelhampton House & Gardens, Dorchester
- Chiffchaffs, Chaffeymoor
- Compton Acres Gardens, Poole
- Cranborne Manor Garden, Cranborne
- Friars Way, Upwey
- Horn Park, Beaminster
- Ivy Cottage, Ansty
- Kingston Maurward Gardens, Dorchester
- Knoll Gardens and Nursery, Hampreston
- Leigh Farm, Halstock
- Mapperton Gardens, nr Beaminster
- Minterne, Minterne Magna
- Moreton Gardens, nr Dorchester
- Parnham, Beaminster
- Snape Cottage, Chaffeymoor
- Springhead, Fontmell Magna
- Stapehill Abbey, Ferndown
- Star Cottage, Cowgrove
- Sticky Wicket, Buckland Newton
- Upwey Wishing Well, Upwey
- White Pit Cottage, Shillingstone
- Wimborne Minster Model Town

By appointment only

For telephone numbers and other details see garden descriptions. Private visits welcomed

- Arne View, Hamworthy
- Highbury, West Moors
- Moulin Huet, West Moors

March 5 Sunday
Chiffchaffs, Chaffeymoor

March 9 Thursday
Farrs Coach House, Wimborne

March 12 Sunday
Aurelia Gardens, West Moors
Mews Cottage, Portland
Welcome Thatch, Witchampton
Witchcroft, Southwell

March 19 Sunday
Langebride House, Long Bredy
Stour House, Blandford

March 26 Sunday
Aurelia Gardens, West Moors

April 2 Sunday
Chiffchaffs, Chaffeymoor
Langebride House, Long Bredy
1 Manor Close, Stratton
Manor Orchard, Stratton

April 5 Wednesday
Cranborne Manor Garden, Cranborne
Edmondsham House, nr Cranborne
1 Manor Close, Stratton
Manor Orchard, Stratton

April 6 Thursday
Friars Way, Upwey

April 9 Sunday
Ashley Park Farm, Damerham
Boveridge Farm, Cranborne
Domineys Yard, Buckland Newton
Fernhill Gardens, Witchampton
Welcome Thatch, Witchampton

April 10 Monday
Wall Farm, Broadwindsor

April 12 Wednesday
Edmondsham House, nr Cranborne
Horn Park, Beaminster

April 13 Thursday
Farrs Coach House, Wimborne
Friars Way, Upwey

April 16 Sunday
Bexington, Lytchett Matravers
Cartref, Stalbridge
Chiffchaffs, Chaffeymoor
Stour House, Blandford

April 17 Monday
Wall Farm, Broadwindsor

April 19 Wednesday
Edmondsham House, nr Cranborne
Springhead, Fontmell Magna

April 20 Thursday
Friars Way, Upwey

April 21 Friday
Aurelia Gardens, West Moors

April 22 Saturday
Glebe Cottage, Woodsford

April 23 Sunday
Ashley Park Farm, Damerham
Aurelia Gardens, West Moors
Chiffchaffs, Chaffeymoor
Deans Court, Wimborne
Frankham Farm, Ryme Intrinseca
Friars Way, Upwey
The Old Rectory, Litton Cheney
The Old Rectory, West Compton
Snape Cottage, Chaffeymoor

April 24 Monday
Aurelia Gardens, West Moors
Chiffchaffs, Chaffeymoor
Deans Court, Wimborne
Edmondsham House, nr Cranborne

April 25 Tuesday
Puck's Knoll, Marshwood

April 26 Wednesday
Edmondsham House, nr Cranborne
Rampisham Manor, Rampisham

April 27 Thursday
Friars Way, Upwey

April 30 Sunday
Ashley Park Farm, Damerham
Aurelia Gardens, West Moors
Boveridge Farm, Cranborne
Chiffchaffs, Chaffeymoor
Corfe Barn, Broadstone
Deans Court, Wimborne

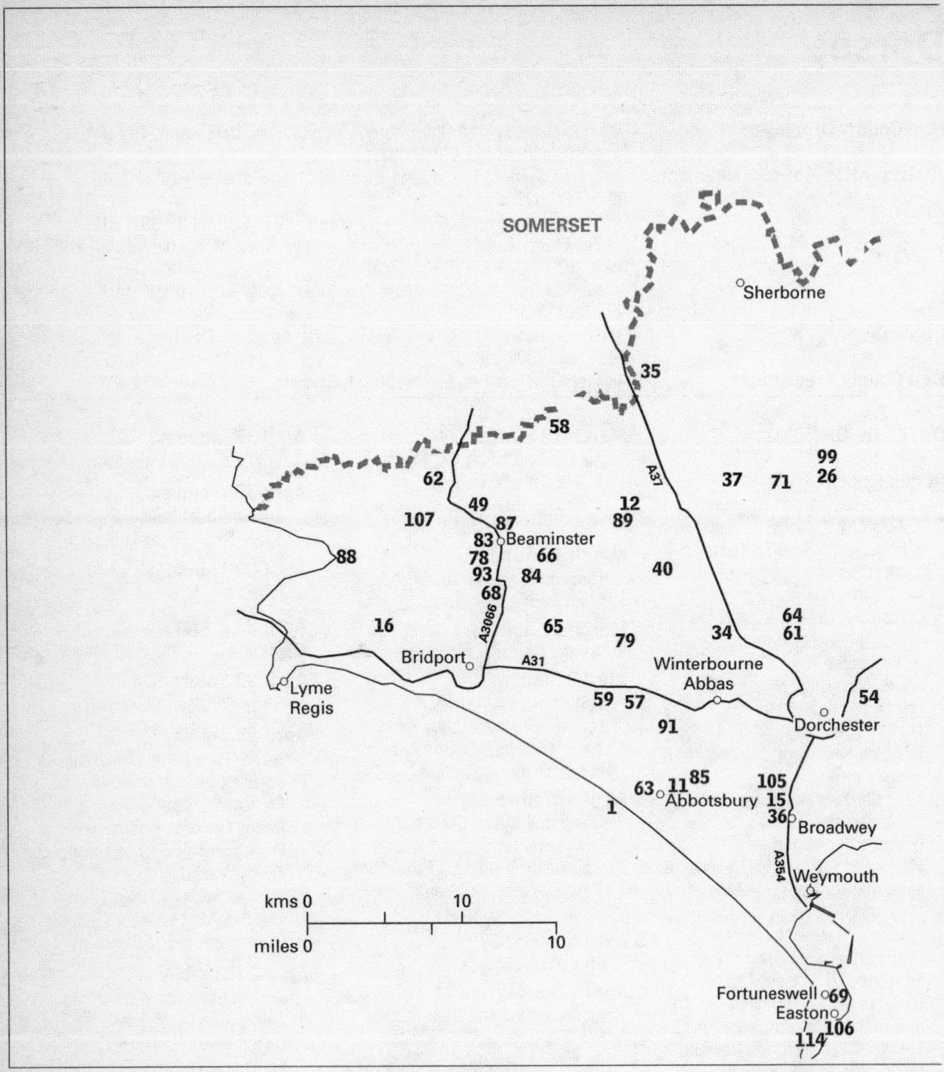

KEY

1 Abbotsbury Gardens
2 Aller Green
3 Arne Barn
4 Arne View
5 Ashley Park Farm
6 Athelhampton House & Gardens
7 Aurelia Gardens
8 34 Avon Avenue
9 Bexington
10 Boveridge Farm
11 Bridge House
12 Broomhill
13 Cartref
14 Chiffchaffs
15 7 Church Street
16 Clent Cottage
17 Compton Acres Gardens
18 Coombe Cottage
19 Corfe Barn
20 Cothayes House & Vine Cottage
21 Cottesmore Farm
22 Cranborne Manor Garden
23 Cucumber Cottage
24 2 Curlew Road
25 Deans Court
26 Domineys Yard
27 Edmondsham House
28 Farriers
29 Farrs Coach House
30 Fernhill Gardens
31 Fiddleford Gardens
32 29 Filleul Road
33 4 Flower Cottage
34 Frampton Rose Garden
35 Frankham Farm
36 Friars Way
37 The Friary
38 Glebe Cottage
39 Glebe House
40 Greenings
41 2 Greenwood Avenue
42 Highbury
43 Higher Melcombe
44 7 Highfield Close
45 Highwood Garden
46 Hilltop
47 Holworth Farmhouse
48 Hookeswood House
49 Horn Park
50 Ivy Cottage
51 Japanese Gardens
52 80 Keith Road
53 Kingston Lacy
54 Kingston Maurward Gardens
55 Knitson Old Farmhouse
56 Knoll Gardens and Nursery
57 Langebride House
58 Leigh Farm

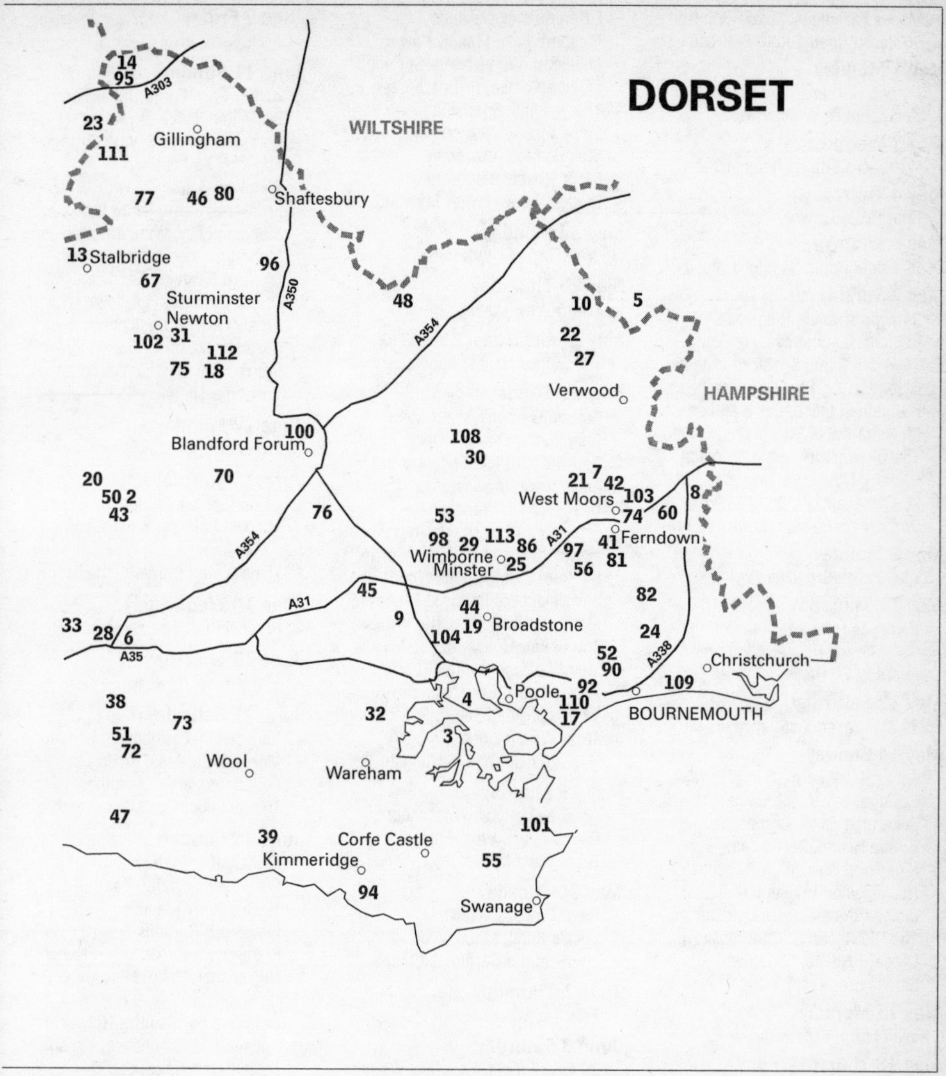

59 Litton Cheney Gardens
60 6 Malmesbury Road
61 1 Manor Close
62 Manor Farmhouse
63 The Manor House
64 Manor Orchard
65 Mappercombe Manor
66 Mapperton Gardens
67 Mead Cottage
68 Melplash Court
69 Mews Cottage
70 Millmead
71 Minterne
72 Moigne Combe
73 Moreton Gardens
74 Moulin Huet
75 Okeford Fitzpaine Gardens
76 The Old Mill, Spetisbury
77 The Old Rectory, Fifehead Magdalen
78 The Old Rectory, Netherbury
79 The Old Rectory, West Compton
80 The Orchard
81 Orchard House
82 Parley Court
83 Parnham
84 Pear Tree Farm
85 Portesham House
86 The Priest's House Museum & Garden
87 Prospect Cottage
88 Puck's Knoll
89 Rampisham Manor
90 46 Roslin Road South
91 The Scented Garden
92 16a Seamoor Road
93 Slape Manor
94 Smedmore
95 Snape Cottage
96 Springhead
97 Stapehill Abbey
98 Star Cottage
99 Sticky Wicket
100 Stour House
101 Studland Bay House
102 Sturminster Newton Gardens
103 Tara
104 Three Bays
105 Upwey Wishing Well
106 78 Wakeham
107 Wall Farm
108 Welcome Thatch
109 Wentworth College
110 24a Western Avenue
111 Weston House
112 White Pit Cottage
113 Wimborne Minster Model Town
114 Witchcroft

Manor Farmhouse, Little Windsor
46 Roslin Road South, Bournemouth

May 1 Monday
Aurelia Gardens, West Moors
Deans Court, Wimborne

May 3 Wednesday
Prospect Cottage, Beaminster

May 4 Thursday
Friars Way, Upwey

May 6 Saturday
29 Filleul Road, Sandford Woods

May 7 Sunday
34 Avon Avenue, Ringwood
Chiffchaffs, Chaffeymoor
29 Filleul Road, Sandford Woods
Glebe House, East Lulworth
7 Highfield Close, Corfe Mullen
Mews Cottage, Portland
The Old Rectory, West Compton
Orchard House, Ferndown
78 Wakeham, Portland
Wentworth College, Bournemouth

May 8 Monday
Wall Farm, Broadwindsor

May 11 Thursday
Cothayes House & Vine Cottage
Farrs Coach House, Wimborne
Friars Way, Upwey

May 13 Saturday
34 Avon Avenue, Ringwood

May 14 Sunday
Ashley Park Farm, Damerham
Bexington, Lytchett Matravers
Boveridge Farm, Cranborne
Bridge House, Portesham
Highwood Garden, Wareham
Hookeswood House, Farnham
Moigne Combe, nr Dorchester
The Old Rectory, Netherbury
Orchard House, Ferndown
Smedmore, Kimmeridge

May 15 Monday
Wall Farm, Broadwindsor

May 18 Thursday
Friars Way, Upwey

May 18 to 19 Thursday to Friday
The Friary, Hilfield

May 20 Saturday
The Friary, Hilfield
Studland Bay House, Studland

May 21 Sunday
34 Avon Avenue, Ringwood
Cartref, Stalbridge
Chiffchaffs, Chaffeymoor
2 Curlew Road, Bournemouth
The Friary, Hilfield
2 Greenwood Avenue, Ferndown
Highwood Garden, Wareham
Leigh Farm, Halstock
Litton Cheney Gardens
Mappercombe Manor, Powerstock
Millmead, Winterborne Stickland
Moigne Combe, nr Dorchester
The Old Mill, Spetisbury
Slape Manor, Netherbury
Star Cottage, Cowgrove
Stour House, Blandford
Studland Bay House, Studland

May 22 Monday
Wall Farm, Broadwindsor

May 25 Thursday
Friars Way, Upwey

May 27 Saturday
The Manor House, Abbotsbury

May 28 Sunday
Aurelia Gardens, West Moors
Chiffchaffs, Chaffeymoor
Coombe Cottage, Shillingstone
Corfe Barn, Broadstone
Deans Court, Wimborne
Frankham Farm, Ryme Intrinseca
Holworth Farmhouse, Holworth
80 Keith Road, Talbot Woods
6 Malmesbury Road, St Leonards
Manor Farmhouse, Little Windsor
The Manor House, Abbotsbury
Mead Cottage, Hinton St Mary
Parley Court, Christchurch
46 Roslin Road South, Bournemouth
Tara, West Moors
White Pit Cottage, Shillingstone

May 29 Monday
Aurelia Gardens, West Moors
Deans Court, Wimborne
Tara, West Moors

May 30 Tuesday
Clent Cottage, Ryall
Puck's Knoll, Marshwood
The Scented Garden, Littlebredy

June 1 Thursday
Friars Way, Upwey

June 3 Saturday
29 Filleul Road, Sandford Woods

June 4 Sunday
Chiffchaffs, Chaffeymoor
29 Filleul Road, Sandford Woods
2 Greenwood Avenue, Ferndown
Orchard House, Ferndown
Wimborne Minster Model Town

June 5 Monday
Wall Farm, Broadwindsor

June 6 Tuesday
Horn Park, Beaminster
The Scented Garden, Littlebredy

June 8 Thursday
Friars Way, Upwey
Mappercombe Manor, Powerstock

June 9 Friday
Arne Barn, Arne

June 11 Sunday
Ashley Park Farm, Damerham
Bexington, Lytchett Matravers
Cothayes House & Vine Cottage
Farriers, Puddletown
4 Flower Cottage, Lower Waterston
Frankham Farm, Ryme Intrinseca
Kingston Lacy, Wimborne Minster
Mead Cottage, Hinton St Mary
Okeford Fitzpaine Gardens
Orchard House, Ferndown
Parley Court, Christchurch
Portesham House, Portesham
Sturminster Newton Gardens
Welcome Thatch, Witchampton

June 12 Monday
Wall Farm, Broadwindsor

June 13 Tuesday
Litton Cheney Gardens
The Old Rectory, West Compton (evening)
The Scented Garden, Littlebredy

June 14 Wednesday
Prospect Cottage, Beaminster

June 15 Thursday
Friars Way, Upwey

June 17 Saturday
Knitson Old Farmhouse, Knitson
Moreton Gardens, nr Dorchester
Pear Tree Farm, Loscombe
16a Seamoor Road, Westbourne

June 18 Sunday
Chiffchaffs, Chaffeymoor
Cucumber Cottage, Rodgrove, Buckhorn Weston
Fiddleford Gardens
Frampton Rose Garden, Frampton
Higher Melcombe, Melcombe Bingham
Holworth Farmhouse, Holworth
Knitson Old Farmhouse, Knitson
Leigh Farm, Halstock
Mews Cottage, Portland
Moreton Gardens, nr Dorchester
The Old Rectory, Fifehead Magdalen
The Old Rectory, West Compton
Pear Tree Farm, Loscombe
Portesham House, Portesham
16a Seamoor Road, Westbourne
Snape Cottage, Chaffeymoor
Sticky Wicket, Buckland Newton
Stour House, Blandford
78 Wakeham, Portland
Weston House, Buckhorn Weston
Witchcroft, Southwell

June 19 Monday
Wall Farm, Broadwindsor

June 20 Tuesday
The Scented Garden, Littlebredy

June 21 Wednesday
The Orchard, Blynfield Gate

June 22 Thursday
Clent Cottage, Ryall
Friars Way, Upwey

June 24 Saturday
Tara, West Moors

June 25 Sunday
7 Church Street, Upwey
Coombe Cottage, Shillingstone
Corfe Barn, Broadstone
Cottesmore Farm, West Moors
Cranborne Manor Garden, Cranborne
Farrs Coach House, Wimborne
Frampton Rose Garden, Frampton
2 Greenwood Avenue, Ferndown
Hookeswood House, Farnham
Japanese Garden, 38 Bingham's Road, Crossways
1 Manor Close, Stratton
Manor Orchard, Stratton
Parley Court, Christchurch
The Priest's House Museum & Garden, Wimborne
46 Roslin Road South, Bournemouth
Star Cottage, Cowgrove
Tara, West Moors
White Pit Cottage, Shillingstone

June 26 Monday
Wall Farm, Broadwindsor

June 27 Tuesday
Clent Cottage, Ryall
Friars Way, Upwey
The Old Rectory, West Compton (evening)
Puck's Knoll, Marshwood
The Scented Garden, Littlebredy

June 28 Wednesday
1 Manor Close, Stratton
Manor Orchard, Stratton

June 29 Thursday
Friars Way, Upwey

July 1 Saturday
29 Filleul Road, Sandford Woods
Three Bays, Beacon Hill

July 2 Sunday
Aurelia Gardens, West Moors
Chiffchaffs, Chaffeymoor
Cucumber Cottage, Rodgrove, Buckhorn Weston
Domineys Yard, Buckland Newton
29 Filleul Road, Sandford Woods
Frampton Rose Garden, Frampton
7 Highfield Close, Corfe Mullen
Rampisham Manor, Rampisham
Three Bays, Beacon Hill
24a Western Avenue, Poole
Weston House, Buckhorn Weston
Wimborne Minster Model Town

July 4 Tuesday
The Scented Garden, Littlebredy

July 5 Wednesday
Aurelia Gardens, West Moors
Prospect Cottage, Beaminster

July 6 Thursday
Friars Way, Upwey
Greenings, Chilfrome

July 9 Sunday
Aurelia Gardens, West Moors
Bexington, Lytchett Matravers
Broomhill, Rampisham
Farriers, Puddletown
Frampton Rose Garden, Frampton
Friars Way, Upwey
Leigh Farm, Halstock

July 11 Tuesday
The Scented Garden, Littlebredy

July 12 Wednesday
Aurelia Gardens, West Moors

July 13 Thursday
Friars Way, Upwey

July 14 Friday
Clent Cottage, Ryall

July 16 Sunday
Aurelia Gardens, West Moors
Hilltop, Woodville, Stour Provost
Mews Cottage, Portland
The Orchard, Blynfield Gate
Star Cottage, Cowgrove
Stour House, Blandford
78 Wakeham, Portland
Witchcroft, Southwell

July 18 Tuesday
The Scented Garden, Littlebredy

July 19 Wednesday
Aurelia Gardens, West Moors

July 20 Thursday
Friars Way, Upwey

July 22 Saturday
Melplash Court, Melplash

July 23 Sunday
Aurelia Gardens, West Moors
7 Church Street, Upwey
Cottesmore Farm, West Moors
Deans Court, Wimborne
Hilltop, Woodville, Stour Provost

July 25 Tuesday
Clent Cottage, Ryall
Puck's Knoll, Marshwood
The Scented Garden, Littlebredy

July 26 Wednesday
Aurelia Gardens, West Moors

July 27 Thursday
Friars Way, Upwey

July 28 Friday
Holworth Farmhouse, Holworth (evening)

July 30 Sunday
Aurelia Gardens, West Moors
2 Curlew Road, Bournemouth
Hilltop, Woodville, Stour Provost
White Pit Cottage, Shillingstone

August 2 Wednesday
Aurelia Gardens, West Moors
Hilltop, Woodville, Stour Provost

August 5 Saturday
Knitson Old Farmhouse, Knitson
Springhead, Fontmell Magna

August 6 Sunday
Aurelia Gardens, West Moors
Chiffchaffs, Chaffeymoor
Hilltop, Woodville, Stour Provost
Knitson Old Farmhouse, Knitson
Leigh Farm, Halstock

August 9 Wednesday
Aurelia Gardens, West Moors

August 10 Thursday
Greenings, Chilfrome

August 13 Sunday
Aurelia Gardens, West Moors
Bexington, Lytchett Matravers
Domineys Yard, Buckland Newton
Hilltop, Woodville, Stour Provost
Mews Cottage, Portland

August 15 Tuesday
Clent Cottage, Ryall

August 16 Wednesday
Aurelia Gardens, West Moors
The Orchard, Blynfield Gate

August 20 Sunday
Aurelia Gardens, West Moors
7 Church Street, Upwey
Hilltop, Woodville, Stour Provost
Sticky Wicket, Buckland Newton
Stour House, Blandford

August 23 Wednesday
Aurelia Gardens, West Moors
The Old Rectory, West Compton

August 27 Sunday
Aller Green, Ansty
Aurelia Gardens, West Moors
Chiffchaffs, Chaffeymoor
Coombe Cottage, Shillingstone
Cottesmore Farm, West Moors
Deans Court, Wimborne
Ivy Cottage, Ansty
80 Keith Road, Talbot Woods
6 Malmesbury Road, St Leonards
White Pit Cottage, Shillingstone

August 28 Monday
Aurelia Gardens, West Moors
Deans Court, Wimborne
Holworth Farmhouse, Holworth

August 29 Tuesday
Clent Cottage, Ryall
Puck's Knoll, Marshwood

August 30 Wednesday
Aurelia Gardens, West Moors
Rampisham Manor, Rampisham

September 3 Sunday
Chiffchaffs, Chaffeymoor
Leigh Farm, Halstock
Wimborne Minster Model Town

September 10 Sunday
Bexington, Lytchett Matravers
4 Flower Cottage, Lower Waterston

September 13 Wednesday
The Orchard, Blynfield Gate

September 15 Friday
Arne Barn, Arne
Clent Cottage, Ryall

September 16 Saturday
Arne Barn, Arne

September 17 Sunday
Aurelia Gardens, West Moors
Deans Court, Wimborne
Stour House, Blandford

September 24 Sunday
Leigh Farm, Halstock
6 Malmesbury Road, St Leonards
Mews Cottage, Portland

September 26 Tuesday
Clent Cottage, Ryall
Puck's Knoll, Marshwood

October 1 Sunday
Chiffchaffs, Chaffeymoor

October 4 Wednesday
Edmondsham House, nr Cranborne

October 11 Wednesday
Edmondsham House, nr Cranborne

October 15 Sunday
Aurelia Gardens, West Moors
Stour House, Blandford

October 18 Wednesday
Edmondsham House, nr Cranborne

October 25 Wednesday
Edmondsham House, nr Cranborne

October 31 Tuesday
Puck's Knoll, Marshwood

DESCRIPTIONS OF GARDENS

● **Abbotsbury Gardens, nr Weymouth** &✿ (Curator/Head Gardener, Ilchester Estates) *From B3157 Weymouth-Bridport, 200yds W of Abbotsbury village.* 20 acres; uniquely mild Mediterranean-type climate, started in 1760 and considerably extended in C19; much replanting during past few years; very fine collection of rhododendrons, camellias, azaleas. In high summer there are many tender exotics like palm trees, bananas, cannas; along with a wide variety of Australasian plants. Peacocks. Children's play area, woodland trail, aviaries and plant centre. Partly suitable for wheelchairs. TEAS. *Adm £4.20 OAPs £4 Chd £2.50, Family £12 Reduced rate in winter (For party rate). Easter to Oct 31 (10-6), Nov to Feb (10-dusk)* **Tel 01305 871387**

Aller Green, Ansty ✗ (A J Thomas Esq) *Aller Lane, 12m N of Dorchester. Ansty is 6m N of Puddletown and 4m W of Milton Abbas. Aller Lane is a turning near the Fox Inn, Ansty.* 1-acre typical Dorset cottage garden; unusual trees, shrubs and perennials in old orchard setting and many perennials grown for autumn colour. Teas at Ivy Cottage. *Combined adm with Ivy Cottage £2.50 Chd 50p (ACNO to the Red Cross). Sun Aug 27 (2-5.30)*

NEW **Arne Barn, Arne** &✗ (Dinah Thompson and Friends) *4m SE of Wareham 1st L on A351 Wareham to Corfe rd. 3m to village of Arne, leave cars at R.S.P.B. car park as you enter village and procéd on foot 300yds.* ½ acre unconventional garden surrounding architect's converted barn. Strong sense of design in the layout. Created from farmyard and field to give distinctive character changes, incorporating sculpture and special effects planting of both wet and dry areas. Indigenous planting used to merge with surrounding countryside. The emphasis is on low upkeep, maximum enjoyment for minimal effort. TEAS in aid of Money for Madagascar. *Adm £1.50 Chd free. Fri June 9, Fri, Sat Sept 15, 16 (10-5)*

NEW **Arne View, Hamworthy** ✗ (Carol & Alan Hawes) *1 Napier Road. Follow signs for Rockley Park, ¼m past The Yachtsman, on L.* Exotic 100' x 35' rear garden with themed plantings for yr-round sub-tropical effect. Desert area with collection of succulents; Australasian garden with cordylines, acacias, callistemons and phormiums; mini-jungle of South American trees and shrubs; Mediterranean-style garden with swimming pool and large collection of palms and tender shrubs in pots; several conservatories and greenhouses. Not suitable for young children. TEA. *Adm £2. Private visits welcome by appt at any time,* **Tel 01202 671263**

Ashley Park Farm, Damerham &✿ (David Dampney Esq) *Between Cranborne and Fordingbridge. Follow yellow signs off the old B3078, immediately W of village.* Gardens of 5 acres with woodland walks. Arboretum with many interesting trees, eucalyptus grove; wild flower meadow. Many exciting plants for south-facing walls, borders. Growing collections of ferns and hellebores. New water feature. TEAS. *Adm £1.50 Chd free (ACNO to Damerham Church). Suns April 9, 23, 30, May 14, June 11 (2-5.30). (See also Boveridge Farm)). Private visits welcome, please* **Tel 01725 518 200**

● **Athelhampton House & Gardens, Dorchester** &✗✿ (Patrick Cooke Esq) *5m E of Dorchester signed off A35 at Puddletown.* The Gardens date from 1891 incl the Great Court with 12 giant yew topiary pyramids overlooked by two terraced pavilions. This glorious Grade I architectural garden is full of vistas and surprises with spectacular fountains and River Piddle flowing through it. C15 Manor house. Lunches and cream teas. *Adm House & Gardens £5.25, OAPs £4.95, Chd £1.50. Gardens only adults & OAPs £3.75 Chd free. Reduced rates for groups. Open March to Oct daily (except Sats). Nov to Feb on Suns* **Tel 01305 848363**

Aurelia Gardens, West Moors &✗✿ (Mr & Mrs R J Knight) *Newman's Lane. N of village off B3072 Bournemouth-Verwood rd.* Emphasis on coloured foliage with approx 20,000 plants propagated in own nursery, to create massed blocks of colour in an unusual maze-like design. Restless tall grasses provide movement to contrast with natural wildlife pond, its calming effect relying on water table. Rare breeds of poultry, some with powder puff crests and spectacular plumage. Featured on TV and in magazines. TEAS. *Adm £1.50 Not suitable for children. Suns March 12, 26, April 23, 30,*

May 28, July 2, 9, 16, 23, 30, Aug 6, 13, 20, 27, Sept 17, Oct 15, Mons April 24, May 1, 29, Aug 28, Weds July 5, 12, 19, 26, Aug 2, 9, 16, 23, 30, Fri April 21 (2-6)

34 Avon Avenue, Ringwood ♿✄❀ (Mr & Mrs Robert Ives) *Avon Castle. Avon Ave is E off Hurn/Matchams Lane, most readily approached from Boundary Lane, turning NE over bridge over A338 (Spur Rd).* Garden of ¾-acre. A pleasant prospect of vistas designed and maintained by owners over nineteen yrs. A foliage garden of yr-round interest in rooms, with rare and unusual shrubs and herbaceous plants. Collections of conifers, rhododendrons and azaleas, hellebores and alliums. Specimen Juniperus 'Pfitzerana Aurea'. Vegetable and fruit garden. TEAS. *Adm £1.50 Chd free (ACNO May 7 to RNLI and The Soroptomists, May 13 to Ringwood Parish Church). Suns May 7, 21, Sat May 13 (2-5.30)*

Bexington, Lytchett Matravers ♿✄❀ (Mr & Mrs Robin Crumpler) *In Lime Kiln Rd, opp old School at W end of village.* Colourful garden of ½-acre maintained by owners, with mixed borders of many interesting and unusual plants, shrubs and trees. Bog garden of primulas and hostas etc. Four rockeries of alpines, with walkways over bog area connecting two lawns, making a garden of interest from spring bulbs to autumn colour. Cream TEAS & plant stall for Alzheimer's Disease Society & gardening charities. *Adm £1 Chd 20p. Suns April 16, May 14, June 11, July 9, Aug 13, Sept 10 (2-6). Group visits welcome by appt, please* **Tel 01202 622068**

Boveridge Farm, Cranborne ✄ (Mr & Mrs Michael Yarrow) *Leave Cranborne on Martin Rd, thence take 2nd R Boveridge Farm.* A plantsman's garden of 2 acres on 3 levels, part chalk and part acid; with lawns around old farmhouse, formerly manor house of the Hooper family; in rural surroundings with fine views. Fern bank and many rare and interesting trees and shrubs. Specimen acer 'Brilliantissimum', prunus 'Shidare Yoshino', prunus 'Pendula Rubra', Paulownia tomentosa. TEAS at Ashley Park, Damerham (next village 3m). *Adm £1 Chd free (ACNO to Cranborne Village Hall Appeal). Suns April 9, 30, May 14 (2-5). (See also Ashley Park Farm)). Group visits welcome by appt, please* **Tel 01725 517241**

Bridge House, Portesham ♿ (Max & Thea Warwick) *13 Fry's Close. 7m W of Weymouth on coast rd, B3157 to Bridport. From Dorchester take A35 W, turn L in Winterbourne Abbas and follow signs to Portesham; parking in village.* Mostly designed in Japanese manner. A popular strolling water garden and knave-sansui garden. New feature pond and waterfall. *Adm £1.50 Chd free. Sun May 14 (2-6). Private visits welcome, please* **Tel 01305 871685**

Broomhill, Rampisham ❀ (Mr & Mrs D Parry) *From Yeovil take A37 towards Dorchester, 7m turn R signed Evershot, follow sign-post to Rampisham. From Dorchester take A37 towards Yeovil, 4m turn L A356 signed Crewkerne; at start of wireless masts R to Rampisham. Small unspoilt village deep in rural Dorset with C14 church.* Approx 1-acre delightful family garden incorporating disused farmyard and paddock. The pretty trellised entrance leads to mixed borders, island beds filled with a great variety of plants. The lawns slope to a large wildlife pond full of ornamental fish. Cream TEAS and Plant Stall in aid of St John Ambulance - Dorset. *Adm £2. Sun July 9 (12-5)*

▲ **Cartref, Stalbridge** ✄❀ (Mrs Nesta Ann Smith) *Station Rd. From A30, S at Henstridge for 1m. Turn L opp Stalbridge PO, house 80yds on R. Free car park nearby.* A plantsman's garden approx ¼-acre, cottage garden and unusual plants. Small woodland area with choice shade-loving plants and wildlife pond. Small potager, organically grown. Enclosed garden of fruit and roses. TEA. *Adm £2 Chd free. For NGS Suns April 16, May 21 (10-5). Private visits by appt, please* **Tel 01963 363705**

■ **Chiffchaffs, Chaffeymoor** ✄❀ (Mr & Mrs K R Potts) *Situated at W end of Bourton village. Leave A303 (Bourton bypass) at junction signposted Gillingham.* A garden for all seasons with many interesting plants, bulbs, shrubs, herbaceous border, shrub roses. Attractive walk to woodland garden with far-reaching views across the Blackmore Vale. Nursery open Tues-Sat and on garden open days. *Adm £2 Chd 50p (ACNO to Penselwood Church). Open Suns March 5, April 2, 16, 23, 30, May 7, 21,28 June 4, 18, July 2, Aug 6, 27, Sept 3 Oct 1. Every Bank Hol Mon and every Weds & Thurs (2-5) For NGS Suns April 23, May 28, June 18, Aug 6 (2-5) plus 10 per cent of all receipts . Private visits, coaches and refreshments by appt please* **Tel 01747 840841**

7 Church Street, Upwey ♿✄❀ (Ann & Gorden Powell) *½m from bottom of Ridgeway Hill on A354 Dorchester-Weymouth rd turn R B3159 (Bridport rd) L turn at bottom of hill. Please park on rd except disabled.* Circular lawns linked by paths surrounded by beds of trees, shrubs and perennials many with coloured foliage. Vegetables, fruit and woodland. Teas at Wishing Well. *Adm £1.50 Acc chd free. Suns June 25, July 23; Aug 20 (2-6). Group visits by appt,* **Tel 01305 812303**

Clent Cottage, Ryall ✄❀ (S Huggins & T Farnden) *7m W of Bridport on A35. Turn R opp garage as you enter Morcombelake, signed Ryall. 1½m narrow lane. Considerate parking on main rd in village please, space limited, and walk to garden.* Exciting plantsman's garden still under development with voluminous borders packed with unusual and exciting perennials and grasses. Small vineyard and orchard. Not ideal for the disabled. *Adm £1.50 Chd free. Tues May 30, June 27, July 25, Aug 15, 29, Sept 26, Thurs June 22, Fris July 14, Sept 15 (10.30-4). Small parties by appt* **Tel 01297 489739**

● **Compton Acres Gardens, Poole** ♿✄❀ (The Administrator) *Canford Cliffs Road. Signed from Bournemouth and Poole. Wilts & Dorset Buses 150, 151. Yellow Buses nos 11 & 12 stop at entrance.* Set in 10 acres with spectacular views overlooking Poole Harbour and the Purbeck Hills beyond. Compton Acres takes you on a relaxing journey around the gardens of the world, from Italy to Japan. 10 distinctive gardens reveal their individual charm, character and beauty. Established in 1920 as one man's dream. Morning coffees, light lunches and Dorset cream teas served daily. *Adm £4.95 OAPs £3.95 Chd £2.95. March 1 to Oct 31 daily (10-6) last admission 5.15pm* **Tel 01202 700778** www.comptonacres.co.uk

Coombe Cottage, Shillingstone ❀ (Mike & Jennie Adams) *Blandford Rd. 5m NW of Blandford on A357 next to PO Stores on main rd. Parking advised in Gunn Lane.* ⅓-acre plantsman's cottage garden, enclosed by walls and hedges, with a dense, catholic mix of herbaceous and woody perennials, climbers, bulbs and self-seeding annuals (many unusual), in broad, mostly rectangular borders, some of them colour co-ordinated. Small formal vegetable plot. Cream TEAS *Adm £1 Chd free Suns May 28, June 25, Aug 27 (2-6)*

Corfe Barn, Broadstone ✲❀ (Mr & Mrs John McDavid) *Corfe Lodge Rd. From main roundabout in Broadstone W along Clarendon Rd, ¾m N into Roman Rd, after 50yds W into Corfe Lodge Rd.* ⅔ acre on three levels on site of C19 lavender farm. Informal country garden with much to interest both gardeners and flower arrangers. Parts of the original farm have been incorporated in the design. A particular feature of the garden is the use made of old walls. TEAS. *Adm £1 Chd free. Suns April 30, May 28, June 25 (2-5)*

Cothayes House & Vine Cottage ✲ *6m off A354 Blandford/Dorchester rd. Leave at Milton Arms in Winterbourne Whitechurch and follow signs for Milton Abbey, pass Abbey and through Hilton village. At top of hill turn R and follow signs for The Fox. Pass the PH on L and for Cothayes take 1st R at Melcombe Park Farm sign. House on L after ¾m, Vine Cottage is in the village of Melcombe Bingham on R after village green.* TEAS at Cothayes in aid of Village Hall. *Combined adm £2 Thurs May 11, Sun June 11 (11-5)*

Cothayes House, Ansty (Pat and David Wells) Tranquil 2-acre garden on sloping land with streams linking ponds; variety of trees and woodland walks. Shrubs and perennials combine to provide colourful borders with stream banks hosting wet-loving plants

Vine Cottage (Mrs Wendy Jackson) Small cottage garden with emphasis on interesting and unusual perennials and a wealth of containers

Cottesmore Farm, West Moors ♿✲❀ (Mr & Mrs Paul Guppy) *Newmans Lane. N of village off B3072 Bournemouth to Verwood rd.* The owners, late of High Hollow, Corfe Mullen, an NGS garden seen on TV, offer visitors the chance of seeing their new display garden. Accent on exotic and unusual plants from many countries, also large colourful herbaceous borders. The acre incls enclosures of rabbits, guinea pigs, sheep and different breeds of fowl. Wildflower area. Parking in field. TEA. *Adm £1 Chd 50p (ACNO to Cats Protection League). Suns June 25, July 23, Aug 27 (2-4.30)*

■ **Cranborne Manor Garden, Cranborne** ♿✲❀ (The Viscount and Viscountess Cranborne) *10m N of Wimborne on B3078.* Beautiful and historic garden laid out in C17 by John Tradescant and enlarged in C20, featuring several gardens surrounded by walls and yew hedges: white garden, herb and mount gardens, water and wild garden. Many interesting plants, with fine trees and avenues. *Adm £3 OAPs £2.50 Chd 50p (ACNO to Cranborne Chase Communities). Weds March to Sept incl (9-5). For NGS Wed April 5 (9-5), Sun June 25 (10-5)*

NEW **Cucumber Cottage, Rodgrove, Buckhorn Weston** ❀ (Mr & Mrs T Bradder) *3m SE of Wincanton. From A30 turn N to Kington Magna, continue to Buckhorn Weston, take 1st L after railway bridge, continue to next junction, turn R to Wincanton. 1st house on R is Cucumber Cottage.* ⅓ acre of organically grown vegetables, raised beds, herbaceous and mixed borders. Fruit cage, wildlife pond. Hardy geraniums, clematis, hostas, greenhouses. No chemicals used. Views of Blackmore Vale. TEAS at Weston House in aid of Buckhorn Weston Church. *Combined adm with Weston house £2 Chd free. Suns June 18, July 2 (2-6)*

2 Curlew Road, Bournemouth ♿✲❀ (Mr & Mrs Gerald Alford) *Strouden Park. From Castle Lane West turn S into East Way, thence E into Curlew Rd.* Small town garden 150′ × 30′ divided into rooms and linked by arches. Conifers, acers, rhododendrons, clematis; spring and summer bedding; three water features. Featured Daily Mail Special Garden '98. The owners are seriously disabled and their garden is thus of especial interest to other disabled people. *Adm £1 Chd 30p. Suns May 21, July 30 (2-6). Private visits welcome of 2 or more please* **Tel 01202 512627**

▲ **Deans Court, Wimborne** ♿✲❀ (Sir Michael and Lady Hanham) *Just off B3073 in centre of Wimborne.* 13 acres; partly wild garden; water, specimen trees, free-roaming peacocks. House (open by written appt) originally the Deanery to the Minster. Herb garden with over 200 species and walled kitchen garden. New rose garden open July. Chemical-free plants and produce for sale. Free car parking. Morning coffee/TEAS. *Adm £2 OAPs £1.50 Chd 50p. For NGS Suns April 23, 30, May 28, July 23, Aug 27, Sept 17 (2-6). Mons April 24, May 1, 29, Aug 28 (10-6). Other openings refer Wimborne T I C* **Tel 01202 886116**

Domineys Yard, Buckland Newton ♿✲❀ (Mr & Mrs W Gueterbock) *Dorchester and Sherborne 11m. 2m E A352 or take B3143. Take 'no through rd' between church and 'Gaggle of Geese'. Entrance 200 metres on L. Park and picnic in field with alder-lined stream and recent tree planting, or in lane if wet.* 2½-acre all seasons garden on chalk, clay and greensand surrounds C17 thatched cottage. Developed since 1961. Unusual plants, shrubs, trees. Camellias in spring, kitchen garden. TEAS. *Adm £1.50 Chd 50p (ACNO to Pulham Church Repairs) Suns April 9, July 2, Aug 13 (2-6). Private visits welcome, please* **Tel 01300 345295**

Edmondsham House, nr Cranborne ♿✲❀ (Mrs Julia Smith) *Edmondsham, off B3081 between Cranborne and Verwood.* Large garden; spring bulbs, trees, shrubs; walled garden with herbaceous border; vegetables and fruit; grass cockpit. Early church nearby. TEAS Weds only. *Adm £1 Chd 50p under 5 free (ACNO to PRAMA). Mon April 24, Weds April 5, 12, 19, 26, Oct 4, 11, 18, 25 (2-5); also private visits and parties welcome, please* **Tel 01725 517207**

Farriers, Puddletown ♿❀ (Mr & Mrs P S Eady) *16 The Moor. On the A354 Puddletown-Blandford rd, close to the Blue Vinny public house, Dorchester 5m.* ⅓-acre informal country garden with much to interest gardeners and flower arrangers, designed and maintained by owners; shrubs, herbaceous, collection of hostas, specialising in sweet peas, vegetable plot, greenhouse with collection streptocarpus, pond. Park in village. Joint opening with Flower Cottage on June 11 only. TEAS at Flower Cottage (June 11). *Adm £1 each*

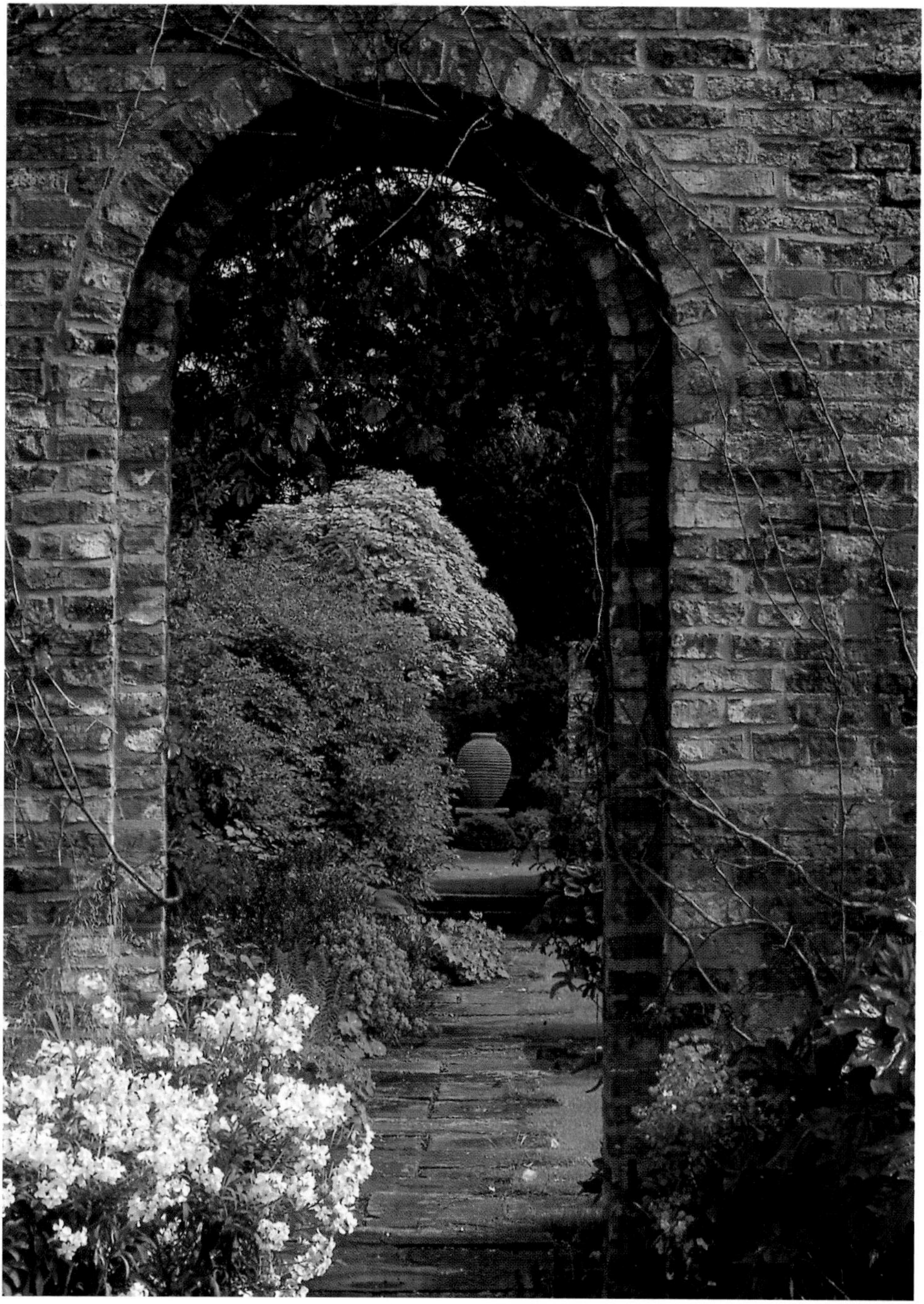

Saltmarshe Hall, Saltmarshe, Yorkshire
An inviting doorway leading from one walled garden into another, past a bank of sweetly scented stock (*Matthiola fruticulosa* subsp. *perennis*). This 10-acre garden on the banks of the River Ouse also includes a pond garden and a large herbaceous border with many unusual varieties.
Photograph by Suzanne Shacklock

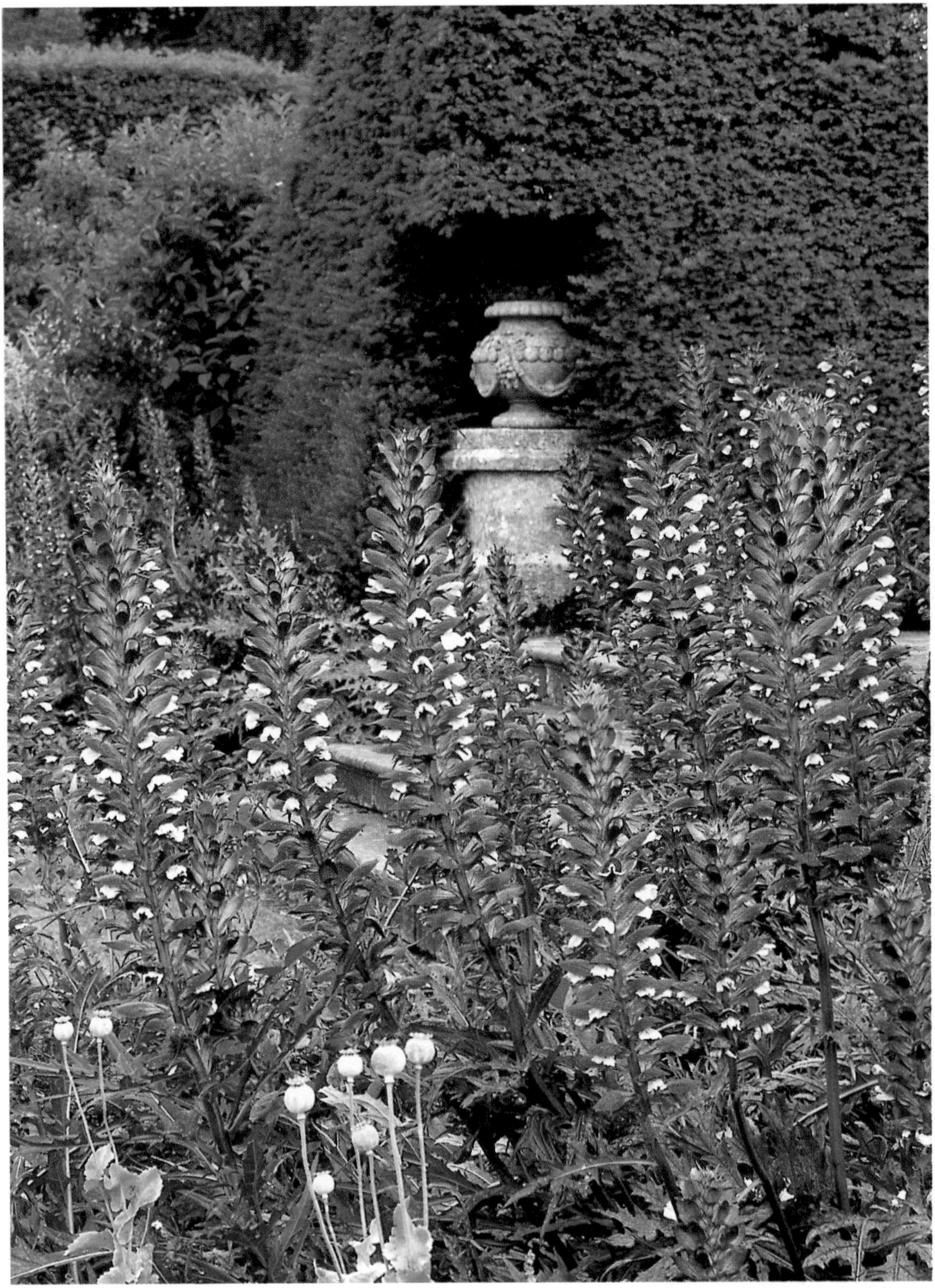

Misarden Park, Miserden, Gloucestershire
Misarden Park will be celebrating 66 years of opening for the National Gardens Scheme in 2000. Created in the 17th century, Misarden has enduring interest. The spectacular views over the Golden Valley remain unchanged, and fine features have been added through the years, including topiary designed by Sir Edwin Lutyens, and a new summerhouse and rill last year. *Acanthus mollis* frames the terrace steps.
Photograph by Andrew Lawson

Chidmere House, Chidham, Sussex
Magnolia x *soulangeana*, flowering cherries, sheets of daffodils and bluebells ensure that spring is superb at Chidmere. The garden is surrounded by a large mere, now a private nature reserve. Chidmere will be celebrating 60 years of opening for the Scheme in 2000.
Photograph by Consie Dunn

Below: **Old Rectory, Sudborough, Northamptonshire**
Spring bulbs and hellebores are a speciality in this classic 3-acre garden, but there are many other rare and unusual plants, a potager designed by Rosemary Verey, herbaceous borders, formal rose garden, a pond and a woodland walk.
Photograph by Andrew Lawson

Moleshill House, Surrey
Visitors looking for design ideas will come away with full notebooks from Moleshill House. Penny Snell, a leading flower arranger, delights in detail. Here *Ligustrum ovalifolium*, underplanted with pittosporum and edged with *Buxus sempervirens*, stands sentinel in a lead cistern garlanded with ivy.
Photograph by Derek St. Romaine

Below: **Croft House, Lincolnshire**
Finely shaped and clipped hedges of *Lonicera nitida* frame the informal planting of aquilegias and *Aegopodium podagraria* 'Variegatum' in the herbaceous border and open the view towards the woodland borders.
Photograph by Suzanne Shacklock

garden Chd free. Also July 9 (2-6). Private visits welcome, please **Tel 01305 848634**

NEW **Farrs Coach House, Wimborne** (Valerie & Michael Evans) *Leave Wimborne on Blandford Road, turn L at hospital into Cowgrove Rd. Farrs Coach House is ½ m on R up steep gravel drive. No cars please. Car park 300 yds further on, on L.* A garden in the making, surrounding a new house on an historic site, with extensive views to the S over the Stour valley. The garden is home to many indigenous species of wildlife which the owners are keen to attract. Shingle beds have recently been planted with heathers and alpines, and there are roses, climbers, a camomile lawn and banks where wild flowers are encouraged. *Adm £1 Chd under 16 free. Thurs March 9 (11-3) April 13, May 11, Sun June 25 (12-4)*

Fernhill Gardens, Witchampton *3½m E of Wimborne B3078 L to Witchampton then L up Lower St. (Blandford rd) houses on R 200yds.* TEAS in aid of Village Hall. *Combined Adm £1.50 Sun April 9 (2-5)*

Fernhill Cottage (Miss Shirley Forwood) Small thatched cottage garden. Hellebores, pulmonarias and unusual perennials *(ACNO to the League of Friends of Hahneman and Herbert Hospitals) Parties by appt, please* **Tel 01258 840321 evenings**

Fernhill House, Witchampton (Mrs Henry Hildyard) Spring bulbs and blossom, woodland walk with water garden and shrubs. *(ACNO to Joseph Weld Hospital Trust). Parties by appt, please* **Tel 01258 840105**

Fiddleford Gardens *1½m from Sturminster Newton on A357 towards Blandford. Sharp R-hand corner with Fiddleford Inn on L. Turn L up lane to hamlet. Parking and* TEAS at Sweetwell *Combined adm £2 Chd free Sun June 18 (2-5)*

Little Brook Cottage (Stella Hayward) Approx ½ acre of garden set against a stone and thatched cottage. Large lawned area with curving borders containing a newly planted mixture of shrubs and cottage garden flowers. A new walk-through rose arch separates the lawned area

Sweetwell (Mrs Ann R Hay) C16 timbered thatched cottage in 1 acre garden, created from derelict site in 1981. Shrub and herbaceous borders, stone garden, old roses, pond

Willow Tree Cottage (Mr & Mrs C Bull) Cottage garden with coveted stream bank (the only one in the hamlet) lawn, pond and beds of mixed planting

Woodview (John & Kath Singleton) 1-acre of maturing woodland/shrub garden planted within the last 15yrs, with vistas over adjoining farmland to the Dorset hills

29 Filleul Road, Sandford Woods (Mr & Mrs Richard Preston) *Nr Wareham. Turn N off A351 opp Shell Petrol Stn, then R into Filleul Rd.* ⅔-acre colourful summer garden, partly suitable for wheelchairs, maintained by owners. Lawns, shrubs, dwarf conifers, herbaceous plantings. Pool, bog garden and cottage plant border. Foliage plants are a special interest for flower arranging. TEAS. *Adm £1 Chd free. Sats, Suns May 6, 7, June 3, 4, July 1, 2, Sats (2-5) Suns (11-5)*

4 Flower Cottage, Lower Waterston (Mrs A J Penniston) *From Puddletown on the B3142 take the rd from bypass to Piddlehinton and Piddletrenthide.* ⅓-acre cottage garden, with herbaceous borders, scree, fernery and vegetables. TEAS. *Joint opening with Farriers June 11 only Adm £1 (each garden) Chd free (ACNO to Dewlish Parish Church). Sun June 11, Sept 10 (2-6). Private visits welcome, please* **Tel 01305 848694**

NEW **Frampton Rose Garden, Frampton** (Kevin Merritt) *34 Dorchester Road. Take A37 from Dorchester heading N. After about 5m turn L on A356.After ¾m, turn L into Southover Lane.* A newly planted ½ acre rose garden featuring over 300 varieties from the very old to the best of the more recent introductions. Set in tranquil setting next to River Frome. Nursery specialising in roses, clematis and ornamental trees. Teas in Village Hall and July 2 at Village Fete. *Adm £1.50 Chd free. Open all year (9-5) except Tues & Weds. For NGS Suns, June 18, 25, July 2, 9 (2-5)*

Frankham Farm, Ryme Intrinseca (Mr & Mrs R G Earle) *A37 Yeovil-Dorchester; 3m S of Yeovil turn east; drive ¼m on L.* 2 acres started in 1960s; plantsman's garden with shrubs, trees, spring bulbs, clematis, roses, vegetables and fruit; extensive wall planting. Recently planted unusual hardwoods. TEAS in aid of Ryme Church. *Adm £2 Chd free. Suns April 23, May 28, June 11 (2-5.30)*

Friars Way, Upwey (Les & Christina Scott) *Church Street. On B3159 Martinstown rd (opp church car park).* C17 thatched cottage with ½-acre hillside cottage garden and specialist nursery, with emphasis on plants for dry situations. A plantsman's paradise with innovative ideas for the smaller garden. Newly created pre 1700 border. *Adm £1.50 Chd free Open Thurs from April 6 to July 27. Suns April 23, July 9 (2-6). Private visits, parties and organisations by appt, please* **Tel 01305 813243**

The Friary, Hilfield (The Society of St Francis) *A352 from Dorchester to Minterne Magna, 1st L after village, 1st turning on R signed The Friary. From Yeovil turn off A37 signed Batcombe, 3rd turning on L.* A small woodland garden begun in 1950's then neglected. Reclamation began in 1984. The Secret Garden has a number of mature trees, rhododendrons, azaleas, magnolias, camellias and other choice shrubs with a stream on all sides crossed by bridges New plantings added in 1998-99 (stout shoes recommended). TEA. *Adm £1.50 Chd free. Thurs, Fri, Sat, Sun May 18, 19, 20, 21 (2-5). The Friary is happy to receive visitors every day apart from Monday*

Glebe Cottage, Woodsford (Mr F K Fletcher) *Take Wareham Rd W out of Dorchester. Follow signs to Crossways and L fork to Woodsford after passing under light controlled bridge. Entrance ¼m after Woodsford Castle on L and labelled Woodsford House. Drive forks to Glebe Cottage. Approach from E by taking sign to Woodsford at Moreton/Woodsford Cross Rd on B3390.* Camellias, mostly in woodland setting. 1½-acre garden with rhododendrons and azaleas and many varieties of trees. TEAS. *Adm £1 Chd 50p. Sat April 22 (2-6)*

Glebe House, East Lulworth ♿❀ (Mr & Mrs J G Thompson) *4m S of Wool, 6m W of Wareham. Take Coombe Keynes rd to East Lulworth. Glebe House just to E of Weld Arms and War Memorial.* Shrub garden with lawns, walks and terrace; 2 acres with interesting and varied planting, nearly 500 varieties of shrubs. TEAS. *Adm £1.25 Chd free (ACNO to Wool & Bovington Cancer Relief). Sun May 7 (2-6)*

Greenings, Chilfrome ♿ (Mr & Mrs A D T Philp) *1m NW of Maiden Newton. Chilfrome lies between Maiden Newton and Cattistock. Garden next to church. Park in village.* A plantsman's country garden with unspoilt view over Frome valley. Well stocked herbaceous borders with unusual plants and grasses, scree garden, vegetables and a wildlife pond with solar powered fountain. Cultivation methods are 95% organic. TEAS. *Adm £1 Chd 25p. Thurs July 6, Aug 10 (2.30-7)*

2 Greenwood Avenue, Ferndown ❀ (Mr & Mrs P D Stogden) *Off Woodside Rd which is between Ringwood Rd (A348) and Wimborne Rd (C50 ex-A31), E of town centre.* ⅓-acre designed and maintained by owners. An interesting and informal garden, with accent on herbaceous plants; many rare and unusual. Hostas, sempervivums and penstemons are a special interest of the owners. Soft fruits and vegetable garden. Arbour and pergola. Dogs must be kept on leads. TEAS. *Adm £1 Acc chd free. Suns May 21, June 4, 25 (11-5)*

Highbury, West Moors ♿✂❀ (Stanley Cherry Esq) *8m N of Bournemouth in Woodside Rd, off B3072 Bournemouth-Verwood rd; last rd at N end of West Moors village.* Woodland garden of ½ acre in mature setting surrounding interesting Edwardian house (1909 listed). Unusual plants and shrubs with ground cover. Weather station. Seen on TV. TEAS in orchard when fine. House and garden, organised parties. *Adm £1 (incl TEA); Otherwise by appt. Garden only 75p (2-6). April to Sept* **Tel 01202 874372**

Higher Melcombe, Melcombe Bingham (Lt Col J M Woodhouse) *11m NNE of Dorchester. Exit A35 bypass at Puddletown. Sign Blandford/Piddlehinton. After 300yds turn R through Cheselbourne to Melcombe Bingham Xrds. Signpost 'Private Rd to Higher Melcombe'.* Fine views and setting, herbaceous beds, annuals, walled garden. Parking in field. Chapel open for TEAS. *Adm £1 Chd free. Sun June 18 (2-5)*

7 Highfield Close, Corfe Mullen ✂❀ (Mr & Mrs M D Bright) *From Wareham Rd turn E in Hanham Rd, thence ahead into Highfield Close.* Colourful ⅓-acre summer garden designed and made by owners over 18yrs. Bedding plants, fuchsias and pelargoniums interplanted with shrubs; fish pond and ornamental pool. Much to interest gardeners in a small area. TEAS. *Adm £1 Chd free. Suns May 7, July 2 (2-5)*

Highwood Garden, Wareham ✂ (H W Drax Esq) *Charborough Park, 6m E of Bere Regis behind long wall. Enter park by any lodge on A31; follow signpost to Estate Office, then Highwood Garden.* Large garden with rhododendrons and azaleas in woodland setting. TEAS *Adm £3 Chd £1.50 (7-16 yrs) (ACNO to Red Post Parish) Suns May 14, 21 (2.30-6)*

Hilltop, Woodville, Stour Provost ✂❀ (Mr & Mrs Emerson) *Approx 5m N Sturminster Newton on B3092 turn R at Stour Provost Xrds, signed Woodville. After 1¼m a thatched cottage on the RH-side.* Well established garden overflowing with a wealth of different and interesting perennials, displayed in curved and sweeping borders. Very colourful and inspirational with misty blue views over Blackmore Vale. TEAS. *Adm £1 Chd free. Nursery open Thurs (9-6) and garden afternoons. Suns July 16, 23, 30, Aug 6, 13, 20; Weds Aug 2, (2-6)* **Tel 01747 838512**

Holworth Farmhouse, Holworth ✂❀ (Anthony & Philippa Bush) *7m E of Dorchester, 1m S of A352. Follow signs to Holworth up the hill, past duck pond on R. After 250yds turn L to C16 Grade II farmhouse on side of hill with magnificent views.* Partially walled and terraced garden uses hedges to protect a wide variety of herbaceous plants, shrubs and old roses from the effects of strong and persistent winds. TEAS in aid of Joseph Weld Hospice & 'Fight for Sight' and International League for the Protection of Horses. *Adm £2 Chd free. Suns May 28, June 18, Mon Aug 28 (2-6).Fri July 28 (6-9) Evening Opening with cheese and wine (donations to Countryside Alliance) Private visits by appt, please* **Tel 01305 852242**

NEW **Hookeswood House, Farnham** ♿✂❀ (Mr & Mrs Nicholas Haydon) *After 9m NE from Blandford on A354 L for Farnham. 1st L Ashmore and Shaftesbury. After Newtown village sign rd bends sharp R, take lane sharp L.* 3yr-old plantsman's garden with newly planted Spring border and separate bed of specialist hellebores, and stretches of primroses and narcissi. Also Summer, 'hot', vegetable and a new autumn border incorporating Piet Oudolf's style of planting - umbellifers, unusual grasses and perennials - in 2½ acres with views of surrounding fields. TEA. *Adm £1.50 Chd free. Suns May 14, June 25 (2-5) Private parties by appt, please* **Tel 01725 516259**

■ **Horn Park, Beaminster** ♿❀ (Mr & Mrs John Kirkpatrick) *On A3066 1½m N of Beaminster on L before tunnel.* Large garden; magnificent view to sea. Featured in RGBS 1999 calendar '12 Gardens to Remember'. Plantsman's garden worth visiting at all seasons; many rare plants and shrubs in terraced, herbaceous, rock and water gardens. Woodland garden and walks in bluebell woods. Good autumn colouring. Wild flower meadow with 164 varieties incl orchids. TEAS by arrangement for groups, toilet, ample parking also TEAS on NGS open days. *Adm £3.50 Chd under 16 free. Open Sun - Thurs incl (2-6) April to Oct 31. For NGS Wed April 12, Tues June 6 (2-6)* **Tel 01308 862212**

■ **Ivy Cottage, Ansty** ✂❀ (Anne & Alan Stevens) *Aller Lane, 12m N of Dorchester. Ansty is 6m N of Puddletown and 4m W of Milton Abbas. Aller Lane is a turning near the Fox Inn, Ansty.* A sparkling little stream runs through the centre of this charming cottage garden of 1 ¾ acres. An excellent plantsman's garden specialising in unusual perennials, moisture-loving plants; specimen trees and shrubs; well laid out vegetable garden. TEAS Sun Aug 27 *Combined adm with Aller Green £2.50 Chd 50p. Also every Thurs April to Oct incl. Adm £2 (Share to NGS) (10-5). For NGS Sun Aug 27 (ACNO to Red Cross) (2-5.30)* **Tel 01258 880053**

NEW **Japanese Garden, 38 Bingham's Road, Crossways** ✂ (Mr & Mrs Geoffrey Northcote) *6m E of*

Dorchester, off Dick O th' Banks Rd, and the B3390. Parking in village. Two unusual small gardens, newly designed by owner. Front garden features 'Turtle' island and contrasting yellow/blue borders. 'Sansui' mural painting. Rear courtyard garden 26' x 36' symbolises 'River of Life' with 'Moon Waves' bridge, amid contrasting red/green foliage and flower forms. RAF memorial park garden adjacent. *Adm £1 Chd free Sun June 25 (2-6) Private visits welcome April to Sept, please* **Tel 01305 854538**

80 Keith Road, Talbot Woods (Howard Ffitch Esq) *W of N end of Glenferness Ave turn into Roslin Road South and follow rd round into Keith Rd.* Enclosed town garden of approx ¼ acre redesigned in the last six years. Divided by hedges and shrub planting into areas of differing mood. Plantings range from rhododendrons to Kiftsgate style roses climbing along walls and over the summerhouse, in addition to mixed plantings in box hedged borders. TEA Sun May 28. *Combined adm with 46 Roslin Rd £2. Sun May 28 (1.30-5) Adm £1 Sun Aug 27 (2-5)*

▲ **Kingston Lacy, Wimborne Minster** ♿✂❀ (The Property Manager, The National Trust) *1½m W of Wimborne Minster on the Wimborne-Blandford rd B3082.* The setting landscaped in the C18, to W J Bankes's Kingston Lacy House. Magnificent trees planted over 175 years by Royal and famous visitors; avenue of limes and cedars; 9 acres of lawn; Dutch garden; sunken garden laid out to 1906 plans. A Victorian fernery, extensive collection of rhododendrons and azaleas, National Collections of anemone nemorosa and convallaria. TEAS and lunches in aid of NT. *Adm House & Garden £6, Gardens £2.50, Chd half price. For NGS Sun June 11 (11.30-6)*

● **Kingston Maurward Gardens, Dorchester** ♿✂❀ *1m E of Dorchester off A35. Follow brown Tourist Information signs.* National collections of penstemons and salvias. Classic Georgian mansion (not open) set in 35 acres of gardens laid out in C18 and C20 with 5-acre lake. Terraces and gardens divided by hedges and stone balustrades. Stone features and interesting plants. Elizabethan walled garden laid out as demonstration. Nature and tree trails. Animal park. Restaurant. *Adm £3.75 Chd £2 Open March 11 to Oct 29 daily (10-5.30). Private visits and guided tours welcome, please* **Tel 01305 215003 (Ginny Rolls or Ruth Whitty)**

Knitson Old Farmhouse, Knitson ✂❀ (Rachel & Mark Helfer) *Signposted L off A351 Knitson, approx 1m W of Swanage 3m E of Corfe Castle. Ample parking in yard or in adjacent level field.* Approx 1 acre of mature cottage garden. Herbaceous borders, rockeries, climbers, shrubs - many interesting cultivars. Large organic kitchen garden, orchard. Purbeck woodcraft. TEAS. *Adm £1.50 Chd 50p. Sats, Suns June 17, 18; Aug 5, 6 (2-5). Private visits and parties welcome, please* **Tel 01929 422836**

● **Knoll Gardens and Nursery, Hampreston** ♿✂❀ (Neil Lucas Esq) *2½m W of Ferndown, ETB brown signs from A31.* Wide collection of trees, shrubs, perennials, and expanding collection of ornamental grasses. Waterfalls, pools and streams; mixed borders. Mediterranean style gravel garden. NCCPG collections of phygelius and deciduous ceanothus. Licensed tea rooms and visitor centre; gift shop, garden accessories. Large car park. Many plants shown available in adjacent nursery. TEAS. *Adm £3.75 OAPs £3.25 Students £2.50 Chd £1.80. Group rates on application. Daily, April 1 to Sept 30 (10-5); March and Oct Wed to Sun (10-4); Nov, Dec Wed to Fri and Suns until Christmas (10-4)*

Langebride House, Long Bredy ❀ (Mrs J Greener) *½-way Bridport and Dorchester, S off A35, well signed.* Substantial old rectory garden with many designs for easier management. 200-yr-old beech trees, pleached limes, yew hedges, extensive collections of spring bulbs, herbaceous plants, flowering trees and shrubs. TEA in aid of Joseph Weld Hospice. *Adm £2 Chd free. Suns March 19, April 2 (2-5). Private visits welcome March to end July*
Tel 01308 482257

■ **Leigh Farm, Halstock** ✂❀ (Mrs L J Lauderdale) *Leave A37 Yeovil-Dorchester rd 2m S of Yeovil to Sutton Bingham and Halstock, continue 3½m to Halstock. R signposted to shop continue 1¾m on R.* 1 acre young, expanding plantsman's garden, being developed by former owners of Ashtree Cottage, Kilmington. Ponds, herbaceous borders, trees, shrubs and roses in beautiful rural setting. Garden and nursery open Tues and Weds, March to Oct 18 (10-5). TEAS. *Adm £2 Chd 50p (ACNO to Woodgreen Animal Shelters and St Margaret's Somerset Hospice). For NGS Suns May 21, June 18, July 9, Aug 6, Sept 3, 24 (2-6). Please*
Tel 01935 891848

Litton Cheney Gardens *1m S of A35, 10m Dorchester, 6m Bridport. Small village in the beautiful Bride Valley. Park in centre of vilage and follow signs.* TEAS in Church Hall in aid of the Church on Sun May 21. TEAS on June 13. *Combined adm £2.50 Chd 50p. Sun May 21, Tues June 13 (2-8)*

2 Litton Hill ✂❀ (Patricia & Malcolm Munro) Garden created since 1991 on difficult site; 1/5 acre. Shallow soil overlying chalk. SE facing with steep slopes. Showing plants that flourish on chalk and plants of interest to dyers. *(Sun May 21 only)*

The Old Rectory, Litton Cheney ❀ (Mr & Mrs Hugh Lindsay) Small walled garden, partly paved and with a prolific quince tree. A steep path leads to 4 acres of natural woodland with many springs, streams and 2 small lakes; mostly native plants, and many primulas. Wild flower lawn; (stout shoes recommended). Featured in Sunday Express and Sunday Telegraph. TEAS on Easter Sunday in aid of Arthritis Care. *Adm £2 Chd free. Also Easter Sun April 23. Private visits welcome April to June, please* **Tel 01308 482383**

NEW **1 Rose Cottages** (Norman and Molly Gardener) Approx ¼ acre cottage garden, restored over the past four years. Shrub and cottage garden, flower borders, potager, wood carving and pottery workshops

Steddings (Brian & Jennie Prentice) 1-acre immaculate garden with lawns, specimen trees, shrubs, herbaceous borders. Fine fruit and vegetable garden

Swallowfield ✂ (Geoffrey & Mary Court) Small irregular shaped garden with long herbaceous border and interesting patio. Adjoining artist's studio open *(Sun May 21 only)*

NEW **6 Malmesbury Road, St Leonards** (Mr & Mrs John Hawkins) *2m W of Ringwood. At A31 St Ives roundabout (Little Chef) turn N into Woolsbridge Rd, then 1st L, 2nd R, 1st L then L again.* Mature ½ acre sloping garden on heathland sand, developed in 1976 by present owners; Since 1995, re-landscaping and planting, now almost complete, for ease of up-keep in their ripening years. Collections of heather, alpines (esp. thymes, sempervivums, saxifrages), with azaleas, rhododendrons, bulbs and herbaceous. All plants labelled and documented. Gravel paths, steps, paving, ponds and lawns. *Adm £1 Chd 50p. Suns May 28, Aug 27, Sept 24 (2-6)*

1 Manor Close, Stratton (Mr & Mrs W A Butcher) *3m NW of Dorchester off A37 to Yeovil, turn into village, gardens signed at Church.* Fifth-acre plantsman's garden. Alpines at front. To the rear interesting shrubs, collection of grasses and herbaceous beds. Intensively cultivated vegetable plot. *Combined adm with Manor Orchard £1.50 Chd free. Suns, Weds April 2, 5, June 25, 28 (2-5.30)*

Manor Farmhouse, Little Windsor (Mr & Mrs E Hornsby) *4m NW of Beaminster; 1m from Broadwindsor. From A3066 turn off at Mosterton, signed Drimpton.* 3 acres landscaped gardens; pond and water garden, with primulas and orchids, unusual trees and shrubs. TEA. *Adm £1.50 Chd free. Suns April 30, May 28 (2-6).Gardening clubs and coach parties welcome by arrangement, please* **Tel 01308 868491**

The Manor House, Abbotsbury (Mr M. G Turnbull & Miss Caroline Dell) *Equidistant 9m from Dorchester, Weymouth and Bridport. The Manor House is in Church St opp St Nicholas Church. Park in the public carpark by the Swan Inn. No parking by The Manor House.* The gardens extending to 2½ acres were designed in 1988 by Ian Teh. They feature 4 inter-connecting ponds surrounded by herbaceous borders, a herb garden and abundance of roses. The gardens lie below St Catherine's chapel with views of the sea. TEAS. *Adm £2 Chd free. Sat, Sun May 27, 28 (2.30-6)*

Manor Orchard, Stratton (Mr & Mrs G B David) *3m NW of Dorchester off A37 to Yeovil, turn into village, gardens signed at Church.* 1-acre garden planted for yr-round interest. Spring bulbs, herbaceous and shrub borders, lawns, pond, roses, vine. Kitchen garden with pergola, fruit tunnel and topiary. New features for AD 2000. Cream TEAS (Suns only). DIY teas on Weds. *Combined adm with 1 Manor Close £1.50 Chd free. Suns, Weds April 2, 5; June 25, 28 (2-5.30)*

Mappercombe Manor, Powerstock (Cdr & Mrs William Crutchley) *4m NE of Bridport. From A35 at Bridport take A3066 towards Beaminster. Turn R at Kings Head. At T-junction turn R towards Loders. Next L to Nettlecombe. After 3m, keeping straight, entrance on RH side.* Monks' rest house with stew pond and dovecote. S facing gardens on 4 levels with ancient monastic route. Approx 2½ acres. Apart from walls and pillars and mature trees, garden has been mostly replanted; mixed borders and young trees and shrubs in last 12 years. TEAS and plants in aid of Powerstock School. *Adm £2 Chd free. Sun May 21, Thurs June 8 (2-5.30)*

● **Mapperton Gardens, nr Beaminster** (The Earl & Countess of Sandwich) *6m N of Bridport off A35. 2m SE of Beaminster off B3163.* Descending valley gardens beside one of Dorset's finest Grade I manor houses (C16-C17). Magnificent walks and views. Fish ponds, orangery, formal Italian-style borders and topiary; specimen trees and shrubs; car park. Upper levels only suitable for wheelchairs. Shop with plants, gifts and terracotta pots. House open to group tours by prior appt Tel 01308 862645 Fax 01308 863348. *Adm garden £3.50 Chd £1.50, under 5 free. March to Oct incl daily (2-6)*

Mead Cottage, Hinton St Mary (Dr J and Mrs J Bolton) *1m NW of Sturminster Newton on B3092. In village of Hinton St Mary, turn into lane opp Turks Garage. 1st on L at top of lane.* 1-acre garden created from a field 6yrs ago. Country garden with colour theming and many unusual plants. Walled Mediterranean area. Small formal garden. TEAS *Adm £1.50 Chd free Suns May 28, June 11 (2-6)*

Melplash Court, Melplash (Mr & Mrs Timothy Lewis) *On A3066 between Beaminster and Bridport, just N of Melplash. Turn W and enter between field gates next to big gates and long ave of chestnut trees.* While the gardens as they exist today were originally designed by Lady Diana Tiarks they continue to evolve and consist of park planting, bog garden, croquet lawn and adjacent borders. Formal kitchen garden and herb garden, ponds, streams and lake; new borders and areas of interest are added and opened up each year. TEAS in aid of Melplash Church *Adm £2.50 Chd free Sat July 22 (2-6)*

Mews Cottage, Portland (Mr & Mrs P J Pitman) *34 Easton Street. Situated in the 1st village on the top of the Island, 50yds past the Punchbowl Inn on the L. Park in the main st and follow signs.* Small cottage-style garden, with a pond, herbaceous plants and unusual shrubs, incl crinodendron hookerianum and callistemon. Hellebores, spring bulbs and snowdrops in spring and a National Collection of Penstemon (190+) from March to November. The garden featured in BBC2 Gardeners World Aug '98. Autumn colour is achieved with a large collection of nerine bowdenii and 20+ varieties of agapanthus. TEAS. *Adm £1 Chd free. Suns March 12, May 7, June 18, July 16, Aug 13, Sept 24 (2-5)*

Millmead, Winterborne Stickland (Michele Barker) *4m SW of Blandford Forum. After 'Shire Horse', turn R down West St, signed Winterborne Houghton. 1st L after 30mph sign.* Although only started in 1990, the garden, which has been designed and constructed by its owners, already has a well established feel. Within ⅓ acre, they have created a beautiful formal country garden on different levels, divided into separate 'rooms', each with its own character. The emphasis is on structure and planting, with many unusual plants. The garden has recently been extended by the addition of a Mediterranean courtyard. *Adm £2 Chd 50p. Sun May 21 (2-5). Also by appt, please* **Tel 01258 880814**

● **Minterne, Minterne Magna** (The Lord Digby) *On A352 Dorchester-Sherborne rd. 2m N Cerne Abbas.* Minterne valley, landscaped in C18, home of the Churchill and Digby families for 350yrs. Wild woodland gardens are laid out in a horseshoe below Minterne House, with over 1m of walks, providing a new vista at each turn. Rhododendrons and magnolias tower over small lakes, streams, and cascades. Maples and many rare trees provide spectacular autumn colouring. *Adm £3 Acc chd and parking free. Open daily March 28 to Nov 10 (10-7)*

Moigne Combe, nr Dorchester (Major General H M G Bond) *6m E of Dorchester. 1½m N of Owermoigne turn off A352 Dorchester-Wareham rd.* Medium-sized garden; wild garden and shrubbery; heathers, azaleas, rhododendrons etc; woodland paths and lake walk. Tea at Post Office, Kit Lane, Owermoigne *Adm £1.50 1st chd 25p Suns May 14, 21 (2-5)*

■ **Moreton Gardens, nr Dorchester** ♿✂❀ (Mrs Philippa Hobbs) *7m E of Dorchester and 3m W of Wool, signed from the B3390 and 1m E of Moreton station. Nr Lawrence of Arabia's grave in the village of Moreton.* A garden re-created in an old setting in the picturesque village of Moreton. 3 acres of lawns, mixed borders, woodland, stream and ponds, bog garden, pergola and fountain. Ample parking. Also plant centre with a wide variety incl shrubs, clematis, heathers, conifers, perennials, climbers, alpines and roses. *Adm £2 Chd free. Open every day March 1 to Oct 31 (10-5). For NGS Sat, Sun June 17, 18, (10-5)* **Tel 01929 405084**

Moulin Huet, West Moors (Harold Judd Esq) *15 Heatherdown Rd. 7m N of Bournemouth. Leave A31 at Shell petrol station into Pinehurst Rd, take 1st R into Uplands Rd, then 3rd L into Heatherdown Rd, thence into cul-de-sac.* ⅓-acre garden made by owner from virgin heathland after retirement. Considerable botanical interest; collections of 90 dwarf conifers and bonsai; many rare plants and shrubs; alpines, sink gardens, rockeries, wood sculpture. TV 'Gardeners' World'. *Adm 75p Chd free. Two Suns in May, see local press. Private visits welcome March to Oct, please* **Tel 01202 875760** (between 11am to 12noon)

NEW **Okeford Fitzpaine Gardens** ♿❀ *Off A357 between Sturminster and Blandford. Go to Royal Oak Public House, Okeford Fitzpaine. Turn into Lower St. After 300yds turn R into Darknoll Lane. For parking for Drove Cottage and The Old Farmhouse follow lane 200yds on the L.* Cream TEAS. *Combined adm £2 Chd free. Sun June 11 (2-6)*

NEW **Drove Cottage, Okeford** (Steve & June Armstrong) A new informal garden designed round a rose-covered central gazebo with ornamental fountain. Mixed and varied planting enhances large lawn with ancient oak trees, adjoining horse paddock. S of the house orchard with cottage garden. Fine views of Dorset Hills leading up to Bulbarrow.

NEW **The Old Farmhouse, Okeford Fitzpaine** (David Conville) Enjoy fine views of North Dorset Hills. An informal garden of 2 acres designed and established over recent years around an C18 thatched former farmhouse. (Not open). Interesting mixed and varied planting round both the house and extensive lawn, also a rose-covered pergola and gazebo, all framing Okeford Hill.

The Old Mill, Spetisbury ♿✂❀ (The Rev & Mrs J Hamilton-Brown) *Spetisbury village opp school on A350 3m SE of Blandford.* 2 acres water gardens and natural ponds by R Stour; choice trees and plants. Caltha collection. Spring bulbs and hellebores. Summer borders, roses and clematis. As seen on Grass Roots. *Adm £2 Chd free. Sun May 21 (2-5). On other days by appt (April-Aug inc, individuals or parties) please* **Tel 01258 453939**

The Old Rectory, Fifehead Magdalen ♿❀ (Mrs Patricia Lidsey) *5m S of Gillingham just S of the A30.* Medium-sized garden with interesting shrubs and perennials; pond; grandchildren's garden; plant stall. TEAS in aid of St Mary Magdalen *Adm £1 Chd free Sun June 18 (2-6). Also private visits welcome, please* **Tel 01258 820293**

The Old Rectory, Litton Cheney *See Litton Cheney Gardens*

The Old Rectory, Netherbury (Amanda & Simon Mehigan) *2m SW of Beaminster; turn off Beaminster/Bridport rd and go over R Brit and into centre of village and up hill. The Old Rectory is on L opp church. Please park considerately in village streets and village hall car park.* Garden of approx 5 acres in process of restoration/development. Formal courtyard, bog garden with stream and pond, wild flower meadows and orchards. A number of large mature trees incl ancient yews and massive gingko. Beech house. TEAS in aid of Netherbury Village Hall *Adm £2 Chd free Sun May 14 (2-6). Also open June 10, 11 as part of Netherbury Gardens weekend*

NEW **The Old Rectory, West Compton** ♿✂ (Robert & Susan Henwood) *3m N of A35 equidistant Dorchester/Bridport; 3m SW of Maiden Newton.* 1 acre of informality around Victorian hamstone house surrounded by hilly farmland and with a wooded backdrop. Garden tended as naturally as possible (ducks control snails, bats tackle aphids). Two ponds with connecting paths through wildlife area (boots recommended after rainfall). TEAS. Wine on Tues June 13, 27. *Adm £1.50 Chd free (ACNO to The Injured Jockeys Fund). Suns April 23, May 7, June 18 (2-6) Tues June 13, 27 (4-8) Wed Aug 23 (2-6)*

The Orchard, Blynfield Gate ✂❀ (Mr & Mrs K S Ferguson) *2m W of Shaftesbury on the rd to Stour Row. From Shaftesbury take B3091 to St James's Church then onto the Stour Row rd.* A 3-acre country garden, orchard and native meadow developed since 1981. Lawns and paths link formal, informal and wild areas. Colourful mixed borders and island beds with a wide variety of plants, several chosen for their intermingling qualities and lengthy flowering period. Hedgebanks of hardy geraniums, interesting trees and shrubs, small natural pond and plenty of seats. Cream TEAS *Adm £2 to incl descriptive guide Chd free (ACNO to Red Cross) Weds June 21, Aug 16, Sept 13, Sun July 16 (2-6)*

Orchard House, Ferndown ♿✂❀ (Mr & Mrs John Norris) *6 Aldridge Rd. From Parley Xrds continue N on A347 (New Rd), after ½m turn R into Golf Links Rd, thence 2nd R into Lone Pine Drive and 1st L into Aldridge Rd.* Colourful ½-acre garden carefully maintained by owners. Spring and summer bulbs, herbaceous plants and ground cover, hostas, increasing collection day lilies, perennial geraniums. Roses, pool and small vegetable garden. Greenhouse and conservatory, dahlias. Many plants are labelled with new plants always being added. TEAS. *Adm £1 Chd free (ACNO to Osborne Day Centre for MS). Suns May 7, 14, June 4, 11 (11-5)*

Parley Court, Christchurch ♿✿ (Mr & Mrs Theo Dampney) *East Parley. On B3073 1¼m E of Xrds at West Parley, off SW corner Hurn airport turn S into Parley Green Lane, fork R thence ½m to house and garden.* A garden of 2½ acres, lawns, herbaceous borders, old roses, specimen trees, pool with fountain and cascade, statuary, all surrounding Queen Anne house (listed Grade 2 not open). Vistas incl new funnel avenue of mixed trees. Ha Ha. Something of interest for at least 11 months of the yr. TEAS. *Adm £1.50 Chd 50p ACNO to CHAOS (Children's Helpers and other support), Portfield School (Wessex Autistic Society) The Fortune Centre of Riding Therapy (Avon Tyrell, nr Bransgore) Suns May 28, June 11, 25 (2-5.30)*

● **Parnham, Beaminster** ♿ (Mr & Mrs J Makepeace) *½m S of Beaminster on A3066, 5m N of Bridport* 14 acres including grand herbaceous borders, intimate courtyard garden, formal terraces; topiary, spring-fed water rills overlooked by gazebos to the south; recognised by English Heritage as very important 1910 period. Riverside walk, many unusual plants and fine old trees. House dates from 1540. Grade 1 listed. Also John Makepeace furniture workshops. Children's play area. Tree trail. Restaurant, coffee, lunches. TEAS *Adm to whole site £5 Chd 5-15 £2 Suns, Tues, Weds, Thurs, Bank Hols Easter or April to end Oct (10-5)* **Tel 01308 862204**

Pear Tree Farm, Loscombe (Major & Mrs J L Poë) *3m S of Beaminster. 3½m N of Bridport, turn off A3066 in Melplash opp public house The Half Moon. After approx ½m take R fork signed Loscombe, approx 1m turn L at T-junction up cul-de-sac for 200yds to carpark on L. (Avoid 2 entrances to 1st house on L).* Approx ½ acre, designed to harmonize with the beauty of the surrounding landscape, developed over last 10yrs, features a number of small rooms all differing in style and composition, packed with many unusual plants and climbers on tripods and archways. Conservatory with many tender plants, 2 small ponds with running water and a wildflower area. TEAS. *Adm £2 Chd under 16 free. Sat, Sun June 17, 18 (2-6)*

Portesham House, Portesham ♿✿❀ (Mrs G J Romanes) *7m W of Weymouth on coast rd, B3157 to Bridport. From Dorchester take A35 W, turn L in Winterborne Abbas and follow signs to Portesham; parking in village.* Home of Admiral Sir Thomas Masterman Hardy, with 300-yr-old mulberry tree; 2 acres of family garden with modern dry stone walling, old walls and recent plantings by stream. Tree paeonies, herbaceous paeonies, unusual trees and shrubs. Lunches and teas at King's Arms Hotel opp. *Adm £1.50 Chd free. Suns June 11, 18 (2-5.30). For early flowering tree paeonies in May, please* **Tel 01305 871300**

▲ **The Priest's House Museum & Garden, Wimborne** ♿✿ (The Curator) *23 High St. Public car parks nearby.* Old 'borough plot' garden of ½ acre, at rear of local museum, in historic town house. Extending to mill stream and containing many unusual plants, trees and exhibits. Tearoom daily. *Adm £2.20 Family £5.50 OAP/Students £1.75 Chd £1. For NGS Sun June 25 (2-5)* **Tel 01202 882533**

Prospect Cottage, Beaminster (Robin & Shirley Samways) *From Beaminster town centre take B3163 towards Evershot then 1st L into East St.* Attractive secluded cottage garden and conservatory in ¼ acre comprising unusual courtyard, traditional cottage garden flowers, small pond and wild garden bounded by the R Brit. Artist's studio. TEAS in aid of Friends of the Earth. *Adm £1.50 Chd free. Weds, May 3, June 14, July 5 (2-5.30)*

NEW **Puck's Knoll, Marshwood** ✿❀ (Mrs Joy Everington) *4m. N of Charmouth on B3165 Lyme Regis to Crewkerne rd, approx 100yds W of Bottle Inn. Limited parking on driveway apron or on verge approx 30yds W.* Relaxed, 3/4 acre hillside garden with splendid views. Trees and shrubs with some choice specimens; herbaceous, ferns, fun features including topiary; organic fruit and vegetables and wild flower patch. Something of interest yr-round. (Stout shoes recommended). TEAS at by appointment visits only. *Adm £1 Chd 50p. Tues April 25, May 30, June 27, July 25, Aug 29, Sept 26, Oct 31 (2-6)* **Tel 01297 678392**

Rampisham Manor, Rampisham ✿❀ (Mr & Mrs Boileau) *From Yeovil take A37 to Dorchester, 7m turn R signed Evershot. From Dorchester take A37 to Yeovil, 4m turn L A356 signed Crewkerne. Then follow signs.* Small unspoilt village in rural Dorset with C14 Church. 3-acre garden. Mixture of formal and flowing planting in rural setting, English roses amongst shrubs, vegetables, grasses bed, hedged walks, water and new woodland garden. TEAS. *Adm £2. Wed April 26, Sun July 2, Wed Aug 30 (2-5)*

46 Roslin Road South, Bournemouth ✿❀ (Dr & Mrs Malcolm Slade) *W of N end of Glenferness Ave in Talbot Woods area of Bournemouth.* Plantswoman's ⅓-acre walled town garden planted with many unusual and rare plants. Sunken gravel garden with collection of grasses, surrounded by colourful mixed borders. Features include many well planted containers, raised octagonal alpine bed, rose pergola leading to enclosed patio, kitchen garden and greenhouses. TEA Sun May 28. *Combined adm with 80 Keith Rd £2. Sun May 28 (1.30-5). Adm £1 Suns April 30, June 25 (1.30-5). Parties by appt,* **Tel 01202 510243**

The Scented Garden, Littlebredy ✿❀ (Chris & Judy Yates) *10m equidistant Dorchester and Bridport. 1½m S off the A35. Park on Littlebredy village green by round bus shelter. 400yd walk to garden (not ideal for the disabled).* 1-acre Victorian walled garden, in tranquil setting, being lovingly restored. Old roses form the backbone to the white and colour themed beds and borders, which contain many unusual plants. Display beds containing National Collection of lavender (over 80). *Adm £1 Chd 20p (ACNO to Littlebredy Church) Tues May 30, June 6, 13, 20, 27 July 4, 11, 18, 25 (2.30-8)*

16a Seamoor Road, Westbourne ✿ (Mr S Siggs & Ms J Chrystal) *Centre of Westbourne, opp arcade, next door to Post Office.* Delightful small town garden 50′ × 20′ fully enclosed, with pergolas and water features, many interesting climbers; roses, clematis, wisteria, trachelospermum.

Charming example of how to fill a small space. *Adm 60p Chd 30p (ACNO to Guide Dogs for the Blind, MS Society). Sat June 17 (10-1), Sun June 18 (2-6)*

Slape Manor, Netherbury (Mr & Mrs Antony Hichens) *1m S of Beaminster turn W off A3066 to village of Netherbury. House ⅓m S of Netherbury on back rd to Bridport.* River valley garden, extensive lawns and lake. Azaleas, rhododendrons, large clump Phyllostachys Boryana nigra and specimen trees. Dogs on leads. TEAS in aid of local charity. *Adm £2 Chd 50p under 5 free. Sun May 21 (2-6)*

Smedmore, Kimmeridge ♿❀ (Dr Philip Mansel) *7m S of Wareham. Turn W off A351 (Wareham-Swanage) at sign to Kimmeridge.* 2 acres of colourful herbaceous borders; display of hydrangeas; interesting plants and shrubs; walled flower gardens; herb courtyard. House also open for NGS. *Adm £3.50 Chd £1 (incl house) Sun May 14 (2-5). Private visits welcome by appt, please* **Tel 01929 480719 (Mr T Gargett)**

■ **Snape Cottage, Chaffeymoor** ✂❀ (Ian & Angela Whinfield) *At W end of Bourton. Opp Chiffchaffs.* ½-acre plantsman's country garden full of old-fashioned and uncommon perennials, most labelled. Organically managed and planted for yr-round interest with large collections of snowdrops, hellebores, pulmonarias, auriculas, geraniums, dianthus, iris, penstemon and asters. Special emphasis on plant history and nature conservation. Beautiful views, wildlife pond. TEA at 11 & 3 only. *Adm £2 Chd free. Suns Feb 20, 27 April 2. Every Weds April to Sept (closed Aug). For NGS Suns April 23, June 18 (2-5). Groups by appt, please* **Tel 01747 840330 (evenings only)**

NEW **Springhead, Fontmell Magna** (The Springhead Trust) *Take the A350 between Shaftesbury and Blandford. In Fontmell at the Xrds turn up Mill St, opp the public house. Springhead is the last on the R.* From Saxon times Springhead was a working mill. In 1926 it became the property of a painter, Harold Squire, who made an atmosphereic garden around the large lake. Over 50yrs the garden was developed by the Gardiner family. Now undergoing restoration. Extraordinary setting below the lynchets: springs rising from under the chalk, mill race, water and bog gardens, early bulbs, interesting shrubs, herbaceous border, long colour themed beds of unusual annuals. Herb garden run by Neal's Yard Herbal Remedies. Lunches and cream TEAS. *Adm £2 Chd free. Mon May 1, Fri June 2, Sun Aug 6 (Countryside Day) Wed Sept 27. For NGS Wed Apr 19, Sat Aug 5 (11-5)*

● **Stapehill Abbey, Ferndown** ♿✂❀ (Mr & Mrs John Pickard, Garden Managers) *Wimborne Rd West. 2½m W of Ferndown on the old A31, towards Wimborne, ½m E of Canford Bottom roundabout* Early C19 Abbey set amidst a walled garden which is a true gardeners' paradise with many rare and unusual plants. It boasts herbaceous borders, a rose garden, water features and a sunken formal garden. New for 2000 a Japanese garden. Free car/coach park. Licensed coffee shop. *Adm £7 OAPs £6.50 Chd £4.50 Open daily April 1 to Oct 1 (10-5); Weds - Suns incl Oct 2 to March 31 (10-4) Closed Dec 20 to Feb 4* **Tel 01202 861686**

■ **Star Cottage, Cowgrove** ✂❀ (Miss Lys de Bray FLS) *8 Roman Way, Cowgrove, nr Wimborne. Leave B3082 at Wimborne Hospital, along Cowgrove Rd for approx 1½m to Roman Way on R.* Created in 1992 from a field, the garden is another 'living library' of RHS gold medallist and author Lys de Bray, whose botanical paintings are on permanent exhibition in her working studio, open all the year at weekends and Bank Holidays. *Adm £1.50 Chd £1 Open Sats & Suns all year. Easter to end Oct (2-6). End Oct to end March (2-4). For NGS Suns May 21, June 25, July 16. Private visits arranged* **Tel 01202 885130**

■ **Sticky Wicket, Buckland Newton** ♿✂❀ (Mr & Mrs Lewis) *11m from Dorchester and Sherborne. 2m E of A352 or take B3143 from Sturminster Newton. T-junction midway Church, School and 300yds from Gaggle of Geese public house.* 2-acre colourist and conservationist's wildlife garden created since 1987, unusual designs, well documented, showing wild life interest; fragrant cottage garden planting with many perennials, grasses and herbs. Unsuitable for children. TEAS. *Adm £2.50 Chd £1.50. Every Thurs June 3 to Sept 30 incl (10.30-8). For NGS Suns June 18, Aug 20 (2-8). Groups welcome by appt, please* **Tel 01300 345476**

Stour House, Blandford ♿✂❀ (T S B Card Esq) *East St. Enter Blandford from the ring rd by the B3082 from Wimborne. 200yds along East St (one-way) on the L.* 2½-acre town garden, half on a romantic island in R Stour reached by a remarkable bridge; bulbs; borders well planted with perennials and many rare shrubs; river views. TEAS. April to Aug. Teas and ACNO to Dorset Rural Music School (June) and to Blandford Parish Church (July). *Adm £1 Chd 20p. Suns Mar 19, April 16, (2-5) May 21, June 18, July 16, Aug 20 (2-6), Sept 17, Oct 15 (2-5)*

Studland Bay House, Studland ♿❀ (Mrs Pauline Ferguson) *On B3351 5m E of Corfe Castle. Through village, entrance on R after Studland Bay House. Ample parking (no coaches). From Bournemouth, take Sandbanks ferry, 2½m, garden on L after Knoll House Hotel.* 6-acre spring garden overlooking Studland Bay. Planted in 1930's; magnificent rhododendrons, azalea walk, camellias, magnolias, ferns and stream; recent drainage and replanting, garden suitable for wheelchairs. Cream TEAS in aid of Swanage Cottage Hospital. *Adm £2.50 Chd free. Sat, Sun May 20, 21 (2-5)*

Sturminster Newton Gardens ♿ *Off A357 between Blandford and Sherborne take turn opp Nat West Bank. Park in car park or behind Stourcastle Lodge. Walk down Penny St for Ham Gate and Goughs Close for Stourcastle Lodge.* TEAS at Ham Gate. *Combined adm £2 Chd free. Sun June 11 (2-6). Parties by appt, please* **Tel 01258 472462 or 01258 472320**

Ham Gate (Mr & Mrs H E M Barnes) Informal 2-acre garden with shrubs, trees, lawns running down to R Stour, pleasant woodland views across water meadows

Stourcastle Lodge (Jill & Ken Hookham-Bassett) S facing secluded cottage garden, with a wide selection of interesting herbs, perennials and shrubs, a dovecote and water features

Tara, West Moors (Mr & Mrs W H Adams) *66 Elmhurst Rd. 7m N of Bournemouth. Leave A31 at Shell petrol station into*

Pinehurst Rd and take 4th R into Elmhurst Rd. Carefully tended garden 130' x 40', lawns with island beds. Small pool and water features, statuary, ivy topiary and bonsai. Featured in Amateur Gardening and Garden News, the garden is also used in its advertising by an organic fertiliser manufacturer. Plants, Teas and other stalls in aid of animal charities. *Collection Box. Sun, Mon May 28, 29, Sat, Sun June 24, 25 (10-4.30)*

Three Bays, Beacon Hill (Mr & Mrs Christopher Garrett) *8 Old Wareham Rd, (nr Limberlost junction with A350). 1½m SW of Corfe Mullen.* Garden of ¼ acre made and maintained by owners. There is a Japanese flavour to the garden, with stone lanterns, dovecote and water features. Shrubs and herbaceous borders with much use of sloping site. TEAS. *Adm £1 (ACNO to Cancer Research Campaign) Sat, Sun July 1, 2. Private visits welcome for groups, please* **Tel 01202 623352**

● **Upwey Wishing Well, Upwey** ♿✂❀ (Mr & Mrs Richard Harrison) *3m N of Weymouth on B3159 and just off Dorchester to Weymouth Rd (A354).* A tranquil, well-stocked water garden, with ponds (¼ acre). The large natural spring, which is the source of the River Wey is known as the Wishing Well and is an ancient monument. A fine show of bog primulas in May/June. Huge gunneras and unusual foliage plants provide a unique and exotic setting. TEAS and lunches *Entrance through cafe, adm free but donations welcomed for National Gardens' charities. Open daily April to Sept;Wed to Sun March, Oct, Dec (10.30-6)*

78 Wakeham, Portland ✂❀ (Mr & Mrs M A Osmond) *Wakeham is a long wide rd leading from the village of Easton at the top of the island. No 78 is 300yds along, on the R-hand side.* Small garden started in spring 1995. Mixture of shrubs and perennials. Interesting features incl patio, rockery, pond and cottage garden area. *Adm £1 Chd free Suns May 7, June 18, July 16 (2-5). Private visits by appt,* **Tel 01305 821299**

Wall Farm, Broadwindsor (Cdr & Mrs P Corson) *1m from Broadwindsor on B3164 Axminster rd. Turn L behind Tin Hut. Very narrow lane, beware cars. Parking limited.* 4-acre garden surrounding C17 thatched farmhouse (not open) in a hidden valley. Garden, started 8 yrs ago and being continued by present owners. A mass of spring bulbs and bluebells. Herbaceous borders, small hedged garden. Streams, ponds and bog garden. A flower arranger's garden. Dogs on leads. *Adm £1.50 Chd free Mons April 10, 17 & May and June (2-5) not Bank Hols. Private visits welcomed, weekdays preferred, please* **Tel 01308 868203**

Welcome Thatch, Witchampton ✂❀ (Mrs Diana Guy) *3½m E of Wimborne, B3078 L to Witchampton, thence through village past church & shop to last but one on R. Please avoid parking close village centre.* Listed thatched cottage (not open). Enthusiast's garden (⅔ acre). Garden 'rooms' packed with unusual plants of all-yr-round interest, ranging from the exotic and tender to hardy perennials and shrubs. Large collection of hardy geraniums. Featured in 'The English Garden', Period Living, Traditional Homes and Gardening Which magazines. TEAS. *Adm £1 Chd free. Suns March 12 (Hellebores for sale), April 9 (Teas in village hall) June 11 (2-5.30). Private parties welcome at weekends by appt, please* **Tel 01258 840894**

Wentworth College, Bournemouth ✂ (The Administrator) *250yds from the beach and Boscombe Overcliff Dr. 3m E of Bournemouth town centre; off A35, off Beechwood Ave.* Originally the seaside estate of Lord Portman, Wentworth Lodge was built in 1872. The main Victorian house has gradually been extended to accommodate the needs of Wentworth College. Formal gardens have been restored to reflect their origins. The grounds also incl woodland with mature specimen trees and rhododendrons in approx 3 acres. TEAS. *Adm £1.50 Chd free. Sun May 7 (2-5)*

24a Western Avenue, Poole ✂ (Mr & Mrs Peter Jackson) *Central in Branksome Park, ½m from Compton Acres.* Award winning 1-acre part Mediterranean, part English garden close to sea. Formal areas incl lawns, cherry tree walk, rose garden, herbaceous beds, topiary and courtyard with tender wall plants. Tree ferns, drimys, bamboo and camellias flourish. Sunny banks are planted with eucalyptus, acacias, and a collection of callistemons, agaves, yuccas and other drought resistant plants. *Adm £1.50 Chd free. Sun July 2 (2-6)*

Weston House, Buckhorn Weston ♿✂❀ (Mr & Mrs E A W Bullock) *4m W of Gillingham and 4m SE of Wincanton. From A30 turn N to Kington Magna, continue towards Buckhorn Weston and after railway bridge take L turn towards Wincanton. 2nd on L is Weston House.* 1 acre plus fields; old and new roses (over 95 varieties); herbaceous and mixed borders backed by old walls with climbers. Small woodland and wild flower areas; wildlife pond; lawns and view of Blackmore Vale. TEAS in aid of Buckhorn Weston Parish Church. *Combined adm with Cucumber Cottage £2 Chd free. Suns June 18, July 2 (2-6)*

■ **White Pit Cottage, Shillingstone** ❀ (Jennifer Burton) *5m NW of Blandford. Turn off A357 by PO into Gunn Lane, after ¼m and turn R into parking area.* Situated in a secluded cottage garden, ¼-acre herb garden is formally laid out in raised beds of medicinal, culinary, dye and scented herbs. Over 200 varieties in total, some quite rare. Plants clearly labelled. TEAS *Adm £1 Chd free. April 1 to Sept 30 (2-5), not Weds, Thurs. For NGS Suns May 28, June 25, July 30, Aug 27 (2-6)*

▲ **Wimborne Minster Model Town** ♿✂❀ (R J Percey Esq Hon Publicity Director) *King St 200yds W of Minster, opp public car park* 1½-acre grounds with one tenth scale models of the town in early fifties, surrounded by landscaped gardens. Herbaceous borders, alpines, herbs, heather and rose gardens, with many rare and unusual plants, with pools and fountain, making a colourful pleasure garden. Visitors' and exhibition centres. Many seats. Views over Stour valley. Refreshments daily. *Adm £3 OAPs £2 Chd £1.50 (3-15) under 3 free For NGS Suns June 4, July 2, Sept 3 (10-5)* **Tel 01202 881924**

Witchcroft, Southwell ✂❀ (Mr Rowland & Mrs Pamela Reynolds) *1 Sweet Hill Rd, Southwell, Portland. Follow the signs for Portland Bill (A354). 'Witchcroft' is the bungalow*

300yds on L, past Eight Kings public house in the village of Southwell. Small cottage garden with pond, shrubs and herbaceous borders and open rural views. Spring bulbs and hellebores, in summer new and old-fashioned roses. Park in main st. TEAS in aid of Cancer and Leukaemia in Childhood Trust. *Adm £1 Chd free. Suns March 12, June 18, July 16 (2-5)*

Evening Opening (See also garden description)

Holworth Farmhouse, Holworth	July 28
The Old Rectory, West Compton	June 13 & 27

MORE THAN JUST A GARDEN...

- Glorious Award Winning Gardens
- Beautiful 19th Century Cistercian Abbey
- Wonderful selection of unique working craft shops
- Outstanding Country World Museum
- Woodland Walk
- Licensed Coffee Shop • Gift Shop • Plant Sales

SPRING 2000 - JAPANESE GARDEN OPENING
16th-19th JUNE - FLOWER & GARDEN FESTIVAL

Special Events throughout the year
Group discounts available

Open daily, 1st April - 1st October, 10am - 5pm
Open Wed-Sun, 2nd October - 31st March, 10am - 4pm
Closed Christmas Holidays & January

STAPEHILL ABBEY CRAFTS & GARDENS
276 Wimborne Road West, Stapehill, Nr Wimborne, Dorset
Tel: 01202 861686

Marie Curie Cancer Care

Cancer is the UK's single biggest killer – one in three people will get it and one in four will die from it. The National Gardens Scheme supports Marie Curie Cancer Care, a comprehensive cancer care charity, helping people with cancer and their families throughout the UK. For more information about Marie Curie Cancer Care, ring 0800 716 146 or visit our web site at www.mariecurie.org.uk.

County Durham

Hon County Organiser: Mrs Elizabeth Carrick, Throstle Gill Farm, Dalton, Richmond, North Yorkshire DL11 7HZ Tel 01833 621363

DATES OF OPENING

Regular openings
For details see garden description
Raby Castle, Staindrop

April 16 Sunday
South Thorpe & Hutton Magna Gardens

May 1 Monday
Birkheads Cottage Garden & Nursery, Nr Causey Arch, Sunniside

May 21 Sunday
Westholme Hall, Winston

May 28 Sunday
Croft Hall, Croft

June 11 Sunday
Barningham Park, nr Barnard Castle

June 18 Sunday
Romaldkirk Gardens
28 Sunnyside Terrace, Trimdon Grange

June 25 Sunday
Birkheads Cottage Garden & Nursery, Nr Causey Arch, Sunniside
Gainford Gardens

July 2 Sunday
Hurworth on Tees Gardens
Low Walworth Hall, Darlington

July 9 Sunday
Broomshiels Hall, Satley

July 16 Sunday
Ravensford Farm, Hamsterley

July 23 Sunday
Bedburn Hall, Hamsterley

August 20 Sunday
Browside, Boldron

DESCRIPTIONS OF GARDENS

Barningham Park, nr Barnard Castle ❀ (Sir Anthony Milbank) *Turn S off A66 at Greta Bridge or A66 Motel via Newsham.* Woodland walks, trees and rock garden on steep slope with ponds and waterfalls. Shrub and perennial borders. House (not open) built 1650. Home-made cream TEAS. *Adm £2.50 Chd under 14 free. Sun June 11 (2-5). Also by appt for parties, please* **Tel 01833 621202**

Bedburn Hall, Hamsterley ♿❀ (Ian Bonas Esq) *9m NW of Bishop Auckland. From A68 at Witton-le-Wear, turn off W to Hamsterley; turn N from Hamsterley to Bedburn rd and down 1m to valley. From Wolsingham on B6293 turn off SE for 3m.* Medium-sized, terraced garden on S-facing hillside with streams, lake, woodland, lawns, rhododendrons, herbaceous borders and roses. TEAS. *Adm £2 Chd 50p. Sun July 23 (2-6)*

▲ Birkheads Cottage Garden & Nursery, Nr Causey Arch, Sunniside ❀ (Christine Liddle) *Leave A1M at junction 63 onto A693 then onto A6076 rd between Stanley and Sunniside. The nursery is signed between the Causey Arch and Tanfield Steam Railway. If in doubt follow the brown Tourist Board signs for Hedley Hall Wood which also has its entrance in Birkheads Lane. Look out for daisy at car park entrance.* Over 4,000 different hardy plants in garden of 3 acres incl wildlife pond, topiary garden, rockeries, gravel garden, herbaceous borders and wildflower garden all set in open countryside with beautiful views. *Adm £1.50 Chd 50p. For NGS Bank Hol Mon May 1, Sun June 25 (1-5). Parties welcome at other times, incl evenings, by appt, please* **Tel 01207 232262**

Broomshiels Hall, Satley ♿ (Mr & Mrs Peter Cook) *1m N of Tow Law on A68 turn off to Satley. After approx 1m turn R at Lodge entrance to main house (not open).* Approx 2 acres of country garden incl rose garden, shrubbery walk, small lake and formal potager. TEAS. *Adm £2 Chd free. Sun July 9 (2-6)*

NEW **Browside, Boldron** ♿ (Mr & Mrs R D Kearton) *On A66 3m W of Greta Bridge, turn R to Boldron, then proceed ½m, entrance opp junction. From Barnard Castle take A67 to Bowes, after 2m turn L to Boldron.* 1¼ acres with unusual water features and large collection of conifers, wide range of plants and imaginative stone objects. TEA. *Adm 1.50 Chd 50p. Sun Aug 20 (2-5.30)*

Croft Hall, Croft ♿ (Mr & Mrs Trevor Chaytor Norris) *Croft village lies 3m S of Darlington on A167 to Northallerton and 6m from Scotch Corner. Croft Hall is 1st house (not open) on R as you enter village from Scotch Corner.* Large mature garden with wide variety and massed planting of spring bulbs with avenue of red may trees and ancient yew hedge. TEAS. *Adm £2.50 Chd 50p. Sun May 28 (2-6)*

Gainford Gardens *On A67 8mW of Darlington, 8m E of Barnard Castle.* One of the loveliest villages in the county lying round a large tranquil village green beside R Tees. About 10-12 gardens open. TEAS in aid of St Mary's Church. *Adm £2.50 Chd free. Sun June 25 (2-5.30)*

NEW **Hurworth on Tees Gardens** *From N, leave A167 5m S of Darlington. From S, take A167 from Northallerton.* 2 mature gardens on bank of R Tees. Roses, long herbaceous border, lavender border, mature trees, willow. Views of river with stream and flower meadow. Home-made TEAS. *Combined adm £2 Chd free. Sun July 2 (2-5.30)*
NEW **Ings Close** (Mr & Mrs Maxey)
The Old Hall (Mr & Mrs Harrison)

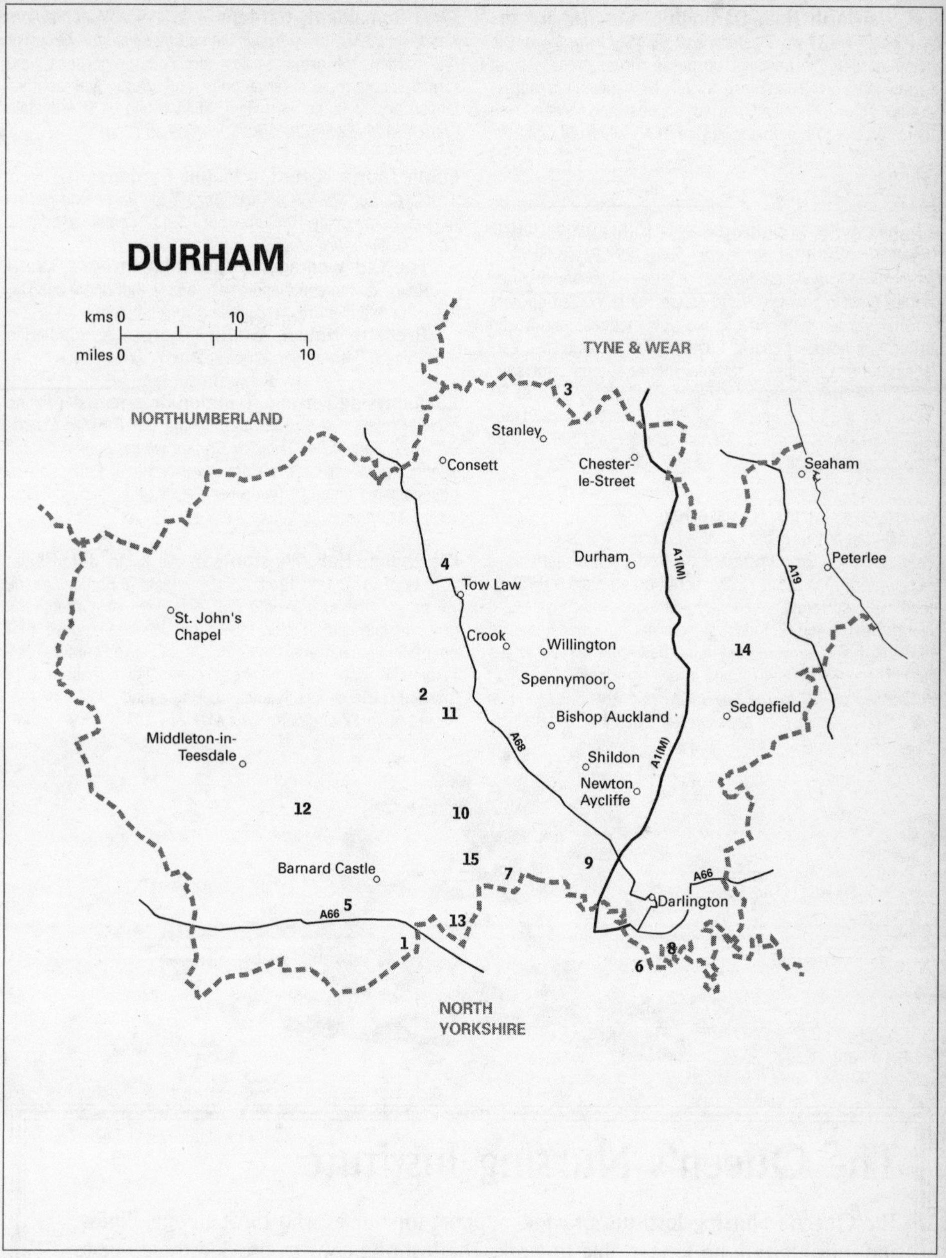

KEY

1 Barningham Park
2 Bedburn Hall
3 Birkheads Cottage Garden & Nursery
4 Broomshiels Hall
5 Browside
6 Croft Hall
7 Gainford Gardens
8 Hurworth on Tees Gardens
9 Low Walworth Hall
10 Raby Castle
11 Ravensford Farm
12 Romaldkirk Gardens
13 South Thorpe & Hutton Magna Gardens
14 28 Sunnyside Terrace
15 Westholme Hall

Low Walworth Hall, Darlington ♿❀ (Mr and Mrs Worrall) *3½m W on Staindrop rd. B6279 (½m drive).* Old walled garden; herbaceous borders, shrubs, roses; trout rearing pond. Small Japanese garden. New millenium fantasy garden. Interesting and varied shrubs and greenhouse plants for sale. Home-made cream TEAS. *Adm £2 Chd 50p. Sun July 2 (2-5.30). Also by appt, please* **Tel 01325 468004**

● **Raby Castle, Staindrop** ♿✗❀ (Lord Barnard) *NW of Darlington. 1m N of Staindrop on A688. Buses: 75, 77 Darlington-Barnard Castle; 8 Bishop Auckland-Barnard Castle; alight Staindrop, North Lodge, ¼m.* Walled garden; informal garden with ericas; old yew hedges; shrub and herbaceous borders; roses. Castle open. Horse-drawn carriages and fire engines. Tearoom. Plants and gifts for sale. *Adm Castle Gardens and carriages £4 OAPs £3 Chd £1.50. Family ticket £10 (2 adults, 2-3 Chd) Gardens & carriages only £1.50 OAPs/Chd £1. Open all Bank Hols; Sat to Wed May, June; Wed and Sun July to end Sept*

Ravensford Farm, Hamsterley ✗❀ (Mr & Mrs J Peacock) *9m NW of Bishop Auckland. From A68 at Witton-le-Wear turn off W to Hamsterley. Go through village and turn L just before tennis courts.* 2½ acres created since 1986 to blend with surrounding countryside and provide yr-round colour. Small wood, 2 ponds, sunken garden, rhododendron walk and mixed borders containing flowering shrubs, roses and herbaceous perennials and a few surprises. TEAS. *Adm £2 Chd 50p (ACNO to The Royal National Rose Society). Sun July 16 (2-5.30). Also by appt, please* **Tel 01388 488305**

NEW **Romaldkirk Gardens** ♿❀ *6m NW of Barnard Castle on B6277, or approach via nearby Eggleston.* Group of 8+ gardens of great variety incl cottage gardens, one formal, another with large pond and grotto, yet another landscaped to blend with view. TEAS in aid of St Romald's Church. *Adm £2.50 Chd 50p. Sun June 18 (2-5)*

South Thorpe & Hutton Magna Gardens ✗❀ *From Scotch Corner 8m NW on A66. Turn R to Thorpe and Hutton Magna.* Home-made TEAS in aid of NSPCC. *Combined adm £2 Chd 50p. Sun April 16 (2-5)*

The Old Vicarage, Hutton Magna (Mr & Mrs D Raw) Garden contemporary to house (not open) specialising in hellebore, primula and spring bulbs

Orchard House, South Thorpe ♿ (Catherine Scrope) Cottage garden of approx ¼ acre

28 Sunnyside Terrace, Trimdon Grange ♿❀ (Dianne Nichol-Brown) *5m E of Durham signposted Trimdon Grange off A181. Far end of Trimdon Grange village behind infants school.* Newly created garden with National Collection of polemoniums among a wide variety of other plants. TEAS. *Adm £1 Chd free. Sun June 18 (2-5)*

Westholme Hall, Winston ♿❀ (Mr & Mrs J H McBain) *11m W of Darlington. From A67 Darlington to Barnard Castle rd, nr Winston turn N onto B6274.* 5 acres of gardens and grounds laid out in 1892 surround Jacobean house (not open). Rhododendrons, flowering shrubs, mixed borders, old-fashioned rose garden. The croquet lawn leads on to orchard, stream and woodland. Home-made TEAS in tearooms. *Adm £2 Chd 50p. Suns May 21 (2-6)*

The Queen's Nursing Institute

The Queen's Nursing Institute provides support for nurses who through age, illness and infirmity are no longer able to work. The Institute aims to provide these nurses with as much independence as possible, in gratitude for the unparalleled quality of care they provided for the community during their working lives, many of them at a time when no formal state pensions infrastructure existed.

More information is available on the NGS website www.ngs.org.uk

Essex

Hon County Organiser: Mrs J Cowley, Park Farm, Chatham Hall Lane, Great Waltham,, Essex CM3 1BZ 01245 360 871

Assistant Hon County Organisers: Mrs Judy Johnson, Saling Hall, Great Saling, Braintree, Essex CM7 5DT 01371 850243
Mrs Rosie Welchman, The Old Rectory, Little Sampford, Essex CB10 2QD 01799 586230

Hon County Treasurer: Mr Eric Brown, 107 Castle Street, Saffron Walden, Essex CB10 1BQ

DATES OF OPENING

Regular openings

For details see garden description

Beth Chatto Gardens, Elmstead Market
Easton Lodge Gardens, Great Dunmow
Feeringbury Manor, Feering
The Gibberd Garden, Marsh Lane, Harlow
Green Island, Radleigh
Hyde Hall RHS Garden
Wickham Place Farm, Wickham Bishops

By appointment only

For telephone numbers and other details see garden descriptions. Private visits welcomed

Woodpeckers, Burnham-on-Crouch

March 12 Sunday
Writtle College, Writtle

March 19 Sunday
The Magnolias, Brentwood

March 26 Sunday
Glen Chantry, Wickham Bishops
The Magnolias, Brentwood

April 2 Sunday
The Magnolias, Brentwood
St Mary's Hall, Great Bentley

April 9 Sunday
Lower Dairy House, Nayland
Park Farm, Great Waltham

April 10 Monday
Park Farm, Great Waltham

April 16 Sunday
Lower Dairy House, Nayland
The Magnolias, Brentwood

April 23 Sunday
Glen Chantry, Wickham Bishops
Hobbans Farm, Bobbingworth
Lower Dairy House, Nayland
The Magnolias, Brentwood
Park Farm, Great Waltham
Saling Hall Lodge, Great Saling

April 24 Monday
Lower Dairy House, Nayland
Park Farm, Great Waltham

April 30 Sunday
Glen Chantry, Wickham Bishops
Lower Dairy House, Nayland
Olivers, Colchester
Park Farm, Great Waltham

May 1 Monday
Glen Chantry, Wickham Bishops
Lower Dairy House, Nayland
Olivers, Colchester
Park Farm, Great Waltham

May 3 Wednesday
Saling Hall, Great Saling
Saling Hall Lodge, Great Saling

May 7 Sunday
Hobbans Farm, Bobbingworth
Lower Dairy House, Nayland
The Magnolias, Brentwood

May 10 Wednesday
Saling Hall, Great Saling

May 14 Sunday
Lower Dairy House, Nayland
The Magnolias, Brentwood
Park Farm, Great Waltham
Shore Hall, Cornish Hall End

May 15 Monday
Park Farm, Great Waltham

May 17 Wednesday
Saling Hall, Great Saling
Shore Hall, Cornish Hall End

May 21 Sunday
Hobbans Farm, Bobbingworth
Lower Dairy House, Nayland
The Magnolias, Brentwood
Saling Hall Lodge, Great Saling

May 24 Wednesday
Saling Hall, Great Saling

May 27 Saturday
Edelweiss, Hornchurch

May 28 Sunday
Edelweiss, Hornchurch
Fanners Farm, Great Waltham
Glen Chantry, Wickham Bishops
Little Sampford Gardens, nr Saffron Walden
Lower Dairy House, Nayland
Park Farm, Great Waltham
Tudor Roost, Fingringhoe

May 29 Monday
Edelweiss, Hornchurch
Fanners Farm, Great Waltham
Glen Chantry, Wickham Bishops
Little Sampford Gardens, nr Saffron Walden
Lower Dairy House, Nayland
Park Farm, Great Waltham
Tudor Roost, Fingringhoe

May 31 Wednesday
Saling Hall, Great Saling

June 3 Saturday
Shrubs Farm, Lamarsh

June 4 Sunday
Hobbans Farm, Bobbingworth
Lower Dairy House, Nayland
The Old Rectory, Boreham
Shrubs Farm, Lamarsh
South Green Farmhouse, Fingringhoe
Tudor Roost, Fingringhoe
Writtle College, Writtle

June 7 Wednesday
Saling Hall, Great Saling
Saling Hall Lodge, Great Saling

June 11 Sunday
Lower Dairy House, Nayland
Park Farm, Great Waltham

June 12 Monday
Park Farm, Great Waltham

June 14 Wednesday
Barnards Farm, West Horndon (evening)
Horkesley Hall, Little Horkesley
Saling Hall, Great Saling

June 16 Friday
Perrymans, Dedham Road, Boxted

June 18 Sunday
Hobbans Farm, Bobbingworth
Lower Dairy House, Nayland
The Magnolias, Brentwood
Saling Hall, Great Saling
Saling Hall Lodge, Great Saling

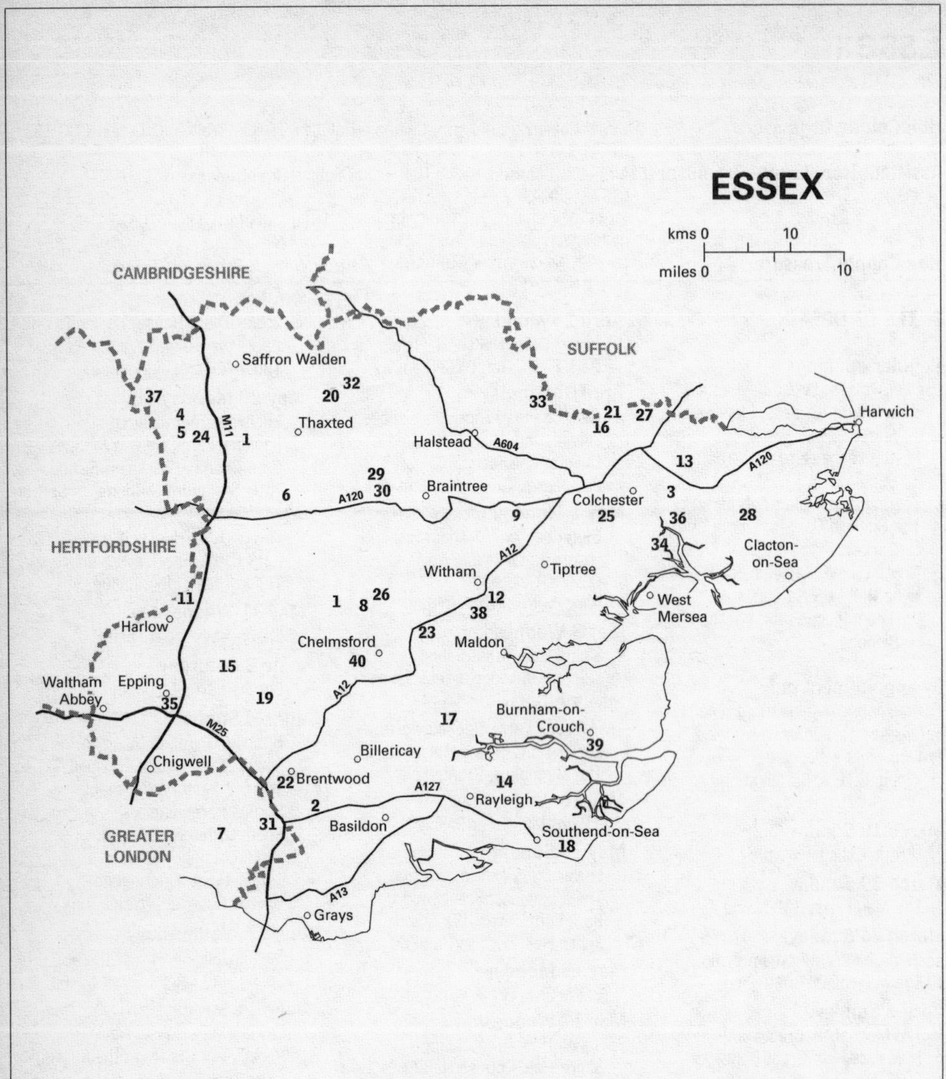

KEY

1 Amberden Hall
2 Barnards Farm
3 Beth Chatto Gardens
4 Clavering Gardens
5 Deers
6 Easton Lodge Gardens
7 Edelweiss
8 Fanners Farm
9 Feeringbury Manor
10 Fudlers Hall
11 The Gibberd Garden
12 Glen Chantry
13 Green Island
14 47 Hill Lane
15 Hobbans Farm
16 Horkesley Hall
17 Hyde Hall RHS Garden
18 Little Foxes
19 Little Myles
20 Little Sampford Gardens
21 Lower Dairy House
22 The Magnolias
23 The Old Rectory, Boreham
24 The Old Vicarage, Rickling
25 Olivers
26 Park Farm
27 Perrymans
28 St Mary's Hall
29 Saling Hall
30 Saling Hall Lodge
31 Schluck
32 Shore Hall
33 Shrubs Farm
34 South Green Farmhouse
35 19 Stewards Close
36 Tudor Roost
37 Wickets
38 Wickham Place Farm
39 Woodpeckers
40 Writtle College

Schluck, Cranham
Shore Hall, Cornish Hall End
Wickets, Langley Upper Green

June 21 Wednesday
Saling Hall, Great Saling
Shore Hall, Cornish Hall End

June 24 Saturday
Edelweiss, Hornchurch

June 25 Sunday
Clavering Gardens, Clavering
Edelweiss, Hornchurch
Fudlers Hall, Mashbury
Lower Dairy House, Nayland
The Old Vicarage, Rickling
Park Farm, Great Waltham

June 26 Monday
Fudlers Hall, Mashbury
Park Farm, Great Waltham

June 28 Wednesday
Saling Hall, Great Saling

June 30 Friday
Perrymans, Dedham Road, Boxted

July 2 Sunday
Hobbans Farm, Bobbingworth
Little Myles, Stondon Massey, Brentwood
Lower Dairy House, Nayland
19 Stewards Close, Epping
Tudor Roost, Fingringhoe

July 5 Wednesday
Saling Hall, Great Saling

July 8 Saturday
Little Foxes, Thorpe Bay

July 9 Sunday
Barnards Farm, West Horndon
Little Foxes, Thorpe Bay
Lower Dairy House, Nayland
Park Farm, Great Waltham
Saling Hall Lodge, Great Saling
19 Stewards Close, Epping

July 10 Monday
Park Farm, Great Waltham

July 12 Wednesday
Saling Hall, Great Saling
Saling Hall Lodge, Great Saling

July 15 Saturday
Amberden Hall, Widdington

July 16 Sunday
Amberden Hall, Widdington
Hobbans Farm, Bobbingworth
The Magnolias, Brentwood
Writtle College, Writtle

July 19 Wednesday
Saling Hall, Great Saling

July 22 Saturday
Edelweiss, Hornchurch

July 23 Sunday
Edelweiss, Hornchurch

July 26 Wednesday
Saling Hall, Great Saling

July 30 Sunday
47 Hill Lane, Hawkwell

August 6 Sunday
Tudor Roost, Fingringhoe

August 16 Wednesday
Horkesley Hall, Little Horkesley

August 20 Sunday
Hobbans Farm, Bobbingworth
The Magnolias, Brentwood

August 26 Saturday
Edelweiss, Hornchurch

August 27 Sunday
Deers, Clavering
Edelweiss, Hornchurch

August 28 Monday
Edelweiss, Hornchurch
Glen Chantry, Wickham Bishops

September 3 Sunday
Barnards Farm, West Horndon
Hobbans Farm, Bobbingworth

September 17 Sunday
Hobbans Farm, Bobbingworth
The Magnolias, Brentwood

October 8 Sunday
Writtle College, Writtle

October 22 Sunday
The Magnolias, Brentwood

DESCRIPTIONS OF GARDENS

Amberden Hall, Widdington ♿✂❀ (Mr and Mrs D Lloyd) *6m from Saffron Walden. E off B1383 nr Newport. Follow signs to Mole Hall Wildlife Park. Drive ½m beyond park on R.* Medium-sized walled garden with collection of unusual hardy plants, shrubs, ivy allée, woodland walk and secret garden. Raised vegetable garden. TEAS. *Adm £2.50 Chd free. Sat, Sun July 15, 16 (2-6)*

Barnards Farm, West Horndon ♿✂❀ (Bernard & Sylvia Holmes and The Christabella Charitable Trust) *On A128, 2km S of A127.* Created from farmland around a Georgian farm house (not open). Partially designed from the air. Aviators welcome. Life size bronzes, sculptured pots and brick and willow mazes. Herbaceous borders, 17 hectares of grounds, ponds, developing woodland, arboretum, living wall malus collection, Japanese garden, long avenue, bog garden, small museum, parterre, and ornamental vegetable garden. Religious service 5.30 to 6. TEAS. Disabled buggy, guided tours. *Adm £3 Chd free (ACNO to St Francis Church West Horndon). Suns July 9, Sept 3 (2-5.30)* **Evening opening** *Adm £5. Wine and Live Music. Wed June 14 (6-9) Private visits welcome by appt, please* **Tel 01277 811262**

● **Beth Chatto Gardens, Elmstead Market** ✂❀ (Mrs Beth Chatto) *On A133, ¼m E of Elmstead Market.* 5 acres of attractively landscaped garden with many unusual plants, shown in wide range of conditions from hot and dry to water garden. Books available by Beth Chatto The Dry Garden, The Damp Garden, Beth Chatto's Garden Notebook, The Green Tapestry, Dear Friend and Gardener. Adjacent nursery open. *Adm £3 Chd free. March 1 to Oct 31, every Mon to Sat but closed Bank Hols (9-5); Nov 1 to end of Feb every Mon to Fri but closed Bank Hols (9-4). Parties by appt*

Clavering Gardens, Clavering ♿❀ *On B1038 7m N of Bishops Stortford. Turn W off B1383 (old A11) at Newport.* TEAS in Cricket Pavilion on village green in aid of Clavering Cricket Club. *Combined adm £3 Chd free. Sun June 25 (1.30-6)*

April Cottage (Mr & Mrs N C Harris) Small cottage garden with old-fashioned perennials and roses, raised alpine bed

Brooklands (Mr & Mrs John Noble) Walled garden, herbaceous and shrub borders, rustic rose trellis, arboretum. Extended garden planting in old orchard; 1½ acres

Clavering Court (Mr & Mrs S R Elvidge) Approx 1½ acres, fine trees, shrubs and borders. Walled garden, Edwardian greenhouse

Deers (Mr & Mrs S H Cooke) *Parking in yard next to house.* For details see separate entry

Piercewebbs (Mr & Mrs B R William-Powlett) Old walled garden, shrubs, lawns, ha ha, yew with topiary and stilt hedges, pond and trellised rose garden. Extensive views

Shovellers (Miss J & Miss E Ludgate) *Stickling Green* 3-acre extended cottage garden, orchard and meadow

Deers, Clavering ♿ (Mr & Mrs S H Cooke) *On B1038 7m N of Bishop's Stortford. Turn W off B1383 (old A11) at Newport; nr Fox & Hounds, in centre of Clavering, turn to Langley and take 2nd L (on bend), to Ford End, house on R ¾m along lane. Parking in yard next to house.* Shrub and herbaceous borders; ponds; old roses in formal garden; pool garden; walled vegetable garden; flower meadow; field and woodland walks. 9 acres. TEAS. *Combined adm with* **Clavering Gardens** *£3 Chd free. Sun June 25 (2-6). Also open alone Adm £3 Chd free. Sun Aug 27 (2-5).*

● **Easton Lodge Gardens, Great Dunmow** ♿❀ (Mr & Mrs B Creasey) *Brown heritage signs from A120, W of Dunmow. 1½m N of Dunmow.* Home of 'Darling Daisy', Countess of Warwick, who in 1903 commissioned Harold Peto to lay out Italian and Japanese Gardens. Abandoned 1950; major restoration since 1993 incl brick and cobble courtyard, ponds, C18th dovecote, conservatory and pavilion. Work started on sunken Italian Garden. History Exhibition. Cream TEAS. *Adm £3.30 OAPs £3 Chd under 12 free (ACNO to Five Parishes). Fris, Sats, Suns, Bank Hols April 21 to Oct 31 (12-6). Private visits welcome, please* **Tel 01371 876979**

Edelweiss, Hornchurch (Joan H Hogg /Pat F Lowery) *20 Hartland Rd. From Romford E along the A124 past Tesco on L, turn R into Albany Rd opp church on corner of Park Lane on the L. Go to the bottom of Albany Rd, humps all the way, turn L at the end into Hartland Rd.* Small town garden 200′ × 25′. Laid out to maximise small narrow plot and featuring many containers, baskets, seasonal bedding and mixed borders. Home-made produce. Narrow access and steps not suitable for push-chairs. Produce, plants. Cream TEAS. *Adm £1 Chd free. Sats, Suns, Bank Hol Mon May 27, 28, 29, June 24, 25, July 22, 23 Aug 26, 27, 28 (3-6). Private visits welcome, June-Aug please* **Tel 01708 454610**

Fanners Farm, Great Waltham ♿✂ (Mr & Mrs P G Lee) *4m N of Chelmsford. In Great Waltham turn into South Street by antique pine shop. After 1¼m turn R into no through rd.* Informal garden of approx 2 acres surrounding C14 house (not open). Secret rose garden, 2 ponds, conservatory and 'potager'. Small collection of vintage and classic cars. TEAS. *Adm £1.75 Chd free. Sun, Mon May 28, 29 (12-5)*

Feeringbury Manor, Feering ♿ (Mr and Mrs Giles Coode-Adams) *Coggeshall Rd, between Coggeshall and Feering.* 7 acres of garden over-flowing with plants both rare and common within a strongly structured design. Intriguing gates, gazebo and benches sculpted by Ben Coode-Adams. Other contemporay sculpture in June, July. Shown in Country Life, Country Living and Passionate Gardener. *Adm £2 Chd free (ACNO to Colchester and District Visual Arts Trust). Thurs, Fris May 4 to July 28 (8.30-4). Private visits welcome, please* **Tel 01376 561946**

Fudlers Hall, Mashbury ✂ (Mr & Mrs A J Meacock) *6m N of Chelmsford. From Great Waltham, turn into Barrack Lane by Beehive Inn. Continue for 2½m. House on R after sharp bend.* 2-acre garden divided into several areas by old walls, with lovely pastoral views surrounding C17 farm house (not open). Many old-fashioned and climbing roses on ropes, pergolas etc. Closely planted mixed herbaceous and shrub borders. Yew-hedged kitchen garden, sweet peas, small orchard. *Adm £1.50 Chd free. Sun, Mon June 25, 26 (2-6)*

● **The Gibberd Garden, Marsh Lane, Harlow** ♿ (The Gibberd Garden Trust) *Marsh Lane is a narrow turning off B183 Rd (to Hatfield Heath), approx 1m E of the junction with A414. Look for 'Garden Open' sign on L.* 7-acre C20 garden designed by Sir Frederick Gibberd, on side of small valley. Terraces, wild garden, landscaped vistas, pools and streams, 'Roman Temple', moated log 'castle', gazebo, tree house and large collection of modern sculpture. TEAS. *Adm £3 Concessions £2 Chd free. Sats, Suns and Bank Hols Easter Sun to end of Sept (2-6). Weekday parties by appt, please* **Tel 01279 442112**

■ **Glen Chantry, Wickham Bishops** ♿✂❀ (Mr & Mrs W G Staines) *1½m SE of Witham. Take Maldon Rd from Witham and 1st L to Wickham Bishops. Cross narrow bridge over R Blackwater. Turn immed L up track by side of Blue Mills.* 3-acre garden, emphasis on mixed borders, unusual perennials and shrub roses. Limestone rock gardens, ponds, formal specialist white garden, foliage beds with grasses and hostas; plant nursery. TEAS in aid of local charities. *Adm £2 Chd 50p. Fris, Sats March 24-Oct 14 (10-4) (DIY TEAS). For NGS Suns March 26, April 23, 30, May 28, Mons May 1, 29, Aug 28 (2-5). Also parties by appt, please* **Tel 01621 891342**

NEW **Green Island, Radleigh** ♿✂❀ (Fiona Edmond) *3m NE of Colchester. Take A137 towards Manningfree, turn R at mini roundabout onto Bromley Rd. Follow for 3m. Park Rd on L.* 'A garden in the making', professionally designed by Fiona Edmond, beautifully situated in 19 acres of woodland. Huge variety of unusual plants with lots of interest all yr round. Japanese garden, mixed borders, woodland walks, secret garden and water garden under development. TEAS. *Adm £2.50 Chd 50p. Weds April 12 to June 28 and Aug 17 to Oct 18, Weds, Sats, Suns April 23, May 13, 14, 20, 21, June 24, 25, July 19, 26, 29, 30, Aug 27, Sept 23, 24 (2-5)*

NEW **47 Hill Lane, Hawkwell** ✂❀ (Margaret Taylor) *Leave A127 at Rayleigh Weir, take A129 to Rayleigh through town. Then B1013 to Hockley-Hawkwell 4m. Train 10 min walk from Hockley Station. Bus no 8 Rayleigh - Southend White Hart Garage stop, 2 min walk.* Exotic colourful garden approx 76' x 10'. Many tender plants and varied perennials, unusual plants in containers, water features, aviary, fish, arches and pergolas. Topiarised conifers. Many different scenes in a smaller garden. Conservatory with bouganvillea and other varieties of plants. TEAS. *Adm £1 Chd 50p (ACNO to Lady McAdden's Appeal B.U.S.T). Sun July 30 (2-5) Groups welcome June to August by appt, please* **Tel 01702 206387**

Hobbans Farm, Bobbingworth ✂❀ (Mrs Ann Webster) *Ongar. N of A414 between Ongar 'Four Wantz' roundabout and N Weald 'Talbot' roundabout just past Blake Hall Gardens. 1st farm entrance on R after St Germain's Church.* Mature, romantic informal gardens, set in 2 acres surrounding C15 farmhouse. Unusual plants; clematis, old roses, small herb, 'potager' and sink gardens, courtyard, orchard and wild garden with ponds, bulbs, trees and shrubs. Set in pastures with fine views. TEAS. *Adm £1.50 Chd free. Suns April 23, May 7, 21, June 4, 18, July 2, 16, Aug 20, Sept 3, 17 (2-6). Private visits and parties by appt, please* **Tel 01277 890245**

Horkesley Hall, Little Horkesley ♿ (Mr & Mrs Richard Eddis) *Colchester. Little Horkesley is W of A134, 3m N of Colchester. House marked on map just beyond church.* A young garden of approx 5 acres within the setting of a classical house, 2 old fishponds and some fine old trees around the perimeter. Its creation began in 1990/91 and the emphasis is on shrubs and trees chosen for colour and effect, incl some which are unusual and rare. *Adm £2 Chd £1. Weds June 14, Aug 16 (2-5); also by appt individuals and parties welcome, please* **Tel 01206 272067**

Hyde Hall RHS Garden ♿✄❀ (J M Calvert, Property Manager) *7m SE of Chelmsford; 6m NE of Wickford. Signed from A130.* 20-acre mixed garden. Many flowering trees, shrubs, perennials and colour theme borders, spring and summer bulbs. Large ponds with water lilies and marginal plants, temperate glasshouse and alpine house. Extensive rose gardens, collections and national collections of ornamental crab apples and viburnum. new farmhouse garden and herb garden. Thatched Barn Restaurant, (licensed), shop. *Adm £3 Chd 70p 6-16 chd under 6 free. Parties 10+ £2.50. Open every day between March 22 and October 29. March to Aug (11-6), Sept, Oct (11-5)*

NEW **Little Foxes, Thorpe Bay** ♿✄❀ (Mrs Dorothy Goode) *Approx 3m E of Southend. Take seafront rd for about 2½m from pier to Thorpe Bay Tennis Courts. Turn L into St Augustines Ave, R into Thorpe Bay Gdns, then 1st L into Marcus Ave. Marcus Gdns is 4th on R.* ⅓ acre enthusiast's garden comprising several island beds and long borders, set in lawns. Trees, shrubs and conifers form a backdrop for mixed beds of perennials, grasses, heathers, variety of foliage plants. Colour themed areas and pretty water feature. RHS/Daily Mail National Gardens Finalist 1998. *Adm £1 Chd 50p. Sat, Sun July 8, 9 (11-4) Private visits groups/clubs welcome by appt, please* **Tel 01702 587972**

Little Myles, Stondon Massey, Brentwood ♿✄❀ (Judy & Adrian Cowan) *Ongar Rd. 1½m SE of Chipping Ongar. Turn off A128 at Stag PH, Marden Ash, (Ongar) towards Stondon Massey. Over bridge, 1st house on R after S bend. (400 yds the Ongar side of Stondon Massey Church).* A romantic garden surrounded by wildflowers and grasses, set in 3 acres. Full borders, hidden features, meandering paths, pond, woodland glade and stream. The herb garden, full of nectar-rich and scented herbs, inspired our handmade herbal cosmetic business. Cosmetics for sale. TEAS. *Adm £2, Chd £1. Sun July 2 (11-4). Groups by arrangement June and July please* **Tel 01277 363176**

Little Sampford Gardens, nr Saffron Walden ✄❀ *B1053 ½m out of Great Sampford on Finchingfield Rd.* Sampford's Society Village Festival, Hill Farm, all week-end (10.30-5).TEAS in aid of Sampford's Churches. *Combined adm £2.50 Chd free. Sun, Mon May 28, 29 (2-6)*

The Grange (Mr & Mrs C P Robinson) Mature garden surrounding C18 house (not open), with charming views. Herbaceous and mixed borders. Rose beds, new shrubbery, small courtyard garden and woodland walk down to the R Pant.

The Old Rectory (Mr & Mrs H Welchman) 2½ acres of formal gardens, with 5 acre ancient wild flower meadow. Many mature trees typical of Rectory gardens, large mixed borders, two ponds, roses, recently planted shrubs and trees, all aimed to produce a long season of interesting colour

Lower Dairy House, Nayland ♿✄❀ (Mr and Mrs D J Burnett) *7m N of Colchester off A134. Turn L at bottom of hill before Nayland village into Water Lane, signed to Little Horkesley. Garden ½m on L past farm buildings.* Plantsman's garden approx 1½ acres. Natural stream with waterside plantings; rockery and raised beds; lawns; herbaceous borders; roses. Many varieties of shrubs and ground cover plants. Spring bulbs and blossom. Tudor House (not open). Teas in village. *Adm £2 Chd 50p. Suns, Bank Hol Mons April 9, 16, 23, 24, 30, May 1, 7, 14, 21, 28, 29, June 4, 11, 18, 25, July 2, 9 (2-6). Also private visits welcome by appt, please* **Tel 01206 262220**

The Magnolias, Brentwood ✄❀ (Mr and Mrs R A Hammond) *18 St John's Ave. From A1023 turn S on A128; after 300yds R at traffic lights; over railway bridge; St John's Ave 3rd on R.* ½ acre informal garden with particular appeal to plantsmen; good collection spring bulbs; ground-cover; trees and shrubs incl maples, rhododendrons, camellias, magnolias and pieris. Koi ponds and other water interests. Featured on Garden Club and Gardeners World. *Adm £1.50 Chd 50p. Suns March 19, 26, April 2, 16, 23, May 7, 14, 21, June 18, July 16, Aug 20, Sept 17, Oct 22 (10-5). Parties by appt March to Oct incl, please* **Tel 01277 220019**

Marsh Lane, Harlow (see The Gibberd Garden)

The Old Rectory, Boreham ♿✄❀ (Sir Jeffery and Lady Bowman) *4m NE of Chelmsford. Take 1137 to Boreham Village, turn into Church Rd at Red Lion Public House. ½m along on R opp church.* 2½ acre garden with ponds, stream, interesting trees and shrubs, herbaceous borders and kitchen garden. TEAS. *Adm £1.50 Chd free. Sun June 4 (2-6)*

The Old Vicarage, Rickling ♿✄ (Mr & Mrs James Jowitt) *7m S from Saffron Walden: from Newport take B1038 W, after 2m, turn L to Rickling. The Old Vicarage is on the L after 1m.* 2-acre garden divided by yew hedges, interesting 'hot' borders, herbaceous and mixed borders; rose garden, shrubbery, herb garden, ornamental potager and lily pond. TEAS in aid of Rickling Church. *Adm £2 Chd 50p. Sun June 25 (2-6)*

Olivers, Colchester ♿✄❀ (Mr and Mrs D Edwards) *3m SW of Colchester, between B1022 & B1026. Follow signs to zoo and continue 1m towards Colchester. Turn R at roundabout (Cunobelin Way) and R into Olivers Lane. From Colchester via Maldon Rd turn L at roundabout, R into Olivers Lane.* C18 house (not open) overlooks Roman R valley, surrounded by terrace and yew-backed borders; closely planted with unusual plants. Lawns; 3 lakes; meadow; woodland with fine trees underplanted with shrubs incl rhododendrons and old roses; spring bulbs and bluebells.

Adm £2 Chd free. Sun, Mon April 30, May 1 (2-6). Other visits by appt, please **Tel 01206 330575/Fax 01206 3303366**

Park Farm, Great Waltham ✇❀ (Mrs J E M Cowley & Mr D Bracey) *Take B1008 N from Chelmsford through Broomfield Village. On Little Waltham bypass turn L into Chatham Hall Lane signed Howe Street; Park Farm ½m on L.* 2 acres of garden in separate 'rooms' formed by yew hedges with climber-obscured old farmhouse and dairy in centre. Many different species of bulbs; shrubs; roses and herbaceous perennials; designing still proceeding with new projects underway. TEAS. *Adm £1.50 Chd 50p. Suns April 9, 23, 30, May 14, 28, June 11, 25, July 9, Mons April 10, 24, May 1, 15, 29, June 12, 26, July 10 (2-6). Parties by appt, please* **Tel 01245 360871**

Perrymans, Dedham Road, Boxted ♿✇❀ (Mr & Mrs H R J Human) *4m NE from Colchester Station to Boxted Cross. Follow Dedham Rd, drive entrance on R 200yds past village shop almost opp Cooks Hill.* 7-acre undulating garden created from scratch since 1970, rose garden overlooking lake, borders, spring bulbs and selection of old and new trees; small vegetable and herb garden. *Adm £2 Chd 50p. Fris June 16, 30 (11-4.30). Private visits welcome, please* **Tel 01206 272297**

St Mary's Hall, Great Bentley ✇❀ (Mrs Mary Fox) *Take A133 to Clacton. Turn R after Little Chef to Gt Bentley (Shair Lane). ½m bear L over railway bridge. After 250yds bear R, gardens are ½m on R. 1m from village centre, 10m from Colchester and Clacton.* 10 acres surrounding Georgian House (not open), large formal rose gardens, box-hedged parterres (ornamental and vegetable), walled gardens, 'rooms', courtyards and terraces. Spectacular parkland display of daffodils and wildflower. Home grown bedding plants, mixed herbaceous and shrub borders, walkways, terrraces, orchard, fruit and vegetable garden and stocked ponds. TEAS. *Adm £2 Chd free. Sun April 2 (2-5)*

Saling Hall, Great Saling ♿✇ (Mr & Mrs Hugh Johnson) *6m NW of Braintree. Turn N off A120 between Braintree and Dunmow at the Saling Oak.* 12 acres; walled garden dated 1698; small park with fine trees; extensive new collection of unusual plants with emphasis on trees; water gardens. Hugh Johnson is 'Tradescant' of the RHS. TEAS Sun only. *Adm £2.50 Chd free (ACNO to St James's Church, Great Saling). Weds in May, June, July (2-5).Combined adm £3 Sun June 18 with* **Saling Hall Lodge**. *(2-6). Parties by appt on weekdays. Written application, please*

Saling Hall Lodge, Great Saling ♿✇❀ (Mr and Mrs K Akers) *6m NW of Braintree. Turn N off A120 between Braintree and Dunmow at the Saling Oak. Drive at end of village on L, please park in village.* Well-designed and maintained ½ acre garden with pond, limestone rock garden, small peat garden, tufa bed and sinks. As seen on Channel 4 and Anglia TV. TEAS (Not Weds). *Adm £1 Chd free. Suns, Weds April 23, May 3, 21, June 7, 18, July 9, 12 (2-5). Combined adm £3 with* **Saling Hall**, *Sun June 18 (2-6)*

Schluck, Cranham ✇❀ (Mr & Mrs W Taylor) *171A Moor Lane. Leave M25 junction 29. Join A127 E to Romford. From A127 take slip rd to Upminster, turning L into Hall Lane. At mini roundabout turn L into Avon Rd. Bottom of Avon Rd (past shops) turn R (Front Lane) 4th turning L into Moor Lane.* ½ acre informal plantsman's garden, created since 1986 and designed as separate areas. Large selection of shrubs, trees and perennials, small alpine collection, vegetable area, 3 large ponds (1 Koi, 2 wildlife), many interesting features. Sorry not suitable for wheelchairs. TEAS. *Adm £2 Chd 50p. Sun June 18 (12-6). Private visits welcome on other Sundays, please* **Tel 01708 221085**

Shore Hall, Cornish Hall End ✇❀ (Mr & Mrs Peter Swete) *nr Braintree. 2½m NE of Finchingfield. ½m W of Cornish Hall End on Gt Sampford Rd. Long drive with poplars.* 3½-acre garden surrounding C17 house (not open) with several enclosed formal areas and interesting shrubs. 100-yr-old box hedges enclose formal beds planted with herbaceous and old roses; rose garden surrounding lily ponds; ornamental vegetable and fruit garden and many young rare trees. TEAS in aid of local charity Suns only. *Adm £2.50 Chd free. Suns May 14, June 18, Weds May 17, June 21 (2-6). Parties by appt weekdays, May to July, please* **Tel 01799 586411**

Shrubs Farm, Lamarsh ♿✇ (Robert & Sara Erith) *1¼m from Bures on the rd to Lamarsh, the drive is signposted to Shrubs Farm.* 2 acres of mature and developing gardens with shrub borders, lawns, roses and trees. For walkers there are 50 acres of parkland and meadow with wildflower paths and woodland trails. Dogs on lead in this area. Much new hedgerow and tree planting has taken place over the past 15 yrs. Superb 10m views to N and E over the Stour valley. TEAS in C18 barn. *Adm £2 Chd free (ACNO Church of the Holy Innocents Lamarsh). Sat, Sun June 3, 4 (2-6)*

South Green Farmhouse, Fingringhoe ♿✇ (Mrs Z E Jopling) *6m S of Colchester. Straight across in centre of village leaving Whalebone PH on R. South Green Farmhouse is 1m from Xrds. N.B. ignore turning to nature reserve.* English cottage garden, of 1-acre surrounding house which looks across marshes and river estuary to Brightlingsea and Mersea Island. Different garden 'rooms', each with its own character; beds of shrub and hybrid musk roses, flag irises, herb garden, border, kitchen garden and grass maze. TEAS. *Adm £1.50 Chd free. Sun June 4 (2-5)*

19 Stewards Close, Epping ✇❀ (Jenny Filby & Geoff Clark) *From London B1393 to Epping. Turn R at 1st mini roundabout. Past Epping station to bottom of hill. Round LH bend; 1st Rd on L. Additional parking, next side road (50yds on).* 105′ × 60′, 350 plant varieties (full planting plan). Focus on foliage shrubs and attractive plant groupings. Wildlife pond, unusual water features, pergola and trellises, rockery, patios, containers. 'Before and after' photos of all planting/construction work. Special quiz for children. New Mediterranean garden and water cascade planned for 2000. TEAS. *Adm £1 Chd free. Suns July 2, 9 (2-5.30)*

NEW **Tudor Roost, Fingringhoe** ♿ (Chris & Linda Pegden) *5m S of Colchester. In centre of village by Whalebone PH. Follow sign to Ballast Quay, after ½m turn R into Brook Hall Rd, then 1st L into Frere Way.* Set in delightful village, compact, 95' x 60' plantsmans garden, offering an abundance of yr round colour, foliage and the exotic. A koi carp pond (tame koi - 2') being the central feature surrounded by borders and walkways. Rose and clematis covered pergola and pillars. Featured on Anglian TV. TEAS. *Adm £1.50 Chd 50p. Suns, Mon May 28, 29, June 4, July 2, Aug 6 (1.30-5.30)*

Wickets, Langley Upper Green ♿✂ (Mr & Mrs D Copeland) *11m N of Bishops Stortford. Turn W off B1383 (old A11) at Newport. After 5m turn R off B1038 at Clavering, signed Langley. Upper Green is 3m further on. Last house on R of cricket green.* Cottage garden and landscaped paddock with long views. 1½ acres. Newly planted in 1990. Island beds, mixed borders, rose borders, new projects always under way, ponds. Highest village in Essex, windy site. TEAS. *Adm £1.50 Chd free. Sun June 18 (2-5.30)*

Wickham Place Farm, Wickham Bishops ♿✂❀ (Mr & Mrs K Kittle) *2½m SE of Witham nr R Blackwater on B1018. Take B1018 from Witham towards Maldon. After going under A12 take 3rd L (Station Road). 1st house on L.* 2-acre walled garden with further 12 acres of woodland. Huge climbers, roses and wisterias cascade down into wide borders filled with shrubs, perennials and bulbs. Planted for yr round colour on light dry soil. Knot garden and natural pond. Mixed woodland with rabbit resistant plants and bulbs alongside wide paths. TEAS. *Fris only April 7, April 28 to July 28 and Sept 1 to 29 (11-4). Also by postal appt. Adm £1.50 Chd 50p*

Woodpeckers, Burnham-on-Crouch ♿✂❀ (Mr & Mrs N J Holdaway & Mrs L M Burton) *Mangapp Chase. B1010 to Burnham-on-Crouch. Just beyond town sign turn L into Green Lane. Turn L after ½m. Garden 200yds on R.* 1½ acres. Planted with old 'cottage' favourites as well as newer varieties of roses, shrubs and herbaceous perennials. 'Potager', rose walk, ponds all set amongst mature trees. TEAS. *Adm £1 Chd 50p. Open for groups visits by appt, please* **Tel 01621 782137**

▲ **Writtle College, Writtle** ♿❀ (The Administrator) *Lordship Rd. On A414 W of Chelmsford, nr Writtle village, clearly signed.* Approx 15 acres; informal lawns with naturalised bulbs in spring and wild flowers in summer, large tree collection, mixed shrub and herbaceous borders, heathers and alpines. Landscaped gardens designed and built by students including a 'Centenary' garden and a sub-tropical 'Hot 'n' Spicy' garden. A new Millennium garden is being constructed by students ready for summer 2000. Landscaped glasshouses. TEA. *Adm £2 Chd free, Cons/OAP £1. For NGS Suns March 12, June 4, July 16, Oct 8 (10-4)*

Evening Opening (See also garden description)

Barnards Farm, West Horndon	June 14

Flintshire & Wrexham

See separate Welsh section on page 410

Glamorgan

See separate Welsh section on page 413

Crossroads Caring For Carers

Crossroads is the leading national charity providing support to carers; giving them a regular break from their caring responsibilities.

For more information, please contact:
Crossroads,
10 Regent Place, Rugby CV21 2PN

Information is also available on the NGS website
(www.ngs.org.uk)

THE COTTAGE GARDEN

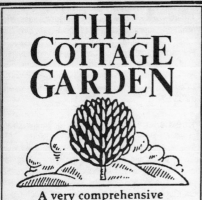

A very comprehensive range of plants to suit all types of gardens and gardeners

PLUS

Garden antiques and many other special things.

LANGHAM ROAD, BOXTED
COLCHESTER, ESSEX CO4 5HU
Telephone (01206) 272269

Macmillan Cancer Relief

Macmillan's nurses and doctors help to increase expertise in cancer treatment and care by sharing their knowledge and skills with other professionals across the country, a process which is aided by formal education programmes.

Macmillan Cancer Relief
Information Line: 0845 601 6161
Macmillan Cancer Relief
Website: www.macmillan.org.uk

LANGTHORNS PLANTERY

FOR HARD TO FIND PLANTS

An outstanding nursery just packed with treasures beautifully grown. A massive range of hardy trees, shrubs, herbaceous and alpine plants as well as a superb conservatory section in summer

Little Canfield, Dunmow, Essex CM6 1TD
Tel/Fax: 01371 872611

Open every day, 10am - 5pm
Please send £1.50 for catalogue

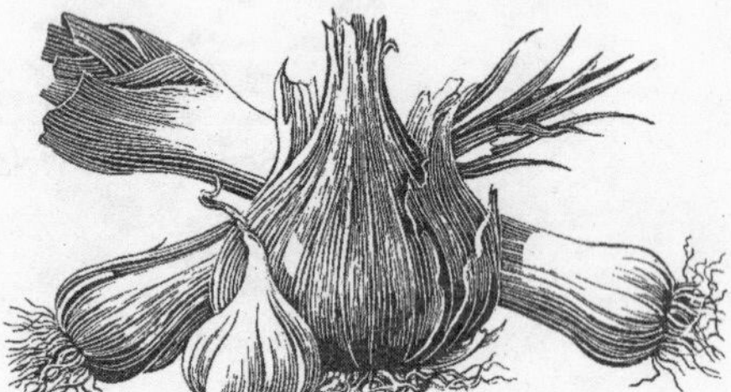

The National Trust Careership Scheme

The National Gardens Scheme sponsors apprenticeships in gardening with the National Trust.

Applications for places are available from January 2000, and the three-year course commences in September 2000.

For more information contact, John McKennall, 01208 74281

Gloucestershire North & Central

Hon County Organiser: Mrs Stella Martin, Dundry Lodge, France Lynch, Stroud GL6 8LP
Tel 01453 883419

Assistant County Organisers: Mrs Barbara Adams, Warners Court, Charfield, Wotton under Edge GL12 8TG
Mrs Lisa Fellows, The Holme House, Jubilee Road, Mitcheldean GL17 0EE
Mrs Meryl King, Springfield, Lower Chedworth, Cheltenham GL54 4AN
Mrs Rosemary Lyons, The Granary, Willington Court, Sandhurst GL2 9NZ
Mr Tony Marlow, Greenedge, 32 Dr Browns Road, Minchinhampton GL6 9BT
Miss Anne Palmer, 10 Vineyard Street, Winchcombe GL54 5LP

Hon County Treasurer: Mr Graham Baber, 11 Corinium Gate, Cirencester GL7 2PX Tel 01285 650961

DATES OF OPENING

Regular openings

For details see garden description

Barnsley House, Nr Cirencester
Batsford Arboretum, nr Moreton-in-Marsh
Bourton House Garden, Bourton-on-the-Hill
Cerney House Gardens, North Cerney
Cinderdine Cottage, Dymock
Ewen Manor, nr Cirencester
Hidcote Manor Garden, Chipping Campden
Hunts Court, North Nibley
Kiftsgate Court, nr Chipping Campden
Lydney Park, Lydney
Mill Dene, Blockley
Misarden Park, Miserden
Painswick Rococo Garden
Rodmarton Manor, Cirencester
Sezincote, nr Moreton-in-Marsh
Snowshill Manor, nr Broadway
Stanway Water Garden, nr Winchcombe
Sudeley Castle, Winchcombe
Tinpenny Farm, Fiddington
Trevi, Hartpury
Trull House, Tetbury
Westbury Court Garden, Westbury-on-Severn

By appointment only

For telephone numbers and other details see garden descriptions. Private visits welcomed

Burnside, Prestbury
The Chestnuts, Minchinhampton
Cotswold Farm, Cirencester
Humphreys End House, Randwick
Orchard Cottage, Gretton
Spring Tyning, Dursley
St Francis, Lammas Park, Minchinhampton

January 30 Sunday
Home Farm, Huntley

February 8 Tuesday
Cinderdine Cottage, Dymock

February 10 Thursday
Cinderdine Cottage, Dymock

February 13 Sunday
Cinderdine Cottage, Dymock
Home Farm, Huntley

February 15 Tuesday
Cinderdine Cottage, Dymock

February 17 Thursday
Cinderdine Cottage, Dymock

February 20 Sunday
Cinderdine Cottage, Dymock
Tinpenny Farm, Fiddington
Trench Hill, Sheepscombe

February 21 Monday
The Old Rectory, Duntisbourne Rous

February 22 Tuesday
Cinderdine Cottage, Dymock

March 4 Saturday
Redwood, Bussage

March 5 Sunday
Cinderdine Cottage, Dymock
Green Cottage, Lydney
Highnam Court
Pear Tree Cottage, Gotherington
Redwood, Bussage

March 7 Tuesday
Cinderdine Cottage, Dymock

March 12 Sunday
Green Cottage, Lydney

March 19 Sunday
Cinderdine Cottage, Dymock
Green Cottage, Lydney
Sheephouse, nr Painswick
Tinpenny Farm, Fiddington

March 21 Tuesday
Cinderdine Cottage, Dymock

March 26 Sunday
Brockweir Gardens
Home Farm, Huntley
Stanway Water Garden, nr Winchcombe

March 27 Monday
The Old Rectory, Duntisbourne Rous

April 1 Saturday
Warners Court, Charfield

April 2 Sunday
Abbotswood, Stow-on-the-Wold
Cinderdine Cottage, Dymock
Highnam Court
Misarden Park, Miserden
Pear Tree Cottage, Gotherington
Trevi, Hartpury
Warners Court, Charfield
Westonbirt School Gardens

April 4 Tuesday
Cinderdine Cottage, Dymock

April 6 Thursday
Trevi, Hartpury

April 9 Sunday
Clover House, Winson
Hodges Barn, Shipton Moyne
Kestrel Cottage, Brand Green
Tinpenny Farm, Fiddington

April 10 Monday
Hodges Barn, Shipton Moyne

April 16 Sunday
The Glebe House, Shipton Moyne
Home Farm, Huntley
Stone House, Wyck Rissington
Upton Wold, nr Moreton-in-Marsh

April 23 Sunday
Beverston Castle
Cinderdine Cottage, Dymock
Ewen Manor, nr Cirencester
Pigeon House, Southam
The Red House, Staunton, nr Gloucester
Trench Hill, Sheepscombe
Trevi, Hartpury

April 24 Monday
Beverston Castle
Cinderdine Cottage, Dymock
Kestrel Cottage, Brand Green

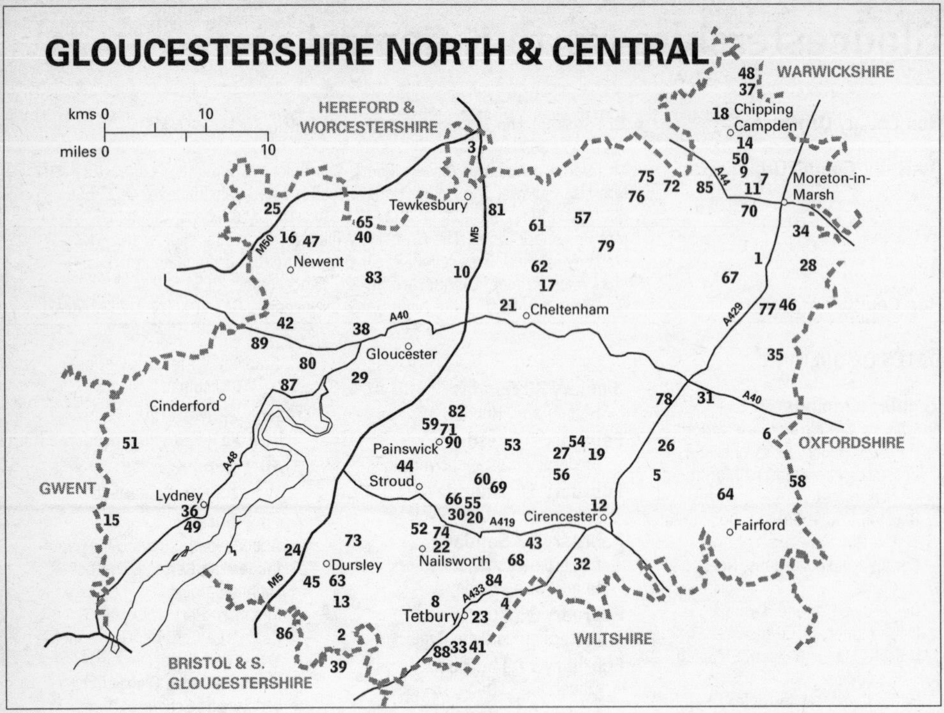

KEY

1 Abbotswood
2 Alderley Grange
3 Apricot Cottage
4 Ashley Manor
5 Barnsley House
6 Barrington Downs
7 Batsford Arboretum
8 Beverston Gardens
9 Blockley Gardens
10 Boddington Manor
11 Bourton House Garden
12 25 Bowling Green Rd
13 Brackenbury
14 Broad Campden Gardens
15 Brockweir Gardens
16 The Bungalow
17 Burnside
18 Campden House
19 Cerney House Gardens
20 Chalford Gardens
21 Cheltenham Gardens
22 The Chestnuts
23 The Chipping Croft
24 Church Cottage
25 Cinderdine Cottage
26 Clover House
27 Cotswold Farm
28 Daylesford House
29 Dower House
30 Eastcombe, Bussage & Brownshill Gardens
31 Eastington Gardens
32 Ewen Manor
33 The Glebe House
34 Grange Farm
35 Great Rissington Farm
36 Green Cottage
37 Hidcote Manor Garden
38 Highnam Court
39 Hillesley House
40 Hillfield
41 Hodges Barn
42 Home Farm
43 Hullasey House
44 Humphreys End House
45 Hunts Court
46 Icomb Place
47 Kestrel Cottage
48 Kiftsgate Court
49 Lydney Park
50 Mill Dene
51 Millend House
52 Minchinhampton Gardens
53 Misarden Park
54 Moor Wood
55 The Old Chapel
56 The Old Rectory
57 Orchard Cottage
58 Oxleaze Farm
59 Painswick Rococo Garden
60 Paulmead
61 Pear Tree Cottage
62 Pigeon House
63 Pitt Court
64 Quenington Gardens
65 The Red House
66 Redwood
67 Rockcliffe
68 Rodmarton Manor
69 Rookwoods
70 Sezincote
71 Sheephouse
72 Snowshill Manor
73 Spring Tyning
74 St Francis
75 Stanton Gardens
76 Stanway Water Garden
77 Stone House
78 Stowell Park
79 Sudeley Castle
80 Sunningdale
81 Tinpenny Farm
82 Trench Hill
83 Trevi
84 Trull House
85 Upton Wold
86 Warners Court
87 Westbury Court Garden
88 Westonbirt School Gardens
89 Willow Lodge
90 Yew Tree House

The Red House, Staunton, nr Gloucester
Trench Hill, Sheepscombe
Trevi, Hartpury

April 25 Tuesday
Cinderdine Cottage, Dymock

April 27 Thursday
Trevi, Hartpury

April 29 Saturday
Barnsley House, Nr Cirencester

April 30 Sunday
Apricot Cottage, Twyning
Brockweir Gardens
Eastcombe, Bussage & Brownshill Gardens
Lydney Park, Lydney
Redwood, Bussage
Sudeley Castle, Winchcombe
Trevi, Hartpury
Willow Lodge, nr Longhope

May 1 Monday
Brockweir Gardens
Eastcombe, Bussage & Brownshill Gardens
Pear Tree Cottage, Gotherington
Redwood, Bussage
Trevi, Hartpury
Willow Lodge, nr Longhope

May 3 Wednesday
Lydney Park, Lydney

May 4 Thursday
Trevi, Hartpury

May 6 Saturday
Malvern Mill
Mill Dene, Blockley

May 7 Sunday
Cinderdine Cottage, Dymock
Hidcote Manor Garden, Chipping Campden
Highnam Court
Snowshill Manor, nr Broadway
Willow Lodge, nr Longhope

May 8 Monday
Willow Lodge, nr Longhope

May 9 Tuesday
Cinderdine Cottage, Dymock
Kestrel Cottage, Brand Green

May 10 Wednesday
Rookwoods, Waterlane

May 13 Saturday
Kiftsgate Court, nr Chipping Campden

May 14 Sunday
Abbotswood, Stow-on-the-Wold
Cerney House Gardens, North Cerney
Green Cottage, Lydney
Home Farm, Huntley
Kestrel Cottage, Brand Green
Oxleaze Farm, Filkins, Lechlade
Pitt Court, North Nibley
Trevi, Hartpury

May 15 Monday
The Old Rectory, Duntisbourne Rous

May 16 Tuesday
Kestrel Cottage, Brand Green

May 17 Wednesday
Pitt Court, North Nibley

May 18 Thursday
Trevi, Hartpury

May 21 Sunday
Batsford Arboretum, nr Moreton-in-Marsh
Dower House, Elmore
Green Cottage, Lydney
Hodges Barn, Shipton Moyne
Millend House, Coleford
Paulmead, Bisley
Pitt Court, North Nibley
Stanway Water Garden, nr Winchcombe
Stowell Park, Northleach
Yew Tree House, Painswick

May 22 Monday
Hodges Barn, Shipton Moyne

May 25 Thursday
Bourton House Garden, Bourton-on-the-Hill
Hillfield, Corse

May 28 Sunday
Apricot Cottage, Twyning
Brockweir Gardens
Cinderdine Cottage, Dymock
Eastington Gardens, nr Northleach
Green Cottage, Lydney
The Red House, Staunton, nr Gloucester
Trevi, Hartpury
Willow Lodge, nr Longhope

May 29 Monday
Apricot Cottage, Twyning
Brackenbury, Coombe
Brockweir Gardens
The Bungalow, nr Newent
Cinderdine Cottage, Dymock
Eastington Gardens, nr Northleach
Kestrel Cottage, Brand Green
The Red House, Staunton, nr Gloucester
Trevi, Hartpury
Willow Lodge, nr Longhope

May 30 Tuesday
Cinderdine Cottage, Dymock

June 1 Thursday
Trevi, Hartpury

June 3 Saturday
Barnsley House, Nr Cirencester

June 4 Sunday
Ashley Manor, nr Tetbury
Boddington Manor
Cheltenham Gardens
Green Cottage, Lydney
Highnam Court
Hodges Barn, Shipton Moyne
Home Farm, Huntley
Kestrel Cottage, Brand Green
Pigeon House, Southam

June 5 Monday
Hodges Barn, Shipton Moyne
Pear Tree Cottage, Gotherington

June 7 Wednesday
Green Cottage, Lydney

June 8 Thursday
Church Cottage, Stinchcombe
Rockcliffe, nr Lower Swell

June 10 Saturday
The Old Chapel, Chalford Vale

June 11 Sunday
Alderley Grange, Alderley
The Bungalow, nr Newent
Chalford Gardens
Cinderdine Cottage, Dymock
The Glebe House, Shipton Moyne
Green Cottage, Lydney
Hunts Court, North Nibley
Kestrel Cottage, Brand Green
Mill Dene, Blockley
The Old Chapel, Chalford Vale
Trench Hill, Sheepscombe
Trevi, Hartpury
Trull House, Tetbury
Willow Lodge, nr Longhope

June 12 Monday
The Old Chapel, Chalford Vale
Trull House, Tetbury
Willow Lodge, nr Longhope

June 13 Tuesday
Cinderdine Cottage, Dymock
Kestrel Cottage, Brand Green

June 13 to 16 Tuesday to Friday
The Old Chapel, Chalford Vale

June 14 Wednesday
Green Cottage, Lydney

June 15 Thursday
Rockcliffe, nr Lower Swell
Trevi, Hartpury

June 17 Saturday
The Old Chapel, Chalford Vale

June 18 Sunday
25 Bowling Green Rd, Cirencester
Cheltenham Gardens
Cinderdine Cottage, Dymock
Grange Farm, Evenlode, nr Moreton-in-Marsh
Green Cottage, Lydney
Hunts Court, North Nibley
Kestrel Cottage, Brand Green

Millend House, Coleford
The Old Chapel, Chalford Vale
The Red House, Staunton, nr Gloucester
Trench Hill, Sheepscombe
Upton Wold, nr Moreton-in-Marsh
Willow Lodge, nr Longhope

June 19 Monday
25 Bowling Green Rd, Cirencester
The Old Chapel, Chalford Vale
The Old Rectory, Duntisbourne Rous
Willow Lodge, nr Longhope

June 20 Tuesday
Cinderdine Cottage, Dymock

June 20 to 23 Tuesday to Friday
The Old Chapel, Chalford Vale

June 21 Wednesday
Green Cottage, Lydney
Rockcliffe, nr Lower Swell

June 22 Thursday
Hillfield, Corse
Sunningdale, nr Westbury-on-Severn

June 24 Saturday
Hullasey House, Tarlton
The Old Chapel, Chalford Vale

June 25 Sunday
Apricot Cottage, Twyning
Blockley Gardens
25 Bowling Green Rd, Cirencester
Brackenbury, Coombe
Brockweir Gardens
Cinderdine Cottage, Dymock
Hillesley House, Hillesley
Hullasey House, Tarlton
Hunts Court, North Nibley
Icomb Place, nr Stow-on-the-Wold
The Old Chapel, Chalford Vale
Quenington Gardens, nr Fairford
Stanton Gardens, Broadway
Stowell Park, Northleach
Sunningdale, nr Westbury-on-Severn
Tinpenny Farm, Fiddington

June 26 Monday
25 Bowling Green Rd, Cirencester
Hullasey House, Tarlton

June 27 Tuesday
Kestrel Cottage, Brand Green

June 28 Wednesday
Great Rissington Farm, Cheltenham
Moor Wood, Woodmancote

June 29 Thursday
Bourton House Garden, Bourton-on-the-Hill
Sunningdale, nr Westbury-on-Severn
Trevi, Hartpury

June 30 Friday
Mill Dene, Blockley (evening)

July 2 Sunday
Beverston Gardens
25 Bowling Green Rd, Cirencester
Broad Campden Gardens
Cinderdine Cottage, Dymock
Highnam Court
Hunts Court, North Nibley
Misarden Park, Miserden
Sunningdale, nr Westbury-on-Severn
Willow Lodge, nr Longhope

July 3 Monday
Beverston Gardens
25 Bowling Green Rd, Cirencester
The Old Rectory, Duntisbourne Rous
Pear Tree Cottage, Gotherington
Willow Lodge, nr Longhope

July 4 Tuesday
Cinderdine Cottage, Dymock
Kestrel Cottage, Brand Green

July 5 Wednesday
Daylesford House, Daylesford

July 6 Thursday
Sunningdale, nr Westbury-on-Severn

July 8 Saturday
Rookwoods, Waterlane

July 9 Sunday
25 Bowling Green Rd, Cirencester
The Bungalow, nr Newent
Campden House, Chipping Campden
Hunts Court, North Nibley
Sezincote, nr Moreton-in-Marsh
Sunningdale, nr Westbury-on-Severn
Trevi, Hartpury

July 10 Monday
25 Bowling Green Rd, Cirencester

July 13 Thursday
Trevi, Hartpury

July 16 Sunday
25 Bowling Green Rd, Cirencester
Cinderdine Cottage, Dymock
Millend House, Coleford
Tinpenny Farm, Fiddington
Willow Lodge, nr Longhope

July 17 Monday
25 Bowling Green Rd, Cirencester
Willow Lodge, nr Longhope

July 18 Tuesday
Cinderdine Cottage, Dymock

July 20 Thursday
Hillfield, Corse
Sunningdale, nr Westbury-on-Severn
Trevi, Hartpury

July 23 Sunday
25 Bowling Green Rd, Cirencester
Sunningdale, nr Westbury-on-Severn

July 24 Monday
25 Bowling Green Rd, Cirencester

July 27 Thursday
Bourton House Garden, Bourton-on-the-Hill

July 29 Saturday
Trevi, Hartpury

July 30 Sunday
Brackenbury, Coombe
Brockweir Gardens
Minchinhampton Gardens
Sunningdale, nr Westbury-on-Severn
Trevi, Hartpury
Willow Lodge, nr Longhope

July 31 Monday
Willow Lodge, nr Longhope

August 3 Thursday
Trevi, Hartpury

August 6 Sunday
Barrington Downs, Aldsworth
Cinderdine Cottage, Dymock
Highnam Court
Trevi, Hartpury
Willow Lodge, nr Longhope

August 7 Monday
Willow Lodge, nr Longhope

August 8 Tuesday
Cinderdine Cottage, Dymock

August 12 Saturday
Kiftsgate Court, nr Chipping Campden

August 13 Sunday
Millend House, Coleford
Tinpenny Farm, Fiddington
Trevi, Hartpury
Westonbirt School Gardens
Willow Lodge, nr Longhope

August 14 Monday
Willow Lodge, nr Longhope

August 17 Thursday
Trevi, Hartpury

August 20 Sunday
Trevi, Hartpury

August 26 Saturday
Rodmarton Manor, Cirencester

August 27 Sunday
Apricot Cottage, Twyning
Brockweir Gardens
Cinderdine Cottage, Dymock
Eastington Gardens, nr Northleach
Trevi, Hartpury

August 28 Monday
Brackenbury, Coombe
Brockweir Gardens
Cinderdine Cottage, Dymock
Eastington Gardens, nr Northleach

Trevi, Hartpury

August 29 Tuesday
Cinderdine Cottage, Dymock

August 31 Thursday
Bourton House Garden, Bourton-on-the-Hill
Trevi, Hartpury

September 3 Sunday
Highnam Court
Pear Tree Cottage, Gotherington
Pitt Court, North Nibley
Trevi, Hartpury
Westbury Court Garden, Westbury-on-Severn

September 6 Wednesday
Pitt Court, North Nibley

September 10 Sunday
Blockley Gardens
The Chipping Croft, Tetbury
Pitt Court, North Nibley
Sudeley Castle, Winchcombe

September 23 Saturday
Warners Court, Charfield

September 24 Sunday
Tinpenny Farm, Fiddington
Warners Court, Charfield

September 28 Thursday
Bourton House Garden, Bourton-on-the-Hill

October 1 Sunday
Highnam Court
Pear Tree Cottage, Gotherington

October 15 Sunday
Tinpenny Farm, Fiddington

October 26 Thursday
Bourton House Garden, Bourton-on-the-Hill

2001

February 11 Sunday
Cinderdine Cottage, Dymock

February 18 Sunday
Cinderdine Cottage, Dymock

February 21 Wednesday
Tinpenny Farm, Fiddington

March 14 Wednesday
Tinpenny Farm, Fiddington

DESCRIPTIONS OF GARDENS

Abbotswood, Stow-on-the-Wold (Mr R Scully) *On B4068 nr Lower Swell.* Several acres of massed plantings of spring bulbs, heathers, flowering shrubs and rhododendrons in dramatic, landscaped hillside stream gardens; fine herbaceous planting in elegant formal gardens with lily pond, terraced lawn and fountain created by Sir Edwin Lutyens. TEAS. Car park free. Dogs on leads. *Adm £2 Chd free. Easter Sun April 23, Suns May 28, June 11. For NGS Suns April 2, May 14 (Plants) (1.30-6)*

Alderley Grange, Alderley (Mr Guy & the Hon Mrs Acloque) *2m S of Wotton-under-Edge. Turn NW off A46 Bath to Stroud rd, at Dunkirk.* Walled garden with fine trees, roses; herb gardens and aromatic plants. *Adm £2 Chd free. Sun June 11 (2-6). Private groups by written request welcome during June*

Apricot Cottage, Twyning (Barbara & Frank Cooke) *2½m N of Tewkesbury. Take A38 Worcester rd. After 2.4m turn R for Twyning, at T junction turn L, at next T junction turn R. On your L just past war memorial. Parking in layby.* Approx ¼ acre, developed over last 4 yrs; terraces, pergola, man-made water course, herbaceous beds and scree. TEA. *Adm £1.50 Chd free. Sun April 30, Sun, Bank Hol Mon May 28, 29, Suns June 25, Aug 27 (2-4.30)*

Ashley Manor, nr Tetbury (Mr & Mrs M J Hoskins) *On A433, turn R through Culkerton to Ashley.* Old garden next to church redesigned by present owners and imaginatively planted. Mature yew hedges divide 4 separate gardens and form backdrop to collection of clematis, shrub roses and herbaceous plants. Kitchen garden. TEAS. *Adm £2 Chd free (ACNO to Ashley Church). Sun June 4 (2-5)*

■ **Barnsley House, Nr Cirencester** (Mr & Mrs Charles Verey) *4m NE of Cirencester on B4425.* Mature garden, created by Rosemary Verey, with interesting collection of shrubs and trees; ground cover; herbaceous borders; pond garden; laburnum walk; knot and herb gardens; formal kitchen garden; C18 summerhouses. C17 house (not open). *Adm £3.75, OAP £3 Chd free (ACNO to Barnsley Church). Mons, Weds, Thurs & Sats (10-5.30) closed Christmas to end Jan. For NGS Sats April 29, June 3 (1.30-5.30). No pre-booked coaches unless NGS specific. Coach parties by appt only* **Tel 01285 740561**

NEW **Barrington Downs, Aldsworth** (Sir Jeremy & Lady Morse) *2m E of Aldsworth. Approached by farm drive off B4425 Cirencester to Burford rd.* Peaceful summer garden of about 2 acres set among fields. Herbaceous borders, trees, shrubs, vegetables and fruit. Water sculpture by William Pye. Children's play area. TEAS. *Adm £2 Chd free. Sun Aug 6 (2-6)*

■ **Batsford Arboretum, nr Moreton-in-Marsh** (Mr David Sherborne Hoar) *Off A44 NW of Moreton-in-Marsh.* Arboretum and wild gardens; over 1500 named trees (many rare) and shrubs; magnolias, flowering cherries, bulbs; beautiful views from Cotswold escarpment. House not open. Teas at Garden Centre. *Adm £3.50 OAP £3 Chd under 16 free. Open daily, March 1 to mid-Nov (10-4.30). For NGS Sun May 21 (2-5)* **Tel 01386 701441**
www.batsford-arboretum.co.uk

Beverston Gardens *2m W of Tetbury on A4135 rd to Dursley.*

Beverston Castle (Mrs L Rook) Overlooked by romantic C12-C17 castle ruin, overflowingly planted paved terrace leads from C18 house (not open) across moat to sloping lawn with spring bulbs in abundance and full herbaceous and shrub borders. Large walled kitchen garden and greenhouses, orchids. TEAS Suns. *Adm £1.50 OAPs & Chd £1 (ACNO to Malt House, Tetbury). Easter Sun, Mon April 23, 24, Sun, Mon July 2, 3. Suns (2-6) Mons (11-6)*

Orchard Cottage (Mr & Mrs H L Pierce) *On corner by memorial garden.* ⅔ acre used to the full with mixed borders, trees, shrubs, climbers, ferns and other shady plants, together with kitchen garden, wall and cordon fruit and herb interest in sheltered back garden. *Adm £1 Chd free. Sun, Mon July 2, 3 (2-6)*

Blockley Gardens *NW of Moreton-in-Marsh. Take A44 Moreton to Broadway rd; turning E.* Popular Cotswold hillside village with great variety of high quality gardens; some walking necessary and some gardens not safe for small children. Teas at St George's Hall and Mill Dene garden in aid of Blockley WI and local charities. *Combined adm £4, single garden £1, Chd free. Suns June 25, Sept 10 (2-6)*

NEW **Cherry Tree Cottage** (Dr Neil Hammatt)
Colebrook House *Sun June 25 only*
3 The Dell (Mr & Mrs Stubbs)
4 The Dell (Mrs D Powell) *Restricted entry*
Haberdashers (Mrs M Stuart-Turner)
Malvern Mill (Mr & Mrs J Bourne) *Sun June 25. Also open with* **Mill Dene**, *Sat May 6*
Mill Dene (Mr & Mrs B S Dare) Open other days, see main entry
4 Millview (Mr & Mrs N Grant) *Sun June 25 only*
21 Millview (Mr & Mrs D Vaughan) *Sun June 25 only*
The Old Silk Mill (Mr & Mrs A Goodrick-Clark) Very dangerous for children. *Sun June 25 only*
Pear Trees (Mrs J Beckwith) *Also by appt*
9 Station Road (Mr & Mrs A Bowell) *Sun June 25 only*

Boddington Manor ♿❀ (Robert Hitchins Ltd) *3m W of Cheltenham off A4019 Cheltenham toTewkesbury rd. After crossing M5, take first turning L, signed to Boddington.* Old garden sympathetically restored since 1985 incl wildflower woodland walk, mature specimen trees, extensive lawns and lakes; established pinetum and bog garden. New planting of acers, birches, liquidambars in meadow setting. Neo-gothic manor house (not open). Gardening with Nature Fair. Cream TEAS in aid of Church of St Mary Magdalene. *Adm £2 Chd free. Sun June 4 (11-5)*

■ **Bourton House Garden, Bourton-on-the-Hill** ❀ (Mr & Mrs R Paice) *2m W of Moreton-in-Marsh on A44.* Intensively planted 3 acres with topiary, knot garden, potager, colour and herbaceous borders, water features and C16 Tithe Barn. Imaginative containers, vast range of unusual plants incl tender and half hardy, providing lots of late season interest; a plantsman's paradise. TEAS in Tithe Barn. *Adm £3.50 Chd free. Every Thurs & Fri May 25 to Oct 20. Also Bank hols Sun, Mon May 28, 29, Aug 27, 28 (10-5). For NGS last Thurs of every month May to Oct (10-5). Parties of 20 minimum welcome, by prior appt, please* **Tel 01386 700121**

25 Bowling Green Rd, Cirencester ❀ (Fr John & Susan Beck) *Take A417 to Gloucester just to t-lights, cross or turn R into The Whiteway then 1st L to no 25 on R of rd bend. Please respect neighbours' driveways, no pavement parking.* Uncontrollable enthusiasts' ever-growing, semi-detached corner plot plant home. Wide range of perennials, daylilies (200+ varieties), roses, clematis etc. Featured in Gardeners Guide to Growing Daylilies (Diana Grenfell), Weekend Times, July 1999 and Central TV. *Adm £1.25 Chd under 16 free. Suns June 18, 25, July 2, 9, 16, 23 (2-5), Mons June 19, 26, July 3, 10, 17, 24 (11-4). Private visits welcome mid-June to mid-Aug, please* **Tel 01285 653778**

Brackenbury, Coombe ❀ (Peter & Margaret Heaton) *1m NE of Wotton-under-Edge. From Wotton Church ½m on Stroud rd B4058 turn R (signed Coombe); from Stroud on B4058, 300yds past Wotton-under-Edge sign turn L, (signed Coombe). Garden on R.* ⅔ acre, plantsman's terraced garden with multi-layer planting; foliage a special feature. Well stocked mixed borders, cottage garden, pool; 1000 different hardy perennials and 200 different shrubs. Vegetables on deep-bed system. National Collection of erigerons June and July. Home-made TEAS. *Adm £2 Chd free (ACNO to Cotswold Care Hospice). Bank Hol Mons May 29, Aug 28, Suns June 25, July 30 (2-6)*

Broad Campden Gardens ♿❀ *5m E of Broadway, 1m SE of Chipping Campden.* Group of gardens of wide appeal and expertise: large and small, old and new, formal and informal, within picturesque popular village with meandering stream. Teas in aid of Village Hall. *Combined adm £3 Chd free. Sun July 2 (2-6). Free car park. Coach parties please* **Tel 01386 840467**

The Angel House, Angel Lane (Mr & Mrs Bill Boddington)
The Farthings (Mr & Mrs John Astbury)
Halfpenny Cottage (Mr & Mrs Kenneth Jones)
The Malt House (Mr & Mrs Nick Brown)
Manor Barn, Angel Lane (Mr M Miles & Mr C Gurney)
Oldstones (Mr & Mrs Hugh Rolfe)
Pinders (Mr & Mrs I R Dunnett)
Sharcomb Furlong (Mr & Mrs Basil Hasberry)
Wold Cottage (Mr & Mrs James Jepson)
Wyldlands (Mr & Mrs John Wadey)

Brockweir Gardens ♿❀ *From A466 Chepstow to Monmouth rd, cross R Wye to Brockweir, ¾m uphill take L turning to Coldharbour. Also from B4228 at Hewelsfield Xrds.* Please consult owners before walking between gardens. TEAS in aid of Marie Curie Cancer Care and RSPCA, at Laurel Cottage. *Adm £1 each garden. Sun March 26, Suns, Bank Hol Mons April 30, May 1, May 28, 29, Aug 27, 28, Suns June 25, July 30 (2-6)*

Laurel Cottage ♿ (David & Jean Taylor) Informal 1-acre cottage garden, very peaceful with lovely views over Offa's Dyke. Dry stone walling creates gardens within a garden with lawns, herbaceous flowers and spring bulbs. Interesting selection of unusual shrubs and plants. *Private visits welcome all year, please* **Tel 01291 689565**

Threeways (Mr & Mrs Iorwerth Williams) *On foot from Laurel Cottage.* 2 acres with unusual shrubs and trees. Small woodland area, bog garden and stream. Extensive views. Formal area with water feature and well stocked herbaceous borders. *Private visits welcome all year, please* **Tel 01291 689686**

The Bungalow, nr Newent ❀ (Mrs Sue Clive) *Birches Lane off B4215, half-way between Newent and Dymock, signposted Botloes Green and Pool Hill. The Bungalow is first on L on edge of Three Choirs Vineyard. Park in Vineyard.* Featured in The English Garden as 'Elements of Surprise', this ½ acre garden incl several unusual water and architectural features, sitting areas, informal plantings of herbaceous and wildflowers, herbs and fruit, merging into landscape with a fine view over Malvern Hills. TEAS. *Adm £1.50 Chd free (ACNO to Downs Syndrome Assoc). Bank Hol Mon May 29, Sun June 11, Sun July 9 (2-6). By appt weekends May, June, July,* **Tel 01531 821640**

Burnside, Prestbury ❀ (Mr & Mrs John Anton-Smith) *Burnside is 300yds E of B4632, up Mill Lane, in village of Prestbury which is 2m NE of Cheltenham.* 1½-acre working garden specialising in plant-breeding of hellebores, pulsatillas, geraniums, erodiums, hepaticas, sedums and origanums, and production of unusual herbaceous plants. Stock beds, large rockery, stream. *Adm £2 Chd free (ACNO to NCCPG Glos Group). Free erodium to each visitor. Visits by appt only, individuals or groups up to 30. Owner will give conducted tour lasting about 1hr describing plants and breeding work. Rare plants for sale and clumps dug up on request. Please* **Tel 01242 244645** for descriptive leaflet or visit website www.j.mann.taylor.clara.net/anton.html

Campden House, Chipping Campden ♿❀ (The Hon Philip & Mrs Smith) *Drive entrance on Chipping Campden to Weston Subedge rd, about ¼m SW of Campden.* 2-acre garden featuring mixed borders of plant and colour interest around Manor House (not open) and C17 Tithe Barn (not open). Set in fine parkland in hidden valley. TEAS and plant stall in aid of Marie Curie Cancer Care. *Adm £2 Chd free. Sun July 9 (2-6)*

■ **Cerney House Gardens, North Cerney** ♿✂❀ (Sir Michael & Lady Angus) *4m NW of Cirencester on A435 Cheltenham rd. Turn L opp Bathurst Arms, past church up hill, pillared gates on R.* Romantic walled garden filled with old-fashioned roses and herbaceous borders. Working kitchen garden, scented garden, well-labelled herb garden, Who's Who beds and genera borders. Spring bulbs in abundance all around the wooded grounds. Bothy pottery. TEAS. *Adm £3 Chd £1. Tues, Weds, Fris, April to Sept (10-5). For NGS Sun May 14 (2-6). Private groups welcome, please* **Tel 01285 831300/831205**

Chalford Gardens ✂ *4m E of Stroud on A419 to Cirencester. Gardens are high above Chalford Vale and reached on foot by steep climb from car park on main rd or from High St. Combined adm £3 Chd free. Sun June 11 (2-5)*

- **Barley Patch Cottage** ✂❀ (Dave & Louise Clark) Medium-sized cottage garden packed with plants incl hosta collection. Started 1991 and still evolving
- **Marle Hill House** (Mike & Leslie Doyle-Davidson) 1-acre newly reclaimed Victorian woodland garden, containing a number of interlinked secret, formal and natural areas on terraced hillside
- **The Old Chapel** ✂ (F J & F Owen) See main entry
- **The Rock House** (Mr & Mrs George Edwards) 1-acre, S-facing old garden. Dramatic 40′ cliff and cave provide backdrop for climbing roses, clematis, shrubbery, rockery, lawn and herbaceous borders. *Private visits welcome, May to July by appt* **Tel 01453 886363**

NEW **Cheltenham Gardens** ✂❀ *Near A46 from Stroud.* Home-made TEAS. *Combined adm £2.50, £1.50 each garden Chd free. Suns June 4, 18 (2-6)*

- **13 Merestones Drive, Cheltenham** ✂❀ (Mr Dennis Moorcraft) *Merestones Drive is turning off The Park.* Town garden shaded by large trees; hostas and ferns a speciality; many unusual plants; scree garden; small brook. *Private visits welcome, please* **Tel 01242 578678**

NEW **45 Moorend Park Road** ❀ (Linda and Steven Ward) *Proceed over hump back bridge, white gates on R.* Town garden with an abundance of unusual plants. Many secret areas and plenty of surprises.

The Chestnuts, Minchinhampton ✂ (Mr & Mrs E H Gwynn) *From Nailsworth by Avening rd B4014, turn L at Weighbridge Inn ¼m up hill. From Minchinhampton 1m via New Rd or Well Hill.* ⅔ acre walled garden plus ⅔ acre well established arboretum with lovely views, offers yr-round interest, with many unusual trees and shrubs, bulbs, roses, clematis, rock garden, pool and wildflower lawn. *Adm £2 Chd free. By appt only, please* **Tel 01453 832863**

The Chipping Croft, Tetbury ❀ (Dr & Mrs P W Taylor) *At bottom of Chipping Hill approached from market place.* 2-acre, secluded, walled town garden on three levels, with mature trees, shrubs, herbaceous borders, rose beds and unusual plants; spring blossom and bulbs. A series of formal gardens, incl fruit and vegetable/flower potager all informally planted; also a water garden. C17 Cotswold house (not open). *Adm £2.50 Chd free. Sun Sept 10 (2-5). Private visits by appt, please* **Tel 01666 503570 or 503178**

Church Cottage, Stinchcombe ✂❀ (Mr & Mrs David Leach) *Off A38, 5m NW of Dursley.* Peacefully situated next to church. A plant lover's cottage garden of about ¼ acre planted since 1992 and still evolving. Good variety of hardy plants. Please use car park. *Adm £1.50 Chd free. Thurs June 8 (1.30-5.30). Private visits and small groups welcome, June and July please* **Tel 01453 542116**

Cinderdine Cottage, Dymock ♿✂❀ (John & Daphne Chappell) *From Newent, take B4215 to Dymock. Cottage ¾m on R of lane signed Ryton/Ketford.* Country garden for all seasons. Unusual snowdrop collection; hellebores, pulmonarias and other spring flowering plants. Large herbaceous borders summer and early autumn. TEA. *Adm £1.50 Chd free (ACNO to St Mary's Church, Dymock) Tues, Thurs, Suns Feb 8, 10, 13, 15, 17, 20, 22 (12-5), Suns, Tues March 5, 7, 19, 21, April 2, 4, Easter Sun, Mon, Tue April 23, 24, 25, Suns, Tue May 7, 9, 28, Bank Hol Mon, Tue May 29, 30, Suns, Tues June 11, 13, 18, 20, 25, July 2, 4, 16, 18, Aug 6, 8, 27, Bank Hol Mon, Tue Aug 28, 29 (2-5),* **2001** *Suns Feb 11, 18 (12-5). Parties welcome, please* **Tel 01531 890265**

Clover House, Winson (Mrs Kenneth Kemble) *Winson lies approx 7m NE of Cirencester. From Cirencester take A433 Bibury rd, turn L just before Bibury signposted Ablington/Winson. On entering Winson, Clover House is 1st house on R.* Well established garden of approx 12 acres fronting R Coln. Daffodils & narcissi feature in spring. *Adm £2 Chd free. Sun April 9 (2-6)*

Conderton Manor see Worcestershire

Cotswold Farm, Cirencester ✂ (Major & Mrs P D Birchall) *5m N of Cirencester on A417. From Cirencester turn L signed Duntisbourne Abbots/Services, then immed R and under underpass. Private drive straight ahead. From Gloucester turn L signed Duntisbourne Abbots/Services past Centurion garage. Private drive on L.* Cotswold garden in lovely position on different levels with terrace designed by

Norman Jewson in 1938; shrubs and trees, mixed borders, alpine border, shrub roses. *Adm £2.50 Chd free. By appt only, also private parties welcome by arrangement with adequate notice, mid-June to mid-Aug, Mon to Fri afternoons, please* **Tel 01285 653856**

Daylesford House, Daylesford ♿✂ (Sir Anthony & Lady Bamford) *Between Stow-on-the-Wold and Chipping Norton off A436.* Magnificent lakeside and wooded walks amidst unusual shrubs and trees. Large, decorative, formal fruit and vegetable walled garden with orchid house, peach house and working glasshouses. Trellised rose garden on raised terrace. Intimate walled garden behind the Orangery with Pavilion. Extensive restoration to large lake undertaken during 1999. Grounds immed around Grade I house not open. Visitors should note this is a very large garden with substantial distances to be walked. No cameras, dogs or coach parties. *Adm £3 Chd free. For NGS Wed July 5 (2-5.30).*

NEW **Dower House, Elmore** ♿✂❀ (Mr & Mrs B R Murray) *From Quedgeley on B4008, 6m S of Gloucester, follow signs for Elmore. In village pass hall, phone and post boxes on L; 2nd house on R after approx 300yds.* Cottage-style garden of about 3/4 acre around late C19 house (not open) with far reaching views. Wide variety of plants with emphasis on drought resistance. Wildlife ponds. About 1/8 acre devoted to 250 vines in 25 varieties grown for personal wine production. *Adm 1.50 Chd free. Sun May 21 (2-6)*

Eastcombe, Bussage & Brownshill Gardens *3m E of Stroud. 2m N of A419 Stroud to Cirencester rd on turning signposted to Bisley and Eastcombe.* Cream TEAS at Eastcombe Village Hall. *Combined adm £3 Chd free incl adm to art exhibition (ACNO to Glos Macmillan Cancer Service and Cotswold Care Day Hospice). Sun, Bank Hol Mon April 30, May 1 (2-6)*

Beechcroft, Brownshill ♿ (Mr & Mrs R H Salt) Much of interest incl conservatory, herb garden and wild area

18 Farmcote Close, Eastcombe ♿ (Mr & Mrs K Chalmers) Small garden planned for retirement

Fidges Hill House, Eastcombe (Mr & Mrs S A Lewis) Secluded and lovely view. No car access, please park in village. Steep descent

Highlands, Eastcombe (Mrs R Page) Small, tranquil and colourful cottage garden

NEW **Maryfield, Bussage** (Mr & Mrs D Brown) Colourful cottage garden with extensive valley views

Mount Pleasant, Eastcombe (Mr & Mrs R Peyton) Medium garden, pool, island beds, views

NEW **Park View, Eastcombe** (Mr & Mrs A Jordan) Cottage garden with yr-round interest provided by colourful shrubs

Pine Corner, Bussage (Mr & Mrs W Burns-Brown) 3/4 acre terraced garden. Spring bulbs, shrubs, alpines; water feature

NEW **Redwood, Bussage** ❀ (Mr & Mrs D F Collins) see main entry

NEW **Three Beeches, Bussage** (Mr & Mrs A H Gardiner) Secluded 3/4 acre mature, sloping garden with old quarry. Trees and shrubs

Eastington Gardens, nr Northleach *A40.* Charming Cotswold village with lovely views. 2 gardens of traditional appeal. *Combined adm £1.50 Chd free. Suns, Bank Hol Mons May 28, 29, Aug 27, 28 (2-6)*

Middle End (Mr & Mrs Owen Slatter) *Ample parking at house.* Medium-sized garden of general interest

Yew Tree Cottage (M Bottone Esq) *Ample parking in village.* Small garden packed with hardy plants for sun and shade

■ **Ewen Manor, nr Cirencester** ♿❀ (Lady Gibbs) *Via A429 3m from Cirencester turn at signpost Ewen 1m.* Profusely planted series of gardens with architectural features, yew hedges, pattern mown lawn, terrace and containers, lily pool, cedar trees over 200yrs old; woodland area all around. Spring bulbs and blossom. Georgian Cotswold manor (not open). TEAS Sun only. *Adm £2 Chd free. Tues, Wed, Thurs May 2 to July 6 (11-4.30) (Share to NGS). For NGS Easter Sun April 23 (2-6), (ACNO to Cotswold Care Hospice). Private visits welcome, please* **Tel 01285 770206**

The Glebe House, Shipton Moyne ♿ (Mr & Mrs Richard Boggis-Rolfe) *In Shipton Moyne 2½m S of Tetbury. Next to church.* Medium-sized garden surrounding former rectory (not open). Mixture of formal and informal planting. Double herbaceous border. Walled kitchen garden, mown walks through young orchard & newly planted woodland with bulbs. Dogs on leads. TEAS. *Adm £2.50 Chd under 10 free. Suns April 16, June 11 (2-6)*

Grange Farm, Evenlode, nr Moreton-in-Marsh ✂ (Lady Aird) *Evenlode 3m from Moreton-in-Marsh and Stow-on-the-Wold. E of A429 Fosseway and 1½m from Broadwell.* This atmospheric garden continues to be developed and C17 rose-covered house (not open) and ancient apple trees provide a wonderful setting for the water garden, wide lawns, grass steps and extensive plantings. Lots of places to sit, vegetable patch and croquet lawn. TEAS. *Adm £2 Chd free (ACNO to St Edward's Church, Evenlode). Sun June 18 (11-6). Private visits welcome May and June, please* **Tel 01608 650607**

Great Rissington Farm, Cheltenham ✂ (The Hon John & Mrs Donovan) *4m SE of Stow-on-the-Wold, 6m NW of Burford off A424 on Barrington Rd. Turn at North Lodge (nr Barn Business Centre), pass farm buildings to bottom of lane.* C16 Cotswold house (not open) in 2 acres; 4 small, walled gardens filled with large collection of roses and herbaceous plants. Wide border has bold planting of large shrubs. Small spinney being replaced with interesting new trees and shrubs. Exciting young garden with great potential complemented by marvellous views over surrounding countryside. TEAS. *Adm £1.50 Chd free (ACNO to Motor Neurone Disease Assoc). Wed June 28 (2-6)*

Green Cottage, Lydney ♿❀ (Mr & Mrs F Baber) *Approaching Lydney from Gloucester, keep to A48 through Lydney. Leaving Lydney turn R into narrow lane at de-limit sign. Garden 1st R. Shady parking.* 1¼ acres planted for seasonal interest and wildlife. Mature trees, stream and bog garden, cottage garden with ferns and hellebores. Herbaceous paeonies featured throughout garden incl National Reference Collection of rare Victorian and Edwardian cultivars. Hellebores March, NRC paeonies June, others May.

TEAS. *Adm £1.50 Chd free. Suns March 5, 12, 19 (1-4), May 14, 21, 28, June 4, 11, 18, (2-6), Weds June 7, 14, 21 (1-5)*

▲ Hidcote Manor Garden, Chipping Campden (The National Trust) One of England's great gardens, a 10½ acre 'Arts & Crafts' masterpiece created by horticulturist Major Lawrence Johnston. Series of outdoor rooms, each with a different character and separated by walls and hedges of many different species. Many rare trees and shrubs, outstanding herbaceous borders and unusual plant species from all over the world. Coffee, lunches and teas. *Adm £5.60 Chd £2.80. For NGS Sun May 7 (11-6)*

Highnam Court (Roger Head) *Leave Gloucester on A40 towards Ross on Wye. DO NOT take Newent turning, but proceed to next big Highnam roundabout. Take R exit for Highnam Court entrance directly off roundabout.* 25 acres of Victorian landscaped gardens surrounding magnificent Grade I house (not open), set out by the artist Thomas Gambier Parry. Lake, shrubberies and listed Pulhamite water gardens with grottos and fernery. TEAS. *Adm £2.50 Chd free (ACNO to Highnam Church). First Suns of month March till Oct (11-5)*

Hillesley House, Hillesley (Mr & Mrs J Walsh) *3m from Wotton-under-Edge on rd to Hawkesbury Upton and A46.* Recently revived garden in 4 acres surrounding Tudor house (not open); walled garden, borders in sun and shade, roses. Recently planted arboretum and secret garden all offering interesting ideas. TEAS. *Adm £2.50 Chd free. Sun June 25 (2-6)*

NEW **Hillfield, Corse** (Leila & David Dawson) *8m NW of Gloucester off A417. Approx 1m after Corse boundary turn L, signed Upleadon and Newent (Oridge St). Garden 3/4m on R. [Map ref SO 783.275].* Pretty 1 acre garden in process or re-development, planned for yr-round interest. Mature trees and shrubs, bulbs, mixed borders, roses, water features. Large productive vegetable garden. Small, wildflower area. Partially suitable for wheelchairs. TEA. *Adm £1.50 Chd free. Thurs May 25, June 22, July 20 (2-6)*

Hodges Barn, Shipton Moyne (Mrs C N Hornby) *3m S of Tetbury on Malmesbury side of village.* Very unusual C15 dovecot converted into a family home (not open). Cotswold stone walls act as host to climbing and rambling roses, clematis, vines and hydrangeas, and together with yew, rose and tapestry hedges create formality around house. Mixed shrub and herbaceous borders, shrub roses and water garden; woodland garden planted with cherries, magnolias and spring bulbs. Also open for NGS, adjoining garden of Hodges Farmhouse by kind permission of Mrs Clive Lamb. *Adm £3 Chd free. Suns, Mons April 9, 10, May 21, 22, June 4, 5 (2-6). Private groups welcome, please* **Tel 01666 880202**

Home Farm, Huntley (Mrs T Freeman) *On B4216 ½m off A40 in Huntley travelling towards Newent.* Set in elevated position with exceptional views. 1m walk through woods and fields to show carpets of spring flowers. Enclosed garden with fern border, sundial and heather bed. Herbaceous borders. White and mixed shrub borders. Stout footwear advisable in winter. *Adm £1.50 Chd free. Suns Jan 30, Feb 13, March 26, April 16, May 14, June 4 (2-5). Private visits welcome, please* **Tel 01452 830209**

Hullasey House, Tarlton (Jonathan & Gail Taylor) *Mid-way between Cirencester and Tetbury off A433.* Cotswold garden with exceptional views. Stone walls, many old roses, gravel gardens round house (not open). Walled herb and fruit potager; walled mixed shrub and herbaceous garden. *Adm £2 Chd free (ACNO to Tarlton Church). Sat, Sun, Mon June 24, 25, 26 (2-5). Other Mons, by appt, mid-May to mid-July, please* **Tel 01285 770132**

Humphreys End House, Randwick (Mr & Mrs J W A Hutton) *Leave M5 at junction 13, 2m W of Stroud follow signs to Cashes Green and Randwick [Map ref SO 832.061].* Different areas of contrasting mood and interesting planting in 1 acre surrounding listed C16 farmhouse (not open). Wildlife pond, herbs, old roses, grasses. Organic vegetable garden. *Adm £1.50 Chd free. Private visits welcome by appt, please* **Tel 01453 765401**

■ Hunts Court, North Nibley (Mr & Mrs T K Marshall) *2m NW of Wotton-under-Edge. From Wotton B4060 Dursley rd turn R in North Nibley at Black Horse; fork L after ¼m.* Unusual shrubs, 450 varieties old roses, large collection of penstemons in peaceful 2½-acre garden with lawns set against tree-clad hills and Tyndale monument. Superb views. House (not open) possible birth place of William Tyndale. Picnic area. Home-made TEAS by local charities (Suns only). *Adm £2 OAP £1.50 Chd free. Garden and nursery open Tues-Sat all year except Aug; also Bank Hol Mons, May 1, 29. For NGS Suns June 11, 18, 25, July 2, 9 (2-6);* **Tel 01453 547440**

Icomb Place, nr Stow-on-the-Wold (Mr & Mrs T L F Royle) *4m S of Stow after 2m on A424 Burford rd turn L to Icomb village.* 100-year-old garden featuring woodland walk through mature and young trees in arboretum; rhododendrons and azaleas; grotto; pools, stream and water garden; parterre; lawned garden with extensive views. C14 manor house (not open). TEAS. *Adm £2 Chd £1 (ACNO to Deus Laudamus Trust). Sun June 25 (2-6)*

Kestrel Cottage, Brand Green (Jo & Mike Howe) *2.5m NE of Newent [OS map SO 739.284]. From Gloucester take A40 W. Turn R onto B4215. After 3.4m, turn R signed Hartpury and Upleadon. Proceed 2.8m, go over Xrds and after 1.2m park at village hall (Pauntley). Garden 200yds on R.* ½ acre, sloping plantsman's garden surrounding pretty half-timbered cottage (not open) with views over Severn Vale. Mixed and herbaceous borders, unusual plants, pond, stone troughs and small alpine beds. *Adm £1.50 Chd free. Sun April 9, Easter Mon April 24, Suns May 14, June 4, 11, 18, Bank Hol Mon May 29, Tues May 9, 16, June 13, 27, July 4 (2-5). Private visits by appt April-June*
Tel 01531 821055

■ Kiftsgate Court, nr Chipping Campden (Mr & Mrs J G Chambers) *Adjacent to Hidcote National Trust Garden. 1m E of B4632 and B4081.* Magnificent situation and views; many unusual plants and shrubs; tree paeonies, hydrangeas, abutilons, species and old-fashioned roses, incl largest rose in England, R. filipes Kiftsgate. TEAS, lunches

June and July. *Adm £4 Chd £1. Suns, Weds, Thurs & Bank Hols Mons April 1 to Sept 30 (2-6). Also Suns, Weds, Thurs, Sats in June & July (12-6). For NGS (ACNO to Sunfield Children's Home, Clent) Sats May 13, Aug 12 (2-6). Coaches by appt, please* **Tel 01386 438777**

■ **Lydney Park, Lydney** ❀ (The Viscount Bledisloe) *On A48 Gloucester to Chepstow rd between Lydney and Aylburton. Drive is directly off A48.* 8 acres of extensive valley garden with many varieties of rhododendron, azaleas and other flowering shrubs; trees and lakes. Garden round house (not open); magnolias and daffodils (April). Roman Temple site and Museum. Deer park with fine trees. TEAS; also picnic area (in park). *Adm £3 Weds £2 Acc chd free. Every Sun, Wed and Bank Hol from March 26 to June 4, every day from Easter Sun April 23 to 28 and May 28 to June 2 (11-6). For NGS Sun April 30, Wed May 3 (11-6). Groups welcome by appt, please* **Tel 01594 842027 or 845497**

■ **Mill Dene, Blockley** ✗❀ (Mr & Mrs B S Dare) *School Lane. From A44, follow brown signs for Bourton-on-the-Hill, turn Blockley. 1.3m down hill turn L (signed) cul-de-sac, behind 30mph sign. Parking for 8 cars.* 2½ acres with steep lawned terraces, stream and mill-pool in frost pocket. Potager; grotto and trompe l'oeil. Dangerous for young children. TEAS. *Adm £2.50 Chd 50p. Open Mon to Fri (10-6) April 1 to Oct 31 and Bank Hols. For NGS Sat May 6 (with* **Malvern Mill**), *Sun June 11 (2-5.30).* **Evening Opening** *Fri June 30 (6.30-8.30). Also open with* **Blockley Gardens** *Suns June 25, Sept 10 (2-6). Private visits welcome all yr, please* **Tel 01386 700457**

Millend House, Coleford ❀ (Mr & Mrs J D'A Tremlett) *1½m SW of Coleford on Newland rd. From centre of Coleford, clocktower signposted, Newland.* Magnificently locate, 2-acre hillside garden contains many unusual herbaceous plants and shrubs, both shade and sun loving, some of which are for sale. Scree and fern beds; gazebo; ornamental pond; small vegetable and soft fruit garden; walk round 200yr-old wood. TEAS. *Adm £1.50 Chd free. Suns, May 21, June 18, July 16, Aug 13 (2-6). Private groups welcome May 1 to Sept 30, please* **Tel 01594 832128**

Minchinhampton Gardens ♿✗❀ *4m SE of Stroud. From Market Sq go down High St for 100yds, then turn R at Xrds. After 300yds turn L.* Cream TEAS at Lammas Park in aid of Minchinhampton Centre for the Elderly. *Combined adm £2 Chd free. Sun July 30 (1.30-5).*

Box Lane Barn ♿❀ (Geoffrey & Joyce Hands) *50yds from Lammas Park.* ½ acre created from rough pasture in 1997. Two long borders planted for summer spectacle; all-yr interest with unusual wall shrubs and climbers

NEW **2 Camp Field** (Mrs Pat Timpson) *Parking in Dr Brown's Rd.* Approx ⅓ acre level garden adjoining the Common. Shrub, herbaceous, rose borders; vegetables and soft fruit

Lammas Park (Mr P Grover) 2½ acres around Cotswold 'Arts & Crafts' style house (not open). Herbaceous borders, pleached lime allee, wild garden, alpines, restored C17 'hanging gardens' with tunnel *Also by appt, please* **Tel 01453 886471**

■ **Misarden Park, Miserden** ♿✗❀ (Major M T N H Wills) *6m NW of Cirencester. Follow signs off A417 or B4070 from Stroud.* Spring flowers, shrubs, fine topiary (some designed by Sir Edwin Lutyens) and herbaceous borders within a walled garden; roses; fine specimen trees; C17 manor house (not open) standing high overlooking Golden Valley. New rill and summerhouse. Garden Nurseries open daily except Mons. TEAS in aid of Miserden School PTA. *Adm £3 Chd free. April 1 to Sept 30 every Tues, Wed & Thurs (10-5). For NGS (ACNO to Museum of Garden History) Suns April 2, July 2 (2-6)* **Tel 01285 821303**

Moor Wood, Woodmancote ✗ (Mr & Mrs Henry Robinson) *3½m from Cirencester turn L off A435 to Cheltenham at North Cerney, signed Woodmancote 1¼m; entrance in village on L beside lodge with white gates.* 2 acres of shrub, orchard and wildflower gardens in isolated valley setting. Holder of the National Collection of Rambler Roses. TEA. *Adm £2 Chd free. Wed June 28 (2-6). Private visits, please* **Tel 01285 831397**

The Old Chapel, Chalford Vale ✗ (F J & F Owen) *4m E of Stroud on A419 to Cirencester. Above Chalford Vale, steep climb from car park on main rd, up Marle Hill.* 1-acre Victorian chapel garden on precipitous hillside. A tiered tapestry of herbaceous borders, formal potager, small orchard, pond and summerhouse, old roses. Gothic pergola and rose tunnel, many unusual plants all laid out on terraced S-facing Marle Cliff. Garden open with Art Exhibition in studio. *Adm £2 Chd free (50% to NGS). Sat June 10 to Sun June 25 (10-5). Also open in conjunction with* **Chalford Gardens** *Sun June 11 (2-5)*

The Old Rectory, Duntisbourne Rous ✗ (Charles & Mary Keen) *NW of Cirencester at Daglingworth take valley rd for the Duntisbournes. After ½m no-through rd joins from R at entrance to Old Rectory. Can also be approached via Duntisbourne Leer off A417; turn L (after crossing ford) at T junction.* Writer and designer's own 1½ acre Cotswold family garden. Listed as one of 50 best gardens to visit in The Independent. Beautiful setting nr Saxon church. Planted for atmosphere and all-yr-interest, this small garden has ten distinct areas and moods. Winter flowers, 100+ auriculas under cover, tender plants and unusual pelargoniums a speciality. *Adm £2.50 Chd free. Mons Feb 21, March 27 (11-4), May 15, June 19, July 3 (11-5). Private visits for groups of 10 or more, by WRITTEN APPT ONLY welcome (adm charges negotiable).*

Orchard Cottage, Gretton ✗ (Mr Rory Stuart) *2m N of Winchcombe. Up Duglinch Lane beside Bugatti Inn. Approx 300yds up lane turn R after Magnolia grandiflora.* Approx 1½ acres. Romantically overplanted, owner-maintained garden, created largely by the late Mrs Nancy Saunders. Always some interest. Teas in Winchcombe. *Adm £1.50. Open all year, by appt only* **Tel 01242 602491**

Oxleaze Farm, Filkins, Lechlade ♿✗❀ (Mr & Mrs Charles Mann) *5m S of Burford, 3m N of Lechlade off A361 to W (signed Barringtons). Take 2nd L then follow signs.* Medium-sized 'developing garden', combining formality and informality. Shrub borders, vegetable potager and decorative fruit cage; pond and sunken garden; proposed gravel garden.

Series of 'garden rooms' surround central lawn with reflective corners giving a chance to enjoy the enthusiasm of this typical Cotswold garden. *Adm £2 Chd free (ACNO to The Countryside Foundation). Sun May 14 (2-6). Private visits very welcome, please* **Tel 01367 850216**

● **Painswick Rococo Garden** ❀ (Painswick Rococo Garden Trust) *½m outside village on B4073.* Unique C18 garden from the brief Rococo period, combining contemporary buildings, vistas, ponds, kitchen garden and winding woodland walks. Newly planted maze. Coach House restaurant for coffee, lunches. 'Present Collection' shop. Specialist plant nursery. *Adm £3.30 OAP £3 Chd £1.75. Jan 12 to Nov 30 Weds to Suns and Bank Hols. July and Aug daily. Restaurant open Weds to Suns (11-5)* **Tel 01452 813204**

NEW **Paulmead, Bisley** ♿✂❀ (Judy & Philip Howard) *On S edge of Bisley at head of Toadsmoor Valley. 5m E of Stroud on top of Cotswolds. Garden and car park well signed in Bisley village.* Approx 1acre landscaped garden constructed in stages over last 12 yrs. Terraced in three main levels: natural stream garden; formal herbaceous and shrub borders; yew and beech hedges; formal vegetable garden; lawns; summerhouse with exterior wooden decking by pond and thatched roof over well head. *Adm £2 Chd free. Sun May 21 (2-6)*

NEW **Pear Tree Cottage, Gotherington** ❀ (Mr & Mrs E Manders-Trett) *A435 N of Cheltenham. Turn R into Gotherington 1m after end of Bishop's Cleeve by-pass. Garden is on L approx 100m past Shutter Inn.* Mainly informal country garden of about ½ acre with pond and gravel garden, grasses and herbaceous borders, trees and shrubs surrounding lawns. Wild garden and orchard lead to greenhouses, herb and vegetable gardens. Aims to provide interest at all seasons. TEA. *Adm £1.50 Chd free. Suns March 5, April 2, Sept 3, Oct 1, Mons May 1, June 5, July 3 (2-6)*

Pigeon House, Southam ✂❀ (Mr & Mrs Julian Taylor) *Southam Lane. 3m from Cheltenham off B4632 toward Winchcombe.* Revitalised 2-acre garden surrounding C14 manor house (not open). Small lake and bubbling water garden with fish and bog plants. Wide range of flowering shrubs and borders designed to create multitude of vistas and plant interest. TEAS in aid of Southam Church of the Ascension. *Adm £1.50 Chd free. Suns April 23 (Easter), June 4 (2-6). Groups welcome by appt, please* **Tel 01242 529342**

Pitt Court, North Nibley ♿✂❀ (Mr & Mrs M W Hall) *Turn off B4060 at North Nibley past Black Horse Inn into Barrs Lane. Continue for approx ¾m. Car parking.* Charming garden surrounded by rolling hills, this shows how a small (⅓ acre) sloping area, designed and converted by architect owner, can create a visibly larger garden. Intensive planting together with excellent use of paving, stones and bricks form settings for interesting trees, shrubs, containers, alpine and herbaceous plants. *Adm £1.50 Chd free. Suns May 14, 21, Sept 3, 10, Weds May 17, Sept 6 (2-6)*

Quenington Gardens, nr Fairford ♿✂❀ *E of Cirencester.* A rarely visited Coln Valley village delighting its infrequent visitors with C12 Norman church and C17 stone cottages (not open). An opportunity to discover the horticultural treasures behind those Cotswold stone walls and visit 7 very different but charming gardens incorporating everything from the exotic and the organic to the simple cottage garden; a range of vistas from riverside to seclusion. TEAS at the Old Rectory. *Combined adm £2.50 Chd free. Sun June 25 (2-6)*

- **Apple Tree Cottage** (Mrs P Butler-Henderson)
- NEW **Bank View** (Mr & Mrs Cliff Moulden)
- **Old Post House** (Mrs D Blackwood)
- **The Old Rectory** (Mr & Mrs D Abel-Smith)
- **Pool Hay** (Mr and Mrs A W Morris)
- **Quenington House** (Mr & Mrs J D'Arcy Clark)
- NEW **Yew Tree Cottages** (Messrs A Watson & J Lindon)

The Red House, Staunton, nr Gloucester ♿❀ (Mr & Mrs W K Turner) *Pillows Green. On A417 from Staunton Xrds ½m off B4208.* Split level 2-acre organic and wildlife garden with herbaceous borders; rockery and terrace with containers; parterre; also flower meadow. C17 house open by appt. Garden designed and maintained by owners. All plants for sale grown from garden stock. TEA. *Adm £1.50 Chd free (ACNO to Glos Wildlife Trust). Easter Sun, Mon April 23, 24, Suns May 28, June 18, Bank Hol Mon May 29 (2-6). Private visits welcome, please* **Tel 01452 840505**

Redwood, Bussage ❀ (Mr & Mrs D F Collins) *3m E of Stroud. 2m N of A419 Stroud to Cirencester on turning signposted to Bisley and Eastcombe.* Terraced garden with lovely array of plants especially hellebores, many for sale. TEAS. *Adm £1. Sat, Sun March 4, 5 (1-5). Also open Sun, Bank Hol Mon April 30, May 1 with Eastcombe Gardens.*

Rockcliffe, nr Lower Swell ✂❀ (Mr & Mrs Simon Keswick) *On B4068. From Stow-on-the-Wold turn R into drive 1½m from Lower Swell.* 7 acres incl herbaceous borders; pink, white and blue gardens; rose terrace; walled kitchen garden and orchard. As featured in Sunday Telegraph Magazine, Oct 99. TEAS in aid of local schools. *Adm £2.50 Chd under 15 free. Thurs June 8, 15, 21 (12-5)*

■ **Rodmarton Manor, Cirencester** ♿✂ (Mr & Mrs Simon Biddulph) *Between Cirencester and Tetbury off A433.* 8-acre garden of this fine 'Arts and Crafts' house is a series of 'outdoor rooms' each with its own distinctive character. Leisure garden, winter garden, troughery, topiary, hedges, lawns, rockery, containers, wild garden, kitchen garden, snowdrops and magnificent herbaceous borders. *Adm £2.50 Acc chd free. Every Wed, Sat and Bank Hol Mon May 10 to Aug 30 (2-5). For NGS Sat Aug 26. Private group visits of 20 or more welcome at other times, please* **Tel 01285 841253 or Fax 01285 841298**

Rookwoods, Waterlane (Mr & Mrs Des Althorp) *5m E of Stroud. Between Sapperton and Bisley. Turn down 'No Through Rd' in Waterlane then follow signs.* 3-acre, well structured garden with herbaceous borders to colour themes. Pleached whitebeam around pool area. Wide variety of old-fashioned and modern climbing and shrub roses (labelled), water gardens and outstanding views. Dogs welcome. TEAS. *Adm £1.75 Chd free. Weds May 10, Sat July 8 (2-6). Coaches by appt. Private visits welcome May and July, please* **Tel 01452 770747**

■ **Sezincote, nr Moreton-in-Marsh** ✂ (Mr & Mrs D Peake) *Turn W along A44 towards Evesham; after 1½m (just before Bourton-on-the-Hill) take turn L, by stone lodge with white gate.* Exotic oriental water garden by Repton and Daniell with lake, pools and meandering stream, banked with massed perennials. Large semi-circular orangery, formal Indian garden, fountain, temple and unusual trees of vast size in lawn and wooded park setting. House in Indian manner designed by Samuel Pepys Cockerell. TEAS NGS day only. *Adm £3.50 Chd £1 under 5 free. Open every Thurs Fri & Bank Hols (except Dec) (2-6). For NGS Sun July 9 (2-6)*

Sheephouse, nr Painswick ♿✂ (Lawrence E Gardiner & Mrs Lindsay J Gardiner) *From A46 through Painswick take Stamages Lane (below car park) and follow signs. Parking in Painswick will assist parking at house and provide lovely 1m walk.* 1¼ acre garden surrounding C15, C17 and C19 country house (not open). Extensively re-designed and developed over last 3 yrs. Formal holly and clipped yew drive; water feature with weir; knot garden; formal potager designed by Robert Bryant; herbaceous and shrub borders; beautiful mature trees. 20,000 spring flowering bulbs. TEA. *Adm £2 Chd free (ACNO to Brimscombe Church Building Project). Sun March 19 (2-5)*

▲ **Snowshill Manor, nr Broadway** ✂ (The National Trust) Small terraced garden in which organic and natural methods only are used. Highlights include tranquil ponds, old roses, old-fashioned flowers and herbaceous borders rich in plants of special interest. House contains collections of fine craftmanship incl musical instruments, clocks, toys and bicycles. TEAS. *Adm house & gdn £6 Chd £3 Garden only £3, Chd £1.50. Family ticket £15. For NGS Sun May 7 (11-5)*

Spring Tyning, Dursley ✂ (Mrs Sally Whittal) *2m NNW of Uley on Cotswold escarpment between Coaley & Uley.* 2 acres with panoramic views over Severn Valley planted in a naturalistic way to blend with unspoilt landscape; some structure and formality around house (not open). Many banks planted for interest and ground cover. Plantsman's garden incl dell, raised pond, landscaped tennis court and planted dry areas. Spring bulbs and colour through to September with many plants labelled. Refreshments available. *Adm £2.50 Chd free (ACNO to Save the Children Fund). All visits welcome by appt, please* **Tel or Fax 01453 860473**

St Francis, Lammas Park, Minchinhampton ♿✂❀ (Mr and Mrs P Falconer) *4m SE of Stroud. From Market Sq go down High St for 100yds, then turn R at Xrds. After 300yds bear L; entrance is 200yds on L at rd junction.* Garden made by present owners over past 50yrs in old park around Cotswold stone house (not open). Fine beech avenue; terraced garden; unusual plants; giant snowdrops in spring; C18 ice-house. *Adm £1.50 Chd free. Open all year, groups or individuals by appt only, please* **Tel 01453 882188**

Stanton Gardens, Broadway ♿❀ (Mr G B Horton) One of the most picturesque and unspoilt C17 Cotswold villages with many gardens to explore (22 open in 1999) ranging from charming cottage to large formal gardens of appeal to visitors of all tastes. Plant and produce stalls. Car park free. TEAS from 3-5.30. *Adm £3 Chd free (ACNO to Stanton Church and village hall). Sun June 25 (2-6). For information, please* **Tel 01386 584212**

■ **Stanway Water Garden, nr Winchcombe** (Lord Neidpath) *1m E of B4632 Cheltenham to Broadway rd or B4077 Toddington to Stow-on-the-Wold rd.* 20 acres of planted landscape in early C18 formal setting. Recent restoration of canal, upper pond and 70′ high fountain have re-created one of the most interesting baroque water gardens in Britain. Striking C16 manor with gatehouse, tithe barn and church. *Adm grounds only £1 Chd 50p; House and grounds £3 OAPs £2.50 Chd £1. House and grounds open Tues & Thurs Aug and Sept (2-5). For NGS Suns March 26, May 21 (2-5)* **Tel 01386 584469**

Stone House, Wyck Rissington ✂❀ (Catherine, Lady Walk-Okeover) *Off A429 between Bourton-on-the-Water and Stow-on-the-Wold. Last house in village behind high bank on R.* 2 acres full of unusual bulbs, shrubs and herbaceous plants. Crab apple walk, rose borders, herb and water garden, woodland walk. A plantman's garden with yr-round interest. TEAS. *Adm £2 Chd free. Sun April 16 (2-5). Private visits welcome, please* **Tel 01451 810337**

Stowell Park, Northleach ♿✂❀ (The Lord and Lady Vestey) *Off Fosseway A429 2m SW of Northleach.* Magnificent lawned terraces with stunning views over Coln Valley. Fine collection of old-fashioned roses and herbaceous plants, with pleached lime approach to C14 house (not open). Two large walled gardens (as featured in Country Life) containing vegetables, fruit, cut flowers and range of greenhouses. Long rose pergola and wide, plant-filled borders divided into colour sections. TEAS. Plant sales May 21 only. Band playing June 25. *Adm £2.50 Chd free. Sun May 21 (ACNO to St Michael's Church, Yanworth), Sun June 25 (ACNO to The Royal British Legion) (2-5)*

■ **Sudeley Castle, Winchcombe** ✂❀ (Lord & Lady Ashcombe) The 11 individual gardens around C15 castle incl Queen's Garden, with old-fashioned roses, perennials, herbs; Tudor knot garden with water features, and recently opened Victorian kitchen garden. Also formal pools, spring bulbs and fine trees in extensive grounds. Specialist plant centre. Teas and lunches at restaurant. *Adm gardens and Emma Dent exhibition £4.70 OAPs £3.70 Chd £2.50. Open daily March 4 to Oct 29 (10.30-5.30). For NGS Suns April 30, Sept 10 (10.30-5.30). Group tours of gardens can be booked, please* **Tel 01242 602308**

Sunningdale, nr Westbury-on-Severn ♿✂❀ (Mr J Mann Taylor) *Grange Court. Turn off A48 in Chaxhil [OS map ref. SO 727.164].* ¾ acre fanfare of fabulous features filled with families of flora, familiar and foreign, fragrant and flamboyant. Be flabbergasted by fifty, fully fledged, fantastic Phlomis (National Plant Collection) featured by a fanatic with finesse and foresight. A foretaste of first-rate foliage and floral focus, from formal to far-fetched. Fishing for frogs forbidden. *Adm £1.50 Chd 50p. Suns June 25, July 2, 9, 23, 30, Thurs June 22, 29, July 6, 20 (2-5)*

Tinpenny Farm, Fiddington ♿✂❀ (E S Horton) *2½m SE of Tewkesbury. From M5 junction 9 take A46 exit towards Evesham. Just after t-lights turn R to Fiddington. After 1½m* *turn R to Walton Cardiff. Entrance is 1st on R.* Interesting collection of plants finding a new home in largish garden 'in the making' on thick clay. Good display of hellebores. TEAS on Suns and Bank Hol Mons. *Adm £1.50 Chd free. Tues, Weds, Thurs all year; Bank Hol Mons; Suns Feb 20, March 19, April 9, June 25, July 16, Aug 13, Sept 24, Oct 15 (12-5).* **2001** *Hellebore Suns Feb 21, March 14. Parties by appt, please* **Tel 01684 292668**

Trench Hill, Sheepscombe ♿✂❀ (Celia & Dave Hargrave) *½m from Painswick on A46 to Cheltenham, turn R to Sheepscombe. Approx 1½m (before reaching village) turn L by telegraph poles, Trench Hill at top of lane.* About 3 acres set in small woodland with panoramic views. Variety of herbaceous and mixed borders, rose garden, extensive vegetable plots, wildflower areas, plantings of spring bulbs, a woodland walk, 2 small ponds, waterfall and larger conservation pond. Run on organic principles. TEAS. *Adm £1.50 Chd free (ACNO to MACE - for the housebound). Sun Feb 20, Easter Sun, Mon April 23, 24 (11-5), Suns June 11, 18 (11-6). Private visits welcome, please* **Tel 01452 814 306**

Trevi, Hartpury ♿✂❀ (Gilbert & Sally Gough) *5m NW of Gloucester via A417.* Tranquil gardens in 1 acre; winding water garden; alpine terrace; clematis walk, rope and pole garden; herbaceous borders. Hardy geraniums, penstemons, epimediums; unusual shrubs and trees. Garden for the connoisseur. TEAS. *Adm £2 Chd free (ACNO to Gurkha Welfare Trust). Sun April 2, Easter Sun, Mon April 23, 24, Suns, Bank Hol Mons April 30, May 1, 28, 29, Suns June 11, July 9 (Hartpury Church), Sat, Sun July 29, 30 (Clematis weekend), Suns Aug 6, 13 (Crack Cancer), 20, Sun, Bank Hol Mon Aug 27, 28, Sun Sept 3, Thurs April 6, 27, May 4, 18, June 1, 15, 29, July 13, 20, Aug 3, 17, 31 (2-6). Coaches and groups by appt on other dates, please* **Tel 01452 700370**

■ **Trull House, Tetbury** ♿✂ (Caroline & Simon Mitchell) *3m NE of Tetbury off A433. From Tetbury pass Trouble House Inn and take 2nd turning L by cottages, then follow signs.* Large garden with mixture of formal and informal areas. Herbaceous borders, walled garden, lily pond, wilderness, mature trees, abundant spring bulbs. Attractive period Cotswold house (not open). TEAS. *Adm £2.25 Chd free. Each Wed and Sat from May 7 to July 9. For NGS Sat and Sun June 11, 12 (2-6). Private visits by appt, please* **Tel 01285 841255**

Upton Wold, nr Moreton-in-Marsh ✂❀ (Mr & Mrs I R S Bond) *On A44 1m past A424 junction at Troopers Lodge Garage.* Ever developing and changing garden architecturally and imaginatively laid out around C17 house (not open) with commanding views. Yew hedges; old shrub roses; herbaceous walk; some unusual plants and trees; vegetable garden; pond garden and woodland garden. Cream TEAS. *Adm £3 Chd free. Sun April 16, June 18 (10-6). Private visits (£4) welcome May to July, please* **Tel 01386 700667**

NEW **Warners Court, Charfield** (Mr & Mrs M Adams) *3m SW of Wotton-under-Edge on B4058 (towards Bristol and 2½m from M5 junction 14) in main st of Charfield.* 1 acre around Cotswold farmhouse (not open) with mixed planting. Owner not yet learned to resist plant sales. Large, new wildlife pond, organic vegetable garden with raised beds, using 'no dig' principles. TEAS. *Adm £2 Chd free. Sats, Suns April 1, 2, Sept 23, 24 (2-5)*

▲ **Westbury Court Garden, Westbury-on-Severn** ♿✂ (The National Trust) *9m SW of Gloucester on A48.* Formal Dutch-style water garden, earliest remaining in England; canals, summerhouse, walled garden; over 100 species of plants grown in England before 1700. *Adm £2.80 Chd £1.40. For NGS Sun Sept 3 (11-6)*

Westonbirt School Gardens ♿ *3 m S of Tetbury. A433 Tetbury to Bristol rd.* 22 acres. Formal Victorian/Italian garden, terraced pleasure garden, rustic walks, lake, statuary and grotto, chapel. Rare, exotic trees and shrubs. Beautiful views of Westonbirt House, now Westonbirt School (not open). Teas in Tetbury or at Hare & Hounds Hotel, Westonbirt ½m; to book tea room for parties Tel 01666 880233. *£2.50 Chd 50p (ACNO to Westonbirt Church Organ Appeal). Suns April 2, Aug 13 (2-4.30)*
Tel 01666 880333

Willow Lodge, nr Longhope ♿✂❀ (John & Sheila Wood) *On A40 between May Hill & Longhope, 10m W of Gloucester, 6m E of Ross-on-Wye.* Plantsman's garden with unusual and rare plants and colour-themed herbaceous borders and shrubs. Alpine walk, stream and pools. Several greenhouses and organic vegetable garden. Young arboretum with over 300 trees and shrubs from around the world, and wild flowers in 4-acre grounds. Plants labelled. Ample parking. TEAS. *Adm £1.50 Chd free. Suns, Mons April 30, May 1, 7, 8, 28, 29, June 11, 12, 18, 19, July 2, 3, 16, 17, 30, 31, Aug 6, 7, 13, 14 (1-5). Groups and private visits especially welcome between May and Aug, please* **Tel 01452 831211**

Yew Tree House, Painswick (Prof & Dr Edward J Burge) *In the centre of Painswick on A46, at t-lights turn R into Bisley St, (L if coming from Cheltenham). At T-junction turn L into Vicarage St. Yew Tree House is 100yds down hill on RH-side. Park in village car park off A46.* Garden with mature trees, yew, tulip and walnut. Mixed herbaceous and shrub borders planned for ease of maintenance, with interesting foliage and plants. Wild garden. Lovely views across Painswick valley from 1668 Grade II* house (not open). TEAS. *Adm £1.50 Chd free. Sun May 21 (2-6). Parking for disabled by arrangement, please* **Tel 01452 813177**

Evening Opening (See also garden description)

Mill Dene, Blockley	June 30

Gwent & Gwynedd

See separate Welsh section on pages 417 & 421

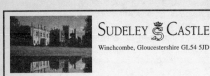

SUDELEY CASTLE

Winchcombe, Gloucestershire GL54 5JD

Once home to Queen Katherine Parr, Henry VIII's sixth wife.

Ten Magnificent Gardens • Historic Castle Apartments & Chapel • Licensed Restaurant • Adventure Playground • Gift Shop • Plant Centre • Wildfowl Lake • Exhibition - The Life and Times of Emma Dent.

Gardens open 4th March - 29th October
Telephone 01242 602308 for opening times and admission.

MILL DENE GARDEN

2 1/2 acres of tranquility surrounding a cotswold water mill

STREAM; GROTTO; TROMPHE L'OEIL;
MILL-POND; DUCKS AND CATS WILL ENCHANT YOU
B&B, TEAS AND PLANT SALES AVAILABLE

ENTRY: £2.50 OPEN: 1ST APRIL TO END OCTOBER, 10AM TO 6PM
BLOCKLEY, MORETON IN MARSH, GLOS. GL56 9HU
TEL: 01386 700457 HTTP.WWW.SMOOTHOUND/HOTELS/MILLDENE/HTML

Nurses Welfare Service

A nurse in charge of a night shift is attacked and tied up by robbers. Who is there to pick up the pieces? The Nurses Welfare Service.

Tel 0171 222 1563.

The Royal Gardeners' Orphan Fund

The RGOF has been helping the orphaned children of professional horticulturists since 1887. In 1995, the scope of the Fund was broadened. Now all the children in need, whose parents are employed in horticulture, may qualify for assistance. The RGOF gives quarterly allowances to orphaned children, and grants to those in need for school expenses, winter clothing, bedding and holidays.

For more information about the RGOF, please contact the Secretary,

Mrs Kate Wallis
14 Scholars Mews,
Welwyn Garden City,
Hertfordshire AL8 7JQ
Tel/Fax: 01707 333663

Information can also be found on the NGS website www.ngs.org.uk

Hampshire

Hon County Organiser:
Central West: Mrs A R Elkington, Little Court, Crawley, Winchester SO21 2PU
Tel 01962 776365 e-mail: elkslc@compuserve.com
Assistant Hon County Organisers:
Central North-West Mr M Walford , Little Acre, Down Farm Lane, Headbourne Worthy SO23 7LA
North-West Miss C Pratt, Field House, Monxton, Andover SP11 8AS
North: Mrs C Oldale, Little Coopers, Coopers Hill, Eversley RG27 0QA Tel 01252 872229
North-East: Mrs E Powell, Broadhatch House, Bentley, Nr Farnham GU10 5JJ
Central-East: Mrs W F Richardson, Hill House, Old Alresford SO24 9DY
East: Mrs D Hart Dyke, Hambledon House, Hambledon PO7 4RU
South: Mrs H Sykes, The Cottage, 16 Lakewood Road, Chandlers Ford SO53 1ES
South-West: Mrs A Dickens, 2 Victoria Place, Lymington SO41 3TD
West: Mr C Stanford, Oakdene, Sandleheath, Fordingbridge SP6 1PA
Hon County Treasurer: Mr R Morcom, White Poplars, Station Road, Chilbolton SO20 6AW

DATES OF OPENING

Regular openings
For details see garden description
Alverstoke Crescent Garden, Gosport
Apple Court
Beechenwood Farm, Odiham
Braxton Gardens, Milford-on-Sea
Little Court
Exbury Gardens, Southampton
Furzey Gardens, Minstead
Hambledon House, Hambledon
The Sir Harold Hillier Gardens & Arboretum, Ampfield
Longstock Park Gardens, nr Stockbridge
Longthatch, Warnford
Macpennys Woodland Garden & Nurseries, Bransgore
Spinners, Boldre
2 Warren Farm Cottages
West Green House, Hartley Wintney

By appointment only
For telephone numbers and other details see garden descriptions. Private visits welcomed
Little Coopers

February 5 Saturday
Brandy Mount House, Alresford

February 20 Sunday
Little Court, Crawley, nr Winchester

February 21 Monday
Little Court, Crawley, nr Winchester

February 22 Tuesday
Little Court, Crawley, nr Winchester

February 27 Sunday
The White Cottage, Beech

March 5 Sunday
Brandy Mount House, Alresford
Longthatch, Warnford

March 12 Sunday
Little Court, Crawley, nr Winchester
Longthatch, Warnford
The White Cottage, Beech

March 14 Tuesday
Little Court, Crawley, nr Winchester

March 19 Sunday
Hayden Barn Cottage, Warnford
Heathlands, Locks Heath
Longthatch, Warnford
Nikendi, Swanmore
Sowley House, Sowley

March 26 Sunday
Fernlea, Chilworth
Mittens, Mapledurwell

April 2 Sunday
Appleshaw Manor, Andover
Chilland, Martyr Worthy
Durmast House, Burley
East Lane, Ovington

April 3 Monday
Chilland, Martyr Worthy

April 5 Wednesday
Beechenwood Farm, Odiham

April 9 Sunday
Abbey Cottage, Itchen Abbas
Brandy Mount House, Alresford
44 Brecon Avenue, Drayton
Fairfield House, Hambledon
Hayden Barn Cottage, Warnford
60 Lealand Road, Drayton
The Old House, Silchester

April 16 Sunday
The Cottage, Chandler's Ford
Crawley Gardens, nr Winchester
Hinton Ampner, Alresford
Houghton Lodge, Stockbridge
Little Court, Crawley, nr Winchester
Longthatch, Warnford
Manor Lodge, Crawley, nr Winchester
Valentine Cottage, Newnham
Weir House, Alresford

April 17 Monday
The Cottage, Chandler's Ford
Crawley Gardens, nr Winchester
Houghton Lodge, Stockbridge
Little Court, Crawley, nr Winchester
Manor Lodge, Crawley, nr Winchester

April 19 Wednesday
Beechenwood Farm, Odiham

April 21 Friday
187 Christchurch Road, Ringwood
Rowans Wood, Ampfield

April 23 Sunday
Bramdean House, Bramdean
187 Christchurch Road, Ringwood
The Coach House, Chilbolton
Fernlea, Chilworth
Rowans Wood, Ampfield
Woodcote Manor, Bramdean

April 24 Monday
Beechenwood Farm, Odiham
Bramdean House, Bramdean

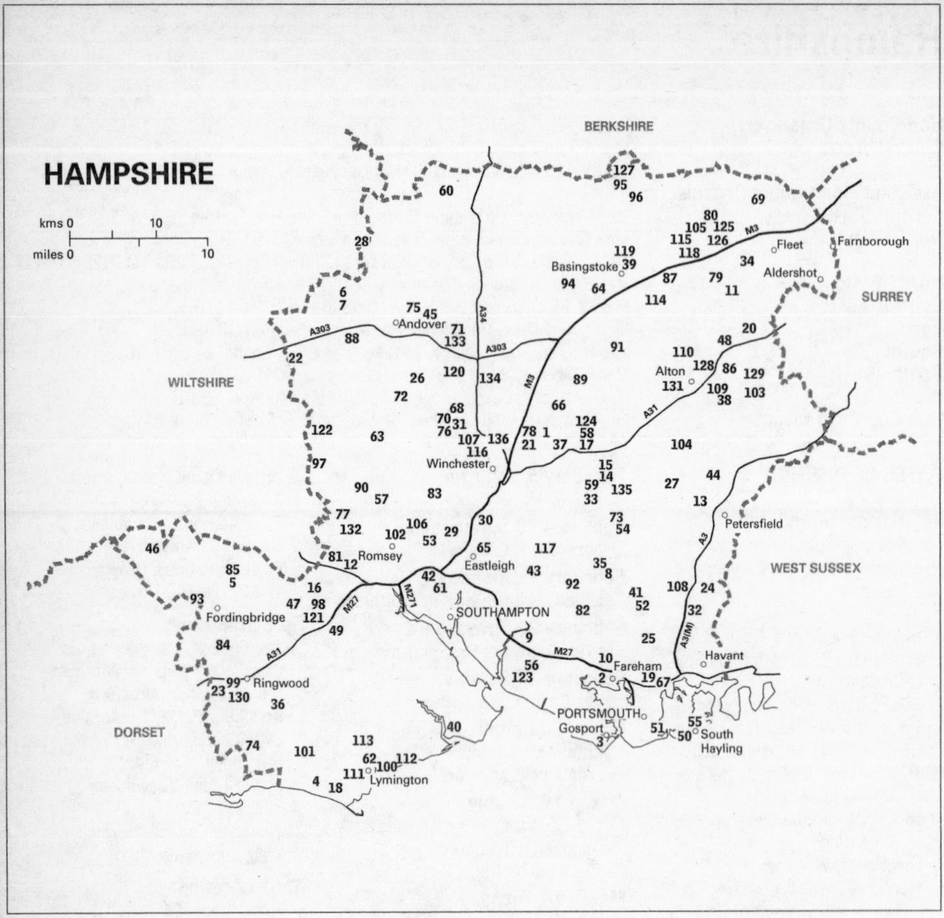

KEY

1 Abbey Cottage
2 Abbey Road Gardens
3 Alverstoke Crescent Garden
4 Apple Court
5 Applecroft
6 Appleshaw Gardens
7 Appleshaw Manor
8 Appletree House
9 Appletrees
10 Barnwood Road
11 Beechenwood Farm
12 Birches
13 Bluebell Cottage
14 Bramdean House
15 Bramdean Lodge
16 Bramshaw Lodge
17 Brandy Mount House
18 Braxton Gardens
19 44 Brecon Avenue
20 Bury Court
21 Chilland
22 Cholderton Gardens
23 187 Christchurch Road
24 Clibdens
25 Closewood House
26 The Coach House
27 Coles
28 Conholt Park
29 The Cottage
30 Cranbury Park
31 Crawley Gardens
32 Crookley Pool
33 Dean House
34 The Dower House
35 Droxford Gardens
36 Durmast House
37 East Lane
38 East Worldham Gardens
39 8 Elbow Corner
40 Exbury Gardens
41 Fairfield House
42 Fernlea
43 Flintstones
44 Forde's Cottage
45 Forest Edge
46 The Forge
47 Fritham Lodge
48 Froyle Cottage Gardens
49 Furzey Gardens
50 Garden Cottage
51 Greenfingers
52 Hambledon House
53 The Sir Harold Hillier Gardens & Arboretum
54 Hayden Barn Cottage
55 Hayling Island Gardens
56 Heathlands
57 The Hedges
58 Hill House
59 Hinton Ampner
60 Hollington Herb Garden
61 93 Holly Hill
62 Hordle Walhampton School
63 Houghton Lodge

64 Jasmine Lodge
65 53 Ladywood
66 Lake House
67 60 Lealand Road
68 Lithend
69 Little Coopers
70 Little Court
71 Longparish Gardens
72 Longstock Park Gardens
73 Longthatch
74 Macpennys Woodland Garden & Nurseries
75 Mandelieu
76 Manor Lodge
77 March End
78 Martyr Worthy Gardens
79 Marycourt
80 Mattingley Green Cottage
81 Maurys Mount
82 Meon Orchard
83 Merdon Manor
84 Merebimur
85 Merrie Cottage
86 Mill Court
87 Mittens
88 Monxton Gardens
89 Moth House
90 Mottisfont Abbey & Garden
91 Moundsmere Manor
92 Nikendi
93 Oakdene
94 Oakley Manor
95 The Old House
96 Old Meadows
97 The Old Rectory
98 Paddocks Way
99 Potters Cot
100 Pylewell Park
101 Robins Return
102 Romsey Gardens
103 Rose Cottage
104 Rotherfield Park
105 Rotherwick Gardens
106 Rowans Wood
107 12 Rozelle Close
108 Rumsey Gardens
109 Selborne
110 Shalden Park House
111 South End House
112 Sowley House
113 Spinners
114 Tunworth Old Rectory
115 Tylney Hall Hotel
116 Ulvik
117 Upham Gardens
118 Valentine Cottage
119 The Vyne
120 Wades House
121 Waldrons
122 2 Warren Farm Cottages
123 319 Warsash Rd
124 Weir House
125 West Green House Cottages
126 West Green House
127 West Silchester Hall
128 Westbrook House
129 Wheatley House
130 White Barn
131 The White Cottage
132 White House
133 White Windows
134 Wonston Lodge
135 Woodcote Manor
136 The Worthys Gardens

187 Christchurch Road, Ringwood
The Coach House, Chilbolton
Coles, Privett
Rowans Wood, Ampfield
Woodcote Manor, Bramdean

April 26 Wednesday
Hayden Barn Cottage, Warnford

April 30 Sunday
Abbey Cottage, Itchen Abbas
Abbey Road Gardens, Fareham
Bluebell Cottage, Froxfield
Coles, Privett
The Cottage, Chandler's Ford
53 Ladywood, Eastleigh
Little Court, Crawley, nr Winchester
The Old House, Silchester
Shalden Park House

May 1 Monday
Abbey Cottage, Itchen Abbas
Bluebell Cottage, Froxfield
Coles, Privett
The Cottage, Chandler's Ford
Hambledon House, Hambledon

May 2 Tuesday
Little Court, Crawley, nr Winchester

May 3 Wednesday
Beechenwood Farm, Odiham
Exbury Gardens, Southampton

May 5 Friday
2 Warren Farm Cottages

May 7 Sunday
Brandy Mount House, Alresford
The Dower House, Dogmersfield
Hordle Walhampton School, Lymington
Rowans Wood, Ampfield
Spinners, Boldre
Tylney Hall Hotel, Rotherwick

May 12 Friday
2 Warren Farm Cottages

May 13 Saturday
Garden Cottage, Hayling Island

May 14 Sunday
Bramdean House, Bramdean
Coles, Privett
The Dower House, Dogmersfield
Garden Cottage, Hayling Island
Greenfingers, Milton
Hayden Barn Cottage, Warnford
Heathlands, Locks Heath
Nikendi, Swanmore
The Old House, Silchester
Pylewell Park, Lymington
Rumsey Gardens, Clanfield
319 Warsash Rd, Titchfield
White Windows, Longparish

May 15 Monday
White Windows, Longparish

May 17 Wednesday
Beechenwood Farm, Odiham
Crookley Pool, Horndean
Rowans Wood, Ampfield (evening)

May 19 Friday
Mill Court, Binsted
2 Warren Farm Cottages

May 20 Saturday
Mill Court, Binsted
Potters Cot, Ringwood

May 21 Sunday
Coles, Privett
Forde's Cottage, Oakshott
Hambledon House, Hambledon
Lithend, Crawley
Little Court, Crawley, nr Winchester
The Old House, Silchester
Paddocks Way, Brook
Potters Cot, Ringwood
Pylewell Park, Lymington
Robins Return, Tiptoe
Rowans Wood, Ampfield
Waldrons, Brook
2 Warren Farm Cottages

May 22 Monday
Hambledon House, Hambledon
2 Warren Farm Cottages

May 23 Tuesday
Lithend, Crawley
Little Court, Crawley, nr Winchester

May 24 Wednesday
Robins Return, Tiptoe

May 26 Friday
2 Warren Farm Cottages

May 27 Saturday
Hayling Island Gardens
Rowans Wood, Ampfield (evening)
Weir House, Alresford

May 28 Sunday
Beechenwood Farm, Odiham
Bluebell Cottage, Froxfield
Bramshaw Lodge, Bramshaw
44 Brecon Avenue, Drayton
Coles, Privett
Hayling Island Gardens
Longthatch, Warnford
Monxton Gardens
Romsey Gardens
Valentine Cottage, Newnham
Weir House, Alresford
West Silchester Hall, Silchester

May 29 Monday
Birches, East Wellow
Bluebell Cottage, Froxfield
Bramshaw Lodge, Bramshaw
Coles, Privett
Longthatch, Warnford
Monxton Gardens
Romsey Gardens
West Silchester Hall, Silchester

May 30 Tuesday
Birches, East Wellow

May 31 Wednesday
Beechenwood Farm, Odiham

June 2 Friday
2 Warren Farm Cottages

June 3 Saturday
Forest Edge, Andover
Froyle Cottage Gardens, nr Alton

June 4 Sunday
Flintstones, Durley
Forest Edge, Andover
Froyle Cottage Gardens, nr Alton
Longparish Gardens, Andover
Maurys Mount, West Wellow
Meon Orchard, Kingsmead
Rose Cottage, Kingsley Common
Tylney Hall Hotel, Rotherwick
Upham Gardens
The White Cottage, Beech

June 5 Monday
Flintstones, Durley
Rose Cottage, Kingsley Common
The White Cottage, Beech

June 7 Wednesday
Appletree House, Soberton
Hambledon House, Hambledon
Upham Gardens

June 9 Friday
2 Warren Farm Cottages
White Barn, Crow Hill

June 10 Saturday
The Forge, Martin
93 Holly Hill, Bassett
White Barn, Crow Hill

June 11 Sunday
Applecroft, Woodgreen
Bramdean House, Bramdean
Bramdean Lodge, Bramdean
Closewood House, Denmead
Cranbury Park, Otterbourne
The Forge, Martin
The Hedges, Timsbury
93 Holly Hill, Bassett
Longthatch, Warnford
Merrie Cottage, Woodgreen
Nikendi, Swanmore
The Vyne, Sherborne St John

June 12 Monday
Applecroft, Woodgreen
Merrie Cottage, Woodgreen
Nikendi, Swanmore

June 14 Wednesday
Beechenwood Farm, Odiham
Closewood House, Denmead
The Hedges, Timsbury

June 14 to 16 Wednesday to Friday
White House, Romsey

June 16 Friday
2 Warren Farm Cottages

June 17 Saturday
Appletrees, Burridge

June 18 Sunday
Appletrees, Burridge
Clibdens
Conholt Park, Chute
East Worldham Gardens
Longstock Park Gardens, nr Stockbridge
Oakdene, Sandleheath
Old Meadows, Silchester
2 Warren Farm Cottages
Westbrook House, Holybourne
Wheatley House, Kingsley Bordon

June 19 Monday
March End, Sherfield English
2 Warren Farm Cottages

June 20 Tuesday
Oakdene, Sandleheath
Wheatley House, Kingsley Bordon

June 21 Wednesday
Crookley Pool, Horndean
Dean House, Kilmeston

June 23 Friday
2 Warren Farm Cottages

June 24 Saturday
West Green House, Hartley Wintney
West Green House Cottage, Hartley Wintney

June 25 Sunday
Abbey Road Gardens, Fareham
Appleshaw Gardens, Andover
19 Barnwood Road, Fareham
Cholderton Gardens
Droxford Gardens
Fairfield House, Hambledon
Fritham Lodge, Lyndhurst
Hinton Ampner, Alresford
53 Ladywood, Eastleigh
Lake House, Northington
March End, Sherfield English
Marycourt, Odiham
Mottisfont Abbey & Garden, Romsey
The Old Rectory, West Tytherley
Robins Return, Tiptoe
Valentine Cottage, Newnham
Wonston Lodge, Wonston

June 26 Monday
Cholderton Gardens
Droxford Gardens
March End, Sherfield English
The Old Rectory, West Tytherley

June 27 Tuesday
Lake House, Northington

June 28 Wednesday
Robins Return, Tiptoe
The Vyne, Sherborne St John (evening)

June 30 Friday
2 Warren Farm Cottages

July 2 Sunday
Conholt Park, Chute
Durmast House, Burley
Forde's Cottage, Oakshott
Mandelieu, Picket Piece
Marycourt, Odiham
Mattingley Green Cottage, Mattingley
Moth House, Brown Candover
Moundsmere Manor, Preston Candover
Tunworth Old Rectory
Wades House, Barton Stacey

July 3 Monday
Mandelieu, Picket Piece

July 4 Tuesday
Wades House, Barton Stacey

July 5 Wednesday
Appletree House, Soberton
Crookley Pool, Horndean
Hambledon House, Hambledon
The Hedges, Timsbury
Marycourt, Odiham

July 7 Friday
2 Warren Farm Cottages

July 9 Sunday
Abbey Cottage, Itchen Abbas
Birches, East Wellow
Bramdean House, Bramdean
Bramdean Lodge, Bramdean
Greenfingers, Milton
The Hedges, Timsbury
Hollington Herb Garden, Woolton Hill
Longthatch, Warnford
Martyr Worthy Gardens

Rotherwick Gardens, Hook
The White Cottage, Beech

July 10 Monday
Chilland, Martyr Worthy
The White Cottage, Beech

July 11 Tuesday
Birches, East Wellow

July 14 Friday
2 Warren Farm Cottages

July 15 Saturday
93 Holly Hill, Bassett
Potters Cot, Ringwood
12 Rozelle Close, Littleton
Ulvik, Winchester

July 16 Sunday
44 Brecon Avenue, Drayton
Hambledon House, Hambledon
Hollington Herb Garden, Woolton Hill
93 Holly Hill, Bassett
60 Lealand Road, Drayton
Merdon Manor, Hursley
Old Meadows, Silchester
Potters Cot, Ringwood
12 Rozelle Close, Littleton
Tylney Hall Hotel, Rotherwick
Ulvik, Winchester
2 Warren Farm Cottages
West Silchester Hall, Silchester

July 17 Monday
Hambledon House, Hambledon
Ulvik, Winchester
2 Warren Farm Cottages

July 21 Friday
Bury Court, Bentley
2 Warren Farm Cottages

July 22 Saturday
Bury Court, Bentley
Elbow Corner, Basingstoke
Merebimur, Mockbeggar

July 23 Sunday
Elbow Corner, Basingstoke
Jasmine Lodge, Kempshott
Merebimur, Mockbeggar
Robins Return, Tiptoe

July 26 Wednesday
Merebimur, Mockbeggar
Robins Return, Tiptoe

July 28 Friday
2 Warren Farm Cottages

July 29 Saturday
Elbow Corner, Basingstoke
Forest Edge, Andover
12 Rozelle Close, Littleton
South End House, Lymington (evening)

July 30 Sunday
Elbow Corner, Basingstoke
Forest Edge, Andover
Jasmine Lodge, Kempshott
Mandelieu, Picket Piece
Meon Orchard, Kingsmead
12 Rozelle Close, Littleton

July 31 Monday
Mandelieu, Picket Piece

August 1 Tuesday
Worthy Gardens

August 4 Friday
2 Warren Farm Cottages

August 5 Saturday
Elbow Corner, Basingstoke

August 6 Sunday
Abbey Road Gardens, Fareham
Elbow Corner, Basingstoke
Hill House, Old Alresford
Oakley Manor, Oakley
Rose Cottage, Kingsley Common
Selborne, East Worldham
West Silchester Hall, Silchester
The White Cottage, Beech

August 7 Monday
Rose Cottage, Kingsley Common
Selborne, East Worldham
West Silchester Hall, Silchester
The White Cottage, Beech

August 8 Tuesday
Hill House, Old Alresford

August 11 Friday
2 Warren Farm Cottages

August 12 Saturday
93 Holly Hill, Bassett

August 13 Sunday
Bramdean House, Bramdean
Bramdean Lodge, Bramdean
Fernlea, Chilworth
93 Holly Hill, Bassett
Little Court, Crawley, nr Winchester
Weir House, Alresford

August 14 Monday
Little Court, Crawley, nr Winchester

August 18 Friday
Bury Court, Bentley
2 Warren Farm Cottages

August 19 Saturday
Bury Court, Bentley

August 20 Sunday
60 Lealand Road, Drayton
2 Warren Farm Cottages

August 21 Monday
2 Warren Farm Cottages

August 25 Friday
2 Warren Farm Cottages

August 27 Sunday
Abbey Cottage, Itchen Abbas

August 28 Monday
Abbey Cottage, Itchen Abbas

September 2 Saturday
West Green House, Hartley Wintney

September 3 Sunday
Lake House, Northington
Manor Lodge, Crawley, nr Winchester
Meon Orchard, Kingsmead
Mittens, Mapledurwell
West Green House, Hartley Wintney
The White Cottage, Beech

September 4 Monday
Manor Lodge, Crawley, nr Winchester

September 5 Tuesday
Lake House, Northington

September 6 Wednesday
Crookley Pool, Horndean

September 9 Saturday
Hinton Ampner, Alresford
West Green House, Hartley Wintney

September 10 Sunday
Bramdean House, Bramdean
Bramdean Lodge, Bramdean
Hambledon House, Hambledon
Hinton Ampner, Alresford
Rotherfield Park, East Tisted
West Green House, Hartley Wintney

September 11 Monday
Hambledon House, Hambledon

September 16 Saturday
West Green House, Hartley Wintney

September 17 Sunday
Nikendi, Swanmore
2 Warren Farm Cottages
West Green House, Hartley Wintney

September 18 Monday
2 Warren Farm Cottages

September 20 Wednesday
Old Meadows, Silchester

September 22 Friday
Bury Court, Bentley

September 23 Saturday
Bury Court, Bentley
West Green House, Hartley Wintney

September 24 Sunday
Mill Court, Binsted
West Green House, Hartley Wintney

September 27 Wednesday
Mill Court, Binsted

October 15 Sunday
Coles, Privett

Nikendi, Swanmore
2 Warren Farm Cottages
Weir House, Alresford

October 16 Monday
2 Warren Farm Cottages

October 22 Sunday
Coles, Privett

2001

February 18 Sunday
Little Court, Crawley, nr Winchester

February 19 Monday
Little Court, Crawley, nr Winchester

February 20 Tuesday
Little Court, Crawley, nr Winchester

DESCRIPTIONS OF GARDENS

Abbey Cottage, Itchen Abbas ♿✗❀ (Colonel P J Daniell) *Rectory Lane. 1m E of Itchen Abbas on B3047.* An inspiring 1½ acres of walled garden and meadow on alkaline soil, designed and created on different levels, and maintained by owner. Trees, hedges and walls provide a strong framework within which a wide range of shrubs and herbaceous plants flourish and provide yr-round interest. Featured on Channel 4's 'C20 Gardens' autumn 1999. TEA. *Adm £2 Chd free (ACNO to Itchen Abbas Church). Sun April 9, Sun, Bank Hol Mon April 30, May 1, Sun July 9, Sun, Bank Hol Mon Aug 27, 28 (12-5)*

Abbey Road Gardens, Fareham ❀ *From M27 junction 9 take A27 towards Fareham. At top of hill past Titchfield Gyratory, turn L at t-lights into Highland Rd. Take 4th turning R into Blackbrook Rd. Abbey Rd is 4th turning on L. Combined adm £1.50 Chd free. Suns April 30, June 25, Aug 6 (11-5)*

80 Abbey Road, Fareham ✗❀ (Brian & Vivienne Garford) Very small garden with extensive collection of herbs, also plants of botanical and historical interest. 2 small ponds, miniscule meadow area, but no lawn. Many original ideas for small gardens

86 Abbey Road, Fareham ✗ (Tricia & Don Purseglove) Front garden with raised bed of shrubs and perennials, small lawn. Trellis arch to side garden, lawn with mixed beds and borders; pergola into paved area with fish pond and waterfall TEA.

Alverstoke Crescent Garden, Gosport ♿❀ (Gosport Borough Council) *From A32 and Gosport follow signs for Stokes Bay then Alverstoke Village. Crescent is off Anglesey Road.* Small recreated Regency garden, being partnership between council and community, opp Grade II* Regency Crescent. Terrace walk with series of small scenes. Central area, site of old reading room and baths, has grassy bays and inlets, shrubs and old roses, authentic plants of the period. *Donations in box by gate. Daily. Private guided visits, please* **Tel 01705 586403**

● **Apple Court** (Mrs Diana Grenfell, Mr Roger Grounds) *From A337 between Lymington and New Milton, turn into Hordle Lane at Royal Oak at Downton Xrds.* 1½ acres within former walled kitchen garden. 3 National Plant Collections incl small-leafed hosta. Theatrical white garden, modern grassery, fern path. American Hemerocallis Society and Hemerocallis Europa Display Garden. Extensively featured in garden owner's recently published books, television and many articles. *Adm £2 Chd 50p. Daily except Weds March to Oct (10-1 & 2-5)*

Applecroft, Woodgreen ✗ (Mr & Mrs J B Milne) *Brook Lane, Woodgreen. 3m N of Fordingbridge on A338 turn E to Woodgreen. Turn R at Horse and Groom and R again along edge of common. Park on common and walk down through 5-barred gate.* Small garden with mixed planting incl annuals and vegetables in cottage style. Shady arbour and pond. Distant view to SW over Avon Valley. TEAS (Mon). Teas (Sun at Merrie Cottage). *Adm £1.50 Chd free. Sun, Mon June 11, 12 (2-6)*

Appleshaw Gardens, Andover *Take A342 Andover to Marlborough rd. Turn to Appleshaw 1m W of Weyhill. Fork L at playing field on R, after ½m, near white church. Combined adm £2 Chd free (ACNO to St Peter in the Wood Church, Appleshaw). Sun June 25 (2-5)*

The Old Vicarage ✗ (Sir Dermot & Lady De Trafford) 2-acre, walled garden with mature trees, bush and rambler roses, shrub borders, shrubs and trees in grass; fruit and herb garden with box hedges. TEAS.

Rose Hill ♿✗ (Mr & Mrs H McCall) 2 acres surrounded by paddocks grazed by thoroughbred horses. Mature trees, herbaceous borders, small orchard and kitchen garden

Appleshaw Manor, Andover ♿✗ (Mr & Mrs Patrick Walker) *Take A342 Andover to Marlborough rd. Turn to Appleshaw 1m W of Weyhill. Fork L at playing field on R after ½m near white church.* 7-acre, walled garden and grounds. Spring flowers, kitchen garden, wood garden and arboretum. Notable beech and yew hedges. TEAS. *Adm £2 Chd free (ACNO to St Peter in the Wood, Appleshaw). Sun April 2 (2-5)*

NEW **Appletree House, Soberton** ✗ (Mrs J Dover) *A32 N to Droxford bridge. B2150 turn R immed under bridge into Station Rd. Garden 1m. Parking in layby 300yds S or in rd.* Delightful small garden developed over 26 yrs and still evolving, showing what can be achieved in limited space. Exuberant planting of trees, shrubs and roses, intermingled with clematis, perennials, bulbs and grasses. *Adm £1.50 Chd 50p. Weds June 7, July 5 (2-5.30). Private visits welcome, please* **Tel 01489 877333**

Appletrees, Burridge ✗❀ (Kath & Ray Butcher) *267 Botley Road. From A27 take A3051 Park Gate to Botley, on L after 1½m. From Botley take A3051, Appletrees is 2m on R.* Flower arrangers' ⅓ acre garden densely planted with perennials, good foliage. Large patio with sinks and containers. Many winding paths with seats, small pond and waterfall. TEA. *Adm £1.50 Chd free. Sat, Sun June 17, 18 (2-5.30)*

Ashley Park Farm see Dorset

19 Barnwood Road, Fareham ✗❀ (Jill & Michael Hill) *From M27 junction 9 take A27 towards Fareham. At top of hill past Titchfield gyratory turn L at t-lights into Highlands Rd.*

Take 4th turning R into Blackbrook Rd, Meadow Bank is 4th turning on R. Barnwood is off Meadow Bank. Small plot, mostly perennials and shrubs with winding paths and surprising vistas. Double pond with bridge. Interesting use of colour in planting schemes and structural features. *Adm £1 Chd free. Sun June 25 (11-5)*

Beechenwood Farm, Odiham ♿❀ (Mr & Mrs M Heber-Percy) *Hillside. Turn S into King St. from Odiham High St. Turn L after cricket ground for Hillside. Take 2nd turn R for Roke after 1m. Modern house ½m.* Garden in many parts incl woodland garden, rock garden, pergola, conservatory, herb garden with exuberant planting, belvedere with spectacular views over Odiham. Newly planted wood of 8 acres. Teas in aid of WI Suns and Mons. *Adm £2 Chd free. Weds April 5, 19, Easter Mon April 24, Weds May 3, 17, 31, Sun May 28, Wed June 14 (2-6); also private visits welcome March to July, please* **Tel 01256 702300**

Birches, East Wellow ♿✂❀ (Mr & Mrs J Vinnicombe) *2m N of M27. Turn R off A36 into Whinwhistle Rd. Good access and parking for disabled.* ¾ acre on acid soil. Beautiful mature trees and shrubs linked by beds of striking texture, contrasting forms and subtle pespectives. Light and shade give added dimension to colour of both blooms and foliage. Result is a variety of moods without contrived compartments. TEA in period gazebo. *Adm £1.50 Chd free. Bank Hol Mon, Tues May 29, 30, Sun, Tues July 9, 11 (11.30-5)*

Bluebell Cottage, Froxfield ✂ (Mr & Mrs T Clarke) *Broadway. 3½m NW of Petersfield. Between top of Stoner Hill and Froxfield Green, or take sign to Froxfield off A272 and follow yellow signs.* 1 acre incl natural woodland with prolific bluebells and ferns. Mixed borders, kitchen garden with raised beds and greenhouse. Conservatory, pool. *Adm £1.50 Chd free. Suns, Bank Hol Mons April 30, May 1, May 28, 29 (2-6)*

Bramdean House, Bramdean ✂ (Mr & Mrs H Wakefield) *In village on A272.* 6½ acres, chalk garden with famous mirror-image herbaceous borders. Carpets of spring bulbs, working kitchen garden, many unusual plants incl large collection of sweet peas. Featured in Daily Mail weekend supplement 1998. TEAS. *Adm £2.50 Chd free (ACNO to Bramdean Parish Church) Easter Sun, Mon April 23, 24, Suns May 14, June 11, July 9, Aug 13, Sept 10 (2-5); also private parties by appt, please* **Tel 01962 771214 Fax 01962 771095**

Bramdean Lodge, Bramdean ♿ (The Hon Peter & Robin Dickinson) *In village, on A272 (car park and TEAS as for Bramdean House). Disabled please use Wood Lane entrance and park in yard.* 1¾ acres around Victorian gothic house (not open). Walled garden. Romantic cottage style with masses of colour. Many rarities. Over 150 varieties of clematis, and 500 of roses. *Adm £2 Chd free. Suns June 11, July 9, Aug 13, Sept 10 (3-6). Private parties welcome, please* **Tel 01962 771324**

Bramshaw Lodge, Bramshaw ♿✂❀ (Dr, Mrs & Miss Couchman) *Lyndhurst. 2m from junction 1 on M27 on B3079. On L past Bramshaw Village Hall.* Victorian garden of 1½ acres, circa 1850, with mature trees, rhododendrons and azaleas and expanding shrub and herbaceous planting surrounded by natural forest. Ponds and rope walk. TEAS. *Adm £2 Chd free. Sun, Bank Hol Mon May 28, 29 (2-6)*

Brandy Mount House, Alresford ♿❀ (Caryl & Michael Baron) *From centre, first R in East St before Sun Lane. Please leave cars in Broad St.* 1-acre, informal plantsman's garden, spring bulbs, hellebores, species geraniums, snowdrop collection, daphne collection, European primulas, herbaceous and woodland plants. Featured in Gardeners' World April 1999. TEAS. *Adm £1.50 Chd free. Sat Feb 5 (11-4), Suns March 5, April 9, May 7 (2-5)*

● **Braxton Gardens, Milford-on-Sea** ♿✂❀ (J D M Aldridge Esq) *Braxton Courtyard. 3m W of Lymington. From A337 at Everton take turning to Milford-on-Sea, 70yds on L is Lymore Lane. Turn into Lane and gardens are at Braxton courtyard on L.* Attractive courtyard with raised lily pool and dovecote. Restored C19 barn leading into formal walled garden. Knot garden, new rose garden, nursery. TEA (dog rings & water provided). *Donations. Open April 1 to Oct 31 Mons to Sats (9-5) and Suns (10-5) and shorter opening hours in winter please enquire* **Tel 01590 642008**

NEW **44 Brecon Avenue, Drayton** ✂❀ (David Lippiett) *1m from Cosham, N of old A27 (Havant Rd) between Cosham and Drayton. Turn into Penarth Ave (by Honda garage) and continue up hill.* Small, newly created town garden with views over Langstone Harbour, Portsmouth, Solent and IOW. Carefully selected plants incl bulbs, clematis (20+ varieties) and lilies. Pond, aviary and orchids. Portsdown Hill adjacent. TEAS. *£1 Chd free (ACNO to Southsea Shakespeare Actors). Suns April 9, May 28, July 16 (11-5)*

▲ **Bury Court, Bentley** ♿✂❀ (John Coke) *1m N of Bentley on Crondall Rd.* New garden designed in co-operation with Piet Oudolf, created from old farmyard. Currently the only pure example of continental 'naturalistic' style, making heavy use of grasses in association with perennials selected for an extended season of interest. TEAS. *Adm £2 Chd 50p. For NGS Fri, Sat July 21, 22, Aug 18, 19, Sept 22, 23 (10-6)*

Chilland, Martyr Worthy (Mr & Mrs John Impey) *Midway between Winchester and Alresford on B3047 between Martyr Worthy and Itchen Abbas signposted Chilland.* 4 acres with stream overlooking R Itchen and watermeadows; woods and farmland beyond. Large collection of mature shrubs planned for yr-round colour effects. Many fine trees incl huge plane and ancient mulberry, nutwalk, spring bulbs, clematis and herbaceous borders. *Adm £2 Chd free. Sun, Mon April 2, 3 (2-5.30), Sun July 9 see* **Martyr Worthy Gardens**, *Mon July 10 (2-6)*

Cholderton Gardens ♿✂❀ *From centre of Cholderton, E towards Grateley at mini roundabout and Crown Inn public house. 1m turn R, signposted.* TEAS. *Combined adm £2.50 Chd free. Sun, Mon June 25, 26 (2-6)*

Barn Cottage (Mr & Mrs Leslie Taylor) *Adjacent to Quarley Down Farm House.* Small cottage garden with a mass of colourful annuals and perennials. Features incl ornamental grass beds, rustic pergolas, pond and ancient hay-drying mill

Quarley Down Farm House (Mr & Mrs Jonathan Walsh) 5 acres surrounding listed Georgian farmhouse (not open), recently deerproofed. Newly created garden with numerous herbaceous and shrub borders. Walled garden with rose and herb beds. Magnificent listed barns. Completely secluded and with extensive views over surrounding farmland and wood

187 Christchurch Road, Ringwood ♿✂❀ (Mr C S & Mrs E M J Fryer) *S of Ringwood on B3347, approx ¾m from A31 turn off into Ringwood, follow signs for Kingston and Sopley. Across 3 roundabouts look L for police station; 187 is 4th turning L past it. Parking in Willow Dr, 3rd L, and in service rd.* Small garden packed with interesting plants, gravelled front garden with many variety of houseleeks, also pulsatillas, hardy geraniums, grasses, ferns and evergreens. TEAS. *Adm £1 Chd £1. Good Fri , Easter Sun, Mon April 21, 23, 24 (11-4.30). Group visits by appt, please* **Tel 01425 478450** (evenings)

Clibdens ✂ (Mrs Jacqueline Budden) *Chalton is 6m S of Petersfield. Turn L off A3 N of Horndean then directly R to Chalton. Clibdens is 1st house on L in village.* 1 acre surrounding farm with fine views to Windmill Hill. Recently developed garden on chalk with interesting collection of shrubs and plants, incl gravel garden and pond. TEAS. *Adm £2 Chd free. Sun June 18 (2-6). By appt May, June and July, please* **Tel 01705 592172**

Closewood House, Denmead ♿ (Mr & Mrs Peter Clowes) *Take Closewood Rd to W of B2150 between Waterlooville and Denmead. Turn L at T-junction after ½m. Signs to car park after 300 metres.* 4½ acres. Collection of scented roses incl large climbers and shrubs with good vistas between sections. Developing tree collection of 100 species and grass walk. Picnics welcome by stream. TEAS (Sun) TEA (Wed). *Adm £2 Chd free. Sun June 11, Wed June 14 (12-6). Private visits welcome, please* **Tel 01705 264213**

The Coach House, Chilbolton ❀ (Dr & Mrs J F Redhead) *On A3057 Andover to Stockbridge Rd, E for Chilbolton, just over bridge from Mayfly Inn, 100yds.* Informal garden on banks of R Test, with a carrier running through. Profusion of rambler roses scramble over walls, outbuildings and trees. Spring bulbs, flowering shrubs and fruit trees. Collection of auricula primulas. 2 greenhouses with vines and figs, vegetables, soft fruit cage, ducks. TEA. *Adm £2 Chd free. Easter Sun, Mon April 23, 24 (2-5)*

● **Coles, Privett** ✂❀ (Mrs Tim Watkins) *Nr Alton and Petersfield. Approx 6m NW of Petersfield between Privett and High Cross. From A32, S of Alton between East Tisted and West Meon Hut, turn E to Froxfield at Pig and Whistle/Lawns inn, after ½m turn L at T-junction and continue for ¾m, entrance on L.* 26 acres specialising in rhododendrons and azaleas, set amongst mixed woodland with rare specimens. Walks, clearings and decorative ponds, spring bluebells; autumn leaf colours. TEAS. *Adm £3, OAP £2.50 Chd 50p. Easter Mon April 24, Sun, Bank Hol Mon April 30, May 1, Suns May 14, 21, Bank Hol Mon May 29, Suns Oct 15, 22 (2-6). Private visits welcome, please* **Tel 01730 828 050**

Compton Lodge see Surrey

Conholt Park, Chute ✂❀ (Ms Caroline Tisdall) *Nr Andover. Turn N off A342 Andover to Devizes rd at Weyhill Church. Proceed 5m N through Clanville and Tangley Bottom. Turn L at Conholt (marked on Ordnance Survey) ½m on R, just off Chute causeway.* 10 acres surrounding Regency house (not open), rose, 'Calor', Shakespeare, winter and secret gardens. 1½ acre walled garden with potager, berry wall, rare fruit orchard, white border, hardy geraniums and allium collections. Romantic Ladies Walk and possibly longest maze in Britain. On farm unusual animals incl bison and shire horses. TEAS. *Adm £2.50 Chd free. Suns June 18, July 2 (2-6)*

The Cottage, Chandler's Ford ✂❀ (Mr & Mrs H Sykes) *16 Lakewood Rd. Leave M3 at junction 12, follow signs to Chandler's Ford. At King Rufus public house on Winchester rd, turn R into Merdon Ave, then 3rd rd on L.* ¾ acre. Planting began in 1950 to give yr-round interest under mature trees and in sunnier borders. Bog garden and ponds. Spring colour from bulbs, large camellias, rhododendrons, azaleas and trilliums. Bantams. TEAS. *Adm £1.50 Chd 10p (ACNO to British Heart Foundation). Suns, Mons April 16, 17 & April 30, May 1 (2-6)*

Cranbury Park, Otterbourne ♿❀ (Mr & Mrs Chamberlayne-Macdonald) *5m S of Winchester. 2m NW of Eastleigh; main entrance on old A33 between Winchester-Southampton, by bus stop at top of Otterbourne Hill. Entrances also in Hocombe Rd, Chandler's Ford.* Extensive pleasure grounds laid out in late C18 and early C19; fountains; rose garden; specimen trees; lakeside walk. Family carriages and collection of prams will be on view. TEAS. *Adm £2 Chd 50p (ACNO to Church of St Matthew, Otterbourne). Sun June 11 (2-6) last admission 5pm*

Crawley Gardens, nr Winchester *5m NW of Winchester, off A272 or A3049 Winchester-Stockbridge Rd. Parking at top of village nr church.* TEAS Sun only in aid of St Mary's, Crawley. *Combined adm £2.50 Chd free. Sun, Mon April 16, 17 (2-5.30)*

Glebe House ♿ (Lt Col & Mrs J Andrews) 1½ acres. Bulbs and shrubs incl eucalyptus collection.

Little Court (Prof & Mrs A R Elkington) see main entry

Manor Lodge ♿✂❀ (Mr & Mrs K Wren) see main entry

Paige Cottage ✂ (Mr and Mrs T.W. Parker) 1 acre of traditional English country garden incl grass tennis court (not open) and walled Italian-style swimming pool (not open); roses climbing into apple trees

Crookley Pool, Horndean ♿✂❀ (Mr & Mrs F S K Privett) *Turn up Blendworth Lane by main bakery from centre of Horndean. Entrance 200yds before church on L. Off A3 5m S of Petersfield.* Medium-sized plantsman's garden with nursery. Large mixed borders of unusual plants and roses, with special interest in colour and plants for hot, dry situations. Wisteria-covered walls and pergolas. Walled kitchen garden with box-edged, herb garden. TEAS. *Adm £2 Chd free. Weds May 17, June 21, July 5, Sept 6 (2-6). Private visits welcome, please* **Tel 01705 592662**

NEW **Dean House, Kilmeston** (Mr P H R Gwyn) *Kileston lies 5m S of Alresford via village of Cheriton or off A272 signposted at Cheriton Xrds.* 7 acres; orchard, paddock with small, formal pond, spacious lawns, mixed and herbaceous borders surrounding symmetrical rose garden, planted tunnel, working, walled kitchen garden and generously stocked glasshouses. TEA. *£2.50 Chd free. Wed June 21 (10-4)*

The Dower House, Dogmersfield (Mr Michael Hoare) *Turn N off A287.* 6 acres including bluebell wood with large and spectacular collection of rhododendrons, azaleas, magnolias and other flowering trees and shrubs; set in parkland with fine views over 20-acre lake. TEAS. *Adm £2 Chd free. Suns May 7, 14 (2-6)*

Droxford Gardens *4½m N of Wickham on A32 approx mid-way between Alton and Portsmouth.* TEAS Sun at The Mill House, Mon at Park View Cottage. *Adm £1 each garden Chd 50p. Sun, Mon June 25, 26 (2-6)*

The Mill House (Mrs Colin MacPherson) 2 acres. Shrubs, climbing roses and rose garden, herbaceous borders, pond, mill stream, orchard, vegetable garden. Car park *Not open Mon June 26*

Mylor Cottage (Dr & Mrs ffrench Constant) *½m S of Droxford on Swanmore Rd. Car park.* Mature beeches and climbing roses set off colourful herbaceous borders, fine lawns and foliage beds. A much-loved and cherished chalk garden with innumerable wildflowers, incl bee orchids in the paddock

Park View Cottage (Mrs F V D Aubert) Small town garden, flowers, shrubs and very small wooded walk. Car park

3 Waltham Close (Mr & Mrs Cartwright) *200yds from Park View Cottage in Union Lane.* ¾ acre, solely created by owners over 11 yrs. Varied collection of shrubs and herbaceous. Seasonal pots, tubs and hanging baskets

Durmast House, Burley (Mr and Mrs P E G Daubeney) *1m SE of Burley, nr White Buck Hotel.* 4 acres designed by Gertrude Jekyll in 1907 in process of being restored from original plans. Formal rose garden edged with lavender, 130-yr-old Monterey pine, large choisya, Victorian rockery, coach-house, large wisteria and Jekyll herbaceous borders. TEAS. *Adm £1.50 Chd 50p (ACNO to Delhi Commonwealth Women's Assoc Clinic). Suns April 2, July 2 (2-5). Private parties welcome, please* **Tel 01425 403527**

East Lane, Ovington (Sir Peter Ramsbotham) *Take A31 from Winchester towards Alresford. Immed after roundabout, 1m W of Alresford, small sign to Ovington turn sharp L up incline, down small country rd to Ovington. East Lane is only house on L, 500yds downhill towards Bush Inn.* 5 acres, spring bulbs, mixed herbaceous and shrubs; woodland plantings; arboretum; walled rose garden. Terraced water garden. Ample parking. *Adm £2 Chd free. Sun April 2 (2-5.30)*

East Worldham Gardens *On B3004, 2m SE of Alton, at edge of village at Alton end. Parking opp in small public house car park or in field at top of East Worldham Hill.* TEAS at East Worldham Manor. *Adm £2 Chd free (ACNO to St Mary's Church Fabric Fund). Sun June 18 (2-6)*

East Worldham Manor (Mrs H V Wood) A return to yellow book after many years for mellow Victorian double walled garden. Approx 2 acres. Restored Victorian greenhouses; rose beds, shrub and perennial borders; fruit and vegetable areas; colourful and unusual plants. Some of best panoramic views in Hampshire

Selborne (Mr & Mrs Brian Jones) see main entry. *Also open Sun, Mon Aug 6, 7*

Elbow Corner, Basingstoke (Mr & Mrs M Penfold) *Off Church Square, Basingstoke. Car park opp Anvil Theatre, Churchill Way in centre of Basingstoke. Walk via Lower Church St or through park from car park to Elbow Garden, adjacent to St Michael's Church.* Short terrace of houses covered with hanging baskets; small front gardens planted with annuals to give a blaze of colour. Past winner of Basingstoke in Bloom competition. TEA. *Adm £2 Chd free. Sats, Suns July 22, 23, 29, 30, Aug 5, 6 (10-5)*

● **Exbury Gardens, Southampton** (Edmund de Rothschild Esq) *Exbury, off B3054 3m SE of Beaulieu off A326.* 200 acres of landscaped woodland gardens with rhododendrons, azaleas, magnolias and camellias. Rock garden, cascades, river walk, rose gardens, heather gardens, seasonal trails and walks. Luncheon and teas. *Spring Season: Sat Feb 26 to mid-March, Adm £3.50 OAPs £3 Chd (10-15) £2.50. Mid-March to mid-June £5, OAPs £4.50 Tues/Weds/Thurs £4 Chd £4. Mid-June to Nov 5 £3.50 OAPs £3 Chd £2.50. All 200 acres open for whole of 2000 season. (Share to NGS on Wed May 3).* www.exbury.co.uk

Fairfield House, Hambledon (Mrs Marion Wake) *Hambledon village. 10m SW of Petersfield. Adjacent car park.* 5 acres, informal garden on chalk with extensive walls, fine mature trees; large collection of shrubs and climbing roses mixed with wide variety of small trees and interesting perennials. Wildflower meadow. Featured in 'A Heritage of Roses' by Hazel Le Rougetel, 'The Rose Gardens of England' by Michael Gibson, 'The Latest Country Gardens' by George Plumptre. TEAS. *Adm £2.50 Chd free. Suns April 9, June 25 (2-6). Also private visits welcome anytime by appt; suitable for groups, please* **Tel 01705 632431**

Fernlea, Chilworth (Mr and Mrs P G Philip) *From Winchester on M3 take exit 14 to Southampton A33 at roundabout follow A27 to Romsey and Chilworth at Clump Inn turn L follow Manor Rd into Chilworth. Dr over motorway bridge turn R. Fernlea last house on L.* 15 acres reclaimed woodland garden now established with naturalised spring plants followed by lilies. Woodland walks, also many Mediterranean plants in informal planting, formal beds around house (not open) and newly created kitchen garden. Seasonal produce and plants for sale. Picnics welcome. TEAS. *Adm £2 Chd free (ACNO to Children's Society). Suns March 26, April 23, Aug 13 (12-5)*

Flintstones, Durley (June & Bill Butler) *Sciviers Lane. From M3 junction 11 follow signs for Marwell Zoo. From B2177 turn R opp Woodman Inn. From M27 junction 7 follow signs for Fair Oak then Durley, turn L at Robin Hood public house.* ¾ acre designed and developed entirely by owners in 7yrs. Plantswoman's garden densely planted, on clay, providing a pleasing tapestry effect of texture and colour. TEAS.

Adm £1.50 Chd free. Sun, Mon June 4, 5 (2-6). Open by appt please **Tel 01489 860880**

Forde's Cottage, Oakshott (Miss L and Dr J Edwards) *Hawkley. 5m N of Petersfield. At only roundabout on A3 turn S on B3006 towards Liss. In 0.6m at Spread Eagle public house turn R, signed Hawkley. After 1.7m at top of steep hill turn L, signed Colemore. Cross Hawkley Green then down hill for 0.6m. Turn L, signed Oakshott. Entrance 200yds on L.* 2 acres with excellent views. Organic garden encouraging wildlife and predators. Walled garden, cottage plantings, peat banks, alpine beds, old roses, herbaceous, fruit, vegetables. More than 2000 labelled varieties. TEAS. *Adm £1.50 Chd 50p. Suns May 21, July 2 (2-6). Private groups welcome, please* **Tel 01730 827 330**

Forest Edge, Andover (Mr & Mrs David Beeson) *On B3400 Andover to Whitchurch rd. Park on rd edge.* 1 acre conservationist's garden. Surrounding the bungalow is a traditional garden with herbaceous plants and shrubs. Wildflower and buttercup lawn. Beyond is the experimental wildlife garden with semi-natural spring and summer meadows rich in native plant species. Wild pond with frogs, newts and dragonflies. Clouds of butterflies some years. A different kind of garden. Featured in two books and Amateur Gardening magazine. *£1.50 Chd free (ACNO to Hampshire Wildlife Trust). Sats, Suns June 3, 4, July 29, 30 (2-6)* www.forest-edge.freeserve.co.uk

The Forge, Martin (Mr and Mrs P J Lockwood) *From Fordingbridge take rd to Damerham turn R at signpost Martin 3m. Garden on LH-side just past green. Parking at church opp village hall.* Situated at foot of Martin Down in ½ acre informal cottage-style garden on chalk, in four sections with fruit and vegetables and small orchard. Much newish planting of roses and clematis plus pond and unusual seating. Teas at village hall. *Adm £1.50 Chd free. Sat, Sun June 10, 11 (2-6)*

Fritham Lodge, Lyndhurst (Mr & Mrs Christopher Powell) *Fritham. 3m NW of M27 junction 1 Cadnam. Follow signs to Fritham. Parking in field.* Set in heart of New Forest in 18 acres; with 1-acre old walled garden round Grade II listed C17 house (not open) originally one of Charles II hunting lodges. Parterre of old roses, potager with wide variety of vegetables, herbs and fruit trees, pergola, herbaceous and blue and white mixed borders, ponds, walk across hay meadows to woodland and stream, with ponies, donkeys, ducks and rare breed hens. TEAS. *Adm £2 Chd free. Sun June 25 (2-5)*

Froyle Cottage Gardens, nr Alton *Access to Lower Froyle from A31 between Alton and Farnham, at Bentley. Follow signs from Lower Froyle to Upper Froyle.* 'The village of Saints'. Teas in village hall at Lower Froyle. *Combined adm £2.50 Chd free. Sat, Sun June 3, 4 (2-6)*

Bramlins (Mr & Mrs Blunt) Plants chosen for colour harmony, interesting foliage and seed heads, as owner is a nationally known flower arranger. Also productive fruit and vegetable section

NEW **The Cottage, Alton** (Mr & Mrs Carr) Not only plants but a collection of animals frequently associated with a true cottage garden

Oklahoma (Mr & Mrs Figgins) Real English garden with foreign sounding name. Recycled items used to make garden structures. Three well stocked greenhouses. Productive vegetable garden and fruit cage. Featured on TV programme 'Grass Roots' *Private group visits welcome, please* **Tel 01420 22220**

The Old School (Mr & Mrs Bulpitt) Moved in after the Old School was converted into a house 10yrs ago. The garden took 3yrs to landscape and now contains maturing shrubs, roses and perennials

Treetops (Mr & Mrs J Cresswell) Medium-sized garden richly planted with many unusual plants. Herbaceous borders, shrubs and pond

Walbury (Mr & Mrs Milam) Real cottage garden atmosphere. Former vegetable area converted to flower garden with formal design incorporating colour co-ordinated beds. Some fruit and vegetables

● **Furzey Gardens, Minstead** (Furzey Gardens Charitable Trust) *8m SW of Southampton. 1½m SW of A31/M27 junction; 3½m NW of Lyndhurst.* 8-acre informal shrub garden; collections of azaleas, rhododendrons and heathers; lake; fernery; summer and winter flowering trees and shrubs. Restored C16 cottage (not open). Will Selwood Galleries (limited opening in winter) Refreshments. *Adm £3 OAPs £2.50 Chd £1.50 Families £8 March to Oct. £1.50 OAPs £1 Chd 50p Families £3 winter (ACNO to Minstead Training Project and other charities). Daily except Christmas (10-5; dusk in winter)* **Tel 01703 812464**

Garden Cottage, Hayling Island (Mr & Mrs Norman Vaughan) *From Beachlands on seafront, turn R, then 3rd turning on R into Staunton Avenue, then 1st L. Parking in drive. Police dispensation for rd parking.* ⅓ acre ornamental garden with variety of conifers. Interesting trees and shrubs; secret garden; water garden; old roses; fine lawns. Thatched summerhouse and well. Prize-winning garden featured in Amateur Gardening magazine. Small painting exhibition. TEAS. *Adm £1. Sat, Sun May 13, 14 (11-5)*

Greenfingers, Milton (St James's Hospital) *Locks Way. From A27 or M27 take A2030 into Portsmouth, at t-lights rd curves R. Continue to Velder Ave until roundabout. Take L turn into Milton Rd (A288) hospital is signposted at top of Locksway Rd 8th rd from roundabout. Greenfingers Horticulture Training Therapy centre is signposted in hospital grounds.* Approx ⅔ acre. Display beds of all kinds, incl vegetables, nature and ornamental ponds, polytunnels and greenhouses. TEA. *Adm £1 Chd free. Suns May 14, July 9 (11-5)*

Hambledon House, Hambledon (Capt & Mrs David Hart Dyke) *8m SW of Petersfield and 5m NW of Waterlooville. In village centre.* 2 acres partly walled plantsman's garden. Large borders filled with wide variety of unusual shrubs and plants. Hidden, secluded areas reveal surprise views of garden and village rooftops. TEAS. *Adm £2 Chd free. Bank Hol Mon May 1, Sun, Mon May 21, 22, July 16, 17, Sept 10, 11, Weds June 7, July 5 (2-6); also private visits and groups welcome, please* **Tel 01705 632380**

● **The Sir Harold Hillier Gardens & Arboretum, Ampfield** *3m NE of Romsey signposted from A3090 and*

A3057. Established 1953, by the late Sir Harold Hillier, 180-acre comprising greatest collection of hardy trees and shrubs in the world. Garden for all seasons, providing stunning range of seasonal colour and interest; 11 National Plant Collections, Champion Trees, largest Winter Garden in Europe. Guided tour available first Sunday each month. Jermyn's House Tearooms and lawns open daily. *Adm April to Oct £4.25 OAPs £3.75 Chd 5-16 £1, under 5 free; Nov to March £3.25, OAPs £2.75 Chd £1. Discount rate for groups of 10 and above when booked in advance. Open all year except Christmas Bank Holiday. April to Oct, weekdays 10.30-6, weekends and Bank Hols 9.30-6, Nov to March 10.30-dusk*

Hayden Barn Cottage, Warnford ♿✂❀ (Captain & Mrs Broadbent) *From A32 take rd signposted to Clanfield, opp George and Falcon public house. Proceed ¾m until red brick cottage on L. Park in field behind house, not in lane. On Sunday please arrive during 1st half of any hour.* Sloping 1-acre garden on chalk, with brick, flint and sleeper-edged terraced beds. Curving herbaceous and mixed borders, shrubberies and many rock plants. Good spring and early summer colour set off by well maintained lawns and hedging. Different levels give delightful surprises and vistas. Vegetable garden. No coaches. TEAS May 14 only. *Adm £2 Chd free. Suns March 19, April 9, May 14, Wed April 26 (1-5.15)*

Hayling Island Gardens *From A27 Havant/Hayling Island roundabout, travel S for 2m, turn R into West Lane and continue for 1m.* TEAS. *Combined adm £2.50 Chd free. Sat, Sun May 27, 28 (11-5)*

Broomhill ♿✂❀ (Mrs Ann Legge) *Entrance on L.* 2 acres with mature trees, shrubs rhododendrons and herbaceous borders surrounding croquet lawn. Two wildlife ponds and rockeries. Vegetable plot, copse with wild orchids. *(ACNO to National Asthma Campaign).*

Littlewood ♿❀ (Mr & Mrs Steven Schrier) *163 West Lane. Littlewood is on R in a wood, opp Broomhill.* 2½-acre woodland garden protected from sea winds by multi-barrier hedge. Woodland walk and access to Hayling Billy harbour trail. Rhododendrons, azaleas, camellias and many other shrubs. Features include pond, bog garden watered from roof of conservatory, house plants. 'Tree' house in woods and propagating greenhouse. New for millennium - summerhouse, arbor and 'mini barn'. Picnickers welcome. Easy access for elderly and wheelchair bound. Dogs on leads.

Heathlands, Locks Heath ♿❀ (Dr & Mrs John Burwell) *47 Locks Rd. Locks Rd runs due S from Park Gate into Locks Heath. No 47 is 1m down on RH-side [Map Ref 513.069].* 1 acre designed and developed by owner since 1967. Yr-round interest against background of evergreens and mature trees. Spring bulbs, rhododendrons, paulownias, cyclamen, ferns and many less usual plants. Topiary peacock, winning feature in Hillier's garden competition 1998, small herbaceous border, scree and moss beds. National Collection of Japanese anemones. TEAS. *Adm £1.50 Chd free. Suns March 19, May 14 (2-5.30)*

The Hedges, Timsbury ♿✂❀ (Betty & Tony Rackham) *Proceed 2½m N of Romsey on A3057 Stockbridge Rd to middle of Timsbury, turn R towards Michelmersh along New Rd. Chapel Lane is gravel track 400yds along New Rd on R. 1st bungalow on R along lane.* 2 acres. Botanists' garden of gravel beds, ponds, formal beds and many natural areas with varied plant collection incl many oenothera species and unusual perennials. Meadow and woodland areas are managed to encourage wild flowers especially prolific orchids. Interesting vegetable garden. Photographic exhibition. TEAS. *Adm £1.50 Chd free. Suns June 11, July 9, Weds June 14, July 5 (2-5.30)*

Hill House, Old Alresford ♿ (Major & Mrs W F Richardson) *From Alresford 1m along B3046 towards Basingstoke, then R by church.* 2 acres with large old-fashioned herbaceous border, established in 1938, and shrub beds set around large lawn; kitchen garden. TEAS. *Adm £1.50 Chd free. Sun, Tue Aug 6, 8 (1.30-5)*

▲ **Hinton Ampner, Alresford** ♿✂ (The National Trust) *S on Petersfield to Winchester rd A272. 1m W of Bramdean village.* 12 acre; C20 shrub garden designed by Ralph Dutton. Strong architectural elements using yew and box topiary; spectacular views. Bold effects using simple plants, restrained and dramatic bedding. Orchard with spring wildflowers and bulbs within formal box hedges; magnolia and philadelphus walks. Dell garden made from chalk pit. Shrub rose border dating from 1950s. Chosen for Alan Titchmarsh's Favourite Gardens. TEAS. *Adm £3.50 Chd £1.75. For NGS Suns April 16, June 25, Sat, Sun Sept 9, 10 (1.30-5)*

NEW **Hollington Herb Garden, Woolton Hill** ♿✂❀ (Simon and Judith Hopkinson) *Off A343 Newbury to Andover rd, 5m S of Newbury. 1m from main rd, adjacent to Hollington House Hotel.* Walled herb garden in 13 areas. Knot gardens using many different hedging plants incl varieties of box, santolina, berberis, euonymous and lavender. Pergola, wall climbers, roses, topiary, bubble fountains and a feast of culinary and aromatic plants. Definitely a garden to give you ideas. TEA. *Adm £2 Chd 50p. Suns July 9, 16 (12-5)* www.herb-garden.co.uk

93 Holly Hill, Bassett ✂❀ (Mrs Myra Burville) *2½m N of Southampton. Leave M3 exit 14. Take avenue towards Southampton. At 1st roundabout, go right around and back up avenue, take 1st L, 1st L again, approx 400m on L.* Award winning owner-designed ⅓-acre with tapestry of evergreens and perennnials in 'rooms'. Unusual water features, streams, fish and wildlife ponds. Bamboo and grass bed. Hidden shade walk. Baskets and many pots with hostas, fuchsias, tender and summer plants. Shown on Grass Roots 1999. Teas and plants in aid of British Diabetic Association. *Adm £1.50 Chd 50p. Sats, Suns June 10, 11, July 15, 16, Aug 12, 13 (2-6). Private visits welcome,* **Tel 02380 767704**

Hordle Walhampton School, Lymington (Hordle Walhampton School Trust Ltd) *1m E of Lymington on Beaulieu rd.* Fine walks around 97 acres of managed woodland, lakes, lawns and formal gardens in grounds of C18 manor house (not open). TEAS. *Adm £2 Chd 50p. Sun May 7 (2-6)*

● **Houghton Lodge, Stockbridge** ♿❀ (Captain M W Busk) *1½m S of Stockbridge A30 on rd to Houghton.* Spacious informal landscape (Grade II*) with fine trees surrounds an C18 cottage ornée overlooking tranquil beauty of R Test. Walled garden, espaliers, greenhouses, herb garden. Serene formal topiary 'peacock garden'. Wildflowers. Children's puffing topiary dragon. Popular tv/film location, as in BBC's David Copperfield. Indoor hydroponicum: learn how to garden without soil, toil or pesticides! Recently featured on 'Grass Roots'. Hydroponicum; gardening without soil or toil! Biological control of greenhouse pests. Tea/coffee in visitor centre. *Adm £3 Chd free, Hydroponicum £2. Daily March 1 to Sept 30. Sat, Sun and Bank Hols (10-5), weekdays (2-5). For NGS Sun, Mon April 16, 17*

Jasmine Lodge, Kempshott ♿ (Mr & Mrs Nigel Murgatroyd) *Jasmine Rd, Basingstoke. From M3, junction 7, follow Basingstoke signs. At Kempshott roundabout turn L into Heather Way, then immed R into Jasmine Rd. Park on rd away from bend.* Front and back gardens each 30′ × 70′. Over 5,000 summer plants in carpet bedding, baskets and containers. Pond. *Adm £1.50 Chd free (ACNO to St Michael's Hospice, Basingstoke). Suns July 23, 30 (11-5)*

53 Ladywood, Eastleigh ✂❀ (Mr & Mrs D Ward) *Leave M3 junction 12. Follow signs to Eastleigh. Turn R at roundabout into Woodside Ave, then 2nd R into Bosville. Ladywood is 5th on R. Park in Bosville.* 45′ × 45′giving ideas for the small garden. Featured in magazines, books and tv. Over 1800 different plants labelled. Rustic fences give vertical space for many clematis and unusual climbers. Special interest in foliage plants, hardy geraniums and pulmonarias. Afternoon TEAS. *Adm £2 Chd 75p. (ACNO to 14th Eastleigh Scout Band). Suns April 30, June 25 (11-5.30). By appt only Tues afternoons April 4 to Aug 29 (no teas), please* **Tel 01703 615389**

Lake House, Northington ❀ (Lord Ashburton) *4m N of Alresford off B3046. Follow English Heritage signs to The Grange, then directions.* 2 large lakes in Candover valley set off by mature woodland with waterfalls, abundant bird life, long landscaped vistas. 1½-acre walled garden, mixed borders, long herbaceous border, rose pergola leading to moon gate. Formal kitchen garden, flowering pots, conservatory and greenhouses. Picnicking by lakes. TEAS. *Adm £3 Chd free (ACNO to Friends of St John's Church, Northington). Suns, Tues June 25, 27, Sept 3, 5 (11-5). Group visits welcome, please* **Tel 01962 734820** (evenings)

60 Lealand Road, Drayton ♿✂❀ (Mr F G Jacob) *2m from Cosham on E side of Portsmouth. Old A27 (Havant Rd) between Cosham and Bedhampton.* Small prize-winning garden created and designed by owner since 1969. Featured in national gardening magazines. Exotic plants with rockery, ponds, dwarf conifers and collection of grasses, cacti and other exotics in greenhouse. TEAS. *Adm £1 Chd free. Suns April 9, July 16, August 20 (11-5). Also private visits welcome, please* **Tel 01705 370030**

Lithend, Crawley ♿✂❀ (Mrs F L Gunner) *5m NW of Winchester off A272 or A3049 Winchester to Stockbridge rd. Parking at top of village nr church.* Small cottage garden. *Combined adm with* **Little Court** *£2.50 Chd free. Sun, Tues May 21, 23*

Little Coopers (Mr & Mrs J K Oldale) *Please telephone for directions.* 10 acres. A guided walk will take you through woodland (bulbs in spring, colours in autumn), rhododendrons, azaleas, many unusual shrubs, water and bog gardens, extensive lawn with conifers, heather, mediterranean, rose and small Japanese gardens. Clive Nicols's photographs of this garden in numerous books and magazines. *Adm £2 Chd free. Private parties and individuals welcome by appt, March to Oct, please* **Tel 01252 872229**

Little Court, Crawley, nr Winchester ♿✂❀ (Prof & Mrs A R Elkington) *5m NW of Winchester off A272 or B3049 in Crawley village; 300yds from either village pond or church.* 1½ acre, walled Victorian country garden in tranquil setting. Prolific spring bulbs, climbers and perennials in harmonious colours and naturalistic style. Walled kitchen garden. Fine views. Bantams and geese. Featured in The English Garden 1998 and Red Magazine 1999. TEAS Suns only. *Adm £2. (Combined adm with* **Crawley Gardens** *£2.50). Suns, Mons, Tues Feb 20, 21, 22, Sun, Tues March 12, 14, Sun, Mon April 16, 17 (with* **Crawley Gardens***), Sun, Tues Apr 30, May 2, Sun, Tues May 21, 23 (with* **Lithend***), Sun, Mon Aug 13, 14 (2-5.30);* **2001** *Sun, Mon, Tues Feb 18, 19, 20. Group visits welcome, please* **Tel 01962 776365** e-mail: elkslc@compuserve.com

Longparish Gardens, Andover ✂ *2m E of Andover off A303. To village centre on B3048.* TEAS. *Combined adm £3 Chd free. Sun June 4 (2-6)*

> **Longmead House** ❀ (Mr & Mrs J H Ellicock) 2½ acre organic garden. Large, hedged vegetable garden with deep beds, polytunnel, fruit cage and composting display. Fishpond, wildlife, pond. Wildflower meadow. Herbaceous and shrub borders. Conservatory
>
> NEW **Lower Mill** (Mr & Mrs A W Dinesen) Large water garden adjacent to R Test. Substantial new shrub planting and design, since garden was last open

■ **Longstock Park Gardens, nr Stockbridge** ♿✂❀ (Leckford Estate Ltd; part of John Lewis Partnership) *3m N. From A30 turn N on to A3057; follow signs to Longstock.* Famous water garden with extensive collection of aquatic and bog plants set in 7 acres of woodland with rhododendrons and azaleas. A walk through park leads to National Collection of Buddleia and Clematis viticella, arboretum, herbaceous border and nursery. Featured in TV programmes and gardening books. Teas at nursery in aid of local churches. *Adm £3 Chd 50p. 1st and 3rd Sunday in month April to Sept. For NGS Sun June 18 (2-5)*

■ **Longthatch, Warnford** ♿✂❀ (Peter & Vera Short) *Lippen Lane. 1m S of West Meon on A32, turn R from N or L from S at George and Falcon public house. After 100yds turn R at T-junction, continue for ¼m; thatched C17 house on R. Parking opp.* 3½ acres, plantsman's garden on R Meon. Rare trees and shrubs. Part of National Collection of Helleborus. Fine lawns, herbaceous borders, island beds, alpine and bog gardens. Spring-fed ponds, woodland area with hellebores, primulas and shade-loving plants. Featured in Country Homes and Interiors, 1998, The Daily Mail and Saga magazine. TEAS (not March). *Adm £2 Chd free. Every Weds March 1 to July 26 (10-5). For NGS Suns March 5, 12, 19, April 16; Sun, Bank Hol Mon May 28, 29; Suns June 11, July 9 (2-5). Private visits by societies and individuals welcome, please* **Tel 01730 829285**

● **Macpennys Woodland Garden & Nurseries, Bransgore** ❀ (Mr & Mrs T M Lowndes) *154 Burley Road. Mid-way between Christchurch and Burley. From Christchurch via A35, turn L at Cat and Fiddle; at Xrds by The Crown, Bransgore turn R and proceed ¼m. From A31 (travelling towards Bournemouth) L at Picket Post, signed Burley, then R at Burley Cross. Garden on L after 2m.* 12 acres; 4-acre gravel pit converted into woodland garden; many unusual plants. Large selection shrubs and herbaceous plants available. *Collecting box. Daily except Dec 25 & 26 and Jan 1 (Mons to Sats 9-5; Suns 2-5)*

Mandelieu, Picket Piece ✂❀ (Jenny & Roger Bateman) *Approx 2m NE of Andover. From A303 exit onto A3093, at first roundabout take first exit, then follow directions to Picket Piece. In centre of village, opp Andover Patio Centre.* ½ acre, owner-designed shrub and herbaceous garden with carefully chosen plants for yr-round texture and colour. Summerhouse and secret sitting places with postage-stamp vegetable garden and many other interesting features. Fish and wildlife ponds. TEA. *Adm £1.50 Chd 50p. Suns, Mons July 2, 3, July 30, 31 (2-5.30)*

Manor Lodge, Crawley, nr Winchester ♿✂❀ (Mr & Mrs K Wren) *5m NW of Winchester off A272 or B3049 Winchester to Stockbridge rd. Park outside drive near to village pond.* 5 acre, all-season walled garden and planted drive. Interesting shrubs. Extensive lawns. Hellebore collection, old and new shrub and climbing roses. Many clematis, scented flowers a speciality. Good autumn colour and hips. Lily pond, thatched summerhouse, ancient walnut tree. *Adm £2 Chd free. (Combined adm with* **Little Court** *£2.50). Sun, Mon April 16, 17 with* **Crawley Gardens**, *Sun, Mon Sept 3, 4. Private visits welcome in summer months.*
Tel 01962 776372

▲ **March End, Sherfield English** ♿✂❀ (Dr David & Mrs Joan Thomas) *5m W of Romsey on A27 Salisbury rd, at Xrds, turn N into Branches Lane, 1st R Doctor's Hill, 1st house on R.* 1-acre totally organic garden on free-draining, acid sandy soil surrounding C16 thatched cottage (not open). Large vegetable garden of 4 ft beds with different mulches and green manures. S-facing garden wall with kiwi, peach, fig and grape under covered walk. Insect-attractant flowers. TEA. *Adm £1.50 Chd 50p (ACNO to the Romsey Opportunity Group). For NGS Mon June 19, Sun, Mon June 25, 26 (2-6). Private visits welcome, please* **Tel 01794 340255**

Martyr Worthy Gardens ♿ *Mid-way between Winchester and Alresford on B3047. Gardens joined by Pilgrims Way through Itchen Valley, approx ½m.* Teas at, and in aid of, village hall. *Adm £2 each Chilland and Manor House, Cygnet House £1 Chd free. Sun July 9 (2-6)*

Chilland ♿ (Mr & Mrs J Impey) see main entry

NEW **Cygnet House** ♿ (Mr & Mrs Shane Chichester) Still developing garden of 1½ acres with roses, shrubs and interesting perennials. Lovely views over valley

Manor House, Martyr Worthy (Cdr & Mrs Miles Rivett-Carnac) Large garden, roses, mixed borders, lawns, shrubs and fine trees, next to C12 church

Marycourt, Odiham ♿✂ (Mr & Mrs M Conville) *2m S of Hartley Wintney on A30; M3 exit 5. In Odiham High St.* 1 acre with paddocks; old roses, shrubs, ramblers dripping from trees. Silver/pink border; long, colourful herbaceous borders; hostas and delphiniums. Dry stone wall with alpines. Grade II* house (not open). *Adm £2 Chd free. Suns June 25, July 2 (2-6); Wed July 5 (all day). Group visits also welcome, please* **Tel 01256 702100**

NEW **Mattingley Green Cottage, Mattingley** ♿✂❀ (Mr & Mrs M Edwards) *2½m N of Hook on B3349 Reading rd. Take rd to Mattingley Church. Parking at church.* 1½ acre, cottage garden, owner-maintained. Large herbaceous and shrub borders, lavender, roses and cosmos. Views from paddock to R Whitewater. Thatched C14 cottage (not open) overlooking village green and church. TEAS. *Adm £2 Chd free. (ACNO to Samantha Dickson Research Trust). Sun July 2 (2-5.30)*

Maurys Mount, West Wellow ♿❀ (Dr & Mrs P Burrows) *Slab Lane. On A36 mid-way between Salisbury and Southampton. Slab Lane is a turning between roundabout and Red Rover Inn on A36 in West Wellow.* Edwardian-style garden created over 3 generations. 10-acre, mature woodland incl 300-yr-old oak; paddocks, young arboretum, conservatory, formal herb and kitchen gardens. Woodland walk with pond, orchard and wildflower meadow. Jacob sheep, ducks, geese, hens and horses. TEAS in aid of Imperial Cancer Research Fund. *Adm £2 Chd 50p. Sun June 4 (2-5)*

Meon Orchard, Kingsmead ♿❀ (Doug & Linda Smith) *From Wickham take A32 N for 1½m. Turn L at Roebuck Inn. Continue ½m.* All yr 1½-acre garden designed and constructed by current owners over 12yrs. Round lawns and grass paths separate structural plantings of half-hardy and tender perennials incl bananas, cannas and daturas, unusual shrubs and trees incl National Collection of Eucalyptus. Wide range of interesting planters, sizeable palms and other exotics. Pond and water features. Featured in local press. Gardeners available to answer questions. TEA. *Adm £2 Chd 50p. Suns June 4, July 30, Sept 3 (2-6). Major plant sale September 3, (Share to NCCPG). Group visits welcome, please* **Tel or Fax 01329 833253**

Merdon Manor, Hursley ♿✂❀ (Mr & Mrs J C Smith) *SW of Winchester. From A3090 Winchester to Romsey rd, turn R at Standon onto rd to Slackstead; proceed 1½m. Ample car park.* 5 acres with panoramic views; herbaceous and rose borders; fruit-bearing lemon trees; small secret walled water garden as seen on tv. Ha-ha and sheep. TEAS. *Adm £2 Chd 25p. Sun July 16 (2-6); also private visits welcome, please* **Tel 01962 775215 or 775281**

Merebimur, Mockbeggar ♿✂❀ (Mr & Mrs C Snelling) *3m N of Ringwood on A338, turn E to Mockbeggar at The Old Beams Inn. Turn L at next small Xrds then next L into New Rd. Limited parking at garden; park on verge opp end of New Rd, then short walk.* Owner maintained, ½ acre garden intensively planted with original combinations of shrubs and herbaceous plants with good foliage effects. Also pond, pergola, lawns and vegetables. TEAS. *Adm £1.50 Chd free. Sat, Sun July 22, 23, Wed July 26 (2-5.30). Private visits welcome, please* **Tel 01425 473116**

Merrie Cottage, Woodgreen ♿✂❀ (Mr & Mrs C K Thornton) *3m N of Fordingbridge on A338 turn E to Woodgreen. Fork R at PO towards Godshill. Entrance 200 yds on L. Limited parking for disabled or park on common and walk down footpath.* Irregular, sloping shape offers vistas with profusion of iris and primulas in May and June, followed by seed-grown lilies and wide variety of moisture lovers. No hard landscape or colour theme but interesting all year. TEAS (Sun) Teas (Mon at Applecroft). TEAS on private visits for Treloar Trust. *Adm £2 Chd free. Sun, Mon June 11, 12 (2-6). Private visits welcome, please* **Tel 01725 512273**

Mill Court, Binsted ❀ (The Hon Mrs T. M. Ogilvie Thompson) *2m E of Alton on A31, signpost opp Hen and Chicken public house.* 24 acres of woodland and river walk; 4-acre garden. Walled herbaceous border, pergola, azaleas and bulbs. Mixed shrubbery, vegetable garden and greenhouses. Surrounds Tudor barn (not open). TEA. *Adm £2 Chd free. Fri, Sat May 19, 20, Sun, Wed Sept 24, 27 (2-6)*

Mittens, Mapledurwell ✂ (Mr & Mrs David Hooper) *[OS map ref 685.510]. 3½m E of Basingstoke. R off A30 at Hatch, signed Mapledurwell. Over M3 bridge take 2nd R, Frog Lane, to Xrds at pond. 300yds up rd to Tunworth.* 1½ acres. Created from farmyard and field in conservation area. Spring bulbs, red and yellow borders, children's garden with rill and ivy house, wild garden, pergola and series of rooms with shrubs and perennials, separated by hedges. TEAS. *Adm £2 Chd 50p (ACNO to St Mary's Church). Suns March 26, Sept 3 (2-6). Private visits by appt, please* **Tel 01256 321 838**

Monxton Gardens ♿✂❀ *3m W of Andover, between A303 and A343; parking at Field House.* TEAS at village hall in aid of St Mary's Church, Monxton. *Combined adm £2.50 Chd free. Sun, Bank Hol Mon May 28, 29 (2-5.30)*

> **Field House** (Pratt Family) 2 acres created by owners with air of tranquillity, winding paths, 2 ponds with frogs, herbaceous borders, foliage and kitchen garden, car park
>
> **Hutchens Cottage** (Mr & Mrs R A Crick) ¾ acre cottage garden; old roses, clematis, shrubs, mature trees, small orchard; mixed thyme patch and kitchen garden
>
> **White Gables** (Mr & Mrs D Eaglesham) Cottage style garden of ⅓ acre, leading down to Pill Hill Brook. Interesting shrubs, old roses and herbaceous plants

Moth House, Brown Candover (Mrs Melissa Perkins) *Village is on B3046 5m N of Alresford. Garden just past village green on L.* 2 acres; gold and silver garden, herbaceous borders and shrub walk. Speciality roses. Cream TEAS. *Adm £2 Chd free. Sun July 2 (11-5.30)*

▲ Mottisfont Abbey & Garden, Romsey ♿✂❀ (The National Trust) *4½m NW of Romsey. From A3057 Romsey to Stockbridge turn W at sign to Mottisfont. 4 wheelchairs and battery car service available at garden.* 30 acres; originally C12 priory, landscaped grounds with lawns bordering R Test. Magnificent trees, remarkable ancient spring pre-dating priory, walled garden contains NT's famous collection of old-fashioned roses. Lunch and tea available in Abbey. *Adm £5 Chd £2.50. For NGS Sun June 25 (11-8.30), last adm 7.30 pm, Abbey (1-5) last adm 4.30*

Moundsmere Manor, Preston Candover ♿✂ (Mr & Mrs Andreae) *6m S of Basingstoke on B3046. Drive gates on L just after Preston Candover sign.* Authentic Edwardian garden designed by Reginald Blomfield incl period greenhouse in full use. Formal rose garden, long herbaceous borders, unusual mature specimen trees and superb views over Candover Valley. *Adm £2 Chd £1. Sun July 2 (2-5). Coaches by appt.*

Nikendi, Swanmore ❀ (Phil Jeffs) *Swanmore is SE of Bishop's Waltham off B2177. From church, New Rd runs SW. Broad Lane is off New Rd 300 yds from church. Garden at 5th house on R.* Small, plantsman's garden. Wide variety of shrubs, trees and perennials; emphasis on plants with more than one season of interest. Small pond. *Adm £1.50 Chd 50p. Suns March 19, May 14, June 11, Sept 17, Oct 15 (1-dusk) Mon June 12 (4-dusk)*

Oakdene, Sandleheath ♿✂❀ (Mr & Mrs C Stanford) *Just into Sandleheath, 1m from Fordingbridge on RH-side, immediately beyond small church.* Nearly 2 acres with over 400 roses of all types incl rambler covered long pergola, white and red herbaceous beds, orchard with free-range hens, organic kitchen garden with apple and pear arches, colourful flower borders and greenhouses, dovecotes with resident doves. Cream TEAS in aid of Friends of Fordingbridge Hospital. *Adm £2 Chd free. Sun, Tues June 18, 20 (2-5.30). Private visits welcome, please* **Tel 01425 652133**

Oakley Manor, Oakley ♿✂❀ (Mr & Mrs R Priestley) *Rectory Rd. 5m W of Basingstoke. From B3400 Basingstoke to Whitchurch rd turn L into Station Rd and follow signs. Parking at Manor.* Large 5-acre garden surrounded by open farmland with comprehensive planting incl conservation area. Mature trees, shrubs, perennials and annuals. Thatched Wendy House. TEA. *Adm £2 Chd free. Sun Aug 6 (2-5.30)*

The Old House, Silchester ♿❀ (Mr & Mrs M Jurgens) *Bramley Rd, next to Roman Museum.* Queen Anne rectory (not open) with large garden dating from 1920s. Pergola, dell, ponds, spring bulbs, woodland carpeted with bluebells, well-labelled collection of rhododendrons, camellias, azaleas, specimen trees and shrubs; easy walk to Roman town and mediaeval church. Featured in 'The English Garden', March 1999. TEAS in aid of St Mary the Virgin Church, Silchester. *Adm £2 Chd 50p. Suns April 9, 30, May 14, 21 (2-6). Private parties welcome March to June, please* **Tel 01189 700240**

Old Meadows, Silchester ♿✂❀ (Dr & Mrs J M Fowler) *Off A340 between Reading and Basingstoke. 1m S of Silchester on rd to Bramley, signed at Xrds.* 5 acres incl unploughed, wildflower meadow. Walled garden with diverse plants and vegetables, bed of American annuals. Rare geese, peacocks and hens. Carpets of old-fashioned spring bulbs. Hand-made living willow/hazel seats and arches. Three species of wild orchid in lawn. TEAS. *Adm £2 Chd free (ACNO to Basingstoke North Hampshire Medical Fund). Sun June 18, July 16, Wed Sept 20 (2-6). Private visits welcome, please* **Tel 01256 881450**

The Old Rectory, West Tytherley (Mr & Mrs Charles Vincent) *10m E of Salisbury; 10m NW of Romsey, from A30 4½m W of Stockbridge, take turn signed W Tytherley/Norman Court. In village take 1st R turn signed Home Stud.* Queen Anne grade II listed house (not open). Lake and rockery, waterfall with bridges, gazebo, rope pergola walk. Traditional walled kitchen garden. *Adm £2.50 Chd 50p (ACNO to Jonathan Conville Memorial Trust). Sun, Mon June 25, 26 (2-6)*

Paddocks Way, Brook ♿✗ (Mr & Mrs Ken Elcock) *1m W from junction 1 of M27. From B3079 turn L into Canterton Manor Drive before Green Dragon.* Country garden of ¾ acre. Mixed borders and island beds containing spring bulbs, herbaceous perennials, grasses and shrubs grown for flower and foliage effect. Kitchen garden with vegetables, fruit, greenhouse and frames. TEAS. *Adm £2 Chd 50p. Sun May 21 (2-5.30)*

Potters Cot, Ringwood ✗❀ (Mr & Mrs M G Smith) *Hightown Hill. From Southampton, take A31 past Picket Post, then 1st L after two cattle grids. From Bournemouth follow signs to Picket Post, then underpass to Hightown, take 1st L.* 2½ acres, on acid soil with extensive views. Specimen bulbs, lilies, roses, annuals, herbaceous borders and flowering shrubs. 9-yr-old arboretum planted for foliage effect. Small working kitchen garden. Extensive views. TEAS. *Adm £2 Chd £1. Sats, Suns May 20, 21, July 15, 16 (2-6)*

Pylewell Park, Lymington ♿ (Lord Teynham) *2½m E beyond IOW car ferry.* Large garden of botanical interest; fine trees, flowering shrubs, rhododendrons, lake and woodland garden. *Adm £2.50 Chd 50p (ACNO to Wessex Regional Medical Oncology Unit). Suns May 14, 21 (2-5.30). Private visits welcome, please* **Tel 01590 673010**

Robins Return, Tiptoe ♿✗❀ (Marjorie & John Ingrem) *2m NE of New Milton. Take B3055, at Xrds by Tiptoe Church. Car parking.* ⅔ acre; 100' wisteria pergola; box edgings; ornamental pool and rock garden; fern garden. Wall with trained fruit trees, flowering shrubs, greenhouses and organic kitchen garden. TEA (Suns only). *Adm £1.50 Chd free (ACNO to The Evangelical Aid Relief (Tear Fund). Suns May 21, June 25, July 23, Weds May 24, June 28, July 26 (2-5)*

Romsey Gardens ✗ *Centre of Romsey nr Abbey. Combined adm £2 Chd free. Sun, Bank Hol Mon May 28, 29 (11-5.30)*

- **King John's Garden** (Friends of King John's and Test Valley Council) Historic garden planted with material available up to 1700, many herbs. Listed C13 house (open Mon only). TEAS.
- **4 Mill Lane** ❀ (Miss J Flindall) Small, long floriferous town garden

Rose Cottage, Kingsley Common ✗❀ (Ian & Julia Elliot) *On B3004, 5m E of Alton. Park on green below church or in public house car park. 150yds down track on R.* Sheltered ½ acre garden with distinctive areas. Cottage-style herbaceous borders, range of conifers and trees, ornamental pond and rockery, rose garden, grass and bamboo feature, productive kitchen garden and large attractive patio with tubs and baskets. New gravel garden. TEAS. *Adm £1.50 Chd free (ACNO to All Saints Church). Sun, Mon June 4, 5 Aug 6, 7 (2-6)*

Rotherfield Park, East Tisted ✗ (Sir James & Lady Scott) *4m S of Alton on A32.* Picturesque 12-acre garden, many shrubs and trees proposed by Norah Lindsay of Sutton Courtenay Manor in 1928. Walled garden with trained fruit trees, hazel maze and ice house. Picnic in park from noon. TEAS in aid of nominated local charities. *Adm £2 Chd £1. Sun Sept 10 (2-5)*

Rotherwick Gardens, Hook ♿❀ *2½m N of Hook. M3 exit 5 or M4 exit 11 via B3349* TEAS *Adm £2 Chd free (ACNO to Whitewater School) Sun July 9 (2-6)*

- **The Ricks** (Mr J J Morris) 1 acre with herbaceous borders, shrubs and vegetables
- **Whitewater School** Chequerboard garden and nature pond developed as a learning resource
- **1 Wogsbarne Cottages** (Mr & Mrs Whistler) Cottage garden with flowers, vegetables and ornamental pond

Rowans Wood, Ampfield ♿✗❀ (Mrs D C Rowan) *Straight Mile, on A3090 (S side) (old A31); 2m E of Romsey. 2m W of Potters Heron Hotel. Parking on service rd.* Woodland garden developed since 1962 and planted for yr-round interest. Camellias, rhododendrons, flowering trees, spring bulbs followed by azaleas, hostas and other perennials. TEAS. *Adm £2 Chd free (ACNO to Winchester & Romsey Branch RSPCA). Good Fri, Easter Sun, Mon April 21, 23, 24 (2-5), Suns May 7, 21 (2-6).* **Evening Openings** *Wed May 17 & Sat May 27 (5-8.30) Wine. Parties welcome, mid-April to early June, please* **Tel 01794 513072**

12 Rozelle Close, Littleton ✗ (Mr & Mrs Tom Hyatt) *Turn E off Winchester to Stockbridge Rd for Littleton. Rozelle Close is near Running Horse public house.* ⅓ acre spectacular display of 10,000 bedding plants; tubs, troughs and hanging baskets; 2 ponds; 3 greenhouses; vegetables. *Donations. Sats, Suns July 15, 16, 29, 30 (9.30-5.30). By appt in July, please* **Tel 01962 880 662**

Rumsey Gardens, Clanfield ♿✗ (Mr and Mrs N R Giles) *117 Drift Rd. 6m S of Petersfield. Turn off A3 N of Horndean, signed Clanfield.* Created from cornfield since 1956 in poor, shallow, chalk soil. Acid beds constructed enabling lime-hating shrubs and plants to be grown. Rock garden, heather beds, pools and bog gardens. National Collection of Cotoneasters. TROBI/NCCPG. *Adm £1.50 Chd 50p. Sun May 14 (11-5). Private visits by societies welcome, please* **Tel 01705 593367**

Selborne, East Worldham ♿✗❀ (Mr & Mrs Brian Jones) *On B3004, 2m SE of Alton, at edge of village at Alton end. Parking opp in public house car park.* ½ acre mature garden with old established orchard of named varieties. Mixed borders featuring many hardy geraniums, alliums, euphorbias and herbaceous plants designed for yr-round effect. Shrubbery, vegetable and soft fruit garden with greenhouse feature and small conservatory. TEAS. *Adm £1.50 Chd free (ACNO to Tafara Mission, Zimbabwe). Sun Aug 6, 7 (2-6)*

Shalden Park House (Mr & Mrs Michael Campbell) *Take B3349 from either Alton or M3 junction 5. Turn W at Xrds by The Golden Pot public house marked Herriard, Lasham, Shalden. Garden is ¼m on L.* 4-acre woodland garden with extensive views; pond with duckhouse, walled kitchen garden, herbaceous border and beds of annuals. Glasshouses. Embryonic arboretum with wildflower walk. Lunchtime picnics welcome. TEAS. *Adm £1.50 Chd free (ACNO to The Red Cross). Suns April 30 (2-5)*

South End House, Lymington (Mr & Mrs Peter Watson) *At town centre, turn S opp St Thomas Church 70yds, or park behind Waitrose and use walkway.* Walled town garden to Queen Anne house (not open). ¼ acre, architecturally designed as philosophers' garden. Pergolas, trellises and colonnade attractively planted with vines, clematis, wisteria and roses combine with sculpted awnings to form 'outdoor rooms', enhanced by fountains, music and 400 lights. Enjoy an exceptional, sparkling, Millennium evening with champagne, bucks fizz, coffee and biscuits. *Adm £2.* **Evening Opening** *Sat July 29 (6-10 pm)*

Sowley House, Sowley (Mr & Mrs O van der Vorm) *At Lymington follow signs to IOW ferry. Pass ferry and continue E on rd nearest to Solent for 3m until Sowley pond on L. Sowley House is opp.* Beautiful setting overlooking Solent and IO W; 19 acres at high tide and 52 acres at low tide. Stream walk, wild garden with drifts of primroses and violets. Helleborus collection, woodland and walled herb garden with varied planting; roses, clematis. TEA. *Adm £2.50 Chd free. Sun March 19 (2-5). Private visits welcome, March to June (no coaches) please* **Tel 01590 626231**

● **Spinners, Boldre** (Diana & Peter Chappell) *Signed off A337 Brockenhurst to Lymington rd. (Do not take sign to Boldre Church).* Azaleas, rhododendrons, magnolias, hydrangeas and maples interplanted with wide range of plants and bulbs. Subject of many press articles and tv programmes. Nursery for less common and rare trees, shrubs and plants visited by people from all over the world. *Adm £1.50 Chd under 6 free. Fri April 14 then Tues to Sat until Sept 14 (10-5). For NGS May 7 (10-5)*
Tel 01590 673347

Tunworth Old Rectory (The Hon Mrs Julian Berry) *5m SE of Basingstoke. 3m from Basingstoke turn S off A30 at sign to Tunworth.* Garden laid out with yew hedges, enclosing different aspects, double herbaceous border; white garden; ruby wedding garden; pleached hornbeam walk; lime avenue, ornamental pond, interesting trees incl beech-lined walk to church. TEAS. *Adm £2 Chd free (ACNO to All Saints Church Tunworth). Sun July 2 (2-5.30)*

Tylney Hall Hotel, Rotherwick (The Manager) *From M3 exit 5 via A287 and Newnham, M4 exit 11 via B3349 and Rotherwick.* Large garden of 67 acres with extensive woodlands and fine vistas being restored with new planting. Fine avenues of wellingtonias; rhododendrons and azaleas; Italian garden; lakes, large water and rock garden and dry stone walls originally designed with assistance of Gertrude Jekyll. TEA. *Adm £2 Chd free. Suns May 7, June 4, July 16 (10-6)*

Ulvik, Winchester (Mr & Mrs G G Way) *1m N of Winchester. 5th house on L in Harestock Rd off A3049 (old A272).* Long narrow site of ½ acre designed to create interesting shapes and views, incorporating mixed herbaceous borders and shrubberies; secret area; wild section for self-seeding plants; vegetable garden on 4′ bed system; grassed bed, ponds and areas for shade-loving plants. Fun sculptures. Featured in Kitchen Garden Magazine Sept 99. Cold drinks. *Adm £1.50 Chd free. Sat, Sun, Mon July 15, 16, 17 (2-6). Private visits also welcome, please* **Tel 01962 852361**

Upham Gardens *3m NW Bishop's Waltham on B2177, turn R at Woodman's public house. West Hall ¾m on L, Old Rectory next to church. Adm £2 each garden Chd free. Sun June 4, Wed June 7 (2-6)*

The Old Rectory (Mr & Mrs J R Vail) *Beside Norman church.* Approx 1½ acres divided into series of rooms; knot garden, parterre, woodland area and mixed herbaceous borders; vines and roses covering remains of Victorian glasshouse. TEAS on Wed

West Hall (Mr & Mrs Henry Thornton) 5 acres with much new planting, herbaceous borders, rose garden, arboretum, courtyard, landscaped swimming pool and kitchen garden. TEAS on Sun

Valentine Cottage, Newnham (Mr & Mrs P Brown) *Newnham Rd. From Hook follow A30 towards Basingstoke. After approx 1m turn R at Dorchester Arms into Old School Rd, signed Newnham. At end of Old School Rd turn L into Newnham Rd and 200yds on R is car park at village hall. 25yd-walk along Newnham Rd to Valentine Cottage.* Exuberant cottage garden of ⅔ acre, developed over last 8yrs specialising in clematis and roses; laid out into individual smaller gardens. TEAS (not April). *Adm £2 Chd 50p. Suns April 16, May 28, June 25 (2-6). Also private visits welcome, please* **Tel 01256 762049**

▲ **The Vyne, Sherborne St John** (The National Trust) *4m N of Basingstoke. Between Sherborne St John and Bramley. From A340 turn E at NT signs.* 17 acres with extensive lawns, lake, fine trees, herbaceous border and Edwardian summerhouse garden. Garden tour starting at 2pm. Gardeners available to answer questions. TEAS. *Adm £3 Chd £1.50 under 5s free. For NGS Sun June 11 (12.30-5.30).* **Evening Opening** *Wed June 28 (6.30-9.30 grounds only). Bring a picnic and take advantage of peaceful, summer evening. Staff available to answer questions. For details, please* **Tel 01256 881337**

Wades House, Barton Stacey (Mr & Mrs Antony Briscoe) *Mid-way between A303 and A30 near Andover. Approached from S entrance to village.* 2 acres on chalk with spectacular views; large herbaceous borders, over 300 roses; kitchen garden; many containers with diverse planting. TEAS. *Adm £2 Chd free. Sun, Tues July 2, 4 (2-5)*

Waldrons, Brook (Major & Mrs J Robinson) *Lyndhurst. On B3079 1m W from exit 1 M27. 1st house L past Green Dragon public house and directly opp Bell Inn.* 1-acre garden of C18 listed cottage (not open). Conservatory; mixed planting around old orchard trees; raised alpine garden, rose beds, arbour, trellis and arch. Small stableyard; herb garden;

free roaming call ducks and many original garden ideas. Adequate seating throughout. TEAS. *Adm £1.50 Chd free. Sun May 21 (2-5)*

2 Warren Farm Cottages ✂❀ (Dr & Mrs J G Mitchell) *Just off A30 between Stockbridge and Salisbury. Follow yellow 'Garden Open' signs from A30, 4.5m W of Stockbridge, 2.4m E Lopcombe Corner. Proceed 1.8m along 'The Warren'.* Cottage garden packed with unusual ideas. Hardy geraniums, pulmonarias, poppies, salvias, michelmas daisies. Pond. Lounging cats. Vegetables interplanted and in pots. Late season interest. SW Regional Finalist BBC Gardener of the Year 1999. Featured in 'Kitchen Garden' Oct 99, 'Country Homes' June 98 and 'Grassroots' Aug 98. *Adm £1. Suns, Mons May 21, 22, June 18, 19, July 16, 17, Aug, 20, 21, Sept 17, 18, Oct 15, 16 (10-6). Every Fri, May to Sept (10-6).* **Tel 01980 863101**

319 Warsash Rd, Titchfield (Sheila & Asley Powell) *Leave A27 at Park Gate, proceed down Locks Rd, at end turn L into Warsash Rd, 319 is on LH-side.* Small, long narrow garden subdivided and designed for all-yr effect; phormiums, heathers, ivies and irises. New features. TEA. *Adm £1 Chd free (ACNO to British Heart Foundation). Sun May 14 (2-6)*

Weir House, Alresford ♿ (Mr & Mrs George Hollingbery) *From Alresford go down Broad St (B3046) past Globe public house. Take 1st L (signed Abbotstone). Park in field as signed (150yds).* 3 acres. Lutyens-style house (not open) with terrace enveloped in modern flowing planting, set in riverside garden. Brick and flint walls back major new herbaceous border. Rose garden with stream surround and new earth sculpture. Restored 'Vulcan Rams'; modernist vegetable garden; animals to see; playground. October opening will incl garden lighting after dark; approx 6.45pm. Cream TEAS Aug 13. *Adm £2 Chd free (ACNO to The 0Millennium Walk). Suns April 16, Sat, Sun May 27, 28 (2-5), Sun Aug 13 (2-6), Sun Oct 15 (4-7.15)*

● **West Green House, Hartley Wintney** ♿✂ (Miss Marylyn Abbott) *Turn N off A30 at Phoenix Green (about 1m W of Hartley Wintney) at Thackhams Lane from where signed.* Within C18 walls, herbaceous borders, pottager, parterres, orangery and green theatre surrounded by neoclassical garden studded with follies beside a lake. Nymphaeum water garden cascades down descending steps. TEAS. *Adm £3 Chd £1. Wed to Suns and Bank Hols May 1 to Aug 31. For NGS Sat June 24 (11- 5). Also weekends in Sept.*

NEW **West Green House Cottage, Hartley Wintney** ✂ (Mr D Chase) *Turn N off A30 at Phoenix Green (about 1m W of Hartley Wintney) into Thackhams Lane, then follow signs for West Green House. Garden Cottage is adjacent.* ½ acre laid out into 'rooms'. Oriental-themed garden, seaside garden surrounding fish-shaped lawn. Small water feature; herbaceous plants and shrubs, 100 varieties of hebe; herb garden; unusual plants and planting ideas. Places to sit in tranquil setting. *Adm £1 Chd free. Sat June 24 (11-5)*

West Silchester Hall, Silchester ♿❀ (Mrs Jenny Jowett) *Bramley Rd, Silchester. Off A340 between Reading and Basingstoke (signed from centre of village).* 1½ acres, plantsman artist's garden, good collection of herbaceous plants, rose and shrub borders, rhododendrons and many acid-loving plants. Small pond and bog garden, kitchen garden, interesting display of half hardies. Exhibition of botanical and landscape paintings. TEAS. *Adm £2. Sun, Bank Hol Mon May 28, 29, Sun July 16, Sun, Mon Aug 6, 7 (2-6). Parties welcome by appt March to Sept, please* **Tel 01189 700278**

Westbrook House, Holybourne ✂❀ (Andrew Lyndon-Skeggs Esq) *Howards Lane. Turn off A31 at roundabout immed to NE of Alton towards Holybourne and Alton. 1st R to Holybourne. 1st L up Howards Lane. Entrance on R.* 2½ acres with continuing design and development. Mature trees and impressive formal planting of shrubs and herbaceous with 'maze' garden leading to orchard, woodland, stream and unexpected view. Featured in Country Life. Cream TEAS. *Adm £2 Chd free. Sun June 18 (2.30-5.30)*

Wheatley House, Kingsley Bordon ♿✂❀ (Mr & Mrs Michael Adlington) *4m E of Alton, between Binsted and Kingsley, 5m SW of Farnham. From Alton follow signs to Holybourne and Binsted. At end of Binsted turn R signed Wheatley. ¾m down lane on L.* Magnificent setting with panoramic views over fields and forests. Sweeping mixed borders, shrubberies, roses and rockery. 1½ acres, designed by artist-owner, with particular emphasis on colour and form. TEAS in Barn. *Adm £1.50 Chd 50p (ACNO to Red Cross). Sun June 18 (11-5.30), Tues June 20 (2-5.30)*

NEW **White Barn, Crow Hill** ♿✂❀ (Marilyn & Barrie Knight) *From Ringwood take B3347 Christchurch rd. After 1m turn L for Burley and proceed 1m. Park at Methodist church on R almost opp Woodend Rd.* ½ acre with lovely views. Cottage and country style. Large mixture of much loved and unusual plants combined with roses and clematis. Still developing with good colour and tranquil atmosphere. TEAS. *Adm £1.50 Chd free (ACNO to Crow Hill Methodist Church Flower Fund). Fri, Sat June 9, 10 (2-5.30)*

The White Cottage, Beech ♿✂❀ (Mr & Mrs P Conyers) *35 Wellhouse Rd. Leave Alton on Basingstoke Rd A339. After approx 1m turn L to Medstead and Beech. Wellhouse Rd is 2nd turning on R. Parking at village hall at bottom of rd, limited parking at house.* 1-acre chalk garden with a wide range of shrubs and plants; colourful herbaceous borders, hellebores and bulbs. Conservatory with exotics, collection of carnivorous plants featured on TV, pond and scree bed. TEA. *Adm £1.50 Chd free. Suns, Feb 27 March 12 (11-5), Suns, Mons June 4, 5, July 9, 10, Aug 6, 7, Sept Sun 3 (11-6). Private visits by individuals and associations welcome, please* **Tel 01420 89355**

White House, Romsey ♿✂ (Mrs A Burn) *The Frenches. Take A27 towards Whiteparish. After 3m turn L at Shootash Xrds, turn immediately R, entrance ½m on R.* 1-acre, sloping country garden with distant views. Borders with varied plant collection; hidden corners; winding paths to wild pond and bog garden; enclosed swimming pool (not in use); formal pond. Pergolas and trellis with many roses and clematis. TEA. *Adm £1.50 Chd free. Wed, Thurs, Fri June 14, 15, 16 (11-5)*

White Windows, Longparish ♿✂❀ (Mr & Mrs B Sterndale-Bennett) *E of Andover off A303 to village centre on B3048.* ⅔ acre with glorious range of hardy perennials, trees and shrubs planted for yr-round foliage interest and subtle colour blendings. Many hellebores, pulmonarias, hardy geraniums, asters and euphorbias. Garden featured on TV and in books and magazines. TEAS (Sun only). *Adm £2 Chd free. Sun, Mon May 14, 15 (1.30-5.30). Private visits welcome Weds April to Aug, please* **Tel 01264 720222**

Wonston Lodge, Wonston ♿ (Mr & Mrs N J A Wood) *Take A34 or A30 to Sutton Scotney. At War Memorial turn for Wonston and Stoke Charity; ¾m in Wonston centre.* 3 acres; pond with aquatic plants and ornamental ducks; shrub roses and clematis; topiary. TEAS. *Adm £2 Chd free. Sun June 25 (2-6)*

NEW **Woodcote Manor, Bramdean** ♿ (Mrs J S Morton) *On A272 Winchester to Petersfield rd, ½m E of Bramdean.* Woodland garden with bulbs and shrubs. C17 manor house (not open). *Adm £2 Chd free. Easter Sun, Mon April 23, 24 (2-5)*

The Worthys Gardens *Off B3047 N of Winchester. Combined adm £3. Tues Aug 1 (2-5)*

Little Acre (Mr M Walford) *Headbourne Worthy. Just off S end of Springvale, in Down Farm Lane.* 1½ acres with trees and shrubs planted by owner, for foliar effect and low maintenance. Collection of over 70 aurea trees and shrubs. TEA.

NEW **Meadowsweet** ♿✂ (Mr & Mrs R White) *Kings Worthy. Opp school at junction of Nations Hill and Church Lane.* 1¾ acres on sloping chalk site. Extensive herbaceous beds. Long pergola. Pink and purple colour scheme; grasses; dovecote; shrubs and ground cover; roses; large fish pond with bridge.

22 Springvale Road ✂ (Mr & Mrs Fry) *Kings Worthy. N end of Springwell Rd. Kingsworthy almost opp Dairiall's shop.* ¾ acre. Magnolias, snowdrops, crocuses and daffodils. From late June comprehensive display of agapanthus Headbourne hybrids being Lewis Palmer's stock: he lived nearby. Sept for drifts of cyclamen, heathers and fine display of foliage. *Private visits welcome, please* **Tel 01962 882288**

Evening Opening (See also garden description)

Rowans Wood, Ampfield	May 17 & 27
South End House, Lymington	July 29
The Vyne, Sherborne St John	June 28

THRIVE

Thrive have four integrated garden projects around the country – one in the Midlands, two in London, and one in Reading, and are developing others across the UK. These integrated gardens are a place for people with different abilities to work with horticultural therapists in individually structured programmes. These programmes can help to: build confidence, teach basic numeracy or literacy skills, gain experience in a work-force situation, gain qualifications needed to find a job, restore strength after an accident or illness, break down the psychological barriers and prejudice that lead to loneliness and isolation.

For more information please contact:

Thrive,

The Geoffrey Udall Building, Beech Hill, Reading RG7 2AT.

Tel: 0118 988 5688.

Fax: 0118 988 5677.

Email: info@thrive.org.uk

Web site: www.thrive.org.uk

Herefordshire

Hon County Organiser: Lady Curtis, 30 Witherington Road, London N5 1PP
Assistant County Organisers: Dr J A F Evans, 7 St Margarets Road, Hereford HR1 1TS Tel 01432 273000
Mr & Mrs Roger Norman, Ivy Cottage, Upper Ivington, Leominster, Herefordshire HR6 0JN Tel 01568 720344
Hon County Treasurer: Mr Michael Robins, Mewsholme, 77 Bridge Street, Ledbury HR8 2AN

DATES OF OPENING

Regular openings
For details see garden description
Abbey Dore Court, Abbey Dore
Arrow Cottage, nr Weobley
The Bannut, Bringsty
Bryan's Ground, Stapleton
Kingstone Cottages, Ross-on-Wye
Lingen Nursery & Garden, Lingen
The Nest, Moreton, Eye
The Picton Garden, Colwall
Stockton Bury, Kimbolton

By appointment only
For telephone numbers and other details see garden descriptions. Private visits welcomed
Bonjovi, Bromyard
Brilley Court, nr Whitney-on-Wye
Well Cottage, Blakemere

March 26 Sunday
Ivy Croft, Ivington Green, Leominster

April 2 Sunday
Lower Hope, Ullingswick

April 16 Sunday
Longacre, Colwall
Stone House, Scotland

April 20 Thursday
Overcourt Garden Nursery, Sutton St Nicholas

April 22 Saturday
Arrow Cottage, nr Weobley

April 24 Monday
The Nest, Moreton, Eye

April 27 Thursday
Overcourt Garden Nursery, Sutton St Nicholas

April 30 Sunday
Ivy Croft, Ivington Green, Leominster
Stockton Bury, Kimbolton

May 7 Sunday
Lakeside, Whitbourne

May 14 Sunday
Batch Cottage, Almeley

May 18 Thursday
Overcourt Garden Nursery, Sutton St Nicholas

May 21 Sunday
Lingen Nursery & Garden, Lingen
Stone House, Scotland

May 22 Monday
Darkley House, Norton Canon

May 25 Thursday
Overcourt Garden Nursery, Sutton St Nicholas

May 27 Saturday
Arrow Cottage, nr Weobley
Bryan's Ground, Stapleton

May 28 Sunday
Caves Folly Nursery, Colwall
Ivy Croft, Ivington Green, Leominster
Lower Hope, Ullingswick
Waterpump Farm, Ryeford

May 29 Monday
The Nest, Moreton, Eye

June 4 Sunday
Ash Farm, Much Birch
How Caple Court, How Caple
The Nest, Moreton, Eye
Whitfield, Wormbridge

June 9 Friday
Michaelchurch Court, St Owens Cross

June 10 Saturday
Overcourt Garden Nursery, Sutton St Nicholas

June 11 Sunday
The Bannut, Bringsty
Grantsfield, nr Kimbolton
Overcourt Garden Nursery, Sutton St Nicholas

June 17 Saturday
Arrow Cottage, nr Weobley
Hergest Croft Gardens, Kington
Michaelchurch Court, St Owens Cross

June 18 Sunday
Batch Cottage, Almeley
Darkley House, Norton Canon
Lakeside, Whitbourne
Moccas Court, nr Hereford
Torwood, Whitchurch

June 20 Tuesday
Croft Castle, Kingsland

June 20 to 21 Tuesday to Wednesday
Michaelchurch Court, St Owens Cross

June 25 Sunday
Berrington Hall, Leominster
Caves Folly Nursery, Colwall
Longacre, Colwall
The Nest, Moreton, Eye
Shucknall Court, Weston Beggard
Stone House, Scotland

July 2 Sunday
Bryan's Ground, Stapleton
Dogberry, The Common, Wellington Heath
The Nest, Moreton, Eye
The View, Ochre Hill, Wellington Heath
Waterpump Farm, Ryeford

July 9 Sunday
The Bannut, Bringsty
Linton Gardens
Lower Hope, Ullingswick
Whitfield, Wormbridge

July 12 Wednesday
Darkley House, Norton Canon

July 16 Sunday
Kilima Lodge, Colwall

July 22 Saturday
Arrow Cottage, nr Weobley

July 23 Sunday
Coddington Vineyard, Coddington

July 29 Saturday
Wyche & Colwall Horticultural Society Show, Colwall Green

July 30 Sunday
Elton Hall, Elton
Ivy Croft, Ivington Green, Leominster
The Nest, Moreton, Eye

August 6 Sunday
Bringsty Gardens
Stockton Bury, Kimbolton

August 20 Sunday
Lingen Nursery & Garden, Lingen

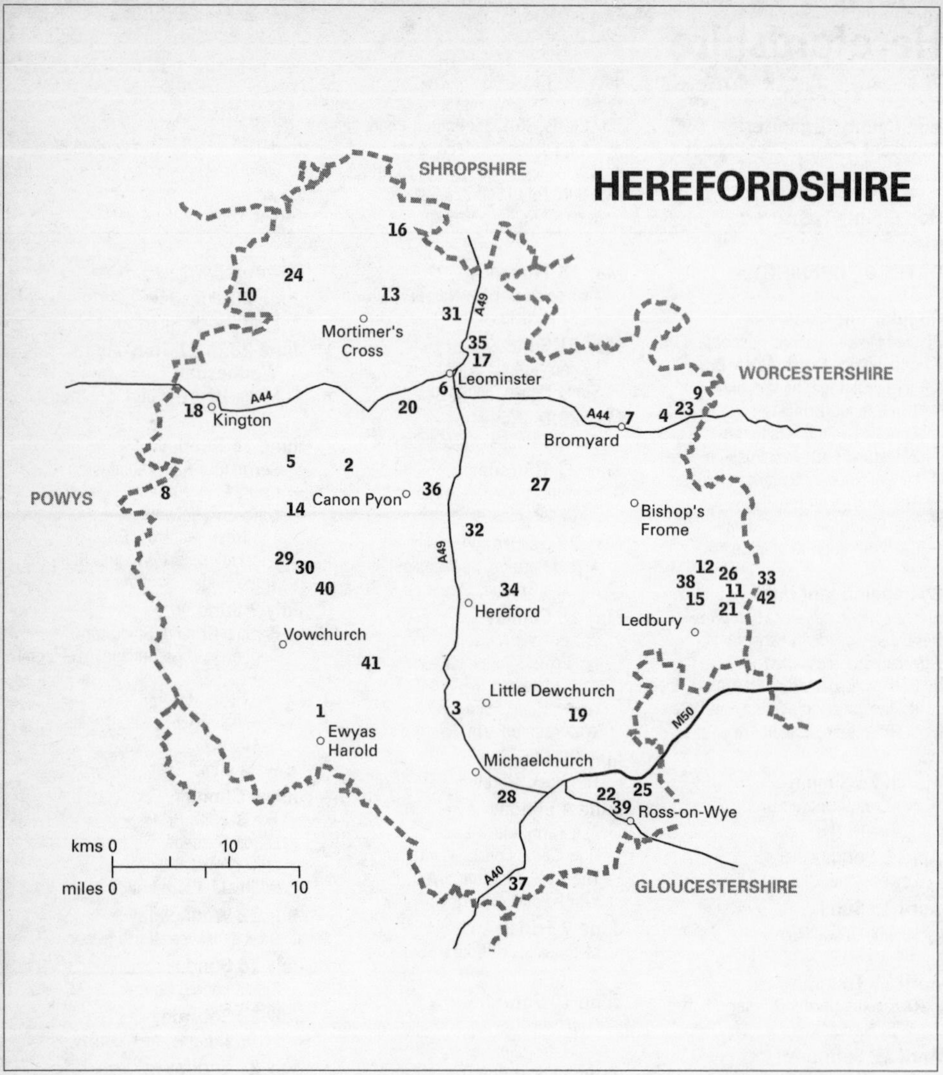

KEY

1 Abbey Dore Court
2 Arrow Cottage
3 Ash Farm
4 The Bannut
5 Batch Cottage
6 Berrington Hall
7 Bonjovi
8 Brilley Court
9 Bringsty Gardens
10 Bryan's Ground
11 Caves Folly Nursery
12 Coddington Vineyard
13 Croft Castle
14 Darkley House
15 Dogberry
16 Elton Hall
17 Grantsfield
18 Hergest Croft Gardens
19 How Caple Court
20 Ivy Croft
21 Kilima Lodge
22 Kingstone Cottages
23 Lakeside
24 Lingen Nursery & Garden
25 Linton Gardens
26 Longacre
27 Lower Hope
28 Michaelchurch Court
29 Moccas Court
30 Monnington Court
31 The Nest
32 Overcourt Garden Nursery
33 The Picton Garden
34 Shucknall Court
35 Stockton Bury
36 Stone House
37 Torwood
38 The View
39 Waterpump Farm
40 Well Cottage
41 Whitfield
42 Wyche & Colwall Horticultural Society Show

August 26 Saturday
Arrow Cottage, nr Weobley
Monnington Court, Hereford

August 27 Sunday
Ivy Croft, Ivington Green, Leominster
Monnington Court, Hereford

August 28 Monday
Monnington Court, Hereford

September 2 Saturday
Arrow Cottage, nr Weobley

September 12 Tuesday
Darkley House, Norton Canon

September 24 Sunday
Ivy Croft, Ivington Green, Leominster

October 8 Sunday
Lower Hope, Ullingswick

October 22 Sunday
Longacre, Colwall

DESCRIPTIONS OF GARDENS

● **Abbey Dore Court, Abbey Dore** ♿✂❀ (Mrs C L Ward) *nr Hereford. 11m SW of Hereford. From A465 midway Hereford-Abergavenny turn W, signed Abbey Dore; then 2½m* 6 acres, bordered by R Dore, of rambling and semi formal garden with unusual shrubs, perennials and clematis in large borders. Pond, rock garden and newly planted trees. River walk with ferns and hellebores leading to borders planted for foliage colour. New cottage garden evolving out of a field. Small nursery selling mainly herbaceous perennials. Coffee, lunch and TEAS (11-5). *Adm £2.50 Chd 50p (ACNO to Mother Theresa). Sat April 8 to Sun Oct 1 closed Mons (except Bank Hols) & Weds (11-6)*

■ **Arrow Cottage, nr Weobley** ✂❀ (Mr & Mrs Lance Hattatt) *From Weobley take unclassified rd direction Wormsley (Kings Pyon/Canon Pyon). After 1m, turn L signposted Ledgemoor. 2nd R (no through rd). 1st house on L.* Design is at its most stylish in this 2-acre plant lover's garden. Colour-themed enclosures, old roses, clematis, a formal 170ft rill and natural stream create mystery and delight at every turn. Featured on BBC2 1999 and in all major garden guides. Unusual plants for sale. Regret no children. TEAS. *Adm £2.50. Wed - Sun, April to Sept. For NGS Sats April 22, May 27, June 17, July 22, Aug 26, Sept 2 (2-5)*

Ash Farm, Much Birch ✂❀ (Alison & David Lewis) *From Hereford take A49 S to Much Birch (approx 7m). After the Pilgrim Hotel take 1st turning R at Xrds into Tump Lane. Garden is on L.* Ample parking. Small walled farmhouse garden and a new garden created from old fold yard for all-yr interest over past 9 yrs. Small trees, herbaceous borders, blue and white borders. *Adm £2 Chd free Sun June 4 (10-6)*

■ **The Bannut, Bringsty** ♿❀ (Mr Maurice & Mrs Daphne Everett) *2½m E of Bromyard on A44 Worcester Rd. (½m E of entrance to National Trust, Brockhampton).* 2½-acres of formal and informal gardens with lovely views to the Malvern Hills. Manicured hedges divide garden rooms, containing a colourful mix of lawns, shrubs, herbaceous plants and an unusual knot garden. The spectacular heather garden leads visitors to grassy paths meandering through trees and shrubs, and masses of cowslips in spring. TEAS. *Adm £2 Chd £1. Weds, Suns & Bank Hol Mons, Easter to Sept. For NGS Suns June 11, July 9 (2-5); also Aug 6, see Bringsty Gardens. Groups by appt, please* **Tel 01885 482206**

Batch Cottage, Almeley ♿✂❀ (Jeremy & Elizabeth Russell) *16m NW of Hereford 2m off A438/4111 to Kington, turn R at Eardisley* Conservation-oriented natural valley garden set in woodland and orchard, with streams and large pond. In all, some 4 acres. Over 300 labelled trees and shrubs; mixed borders, fern and bog beds, wild flower bank and woodland walk. Waterfowl and wildlife. TEAS in aid of Almeley Parish Church. *Adm £2 Chd free. Suns May 14, June 18 (2-6). Private visits welcome, please* **Tel 01544 327469**

▲ **Berrington Hall, Leominster** ♿✂ (The National Trust) *3m N of Leominster on A49. Signposted. Bus Midland Red (W) x 92, 292 alight Luston, 2m* Extensive views over Capability Brown Park; formal garden; wall plants, unusual trees, camellia collection, herbaceous plants, wisteria. Woodland walk, rhododendrons, walled garden with historic apple collection. Light lunches and TEAS *Adm house & garden £4.20 Chd £2.10. Grounds only £2. April to 31 Oct daily except Thurs and Fris (Bank Hol Mons, open Good Friday), Oct 5.30. For NGS Sun June 25 (12.30-6)*

NEW **Bonjovi, Bromyard** (Mr & Mrs John Evans) *¼m E of Bromyard on A44. Turn into Linton Retirement Park, car park for visitors on L of entrance. Take 1st rd on R to no. 47.* Unusual small garden, featured in Amateur Gardening 1999, in a larger than average plot around a retirement bungalow. Many innovative ideas for old and young. 60' stream, thatched well with pond, mosaic floored patio. Closely planted borders and a variety of containers. Very colourful. TEA *Adm £2 Chd 50p 12 yrs and over. Open April 14 - Oct 29 by appt only, please* **Tel 01885 488400**

Brilley Court, nr Whitney-on-Wye ♿✂ (Mr & Mrs D Bulmer) *6m E Hay-on-Wye. 1½m off main A438 Hereford to Brecon Rd signposted to Brilley* Medium-sized walled garden, spring and herbaceous. Valley stream garden; spring colour. Ornamental kitchen garden. Large quantity of roses. Wonderful views. TEAS by appt only *Adm £2 Chd 50p (ACNO to MCR) Owing to renovations of the garden, open by appt only, please* **Tel 01497 831467**

Bringsty Gardens ✂❀ *3m E of Bromyard via A44 10m W of Worcester; Bringsty Common. Three gardens S of rd.* Tickets and maps available from Wittanacre & The Bannut. TEAS at Brookside and The Bannut *Combined adm £3 Chd free Sun Aug 6 (2-5.30)*

Brookside (Mr & Mrs John Dodd) *Turn down track by large oak tree.* Cottage with 2-acre garden. Specimen trees and shrubs in grass sloping to lake. Mixed beds with all yr interest. *Parties and private visits welcome, please* **Tel 01886 821835**

Wittanacre (Mr & Mrs Stephen Dodd) *behind Wintergreen Nurseries.* New garden with range of unusual and interesting plants. *Adm £1.50 Open April 1 to Sept 15 Wed, Thurs, Fri (11-6)*

■ **Bryan's Ground, Stapleton** ♿✂❀ (David Wheeler & Simon Dorrell) *between Kinsham and Stapleton. 12m NW of Leominster. At Mortimers Cross take B4362 signed Presteigne. At Combe, follow signs* 3-acre Edwardian garden. Home of Hortus, The International Garden Journal. Yew and box topiary, parterres, formal herb garden, partly walled kitchen garden. Flower and shrub borders with 'Sulking House'. Shrubbery with spring bulbs, 'Heritage' apple orchard, lighthouse and Edwardian greenhouse. Featured in New York Times, The Observer, House and Garden. TEAS. *Adm £2.50 Chd 50p. Sats, Suns, Mons April 15 to Sept 18. For NGS Sat May 27, Sun July 2 (2-5)*

Caves Folly Nursery, Colwall ♿✂ (Mr Leaper & Mrs Evans) *Evendine Lane, off Colwall Green. B4218 between Malvern and Ledbury. Car parking at Caves Folly.* Nursery established 14 yrs specialising in herbaceous perennials and grasses, some unusual. All plants are grown organically. Herbaceous borders, solar powered water features and display gardens. Meadow walk with pond, chickens and ducks. TEAS. *Adm £1.50 Chd free. Sun May 28 (2-5). Combined adm with Longacre £3 Chd free. Sun June 25 (2-6). Group visits welcome. Nursery open Thurs-Sat (10-5) all yr*

Coddington Vineyard, Coddington ♿ (Denis & Ann Savage) *nr Ledbury. From Ledbury take Bromyard rd, 1st R after railway bridge signposted Wellington Heath, turn R at next T-junction (oak tree on island) and follow signs to Coddington. Vineyard signposted.* 5 acres incl 2-acre vineyard, listed farmhouse, threshing barn and cider mill. Garden and vineyard planted 1985 with terraces, woodland, pond and stream. Interesting trees and shrubs. Wine tasting incl *adm £2 Chd free. Sun July 23 (2-6)*

▲ **Croft Castle, Kingsland** ♿✂ (The National Trust) *5m NW of Leominster. On B4362 (off B4361, Leominster-Ludlow).* Large garden; borders; walled garden; landscaped park and walks in Fishpool Valley; fine old avenues. Special garden open for NGS (Castle closed). *Adm £1 Chd 50p For NGS Tues June 20 (1.30-4.30)*

NEW **Darkley House, Norton Canon** ✂❀ (Malcolm & Jill Ainslie) *10m NW of Hereford off A480. Follow signs to Norton Wood and Hurstley. Gardens are 1.2m on LH side, please drive slowly on the narrow lane.* 3½-acre garden plus wildflower meadows, features-walled garden-rose pergola, 150 varieties of clematis some forming clematis walk; wildlife and formal ponds; herbaceous borders; potager; cottage garden; stunning views. Something for everyone incl small nursery. TEAS. *Adm £2.50 Chd free. Mon May 22, Sun June 18, Wed July 12, Tues Sept 12 (10-4). Open May - Sept Mon, Tues, Wed private visits welcome, please* **Tel 01544 318121**

NEW **Dogberry, The Common, Wellington Heath** (Brian Snell) *From Ledbury take Bromyard Rd. 1st R after Railway Bridge, signposted Wellington Heath & Farmers Arms. At T-junction 1¼m Oak Tree on Island turn R, after 30 yds turn R again down "The Common". Dogberry is on the bend at bottom of Common. Roadside parking on the "The Common" and in Farmers Arms car park.* ½-acre mature garden with lovely view to Frith Wood; densely planted mixed borders for interest over many months. Many unusual plants incl streamside and shade planting. TEAS at The View. *Combined adm with* **The View** *£2.50 Chd free. Sun July 2, (2-5.30). Private visits welcome, please* **Tel 01531 663149**

Elton Hall, Elton ♿✂❀ (Mr & Mrs James Hepworth) *6m SW of Ludlow. From Ludlow take 1st turn R after crossing Ludford bridge, signed Wigmore/Burrington* 5-acre garden being developed. Georgian house (not open) former home of Thomas Andrew Knight, founder of (later Royal) Horticultural Society. Apple orchard includes C18 Elton varieties. Walled herb garden, decorative kitchen garden. Herbaceous borders with unusual perennials. Nuttery, wild flower meadow, Victorian greenhouse, tortoise castle, gothic temple, Moorish sheep palace, new Hermitage. NCCPG Echinacea + Rudbeckia Collection. Featured in Gardens Illustrated, New York Times & The Garden. TEA. *Adm £2 Chd free. Sun July 30 (2-6). Clubs, societies welcome*

Grantsfield, nr Kimbolton ♿✂❀ (Colonel & Mrs J G T Polley) *3m NE of Leominster. A49 N from Leominster, turn R to Grantsfield.* Car parking in field; not coaches which must drop and collect visitors in the village. Minibus acceptable. Contrasting styles in gardens of old stone farmhouse; wide variety of unusual plants and shrubs, old roses, climbers; herbaceous borders; superb views. 1-acre orchard and kitchen garden with flowering and specimen trees. Spring bulbs. TEAS *Adm £1.50 Chd free (ACNO to Red Cross). Sun June 11 (2-5.30). Private visits welcome April to end Sept, please* **Tel 01568 613338**

▲ **Hergest Croft Gardens, Kington** ♿❀ (W L Banks Esq) *½m off A44 on Welsh side of Kington, 20m NW of Hereford: Turn L at Rhayader end of bypass; then 1st R; gardens ¼m on L* 50 acres of garden owned by Banks family for 4 generations. Edwardian garden surrounding house; Park wood with rhododendrons up to 30ft tall; old-fashioned kitchen garden with spring and herbaceous borders. One of finest private collections of trees and shrubs; selected to hold National Collections maples, birches and zelkova. Hergest Croft celebrated its centenary in 1996. TEAS *Adm £3.50 Chd under 16 free (ACNO to NCCPG) For NGS Sat June 17 (1.30-6)* **Tel 01544 230160**

▲ **How Caple Court, How Caple** ❀ (Mr & Mrs Roger Lee) *5m N of Ross on Wye 10m S of Hereford on B4224; turn R at How Caple Xrds, garden 400 yds on L.* 11 acres; Edwardian gardens set high above R Wye in park and woodland; formal terraces: yew hedges, statues and pools; sunken Florentine water garden under restoration; woodland walks; herbaceous and shrub borders, shrub roses, mature trees: Mediaeval Church with newly restored C16 Diptych. Nursery. Dried flowers. TEAS *Adm £2.50 Chd £1.25 For NGS Sun June 4 (10-5)* **Tel 01989 740626**

Ivy Croft, Ivington Green, Leominster ✂❀ (Sue & Roger Norman) *[OS Ref SO 464562] 3m SW of Leominster, between A44 and B4361, 0.7m W of Ivington, towards Dilwyn.* Garden started in 1997. Mixed borders surrround cottage, planted for all yr interest. Willow water treatment system, seasonal pond, formal vegetable garden, alpines, troughs, young wood, collection of snowdrops. TEA. *Adm £2 Chd free. Suns March 26, April 30, May 28, July 30, Aug 27,*

Sept 24 (2-5). Private visits and parties welcome all year, please **Tel 01568 720344**

NEW **Kilima Lodge, Colwall** ♿ (Mr & Mrs W B Stallard) *Evendine Lane off Colwall Green, SW of Malvern . Take A449 S from Malvern, R on to B4218 to Colwall, L just before Yew Tree PH. Garden on R past Cave's Folly Nursery.* 1½-acre garden which has evolved over the last 4 yrs with a background of established trees and shrubs and dramatic views of the Malvern Hills. Mixed borders of shrubs and herbaceous plants with the accent on foliage; water feature with mixed planting. TEAS. *Adm £2 Chd 50p. Sun July 16 (2-5.30)*

Kingstone Cottages, Ross-on-Wye ✲❀ (Mr & Mrs M Hughes) *A40 Ross-Gloucester, turn L at Weston Cross PH to Bollitree Castle, then L to Rudhall.* Informal 1½-acre cottage garden containing National Collection of old pinks and carnations and other unusual plants. Terraced beds, ponds, grotto, summerhouse, lovely views. Separate parterre garden containing the Collection. Featured in several TV programmes & magazines. *Adm £1 Chd free. Mons to Fris May 2 to July 7 (9-4). Private visits welcome, please* **Tel 01989 565267**

Lakeside, Whitbourne ✲❀ (Mr D Gueroult) *Gaines Rd. 9m W of Worcester off A44 at County boundary sign (ignore sign to Whitbourne Village)* 6-acres, large walled garden with many mixed beds and borders; spring bulbs, climbers, small maturing pinetum, heather garden, bog garden, medieval carp lake with fountain. STEEP STEPS AND SLOPES. TEAS in aid of St Michael's Hospice *Adm £2 Chd free Sun May 7, June 18 (2-5). Parties of 10 or more by appt, please* **Tel 01886 821119**

■ **Lingen Nursery & Garden, Lingen** ♿✲❀ (Mr K Davis) *Off B4362 E from Presteigne, 3m opposite Chapel in village.* Specialist alpine and herbaceous nursery and general garden, rock garden and herbaceous borders, peat bed, raised screes and Alpine House. Stock beds incl a large collection of show auriculas. 2 acres of developing garden. Unusual plants with labelling. Nursery. Catalogue available. National collection of Iris sibirica and herbaceous Campanula held for NCCPG. Cream TEAS *Adm £1.50 Chd free. Feb-Oct every day (10-5). For NGS Suns May 21; Aug 20 (10-5). Coach parties by appt* **Tel 01544 267720**

Linton Gardens *6m E of Ross-on-Wye, S of B4221. Signposting within village, improved parking.* Some Linton gardens are steep. Teas in Village Hall (3-5) *Combined adm £2 Chd free Sun July 9 (2-6)*

NEW **Appledown** ❀ (K D P Downham) *Some 300 yds down from Linton Church.* ½-acre cottage garden is S facing and slopes from E to W with lawns linking beds containing a variety of perennials, shrubs and vegetables. Other major features incl a yew and a walnut and several fruit trees.

NEW **Barn House** ♿ (Mr & Mrs C R Arnold) *From the centre of the village take Ridge Rd towards Aston Crews. Barn House is 400 yds along the ridge on the R.* ½ acre cottage style garden situated on a ridge with wonderful views to the Brecons and Black Mountains. Patio area has many containers of perennials and colourful bedding plants; small alpine beds; mixed borders of flowering shrubs and perennials lead the visitor to explore other areas in garden. Trees and shrubs protect against prevailing winds, as well as providing a framework for climbers, clematis, honeysuckle, wisteria and roses.

Bickerton Cottage (Miss A Gittings) A garden of approx 1½ acres, on a slope but not difficult to negotiate. It contains an interesting collection of trees and shrubs, some of them quite rare, a few flower beds and 3 small fish ponds. From the top of the garden one gets a lovely view of the Malvern Hills and part of the Cotswolds

Elmtree Cottage ✲❀ (Noel Kingsbury & Jo Eliot) New ¾-acre garden created by author of 'The New Perennial Garden'. Eclectic influences incl German parks and the American prairie. Wide range perennials and grasses

Kamberg Cottage ❀ (John & Rosemary Verity) Hillside cottage garden on several levels densely planted with perennials, shrubs and ornamental trees. Ample seating with panoramic views to Malvern Hills

Longacre, Colwall ♿✲ (Mr D M & Mrs H Pudsey) *Evendine Lane, off Colwall Green. Between Malvern and Ledbury, off B4218* 1½-acre garden developed since 1970. Emphasis on multi-season trees and shrubs planted to create vistas across lawns, down paths and along avenues. TEAS and car parking at Caves Folly Nursery. *Adm £1.50. Sun April 16, Oct 22 (2-6). Combined adm with Caves Folly Nursery £3 Chd free. Sun June 25 (2-6)*

Lower Hope, Ullingswick ♿✲❀ (Mr & Mrs Clive Richards) *From Hereford take A465 N to Bromyard. After 6m turn L at Burley Gate on A417 signed Leominster. Approx 2m take 3rd turning on R signed Lower Hope and Pencombe, 0.6m on LH-side.* 5-acre garden facing S and W. Herbaceous borders, rose walks and gardens, laburnum tunnel, Mediterranean garden, bog gardens. New lime tree walk, lake landscaped with wild flowers; streams, ponds. Conservatories with exotic species orchids, bougainvilleas. Prize-winning herd of pedigree Hereford cattle, flock of pedigree Suffolk sheep. TEAS. *Adm £2 Chd £1 (ACNO to Belmont Abbey Mission Trust). Suns April 2, May 28, July 9, Oct 8 (2-6)*

NEW **Michaelchurch Court, St Owens Cross** ✲ (Dr & Mrs D J L Smith) *From Ross-on-Wye approx 7m. N on A49, turn L onto B4521 signed Abergavenny; turn R at Xroads. After ¼m turn L at 1st opportunity into narrow rd; to Michaelchurch Court. From Hereford approx 12m S on A49; approx ¼m after Harewood End turn R signed Orcop, 1st minor Xroads turn L. At next minor Xroads turn L into narrow road to Michaelchurch Court.* C17 Farmhouse (not open), set in open countryside near to Norman Church, worth a visit. Approx 3 acres incl large pond a stream with flower border. Old fashioned roses and herbaeous borders set amongst lawns; one long border is backed by a high wall covered with climbing roses and honeysuckle. A long pergola covered with roses, honeysuckle, clematis and wisteria leads to a sunken garden with water feature and seating area. Climbing roses and hydrangeas cover the house. TEA. *Adm £2 Chd £1. Fri, Sat, Tues, Wed June 9, 17, 20, 21 (2-7)*

Moccas Court, nr Hereford ♿ (Francis Chester-Master Esq) *10m W of Hereford. 1m off B4352. 7-acres; Capability Brown parkland on S bank of R. Wye.* House designed by

Adam and built by Keck in 1775. Teas in village hall. *Adm house & garden £2 Chd £1 (ACNO to Moccas Church) Sun June 18 (2-6). By appt for groups of 20 or over, please* **Tel 01981 500381**

Monnington Court, Hereford ♿ (Mr & Mrs Bulmer) *Monnington-on-Wye. Lane to village and Monnington Court S off A438 halfway between Hereford & Hay on Wye.* 20 acres, lake, river, sculpture garden (Mrs Bulmer is sculptor Angela Conner). Famous mile long avenue of pines and yews, favourite of Sir John Betjeman and in Kilvert's Diary. Foundation Farm of British Morgan Horse, living replicas of statues in Trafalgar Square, etc, cider press. C13 Moot Hall, C15 C17 house. TEAS/Barbecue 10-7. Horse display 4.00. *Adm house, garden, display £5 for 1st 2 adults £4 per additional adult Chd £3.50. Garden, display only £4.50 Chd £3 (ACNO to British Morgan Horse Foundation Farm). Sat, Sun, Mon Aug 26, 27, 28 (10-7). Private visits by appt, please* **Tel 01981 500698**

■ **The Nest, Moreton, Eye** ♿✿❀ (Sue Evans) *A49 3m N of Leominster. L in Ashton. 1m on L signed 'The Nest Cottage Garden'.* Drive entrance between Stourport/Leominster canal remnant and 3 acre field (millennium project, conversion to wildflower meadow). House, 1530's Yeoman's timber framed. Established potager and fruits. Rockeries, scree and gravel gardens. Shrubberies and summer garden with water feature. Wet area incl lobelias, primulas, ferns (25 varieties). TEAS *Adm £2 (ACNO to Eye Parish Church) Suns April 23; May 28, every sun in June & July; Sun Aug 27, Mon Aug 28. For NGS Mons April 24; May 29; Suns June 4, 25;: July 2, 30 (2-5)*

Orchard Bungalow see Worcestershire

Overcourt Garden Nursery, Sutton St Nicholas ♿✿❀ (Mr & Mrs Peter Harper) *3m N of Hereford. Turn L at Xrds in village towards Marden for ¼m* Grade II C16 house once a vicarage and school house, with connections to Crusader Knights of St John. Views to the Black Mountains. 1½-acre garden developed over the last few yrs with large shrub and flower borders. Wide range of unusual plants for sale in nursery. TEAS. Nursery open March 1 to October 31 Wed - Sat 10-5. *Adm £1.50 Chd free For NGS Thurs, April 20, 27, May 18, 25; Sat, Sun June 10, 11 (2-5.30). Private visits welcome by appt, please* **Tel 01432 880845**

● **The Picton Garden, Colwall** ♿✿❀ (Mr & Mrs Paul Picton) *Walwyn Rd. 3m W of Malvern on B4218. 1½-acres W of Malvern Hills.* A plantsman's garden specialising in Summer and Autumn colour. Wide range of interesting herbaceous perennials precede Sept/Oct flowering of NCCPG collection of Autumn flowering asters (Michaelmas Dasies). Many unusual plants to be seen. *Adm £2 Chd free. Sun July 16, 23; Aug 2 to Aug 29 Wed to Sun; Mon Aug 28. Aug 30 to Oct 15, daily. Oct 18 to Oct 29, Wed to Sun. (11-5). Group visits welcome, please* **Tel 01684 540416** For more information visit our website www.autumnasters.co.uk

Shucknall Court, Weston Beggard ✿ (Mr & Mrs Henry Moore) *5½m E of Hereford off A4103 signposted Weston Beggard. Garden 100yds from main rd.* Large collection of specie, old-fashioned and shrub roses. Mixed borders in the old walled farmhouse garden. Wild garden, small stream garden, vegetables and fruit. Partly suitable for wheelchairs. TEAS in aid of St John Ambulance. *Adm £2 Chd free. Sun June 25 (11-6)*

Shuttifield Cottage see Worcestershire

■ **Stockton Bury, Kimbolton** ♿✿❀ (Raymond G Treasure Esq) *2m N of Leominster on the A49. Turn R onto the A4112 Kimbolton Rd. The gardens are 300yds on the R.* A superb, sheltered, 4-acre garden with a very long growing season giving colour and interest all-yr long. An extensive collection of plants, many rare and unusual set amongst Mediaeval buildings, a real kitchen garden. Pigeon house, Tithe Barn, Grotto, cider press, pools, ruined Chapel and rill, all surrounded by unspoilt countryside. Home grown plants for sale. TEAS and refreshments in the Tithe Barn. *Adm £3 Open April to October, Wed, Thurs, Fri, Sat, Sun and Bank Hols (12-5). For NGS Suns April 30, Aug 6 (2-6)*

Stone House, Scotland ❀ (Peter & Sheila Smellie) *Wellington. A49 6m N of Hereford, end of dual carriageway, turn L for Westhope. ¾m turn R up narrow track. Parking ¼m.* Parking difficult in wet conditions. 1-acre S sloping garden with magnificent views over countryside. Winding paths traverse the bank and terraced areas which contain a wide selection of unusual shrubs and herbaceous plants. Children welcome. *Adm £2 Chd 50p Suns April 16, May 21, June 25 (1-6). Private visits welcome, please* **Tel 01432 830470**

Torwood, Whitchurch ♿✿❀ (Mr & Mrs S G Woodward) *Ross-on-Wye. A40 turn to Symonds Yat W. Adjacent to village school and roundabout.* Interesting cottage garden; shrubs, conifers, herbaceous plants, etc. Featured by Central TV and in several books. TEAS. *Adm £1.50 Chd free. Sun June 18 (2-6). Private visits welcome all year, please* **Tel 01600 890306**

NEW **The View, Ochre Hill, Wellington Heath** ✿❀ (Mr & Mrs David Evans) *From Ledbury take Bromyard Rd, 1st turning R after railway bridge signposted Wellington Heath. Turn R at next T-junction (Oak Tree with seat round it). After 40 yds turn R down The Common. Ochre Hill is on the L 'The View' is at the top of the hill (access on foot only). Continue down The Common to 'Dogberry'. Parking available at the Farmers Arms PH car park opp.* 2-acre sloping garden, part terraced, planted to encourage wildlife. Mixed beds, herb garden, pond, water feature, new orchard planted with old varieties of trees. Other trees incl medlar, quince, walnut, mulberry. Hedge enclosed vegetable garden. Small woodland walk. Cider mill & press. Most hard landscaping recycled from material on site. Magnificent views over Malvern Hills & Black Mountains. TEAS in aid of Wellington Heath Memorial Hall. *Combined adm with* **Dogberry** *£2.50 Chd free. Sun July 2 (2.5.30)*

NEW **Waterpump Farm, Ryeford** ✿❀ (Mrs Liz Sugden) *On the A40 3m SW of Ross-on-Wye, 13m NE of Gloucester.* A developing 3-acre informal and wildlife garden with herbaceous plants and shrubs, some unusual. Hardy geranium collection. Lake; stream and ponds; tree walk; llamas in paddock. Small nursery specialising in herbaceous and water garden plants all organically grown. TEA. *Adm £1.50 Chd free. Suns May 28, July 2 (1-5)*

Well Cottage, Blakemere ♿ (R S Edwards Esq) *10m due W of Hereford. Leave Hereford on A465 (Abergavenny) rd. After 3m turn R towards Hay B4349 (B4348). At Clehonger keep straight on the B4352 towards Bredwardine. Well Cottage is on L by phone box.* 1¼-acre garden of mixed plantings incl meadow area suitable for picnics. There is a natural pool with gunnera and primulae. Good views over local hills and fields. Featured in Diana Saville's book 'Gardens for Small Country Houses', Jane Taylor's 'The English Cottage Garden' and ITV 1999. *Adm £1.50 OAPS £1 Chd free. Private visits welcome May to Aug, please* **Tel 01981 500475**

Whitfield, Wormbridge ♿❀ (Mr & Mrs Edward Clive) *8m SW of Hereford on A465 Hereford-Abergavenny Rd* Parkland, large garden, ponds, walled kitchen garden, 1780 gingko tree, 1½m woodland walk with 1851 Redwood grove. Picnic parties welcome. TEAS. *Adm £2.50 Chd free (ACNO to Abbey Dore Appeal). Sun June 4, July 9 (2-6). Groups by appt welcome, please* **Tel 0198 570 727**

● **Wyche & Colwall Horticultural Society Show, Colwall Green** ♿❀ (L A C Ashby Esq) *The Elms School.* Medium-sized garden, herbaceous borders, fine views of Malvern Hills. Classes for flowers, vegetables, cookery & handicrafts. Plant sales and other stalls. TEAS. *Adm to show and garden £1 (Share to NGS). Sat July 29 (2-5.30)*

DARKLEY HOUSE and Gardens

17th century self-catering units or B & B and Evening Meal ❋ Views to Black Mountains Seven acres gardens and meadows ❋ Very rural ❋ Personal service ❋ No Smoking, children or pets ❋ Central to many other gardens ❋ Member 'Bed and Breakfast for Garden Lovers'

For brochure please ring Jill and Malcolm Ainslie,
Darkley House, Norton Canon, Herefordshire HR4 7BT
Tel: 01544 318121

The Herb Society

Deddington Hill Farm, Warmington, Banbury OX17 1XB
Tel: 01295 692000
Fax: 01295 692004
Email: email@herbsociety.co.uk

The Herb Society is an educational charity whose objective is to broaden the knowledge and use of herbs for the health and well-being of the individual and the community.

Members of the Herb Society receive four issues each year of Herbs, the UK's only specialist herb magazine, which features plant profiles, herb nurseries, gardening, cooking, herbal medicine, book reviews, and a diary of events at home – with special emphasis on regional group activities – and abroad.

There is also a mail order service for books and products, and a list of herb suppliers offering discounts to members.

Hertfordshire

Hon County Organiser: Mrs Edward Harvey, Wickham Hall, Bishop's Stortford, Herts CM23 1JQ
Assistant Hon County Organisers: Mr Michael Belderbos, 6 High Elms, Hatching Green, Harpenden, Hertfordshire AL5 2JU
Mrs Hedley Newton, Moat Farm House, Much Hadham, Herts SG10 6AE
Mrs Barry Fox, Jenningsbury, London Road, Hertford, Hertfordshire SG13 7NS
Hon County Treasurer: Mrs Rösli Lancaster, Manor Cottage, Aspenden, Buntingford, Herts SG9 9PB

DATES OF OPENING

Regular openings
For details see garden description
Benington Lordship, nr Stevenage
Capel Manor Gardens, Enfield

By appointment only
For telephone numbers and other details see garden descriptions. Private visits welcomed
207 East Barnet Road, New Barnet
94 Gallants Farm Road, East Barnet

March 26 Sunday
Holwell Manor, nr Hatfield

April 2 Sunday
Pelham House, Brent Pelham
23 Wroxham Way, Harpenden

April 16 Sunday
St Paul's Walden Bury, Hitchin
Widford Gardens, nr Ware

April 30 Sunday
The Abbots House, Abbots Langley

May 1 Monday
23 Wroxham Way, Harpenden

May 7 Sunday
Odsey Park, Ashwell

May 14 Sunday
Great Munden House, nr Ware
Hunton Park, Hunton Bridge nr Abbots Langley
St Paul's Walden Bury, Hitchin

May 21 Sunday
Cockhamsted, Braughing
Rustling End Cottage, Rustling End
Thundridge Hill House, Ware
West Lodge Park, Hadley Wood

May 28 Sunday
Great Sarratt Hall, Rickmansworth
Moor Place, Much Hadham
20 Park Avenue South, Harpenden
Queenswood School, Hatfield

May 29 Monday
Queenswood School, Hatfield
23 Wroxham Way, Harpenden

June 4 Sunday
Kettle Green Gardens, Kettle Green
Roxford House, Hertingfordbury
St Mary's Croft, Elstree

June 5 Monday
Knebworth House Gardens, Knebworth

June 11 Sunday
Ashridge, Berkhamsted
Hill House, Stanstead Abbotts, nr Ware
Hunton Park, Hunton Bridge nr Abbots Langley
Shaw's Corner, Ayot St Lawrence
Wickham Hall, Bishop's Stortford
23 Wroxham Way, Harpenden

June 18 Sunday
3 Gardens at Serge Hill, Abbots Langley
The Gardens of Charles Lamb, Mackerye End, Harpenden
St Paul's Walden Bury, Hitchin

June 24 Saturday
Benington Lordship, nr Stevenage
Tanglewood, Tring

June 25 Sunday
Bayford Village Gardens, Bayford
Benington Lordship, nr Stevenage
Childwick Green
The Mill House, Tewin, nr Welwyn
Tanglewood, Tring

June 30 Friday
Rustling End Cottage, Rustling End (evening)

July 2 Sunday
Kennel Farm, Little Hadham
Ragged Hall, Gaddesden Row, nr Hemel Hempstead
Waterdell House, Croxley Green

July 9 Sunday
The Abbots House, Abbots Langley
Hunton Park, Hunton Bridge nr Abbots Langley
Oxhey Hall Gardens, Watford

July 16 Sunday
Putteridge Bury
'Stresa', 126 The Drive, Rickmansworth

July 23 Sunday
20 Park Avenue South, Harpenden
23 Wroxham Way, Harpenden

August 27 Sunday
The Abbots House, Abbots Langley

August 28 Monday
23 Wroxham Way, Harpenden

September 3 Sunday
Hunton Park, Hunton Bridge nr Abbots Langley

September 10 Sunday
23 Wroxham Way, Harpenden

September 17 Sunday
20 Park Avenue South, Harpenden

October 8 Sunday
Capel Manor Gardens, Enfield

October 29 Sunday
West Lodge Park, Hadley Wood

By Appointment Gardens. These owners do not have a fixed opening day, usually because they cannot accommodate large numbers or have insufficient parking space.

Regular Openings. Open throughout the year. They are listed at the beginning of the Diary Section.

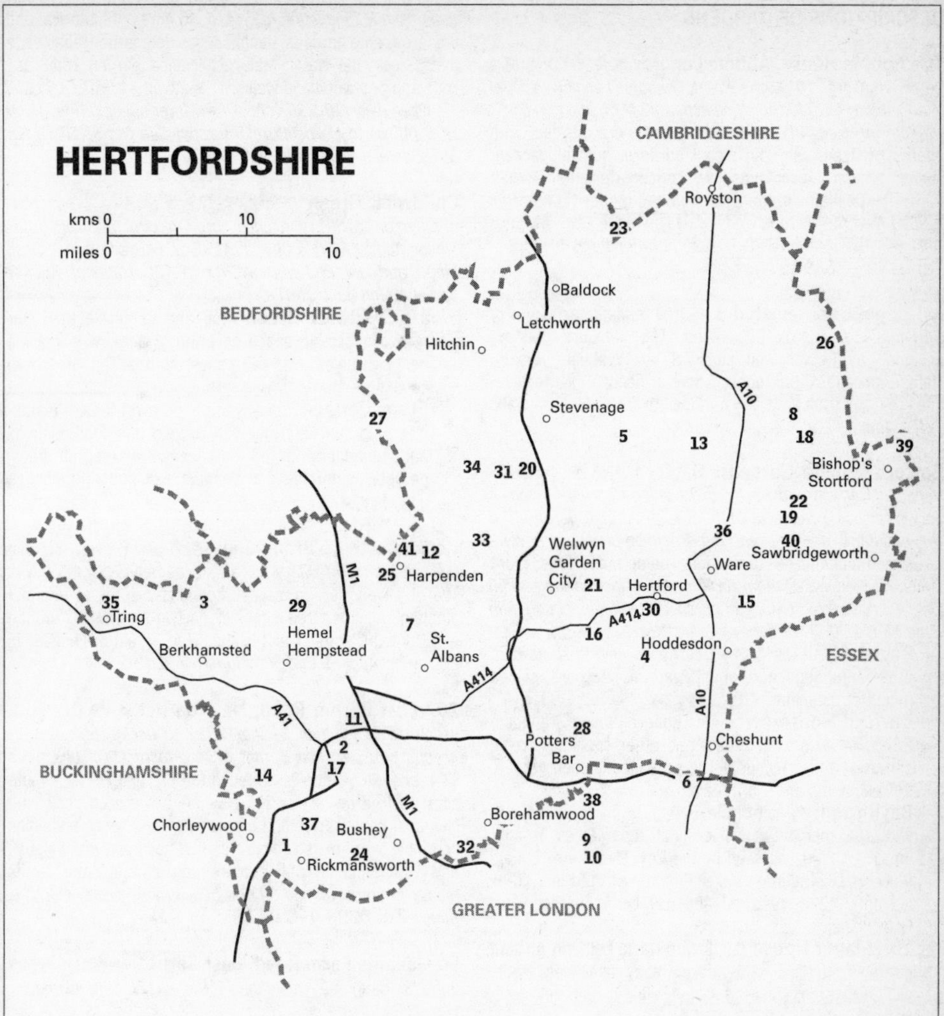

KEY

1 'Stresa'
2 The Abbots House
3 Ashridge
4 Bayford Village Gardens
5 Benington Lordship
6 Capel Manor Gardens
7 Childwick Green
8 Cockhamsted
9 207 East Barnet Road
10 94 Gallants Farm Road
11 3 Gardens at Serge Hill
12 The Gardens of Charles Lamb
13 Great Munden House
14 Great Sarratt Hall
15 Hill House
16 Holwell Manor
17 Hunton Park
18 Kennel Farm
19 Kettle Green Gardens
20 Knebworth House Gardens
21 The Mill House
22 Moor Place
23 Odsey Park
24 Oxhey Hall Gardens
25 20 Park Avenue South
26 Pelham House
27 Putteridge Bury
28 Queenswood School
29 Ragged Hall
30 Roxford House
31 Rustling End Cottage
32 St Mary's Croft
33 Shaw's Corner
34 St Paul's Walden Bury
35 Tanglewood
36 Thundridge Hill House
37 Waterdell House
38 West Lodge Park
39 Wickham Hall
40 Widford Gardens
41 23 Wroxham Way

DESCRIPTIONS OF GARDENS

The Abbots House, Abbots Langley ♿✂❀ (Dr & Mrs Peter Tomson) *10 High Street, Abbots Langley NW of Watford (5m from Watford). Junction 20 M25, junction 6 M1. Parking in free village car park.* 1¾-acre garden with interesting trees; shrubs; mixed borders; sunken garden; ponds; annual flower meadow; conservatory. Many half hardy plants. Plants propagated from the garden. TEAS. *Adm £2 Chd free (ACNO to Friends of St Lawrence Church). Suns April 30, July 9, Aug 27 (2-5). Also at other times by appt* **Tel 01923 264946**

Ashridge, Berkhamsted ♿ (Gardens Manager) *3m N of Berkhamsted.* Approx 200 acres. The pleasure gardens designed by Repton and modified by Wyatville. Rosary, Italian garden, skating pond, Armorial garden, grotto. Avenues of trees from Victorian period with rhododendron walk. TEAS. *Adm £2 Chd £1. Sun June 11 (2-6)*

Bayford Village Gardens, Bayford ♿✂❀ *Off B158 between Hatfield and Hertford. 14 village gardens open. A very interesting range of both large and small gardens for this popular bi-annual event. Bands will be playing in several gardens.* Ploughman's lunch, bars, home-made teas, plant stalls, Marked walks. *Adm to all gardens incl parking £4.50 Chd 50p (Share to St Mary's Church, and Village School). Sun June 25 (11.30-5) Gardens open include*

Bayford Hall (Mr & Mrs George Rowley) Rose garden, ornamental pond, acre of wild garden, peacocks, guinea fowl. Refreshments

Bayford House (Mr & Mrs Robert Wilson Stephens) Extensive lawns, old cedars and other specimen trees, shrubs and herbaceous borders. Walled kitchen garden. Refreshments and Plant Stall

Bayfordbury (Rialto Holmes Plc) 14 acres of grounds with specimen trees incl original cedar trees brought into the country as seed by the Rev. Uvedale of Enfield Place in 1754. Clinton Baker Pinetum started in 1837 is currently being restored and will be open this year. Refreshments

The Manor House (Mr & Mrs David Latham) Ancient garden with ornamental lake, many specimen trees, walled garden, John of Gaunt 900 yr old oak tree. Refreshments

The Warren House (Mr & Mrs Neville Hudson) Mature garden with extensive views; ornamental lake with island and cascade. Refreshments

■ **Benington Lordship, nr Stevenage** ✂❀ (Mr and Mrs C H A Bott) *Benington. 5m E of Stevenage, in Benington Village.* Hilltop garden on castle ruins overlooking lakes. Amazing April display of scillas, rose garden, hidden rock/water garden, spectacular borders, ornamental kitchen garden, nursery. *Adm £2.50 Chd free (ACNO to St Peters Church). Spring and Summer Bank Hol Mons, Weds April to Sept 30 (12-5). Suns April to Aug 31, Sun Oct 15 (2-5). For NGS TEAS and Floral Festival in Church adjoining garden. Sat, Sun June 24, 25 (12-6). Private visits of 20 and over, please* **Tel 01438 869668**

■ **Capel Manor Gardens, Enfield** ♿ (Capel Manor Charitable Corporation) *Bullsmoor Lane, Enfield, Middx. 3 mins from M25 junction M25/A10.* 30 Acres of historical and modern theme gardens, Japanese garden, large Italian style maze, rock and water features. Walled garden with rose collecton and woodland walks. TEAS. *Adm £4 OAP £3.50 Chd £2. Open daily (10-5.30 - check for winter opening times). For NGS (ACNO to Horticultural Therapy) Sun Oct 8 (10-5). For other details* **Tel 0208 366 4442**

Childwick Green *Midway between St Albans and Harpenden on A1081. Entrance through wrought iron gates signposted St Mary's Church.* TEAS at Forge Cottage. *Combined adm £2 Chd 50p (ACNO to The National Autistic Society). Sun June 25 (2-6)*

10 Childwick Green (Bob and Catherine Kay) Our own comfortable space covering ½-acre, with mature hedges of yew and cupressus, shrubs and other eye catching features. Idyllic setting

Forge Cottage (Cindy & Stan Andrews) ⅓-acre plantsman's garden. Informal with rockery and pond, troughs and containers, mixed herbaceous and shrub beds, pergolas with roses and clematis. Exhibition of paintings and plant stall

Cockhamsted, Braughing ♿✂❀ (David & Jan Marques) *2m E of village towards Braughing Friars (7m N of Ware).* Lovely garden in open country. 2 acres of informal planting. Alliums, tree peonies, early roses. Walk around water-filled C14 moat and island. TEAS in aid of Leukaemia Research. *Adm £2 Chd 50p. Sun May 21 (2-6)*

207 East Barnet Road, New Barnet ✂❀ (Margaret Arnold) *M25 junction 24 then A111 to Cockfosters. Underground stations High Barnet or Cockfosters. On bus route 84A and 307.* This is a delightful example of a minute courtyard garden 25' x 25'. High fences are covered with clematis, honeysuckle and passion flowers, roses and vines scramble over an arch above a seat. Small pond with goldfish and water plants. Many interesting and unusual plants mainly in pots. *Adm £1.50 Chd 50p. Private visits welcome, please* **Tel 0208 440 0377**

94 Gallants Farm Road, East Barnet ✂❀ (Mr & Mrs John Gething) *M25 junction 24 then A111 to Cockfosters. Underground stations High Barnet, Cockfosters or Arnos Grove. On bus route 84a and 307.* Small town garden 50′ × 30′ approx, designed to give variety of views of hidden rooms. The mixed planting of trees, shrubs and perennials is constantly changing as new plants are acquired and others outgrow their allotted space. Fishpond, rockery, obelisks and a plethora of pots provide plenty of interest. TEA. *Adm £1.50 Chd 50p. Private visits welcome (parties max. 16) please* **Tel 0208 368 4261**

3 Gardens at Serge Hill, Abbots Langley *½m E of Bedmond, past White Hart public house, on Serge Hill Lane.* TEAS at Serge Hill. *Combined adm £3 Chd 50p (ACNO to Tibet Relief Fund UK). Sun June 18 (2-5)*

The Barn, Abbots Langley ✂❀ (Tom Stuart-Smith and Family) 1-acre plantsman's garden. Small sheltered courtyard planted with unusual shrubs and perennials, contrasts with more open formal garden with views over wild flower meadow.

Serge Hill, Abbots Langley ✗✿ (Sir Murray & Lady Stuart-Smith) Regency house (not open) in parkland setting with fine kitchen garden of ½ acre. A range of unusual wall plants, mixed border of 100yds. TEAS
3 Serge Hill Cottages (Tony & Louise Balcombe) Beautifully kept cotage garden, with fruit, vegetables and flowers

The Gardens of Charles Lamb Mackerye End, Harpenden ✗ *A1 junction 4, follow signs for Wheathampstead then Luton. Gardens ½m from Wheathampstead on R. M1 junction 10 follow Lower Luton Rd (B653) to Cherry Tree Inn. Turn L following signs to Mackerye End. Coffee, lunches and TEAS. Adm £2.50 OAP £1.50 Chd £1. Sun June 18 (11-5)*
 Eightacre (Mr J Walker) 2-acre garden incl shrub and herbaceous beds, wild life pond, raised vegetable beds, greenhouse and orchards.
 Hollybush Cottage (Mr & Mrs John Coaton) A well established cottage garden around this listed house (not open)
 Mackerye End Farm &. (Mr & Mrs Andrew Clarke) A delightful new garden in the grounds of the restored C17 farmhouse (not open) with extensive borders, orchard and pond
 Mackerye End House &. (Mr & Mrs David Laing) A 1550 Grade 1 manor house (not open) set in 11 acres of gardens and park. Front garden set in framework of formal yew hedges with a long border and a fine C17 tulip tree. Victorian walled garden now divided into smaller sections; path maze; cutting garden; quiet garden. W garden enclosed by pergola walk of old English roses and vines.

Great Munden House, nr Ware ✗✿ (Mr and Mrs D Wentworth-Stanley) *7m N of Ware. Off A10 on Puckeridge by-pass turn W; or turning off A602 via Dane End.* 3½-acre informal garden with lawns. Mixed shrub and herbaceous borders, a variety of shrub roses, orchard with climbing roses growing through apple trees. Kitchen and herb garden. 2 small pond areas with water lilies. TEAS. *Adm £2 Chd 50p (ACNO to NE Herts NSPCC). Sun May 14 (2.30-5.30). Private visits welcome, please* **Tel 01920 438244**

Great Sarratt Hall, Rickmansworth &.✗✿ (H M Neal Esq, CBE) *Sarratt, N of Rickmansworth. From Watford N via A41 (or M1 Exit 5) to Kings Langley; and left (W) to Sarratt; garden is 1st on R after village sign.* 4 acres; herbaceous and mixed shrub borders; pond, moisture-loving plants and trees; walled kitchen garden; rhododendrons, magnolias, camellias; new planting of specialist conifers and rare trees. TEAS. *Adm £2.50 Chd free (ACNO The Courtauld Institute of Art Fund). Sun May 28 (2-6)*

Hill House, Stanstead Abbotts, nr Ware ✗✿ (Mr & Mrs R C L Pilkington) *From A10 turn E on to A414; then B181 for Stanstead Abbotts; left at end of High St, garden 1st R past Church. Ample car parking.* 9 acres incl wood; species roses, herbaceous border, water garden, conservatory, woodland walks. Lovely view over Lea Valley. Unusual plants for sale. Home-made TEAS. *Adm £2.50 Chd 50p (ACNO to St Andrews Parish Church of Stanstead Abbotts). Sun June 11 (2-5.30). Private visits welcome, please Tel* **01920 870013**

Holwell Manor, nr Hatfield &.✗ (Mr & Mrs John Gillum) *On W side of B1455, short lane linking A414 with B158 between Hatfield (3m) and Hertford (4m). B1455 joins the A414 roundabout and is signposted Essendon. Holwell is 500yds from this roundabout.* Natural garden with large pond fed by hydraulic ram powered fountain, mature trees, river walks; approx 2-3 acres. Island in pond covered with daffodils and narcissi in spring. TEAS. *Adm £2.50 Chd 50p. Sun March 26 (2-5.30)*

Hunton Park, Hunton Bridge nr Abbots Langley ✿ (The Administrator) *1m S of Junction 20 off M25 and 3m N of Watford. On exiting from Junction 20 follow signs to Watford (A41), turn L at traffic lights after ½m signposted Abbots Langley. Follow Bridge Rd for ½m up hill and Hunton Park on the RH-side.* The 22 acre grounds incl terraced lawns, woodland and woodland plantings, small pond, herbaceous border, heather garden. Rose beds, mature trees and plants of seasonal interest. A picnic area is provided. TEA. *Adm £2 OAP £1.50 Chd free. (ACNO to British heart Foundation) Suns May 14, June 11, July 9, Sept 3 (1-5)* **Tel 01923 261511**

Kennel Farm, Little Hadham &.✗ (Mr & Mrs Oliver Weaver) *From A10 leave at junction with A120 marked Colchester/Stansted. 3m turn L marked Albury School/Albury End. 1st house on L after ½m. From M11 leave at junction 8. Follow signs marked A120 Hertford. T-lights after 6m, at Little Hadham carry straight on approx 1m turn R marked Albury End.* Listed C16 house (not open) with tranquil country garden of 1½ acres; mature native trees, mixed herbaceous and shrub borders; container garden. Adjoining park with excellent parking. TEAS. *Adm £2 Chd 50p. Sun July 2 (2-6)*

NEW Kettle Green Gardens, Kettle Green &.✗ *3/4m W of Much Hadham on Kettle Green Road. TEA. Combined adm £2 Chd 50p. Sun June 4 (2-6)*
 NEW Kettle Barn (Mr & Mrs John Wiseman) Unusual new courtyard garden designed and planted by an artist. Pond, architectural plants and sculptures by Bernard Sindall
 NEW Moat Farm House (Mr & Mrs Hedley Newton) C17 Century moated farmhouse on island with ancient mulberry tree, mixed borders and orchard. Approx 1 acre

▲ Knebworth House Gardens, Knebworth &.✗ (The Lord Cobbold) *28m N of London; direct access from A1(M) at Stevenage. Station and Bus stop: Stevenage 3m.* Historic house, home of Bulwer Lytton; Victorian novelist and statesman. Knebworth's magnificent gardens, laid out by Lutyens in 1908, have benefited from 15 years of restoration and embellishment. Lutyens' pollarded lime avenues, Gertrude Jekyll's herb garden, the newly restored maze, yew hedges, roses and herbaceous borders are key features of the formal gardens with peaceful woodland walks beyond. Tea Room. *Adm £2.50 Chd £1.50. For NGS Mon June 5 (11-5.30)*

The Mill House, Tewin, nr Welwyn &.✗✿ (Dr & Mrs R V Knight) *3½m W of Hertford and 3½m E of Welwyn on B1000. Parking at Archers Green which is signposted on B1000. On the banks of the R Mimram.* Approx 20 acres; mature gardens incl fine hedges, woodlands, many rare trees labelled, shrub and herbaceous borders, spring fed water gardens, with an abundance of wildlife in a lovely valley setting. Plants and TEAS in aid of Isabel Hospice. *Adm £2.50 Chd under 10 free. Sun June 25 (2-6)*

Moor Place, Much Hadham &🌼 (Mr and Mrs B M Norman) *Entrance either at war memorial or at Hadham Cross.* 2 C18 walled gardens. Herbaceous borders. Large area of shrubbery, lawns, hedges and trees. 2 ponds. Approx 10 acres. TEAS. *Adm £3 Chd 50p. Sun May 28 (2-5.30)*

Odsey Park, Ashwell &✗ (Mr & The Hon Mrs Jeremy Fordham) *4½m on A505 between Royston and Baldock. Enter by Lodge on the N carriageway of A505 (going towards Royston), over cattle grid, follow signs to parking area. The A505 is a fast rd so take care when both entering and leaving. Sign on the N carriageway 350yds before the Lodge indicating Odsey Park.* A re-modelled 4-acre Victorian garden. Lawns, walled garden, tulips and spring bulbs, new parterre, herbaceous and shrub borders, iris garden and yew walks. TEAS. *Adm £2 Chd under 10 free (ACNO to St Mary's Church, Ashwell). Sun May 7 (2-5)*

NEW **Oxhey Hall Gardens, Watford** ✗🌼 TEA at 156 Hillcroft Crescent. *Combined adm £2 Chd 50p. Sun July 9 (2-6)*

NEW **37 Oaklands Avenue** (Carolyn & Tony Huntley) *From A41 Watford by-pass take B462 S to Bushey and Oxhey station. Turn R then L on A4125 to Northwood. Oaklands Avenue approx 1½m on L.* Narrow garden approx 200' x 25' featuring an ever increasing number of shrubs, perennials and grasses. Pergola, gravel garden and summerhouse plus many other interesting features
NEW **143 Hillcroft Crescent** (Tertia & Robert Carter) A compact garden which is now bursting at the seams; includes small herbaceous borders, gigantic hostas, several alpine troughs, a pond, wild flower section, and an ever growing collection of plants in pots
NEW **156 Hillcroft Crescent** (Ian & Hazel Jones) *In Northwood Road, turn L opposite wooden bus shelter into Hillcroft Crescent.* ½-acre garden with herbaceous and shrub borders and fruit trees which include a large fig tree covering wall above conservatory with grape vine inside

20 Park Avenue South, Harpenden &✗🌼 (Miss Isobel Leek) *Off A1081 turn W by The Cock Inn and War Memorial up Rothamsted Ave; 3rd on L.* ½-acre plantsman's garden with trees, shrub and herbaceous borders, alpine gravel bed, ponds and bog garden planted for yr-long interest and colour; aviary. Plants and TEAS. *Adm £1.50 Chd 50p. Suns May 28, July 23, Sept 17 (2-5.30)*

Pelham House, Brent Pelham &✗🌼 (Mr David Haselgrove) *On E side of Brent Pelham on B1038. When travelling from Clavering immed after the village sign.* 3½-acre informal garden on alkaline clay started by present owner in 1986. Plenty of interest to the plantsman. Wide variety of trees and shrubs especially birches and oaks. Bulb frames, raised beds with alpines and acid-loving plants and small formal area with ponds. Many daffodils and tulips. *Adm £2.50 Chd free (ACNO to Brent Pelham Church). Sun April 2 (2-5)*

Putteridge Bury ✗ (University of Luton) *On A505 Hitchin/Luton rd 2m NE of Luton on S side of dual carriageway.* Gertrude Jekyll's plans for the rose garden and mixed border have been faithfully restored by the Herts Gardens Trust and are maintained by the University. Edwin Lutyens' reflecting pool and massive yew hedges are important features. Wide lawns, mature trees and new specimens make this an enjoyable garden to visit. It provides an insight into garden design by Lutyens and Jekyll. TEAS. *Adm £3 Chd £1 (ACNO to Herts Gardens Trust). Sun July 16 (10-5)*

Queenswood School, Hatfield &✗🌼 (The Estate Manager) *Shepherds Way. From S: M25 junction 24 signposted Potters Bar. In ½m at lights turn R onto A1000 signposted Hatfield. In 2m turn R onto B157. School is ½m on the R. From N: A1000 from Hatfield. In 5m turn L onto B157.* 120 acres informal gardens and woodlands. Rhododendrons, fine specimen trees, shrubs and herbaceous borders. Glasshouses; fine views to Chiltern Hills. Picnic area. Lunches and TEAS. *Adm £2 OAPS/Chd £1. Sun, Mon May 28, 29 (11-6)*

Ragged Hall, Gaddesden Row, nr Hemel Hempstead &✗🌼 (Mr & Mrs Anthony Vincent) *4m N of Hemel Hempstead. Take A4146 to Water End. Turn R up hill for 2m, turn R at T-junction. House is 3rd L, ⅓m.* Garden of 1½ acres.Some new landscaping and new late summer border. Mixed borders. Some unusual plants. Enclosed rose garden with old and new roses. Potager with vegetables and flowers. TEAS in aid of Dream Flight. *Adm £2 Chd 50p. Sun July 2 (2-6)*

NEW **Roxford House, Hertingfordbury** (Mr & Mrs David Haysey) *On W side of St Mary's Lane linking A414 with B158 to W of Hertford (3m). Take track on RHS before humpbacked bridge.* 3½ acre garden. Listed C18 farm house (not open) with modern extension. Newly designed (Julie Toll) and planted garden. Mix of shrub and natural beds and herbaceous borders. Modern planting in pool area. Moat and orchard area. TEAS in aid of St Mary's Hertingfordbury Parish Church. *Adm £2 Chd 50p. Sun June 4 (2-5)*

NEW **Rustling End Cottage, Rustling End** (Julia & Tim Wise) *1m N of Codicote. From B656 turn L into "3 Houses lane" then R to Rustling End. House is 2nd on L.* Attractive early C18 cottage (not open) under restoration surrounded by fields and woodland. A ½ acre plantswoman's garden, started by the owners 6 yrs ago and still developing. Terraces with drought tolerant plants, deep herbaceous borders, wild garden and pond with bog planting. Small ornamental kitchen garden. *Adm £1.50 Chd 50p. Sun May 21 (2-5) Fri June 30 (6.30-9.30)*

Shaw's Corner, Ayot St Lawrence &✗🌼 (The Custodian) *At SW end of village, 2m NE of Wheathampstead; approx 2m from B653 (A1 junction 4).* Approx 4 acres with richly planted borders, orchard, small meadow, wooded areas and views over the Hertfordshire countryside. An historical garden, belonging to George Bernard Shaw from 1906 until his death in 1950. Hidden among the trees is the revolving summerhouse where Shaw retreated to write. TEAS. *Adm £1.50 Chd 75p. Sun June 11 (1-5)*

NEW St Mary's Croft, Elstree (Hilde & Lionel Wainstein) *Off A411 which runs between the A41 and A1. Leave M25 at J23, then take A1 London. R at first roundabout, L at next roundabout into Barnet Lane, Fortune Lane is on L in Elstree Village. Careful parking on Barnet Lane and limited parking in Fortune Lane (L only).* 1 acre plantsman's garden has many different facets and is constantly being developed. Wander through the woodland to the large wildlife pond, bog garden and summerhouse. Wildflower meadow, herb garden, rockery and many nooks and crannies as well as a magnificent conservatory and extensive mixed plantings. TEA. *Adm £2 Chd £1. Sun June 4 (2-6)*

St Paul's Walden Bury, Hitchin ♿ (Mr and Mrs Simon Bowes Lyon) *on B651 5m S of Hitchin; ½m N of Whitwell.* Childhood home of The Queen Mother. Formal woodland garden listed Grade 1. Laid out about 1730, influenced by French tastes. Long rides and avenues span about 40 acres, leading to temples, statues, lake and ponds. Also more recent flower gardens and woodland garden with rhododendrons, azaleas and magnolias. Dogs on leads. TEAS. *Adm £2.50 Chd 50p (ACNO to St Pauls Walden Church). Suns April 16, May 14, June 18 (2-7). Lakeside concert July. Also other times by appt adm £5* **Tel 01438 871218 or 871229**

NEW 'Stresa', 126 The Drive, Rickmansworth (Roger and Patt Trigg) *From M25 junction 18 take A404 towards Rickmansowrth for 200yds, turn R into The Clump, then 1st L into the Drive. From Rickmansworth take A404 toward Amersham for approx ⅓m, L into Valley Road, 1st L into The Drive.* Approx ½ acre, herbaceous perennials and shrubs, particularly hostas and shade loving plants; euphorbias, dicentras, rhododendrons, phlox, hebes and grasses; new conservatory. TEAS. *Adm £1.50 Chd 75p. Sun July 16 (2-6)*

Tanglewood, Tring ✻❀ (Mr & Mrs E Page) *Nursery gardens. E of Tring High St. Turn L at roundabout, then R into Mortimer Hill. Nursery gardens is 1st L. Free parking in town or on Mortimer Hill.* Mature trees give this garden a woodland effect. Mixed planting with shrubs and perennials, rose arches, rock garden, gravel garden with small pool. Planted for yr-round interest. TEAS *Adm £1.50 Chd 50p Sat, Sun June 24, 25 (2-6). Also by appt,* **Tel 01442 823659**

Thundridge Hill House, Ware ♿❀ (Mr & Mrs Christopher Melluish) *¾m from The Sow & Pigs Inn off the A10 down Cold Christmas Lane. 2m from Ware to the N [Map Ref: OS 814 359].* Well-established garden of approx 2½ acres; good variety of plants and shrubs incl old roses. Fine views down to Rib Valley. TEAS in aid of St Mary's Thundridge Parish Church. *Adm £3 Chd 50p. Sun May 21 (2-5)*

Waterdell House, Croxley Green ♿✻❀ (Mr and Mrs Peter Ward) *1½m from Rickmansworth. Exit 18 from M25. Direction R'worth to join A412 towards Watford. From A412 turn left signed Sarratt, along Croxley Green, fork right past Coach & Horses, cross Baldwins Lane into Little Green Lane, then left at top.* 1½-acre walled garden systematically developed over more than 45 years: mature and young trees, topiary holly hedge, herbaceous borders, modern island beds of shrubs, old-fashioned roses, vegetable, fruit and pond gardens. TEAS £1 *Adm £2 OAPs/Chd £1.50 Sun July 2 (2-6) and private visits welcome by appt yr round, please* **Tel 01923 772775**

West Lodge Park, Hadley Wood ♿ (Trevor Beale Esq) *Cockfosters Rd. On A111 between Potters Bar and Southgate. Exit 24 from M25 signed Cockfosters.* The 10-acre Beale Arboretum consists of over 700 varieties of trees and shrubs, incl national plant collections of eleagnus and hornbeam cultivars, with a good selection of conifers, oaks, maples and mountain ash. A network of paths has been laid out, and most specimens are labelled. Lunch or teas can be booked in West Lodge Park hotel in the grounds *Adm £2 Chd free Suns May 21 (2-5), Oct 29 (12-4). Organised parties anytime by appt* **Tel 0208 216 3900**

Wickham Hall, Bishop's Stortford ♿✻❀ (Mr & Mrs Ted Harvey) *1m NW of Bishop's Stortford. From A120 roundabout W of Bishop's Stortford take exit as for town. Wickham Hall drive is 300yds on LH-side* 1-acre garden surrounding Elizabethan farm house. Mixed borders of shrubs and old-fashioned roses. Large walled garden. TEAS *Adm £2 Chd 50p Sun June 11 (2-6)*

Widford Gardens, nr Ware ✻ *Approx 4m from Ware on the B1004 signposted Widford and Much Hadham. At Widford village sign take 1st turn on R into Abbotts Lane. Follow signs to car park on L.* TEAS in aid of St John the Baptist, Widford *Combined adm £3 Chd £1 Sun April 16 (2-5)*

> **Abbotts Farm, nr Ware** ❀ (Mr & Mrs Michael Franzman) 4-acre garden with mixed borders, roses, shrubs, nut walk, pond and rockery. Large selection of trees. Wonderful commanding views of surrounding countryside. All-yr interest especially in spring
>
> **1Daintrees** ✻❀ (John and Bernadette Thompson) A walled garden with pleached limes. Paved and gravelled with many interesting plants. Garden designed to flourish in dry conditions. All-yr interest. Private visits welcome, please, Tel 01279 843627

23 Wroxham Way, Harpenden ✻❀ (Mrs Margaret Easter) *NE Harpenden A1081 and B652 Station Rd or B653 Lower Luton Rd and Station Rd to Coldharbour Lane, L into Ox Lane, then 1st L.* Plantsman's garden 70′ × 35′. Sloping site with steps and walls. Large mixed border at front. Planted for yr-round interest. Galanthus, crocus, helleborus, diascia, old dianthus, geranium, penstemon, alpine scree, herbs, camomile lawn. National Collection of Thymus. Featured in Garden News Sept 1999. *Adm £1 (ACNO to Gt Ormond St Children's Hospital). Mons May 1, 29, Aug 28, Suns Apr 2, June 11, July 23, Sept 10 (2-5.30). Private visits welcome, please* **Tel 01582 768467**

Evening Opening (See also garden description)

Rustling End Cottage, Rustling End	June 30

Isle of Wight

Hon County Organiser: Mrs John Harrison, North Court, Shorwell PO30 3JG
Hon Assistant County Organiser: Mrs M Hammond, Norton House, Pixley Hill, Freshwater PO40 9TJ
Hon County Treasurer: Mrs R Hillyard, The Coach House, Duver Road, St Helens, Ryde PO33 1XY

DATES OF OPENING

By appointment only
For telephone numbers and other details see garden descriptions. Private visits welcomed
Old Barn, Shalfleet

March 26 Sunday
Kings Manor, Freshwater

April 16 Sunday
Woolverton House, St Lawrence

April 23 Sunday
Northcourt Gardens, Shorwell

April 30 Sunday
Badminton, Clatterford Shute

May 21 Sunday
7 Hilton Road, Gurnard

May 28 Sunday
Northcourt Gardens, Shorwell

June 4 Sunday
Nunwell House, Brading

June 11 Sunday
Dog Kennel Cottage, Thorley

June 18 Sunday
Niton Gardens

June 20 Tuesday
Mottistone Manor Garden, Mottistone

June 21 Wednesday
Northcourt Gardens, Shorwell (evening)

June 25 Sunday
Pitt House, Bembridge

July 1 Saturday
Highwood, Cranmore

July 2 Sunday
Highwood, Cranmore

July 9 Sunday
Ashknowle House, Whitwell

July 16 Sunday
Cassies, Billingham

August 13 Sunday
Crab Cottage, Shalfleet

October 15 Sunday
Spring Bank Nursery, Newchurch

DESCRIPTIONS OF GARDENS

Ashknowle House, Whitwell ⚘❀ (Mr & Mrs K Fradgley) *From Ventnor Rd turn for Ashknowle Lane in Whitwell close to church; lane is unmarked and unmade. Cars can be left in village but field parking is provided in grounds.* 3 acres. Mature but developing garden with trees, shrubs, lawned areas and new pond. Of special interest is vegetable garden and nursery with glasshouses and raised beds. Garden has recently been extended by further acre of young trees. TEA. *Adm £1.50 Chd free. Sun July 9 (2-5)*

Badminton, Clatterford Shute ❀ (Mr & Mrs G S Montrose) *Free parking in Carisbrooke Castle car park. Public footpath in corner of car park leads down to garden.* ¾ acre garden with natural chalk stream. Mixed borders planted by owners during last 22 yrs, for all-yr interest. Lovely views. Continuing development of parts of garden. *Adm £2 Chd 25p. Sun April 30 (2-5)*

NEW **Cassies, Billingham** ❀ (Barbara Smith) *S of Newport on Chillerton to Chale rd, 1m on L beyond Chillerton. Parking and entrance in adjoining field.* Strictly organic country garden of about an acre in an old sand pit. Light, dry, slightly alkaline soil. Herbaceous borders, pebble beds, shrubs, bark and grass paths, lawns and rockery. Mini wild flower meadow. Large pond. Deep ornamental vegetable bed. TEAS. *£2 Chd free (ACNO to Peter Smith Wavenden Student Award). Sun July 16 (2-5)*

Crab Cottage, Shalfleet ♿❀ (Mr & Mrs Peter Scott) *Turn past New Inn into Mill Rd. Go through NT gates. Entrance is first on L. Please park before going through NT gates. Less than 5 mins walk.* Just over 1 acre on gravelly soil, exposed to Westerlies. Walled garden with semi-tropical plants. Croquet lawn with fine views over Newtown Creek and Solent. Wildflower meadow leading to waterlily pond. TEA. *Adm £1.50 Chd free. Sun Aug 13 (2-5.30)*

NEW **Dog Kennel Cottage, Thorley** ♿❀ (Mr & Mrs C M Peplow) *2m E of Yarmouth on B3401. Turn R at Thorley X-roads 100yds prior to Thorley Church into Broad Lane. 8m W of Newport on B3401 via Calbourne, Newbridge, Wellow and Thorley. Turn L 100yds after Thorley Church into Broad Lane. Proceed 800yds up Broad Lane. Parking in field.* 2 acres newly developed garden. Large rockery, stream, climbing roses. Panoramic view of Yarmouth and Solent. Teas in aid of NSPCC. *£2 Chd 25p. Sun June 11 (2-5.30)*

Highwood, Cranmore ⚘❀ (Mr & Mrs Cooper) *Cranmore Ave is approx halfway between Yarmouth and Shalfleet village on A3054. From Yarmouth, turning is on LH-side, opp bus shelter, 3m out of Yarmouth on unmade rd.* 10 acre site with several acres under cultivation. Garden for all seasons and plant enthusiasts. Pond, woodland area with hellebores, borders and island beds. TEAS. *Adm £2 Chd free. Sat, Sun July 1, 2 (2-5). Private visits welcome, please* **Tel 01983 760550**

7 Hilton Road, Gurnard ♿❀ (Derek & Evelyn Hardy) *From Newport on A3020 bear L at garage, continue to Round House, at mini roundabout turn L into Tuttons Hill, L just after church. Parking in Tuttons Hill. 3 spaces for disabled in Hilton Rd.* ⅓ acre. Curved raised beds planted mostly with shrubs and perennials to give yr-round interest. TEAS. *Adm £1.50 Chd free. Sun May 21 (2-4.30)*

ISLE OF WIGHT

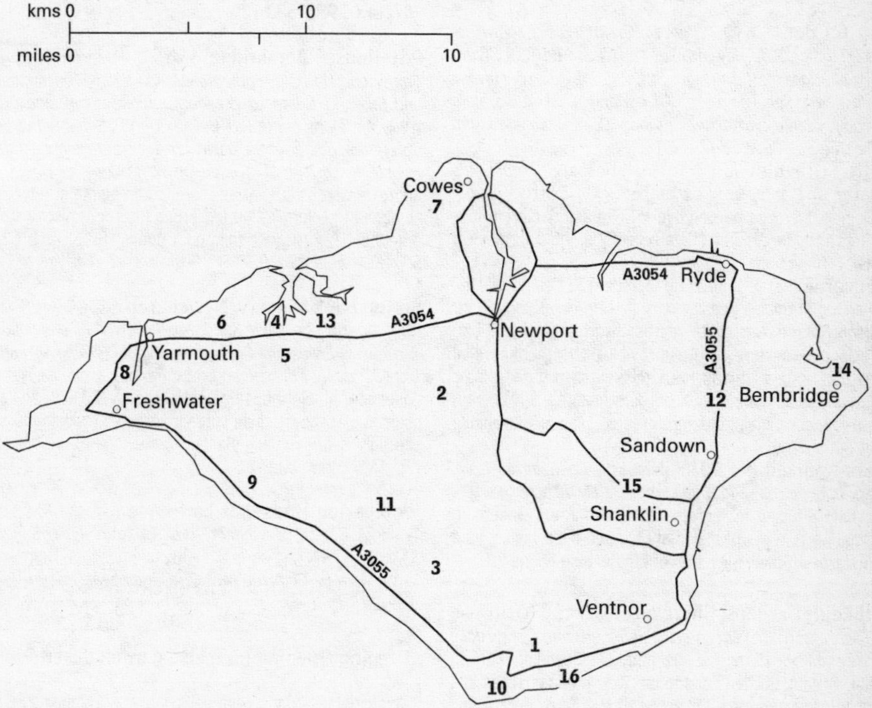

KEY

1 Ashknowle House
2 Badminton
3 Cassies
4 Crab Cottage
5 Dog Kennel Cottage
6 Highwood
7 7 Hilton Road
8 Kings Manor
9 Mottistone Manor Garden
10 Niton Gardens
11 Northcourt Gardens
12 Nunwell House
13 Old Barn
14 Pitt House
15 Spring Bank Nursery
16 Woolverton House

Kings Manor, Freshwater ♿✂❀ (Mr & Mrs Jamie Sheldon) *Head E out of Yarmouth over R Yar Bridge. Approx 1m turn L at top of Pixleys Hill. Entrance on L at top of next hill.* 3 acre informal garden with shrubs and spring bulbs and frontage onto marshes. Special features incl views of estuary and saltings, formal garden around lily pond. TEAS. *Adm £2 Chd free (ACNO to IOW Guides) Sun March 26 (2.30-5)*

▲ **Mottistone Manor Garden, Mottistone** (The National Trust) *8m SW Newport on B3399 between Brighstone and Brook.* Medium-sized formal terraced garden, backing onto Mediaeval and Elizabethan manor house, set in wooded valley with fine views of English Channel. Teas. *Adm £2 Chd £1. For NGS Tues June 20 (2-5.30)*

Niton Gardens ✂❀ *Niton Undercliff. From centre of Niton village go S by way of Institute Hill and Barrack Shute. 200yds past garage turn R into St Catherine's Road. Further 200yds to Castlehaven Lane. All parking in St Catherine's Road only, due to narrowness of lane.* TEAS. *Combined adm £2 Chd 25p Sun June 18 (2-5.30)*

NEW **Graytiles** ✂ (Mr & Mrs C Hobbs) *St Catherine's Road. On L at top of St Catherine's Road.* 5 acre S-facing, sloping, terraced garden overlooking sea. Victorian features include circular steps recently planted to make a daisy 'fountain'.

Lucerne (Peter & Elizabeth Marsden) *St Catherine's Rd. Parking in Buddle Inn car park by kind permission of Mr John Bourne.* Approx 1½ acres. S-facing garden is old-fashioned mixture with sea views. Northern walled garden across rd was formerly a kitchen garden, now grass tennis court with borders planted 199⅔ with shrubs, perennials and shrub roses. Teas also available at Buddle Inn.

Springmead (Mr & Mrs John Hill) *Castlehaven Lane. Springmead is 2nd bungalow on R.* ¼-acre garden, mainly S-facing in temperate area of Niton Undercliff. Planting consists of mixed shrubs and perennials plus a few trees. Small collection of lithops also on view.

Northcourt Gardens, Shorwell ♿❀ (Mrs C D Harrison, Mr & Mrs J Harrison) *On entering Shorwell from Carisbrooke entrance on R.* 15 acres incl bathhouse, walled kitchen garden, stream. Garden rises to mediterranean terraces and new sub-tropical garden. Collection of 100 hardy geraniums. Jacobean Manor House (part open). TEAS. *Adm £2 Chd 25p. Easter Sun April 23, Sun May 28 (2-5.30).* **Evening Opening** *Wed June 21 (6-8) guided tour. Wine. Adm £4. Pre-booked only, please* **Tel 01983 740415**

Nunwell House, Brading ✂❀ (Colonel and Mrs J A Aylmer) *3m S of Ryde; signed off A3055 in Brading into Coach Lane.* 5 acre, beautifully set formal and shrub gardens with exceptional view of Solent. 1acre walled garden recently re-planned. House developed over 5 centuries (not open), full of architectural interest. Coaches by appt only. TEAS. *Adm £2 Acc chd free. Sun June 4 (2-5)*

Old Barn, Shalfleet ✂❀ (Mrs M Hampton) *Take rd to Newtown, E of Shalfleet. Corf Lane 1st on L.* 1¼ acre, attractive spring garden. Also 2 herbaceous borders, shrubs and bog garden. *Adm £1.50. By appt March-July, ring before 10,* **Tel 01983 531420**

Pitt House, Bembridge ♿✂ (L J Martin Esq.) *E of Bembridge Harbour. Enter Bembridge Village, pass museum and take 1st L into Love Lane. Continue down lane (5 min walk) as far as bend; Pitt House is on L. Enter tall wrought iron gates. By car enter Ducie Ave 1st L before museum. Pitt House at bottom of avenue on R. Parking in Ducie Ave.* Approx 4 acres with varied aspects and points of interest. A number of sculptures dotted around garden; also Victorian greenhouse, mini waterfall and 4 ponds. TEAS. *Adm £2 Chd 50p. Sun June 25 (10.30-5)*

Spring Bank Nursery, Newchurch ♿✂❀ (Mr & Mrs K Hall) *Approx 3m from Sandown. Follow A3056 signposted Arreton, at Branstone Cross, take R-hand turning Springbank lies 400yds N of Branstone Cross. Parking available.* National Collection of Nerine sarniensis, approx 20,000 flowering bulbs in glasshouse. Also outdoor Nerine bowdenii and other species. Award winning plants. *Adm £2 Chd free. Sun Oct 15 (10-4.30)*

Woolverton House, St Lawrence (Mr and Mrs S H G Twining) *3m W of Ventnor; Bus 16 from Ryde, Sandown, Shanklin.* Flowering shrubs, bulbs, fine position. Home-made TEAS. *Adm £2 Chd free (ACNO to Crimebeat, Isle of Wight). Sun April 16 (2-5)*

Evening Opening (See also garden description)

Northcourt Gardens, Shorwell	June 21

Kent

Hon County Organiser: Mrs Valentine Fleming, Stonewall Park, Edenbridge, Kent TN8 7DG
Deputy Hon County Organiser: Mrs Mervyn Streatfeild, Hoath House, Edenbridge, Kent TN8 7DB
Asst Hon County Organisers: Mrs Jeremy Gibbs, Upper Kennards, Leigh, Tonbridge, Kent TN11 8RE
Mrs Nicholas Irwin, Hoo Farmhouse, Minster, Ramsgate, Kent CT12 4JB
Mrs Richard Latham, Stowting Hill House, Ashford, Kent TN25 6BE
Miss Elspeth Napier, 447 Wateringbury Road, East Malling, Kent ME19 6JQ
Mrs Simon Toynbee, Old Tong Farm, Brenchley, Kent TN12 7HT
Hon County Treasurer: Mr Valentine Fleming, Stonewall Park, Edenbridge, Kent TN8 7DG

DATES OF OPENING

Regular openings
For details see garden description
Beech Court Gardens, Challock
Cobham Hall, Cobham
Doddington Place, nr Sittingbourne
Finchcocks, Goudhurst
Gardens of Gaia, Cranbrook
Goodnestone Park, Wingham
Great Comp, Borough Green
Groombridge Place Gardens, Groombridge
Hever Castle, nr Edenbridge
Higham Park, Bridge
Hole Park, Rolvenden, Cranbrook
Marle Place, Brenchley
Mount Ephraim, Hernhill, Faversham
Old Buckhurst, Markbeech
Owl House, Lamberhurst
Penshurst Place, Penshurst
The Pines Garden, St Margaret's Bay
Riverhill House, Sevenoaks
Rock Farm, Nettlestead
Squerryes Court, Westerham
Yalding Organic Gardens, Yalding

By appointment only
For telephone numbers and other details see garden descriptions. Private visits welcomed
Cares Cross, Chiddingstone Hoath
Dolly's Garden, 43 Layhams Road, West Wickham
Little Trafalgar, Selling
Oswalds, Bishopsbourne
The Pear House, Sellindge
2 Thorndale Close, Chatham
Westview, Hempstead

February 20 Sunday
Goodnestone Park, Wingham
190 Maidstone Road, Chatham

February 24 Thursday
Broadview Gardens, Hadlow College, Hadlow

February 27 Sunday
Owl House, Lamberhurst

March 5 Sunday
Copton Ash, Faversham
Great Comp, Borough Green

March 12 Sunday
Great Comp, Borough Green
Old Orchard, Loose, Maidstone
Weeks Farm, Egerton Forstal

March 19 Sunday
Church Hill Cottage, Charing Heath
Copton Ash, Faversham
Godinton House, Ashford
Goodnestone Park, Wingham
Great Comp, Borough Green

March 26 Sunday
Church Hill Cottage, Charing Heath
Godinton House, Ashford
Great Comp, Borough Green
Stonewall Park Gardens, Chiddingstone Hoath

April 1 Saturday
Riverhill House, Sevenoaks
Sissinghurst Place, Sissinghurst

April 2 Sunday
Church Hill Cottage, Charing Heath
Cobham Hall, Cobham
Copton Ash, Faversham
Godmersham Park, Godmersham
Hole Park, Rolvenden, Cranbrook
190 Maidstone Road, Chatham
Mere House, Mereworth
Sissinghurst Place, Sissinghurst
Spilsill Court, Staplehurst
Stoneacre, Otham
Weald Cottage, Edenbridge

April 9 Sunday
Hole Park, Rolvenden, Cranbrook
Longacre, Selling
Old Orchard, Loose, Maidstone
Weald Cottage, Edenbridge
Weeks Farm, Egerton Forstal

April 16 Sunday
Church Hill Cottage, Charing Heath
Edenbridge House, Edenbridge
Mount Ephraim, Hernhill, Faversham
St Michael's Gardens, Roydon, Peckham Bush
Sotts Hole Cottage, Borough Green
Torry Hill, Sittingbourne
Withersdane Hall, Wye
Yalding Gardens

April 17 Monday
Groombridge Place Gardens, Groombridge

April 19 Wednesday
Sissinghurst Garden, Sissinghurst

April 22 Saturday
Great Maytham Hall, Rolvenden
Riverhill House, Sevenoaks

April 23 Sunday
Church Hill Cottage, Charing Heath
Copton Ash, Faversham
Higham Park, Bridge
Hole Park, Rolvenden, Cranbrook
Longacre, Selling
Olantigh, Wye
The Pines Garden, St Margaret's Bay
Weald Cottage, Edenbridge

April 24 Monday
Church Hill Cottage, Charing Heath
Copton Ash, Faversham
Crittenden House, Matfield
Godinton House, Ashford
Longacre, Selling
Weald Cottage, Edenbridge

April 29 Saturday
Pett Place, Charing

April 30 Sunday
Beechmont, Sevenoaks Weald
Bradbourne House Gardens, East Malling
Brogdale Horticultural Trust, Faversham
Copton Ash, Faversham
Hole Park, Rolvenden, Cranbrook
Ladham House, Goudhurst
Longacre, Selling
Marle Place, Brenchley
Pett Place, Charing

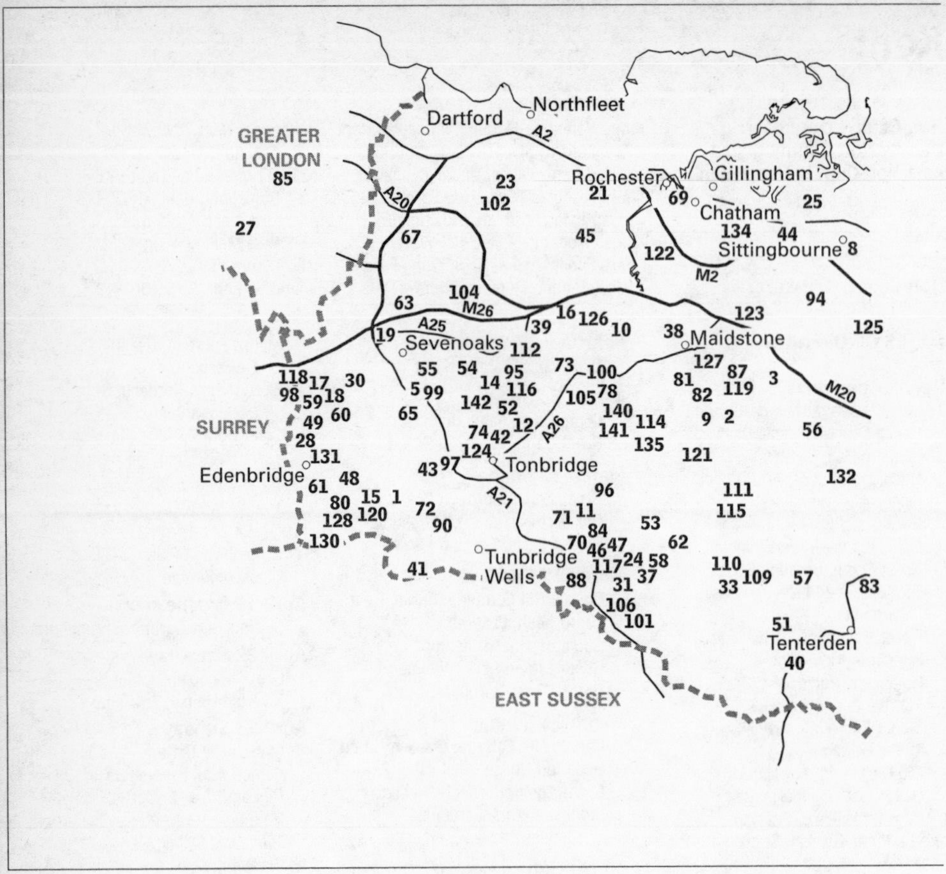

KEY

1 Abbotsmerry Barn
2 Amber Green Farmhouse
3 Battel Hall
4 Beech Court Gardens
5 Beechmont
6 The Beehive
7 Bilting House
8 185 Borden Lane
9 Boughton Monchelsea Place
10 Bradbourne House Gardens
11 Brenchley Gardens
12 Broadview Gardens
13 Brogdale Horticultural Trust
14 Brookers Cottage
15 Cares Cross
16 Cedar House
17 Charts Edge
18 Chartwell
19 Chevening
20 Church Hill Cottage
21 Cobham Hall
22 Copton Ash
23 Crawden Bank
24 Crittenden House
25 25 Crouch Hill Court
26 Doddington Place
27 Dolly's Garden
28 Edenbridge House
29 Elham Gardens
30 Emmetts Garden
31 Finchcocks
32 Flint Cottage
33 Gardens of Gaia
34 Godinton House
35 Godmersham Park
36 Goodnestone Park
37 Goudhurst Gardens
38 45 Grace Avenue
39 Great Comp
40 Great Maytham Hall
41 Groombridge Place
42 115 Hadlow Road
43 Hall Place
44 Hartlip Gardens
45 Haydown
46 Hayle Farm & Hayle Oast
47 Hazel Street Farmhouse
48 Hever Castle
49 High Quarry
50 Higham Park
51 Hole Park
52 Hookwood House
53 Horsmonden Gardens
54 Ightham Mote
55 Knole
56 Knowle Hill Farm
57 Kypp Cottage
58 Ladham House
59 Larksfield
60 Larksfield Cottage
61 Leydens
62 Little Combourne Farmhouse
63 Little Oast
64 Little Trafalgar
65 Long Barn
66 Longacre
67 Lullingstone Castle
68 Luton House
69 190 Maidstone Road
70 Marle Place

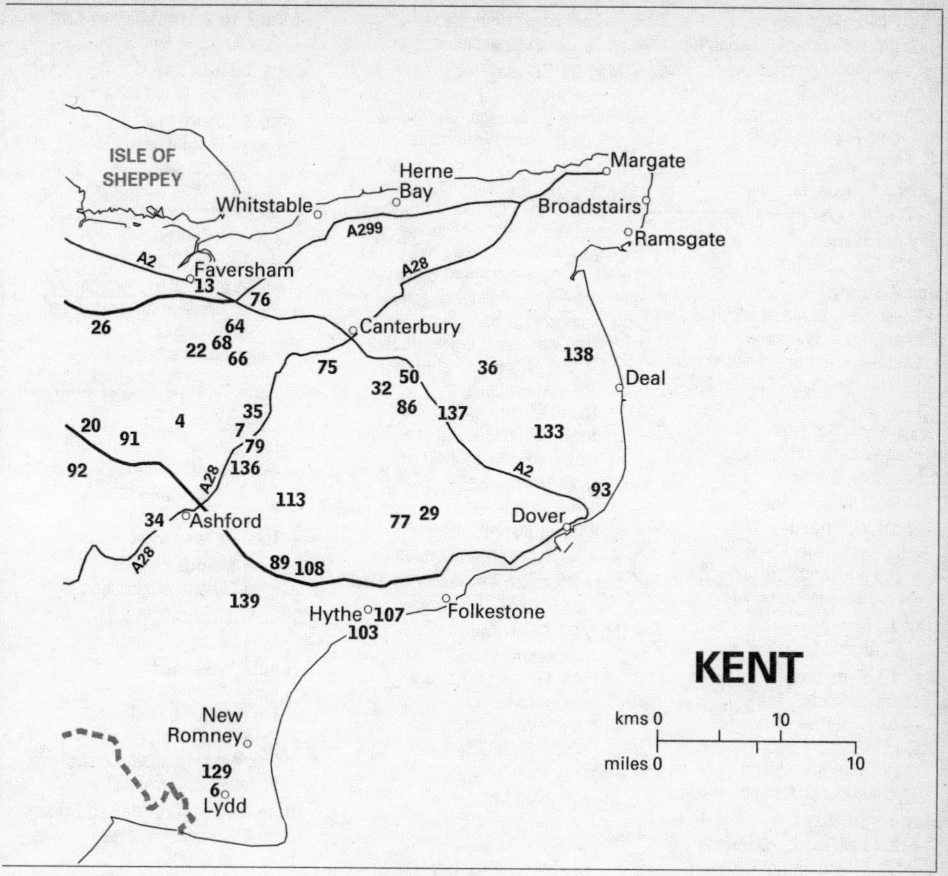

71	Maycotts
72	Meadow Wood
73	Mere House
74	Mill House
75	Milton Manor
76	Mount Ephraim
77	Mounts Court Farmhouse
78	Nettlestead Place
79	Olantigh
80	Old Buckhurst
81	Old Orchard
82	Old Orchard Bungalow
83	Old Place Farm
84	Old Tong Farm
85	Orchard Cottage
86	Oswalds
87	Otham Gardens
88	Owl House
89	The Pear House
90	Penshurst Place
91	Pett Place
92	Pevington Farm
93	The Pines Garden
94	Placketts Hole
95	Plaxtol Gardens
96	Puxted House
97	Ramhurst Manor
98	The Red House
99	Riverhill House
100	Rock Farm
101	Rogers Rough
102	Rose Cottage
103	Rose Lodge
104	St Clere
105	St Michael's Gardens
106	Scotney Castle
107	Sea Close
108	The Silver Spray
109	Sissinghurst Garden
110	Sissinghurst Place
111	Slaney Cottage
112	Sotts Hole Cottage
113	South Hill Farm
114	Southover
115	Spilsill Court
116	Spoute Cottage
117	Sprivers
118	Squerryes Court
119	Stoneacre
120	Stonewall Park Gardens
121	Swan Oast
122	2 Thorndale Close
123	Thornham Friars
124	Tonbridge School
125	Torry Hill
126	Town Hill Cottage
127	Turkey Court
128	Upper Pryors
129	Vine House
130	Waystrode Manor
131	Weald Cottage
132	Weeks Farm
133	West Studdal Farm
134	Westview
135	Whitehurst
136	Withersdane Hall
137	Womenswold Gardens
138	Worth Gardens
139	Wyckhurst
140	Yalding Gardens
141	Yalding Organic Gardens
142	Yew Tree Cottage

May 1 Monday
Church Hill Cottage, Charing Heath
Copton Ash, Faversham
Longacre, Selling
Stonewall Park Gardens, Chiddingstone Hoath

May 3 Wednesday
Old Buckhurst, Markbeech
Rock Farm, Nettlestead

May 6 Saturday
Rock Farm, Nettlestead

May 7 Sunday
Beechmont, Sevenoaks Weald
Charts Edge, Westerham
Church Hill Cottage, Charing Heath
Edenbridge House, Edenbridge
Finchcocks, Goudhurst
Goudhurst Gardens
Hole Park, Rolvenden, Cranbrook
Longacre, Selling
Luton House, Selling

May 10 Wednesday
Penshurst Place, Penshurst
Rock Farm, Nettlestead
Waystrode Manor, Cowden

May 12 Friday
High Quarry, Crockham Hill

May 13 Saturday
Emmetts Garden, Ide Hill
Gardens of Gaia, Cranbrook
Great Maytham Hall, Rolvenden
Rock Farm, Nettlestead
Yalding Organic Gardens, Yalding

May 14 Sunday
Battel Hall, Leeds, Maidstone
Bilting House, nr Ashford
Brenchley Gardens
Crawden Bank, Hartley
Flint Cottage, Bishopsbourne
Goudhurst Gardens
Larksfield, Crockham Hill
Larksfield Cottage, Crockham Hill
Longacre, Selling
Old Orchard, Loose, Maidstone
Old Orchard Bungalow, Loose, Maidstone
The Red House, Crockham Hill
Sea Close, Hythe
Stoneacre, Otham
Weald Cottage, Edenbridge

May 17 Wednesday
Brookers Cottage, Shipbourne
Edenbridge House, Edenbridge
Hazel Street Farmhouse, Horsmonden (evening)
Rock Farm, Nettlestead

May 20 Saturday
Hazel Street Farmhouse, Horsmonden
Old Buckhurst, Markbeech
Rock Farm, Nettlestead
Sprivers, Horsmonden

May 21 Sunday
Beech Court Gardens, Challock
Brookers Cottage, Shipbourne
Charts Edge, Westerham
Church Hill Cottage, Charing Heath
45 Grace Avenue, Maidstone
Hole Park, Rolvenden, Cranbrook
Ladham House, Goudhurst
Larksfield, Crockham Hill
Larksfield Cottage, Crockham Hill
Old Buckhurst, Markbeech
Ramhurst Manor, Leigh
The Red House, Crockham Hill
St Michael's Gardens, Roydon, Peckham Bush
Thornham Friars, Thurnham
Town Hill Cottage, West Malling
Waystrode Manor, Cowden

May 24 Wednesday
Doddington Place, nr Sittingbourne
Rock Farm, Nettlestead
Waystrode Manor, Cowden

May 25 to 26 Thursday to Friday
Kypp Cottage, Biddenden

May 27 Saturday
The Beehive, Lydd
Hayle Farm & Hayle Oast, Horsmonden
Kypp Cottage, Biddenden
Rock Farm, Nettlestead
Vine House, Lydd

May 28 Sunday
The Beehive, Lydd
Hall Place, Leigh
Hole Park, Rolvenden, Cranbrook
Kypp Cottage, Biddenden
Longacre, Selling
190 Maidstone Road, Chatham
Marle Place, Brenchley
The Pines Garden, St Margaret's Bay
Vine House, Lydd
Waystrode Manor, Cowden
Weald Cottage, Edenbridge

May 29 Monday
The Beehive, Lydd
Church Hill Cottage, Charing Heath
Kypp Cottage, Biddenden
Longacre, Selling
Meadow Wood, Penshurst
Scotney Castle, Lamberhurst
Vine House, Lydd
Weald Cottage, Edenbridge

May 30 Tuesday
Kypp Cottage, Biddenden

May 31 Wednesday
Haydown, Great Buckland (evening)
Rock Farm, Nettlestead
Whitehurst, Chainhurst

June 1 to 2 Thursday to Friday
Kypp Cottage, Biddenden

June 1 Thursday
Penshurst Place, Penshurst

June 3 Saturday
Boughton Monchelsea Place, Boughton Monchelsea
Old Buckhurst, Markbeech
Rock Farm, Nettlestead
The Silver Spray, Sellindge

June 4 Sunday
Abbotsmerry Barn, Penshurst
Amber Green Farmhouse, Chart Sutton
Boughton Monchelsea Place, Boughton Monchelsea
Copton Ash, Faversham
Crawden Bank, Hartley
Lullingstone Castle, Eynsford
Nettlestead Place, Nettlestead
Old Buckhurst, Markbeech
Rose Cottage, Hartley
The Silver Spray, Sellindge

June 5 Monday
Kypp Cottage, Biddenden

June 6 Tuesday
Kypp Cottage, Biddenden

June 7 Wednesday
Knole, Sevenoaks
Old Buckhurst, Markbeech
Rock Farm, Nettlestead
Sissinghurst Garden, Sissinghurst
Whitehurst, Chainhurst

June 8 to 9 Thursday to Friday
Kypp Cottage, Biddenden

June 9 Friday
Old Tong Farm, Brenchley

June 10 Saturday
25 Crouch Hill Court, Lower Halstow
Old Tong Farm, Brenchley
Rock Farm, Nettlestead

June 11 Sunday
Abbotsmerry Barn, Penshurst
Bilting House, nr Ashford
Church Hill Cottage, Charing Heath
Doddington Place, nr Sittingbourne
Edenbridge House, Edenbridge
Godmersham Park, Godmersham
Goudhurst Gardens
Hartlip Gardens
Longacre, Selling
Mill House, Hildenborough
Olantigh, Wye
Old Place Farm, High Halden
Old Tong Farm, Brenchley
Plaxtol Gardens, Plaxtol
St Clere, Kemsing
St Michael's Gardens, Roydon, Peckham Bush

Sea Close, Hythe
Waystrode Manor, Cowden
Weald Cottage, Edenbridge
Withersdane Hall, Wye

June 12 Monday
Kypp Cottage, Biddenden
Old Tong Farm, Brenchley

June 13 Tuesday
Kypp Cottage, Biddenden

June 14 Wednesday
Edenbridge House, Edenbridge (evening)
Little Combourne Farmhouse, Curtisden Green
Rock Farm, Nettlestead
The Silver Spray, Sellindge
Upper Pryors, Cowden
Waystrode Manor, Cowden

June 15 to 16 Thursday to Friday
Kypp Cottage, Biddenden

June 16 Friday
Plaxtol Gardens (Evening Openings)

June 17 Saturday
Great Maytham Hall, Rolvenden
Kypp Cottage, Biddenden
Little Combourne Farmhouse, Curtisden Green
Rock Farm, Nettlestead

June 18 Sunday
Chevening, nr Sevenoaks
45 Grace Avenue, Maidstone
Little Combourne Farmhouse, Curtisden Green
Long Barn, Weald
Maycotts, Matfield
Pevington Farm, Pluckley
Puxted House, Brenchley
The Silver Spray, Sellindge
Slaney Cottage, Staplehurst
Sotts Hole Cottage, Borough Green
South Hill Farm, Hastingleigh
Turkey Court, Maidstone
Weald Cottage, Edenbridge

June 19 Monday
Kypp Cottage, Biddenden

June 20 Tuesday
Kypp Cottage, Biddenden

June 21 Wednesday
Horsmonden Gardens
Nettlestead Place, Nettlestead (evening)
Rock Farm, Nettlestead
Wyckhurst, Aldington

June 22 Thursday
Ightham Mote, Ivy Hatch

June 22 to 23 Thursday to Friday
Kypp Cottage, Biddenden

June 22 Thursday
Southover, Hunton, Maidstone

June 24 Saturday
Elham Gardens
Kypp Cottage, Biddenden
Milton Manor, Thanington Without
Rock Farm, Nettlestead
Wyckhurst, Aldington (evening)

June 25 Sunday
Cedar House, Addington
Hookwood House, Shipbourne
Horsmonden Gardens
Longacre, Selling
Milton Manor, Thanington Without
Mounts Court Farmhouse, Acrise
Otham Gardens
Placketts Hole, Bicknor
Torry Hill, Sittingbourne
Waystrode Manor, Cowden
Wyckhurst, Aldington
Yew Tree Cottage, Shipbourne

June 28 Wednesday
Hazel Street Farmhouse, Horsmonden (evening)
Rock Farm, Nettlestead
Waystrode Manor, Cowden
Worth Gardens (evening)

July 1 Saturday
Hazel Street Farmhouse, Horsmonden
Rock Farm, Nettlestead
Womenswold Gardens

July 2 Sunday
Cedar House, Addington
The Silver Spray, Sellindge
South Hill Farm, Hastingleigh
Waystrode Manor, Cowden
Womenswold Gardens
Worth Gardens

July 5 Wednesday
Chartwell, nr Westerham
Old Buckhurst, Markbeech
Rock Farm, Nettlestead

July 6 Thursday
Ladham House, Goudhurst (evening)

July 8 Saturday
25 Crouch Hill Court, Lower Halstow
Little Oast, Otford (evening)
Pett Place, Charing
Rock Farm, Nettlestead
Squerryes Court, Westerham

July 9 Sunday
Charts Edge, Westerham
Edenbridge House, Edenbridge
115 Hadlow Road, Tonbridge
Longacre, Selling
Mounts Court Farmhouse, Acrise
Pett Place, Charing
Rogers Rough, Kilndown
Sea Close & Rose Lodge, Hythe
Squerryes Court, Westerham
Swan Oast, Stilebridge, Marden

July 12 Wednesday
Doddington Place, nr Sittingbourne
Rock Farm, Nettlestead
Sissinghurst Garden, Sissinghurst

July 15 Saturday
Old Buckhurst, Markbeech
Rock Farm, Nettlestead

July 16 Sunday
Cobham Hall, Cobham
Crawden Bank, Hartley
Long Barn, Weald
The Silver Spray, Sellindge
Swan Oast, Stilebridge, Marden

July 19 Wednesday
Haydown, Great Buckland (evening)
Rock Farm, Nettlestead
Torry Hill, Sittingbourne (evening)

July 22 Saturday
Great Maytham Hall, Rolvenden
Rock Farm, Nettlestead

July 23 Sunday
Copton Ash, Faversham
Longacre, Selling
Orchard Cottage, Bickley
Swan Oast, Stilebridge, Marden
Tonbridge School, Tonbridge

July 26 Wednesday
Rock Farm, Nettlestead
The Silver Spray, Sellindge

July 29 Saturday
Rock Farm, Nettlestead
The Silver Spray, Sellindge

July 30 Sunday
185 Borden Lane, Sittingbourne
Church Hill Cottage, Charing Heath
115 Hadlow Road, Tonbridge
190 Maidstone Road, Chatham
Spilsill Court, Staplehurst
Swan Oast, Stilebridge, Marden

August 2 Wednesday
185 Borden Lane, Sittingbourne
Knole, Sevenoaks
Old Buckhurst, Markbeech

August 4 Friday
High Quarry, Crockham Hill

August 6 Sunday
Beech Court Gardens, Challock
185 Borden Lane, Sittingbourne
Leydens, Edenbridge
Sotts Hole Cottage, Borough Green
Swan Oast, Stilebridge, Marden

August 12 Saturday
25 Crouch Hill Court, Lower Halstow

August 13 Sunday
Crawden Bank, Hartley

Doddington Place, nr Sittingbourne
Rose Cottage, Hartley
Swan Oast, Stilebridge, Marden

August 20 Sunday
Church Hill Cottage, Charing Heath
Swan Oast, Stilebridge, Marden
West Studdal Farm, West Studdal

August 23 Wednesday
Godinton House, Ashford (evening)
The Silver Spray, Sellindge

August 26 Saturday
Great Maytham Hall, Rolvenden

August 27 Sunday
Copton Ash, Faversham
115 Hadlow Road, Tonbridge
Longacre, Selling
The Pines Garden, St Margaret's Bay
The Silver Spray, Sellindge
Swan Oast, Stilebridge, Marden
Withersdane Hall, Wye

August 28 Monday
Copton Ash, Faversham
Longacre, Selling
The Silver Spray, Sellindge

September 3 Sunday
Swan Oast, Stilebridge, Marden
Turkey Court, Maidstone

September 6 Wednesday
Old Buckhurst, Markbeech

September 9 Saturday
25 Crouch Hill Court, Lower Halstow
Old Buckhurst, Markbeech

September 10 Sunday
Broadview Gardens, Hadlow College, Hadlow
Crawden Bank, Hartley
45 Grace Avenue, Maidstone
Leydens, Edenbridge
Little Oast, Otford
Longacre, Selling

September 16 Saturday
Gardens of Gaia, Cranbrook

September 17 Sunday
Copton Ash, Faversham
Goodnestone Park, Wingham
Knowle Hill Farm, Ulcombe
Mount Ephraim, Hernhill, Faversham
Nettlestead Place, Nettlestead
Old Orchard, Loose, Maidstone
Sotts Hole Cottage, Borough Green
Spoute Cottage, Plaxtol

September 20 Wednesday
Edenbridge House, Edenbridge

September 24 Sunday
Edenbridge House, Edenbridge
Finchcocks, Goudhurst

October 1 Sunday
Copton Ash, Faversham
Sea Close, Hythe

October 4 Wednesday
Sissinghurst Garden, Sissinghurst

October 8 Sunday
Hole Park, Rolvenden, Cranbrook
Marle Place, Brenchley
Owl House, Lamberhurst
Yalding Organic Gardens, Yalding

October 15 Sunday
Hole Park, Rolvenden, Cranbrook
Mere House, Mereworth

October 16 Monday
Groombridge Place Gardens, Groombridge

October 29 Sunday
Beech Court Gardens, Challock
Brogdale Horticultural Trust, Faversham

November 5 Sunday
Great Comp, Borough Green

DESCRIPTIONS OF GARDENS

Abbotsmerry Barn, Penshurst ✲❀ (Margaret & Keith Wallis) *Salmans Lane. Off B2176 in direction Leigh: 200yds N of Penshurst turn L, 1m down lane with speed ramps.* 5½-acre plantsman's garden on S-facing slope overlooking the Eden valley, developed since 1984 to take advantage of interesting combination of features and containing wide variety of trees, shrubs and plants, many of them unusual. TEAS. Hardy Plant Society Plant Sale June 11 (11-5). *Adm £2 Acc chd free (ACNO to James House Hospice Trust). Suns June 4, 11 (2-5.30)*

Amber Green Farmhouse, Chart Sutton (Mr & Mrs J Groves) *7m SE of Maidstone. Turn W off A274 onto B2163, in 1m turn L at Chart Corner, next R into Amber Lane. 50yds W.* C16 listed house (not open) in enchanting 1-acre cottage garden with abundant hardy perennials, shrubs, old fashioned roses and 2 natural ponds. TEAS in aid of Chart Sutton Village Hall. *Adm £1.50 Acc chd free. Sun June 4 (2-5.30)*

Battel Hall, Leeds, Maidstone ♿✲ (John D Money Esq) *From A20 Hollingbourne roundabouts take B2163 S (signed Leeds Castle), at top of hill take Burberry Lane, house 100yds on R.* Garden of approx 1 acre created since 1954 around mediaeval house (not open); very ancient wisteria, mixed planting of bulbs, shrubs, roses and herbaceous plants. TEAS. *Adm £2 Chd £1 (ACNO to Macmillan Cancer Relief). Sun May 14 (2-6)*

■ **Beech Court Gardens, Challock** ♿✲❀ (Mr & Mrs Vyvyan Harmsworth) *W of crossroads A251/A252, off the Lees.* Informal woodland garden surrounding mediaeval farmhouse. Spring bulbs, rhododendrons, azaleas and viburnums give superb spring colour: roses, summer borders and hydrangeas follow: fine collection of trees incl acers giving colour in autumn: plus extensive lawns, meandering paths and surprising vistas. Picnic area. TEAS. *Adm £2.50, OAP £2.30 Chd £1, under 5 free. Open every day April-mid Nov (Mon-Thurs 10-5.30; Fri-Sun 12-6) Closed Good Friday. For NGS Suns May 21, Aug 6, Oct 29 (12-6)*

Beechmont, Sevenoaks Weald ♿ (Dr & Mrs F J Lindars) *Gracious Lane. From A225 (to Tonbridge) 2m S of Sevenoaks turn R into Gracious Lane, garden on L after ⅓m. From A21 take N Tonbridge/Sevenoaks exit onto A225, 1m up Riverhill turn L into Gracious Lane (signed Ide Hill).* 10 acre early C19 garden of former Lambarde estate, at 700ft on greensand ridge: spectacular views: S-facing Victorian walled terraces, rhododendrons, cedars, redwoods. Ongoing restoration after 30 yrs' abandonment in midcentury and devastation in 1987 storm. TEA. *Adm £2.50 Chd free (ACNO to St George's Church, Weald). Suns April 30, May 7 (2-6)*

The Beehive, Lydd ♿✲ (C G Brown Esq) *10 High Street. S of New Romney on B2075, in centre of Lydd opp Church.* Small walled garden, tucked behind village street house dating from 1550 (not open), with many varieties of plants. There are paths and cosy corners in this cottage garden with pond and pergola; a pool of seclusion; the busy world outside unnoticed passes by. **Vine House** open same days. Teas usually available in the church. *Adm £1.50 Acc chd free (ACNO to Horder Centre for Arthritis, Crowborough). Sat, Sun, Mon May 27, 28, 29 (2.30-5)*

Bilting House, nr Ashford ♿✂❀ (John Erle-Drax Esq) *A28, 5m NE of Ashford, 9m from Canterbury. Wye 1½m.* Old-fashioned garden with ha-ha; rhododendrons, azaleas; shrubs. In beautiful part of Stour Valley. TEAS. *Adm £2 Chd £1 (ACNO to BRCS). Suns May 14, June 11 (2-6)*

185 Borden Lane, Sittingbourne ♿✂ (Mr & Mrs P A Boyce) *½m S of Sittingbourne. 1m from Sittingbourne side of A2/A249 junction.* Formal herb garden at front. To the rear, informal garden with trees, shrubs, herbaceous borders, pond and mini oak barn/summerhouse; fruit and vegetable potager. Maintained by owners. Home-made TEAS. *Adm £1.50 Acc chd free. Suns July 30, Aug 6, Wed Aug 2 (1.30-5); also private visits welcome, please* **Tel 01795 472243**

NEW **Boughton Monchelsea Place, Boughton Monchelsea** ✂ (Mr & Mrs Dominic Kendrick) *From Maidstone follow A229 (Hastings Rd) S for 3½m to major traffic lights at Linton Xrds, turn L onto B2163, house 1m on R. Take junction8 off M20 and follow Leeds Castle signs to B2163, house 5½m along B2163 on L.* Small estate (150 acres), mainly parkland and woodland, spectacular views over own deer park and the Weald. Grade 1 manor house (not open). Intimate walled gardens, box hedges, gravel walks, herbaceous borders. Not particularly well planned or properly tended, but very charming in an old-fashioned way! Do not miss St Peter's Church next door. TEAS. *Adm £3 Acc chd free (ACNO to Holy Family Church, Parkwood). Sat, Sun June 3, 4 (2-5)*

Bradbourne House Gardens, East Malling ♿ (East Malling Trust for Horticultural Research) *4m W of Maidstone. Entrance is E of New Road, which runs from Larkfield on A20 S to E Malling.* The Hatton Fruit Garden consists of demonstration fruit gardens of particular interest to amateurs, in a walled former kitchen garden and incl intensive forms of apples and pears. Members of staff available for questions. TEAS. *Adm £2.50 (incl entry to ground floor of House) Acc chd free. Sun April 30 (2-5)*

Brenchley Gardens *6m SE of Tonbridge. From A21 1m S of Pembury turn N on to B2160, turn R at Xrds in Matfield signed Brenchley. Combined adm £3 Acc chd free. Sun May 14 (2-6)*

Holmbush ♿ (Brian & Cathy Worden Hodge) 1½-acre informal garden, mainly lawns, trees and shrub borders, planted since 1960

Puxted House (P J Oliver-Smith Esq) 1½ acres with rare and coloured foliage shrubs, water and woodland plants. Alpine and rose garden all labelled. Present owner cleared 20yrs of brambles in 1981 before replanting. Cream TEAS. *Also opening on June 11*

Broadview Gardens, Hadlow College, Hadlow ♿✂❀ (Hadlow College) *On A26 9m SW of Maidstone and 4m NE of Tonbridge.* 9 acres of ornamental planting in attractive landscape setting; island beds with mixed plantings, rock garden, lake and water gardens; series of demonstration gardens incl oriental, Italian and cottage gardens. TEAS only on Feb 24. *Adm £2 Acc chd (under 12) free. Thurs Feb 24 (hellebores); Sun Sept 10 (10-5)*

NEW **Brogdale Horticultural Trust, Faversham** ♿✂❀ (Brogdale Horticultural Trust) *Leave M2 at junction 6, turn L towards Faversham, follow brown tourist signs.* The National Fruit Collections. 60 acres of of orchards with 4000 old and new varieties of apples, pears, plums and cherries. Guided tours and expert advice. TEAS. *Adm £2.50 Chd £1. Open Easter-mid November. For NGS £2 Chd £1. Suns April 30 (fruit blossom), Oct 29 (apple display) (9.30-5.30)*

Brookers Cottage, Shipbourne ♿❀ (Ann & Peter Johnson) *Back Lane. 3m N of Tonbridge, 5m E of Sevenoaks just off A227.* Plantsman's garden with over 1,000 plants, mostly labelled. ⅔-acre garden with natural pond, scree bed, herbaceous borders and island beds; large collection of hardy geraniums (cranesbills); small fruit and vegetable patch. *Adm £1.50 Chd 50p. Wed May 17; Sun May 21 (2-6); also by appt for groups and private visitors, please* **Tel 01732 810472**

Cares Cross, Chiddingstone Hoath ♿❀ (Mr & Mrs R L Wadsworth) *[Ordnance Survey Grid ref. TQ 496 431]* Delightful location for small group garden visits. Landscaped 3-acre formal gardens surrounding C15 house. Splendid views to N Downs: tropical-look water garden, wild flower meadow, old roses. TEAS for daytime visits: wine & cheese in evenings *Adm £3.50. By appt only to groups of 5-20, weekdays May to Aug. Write to Mrs R L Wadsworth, Cares Cross, Chiddingstone Hoath, Kent TN8 7BP*

Cedar House, Addington ♿❀ (Mr & Mrs J W Hull) *Trottiscliffe Road, 1½m W of West Malling. Turn N from A20 into Trottiscliffe Road, continue for about ½m, garden on R.* ½-acre garden with wide range of trees, shrubs and perennials. Emphasis also on old roses and foliage plants for year-round interest. TEAS. Share to Concern for Chernobyl Children. *Adm £1.50 Acc chd free. Suns June 25, July 2 (2-6)*

Charts Edge, Westerham ♿❀ (Mr & Mrs J Bigwood) *½m S of Westerham on B2026 towards Chartwell.* 7-acre hillside garden being restored by present owners; large collection of rhododendrons, azaleas & magnolias; specimen trees & newly-planted mixed borders; Victorian folly; walled vegetable garden; rock garden. Fine views over N Downs. TEAS. *Adm £2 Chd free (ACNO to BHS Dressage Group). Suns May 7, 21, July 9 (2-5)*

▲ **Chartwell, nr Westerham** ♿ (The National Trust) *2m S of Westerham, fork L off B2026 after 1½m, well signed.* 12-acre informal gardens on a hillside with glorious views over Weald of Kent. Water garden and lakes together with red-brick wall built by Sir Winston Churchill, the former owner of Chartwell. The avenue of golden roses given by the children of Sir Winston on his golden wedding anniversary should be at its best. Licensed self-service restaurant serving coffee, lunches and teas *Adm to garden only £2.75 Chd £1.35 For NGS Wed July 5 (11-4.15)*

Chevening, nr Sevenoaks ♿ (The Board of Trustees of Chevening Estate) *4m NW of Sevenoaks. Turn N off A25 at Sundridge traffic lights on to B2211; at Chevening Xrds 1½m* *turn L.* 27 acres with lawns and woodland garden, lake, maze, formal rides, parterre. Millennium Flower Festival at St Botolph's Church opposite. TEAS in aid of various Church Charities and NGS. *Adm £2 Chd £1. Sun June 18 (2-6)*

Church Hill Cottage, Charing Heath ♿✂❀ (Mr & Mrs Michael Metianu) *10m NW of Ashford. Leave M20 at junction 8 (Lenham) if Folkestone-bound or junction 9 (Ashford West) if London-bound, then leave A20 dual carriageway ½m W of Charing signed Charing Heath and Egerton. After 1m fork R at Red Lion, then R again; cottage 250yds on R.* C16 cottage (not open) surrounded by garden of 1½ acres, developed & planted by present owners since 1981. Several separate connected areas each containing island beds & borders planted with extensive range of perennials, shrubs, spring bulbs, ferns and hostas. Picnic area. *Adm £2 Chd 50p (ACNO to Paula Carr Trust). Open every day except Mon, from March 23 to Sept 30. For NGS Suns March 19, 26, April 2, 16, 23, May 7, 21, June 11, July 30, Aug 20; Mons April 24, May 1, 29 (11-5)*

▲ **Cobham Hall, Cobham** ♿❀ (Westwood Educational Trust) *8m E of junction 2 of M25, midway between Gravesend and Rochester. Driveway entrance off B2009 within 110yds of A2 signposted Cobham, Shorne, Higham.* Beautiful Elizabethan mansion in 150 acres, landscaped by Humphry Repton at end of C18. Classical garden buildings. Acres of daffodils and flowering trees planted in 1930s. House being restored by English Heritage grant aid. Cream TEAS. *Adm House £3.50 OAP/Chd £2.50 Garden £1.50 (ACNO to Cobham Hall Heritage Trust). For NGS Suns April 2, July 16 (2-5)* **Tel 01474 823371**

Copton Ash, Faversham ♿✂❀ (Drs Tim & Gillian Ingram) *105 Ashford Rd. On A251 Faversham-Ashford rd opp E-bound junction with M2.* 1½-acre plantsman's garden developed since 1978 on site of old cherry orchard. Wide range of plants in mixed borders and informal island beds; incl spring bulbs, alpine and herbaceous plants, shrubs, young trees and collection of fruit varieties. Special interest in plants from Mediterranean-type climates. Good autumn colour. TEAS. *Adm £1.50 Acc chd free (ACNO to National Schizophrenia Fellowship, East Kent Group). Suns March 5, 19, April 2, 23, 30, June 4, July 23, Aug 27, Sept 17, Oct 1; Mons April 24, May 1, Aug 28 (2-6)*

Crawden Bank, Hartley ♿✂❀ (Jacqueline Adams) *Merton Avenue, 4m SE of Dartford. From A2, at Longfield mini-roundabout, follow signs to Hartley into Ash Rd, after ½m Merton Ave is on L. From A20, at New Ash Green roundabout follow sign to Hartley, after 1½m Merton Ave on R.* 1/5 acre gardened in cottage style. Very little grass, very many plants, very attractive. TEA. **Rose Cottage, Hartley** open June 4, Aug 13. *Adm £1.50 Acc chd free (ACNO to Alzheimer's Disease Society). Suns May 14, June 4, July 16, Aug 13, Sept 10 (1-5.30); also by appt, please* **Tel 01474 706327**

Crittenden House, Matfield ♿✂ (B P Tompsett Esq) *6m SE of Tonbridge. Bus: MD 6 or 297, alight Standings Cross, Matfield, 1m.* Garden around early C17 house (not open) completely planned and planted since 1956 on labour saving lines. Featuring spring shrubs (rhododendrons, magnolias), roses, lilies, foliage, waterside planting of ponds in old iron workings, of interest from early spring bulbs to autumn colour. *Adm £2 Chd (under 12) 25p. Mon April 24 (2-5)*

25 Crouch Hill Court, Lower Halstow ✂❀ (Mrs Sue Hartfree) *5m NW of Sittingbourne. 1m W of Newington on A2, turn N to Lower Halstow; continue to T-junc, turn R, pass The Three Tuns on R, take next R (Vicarage Lane), then first R and fork R. Please park with consideration in cul de sac.* Long narrow garden (300ft × 25ft), landscaped on various levels with mixed borders, rock garden, small woodland area, natural stream and islands; wide range of plants, many rare and unusual. *Adm £2 Chd £1. Sats June 10, July 8, Aug 12, Sept 9 (2.30-5); private visits also welcome, please* **Tel 01795 842426**

■ **Doddington Place, nr Sittingbourne** ♿❀ (Mr & Mrs Richard Oldfield) *6m SE of Sittingbourne. From A20 turn N opp Lenham or from A2 turn S at Teynham or Ospringe (Faversham) (all 4m).* Large garden, landscaped with wide views; trees and yew hedges; woodland garden with azaleas and rhododendrons, Edwardian rock garden; formal garden with mixed borders.Gothic Folly. TEAS, shop. *Adm £3 Chd 50p (ACNO to Kent Assoc for the Blind and Doddington Church). May to Aug: Suns 2-6; Weds and Bank Hol Mons 11-6. For NGS Suns June 11, Aug 13 (2-6); Weds May 24, July 12 (11-6)*

Dolly's Garden, 43 Layhams Road, West Wickham ♿✂ (Mrs Dolly Robertson) *Semi-detached house recognisable by small sunken flower garden in the front. Opp Wickham Court Farm.* A raised vegetable garden, purpose-built for the disabled owner with easy access to wide terraced walkways. The owner - now in her 80's- who maintains the 24ft × 70ft area with her daughter, would be pleased to pass on her experiences as a disabled gardener so that others may share her joy and interest. *Collecting Box. Private visits welcome all year, please* **Tel 0208 462 4196**

Edenbridge House, Edenbridge ♿❀ (Mrs M T Lloyd) *Crockham Hill Rd, 1½m N of Edenbridge, nr Marlpit Hill, on B2026.* 5-acre garden of bulbs, spring shrubs, herbaceous borders, alpines, roses and water garden. House part C16 (not open). TEAS. Hardy Plant Society's Plant Sale April 16. *Adm £2 Chd 25p (ACNO to Rose 2000, June 11). Suns April 16, May 7, June 11, July 9, Sept 24 (2-6); Weds May 17, Sept 20 (1-5).* **Evening Opening** *£3. Wine, June 14 (6-9) ; also private visits welcome for groups, please* **Tel 01732 862122**

Elham Gardens ✂❀ *7m from Hythe, 11m from Canterbury. Enter Elham on B2065 from Lyminge or Barham (Hythe/Canterbury). Start at the Old School House, entrance on E side of High Street between Browns (estate agent) and St Marys Road.* A collection of at least four small gardens, full of colour and all very different, within easy walking distance from **The Old School House** (maps available) from Millennium Festival, Flowers in church. TEAS. *Combined adm £2.50 Chd 50p. Sat June 24 (2-6)*

▲ **Emmetts Garden, Ide Hill** ♿ (The National Trust) *5m SW of Sevenoaks. 1½m S of A25 on Sundridge-Ide Hill Rd. 1½m N of Ide Hill off B2042.* 5-acre hillside garden, with the highest tree-top in Kent, noted for its fine collection of rare trees and shrubs; lovely spring and autumn colour. TEAS. *Adm £3 Chd £1.50. For NGS Sat May 13 (11-5.30)*

■ **Finchcocks, Goudhurst** ♿✇❀ (Mr & Mrs Richard Burnett) *2m W of Goudhurst, off A262.* 4-acre garden surrounding early C18 manor, well-known for its collection of historical keyboard instruments. Spring bulbs; mixed borders; autumn garden with unusual trees & rare shrubs; recently restored walled garden on lines of C18 pleasure garden. TEAS. *Adm £6 House & garden, £2 Garden, Chd £4 & 50p. Suns Easter to Sept 26; Bank Hol Mons; Aug every Wed, Thurs & Sun (2-6). For NGS Suns May 7, Sept 24 (2-6)*

Flint Cottage, Bishopsbourne ✇❀ (Mr & Mrs P J Sinnock) *Bourne Park. 4m S of Canterbury turn off A2 to Bridge, through village, turn W at church, follow garden signs.* Small garden; alpines in gravel beds, sink gardens; water features; mixed borders and vegetables grown in raised beds; herb garden. TEAS. *Adm £2 Chd 50p. Sun May 14 (2-6)*

■ **Gardens of Gaia, Cranbrook** ✇ (Peter Bartlett) *Little Swallows. ¾m E of Cranbrook on rd to Tenterden.* 30 acres of mixed and magical woodland with Crane Brook running through it and Lake Chad at its heart. Over 30 large sculptures punctuate the walk. Not a formal garden, but an untamed setting for sculpture and imagination. *Adm £3.50 OAPs and students £3 Chd £2.50 Family £9. Open April, May, June, July, Sept, Fris, Sats, Suns. Aug every day (10-6) Oct for details, please* **Tel 01580 715289.** *For NGS Sats May 13, Sept 16 (10-6)*

▲ **Godinton House, Ashford** ♿✇ (Godinton House Preservation Trust) *Entrance off Godinton Lane. 1½m W of Ashford at Potter's Corner on A20. Bus: Folkestone-Ashford-Maidstone, alight Hare & Hounds, Potter's Corner.* Formal garden designed c1900 by Reginald Blomfield. Famous for its vast yew hedge (one of the longest in the country), champion Ti Haru cherries, topiary, formal and informal ponds. In spring the wild garden is a mass of daffodils. The Italian garden, walled garden and greenhouses are undergoing restoration. House closed on NGS open days. *Adm £2 Chd under 16 free. For NGS Suns March 19, 26, Mon April 24 (2-4.30).* **Evening Opening** *Wed Aug 23 (2-8)*

Godmersham Park, Godmersham ♿ (John B Sunley Esq) *Off A28 midway between Canterbury and Ashford.* Associations with Jane Austen. Early Georgian mansion (not open) in beautiful downland setting, 24 acres of formal and landscaped gardens, topiary, rose beds, herbaceous borders and superb daffodils in restored wilderness. TEAS. *Adm £2.50 Acc chd free (ACNO to Godmersham Church). Suns April 2, June 11 (11-6)*

■ **Goodnestone Park, Wingham** ♿✇❀ (The Lady FitzWalter) *Canterbury. Village lies S of B2046 from A2 to Wingham. Brown tourist signs off B2046 say Goodnestone Park gardens.* 10 to 12 acres; good trees; woodland garden, snowdrops, spring bulbs, walled garden with old-fashioned roses. Connections with Jane Austen who stayed here. Picnics allowed. TEAS (not in Feb, March). *Adm £3 OAP £2.50 Chd (under 12) 30p (Disabled people in wheelchair £1). No discounts on NGS Suns. Suns April 1 to Oct 15 (12-6); Mons, Weds to Fris March 27 to Oct 27 (11-5). Closed Tues and Sats. For NGS Suns Feb 20 (snowdrops), March 19 (spring bulbs and hellebores), Sept 17 (12-6)*

Goudhurst Gardens *4m W of Cranbrook on A262.* TEAS at Tulip Tree Cottage. *Combined adm £2.50 Acc chd free. Suns May 7, 14, June 11 (1-6)*

Garden Cottage ♿❀ (Mr & Mrs Peter Sowerby) 3/4-acre garden with small trees, shrubs, perennials and grass, to provide year-round softly coloured foreground to outstanding views of Teise valley. First laid out in 1930s with extensive planting since 1980s

Hyland (Mr & Mrs K Bronwin) Small garden adjacent to village car park, featuring topiary (at least 25 creations) for the small garden. Small water feature and southerly views

Tulip Tree Cottage ✇❀ (Mr & Mrs K A Owen) 1½ acres with sweeping lawn, established trees in herbaceous and shrub borders; 93ft *Liriodendron tulipifera*, said to be one of finest in country, also fine *Cedrus atlantica glauca*. In May azalea garden of ½-acre, established 1902; *also visitors welcome by appointment, please* **Tel 01580 211423**

45 Grace Avenue, Maidstone (Mrs S Kitchin) *On W side of Maidstone. Leave M20 at junction 5, take A20 towards Maidstone: at 3rd set of T-lights turn L into Grace Ave.* Former rubble heap of 30ft × 150ft transformed into four garden rooms, linked by informal mixed borders and pergolas. Designed to give a peaceful balm to the senses at the end of a working day. TEAS. *Adm £1.50 Chd under 10 free. Suns May 21, June 18, Sept 10 (1-6)*

■ **Great Comp, Borough Green** ♿✇❀ (R Cameron Esq) *2m E of Borough Green. A20 at Wrotham Heath, take Seven Mile Lane, B2016; at 1st Xrds turn R; garden on L ½m.* Skilfully designed 7-acre garden of exceptional beauty. Spacious setting of well-maintained lawns and paths lead visitors through plantsman's collection of trees, shrubs, heathers and herbaceous plants. Good autumn colour. Early C17 house (not open). TEAS on Suns, Bank Hols and NGS days (2-5). *Adm £3.50 Chd £1. Open Suns in March and every day April 1 to Oct 31 (11-6). For NGS (ACNO to Tradescant Trust) Suns March 5, 12, 19, 26 (for hellebores, heathers and snowflakes), Nov 5 (for autumn colour) (11-6)*

▲ **Great Maytham Hall, Rolvenden** ✇❀ (Country Houses Association) *4m SW of Tenterden. On A28 in Rolvenden turn L at church towards Rolvenden Layne; Hall ½m on R.* Lutyens house (not open on NGS days) and garden, 18 acres of parkland with bluebells, daffodils and flowering trees in spring; formal gardens incl blue and silver border, roses, hydrangeas and autumn colour. Walled garden inspired Frances Hodgson Burnett to write her novel 'The Secret Garden'. TEAS. *Adm £2 Chd £1 (ACNO to Country Houses Association). For NGS Sats April 22, May 13, June 17, July 22, Aug 26 (2-5)* **Tel 01580 241346**

■ **Groombridge Place Gardens, Groombridge** ✇❀ (Andrew de Candole, Esq) *4m SW of Tunbridge Wells. Take A264 towards East Grinstead, after 2m take B2110. Gardens entrance on L, past church.* 'Groombridge Place is wonderful because it is so different' is what our visitors say! Come and experience the history, mystery and excitement for yourself. Enjoy stunning formal gardens beyond compare and the sheer magic of The Enchanted Forest. Plus Country Store, tea room and Birds of Prey flying displays. *Adm fees for 2000 available on application. Open daily April to Oct (9-6). For NGS Mons April 17, Oct 16 (9-6)* **Tel 01892 863999**

115 Hadlow Road, Tonbridge ✇ (Mr & Mrs Richard Esdale) *Take A26 from N end of High St signed Maidstone, house 1m on L in service rd.* ⅓-acre unusual terraced garden with large collection of modern roses, island herbaceous border, many clematis, hardy fuchsias, heathers, grasses and ferns, shrub borders, alpines, annuals, kitchen garden and pond; well labelled. TEA. *Adm £1.50 Acc chd free. Suns July 9, 30, Aug 27 (2-6); also private visits welcome, please* **Tel 01732 353738**

Hall Place, Leigh ♿ (The Lady Hollenden) *4m W of Tonbridge. From A21 Sevenoaks-Tonbridge, B245 to Hildenborough, then R onto B2027. Through Leigh and on R.* Large outstanding garden with 11-acre lake, lakeside walk crossing over picturesque bridges. Many rare and interesting trees and shrubs. TEAS. *Adm £2.50 Chd 50p under 12 free. Sun May 28 (2-6)*

Hartlip Gardens *6m W of Sittingbourne, 1m S of A2 midway between Rainham and Newington. Parking for Craiglea in village hall car park and The Street. Combined adm £2 Acc chd free. Sun June 11 (2-6)*

Craiglea Cottage ♿✇ (Mrs Ruth Bellord) *The Street* Cottage garden crammed with interesting shrubs and plants; vegetable garden; small pond

Hartlip Place ✇ (Lt Colonel & Mrs J R Yerburgh) Secret garden concealed by rhododendrons, planted with old roses; shrub borders; wilderness walk; sloping lawns; pond. TEAS in aid of Kent Gardens Trust

Haydown, Great Buckland ✇❀ (Dr & Mrs I D Edeleanu) *nr Cobham, 4m S of A2. Take turning for Cobham, at war memorial straight ahead down hill, under railway bridge to T-junc, turn R, after 200yds take L fork, follow narrow lane for 1½m. Entrance on L after riding stables.* North Downs 9-acre hillside garden developed since 1980, with woodland and meadowland, incl native and unusual trees, shrubs, small vineyard, orchard, ponds, bog garden; patio with terracing; pergola, roses. *Adm £3. Haydown wine.* **Evening Opening** *Weds May 31, July 19 (6-9). Private visits welcome, please* **Tel 01474 814329**

Hayle Farm & Hayle Oast, Horsmonden *1m SW of Horsmonden. From B2162 turn L onto Marle Place Rd, then 400yds on L. Combined adm £2.50 Acc chd free. Sat May 27 (2-6)*

Hayle Farm House (Mr & Mrs L Goss) 4-acre garden and orchard surrounding C16 farmhouse (not open). Recently re-established garden with spring bulbs, azaleas, rhododendrons, rose beds and mixed borders. A small stream connects with Hayle Oast

Hayle Oast (Mr A De Raedt) Amateur collection of mini-gardens over 4 acres; herbs and flowers around the oast house; small Japanese garden; mini-Italian garden; mini-Jurassic park with little waterfall; pond with gunnera, stocked with carp and koi. The elevated section of the garden incls a bluebell and daffodil garden, collection of mature trees, young arboretum, mini-stonehenge and millennium feature: the Horsmonden meridian and large sundial, inspired on bygone centuries

Hazel Street Farmhouse, Horsmonden ✇ (Mr & Mrs Stephen Moir) *Spelmonden Road. From A21 going S, turn E before Lamberhurst on to A262 direction Goudhurst; then N on B2162 towards Horsmonden; after 2m turn R into Spelmonden Rd (signed Horsmonden Church), garden is 1st on R.* 3-acre garden designed in 1939, restored and replanted over last 9yrs; sunken terrace, rose garden, pergola, herb and herbaceous borders and wild meadow with pond. TEA May 20, July 1. *Adm £2 Acc chd free (ACNO to Sacred Heart RC Church, Goudhurst). Sats May 20, July 1 (2-6);* **Evening Openings** *Weds May 17 (5-8.30), June 28 (5-9)*

● Hever Castle, nr Edenbridge ♿❀ (Broadland Properties Ltd) *3m SE of Edenbridge, between Sevenoaks and East Grinstead. Signed from junctions 5 and 6 of M25, from A21 and from A264.* Reinstated 120 yds of herbaceous border, also formal Italian gardens with statuary, sculpture and fountains; large lake; 'splashing' water maze; rose garden and Tudor herb and knot garden, topiary and maze. Romantic moated castle, the childhood home of Anne Boleyn, also open. Refreshments available. *Adm Castle and gardens £7.80, Chd £4.20, gardens only £6.10, Chd £4. Open every day from March 1 to Nov 30 (11-6 last adm 5, March & Nov 11-4, Castle opens 12 noon)*

NEW **High Quarry, Crockham Hill** (The Hon Mrs Denise Harris) *Take B2026 (Hosey Hill Rd) from Westerham, or Crockham Hill. Froghole Lane is at the brow of the hill (3m from Westerham but close to Crockham Hill) follow the NGS signs and High Quarry is 1st drive on L.* 5-acre hillside garden with stunning views, established approx 10yrs. Japanese garden, woodland area, rhododendrons, herbaceous borders, meadow and water features incl 30ft deep carp pond, fountain pond and swimming pool. Therefore sadly, this garden is not suitable for children. TEA. *Adm £3. Fris May 12, Aug 4 (11-3)*

■ Higham Park, Bridge ♿✇❀ (Mrs P Gibb) *On A2, 3m SE of Canterbury: use exit sign Bridge, Higham Park at top of Bridge Hill.* Palladian house and garden, hidden for 80yrs. Wander through secret garden, Italian water garden, rose gardens; spring bulbs; other gardens in process of restoration. Discuss restoration problems with owners. Light lunches and TEAS. *House Tours £1.50. Adm gardens £2.50 Acc chd 50p. Open April to end Sept, Suns to Thurs (11-6). For NGS Sun April 23 (11-6). Groups welcome, please* **Tel/fax 01227 830830** www.higham-park.co.uk

■ Hole Park, Rolvenden, Cranbrook ♿✇❀ (Mr & Mrs D G W Barham) *On B2086 4m SW of Tenterden.* Set in beautiful parkland with lovely views, 15-acre garden with extensive yew hedges a special feature amidst lawns and fine trees. Walled gardens, pools and mixed borders combine with bulbs, rhododendrons and azaleas in the dell to make a garden for all seasons. Massed bluebells in woodland walk. Good autumn colours. TEAS May 7only with Hardy Plant Society Spring plant sale. *Adm £3 Chd (under 12) 50p (ACNO to St Mary's Church, Rolvenden). Weds April, May, June and*

October (2-6). For NGS Suns April 2, 9, 23, 30, May 7, 21, 28, Oct 8, 15 (2-6). Private visits and parties by arrangement, please **Tel 01580 241251**

Hookwood House, Shipbourne ♿✂❀ (Mr & Mrs Nicholas Ward) *Puttenden Road. 7m SE of Sevenoaks, S of village. Puttenden Rd joins A227 on sharp bend 3m N of Tonbridge, signed Plaxtol: house 1m on RH side.* Charming country garden of 2 acres of formal features; old brick paths lead through small garden rooms enclosed by clipped native and yew hedges; mixed and herbaceous borders, perennials, old-fashioned roses, topiary, silver, herb and vegetable gardens, nut plat, apple orchard, cobbled Kentish ragstone yard and planted containers. *Adm £2 Acc chd free . Sun June 25 (2-6). Private visits welcome by appt April 1 - June 30, please* **Tel 01732 810525**

Horsmonden Gardens *approx 8m SE of Tonbridge. Take B2162 out of Horsmonden towards Marden, after just under 1m R up Haymans Hill. For Cacketts Farm turn L after 100yds: for Bainden Farmhouse follow signs.* TEA. *Combined adm £3 Chd £1 (ACNO to Horsmonden Church). Wed June 21; Sun June 25 (11-5) Groups welcome anytime by appt, please* **Tel 01892 722528**

Bainden Farmhouse (Mr & Mrs M Coulman) *School House Lane.* Spacious family garden, approx 2 acres, evolved over many years; mixed plantings with many roses

Cacketts Farmhouse ❀ (Mr & Mrs L P Morrish) 1½-acre garden created since 1988, surrounding C17 farmhouse (not open). Walled garden, bog garden and ponds, woodland garden with unusual plants (picnic area)

▲ **Ightham Mote, Ivy Hatch** ♿✂❀ (The National Trust) *6m E of Sevenoaks, off A25 and 2½m S of Ightham [188: TQ584535] Buses from rail stations Sevenoaks or Borough Green to Ivy Hatch, ½m walk to Ightham Mote.* 14-acre garden and moated mediaeval manor c.1340. Mixed borders with many unusual plants; lawns; courtyard; orchard of Kent apples; water features incl small lake, leading to woodland walk with trees, rhododendrons and other shrubs. TEAS. *Adm £5 Chd £2.50. House and garden. Open as normal. Tours of garden 1.30pm, 2.30pm, 3.30pm. For NGS Thurs June 22 (11.30-5.30 last admission 4.30pm)*

▲ **Knole, Sevenoaks** ♿✂ (The Lord Sackville) *Station: Sevenoaks. Well signposted.* Pleasance, deer park, landscape garden, herb garden. TEAS *Adm Car park £2.50: garden £1 Chd 50p; house £5 Chd £2.50 For NGS Weds June 7, Aug 2 (11-4 last adm 3)*

Knowle Hill Farm, Ulcombe ♿✂❀ (The Hon Andrew & Mrs Cairns) *7m E of Maidstone. From M20 exit 8 follow A20 towards Lenham for 3m. R to Ulcombe. After 1½m, L at crossroads to Lenham. Take first R, past Pepper Box pub then L.* 1½-acre garden planted in last 10 years with wonderful views over Weald. Designed to create a tapestry of colour and texture which is interesting all yr. Mediterranean plants such as cistus, rosemary and lavender thrive on the warm southerly hillside with hebes, myrtles and penstemons. TEAS in aid of All Saints Church Ulcombe. *Adm £2 Acc child free. Sun Sept 17 (2-6); visits by appt welcome, please* **Tel 01622 850240**

Kypp Cottage, Biddenden ✂❀ (Mrs Zena Grant) *Woolpack Corner. At Tenterden Rd A262 junction with Benenden Rd.* Not for the tidy minded! A small romantic foliage enfolding garden where shrubs, scented roses and clematis entwine. Thick tapestry of ground cover predominately geraniums, ferns and shade lovers. TEAS. *Adm £1.50 Chd 30p (ACNO to Royal National Rose Society). Sun May 28 (2-6); Thurs May 25, June 1, 8, 15, 22; Fris May 26, June, 2, 9, 16, 23; Sats May 27, June 17, 24; Mons May 29; June 5, 12, 19; Tues May 30, June 6, 13, 20 (10.30-6); open in July by appt , also private visits welcome, please* **Tel 01580 291480**

Ladham House, Goudhurst ♿❀ (Mr & Mrs Alastair Jessel) *On NE of village, off A262.* 10 acres with rolling lawns, fine specimen trees, rhododendrons, camellias, azaleas, shrubs and magnolias. Arboretum. Spectacular twin mixed borders; fountain and bog gardens. Fine view. Subject of many magazine articles. TEAS. *Adm £2.50 Chd (under 12) 50p (ACNO to Gardening for Disabled Trust). Suns April 30, May 21 (1-5.30).* **Evening Opening** *£3. Wine. Thurs July 6 (6-9) Groups by appt, please* **Tel 01580 212674/211203. Fax 01580 212596**

Larksfield, Crockham Hill ♿❀ (Mr & Mrs Peter Dickinson) *3m N of Edenbridge. On Limpsfield-Oxted Rd, B269.* Octavia Hill, a founder of the NT, lived here and helped create the original garden; fine collection of azaleas, shrubs, herbaceous plants, rose beds and woodlands; views over Weald and Ashdown Forest. **Larksfield Cottage** and **The Red House** gardens open on same days. TEAS at **The Red House**. *Combined adm £3 Chd 50p (ACNO to St John Ambulance Kent and the League of Friends of Edenbridge Hospital). Suns May 14, 21 (2-6)*

Larksfield Cottage, Crockham Hill ♿❀ (Mr & Mrs John Manwaring) *3m N of Edenbridge. On Limpsfield-Oxted Rd, B269.* An enchanting garden redesigned in 1981 with attractive lawns and shrubs. Views over the Weald and Ashdown Forest.**Larksfield** and **The Red House** gardens open on same days. TEAS at **The Red House**. *Combined adm £3 Chd 50p (ACNO to St John Ambulance Kent and the League of Friends of Edenbridge Hospital). Suns May 14, 21 (2-6)*

NEW **Leydens, Edenbridge** ♿❀ (Mr Roger Platts) *1m S of Edenbridge on B2026 towards Hartfield (use Nursery entrance and car park).* Private garden of garden designer/nursery owner, created during 1999 and still under development. ⅓-acre surrounding house (not open) with small natural style pond, beds planted with wide range of shrubs and perennials. Plenty of planting ideas and good selection of unusual varieties. Adjacent to nursery. TEAS. *Adm £2 Chd free. Suns Aug 6, Sept 10 (12-6)*

Little Combourne Farmhouse, Curtisden Green ♿✂❀ (Mr & Mrs Grant Whytock) *5m NW of Cranbrook. Turn off A262 at Chequers Inn in Goudhurst, then 2nd R signed Blantyre House and Curtisden Green* Family garden of 1½ acres with old-fashioned roses, set in idyllic rural countryside, created by present owners around C16 farmhouse (not open). TEAS. *Adm £2 Acc chd free. Wed June 14, Sat, Sun June 17, 18 (2-6)*

Little Oast, Otford ❀ (Mrs Pam Hadrill) *High Street, 3m N of Sevenoaks at W end of village, just past Horns Inn, turn R into private drive. (Please park in public car park opp Bull Inn or in Catholic church car park 80yds past Little Oast.)* ½-acre garden of varied planting, designed to complement circular oast; patios, pots, a pond and 3 summer-houses. TEAS. *Adm £1.50 Acc chd free. Sun Sept 10 (2-5).* **Evening Opening** *Sat July 8 £3. Wine (6-8)*

Little Trafalgar, Selling ♿✄❀ (Mr & Mrs R J Dunnett) *4m SE of Faversham.* ¾-acre garden of great interest both for its wealth of attractive and unusual plants, and its intimate, restful design. Emphasis is placed on the creative and artistic use of plants. TEAS. *Adm £2 Acc chd free. Private visits and groups welcome by appt any time between May and Sept, please* **Tel 01227 752219**

Long Barn, Weald ✄ (Brandon & Sarah Gough) *3m S of Sevenoaks. Signed to Weald at junction of A21 and B245. Garden at W end of village.* 1st garden of Harold Nicolson and Vita Sackville-West. 3 acres with terraces and slopes, giving considerable variety. Dutch garden designed by Lutyens, features mixed planting in raised beds. Teas in village. *Adm £2 OAP £1.50 Chd 50p, under 5 free (ACNO to Hospice in the Weald). Suns June 18, July 16 (2-5)*

Longacre, Selling ♿✄❀ (Dr & Mrs G Thomas) *5m SE of Faversham. From A2 (M2) or A251 follow signs for Selling, passing White Lion on L, 2nd R and immediately L, continue for ¼m. From A252 at Chilham, take turning signed Selling at Badgers Hill Fruit Farm. L at 2nd Xrds, next R, L and then R.* Small, ¾-acre plantsman's garden with wide variety of interesting plants, created and maintained entirely by owners. New gravel garden. Lovely walks in Perry Woods adjacent to garden. TEAS in aid of local charities. *Adm £1.50 Acc chd free (ACNO to Canterbury Pilgrims Hospice). Suns April 9, 23, 30, May 7, 14, 28, June 11, 25, July 9, 23, Aug 27, Sept 10; Mons April 24, May 1, 29, Aug 28 (2-5); also private visits welcome, please* **Tel 01227 752254**

Lullingstone Castle, Eynsford ♿✄❀ (Mr & Mrs Guy Hart Dyke) *In the Darenth Valley via Eynsford on A225. Eynsford Station ½m. All cars and coaches via Roman Villa.* Lawns, woodland and lake, mixed border, small herb garden. Henry VII gateway; Church on the lawn open. TEAS. *Adm garden £2.50 OAPs/Chd £1; house £1 extra. Sun June 4 (2-6)*

Luton House, Selling ✄ (Sir John & Lady Swire) *4m SE of Faversham. From A2 (M2) or A251 make for White Lion, entrance 30yds E on same side of rd.* 5 acres; C19 landscaped garden; ornamental ponds; trees underplanted with azaleas, camellias, woodland plants. *Adm £2 Acc chd free. Sun May 7 (2-6)*

190 Maidstone Road, Chatham ✄❀ (Dr M K Douglas) *On A230 Chatham-Maidstone, about 1m out of Chatham and 7m from Maidstone.* Informal ¼-acre garden; herbaceous borders on either side of former tennis court; scree garden and pool; many snowdrops and other spring bulbs. TEAS (not Feb). *Adm £1.50 Acc chd free. Suns Feb 20 (2-5) (snowdrops), April 2, May 28, July 30 (2-6)*

■ **Marle Place, Brenchley** ♿✄❀ (Mr& Mrs Gerald Williams) *8m SE of Tonbridge, signed from Brenchley.* Victorian gazebo; plantsman's shrub borders; walled scented garden, large Edwardian rockery; herbaceous borders and bog garden. Woodland walk. Mosaic terrace and artist's studio, autumn colour. C17 listed house (not open). TEAS. *Adm £3.50 Chd £3. Every day April 1 to Oct 1 (10-5). For NGS Suns April 30, May 28, Oct 8 (10-6); also by appt, please* **Tel 01892 722304**

Maycotts, Matfield ♿✄❀ (Mr & Mrs David Jolley) *6m SE of Tonbridge. From A21, 1m S of Pembury, turn N onto B2160, turn L at Xrds in Matfield, and first L at Five Wents into Maycotts Lane.* Medium-sized, partly walled garden around C16 farmhouse (not open) being developed by garden designer-owner. Herbaceous borders; old-fashioned and shrub roses; herb garden and potager; unusual perennials and foliage plants, wild life ponds. TEAS if fine in aid of St Luke's, Matfield. *Adm £2 Acc chd free. Sun June 18 (2-6); also private visits and groups welcome, please* **Tel 01892 722203**

Meadow Wood, Penshurst ♿ (Mr & Mrs James Lee) *1¼m SE of Penshurst on B2176 in direction of Bidborough.* 1920s garden, on edge of wood with long southerly views over the Weald, and with interesting trees and shrubs; azaleas, rhododendrons and naturalised bulbs in woods with mown walks. Cream TEAS. *Adm £3 Chd £1 (ACNO to Relate). Mon May 29 (2-6)*

Mere House, Mereworth ♿❀ (Mr & Mrs Andrew Wells) *Midway between Tonbridge & Maidstone. From A26 turn N on to B2016 and then into Mereworth village.* 6-acre garden with C18 lake; ornamental shrubs and trees with foliage contrast; lawns, daffodils; Kentish cobnut plat; woodland walk. TEAS. *Adm £2 Acc chd free. Suns April 2, Oct 15 (2-5.30)*

Mill House, Hildenborough ♿❀ (Dr & Mrs Brian Glaisher) *Mill Lane, ½m N of Hildenborough, 5m S of Sevenoaks. From B245 turn into Mill Lane at Mill garage.* 2½-acre garden laid out in 1906; herbaceous and mixed borders; new secluded herb garden; old shrub roses and climbers; clematis and many fine trees. Newly-designed golden garden. Formal garden with topiary; ruins of windmill with tree ferns and conservatory with exotics. TEAS. *Adm £2 Chd 25p. Sun June 11 (2-6)*

NEW **Milton Manor, Thanington Without** ✄ (Mr & Mrs M Coburn) *From Canterbury City ring rd, take A28 towards Ashford. After 2½m turn L at the Milton roundabout towards Chartham Downs and St Augustines. Approx 100yds up the hill turn L into drive.* Double herbaceous borders, woodland garden, temple garden, white garden, many roses and clematis. Extensive lawns with valley views. TEAS. *Adm £2 Chd free (ACNO to Canterbury Pilgrims Hospice). Sat, Sun June 24, 25 (2-5)*

■ **Mount Ephraim, Hernhill, Faversham** (Mrs M N Dawes, Mr & Mrs E S Dawes) *From M2 and A299 take Hernhill turning at Duke of Kent.* Herbaceous border; topiary; daffodils and rhododendrons; rose terraces leading to a small lake. Rock garden with pools; water garden; small vineyard. TEAS. *Adm £3 Chd £1. Open early April to end Sept Mon, Wed, Thurs, Sat, Sun (1-6); Bank Hols (11-6). For NGS Suns April 16, Sept 17 (1-6)*

Mounts Court Farmhouse, Acrise ♿✂❀ (Graham & Geraldine Fish) *6m NW of Folkestone. From A260 Folkestone-Canterbury Rd, turn L at Swingfield (Densole) opp Black Horse Inn, 1½m towards Elham and Lyminge, on N side.* 1½ acres surrounded by open farmland; variety of trees, shrubs, grasses and herbaceous plants; pond and bog garden. TEAS in aid of Elham Village Hall. *Adm £2 Chd £1. Suns June 25, July 9 (2-5)*

Nettlestead Place, Nettlestead ♿✂ (Mr & Mrs Roy Tucker) *6m W/SW of Maidstone. Turn S off A26 onto B2015 then 1m on L (next to Nettlestead Church).* C13 manor house (not open) set in 7-acre plantsman's garden on different levels with fine views over open countryside; many plant collections incl herbaceous and shrub island beds; formal garden with shrub and species roses; hardy geranium border; sunken pond garden; terraces and glen garden. Picnic area. St Mary's Church, Nettlestead, with fine mediaeval glass, also open; entrance from garden. *Adm £3 Acc chd free (ACNO to Friedreich's Ataxia Group Research). Suns June 4, Sept 17 (2-5.30).* **Evening Opening** *£4. Wine. Wed June 21 (6.15-9.15)*

Olantigh, Wye ✂ (Mr & Mrs J R H Loudon) *6m NE of Ashford. Turn off A28 either to Wye or at Godmersham; ¾m from Wye on rd to Godmersham.* Edwardian garden in beautiful setting; water garden; rockery; shrubbery; herbaceous border; extensive lawns. *Adm £2 Acc chd free. Suns April 23, June 11 (2-5)*

■ **Old Buckhurst, Markbeech** ❀ (Mr & Mrs J Gladstone) *4m E of Edenbridge via B2026, at Queens Arms PH turn E to Markbeech. 1st house on R after leaving Markbeech.* 1-acre partly walled cottage garden around C15 farmhouse (not open). Wide range shrubs, clematis, shrub roses, herbaceous incl campanulas, eryngiums, daylilies, hardy geraniums, iris, poppies, penstemons chosen for yr round interest using colour, texture, scent and shape. *Adm £2.50 Acc chd free (ACNO to St Mary's Church, Chiddingstone). Every Wed May to end Sept. For NGS 1st Wed each month, Sats, Suns May 20, 21, June 3, 4; Sats July 15, Sept 9 (11-5.30)*

Old Orchard, Loose, Maidstone ♿✂❀ (Mr & Mrs M J Brett) *56 Valley Drive. 2½m S of Maidstone on A229. Turn R towards Loose village, parking on hill; at top of hill take footpath to Valley Drive. Limited parking for disabled people at house (in cul-de-sac).* About an acre, plant lovers' informal garden with rockeries, raised beds, scree and island beds containing many unusual plants. Started in 1994 and under continuous development by owners. **Old Orchard Bungalow** also open May 14. TEAS. *Adm £2 Chd £1 (ACNO to Talking Newspapers Association UK). Suns March 12, April 9, May 14, Sept 17 (2-6); group visits welcome by appt, please* **Tel 01622 746941**

NEW **Old Orchard Bungalow, Loose, Maidstone** ✂❀ (Mr & Mrs D J Robinson) *703 Loose Road.2½m S from Maidstone on A229. Turn R towards Loose Village. Parking at top of Old Loose Hill. Follow signs for bungalow. No Parking at Property.* ¼ acre garden with interesting nooks and crannies - incl water features - and ongoing projects. Planting for foliage effect with trees, shrubs, bulbs. **Old Orchard** open on same day. TEAS share to Heart of Kent Hospice. *Adm £1.50 Chd 50p. Sun May 14 (2-6)*

Old Place Farm, High Halden ♿✂❀ (Mr & Mrs Jeffrey Eker) *3m NE of Tenterden. From A28 take Woodchurch Rd (opp Chequers public house) in High Halden, and follow for ½m.* 3½-acre garden, mainly designed by Anthony du Gard Pasley, surrounding period farmhouse (not open) and buildings with paved herb garden and parterres, small lake, ponds, lawns, mixed borders, cutting garden, old shrub roses, lilies and foliage plants; all created since 1969. Featured in Country Life, House & Garden and several books. TEAS in aid of St Mary's Church, High Halden. *Adm £2.50 Chd 50p. Sun June 11 (2-6)*

Old Tong Farm, Brenchley ✂❀ (Mr & Mrs Simon Toynbee) *1½m S of Brenchley. Follow Horsmonden rd from Brenchley, take first R into Fairmans Rd.* Open once again after a year of extensive earthworks. Although this part of the garden is still in its formative stage the rest of the 3 acres still go on in a state of controlled wilderness! TEAS. *Adm £2 Acc chd free. Fri, Sat, Sun, Mon June 9, 10, 11, 12 (11-5)*

Orchard Cottage, Bickley ♿✂❀ (Mrs J M Wall) *1½m E of Bromley, about 400 yds from the A222. From Bickley Park Road turn into Pines Road, then 1st R into Woodlands Road, no 3 is 1st house on L.* Attractive ⅓-acre garden with mixed borders and many interesting herbaceous plants and shrubs; scree beds and troughs with alpines and other small plants. TEAS. *Adm £2 Acc chd free (ACNO to Downs Syndrome Association). Sun July 23 (2-5.30)*

Oswalds, Bishopsbourne (Mr & Mrs Wolfgang Kerck) *4m S of Canterbury. Turn off A2 at B2065, follow signs to Bishopsbourne, house next to church.* 3-acre plantsman's garden. Year round interest includes bulbs, spring garden, mixed borders, rockeries, pools, bog garden, potager, pergola, old roses and many fruit varieties. House (not open) has interesting literary connections. *Adm £2 Chd 50p. Visits welcome by appointment April to end June, please* **Tel 01227 830340**

Otham Gardens *4M SE of Maidstone. From A2020 or A274 follow signs for Otham 1m. Parking restricted to official car parks except for disabled people.* TEAS. *Combined adm £3 Acc chd free (ACNO to Maidstone Mencap). Sun June 25 (2-6)*

Bramley (Miss Ware) Interesting old garden on different levels, wildlife pond, new tree and rose planting

Greenhill House (Dr & Mrs Hugh Vaux) Established herbaceous and shrub border; wildflower garden; alpines

The Limes (Mrs John Stephens) Well-established garden with herbaceous borders and wisteria pergola

Little Squerryes (Mr & Mrs Gerald Coomb) Established garden, herbaceous borders; interesting trees. Car Parking available.

NEW **Senacre Farm House** (Mr & Mrs Richard Baxter) An artist's garden of several rooms

Stoneacre Special opening; NT members to pay. *For garden description, see individual entry*

Swallows (Mrs Eric Maidment) Cottage garden with colourful terrace

Tulip Cottage (Mrs Gloria Adams) Shows what can be done in a small space

■ Owl House, Lamberhurst ♿ (The Iveagh Trust) *1m W of A21, signed from Lamberhurst.* 16½-acre romantic woodland garden surrounding C16 cottage (not open), created by the late Maureen, Marchioness of Dufferin and Ava over 45yrs and continued by her family. Spring bulbs, rhododendrons, camellias, unusual roses, water garden, herbaceous border and good autumn colour Tea Rooms. *Adm £4 Chd £1 (ACNO to Maureen's Oast House for Arthritics). Open daily except Christmas Day and New Years Day, for further information* **Tel 01892 89120**. *For NGS Suns Feb 27, Oct 8 (11-6)*

The Pear House, Sellindge ❀ (Mrs Nicholas Snowdon) *Stone Hill. 6m E of Ashford. Turn L off A20 at Sellindge Church towards Brabourne into Stone Hill.* ⅔ acre developed by present owner. Contains smaller gardens with informal planting; bulbs, roses (mostly old-fashioned), shrubs, small orchard with climbing roses, pond garden, shady areas. *Adm £1.50 Chd 50p. Due to limited parking, private or group visits welcome by appt anytime between April 30 to July 2, please* **Tel 01303 812147**

■ Penshurst Place, Penshurst ♿ (Viscount De L'Isle) *S of Tonbridge on B2176, N of Tunbridge Wells on A26.* 10 acres of garden dating back to C14; garden divided into series of 'rooms' by over a mile of clipped yew hedge; profusion of spring bulbs: herbaceous borders; formal rose garden; famous peony border. All year interest. TEAS and light refreshments. *Adm House & Gardens £6 Concessions £5.50 Chd £4 Family Ticket £16: Gardens £4.50 Concessions £4 Chd £3.50 Family Ticket £13. Open daily April 1 to Oct 31. For NGS Wed May 10, Thurs June 1 (10.30-6)*

Pett Place, Charing ❀ (Mrs I Mills, C I Richmond-Watson Esq & A Rolla Esq) *6m NW of Ashford. From A20 turn N into Charing High St. At end turn R into Pett Lane towards Westwell.* Walled gardens covering nearly 4 acres. A garden of pleasing vistas and secret places which has been featured in Country Life, House and Garden etc. A ruined C13 chapel is a romantic feature beside the manor house (not open), which was re-fronted about 1700 and which Pevsner describes as 'presenting grandiloquently towards the road'. TEAS. *Adm £3 Chd 50p (ACNO to Kent Gardens Trust). Sats, Suns April 29, 30, July 8, 9 (2.30-5)*

Pevington Farm, Pluckley ♿❀ (Mr & Mrs David Mure) *3m SW of Charing. From Charing take B2077 towards Pluckley, before Pluckley turn R towards Egerton, Pevington Farm ½m on. From SW go through Pluckley, turn L for Egerton.* 1½-acre garden with wonderful views over the Weald. Mixed borders with many interesting plants are protected by old walls and yew hedges which form gardens within the whole. TEAS in aid of Friends of St Nicholas Church, Pluckley. *Adm £2 Chd 50p. Sun June 18 (11-5); private visits welcome in May, June, July, please* **Tel 01233 840317**

■ The Pines Garden, St Margaret's Bay ♿❀ (St Margaret's Bay Trust) *Beach Rd, 4½m NE of Dover.* Beautiful 6-acre seaside garden. Water garden with waterfall and lake. Statue of Sir Winston Churchill complemented by the St Margaret's Museum opposite. Fascinating maritime and local interest. TEAS *Adm £1.50 Chd 35p. Gardens Open daily except Christmas Day. Museum open May to early Sept (closed Mon, except Bank Hols, and Tues). For NGS Suns April 23, May 28, Aug 27 (10-5)*

Placketts Hole, Bicknor ♿❀ (Mr & Mrs D P Wainman) *5m S of Sittingbourne, and W of B2163. Signposted from B2163 at top of Hollingbourne Hill, and from A249 at Stockbury Valley.* Owners have designed and planted 2-acre garden around charming old house (C16 with Georgian additions (not open)); interesting mix of shrubs, large borders, rose garden, a formal herb garden and sweet-smelling plants. TEAS. *Adm £1.50 Acc chd free (ACNO to Kent Gardens Trust). Sun June 25 (2-6.30)*

Plaxtol Gardens, Plaxtol *5m N of Tonbridge, 6m E of Sevenoaks, turn E off A227 to Plaxtol village.* TEAS. Tickets and maps available at all gardens. Parking at Spoute Cottage. *Combined adm £3 Acc chd free (ACNO to Friends of Plaxtol Church). Sun June 11 (2-6)*

Ducks Farm (Mr & Mrs H Puleston Jones) *Dux Lane.* 2 acres surrounding mediaeval/Victorian farmhouse (not open). Mixed herbaceous borders; walled garden; vegetable garden; herb garden

Spoute Cottage ♿❀ (Mr & Mrs Donald Forbes) *situated at the bottom of Plaxtol St on L side opp Hyders Forge.* ¾ acre of mixed borders of contrasting flowering and foliage plants, especially for flower arranging; small pond & stream. Japanese garden. Plant nursery attached. Large car park. *Also open Sun Sept 17*

Stonewold House (Mr & Mrs John Young) *The Street. Situated by 2nd lamp post down the Street on R before Papermakers Arms.* 4½ acres of mixed borders, vegetable plots, wisteria pergola and fruit trees. Wonderful views overlooking small lake planted to encourage wildlife

Watermead ❀ (Mr & Mrs M Scott) *Long Mill Lane (next to Plaxtol Nursery).* ¼-acre of varied perennial and shrub planting. Small pond, vegetable plot, greenhouse. Many hardy geraniums. Aiming for flowers and colour throughout the year. Rainbow themed garden

Wickenden Farm (Mr & Mrs S Furness) *On the L going down The Street passing the Papermakers Arms on R.* 3/4-acre sloping garden with views over the Bourne Valley. Areas of interest incl gravel garden, sunken herb garden, pond and organic kitchen garden

NEW **Plaxtol Gardens (Evening Opening)** ♿ *5m N of Tonbridge, 6m E of Sevenoaks, 1m Plaxtol Church, at junction of Brook Lane and Allens Lane. Combined adm £4 Chd free. Wine.* **Evening Opening** *Fri June 16 (5-8)*

Old Allens (Mr & Mrs Martin Adamson) An undulating garden and orchards of 5 acres, surrounding a listed Grade II Kent Hall house (not open) with stream and ponds. Nut plat and beautiful views with formal and informal planting. Drinks in barn if wet

Allens House (Sir Lewis & Lady Hodges) 1½-acre garden with mixed borders, trees, fruit and vegetables. Good views. War-time air raid shelter

Puxted House, Brenchley ♿❀ (P J Oliver-Smith Esq) *6m SE of Tonbridge. From A21 1m S of Pembury turn N onto B2160, turn R at Xrds in Matfield signed Brenchley.* 1½ acres with rare and coloured foliage shrubs, water and woodland plants. Alpine and rose garden all labelled. Present owner cleared 20yrs of brambles in 1981 before replanting. Cream TEAS. *Adm £2 Acc chd free. Sun June 18 (2-6). Also opening with Brenchley Gardens May 14*

Ramhurst Manor, Leigh ♿ (The Lady Rosie Kindersley) *Powder Mill Lane, Tonbridge.* Historic property once belonged to the Black Prince and Culpepper family. Formal gardens; roses, azaleas, rhododendrons, wild flowers. TEA. *Adm £2 Acc chd free. Sun May 21 (2.30-6)*

The Red House, Crockham Hill ♿❀ (K C L Webb Esq) *3m N of Edenbridge. On Limpsfield-Oxted Rd, B269.* Formal features of this large garden are kept to a minimum; rose walk leads on to acres of rolling lawns flanked by fine trees and shrubs incl rhododendrons, azaleas, magnolias, and woodlands. Views over the Weald and Ashdown Forest. TEAS. **Larksfield** and **Larksfield Cottage** gardens open same days. *Combined adm £3 Chd 50p (ACNO to St John Ambulance Kent and the League of Friends of Edenbridge Hospital). Suns May 14, 21 (2-6)*

■ **Riverhill House, Sevenoaks** ✂ (The Rogers Family) *2m S of Sevenoaks on A225.* Mature hillside garden with extensive views; specimen trees, sheltered terraces with roses and choice shrubs; bluebell wood with rhododendrons and azaleas; picnics allowed. TEAS. *Adm £2.50 Chd 50p. Every Wed, Sun and Bank Hol weekends in April, May and June only (12-6). For NGS Sats April 1, 22 (12-6)*

■ **Rock Farm, Nettlestead** ✂❀ (Mrs S E Corfe) *6m W of Maidstone. Turn S off A26 onto B2015 then 1m S of Wateringbury turn R.* 2-acre garden set around old Kentish farmhouse in beautiful setting; created with emphasis on all-year interest and ease of maintenance. Plantsman's collection of shrubs, trees and perennials for alkaline soil: extensive herbaceous border, vegetable area, bog garden and plantings around two large natural ponds. Plant nursery adjoining garden. *Adm £2 Chd 50p (ACNO to St Mary's Church, Nettlestead). Open Every Wed & Sat (11-5) & Sun (2-5) in April to July; Aug 2, 5, 6. For NGS every Wed & Sat in May, June and July (11-5)*

Rogers Rough, Kilndown ♿✂❀ (Richard & Hilary Bird) *10m S of Tonbridge. From A21 2m S of Lamberhurst turn E into Kilndown; take 1st R down Chick's Lane until rd divides.* Garden writer's 1½-acre garden, mainly herbaceous borders, but also rock gardens, shrubs, a small wood and pond. Extensive views. TEAS in aid of local charities. *Adm £2 Chd 50p. Sun July 9 (2-5.30); parties welcome by appointment*

Rose Cottage, Hartley ♿✂❀ (Mr & Mrs B D Crowe) *Castle Hil. 3m NE of Swanley and 4m SE of Dartford. From B260 at Longfield, turn S at main roundabout, ½m up hill to Hartley Green with war memorial, where Castle Hill runs down to Fawkham Church: Rose Cottage garden is 100yds down Castle Hill on L. No parking on Castle Hill.* 1-acre garden created from field since 1988, variety of shrubs and perennials, wild life pond, aviary and paved garden. New woodland area being developed. TEA in aid of Demelza Childrens Hospice. **Crawden Bank, Hartley** open on same days. *Adm £1.50 Acc chd free. Suns June 4, Aug 13 (1.30-5.30): private visits also welcome, please* **Tel 01474 707376**

Rose Lodge, Hythe see under Sea Close

St Clere, Kemsing ♿✂ (Mr & Mrs Ronnie Norman) *6m NE of Sevenoaks. Take A25 from Sevenoaks toward Maidstone; 1m past Seal turn L signed Heaverham and Kemsing; in Heaverham take rd to R signed Wrotham and West Kingsdown; in 75yds straight ahead marked Private rd; 1st L and follow rd to house.* 4-acre garden with herbaceous borders, shrubs, rare trees. C17 mansion (not open). TEAS. *Adm £2.50 Chd 50p. Sun June 11 (2-6)*

St Michael's Gardens, Roydon, Peckham Bush *Roydon Road, Seven Mile Lane, 5m NE of Tonbridge, 5m SW of Maidstone. On A26 at Mereworth roundabout take S exit (A228) signed Paddock Wood, after 1½m turn L at top of rise (signed Roydon). Gardens ¼m up hill on L.* TEAS. *Combined adm £3 OAPs £1.50 Chd 50p. Suns April 16 (tulips), May 21 (irises) (2-6), June 11 (roses) (2-6)*

St Michael's House ♿❀ (Brig & Mrs W Magan) Grey stone old Vicarage with yew topiary hedges surrounding what has been described as a very feminine garden in co-ordinated colours. Lovely display of tulips followed by splendid irises, then a mass of roses from red-hot to old soft colours. Wonderful views from the meadow.

St Michael's Cottage ♿❀ (Mr & Mrs Peter Fox) This garden has been designed so it cannot be seen all at once. Gates and features lead you around the garden from a formal garden into a woodland area. Wildlife area with pond and collection of ornamental grasses to a herb garden. There is a traditional cottage garden with lawn and roses. A collection of lavenders, pinks, hostas, heathers alpines and over 30 varieties of climbers.

■ **Scotney Castle, Lamberhurst** ♿✂ (Mrs Christopher Hussey, The National Trust) *On A21 London-Hastings, 1¼m S of Lamberhurst. Bus: (Mon to Sat) Tunbridge Wells-Wadhurst; alight Lamberhurst Green.* Famous picturesque landscape garden, created by the Hussey family in the 1840s surrounding moated C14 Castle. House (not open) by Salvin, 1837. Old Castle open May-mid-Sept (same times as garden). Gift Shop. Picnic area in car park. Tea Lamberhurst. *Adm £4.20 Chd £2.10; Family ticket £10.50; Pre-booked parties of 15 or more. (Wed-Fri) £3.60 Chd £1.80. March 4-March 26, Sats, Suns (12-4) April 1-Oct 2, daily except Mons & Tues, but open Bank Hol Mons (closed Good Fri). Wed-Fri (11-6), Sats & Suns 2-6 or sunset if earlier; Bank Hol Mons & Suns preceding (12-6). For NGS (ACNO to Trinity Hospice, Clapham Common). Mon May 29 (12-6)*

Sea Close & Rose Lodge, Hythe *1m apart. Combined adm £3 Acc chd free. Sun July 9 (2-5)* **Sea Close**, *for other dates see description below*

Sea Close, Hythe (Major & Mrs R H Blizard) *Cannongate Rd. A259 ½m from Hythe, signed.* 23nd year of opening. An all-the-yr-round plantsman's garden on an outstanding 1¼ acre site overlooking the Channel. Created and maintained by present owners since 1966 without any assistance. Over 1000 varieties of plants and shrubs, many unusual, displayed for maximum effect (enhanced by lots of borrowed ideas!) Cold refreshments. *Adm £2 Acc chd free (ACNO to Royal Signals Benevolent Fund). Suns May 14 , June 11 (2-5), Oct 1 (2-4); also open by appt for groups and private visits, please* **Tel 01303 266093**

Rose Lodge, Hythe (S Brint Esq) *40 Albert Rd. 100yds behind sea front, ½ way between Stade St and the fishing boats. Signed.* Fuchsia grower with many years' experience. Small, old walled town garden, crammed with colour and knowledge. *Adm £1.50 (ACNO to Demelza House Childrens Hospice)*

The Silver Spray, Sellindge ♿✂❀ (Mr & Mrs C T Orsbourne) *7m SE of Ashford on A20 opposite school.* 1-acre garden developed and planted since 1983 and maintained by owners. Attractively laid out gardens and wild area combine a keen interest in conservation (especially butterflies) with a love of unusual hardy and tender plants. Hardy Plant Society's Plant Sale July 16. TEAS. *Adm £1.50 Acc chd free (ACNO to St Mary's Church, Sellindge). Suns June 4, 18, July 2, 16, Aug 27; Mon Aug 28; Weds June 14, July 26, Aug 23; Sats June 3, July 29 (2-5)*

■ **Sissinghurst Garden, Sissinghurst** ♿✂❀ (Nigel Nicolson Esq, The National Trust) *Station: Staplehurst. Bus: from Maidstone 14m; Tunbridge Wells (not Suns) 15m. Well signposted.* Garden created by the late V Sackville-West and Sir Harold Nicolson. Spring garden, herb garden. Tudor building and tower, partly open to public. Moat. **Timed tickets are in operation and visitors may have a short wait before entry**. Lunches and TEAS. *Adm £6.50 Chd £3. Garden open April 1 to Oct 15. (Closed Mons incl Bank Hols). Tues to Fri 1-6.30 (last adm 6pm); Sats and Suns 10-5.30 (last adm 5pm). For NGS (ACNO to Charleston Farmhouse Trust). Weds April 19, June 7, July 12, Oct 4 (1-6.30)*

Sissinghurst Place, Sissinghurst ♿✂ (Mr & Mrs Simon macLachlan) *2m NE of Cranbrook, E of Sissinghurst village ½m from Sissinghurst NT garden on A262.* Large Victorian garden of beds, lawns, fine trees, and established yew hedges; spring woodland garden with daffodils, hellebores and pond; herbs and climbers in ruin of original house. *Adm £2 (ACNO to Sissinghurst Bun Penny Club). Sat, Sun April 1, 2 (12-4.30)*

Slaney Cottage, Staplehurst ❀ (Roger & Trisha Fermor) *Headcorn Road, about 1m to E of A229 (Maidstone-Hastings). Please park in field adjoining cottage - not on road outside.* 2-acre cottage garden in the making, surrounding C18 cottage (not open): old roses, clematis species, hardy geraniums and other herbaceous plants, both unusual and favourites: wildlife pond and new woodland area. TEAS. *Adm £1.50 Acc chd free. Sun June 18 (2-5)*

Sotts Hole Cottage, Borough Green ✂ (Mr & Mrs Jim Vinson) *Crouch Lane. Crouch Lane runs SE from A25 between Esso garage and Black Horse public house, garden at bottom of 2nd hill (approx ¾m).* 6 acres of landscaped cottage garden relying entirely on the threat of visitors to motivate the owners to maintain it. Probably at its best in August when the sun shines. TEAS. *Adm £2 Chd £1 (ACNO to Heart of Kent Hospice). Suns April 16, June 18, Aug 6, Sept 17 (10-6)*

South Hill Farm, Hastingleigh ♿✂❀ (Sir Charles Jessel) *E of Ashford. Turn off A28 to Wye, go through village and ascend Wye Downs, in 2m turn R at Xrds marked Brabourne and South Hill, then first L. Or from Stone Street (B2068) turn W opp Stelling Minnis, follow signs to Hastingleigh, continue towards Wye and turn L at Xrds marked Brabourne and South Hill, then first L.* 2 acres high up on N Downs, C17/18 house (not open); old walls; ha-ha; formal water garden; old and new roses; unusual shrubs, perennials and foliage plants. TEAS. *Adm £2 Chd 25p (ACNO to Kent Assoc for the Blind). Suns June 18, July 2 (2-6)*

Southover, Hunton, Maidstone ♿❀ (Mr & Mrs David Way) *6m S of Maidstone. Via B2163 turn S down Hunton Hill and West St. By school, R into Grove Lane, parking beyond garden.* 1½ acres of plant diversity, changing environments and contrasting atmospheres; a garden of gardens. Strong on internal and external vistas, herbaceous plants, wildlife habitats; good collection penstemons. Featured on TV, in 'Beautiful Borders' and in RHS Journal. TEA. *Adm £2 Acc chd free. Thurs June 22 (11-5); also by appt for groups, please* **Tel 01622 820876**

Spilsill Court, Staplehurst ♿✂❀ (Mr & Mrs C G Marshall) *Frittenden Road. Proceed to Staplehurst on A229 (Maidstone-Hastings). From S enter village, turn R immediately after garage on R & just before 30mph sign, into Frittenden Rd; garden ½m on, on L. From N go through village to 40mph sign, immediately turn L into Frittenden Rd.* Approx 4 acres of garden, orchard and paddock; series of gardens incl blue, white and silver; roses; lawns; shrubs, trees and ponds. Small private chapel. Jacob sheep & unusual poultry. COFFEE/TEA April. Cream TEAS July. *Adm £2 Chd (under 16) 50p (ACNO to Gardening for the Disabled Trust). Suns April 2, July 30 (11-5)*

Spoute Cottage, Plaxtol ♿❀ (Mr & Mrs Donald Forbes) *5m N of Tonbridge, 6m E of Sevenoaks, turn E off A227 to Plaxtol Village. Situated at the bottom of Plaxtol St on L side opp Hyders Forge. Large car park.* ¾ acre of mixed borders of contrasting flowering and foliage plants especially for flower arranging; small pond and stream. Japanese garden. Plant nursery attached. *Adm £1.50 Chd free. Sun Sept 17 (10-5); also open with* **Plaxtol Gardens** *Sun June 11*

NEW **Sprivers, Horsmonden** ♿ (Mr & Mrs N Sanderson) *Approx 8m SE of Tonbridge. From Horsmonden Village Xrds take Lamberhurst Rd B2162. House can be found approx 1m on RH-side.* 3-acre garden to wisteria clad Georgian House (not open) with Tudor origins. Yew hedges surround rhododendron garden and shrubbery. Two newly planted herbaceous borders and walled rose garden. Lawns to the rear of house lead to a wild flower meadow bordering ponds. TEA. *Adm £2 Chd £1. Sat May 20 (2-5)*

■ **Squerryes Court, Westerham** (Mrs John Warde) *½m W of Westerham signed from A25.* 15 acres of well-documented historic garden, C18 landscape. Part of the formal garden has been restored by the family using C17 plan. Lake, spring bulbs, azaleas, herbaceous borders, C18 dovecote, cenotaph commemorating Gen Wolfe; woodland walks. Childrens Garden Trail for Kent Gardens Trust. TEAS on NGS days for St Mary's Church, Westerham. Picnics welcome. *Adm £2.50 OAP £2.20 Chd £1.50 (House and garden £4.20 OAP £3.80 Chd £2.50) Weds, Sats, Suns from April 1 to Sept 30 (Garden 12-5.30: House 1.30-5.30). For NGS Sat, Sun July 8, 9 (12-5.30)*

■ **Stoneacre, Otham** (Mrs Rosemary Alexander & The National Trust) *4m SE of Maidstone, between A2020 and A274.* Old world garden with many unusual plants, recently replanted. Yew hedges; herbaceous borders; ginkgo tree; small kitchen garden. Timber-framed Hall House dated 1480. Subject of newspaper and magazine articles, and country outlet of The English Gardening School, Chelsea. (National Trust members please note that openings in aid of the NGS are on days when the property would not normally be open, therefore adm charges apply. TEAS. *Adm £2.50 Chd 50p. Open Weds & Sats April-Oct 31 (2-5). For NGS Suns April 2, May 14 (2-5); also open with* **Otham Gardens** *Sun June 25. Private visits welcome, please* **Tel 01622 862871**

Stonewall Park Gardens, Chiddingstone Hoath *5m SE of Edenbridge. ½-way between Markbeech and Penshurst.* TEAS. *Combined adm £2.50 Acc chd free (ACNO to The Sarah Matheson Trust and St Mary, Chiddingstone). Sun March 26; Mon May 1 (1.30-5)*

Stonewall Park (Mr & Mrs Valentine Fleming) Large walled garden with herbaceous borders. Daffodils in March. Extensive woodland garden, featuring species and hybrid rhododendrons, magnolias, azaleas; wandering paths, lakes

North Lodge (Mrs Dorothy Michie) Traditional cottage garden full of interest.

Swan Oast, Stilebridge, Marden ♿ (Mr & Mrs Bedford) *6m S of Maidstone. On A229 (Maidstone-Hastings) ½m S of Stilebridge inn, 3m N of Staplehurst.* 28-yr-old 1¾-acre garden, incl ¼ acre of water, landscaped with shrubberies, rockeries, with dwarf conifers and heathers, raised beds of seasonal bedding, kitchen garden; ornamental fish and small collection of waterfowl. Cream TEAS in aid of The Mike Colinwood Trust. *Adm £2 Acc chd free. Suns July 9, 16, 23, 30, Aug 6, 13, 20, 27, Sept 3 (2-5)*

2 Thorndale Close, Chatham (Mr & Mrs L O Miles) *From A229 Chatham-Maidstone rd turn E opp Forte Posthouse into Watson Ave, next R to Thorndale Close.* Minute front and rear gardens of 11ft × 18ft and 20ft × 22ft. Plantsman's garden with alpines, pool, bog garden, rockery, peat and herbaceous beds. Partly suitable for wheelchairs. *Adm £2 Acc chd under 10 free. By appt only, private visits welcome, please* **Tel 01634 863329**

Thornham Friars, Thurnham ♿ (Geoffrey Fletcher Esq) *Pilgrims Way, 4m NE of Maidstone. From M20 or M2 take A249, at bottom of Detling Hill turn into Detling and 1m along Pilgrims Way to garden.* 2-acre garden on chalk. 12-acre park and magnificent views. Many unusual shrubs; trees; lawns with special beds for ericaceous shrubs. Tudor house. TEAS. *Adm £2 Chd 50p (ACNO to The Children's Society). Sun May 21 (2-5.30)*

Tonbridge School, Tonbridge ♿ (The Governors) *At the N end of Tonbridge High Street. Parking signposted off London Rd (B245 Tonbridge-Sevenoaks).* Behind the school lie 150 acres of sports grounds and gardens, with magnificent trees, incl the Headmaster's garden, and Ferox Hall garden . St Augustine's Chapel (restored after fire in 1988) will be open. TEAS *Adm £2.50 Acc chd free (ACNO to St Augustine's Chapel Charity). Sun July 23 (2-5.30)*

Torry Hill, Sittingbourne ♿ (The Lord & Lady Kingsdown) *5m S of Sittingbourne. Situated in triangle formed by Frinsted, Milstead and Doddington [OS map ref 909 573]. Leave M20 at junction 8 for A20 (Lenham), at Great Danes roundabout turn L for Hollingbourne and Frinsted (B2163). From M2 Intersection 5 towards Maidstone, then L through Bredgar/Milstead.* 8 acres; large lawns, specimen trees, flowering cherries, rhododendrons, azaleas and naturalised daffodils; walled gardens with lawns, shrubs, roses, herbaceous borders, wild flower areas and vegetables. Extensive views to Medway and Thames estuaries. TEA; refreshments on July 19. *Adm £2 Chd (over 12) 50p (ACNO to St Dunstan's Church, Frinsted). Suns April 16, June 25 (2-5).* **Evening Opening** *Wed July 19 (6.30-9)*

Town Hill Cottage, West Malling (Mr & Mrs P Cosier) *58 Town Hill. From A20 6m W of Maidstone, turn S onto A228. Top of Town Hill at N end of High St.* Small, part-walled village garden of C16/C18 house (not open), with many interesting plants. TEAS. *Adm £1.50 Chd 75p. Sun May 21 (2-5)*

NEW **Turkey Court, Maidstone** (Turkey Mill Investments) *Ashford Rd A20, approx 1m E of Maidstone town centre.* Historic gardens of approx 10 acres around a water mill, parkland with notable trees. Lakes and waterfall from the C18, and recent design and replanting of walled and rock gardens. Partially suitable for wheelchairs. TEAS. *Adm £2.50 Chd £1 (ACNO to Leukaemia & Cancer Equipment Fund). Suns June 18, Sept 3 (2-6)*

Upper Pryors, Cowden (Mr & Mrs S G Smith) *4½m SE of Edenbridge. From B2026 Edenbridge-Hartfield, turn R at Cowden Xrds and take 1st drive on R.* 10 acres of country garden featuring variety, profusion of plants, water and magnificent lawns. TEAS. *Adm £2 Chd 50p. Wed June 14 (2-5)*

Vine House, Lydd ♿ (Dr & Mrs Peter Huxley-Williams) *62 High St. S of New Romney on B2075, past the church in High St on R-side.* Informal gardens of about 1 acre surrounding C16 farmhouse; many unusual small trees and shrubs; ponds with waterfall; rose pergola through vineyard; new planting of old roses. **The Beehive** open same days. Teas usually available in the church. *Adm £1.50 Acc chd free (ACNO to The Royal National Rose Society). Sat, Sun, Mon May 27, 28 29 (2.30-5)*

Waystrode Manor, Cowden ♿ (Mr and Mrs Peter Wright) *4½m S of Edenbridge. From B2026 Edenbridge-*

Hartfield, turn off at Cowden Pound. 8 acres; sweeping lawns, borders, ponds, bulbs, shrub roses, clematis and many tender plants. Orangery. All trees, plants and shrubs labelled. House C15 (not open). Last entry ½-hour before closing time. Subject of TV Winter Gardens. TEAS. Gift shop. *Adm £3 Chd 50p (ACNO to Cowden Church Bell Restoration Fund, June 11). Weds May 10, 24, June 14, 28 (1.30-5.30); Suns May 21, 28, June 11, 25, July 2 (2-6); also open for groups of 15 or more by appt* **Tel 01342 850695**

Weald Cottage, Edenbridge ♿❀ (Mrs Pauline Abraham) *Four Elms Road, just N of Edenbridge on B2027, opp Eden Valley School.* Small garden with theme areas including French, Roman and Japanese; mixed planting of bulbs, herbaceous, shrubs and trees, vegetables and fruit trees, conservatory. TEAS. *Adm £1.50 Chd 25p. Suns April 2, 9, 23, May 14, 28, June 11, 18; Mons April 24, May 29 (2-5). Private visits welcome, please* **Tel 01732 508514**

Weeks Farm, Egerton Forstal ♿✂❀ (Robin & Monica De Garston) *Ashford, 3½m E of Headcorn. Take Smarden Road out of Headcorn, Bedlam Lane is 3rd turning on L, Weeks Farm approx 1½m on R.* 2-acre garden on Wealden clay, showing varied use of badly drained site; double herbaceous borders flanking gateway, vista a feature; orchard with crocus & fritillaria. Water garden, ponds with abundance of wild life. TEAS. *Adm £1.50 Acc chd free. Suns March 12 (12-5), April 9 (12-6). Private visits welcome, please* **Tel 01233 756252 (evenings)**

West Studdal Farm, West Studdal ♿❀ (Mr & Mrs Peter Lumsden) *N of Dover half-way between Eastry and Whitfield. Take A256. Then rd signposted to Studdal at roundabout. At top of hill turn R and entrance ¼m on L.* Medium-sized garden around old farmhouse(not open) set by itself in small valley; herbaceous borders, roses and fine lawns protected by old walls and beech hedges. TEAS in Dodecagonal folly. *Adm £1.50 Chd 50p. Sun Aug 20 (2-6)*

Westview, Hempstead ❀ (Mr & Mrs J G Jackson) *Spekes Rd. From M2 take A278 to Gillingham; at 1st roundabout follow sign to Wigmore, proceed to junction with Fairview Av, turn L & park on motorway link rd bridge, walk into Spekes Rd, Westview 3rd on L.* ¼-acre town garden on very sloping site with many steps; good collection of plants & shrubs suitable for a chalk soil; designed by owners for all-year interest and low maintenance. Good autumn colour. TEAS. *Adm £1.50 Acc chd free. By appointment only, private visits and clubs welcome, please* **Tel 01634 230987**

Whitehurst, Chainhurst ♿✂ (Mr & Mrs John Mercy) *3m N of Marden. From Marden station turn R into Pattenden Lane and under railway bridge; at T-junc turn L; at next fork bear R to Chainhurst, then second turning on L.* 1½ acres of trees, roses & water garden. Victorian spiral staircase leading to aerial walkway through the tree tops. Exhibition of root dwellings. TEAS. *Adm £2 Chd £1 (ACNO to Stroke Assoc). Weds May 31, June 7 (2-5.30); also private visits welcome, please* **Tel 01622 820616**

Withersdane Hall, Wye ♿ (University of London) *3m NE of Ashford. A28 take fork signed Wye. Bus Ashford-Canterbury via Wye.* Well-labelled garden of educational and botanical interest, containing several small carefully designed gardens; flower and shrub borders; spring bulbs; herb garden. Rain-fed garden. Free guide book with map available. *Adm £1.50 Chd 50p. Suns April 16, June 11, Aug 27 (2-5)*

Womenswold Gardens ♿❀ *Midway between Canterbury and Dover, SE of A2, take B2046 signed Wingham at Barham crossover, after about ¼m turn R at Armada beacon, follow signs for gardens.* Five diverse and colourful cottage gardens within easy walking distance. A sixth garden not to be missed is near the Beacon. St Margaret's Church will be open with an exhibition of embroidery. TEAS. *Combined adm £2.50 Acc chd free (ACNO to St Margaret's Church). Sat, Sun July 1, 2 (2-6)*

Worth Gardens ♿✂❀ *2m SE of Sandwich and 5m NW of Deal, from A258 signed Worth.* A group of cottage gardens in wide variety in peaceful village setting. Maps available at each garden. TEA. *Combined adm £2 Acc chd free. Sun July 2 (1-5).* **Evening Opening** *Wed June 28 (5-8)*

Wyckhurst, Aldington ♿✂❀ (Mr & Mrs C D Older) *Mill Road, 4m SE of Ashford. Leave M20 at junction 10, on A20 travel S to Aldington turning; proceed 1½m to Aldington village hall, at 'Walnut Tree' take rd signed to Dymchurch, after ¼m turn R into Mill Road.* C16 cottage (not open) surrounded by 1-acre cottage garden; old roses; herbaceous borders; unusual perennials and topiary. Extensive views across Romney Marsh. TEAS in aid of Bonnington Church. *Adm £2 Chd 50p. Wed June 21, Sun June 25 (11-6);* **Evening Opening** *£3. Wine. Sat June 24 (6 till dusk),*

Yalding Gardens *6m SW of Maidstone, 3 gardens in centre, S & W of village. Combined adm £3 (family ticket £6). Sun April 16 (2-5.30)*

NEW **The Court Lodge** (Jonathan & Joy Virden) *High Street between Bridges and Kenward Rd.* Small family garden surrounding old Farm House (not open). Interesting deep-dug vegetable strips, dwarf fruit trees, spring flowers

Parsonage Oasts ✂ (Edward & Jennifer Raikes) *Between Yalding village and station turn off at Anchor public house over bridge over canal, continue 100yds up the lane.* 3/4-acre riverside garden with walls, shrubs, daffodils. TEAS in aid of the Fifth Trust for Mentally Handicapped Adults

Rugmer Farmhouse ✂❀ (Mr & Mrs R Lawrence) *S of village, off Benover Rd (B2162), 440yds past Woolpack Inn.* 2-acre garden, surrounding C16 cottage (not open), developed by present owners since 1975; spring bulbs, mixed borders and vegetables, on Wealden clay

■ **Yalding Organic Gardens, Yalding** ♿✂❀ (Henry Doubleday Research Association) *Benover Road. 6m SE of Maidstone, ½m S of Yalding on B2162. Yalding served by buses from Maidstone and Tonbridge, railway station 1½m.* 14 individual gardens illustrating gardening through the ages, from mediaeval times to the present day, set in 6 beautifully landscaped acres. Incl C13 apothecary's garden, paradise garden, Tudor knot, Jekyll borders, rare heritage vegetable varieties, composting and natural pest control displays, large pergola. TEAS. *Adm £3 Chd under 16 free. Wed-Sun May to Sept; weekends only during April and Oct. Also open Easter and all Bank Hol weekends. For NGS Sat May 13; Sun Oct 8 (10-5)*

Yew Tree Cottage, Shipbourne (Susan & Ian Bowles) *The Green. 3m N of Tonbridge, 5m E of Sevenoaks on A227.* Small cottage garden, partly walled, with herb garden, gravel garden, herbaceous borders and old roses. Formation of new garden in progress. Studio of wild-life artist Ian Bowles will also be open. **Hookwood House, Shipbourne** open same day. TEAS in Shipbourne village hall. *Adm £1.50 Acc chd free. Sun June 25 (2-6)*

Evening Opening (See also garden description)

Edenbridge House, Edenbridge	June 14
Godinton House, Ashford	August 23
Haydown, Great Buckland	May 31 & July 19
Hazel Street Farmhouse, Horsmonden	May 17 & June 28
Ladham House, Goudhurst	July 6
Little Oast, Otford	July 8
Nettlestead Place, Nettlestead	June 21
Plaxtol Gardens (Evening Opening)	June 16
Torry Hill, Sittingbourne	July 19
Worth Gardens	June 28
Wyckhurst, Aldington	June 24

Marie Curie Cancer Care

Cancer is the UK's single biggest killer – one in three people will get it and one in four will die from it. The National Gardens Scheme supports Marie Curie Cancer Care, a comprehensive cancer care charity, helping people with cancer and their families throughout the UK. For more information about Marie Curie Cancer Care, ring 0800 716 146 or visit our web site at www.mariecurie.org.uk.

THE GARDEN CONSERVANCY

The Garden Conservancy is a not-for-profit organisation in the United States dedicated to preserving America's exceptional private gardens and facilitating their transition from private to independent not-for-profit ownership and operation. The Garden Conservancy works in partnership with individual garden owners, and public and private organisations, and uses its legal, financial, and horticultural resources to secure each garden's future and to make it permanently accessible to the public.

In 2000, the Conservancy's Open Days Program will once again invite the public to peek behind the gates of over 400 of America's best private gardens which range from a Feng Shui-inspired Arizona desert garden to a New Hampshire parlour garden with a thyme lawn and herbaceous border. By opening these otherwise private gardens, the Conservancy brings to light the importance of preserving fine gardens for future generations and is building a constituency of committed individuals willing to act on behalf of exceptional gardens.

We are a Specialist Nursery
supplying rare and unusual shrubs including
MAGNOLIAS, ACERS, CORNUS, DAPHNE AND CLIMBERS

We are open from **10.00am - 4.00pm**
Closed on **Sundays (Also January, July and August).**

Visit us on the B2028 at

STARBOROUGH NURSERY

Marsh Green, Edenbridge, Kent TN8 5RB

Tel: (01732) 865614 or Fax: (01732) 862166

You are also invited to visit our
Specialist RHODODENDRON & AZALEAS Nursery
on the main A25 between Seal and Ightham

G. REUTHE LTD.

Crown Point Nursery,

Ightham, Sevenoaks, Kent TN15 0HB
(Chelsea Gold Medallists)

which is open from **10.00am - 4.00pm**
Monday to Saturday (but also closed **Sundays January, July and August)**
However, we do open **Sundays & Bank Holidays in April & May.**

Combined price list available.

Lancashire, Merseyside & Greater Manchester

Hon County Organisers: Mr & Mrs Ray Doldon, please contact at address below
Assistant County Organiser: Mr James Bowker, Swiss Cottage, 8 Hammond Drive, Burnley, Lancashire BB12 7RE

DATES OF OPENING

Regular openings
For details see garden description
Catforth Gardens
Weeping Ash, Glazebury

By appointment only
For telephone numbers and other details see garden descriptions. Private visits welcomed
Bank House, Borwick
Cross Gaits Cottage, Blacko, Nelson
Lindeth Dene, Silverdale
Swiss Cottage, Read

April 2 Sunday
The Reginald Kaye Garden, Silverdale

April 30 Sunday
The Ridges, Cowling Road, Limbrick nr Chorley

May 14 Sunday
Woodside, Shevington

May 21 Sunday
Speke Hall, Liverpool
Weeping Ash, Glazebury

May 28 Sunday
Linden Hall, Borwick
The Reginald Kaye Garden, Silverdale
Willow House, Walton-le-Dale

May 29 Monday
480 Aigburth Road, Liverpool

June 4 Sunday
Catforth Gardens

June 9 Friday
Mill Barn, Samlesbury Bottoms

June 10 Saturday
Mill Barn, Samlesbury Bottoms

June 11 Sunday
Mill Barn, Samlesbury Bottoms
Rufford Old Hall, Rufford

June 12 Monday
Mill Barn, Samlesbury Bottoms

June 18 Sunday
Linden Hall, Borwick
7 Marmion Close, Lowton, nr Leigh
South View Cottage, Treales
Willow House, Walton-le-Dale

June 25 Sunday
Clearbeck House, Higher Tatham
Hesketh Bank Village Gardens
Old Malleys, Read

July 2 Sunday
Clearbeck House, Higher Tatham
Rainford Village Gardens

July 6 Thursday
Ivy Cottage, Forest Beck

July 9 Sunday
Catforth Gardens
Cliviger Gardens
Ivy Cottage, Forest Beck
Mill Bridge Barn, Lowgill, Lancaster

July 16 Sunday
Mill Bridge Barn, Lowgill, Lancaster
Piked Edge Farm, Colne
Weeping Ash, Glazebury
Willow House, Walton-le-Dale

July 22 Saturday
Montford Cottage, Fence-in-Pendle

July 23 Sunday
Montford Cottage, Fence-in-Pendle

August 6 Sunday
Woodside, Shevington

August 27 Sunday
The Ridges, Cowling Road, Limbrick nr Chorley

September 3 Sunday
7 Marmion Close, Lowton, nr Leigh

September 17 Sunday
Weeping Ash, Glazebury

Macmillan Cancer Relief

Many people with cancer are unable to work, meaning that they face the additional burden of financial problems. Macmillan's patient grants are awarded to help meet extra costs associated with the illness, such as heating, bedding, telephone and travel bills, care and convalescent breaks. Each week more than 300 people will receive patient grants.

Macmillan Cancer Relief Information Line: 0845 601 6161
Macmillan Cancer Relief Website: www.macmillan.org.uk

LANCASHIRE, MERSEYSIDE & GREATER MANCHESTER

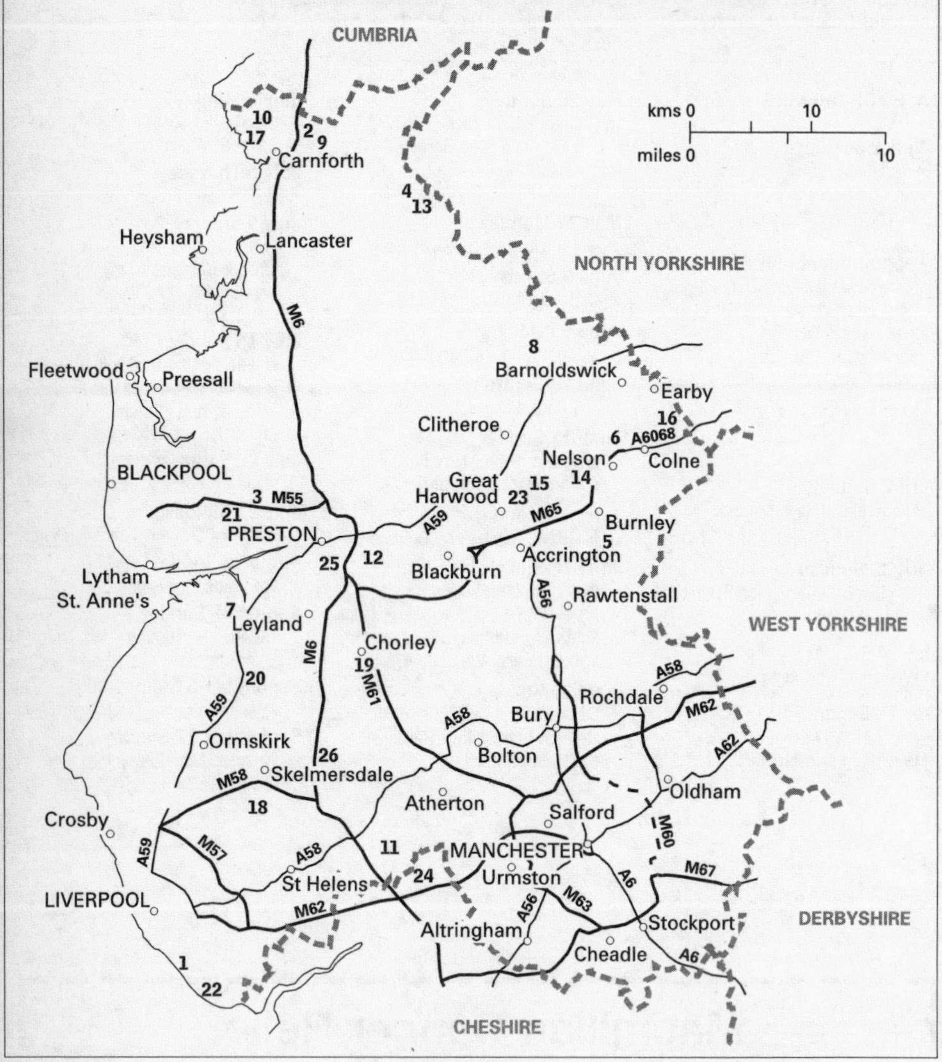

KEY

1 480 Aigburth Road
2 Bank House
3 Catforth Gardens
4 Clearbeck House
5 Cliviger Gardens
6 Cross Gaits Cottage
7 Hesketh Bank Village Gardens
8 Ivy Cottage
9 Linden Hall
10 Lindeth Dene
11 7 Marmion Close
12 Mill Barn
13 Mill Bridge Barn
14 Montford Cottage
15 Old Malleys
16 Piked Edge Farm
17 The Reginald Kaye Garden
18 Rainford Village Gardens
19 The Ridges
20 Rufford Old Hall
21 South View Cottage
22 Speke Hall
23 Swiss Cottage
24 Weeping Ash
25 Willow House
26 Woodside

DESCRIPTIONS OF GARDENS

480 Aigburth Road, Liverpool (Mrs Bridget Spiegl) *S Liverpool, on main rd (A561) between city and Runcorn bridge. Just past Liverpool Cricket Club, on LH side of rd going towards the city.* Plantswoman's small town garden. Mixed herbaceous and shrubs. Some interesting and unusual plants. Spring bulbs, particularly good display of species crocus late February - early March. *Adm £1.50 Chd free (ACNO to Old Peoples' Homes Assoc). Mon May 29 (2-5). Private visits welcome, please* **Tel 0151 427 2344**

Bank House, Borwick (Mr and Mrs R G McBurnie) *2m NE of Carnforth off A6. Leave M6 at junction 35.* Plantsman's garden of 2 acres designed to provide all-yr round shape, colour and form. Divided into different areas of interest incl shady borders, sunny gravel area with old-fashioned roses, arboretum, fruit and vegetables. Island beds, silver and gold borders. Collection of carnivorous plants. *Adm £1.50 Chd free. Please* **Tel 01524 732768**

■ **Catforth Gardens** *Leave M6 at junction 32 turning N on A6. Turn L at 1st set of traffic lights; 2m to T-junction, turn R. Turn L at sign for Catforth, L at next T-junction, 1st R into Benson Lane. Bear L at church into Roots Lane.* TEAS NGS days only. *Combined adm £2.50 OAP £2 Chd 50p. Gardens and adjacent nursery. Open April 1 to end of August (10.30-5). For NGS Suns June 4, July 9 (12-5). Parties by appt, please* **Tel 01772 690561/690269. Please tel to confirm all dates for opening**

Cherry Tree Lodge (Mr & Mrs T A Bradshaw) 1-acre informal country garden, planted for yr-round interest and colour. Wide variety of unusual shrubs; trees; rhododendrons, azaleas; rare herbaceous plants incl euphorbias, dicentras, pulmonarias; ground cover plants; national collection of hardy geraniums; 2 ponds with bog gardens, large rockery and woodland garden

Willow Bridge Farm (Mr W Moore) ¼-acre cottage garden with wide variety of herbaceous perennials. Also 1½-acre summer flower garden with 3 natural clay-lined ponds and high banks. Large herbaceous borders and rose garden, shrubs, climbing roses intermingled with perennials

Clearbeck House, Higher Tatham (Peter & Bronwen Osborne) *Signed from Wray (M6 Junction 34, A683, B6480) and Low Bentham.* This creative garden extends beyond traditional terraced borders through vistas and secret ways; many charming surprises. These include follies (a walk-through pyramid) and sculptures (some for sale), fountains, streams, ponds and a 2-acre wildlife lake, attracting many species of birds and insects. Planting incl herbaceous borders, bog plants, bamboos and grasses. TEAS. *Adm £1.50 Chd free Suns June 25, July 2 (11.30-5.30). Private visits welcome (£1.50), please* **Tel 015242 61029**

NEW **Cliviger Gardens** *3m S of Burnley. ¼m on L along the A671 Bacup Rd, signposted Bacup and Rochdale. Visitors are advised to start at Sagar Fold Farm. Combined adm £2 Chd 50p. Sun July 9 (12-5)*

NEW **Dyneley** (Sir Simon & Lady Towneley) 2-acre Pennine upland woodland garden. Herbaceous borders. Rhododendron, azaleas, tree peonies, old-fashioned roses and other shrubs. Interesting trees. TEAS. *(ACNO to RDA Dyneley Group).*

Sagar Fold Farm (Mrs M Cawtherley) Recently created 1-acre organic garden. On open hillside site with dramatic views. Featuring stream and bog garden, wild flower meadow and orchard, cottage garden, rockery, and no-dig vegetable garden. TEAS in aid of local church.

Cross Gaits Cottage, Blacko, Nelson (Mr & Mrs S J Gude) *Take M65 exit junction 13. Follow Barrowford signs then Barnoldswick signs. Garden 1½m on Barnoldswick Rd opp Cross Gaits Inn.* ⅔-acre walled cottage garden featured on Granada TV; shrub and herbaceous borders; 2 ornamental ponds. 700ft above sea level; fine view of Pennines. TEA. *Adm £1.50. Private visits welcome, please* **Tel 01282 617163**

Hesketh Bank Village Gardens *Midway between Preston and Southport. From Preston take A59 towards Liverpool, then turn R at traffic lights for Tarleton village. Straight through Tarleton to Hesketh Bank.* Free vintage bus between gardens. All gardens recently featured on Granada TV. Maps available at each garden TEAS. *Combined adm £2.50 Chd free. Sun June 25 (12-6)*

31 Becconsall Lane (Mr & Mrs J Baxter) Cottage style garden with pond, white and green beds and semi-woodland walk. TEAS

74 Chapel Road (Mr & Mrs T Iddon) Compact colourful garden. Wide variety of plants. Pond, arbour and gazebo. Lancashire garden winner. *Also by appointment* **Tel 01772 813172**

11 Douglas Avenue (Mr & Mrs J Cook) Large established garden with lawns, mature trees, mixed herbaceous borders and naturalised areas

Hawthornes (Mr & Mrs R Hodson) 1-acre garden. Mixed borders; island beds; shrub roses, clematis. Many perennials. Pond. Nursery open daily. *Also by appt, please* **Tel 01772 812379**

155 Station Road (Mr & Mrs G Hale) Large and interesting garden with pond, mixed herbaceous, shrub borders and climbers

Ivy Cottage, Forest Beck (Mr & Mrs R Corless) *Leave A59 through Sawley, take Bolton-by-Bowland rd. Turn L to Settle 100yds past Copy Nook Hotel, 1m to Forest Beck. Toilets in Bolton-by-Bowland village.* ⅓ acre comprising 2 gardens with ponds, herbaceous beds; both gardens have steps to different levels surrounded by mature trees and streams. *Adm £1.50 Chd 50p. Thurs, Sun July 6, 9 (1-5)*

Linden Hall, Borwick (Mr and Mrs E P Sharp) *3m NE of Carnforth. Leave M6 junction 35. Take A6 direction Milnthorpe. Turn R after ½m. Signposted to Borwick. House in centre of Borwick village.* C19 garden of 5 acres. Wide range of trees, shrubs and old-fashioned roses; mixed borders. Ornamental lake with Chinese pagoda. Knot garden. Victorian greenhouses and ornamental kitchen garden. Teas and parking at village hall. *Adm £2 Chd 50p (ACNO to St Mary's Church, Borwick). Suns May 28, June 18 (2-5.30)*

Lindeth Dene, Silverdale (Mrs B M Kershaw) *38 Lindeth Rd. 13m N of Lancaster. Take M6 to junction 35, turn L (S) on A6 to Carnforth t-lights. Turn R follow signs*

Silverdale. After level Xing ¼m uphill turn L down Hollins Lane. At T junction turn R into Lindeth Rd. Garden is 4th gateway on L, park in rd. 1¼ acres overlooking Morecambe Bay. Limestone rock garden; troughs; pools; heathers; veganic kitchen garden, saxifrages, geraniums, Elizabethan primroses, N.Z. plants and hardy perennials. Teas and toilets available in village *Adm £1.50 Acc chd free By appt, only please* **Tel 01524 701314**

7 Marmion Close, Lowton, nr Leigh ♿ (Mr & Mrs G Smith) *Junction 23 M6. A580 towards Manchester. Turn L at 3rd set traffic lights after Golborne Island into Church Lane. R at traffic lights St Luke's Church into Slag Lane, 5th on L Scott Rd, Marmion Close 1st R.* Plantswoman's 'surprise' garden. Rare and unusual plants and shrubs, wildlife ponds. Different types of garden features. *Adm £1.50 Chd free. Suns June 18, Sept 3 (11-6)*

Middle Birks, Clapham See Yorkshire

Mill Barn, Samlesbury Bottoms ♿❀ (Dr C J Mortimer) *and* **Primrose Cottage** (Mrs S Childs) *Goose Foot Close, Samlesbury Bottoms, Preston. 6m E of Preston. From M6 junction 31 2½m on A59/A677 B/burn. Turn S. Nabs Head Lane, then Goose Foot Lane.* 1½ acre tranquil, terraced garden along the banks of the R Darwen, which is constantly evolving. Varied artistic planting incl some uncommon herbaceous perennials. Primrose Cottage opp is a small hillside garden with a formal but creative layout. TEAS. *Adm £1.50 Chd free. Fri, Sat, Sun, Mon June 9, 10, 11, 12 (12-5). Private visits of groups welcome by appt, please* **Tel 01254 853300**

NEW **Mill Bridge Barn, Lowgill, Lancaster** ❀ (John & Barbara Harrison) *M6 Junction 34, A683, B6480, follow signs from Wray and Low Bentham.* This 1-acre garden is set in a steep sided valley bounded by a small river and surrounded by 3 acres of mature woodland and meadows. Large pond, terraces with shrubs and perennials climbers; rhododendron walk; arboretum with varied planting; deep-bed vegetable and soft fruit area, orchard. TEAS served at Old School. *Adm £1.50 Chd free. Suns July 9, 16 (12-5)* johnandbarbaraharrison@ukgateway.net

Montford Cottage, Fence-in-Pendle ♿✂❀ (Craig Bullock & Tony Morris) *From the M65 junction 13, take the A6068 (signs for Fence) and in 2m turn L onto the B6248 (signs for Brierfield). Proceed down the hill for ½m (past the Forest PH). Entrance to garden is on the L, with limited car park further down hill.* Gardens within a garden, within an acre. Particular interest for the plantsman, flower-arranger, lover of foliage and connoisseur of scones. Overall atmosphere of a relaxed country cottage garden, with a few surprises and the odd eccentric thrown in for good measure. TEAS. *Adm £2 Chd 50p. Sat, Sun July 22, 23 (2-6). No coaches*

NEW **Old Malleys, Read** ♿✂❀ (J & C Barnett) *Between Whalley and Padiham on the A671, turn at Spar Grocers into Straits Lane. Garden at top of Straits Lane on L. Parking in lane.* S-facing medium-sized garden on 2 levels with good selection of perennials, lilies and trees. Bog garden and new water features. TEAS in aid of Pendle Hospice. *Adm £1.50 Chd 50p. Sun June 25 (1-5)*

Piked Edge Farm, Colne ❀ (Mr & Mrs R M Box) *From roundabout on A6068 ½m E of Colne follow signs to Lothersdale. Pass Colne Golf Club, continue up hill for 1¼m. Please park on L side of rd facing uphill.* 1½ acres garden at 1000ft above sea level. Very hardy plants! Rockery, stone features, small pond, lawns. Large semi-organic vegetable garden with raised beds. Also short hill walk with magnificent views of Pennines. Cream TEAS. *Adm £1.50 Chd free. Sun July 16 (1-5)* caroline_box@barclays.com

NEW **Rainford Village Gardens** ♿✂❀ *5m N of St Helens off A570 Rainford Bypass. Turn into village from roundabout. L at T-junction then through village ½m. Turn 1st R after Bridge Inn into Junction Rd. Knowsley View is 1st L.* TEAS. *Combined adm £2 Chd free. Sun July 2 (12-5)*

NEW **24 Junction Road** (Mr J Walker & Mr G Elsdon) Large suburban garden with island beds growing flowering shrubs, conifers, clematis and trees. Pond with fish and water feature

NEW **20 Knowsley View** (Mr & Mrs Eccleston) Typical small garden with mixed borders and container planting. Emphasis on easy maintenance and yr-round colour

NEW **22 Knowsley View** (Mr & Mrs Ball) Compact plantswoman's garden generously planted with variety of climbers, perennials, alpines and bulbs in borders, pots and sinks

NEW **38 Knowsley View** (Mr & Mrs Jackson) Cottage type garden with organically raised vegetable and salad beds, soft fruit, etc. Feature pergola covered in wisteria and other climbers. Small pond with lilies and marginal plants

NEW **The Reginald Kaye Garden, Silverdale** ✂ (Linda Kaye) *5m W J35 M6. From centre of village facing S turn R down Stankelt Rd. 100 yds turn L onto Lindeth Rd. Garden 500yds on R.* A recently restored woodland garden originally designed, constructed and planted by the nurseryman and plantsman Reginald Kaye. In a beautiful setting overlooking Morecambe bay, enclosed in an atmosphere of peace and tranquililty. Special features incl natural limestone rock garden; large plantings of hellebores; drifts of meconopsis; woodland plants and choice perennials. *Adm £1.50 Children not admitted. Suns April 2, May 28 (1-5)*

■ **The Ridges, Cowling Road, Limbrick nr Chorley** ♿❀ (Mr & Mrs J M Barlow) *Approx 2m SE of Chorley. Junction 8 M61 approaching Chorley on A6, follow signs for town centre, then signs for Cowling and Rivington. Modernised C17 house on R.* 2¼ acres. Incl old walled kitchen garden, cottage style; herbaceous borders; area for growing annuals to dry; ponds. Laburnum arch leads to large formal lawn, surrounded by natural woodland. TEAS in aid of Junior Diabetic Society. *Adm £1.50 Chd 50p. Open Bank Hols, Suns, Mons April 30, May 1, 28, 29, Aug 27, 28. Also Weds in June & July. For NGS April 30, Aug 27 (11-5). Private visits for 5 & over welcome, please* **Tel 01257 279981**

▲ **Rufford Old Hall, Rufford** ♿❀ (The National Trust) *On A59 Liverpool to Preston rd in village of Rufford, 7m N of Ormskirk.* Set in 14 acres of garden and woodland. Informal garden and walks. Spectacular in May and June for spring flowering rhododendrons and azaleas. TEAS. *Adm £2 Chd £1 (Garden only). For NGS Sun June 11 (12-4.30)*

South View Cottage, Treales ♿✂ (Pauline & Mike Coxon) *Leave M55 junction 3, A585 then B5192 Kirkham, at t-lights turn L B5192 to Preston. Continue through Kirkham centre and after approx ½m, turn L (Carr Lane, signed Treales). Follow rd approx 1m, keeping Derby Arms Hotel on L.* ⅓-acre garden in cottage style. Large pond area, well stocked mixed herbaceous borders, lawns, containers, varied planting incl scented shrub and climbing roses. A garden to sit in, wander round and enjoy! TEAS. *Adm £1.50 Chd free (ACNO to PDSA). Sun June 18, (1-5). Private visits welcome by appt please,* **Tel 01772 686700**

▲ **Speke Hall, Liverpool** ♿✂ (The National Trust) *8m SE of Liverpool adjacent to Liverpool Airport. Follow signs for Liverpool Airport.* A formal garden with herbaceous border, rose garden; moated area with formal lawns and a recently opened stream garden. A wild wood, views of Mersey basin from a high bank. Estate approx 35 acres. TEAS. *Adm £1.60 Chd 80p Family £3.80 (Garden only). Sun May 21 (12-5). Parties of 20 or over welcome, please* **Tel 0151 4277231**

Swiss Cottage, Read ✂❀ (James and Doreen Bowker) *8 Hammond Drive. 3m SE of Whalley on A671 Whalley to Burnley Road, turn by Pollards Garage, up George Lane to T junction, L into Private Rd.* 1½ acre hillside garden designed on 2 levels in mature woodland setting. Variety of shrubs, trees, rhododendrons, azaleas, perennials and alpines. Stream and bog garden feature. *Adm £2. Private visits welcome by appt, please* **Tel 01282 774853**

Weeping Ash, Glazebury ♿✂ (John Bent Esq) *¼m S A580 (East Lancs Rd Greyhound Motel roundabout, Leigh) on A574 Glazebury/Leigh Boundary.* Large garden of yr-round interest on heavy soil. Lawns, mixed borders of shrubs and herbaceous perennials, secret areas with pools, roses and island beds, alpine rockery, hot area with Mediterranean planting. Newly planted bank 100yds long. Teas 100yds N at Garden Centre. *Adm £2 Chd free (ACNO to Wigan/Leigh Hospice). Suns May 21, July 16, Sept 17 (1-5), also 3rd Sun in month, Feb-Nov incl. Private visits welcome, minimum 10* **Tel 01942 262066**

NEW **Willow House, Walton-le-Dale** ✂❀ (Mrs Sue Coupe) *Exit 29 M6. Bungalow on A675 between Preston and Hoghton (nr to Birch House Restaurant).* Approx ⅓ acre, overlooking fields to ancient woodland. Herbaceous borders, small box parterre, pond with koi, rockery and summerhouse. TEAS. *Adm £1.50 Chd free (ACNO to Preston Hospital Renal Unit). Suns May 28, June 18, July 16 (11-4)*

Woodside, Shevington ✂❀ (Mr & Mrs B Seddon) *M6 Exit 26 or 27. Follow to Shevington. Princes Park is small side rd off Gathurst Lane almost opp Gathurst Vauxhall Garage.* ⅔ acre undulating garden with several levels. Developed by owners from dense woodland and featuring rhododendron, azalea, camellia, magnolia, acer, eucryphia, hydrangea and specimen paeonies. New water feature in dell. Lancashire Garden winner. TEAS in aid of Derian House Childrens' Hospice, Chorley. *Adm £1.50 Chd free. Suns May 14, Aug 6 (2-5). Private visits welcome, please* **Tel 01257 255255** wseddon@tinyworld.co.uk

THRIVE

If age, illness, or accident force you to give up a hobby that has been an important part of your life, the effects can be devastating. Each year Thrive advises thousands of individuals, and their families and friends, about how to adapt their garden, and find gardening tools and techniques that reflect their lifestyle. Thrive also runs a service for visually impaired gardeners with talking tapes and a specifically-designed newsletter.

For more information please contact:

Thrive,
The Geoffrey Udall Building, Beech Hill, Reading RG7 2AT.
Tel: 0118 988 5688.
Fax: 0118 988 5677.
Email: info@thrive.org.uk
Web site: www.thrive.org.uk

Leicestershire & Rutland

Hon County Organiser: Leicestershire Mr John Oakland, Long Close, Woodhouse Eaves, Loughborough LE12 8RZ Tel/Fax 01509 890376 or 01509 890616 (Business Hours)
Hon County Organiser: Rutland Mrs Jennifer Wood, Townsend House, Morcott Road, Wing, Nr Oakham, Rutland LE15 8SE 01572 737465
Assistand Hon County Organser: Rutland Mrs Rose Dejardin, 5 Top Street, Wing, Nr Oakham, Rutland LE15 8SE Tel 01572 737727
Hon County Treasurer:Rutland Mr David Wood
Hon County Treasurer: Leicestershire Mr John Oakland

DATES OF OPENING

Regular openings
For details see garden description
Barnsdale Gardens, Exton
Brooksby Agricultural College, Melton Mowbray
Long Close, Woodhouse Eaves
1700 Melton Road, Rearsby
Orchards, Walton
Stoke Albany House, Stoke Albany

March 5 Sunday
1700 Melton Road, Rearsby

March 19 Sunday
The Homestead, Normanton

March 29 Wednesday
Burbage Gardens

April 1 Saturday
Paddocks, Shelbrook

April 2 Sunday
Paddocks, Shelbrook
Warren Hills Cottage, Warren Hills Road

April 9 Sunday
Long Close, Woodhouse Eaves

April 16 Sunday
Barnsdale Gardens, Exton

April 23 Sunday
Warren Hills Cottage, Warren Hills Road
Whatton Gardens, Loughborough

April 30 Sunday
Pine House, Gaddesby
Wartnaby Gardens, Wartnaby

May 1 Monday
Burbage Gardens
Pine House, Gaddesby

May 7 Sunday
High Trees, Kirby Muxloe

May 10 Wednesday
Arthingworth Manor, Arthingworth, Market Harborough
High Trees, Kirby Muxloe

May 14 Sunday
The Firs, Beveridge Lane, Bardon Hill
Gower Lodge, Uppingham
The Homestead, Normanton
Owston Gardens, nr Oakham
18 Park Road, Birstall

May 15 Monday
18 Park Road, Birstall

May 17 Wednesday
Arthingworth Manor, Arthingworth, Market Harborough

May 20 Saturday
Holly Hayes, Birstall

May 21 Sunday
Hambleton Gardens, Hambleton
Holly Hayes, Birstall

May 24 Wednesday
Arthingworth Manor, Arthingworth, Market Harborough

May 27 Saturday
Paddocks, Shelbrook

May 28 Sunday
Long Close, Woodhouse Eaves
Orchards, Walton
Paddocks, Shelbrook
Warren Hills Cottage, Warren Hills Road

May 29 Monday
Paddocks, Shelbrook

May 31 Wednesday
Arthingworth Manor, Arthingworth, Market Harborough
Orchards, Walton

June 4 Sunday
Botany Bay, Coleorton
The Dairy, Coleorton
Osbaston Kitchen Garden, Osbaston
Wakerley Manor, Oakham

June 7 Wednesday
Arthingworth Manor, Arthingworth, Market Harborough
Stoke Albany House, Stoke Albany

June 11 Sunday
Burbage Gardens
Prebendal House, Empingham

June 14 Wednesday
Arthingworth Manor, Arthingworth, Market Harborough
Stoke Albany House, Stoke Albany

June 17 Saturday
Paddocks, Shelbrook

June 18 Sunday
Ashwell Lodge, Ashwell
Gilmorton Gardens
Harby Gardens, Harby nr Melton Mowbray
Langham Lodge, Oakham
Paddocks, Shelbrook
Whatton Gardens, Loughborough

June 21 Wednesday
Arthingworth Manor, Arthingworth, Market Harborough
Gilmorton Gardens (evening)
Stoke Albany House, Stoke Albany

June 24 Saturday
Sheepy Magna Gardens

June 25 Sunday
Brooksby Agricultural College, Melton Mowbray
Chestnuts, Hambleton
Great Dalby House, Great Dalby nr Melton Mowbray
The Old Manor House, Market Overton
Sheepy Magna Gardens
Wartnaby Gardens, Wartnaby

June 28 Wednesday
Arthingworth Manor, Arthingworth, Market Harborough
The Court House, Geeston, Ketton Stamford (evening)
Stoke Albany House, Stoke Albany

July 2 Sunday
The Firs, Beveridge Lane, Bardon Hill
Wing Gardens, nr Oakham

July 5 Wednesday
Arthingworth Manor, Arthingworth, Market Harborough

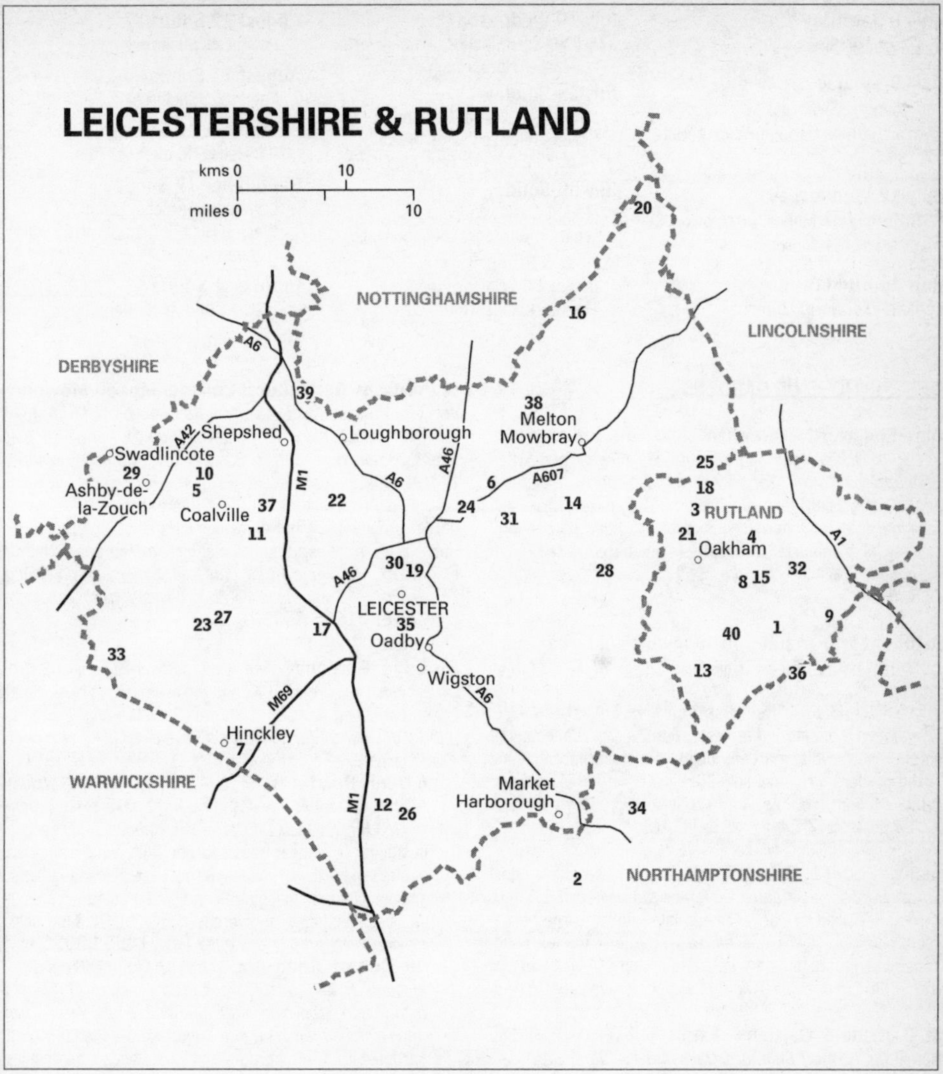

KEY

1 Acre End
2 Arthingworth Manor
3 Ashwell Lodge
4 Barnsdale Gardens
5 Botany Bay
6 Brooksby Agricultural College
7 Burbage Gardens
8 Chestnuts
9 The Court House
10 The Dairy
11 The Firs
12 Gilmorton Gardens
13 Gower Lodge
14 Great Dalby House
15 Hambleton Gardens
16 Harby Gardens
17 High Trees
18 Hill House
19 Holly Hayes
20 The Homestead
21 Langham Lodge
22 Long Close
23 Market Bosworth Gardens
24 1700 Melton Road
25 The Old Manor House
26 Orchards
27 Osbaston Kitchen Garden
28 Owston Gardens
29 Paddocks
30 18 Park Road
31 Pine House
32 Prebendal House
33 Sheepy Magna Gardens
34 Stoke Albany House
35 University of Leicester 'Harold Martin' Botanic Garden
36 Wakerley Manor
37 Warren Hills Cottage
38 Wartnaby Gardens
39 Whatton Gardens
40 Wing Gardens

July 8 Saturday
Paddocks, Shelbrook

July 9 Sunday
Paddocks, Shelbrook
Warren Hills Cottage, Warren Hills Road

July 12 Wednesday
Arthingworth Manor, Arthingworth, Market Harborough

July 16 Sunday
Acre End, North Luffenham

July 19 Wednesday
Arthingworth Manor, Arthingworth, Market Harborough

July 23 Sunday
Hill House, Market Overton
University of Leicester 'Harold Martin' Botanic Garden, Oadby

July 30 Sunday
Market Bosworth Gardens
Whatton Gardens, Loughborough

August 6 Sunday
Botany Bay, Coleorton
The Dairy, Coleorton

August 12 Saturday
Paddocks, Shelbrook

August 13 Sunday
Paddocks, Shelbrook

September 10 Sunday
Hill House, Market Overton

September 17 Sunday
Barnsdale Gardens, Exton
Warren Hills Cottage, Warren Hills Road

October 1 Sunday
1700 Melton Road, Rearsby

DESCRIPTIONS OF GARDENS

Acre End, North Luffenham ✄❀ (Mr & Mrs J R Bolton) *7m SE of Oakham via Manton and Edith Weston and SW of Stamford via Ketton. 2m off A47 through Morcott village.* 1 acre. Knot garden, terrace, studio garden, mixed shrub and rose garden, long herbaceous borders, herb garden and spinney. Many unusual shrubs, trees and perennials. TEAS in aid of Luffenham church. *Adm £1.50 Acc chd free. Sun July 16 (2-5.30)*

Arthingworth Manor, Arthingworth, Market Harborough ✄❀ (Mr W Guinness) *5m S of Market Harborough via A508 at 4m L to Arthingworth; from Northampton via A508. At Kelmarsh turn R at bottom of hill. In village turn R at church then 1st L.* 6 to 7-acres. Collection of shrub roses; white garden; delphiniums, herbaceous and mixed borders; greenhouses. 3-acre arboretum. Art gallery, British Modern Pictures. *Adm £1.75 Chd 50p. Weds May 10, 17, 24, 3l, June 7, 14, 21, 28 July 5, 12, 19 (2-5)*

Ashwell Lodge, Ashwell ♿✄ (Mr & Mrs L J Wigoder) *3m N of Oakham. Garden is on R next to village hall.* 1½ acre garden designed by Percy Cane in late 1960's. Large herbaceous border, lawns, paved rose garden, formal pond. Vegetable garden and newly planted orchard. *Adm £1.50 Chd free (ACNO to Bar Benevolent Association) Sun June 18 (2-6)*

■ **Barnsdale Gardens, Exton** ♿✄❀ (Nick & Sue Hamilton) *Turn off Stamford/Oakham rd A606 at Barnsdale Lodge Hotel then 1m.* 8 acres of individual gardens used by Geoff Hamilton for BBC TV 'Gardeners World'. Wide variety of ideas and garden designs for all year interest. TEAS, light refreshments, nursery. *Adm £5 Chd free (ACNO to Plant Life). Gardens and Nursery open Mar-Oct (10-5), Nursery open Nov - Feb (10-4). For NGS Suns April 16, Sept 17 (10-5)*

Botany Bay, Coleorton ♿✄❀ (Mr & Mrs R W Platts) *100 The Moorlands. Follow sign Sinope at Coleorton Xrds. From A512 Ashby-Louborough Rd for ¾m. Down drive on L. From A511 Coalville-Ashby follow sign Coleorton 400yd on R. Off-road parking.* Mature garden of ⅔ acre; trees, shrubs, herbaceous borders and island beds. Wide variety of plants and shrubs planted with fragrance in mind; viburnums, old roses, honeysuckle, lilac, daphnes, philadelphus, etc. TEAS. *Adm £1.50 Chd 50p. Suns June 4, Aug 6 (2-6)*

■ **Brooksby Agricultural College, Melton Mowbray** ❀ (The Principal) *6m SW of Melton Mowbray. From A607 (9m from Leicester or 6m from Melton Mowbray) turn at Brooksby; entrance 100yds. Bus: Leicester-Melton Mowbray; alight Brooksby turn, 100yds.* Extensive lawns, lake, stream, specimen trees, shrub borders, herbaceous beds, rose garden, topiary, wildflower meadows, national plant collections, rock gardens, pergola, plant centre/nursery. Church built 1220. TEA. *Adm £1.50 Chd free. Every Sun July, Aug (11-4). For NGS Sun June 25 (1-5). Private visits welcome, please* **Tel 01664 434291**

Burbage Gardens *From M69 junction 1, take B4109 signed Hinckley.* Cream TEAS and refreshments at No 7 Denis Road. *Combined adm £2 Chd free (ACNO to Hinckley Hospital). Sun June 11 (11-5). 6 Denis Rd and 7 Hall Rd also open Wed March 29 (2-5), Mon May 1 (1-6)*

6 Denis Road ✄❀ (Mr & Mrs D A Dawkins) *Sketchley Manor Estate. From M69 junction 1 take B4109 signposted Hinkley then 1st L after roundabout.* Small garden designed to appear much larger with wide range of plants incl hardy geraniums, ferns, hostas, foliage plants, species clematis, hellebores and spring bulbs. Alpines in sinks. Collection of snowdrops. TEAS Wed & Mon only. *Private visits welcome, please* **Tel 01455 230509**

40 Duport Road (Mr & Mrs J Griffin) *From M69 junction 1, take B4109 signposted Hinckley at T-lights turn R into Brookside after approx 1m take 6th R turn into Hill Rise then 1st R into Duport Rd.* Medium terraced garden with mixed borders and island beds containing a wide variety of herbaceous plants and shrubs, including a small collection of hardy geraniums. *Sun June 11 (only)*

7 Hall Road ❀ (Mr and Mrs D R Baker) *Sketchley Manor Estate. From M69 roundabout take B4109 to Hinckley at 1st roundabout L then R to Sketchley Lane. 1st R; 1st R; 1st L into Hall Rd.* Medium-sized garden; mixed borders; foliage plants; good mixture of shrubs. Collection of hellebores, spring bulbs and plants; small collection of snowdrops. Hosta, hardy geraniums and unusual perennials; pond, good design ideas. Partially suitable for wheelchairs. *Private visits welcome, please* **Tel 01455 635616**

NEW **12 Johns Close** (Mr & Mrs C Roberts) *From M 69 junction 1 take B4109 signposted Hinckley, turn L at roundabout then R into Sketchley Lane. 1st R, 1st R and 1st R again into Johns Close.* Medium sized garden

Lady Elizabeth Bowes Lyon and her younger brother, the Hon. David Bowes Lyon, wearing their garden smocks, at their childhood home, St. Paul's Walden Bury, Hertfordshire, 1905. The garden was laid out by Edward Gilbert in about 1730. The Hon. David Bowes Lyon, who became Sir David, served as President of the Royal Horticultural Society from 1953-1961.
Photograph courtesy of Mr. and Mrs. Simon Bowes Lyon.

Lady Elizabeth Bowes Lyon and her father, the 14th Earl of Strathmore and Kinghorne, September 29th, 1921. Both the Earl and Countess of Strathmore, who was a keen gardener and knowledgeable botanist, encouraged their daughter's love of gardening.
Photograph by PA photos

Lady Elizabeth Bowes Lyon and the Duke of York, second son of King George V, working in the garden at St. Paul's Walden Bury, where they became engaged in January, 1923. The wedding took place in Westminster Abbey on 26 April, 1923, and thirteen years later the Duke and Duchess of York became King and Queen.
Photograph by ILN, Camera Press London

Below: The Women's Land Army take a break from hoeing a field of beets to meet Queen Elizabeth and King George VI (standing behind Her Majesty), on a morale-boosting tour of Berkshire in 1944.
Photograph by The Times, Camera Press London

Her Majesty Queen Elizabeth The Queen Mother visits a rose walk in St. James's Park, London, on 15th July, 1980. The National Gardens Scheme raised donations for the planting of the rose walk as a tribute the their Patron's 80th birthday.
Photograph Ron Bell, PA Photos

Below: Her Majesty Queen Elizabeth visits two gardens at once in Fentiman Road on 14th July, 1958. Welcomed by Mr. and Mrs. Godfrey, Her Majesty also enjoys the garden of Mr. and Mrs. Albert Hayday on the other side of the fence.
Photograph courtesy of PA Photos

planted in cottage style. Herbaceous borders with shrubs and trees. Raised bed and vegetable plot. *Sun June 11 (only) also private visits welcome May to Sept, please* **Tel 01455 634050**

NEW **16 Johns Close** (Mrs D L Gowland) *From M69 junction 1 take B4109 signposted Hickley turn L at roundabout then R into Sketchley Lane. 1st R, 1st R and 1st R again into Johns Close.* Small garden with interesting shrubs and perannials. Emphasis on contrasting colour shape and texture. *Sun June 11 (only)*

Chestnuts, Hambleton ♿✂❀ (Mr & Mrs A Tibbert) *Turn R at church. 70yds down hill. Turn L at village hall on to a track 4th on R. Only gravel drive.* A sloping S-facing garden of approx 1½ acres overlooking Rutland Water. Various borders of shrubs and perennials lead down to rose arbour and then to a natural pond hidden by willow trees at the bottom of the garden. TEAS. *Adm £1.50 Chd free. Sun May 21 with Hambleton Gardens, Sun June 25 (10-5)*

The Court House, Geeston, Ketton Stamford ❀ (Bas & Jane Clarke) *3m W of Stamford on the A43 for Collyweston. In middle of Collyweston take rd to Ketton (1½m). Turn into Geeston Rd, the Court House 200yds on R.* 2½-acre garden incl formal garden (designed by Bunny Guinness) walled vegetable garden, immaculate lawns, wild flower meadow woodland and river. TEA. *Adm £1.50 Chd free.* **Evening Opening** *Wed June 28 (5-9)*

The Dairy, Coleorton ♿✂❀ (Mr & Mrs J B Moseley) *Moor Lane off A512 W of Peggs Green Roundabout.* Approx ⅓-acre of mature trees, shrubs and herbaceous borders containing many unusual plants. Herb garden and pergola lead to new Japanese Garden. Surprise round every corner. TEAS. *Adm £1.50 Chd 50p. Suns June 4, Aug 6 (2-6)*

NEW **The Firs, Beveridge Lane, Bardon Hill** ✂❀ (Mr & Mrs G C Clemerson) *From M1 junction 22 take A511 towards Coalville. Turn L after 1½m onto B585 towards Ibstock. Entrance 200yds on L opposite Charnwood Arms Hotel.* 3/4 acre garden with trees, rhododendrons, shrubs and perennials. Many interesting varieties. Unusual inner feature water garden. TEAS. *Adm £1 Chd 50p. Suns May 14, July 2 (2-6)*

Gilmorton Gardens *Gilmorton is 12m S of Leicester and 4m from junction 20 of the M1. Proceed through Lutterworth town centre, turn R at police station. Follow signs to Gilmorton. Can also be reached via A50 Leicester/Northampton Rd via Bruntingthorpe from A426 Leicester/Lutterworth Rd by turning off at Dunton Basset (rd signposted to Gilmorton).* Park in village. All gardens are within the village a few minutes walk apart. Teas in village hall. *Combined adm £2 Chd free. Sun June 18 (11-5), Wed June 21 (2-9)*

'Al Manzel' ♿✂❀ (Mr David Grundy) *Nr Crown public house end of Main St opp Porlock Drive.* Average size plant lovers garden constructed from an old walled farmyard, with many interesting plants, structures and features. Pond/waterfall, rockery, gravel gardens, greenhouse, raised vegetable plot. Extensive use of grasses, clematis and plants in pots

Moatfield ✂❀ (Mr & Mrs R P Morgan) *Church Lane.* New garden around barn conversion next to church. Lawns, climbers, roses, shrub and flower borders and raised beds for acid loving plants in original walled farmyard area. Field with large natural pond, collections of trees; rowans, birches, hollies etc and old moat area. Open views of countryside

Ulverscroft Close ✂❀ (Mr & Mrs M J Maddock) *Ashby Road.* ½-acre mature garden developed over 17yrs. Full of plantswoman's choice of herbaceous plants, shrubs and climbers. Pond and bog garden planted for natural effect. Pergola and decorative screen covered with an abundance of roses and clematis; vegetable plot. Conservatory. Places to sit and ponder

Gower Lodge, Uppingham ❀ (Dr & Mrs Clive R Jones) *From Market Sq in centre of Uppingham W along High St past Uppingham school. Take 1st L opp Minerva down Spring Back Way.* 1-acre S-facing sloping garden. Sandstone overlying clay with spring at interface and small stream with damp fringe and wildflower areas. Upper garden mainly flowers with meconopsis and primulas, herbaceous borders and some interesting trees. Kitchen garden on lower slope. Steps and some steep slopes. Teas in the Church Hall, Uppingham Market Place in aid of the Church. Plant Stall by Wingwell Nursery % to the NGS. *Adm £1.50 Chd free. Sun May 14 (2-6)*

Great Dalby House, Great Dalby nr Melton Mowbray ✂❀ (Mr & Mrs E Cobley) *3m S of Melton Mowbray on B6047.* 1¾-acre garden with mature trees, herbaceous borders, potager, vegetable garden with old rare varieties. Alpine house. Collection of Zonal pelargoniums. Greenhouse. TEAS. *£1.50 Chd free. Sun June 25 (2-6). Private parties welcome by appt,* **Tel 01664 564388**

Hambleton Gardens, Hambleton ❀ *3m E of Oakham on A606 Oakham to Stamford rd. Turn R at signpost for Hambleton and Egleton.* TEAS. *Combined adm £2.50 Chd free. Sun May 21 (10-5)*

Chestnuts (Mr & Mrs A Tibbert) *Turn at church. 70yds down hill. Turn L at village hall on to a track, 4th on R. Only gravel drive. For garden details see separate entry; also open Sun June 25 (10-5)*

Orchard House (Mr & Mrs J L Cookson) *Lyndon Rd. In village, church on R, immed turn R, go to bottom of hill, house is last on R, before cattle grid.* Small 4-sectioned, walled and hedged gardens, mainly herbaceous and bulbs, on the edge of Rutland Water. New terrace and further gardens at rear under development. 2 acres

Stone Cottage (Malcolm Bonser) *Ketton Rd. Opp Hambleton Hall.* Approx 1-acre garden with interesting plants; shrubs, roses, herb garden and water features. Orchard underplanted with bulbs and shrubs. Views of Rutland Water

Harby Gardens, Harby nr Melton Mowbray *From Leicester travel to Melton Mowbray, follow outer ring rd 607 (Grantham) signs which take you to Waltham on the Wolds 5m. Turn L at the Royal Horseshoes public house carry straight on to Harby.* TEAS. *Combined adm £1.50 Chd free Sun June 18 (2-5.30)*

NEW **70 Boyers Orchard** (Bernard Clarke) A medium sized garden with a gradual slope on 3 levels: trees, conifers, herbaceous borders, shrubs, grasses, alpines a stone troughs, water features.

The Hollies, 17 Main Street (Mr & Mrs L Partridge) Mediterranean plants on terrace with small pool. Cottage garden, mixed shrubs, herbaceous borders with arbour and thatched gazebo. Cream TEAS.

The Walnuts (Mrs Stephanie Tetley) 1 acre comprising mixed herbaceous borders, shrubs, trees, vegetables and orchard (with damsons, pears, apples, walnut tree, hazelnut bushes, plums, geese and chickens) all organically grown

High Trees, Kirby Muxloe ✀❀ (Ann & Steve Foster) *Take A47 W of Leicester. At T-lights in Leicester Forest East turn R on to the B5380. Forest Drive is ½m on the R, at the bottom of the hill.* ⅓-acre 'all seasons' garden with large number of hardy perennials and ferns. There are 2 ponds and 2 greenhouses containing grapevines, a collection of cacti and many half hardy plants. TEAS (Sun), TEA (Wed). *Adm £1 Chd 50p. Sun May 7 (11-5), Wed May 10 (2-5)*

Hill House, Market Overton ♿❀ (Brian & Judith Taylor) *Teigh Rd, Market Overton. 6m N of Oakham beyond Cottesmore, 5m from the A1 via Thistleton, 10m E from Melton Mowbray via Wymondham.* ½-acre plant enthusiasts' garden consisting mainly of mixed beds designed for seasonal interest and 'architectural' plants comprising many unusual hardy and tender perennials. TEAS. *Adm £1 Chd free. Suns July 23, Sept 10 (11-5). Private group visits welcome July to Sept, please* **Tel 01572 767337**

Holly Hayes, Birstall ♿ (Mrs Edith A Murphy) *216 Birstall Rd, adjoining Ecology Centre. Take Birstall Rd from Redhill island. Near village hall.* 4-acre garden with rhododendrons, azaleas, fine old trees incl redwoods, wisteria, pergola, flower borders and pond. TEAS. *Adm £1 Chd 20p. Sat, Sun May 20, 21 (2-6)*

The Homestead, Normanton ❀ (Mr & Mrs J E Palmer) *10m W of Grantham on A52. In Bottesford turn N, signposted Normanton; last house on R before disused airfield.* ¾-acre informal plant lover's garden. Vegetable garden, small orchard, woodland area, many hellebores and single paeonies. Collections of hostas and sempervivums. TEAS. *Adm £1 Chd free (ACNO to NCCPG). Suns March 19, May 14 (2-6)*

Langham Lodge, Oakham ♿✀❀ (Mr and Mrs H N Hemsley) *½m out of Langham on Burley Rd.* 1 acre; shrubs; interesting foliage; stone walls; shrub and climbing roses. TEAS in aid of Langham Church. *Adm £1.50 Chd free. Sun June 18 (2-6) Private visits welcome, please* **Tel 01572 722912**

Long Close, Woodhouse Eaves ❀ (John Oakland & Pene Johnson) *Main St. S of Loughborough nr M1 junction 23. From A6, W in Quorn.* 5 acres spring bulbs, rhododendrons, azaleas, flowering shrubs, camellias, magnolias, many rare shrubs, mature trees, lily ponds; terraced lawns, herbaceous borders, new potager in walled kitchen garden, penstemon collection, wild flower meadow walk. TEAS. *Adm £2 Chd free. Suns April 9 with Mini Plant Fair (2-5.30); May 28 (2-6); Daily Mons-Sats March-July (9.30-1 & 2-5.30), Tickets Pene Crafts Shop opp. Also private parties welcome, catering by arrangment, please* **Tel 01509 890616 or Fax 01509 890376 (business hours)**

Market Bosworth Gardens ♿ *1m off A447 Coalville to Hinckley Rd, 3m off A444. Village plan available. East Midlands in Bloom winner 1999, National finalist 1998. Free car parking.* TEAS. *Combined adm £2 Chd free. Pay on Market Bosworth Market Place. Sun July 30 (2-6)*

NEW **68 Heath Road** (Mrs I Harrison) Small patio garden

NEW **70 Heath Road** (Mrs M Morgan) Small three tier patio garden and pond

NEW **80 Heath Road** (Mrs R Reid) A cottage garden

Home Farm Cottage (Mr & Mrs Kitching) Farm garden with lawn, flowers, shrubs

16 Northumberland Avenue (Mr & Mrs K McCarthy) Landscaped garden

24 Northumberland Avenue (Mr & Mrs E G Watkins) Flowers, shrubs and lawns

NEW **12 Rectory Lane** (Mr & Mrs S J Holden) Flowers, shrubs and lawn

NEW **15 Shenton Lane** (Mr & Mrs B Claybrook) A newly laid-out grden with water feature

13 Spinney Hill (Mrs J Buckell) Well tended estate garden

11 Stanley Road (Mrs O Caldwell) Small mature garden with shrubs

NEW **13 Station Road** (Mrs C Graham) A cottage garden

273 Station Road (Mr & Mrs C Baker) Flower garden and model village

1700 Melton Road, Rearsby ♿✀❀ (Mrs Hazel Kaye) *N of Leicester on A607.* A garden for all seasons opening in early March and October to tempt the hardiest of garden visitors. 1½ acres with extensive borders, shade beds, pergola and water feature with wide range of interesting hardy plants. Featured in Country Life Sept 1999. Nursery. TEAS. *Adm £2 Chd 10p. Daily March to Oct (Tues to Sat 10-5, Sun 10-12). Also SPECIAL OPEN DAYS Sun March 5 (2-5) and Sun Oct 1 (2-5)* **Tel 01664 424578**

The Old Manor House, Market Overton ✀ (Dr and Mrs Evans) *6m N of Oakham beyond Cottesmore; 5m from the A1 via Thistleton; 10m E from Melton Mowbray via Wymondham.* Medium walled garden to inspire the botanical painter. Herbaceous borders, collection of old roses. *Adm £1.50 Chd free. Sun June 25 (2-6)*

■ **Orchards, Walton** ✀❀ (Mr & Mrs G Cousins) *Hall Lane, Walton nr Lutterworth. 8m S of Leicester via the A5199 take a R turn just after Shearsby (sign-posted Bruntingthorpe); thereafter follow signs for Walton.* A garden of surprises. It is full of rare and unusual plants which are grown in colour-theme garden 'rooms'. Featured on TVs Garden Club and Garden Party. Views of countryside. TEAS. *Adm £1.50 Chd free. Open Suns June to Aug. For NGS Sun May 28, Wed 31 (11-5). Also parties and private visits welcome June to Sept, please* **Tel 01455 556958**

NEW **Osbaston Kitchen Garden, Osbaston** ✀❀ (Mrs L Delisle and Ms Flick Rohde) *The garden is signposted to Osbaston off the A447 between Hinckley and Ibstock. 1½m NE of Market Bosworth. Approx 8m N of Hinckley.* 1 acre walled kitchen garden where fruit and vegetables are grown using organic methods. Large greenhouse contains grapevines and tomatoes plus sunken melon pit, some plantings of shrubs and herbaceous plants. Wilder more natural areas. TEAS. *Adm £1.50 Chd 75p. Sun June 4 (12-4)*

Owston Gardens, nr Oakham ♿❀ *6m W of Oakham via Knossington, 2m S of Somerby. From Leicester turn L 2m E of Tilton.* TEAS. *Combined adm £1.50 Chd free. Sun May 14 (2-6)*

The Homestead (Mr & Mrs David Penny) ⅓ acre with lawn, clematis, ponds, borders, containers, alpine garden, views and photographs. Plants and sundries stalls

Rose Cottage (Mr John Buchanan) Undulating 1¾ acres; shrub and flower borders; spring bulbs, roses, alpines, ponds, waterfall, fine views. *Private visits welcome, please* **Tel 01664 454545**

Paddocks, Shelbrook ♿✂❀ (Mrs A Jackson) *1½m W of Ashby-de-la-Zouch on B5003 towards Moira.* A plantaholic's garden with over 2000 species and varieties in 1 acre incl snowdrops, hellebores, hardy orchids, astrantias and many less common herbaceous plants & shrubs. Plants propagated from garden for sale. NCCPG collection of old named double and single primulas. Silver medallist at Chelsea and Vincent Square. Featured in 'The Garden', March '98. TEAS. *Adm £1.50 Chd free. Sats, Suns April 1, 2, May 27, 28, Mon 29, June 17, 18, July 8, 9, Aug 12, 13 (2-5). Private visits of 10 or more, please* **Tel 01530 412606**

18 Park Road, Birstall ♿❀ (Dr & Mrs D R Ives) *Turn off A6 into Park Rd at crown of the hill on Leicester side of Birstall. Local buses stop at end of Park Rd.* Approx 1 acre of lawn, trees, shrubs and other mixed planting incl bluebells etc with emphasis on foliage and scent. TEAS. *Adm £1.20 Chd 30p (ACNO to LOROS). Sun, Mon May 14, 15 (2-5.30). Private visits welcome end April to end May, please* **Tel 0116 2675118**

Pine House, Gaddesby ✂❀ (Mr & Mrs T Milward) *Rearsby Rd. From A607 Leicester-Melton Mowbray, at Rearsby turn off for Gaddesby.* 2-acre garden with fine mature trees, woodland walk, redesigned water garden. Herb and potager garden and wisteria archway to Victorian vinery. Pleached lime trees, mixed borders with unusual plants and new rock garden; terraced garden with potted standards and a terracotta pot garden. Rare and unusual plant sale. TEAS. *Adm £2 Chd free (ACNO to Red Cross). Sun April 30, Bank Holiday Mon May 1 (2-5). Private visits and groups welcome May to Sept, please* **Tel 01664 840213**

Prebendal House, Empingham ♿❀ (Mr and Mrs J Partridge) *Between Stamford & Oakham on A606.* House (not open) built in 1688; summer palace for the Bishop of Lincoln. Incl herbaceous borders, water garden, topiary and kitchen gardens. TEAS. *Adm £2 Chd free. Sun June 11 (2-6)*

Sheepy Magna Gardens ♿✂❀ *B4116 2½m N of Atherstone on Atherstone to Twycross Rd.* Cream TEAS in aid of Sheepy Magna Church. *Combined adm £2.50 Chd free. Sat, Sun June 24, 25 (2-6)*

Athol House, 108 Main Road (Mr & Mrs A Brown) *Next to village hall.* Old garden now rejuvenated; variety of herbaceous borders, trees, shrubs, vegetable plot, formal pond, container plants and climbers.

Gate Cottage ❀ (Mr & Mrs O P Hall) *Church Lane. Opp church.* Approx ½-acre cottage garden; mixed herbaceous borders; greenhouse; vegetable garden; several specimen trees; lawns, patio and pond, new shrubbery

7 Riverside Close (Miss K Ziemba) Small colourful garden with shrubs, perennials, roses and clematis and small vegetable garden

Sheepy Lodge (Mr & Mrs H D Brogan) *Twycross Road, about ¼m from shop/P Office.* Over 2 acres of formal and informal gardens with extensive lawns. Large circular rose garden, mixed borders, ponds. Some fine trees.

Vine Cottage ❀ (Mr & Mrs T Clark) *26 Main Rd. Opp shop.* Approx ¾-acre cottage garden; mixed herbaceous borders with many unusual plants; alpine gardens; ponds; vegetable plot with greenhouse. Cream TEAS

■ **Stoke Albany House, Stoke Albany** ♿✂❀ (Mr and Mrs A M Vinton) *4m E of Market Harborough via A427 to Corby; turn to Stoke Albany; R at the White Horse (B669); garden ½m on L.* Large garden with fine trees; shrubs; herbaceous borders and grey garden. TEAS on Sun only. *Adm £2.50 Chd free. Weds May 17, 24, 31, July 5, 12 (2-4.30) Sun July 9 (2-5.30). For the NGS Weds June 7, 14, 21, 28 (2-4.30). Private parties welcome May to July Mons to Thurs only, please* **Tel 01858 535227**

University of Leicester 'Harold Martin' Botanic Garden, Oadby ♿✂❀ (Mr B Frankland) *Glebe Road. SE outskirts of city opp race course.* 16-acre garden incl grounds of Beaumont Hall, The Knoll, Southmeade and Hastings House. Wide variety of ornamental features and glasshouses laid out for educational purposes incl NCCPG collections of aubrieta, Lawson Cypress, hardy fuchsia and skimmia. TEAS in aid of the Red Cross. *Adm £1.50 Chd free. Sun July 23 (2-5)*

Wakerley Manor, Oakham ♿❀ (A D A W Forbes Esq) *6m Uppingham.R off A47 Uppingham-Peterborough through Barrowden, or from A43 Stamford to Corby rd between Duddington and Bulwick.* 4 acres lawns, shrubs, herbaceous; kitchen garden; 3 greenhouses. Plant Stall. TEAS. *Adm £2 Chd free (ACNO to St Mary the Virgin Church, South Luffenham). Sun June 4 (2-6)*

NEW **Warren Hills Cottage, Warren Hills Road** ♿✂❀ (Mr & Mrs G Waters) *Approx 4m NW of M1 junction 22 on B587 Copt Oak to Whitwick Road, near schools.* Extensively landscaped gardens on 2 acres aiming for yr-round colour and interest. Large cottage garden area with hundreds of unusual and hardy perennials; lawns, streams and pond. Owners are currently compiling NCCPG collection of astrantias. Small nursery with unusual perennials for sale. TEAS. *Adm £1.50 Chd 50p. Suns April 2, 23, May 28, July 9, Sept 17 (12-5)*

Wartnaby Gardens, Wartnaby ♿❀ (Lord and Lady King) *4m NW of Melton Mowbray. From A606 turn W in Ab Kettleby, from A46 at Six Hills Hotel turn E on A676.* Large garden, shrubs, herbaceous borders, newly laid out rose garden with a good collection of old-fashioned roses and others; small arboretum. Formal vegetable garden. Specialist plant fair on Sun June 25 (11-4), about 20 nurseries selling a wide range of unusual plants. *Adm £2.50 Chd free. Suns April*

30 June 25 (11-4). Private parties welcome, please **Tel 01664 822296 Fax 01664 822900 business hours**

Whatton Gardens, Loughborough ♿❀ (Lord & Lady Crawshaw) *4m NE of Loughborough on A6 between Hathern and Kegworth; 2½m SE of junc 24 on M1.* 15 acres; shrub and herbaceous borders, lawns, rose and wild gardens, pools; arboretum. Nursery open. TEAS in Old Dining Room. *Adm £2.50 OAP/Chd £1.50. Sun April 23, June 18, July 30 (2-6). Private visits welcome for pre-booked parties. Catering by arrangement, please* **Tel/Fax 01509 842268**

Wing Gardens, nr Oakham *2m S of Rutland Water off A6003 between Oakham and Uppingham.* Refreshments. *Combined adm £1.50 Chd free. Sun July 2 (11-6)*

Townsend House (David & Jeffy Wood) Cottage garden with mixed borders, roses and clematis. Walled gravel garden around pool, vegetable garden

Wingwell ❀ (John & Rose Dejardin) Evolving garden and specialist nursery with emphasis on bold use of plants, particularly herbaceous, and interesting use of stone and paving. Includes walled garden with drought resistant plants and ornamental pool.

Evening Opening (See also garden description)

The Court House, Geeston, Ketton Stamford	June 28
Gilmorton Gardens	June 21

SPECIALIST PLANT SALES IN LEICESTERSHIRE

Long Close Gardens
Sunday, April 9th

Pine House
Sunday, April 30th
Monday, May 1st

Wartnaby Gardens
Sunday, June 25th

See garden entries for details

Scotland's Garden Scheme

The National Gardens Scheme has a similar but separate counterpart in Scotland. Called Scotland's Garden Scheme, it raises money for the Queen's Nursing Institute (Scotland), the Gardens Fund of the National Trust for Scotland, and over 160 registered charities nominated by Garden Owners.

The Handbook is available for £3.50 (£4.25 including p&p) from most major bookstores, from the NGS website www.ngs.org.uk or from Scotland's Gardens Scheme, 31 Castle Terrace, Edinburgh EH1 2EL.

Lincolnshire

Hon County Organiser: Mrs Susie Dean, The Orchards, Old Somerby, Grantham, Lincolnshire NG33 4AG 01476 565456
Assistant Hon County Organiser: Lady Bruce-Gardyne, The Old Rectory, Aswardby, Spilsby, Lincs PE23 4JS 01790 752652
Mrs Peter Sandberg, Croft House, Ulceby, Yorkshire East DN39 6SW 01469 588330
Mrs Sally Grant, Holly House, Fishtoft Drove, Boston, Lincolnshire PE22 7ES 01205 750486
Hon County Treasurer: Mrs Julian Gorst, Oxcombe Manor, Horncastle, Lincs LN9 6LU 01507 533227

DATES OF OPENING

By appointment only
For telephone numbers and other details see garden descriptions. Private visits welcomed
Croft House, Ulceby
Park House Farm, Walcott
Pinefields, Bigby
Springtyme, Sibsey
The Villa, South Somercotes

February 19 Saturday
21 Chapel Street, Hacconby
25 High Street, Rippingale
Manor Farm, Keisby

February 20 Sunday
21 Chapel Street, Hacconby
25 High Street, Rippingale
Manor Farm, Keisby

March 2 Thursday
21 Chapel Street, Hacconby

March 16 Thursday
The Old Rectory, East Keal

April 16 Sunday
Grimsthorpe Castle, Bourne
The Old Rectory, East Keal

April 19 Wednesday
The Old Farmhouse, Morton

April 23 Sunday
21 Chapel Street, Hacconby

April 30 Sunday
Becklehon, Wootton
Holton-le-Moor Hall, Holton-le-Moor
Linden House, Wootton

May 4 Thursday
21 Chapel Street, Hacconby

May 6 Saturday
Belton House, Grantham

May 7 Sunday
2 School House, Stixwould

May 10 Wednesday
The Old Farmhouse, Morton

May 11 Thursday
The Old Rectory, East Keal

May 14 Sunday
Aubourn Hall, Aubourn
Doddington Hall, Lincoln
Toft House, Old Leake

May 21 Sunday
Holly House, Boston
70 North Street, Winterton

May 28 Sunday
15 Vicarage Gardens, Scunthorpe

June 1 Thursday
21 Chapel Street, Hacconby

June 4 Sunday
Cosy Cottage, Wainfleet Bank
Houlton Lodge, Goxhill
Station House, Halton Holegate

June 11 Sunday
The Old Rectory, East Keal
The Old Vicarage, Holbeach Hurn
Old White House, Holbeach Hurn
Saxby-all-Saints Gardens

June 15 Thursday
Grimsthorpe Castle, Bourne

June 18 Sunday
Cortaderia, Nettleton
Little Ponton Hall, Grantham
Park View, Holton-le-Moor
Sutton St Edmund Village Gardens

June 21 Wednesday
The Old Farmhouse, Morton

June 25 Sunday
The Holmes, Kirton Holme
Marston Hall, nr Grantham
4 Ringwood Close, Birchwood
Walnut Cottage, Careby

July 2 Sunday
Gunby Hall, Burgh-le-Marsh

July 6 Thursday
21 Chapel Street, Hacconby

July 8 Saturday
Belton House, Grantham

July 9 Sunday
Sturton by Stow Gardens

July 23 Sunday
Harrington Hall, Spilsby

July 30 Sunday
2 School House, Stixwould

August 3 Thursday
21 Chapel Street, Hacconby

August 20 Sunday
70 North Street, Winterton

September 2 Saturday
Belton House, Grantham

September 3 Sunday
Hall Farm, Harpswell

September 7 Thursday
21 Chapel Street, Hacconby

October 8 Sunday
21 Chapel Street, Hacconby
2 School Lane, Stow

2001

February 18 Sunday
21 Chapel Street, Hacconby

February 19 Monday
21 Chapel Street, Hacconby

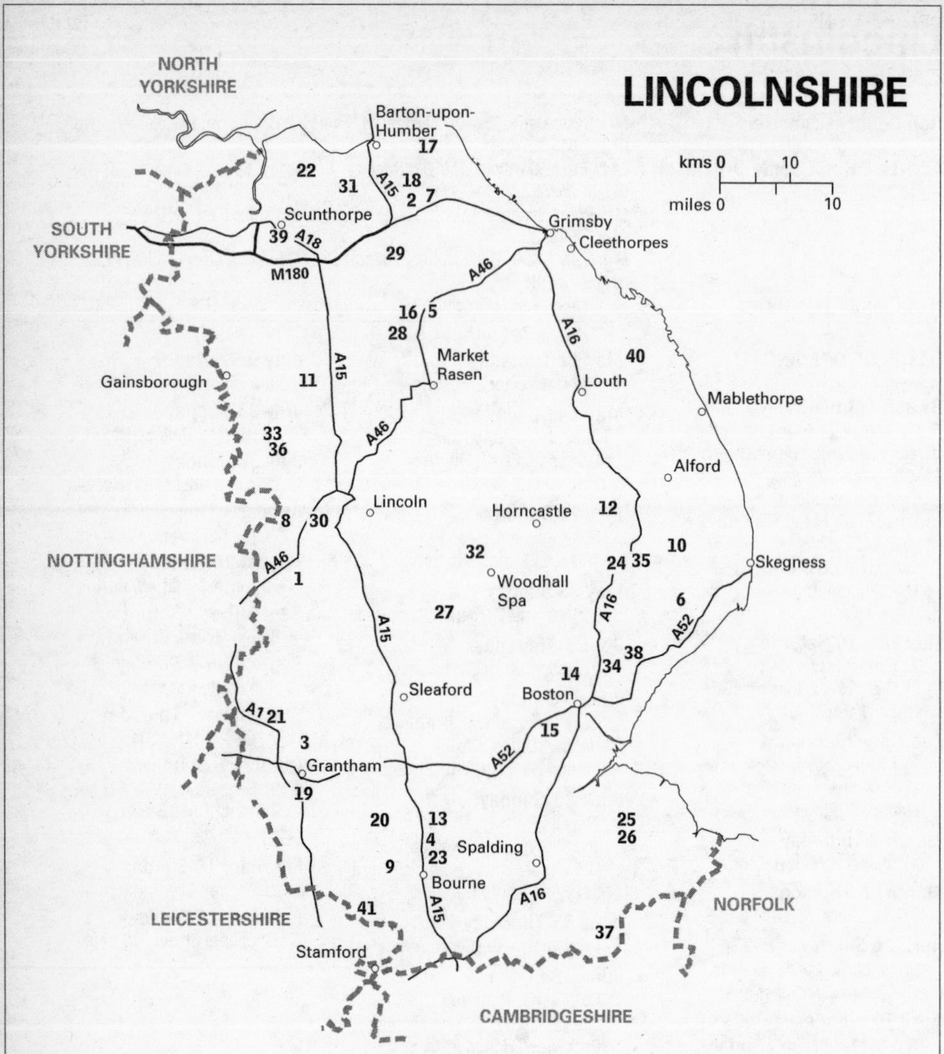

KEY

1 Aubourn Hall
2 Becklehon
3 Belton House
4 21 Chapel Street
5 Cortaderia
6 Cosy Cottage
7 Croft House
8 Doddington Hall
9 Grimsthorpe Castle
10 Gunby Hall
11 Hall Farm
12 Harrington Hall
13 25 High Street
14 Holly House
15 The Holmes
16 Holton-le-Moor Hall
17 Houlton Lodge
18 Linden House
19 Little Ponton Hall
20 Manor Farm
21 Marston Hall
22 70 North Street
23 The Old Farmhouse
24 The Old Rectory
25 The Old Vicarage
26 Old White House
27 Park House Farm
28 Park View
29 Pinefields
30 4 Ringwood Close
31 Saxby-all-Saints
32 2 School House,Stixwould
33 2 School Lane,Stow
34 Springtyme
35 Station House
36 Sturton-by-Stow Gardens
37 Sutton St Edmund Village Gardens
38 Toft House
39 15 Vicarage Gardens
40 The Villa
41 Walnut Cottage

DESCRIPTIONS OF GARDENS

Aubourn Hall, Aubourn ♿✂❀ (Lady Nevile) *7m SW of Lincoln. Signposted off A606 at Harmston.* Approx 3 acres. Lawns, mature trees, shrubs, roses, mixed borders and ponds. C11 church adjoining. Wheelchairs in dry weather only. TEAS. *Adm £2 Chd 50p (ACNO to St. Peters Church Aubourn - repairs). Sun May 14 (2-5.30)*

Becklehon, Wootton ✂❀ (Robert & Pat Musgrove) *4m N of A18 past Melton Ross and Croxton. Garden situated on main High St between PO and Wootton C of E School.* ⅓-acre garden developed during the last six yrs. Large collection of hebes, geraniums and euphorbia. Many unusual plants. Divided into raised alpine bed, rockeries and herbaceous borders. Guide dogs allowed, narrow paths unsuitable for wheelchair access. TEAS. *Combined adm £1.50 with* **Linden House** *Chd free. Sun April 30 (2-5.30)*

▲ **Belton House, Grantham** ♿✂ (The National Trust) *3m NE of Grantham on the A607 Grantham to Lincoln rd. Easily reached and signed from the A1 (Grantham N junction).* 32 acres incl formal Italian and Dutch gardens. Orangery by Sir Jeffrey Wyatville. TEAS. *Adm house & garden £5.30 Chd £2.60. For NGS Sats May 6, July 8, Sept 2 (11-5.30). Group bookings for garden only may be made in advance by post £3.80*

21 Chapel Street, Hacconby ✂❀ (Cliff & Joan Curtis) *A15 3m N of Bourne, turn E at Xrds into Hacconby.* Cottage garden overflowing with plants for yr-round interest; special interest alpines, bulbs, herbaceous. Early opening for hellebores and snowdrop collection. Asters for late opening. Featured on TV. TEAS. *Adm £1 Chd free (ACNO to Marie Curie Memorial Foundation). Sat, Sun Feb 19, 20 (11-4) Thurs March 2 (2-6) Sun April 23 (11-5) Thurs May 4, June 1, July 6, Aug 3, Sept 7 (2-6), Sun Oct 8 (11-5). 2001 Sat, Sun Feb 18, 19 (11-4). Private visits and parties welcome, please* **Tel 01778 570314**

Cortaderia, Nettleton ♿✂❀ (Mr & Mrs A T Moor) *1m SW of Caistor on the A46, just past The Salutation on opposite side.* Approx ⅓ acre front and rear gardens; mixed planting with alpines, pergolas, wildlife pond and stream. TEAS. *Combined adm with* **Park View** *£1.50 Chd free. Sun June 18 (1.30-5.30)*

NEW **Cosy Cottage, Wainfleet Bank** ✂❀ (Mr & Mrs C Sissons) *Over railway crossing in Wainfleet, turn R into Mill Lane, over 'Crows Bridge', ¼m on R.* Started in 1992, rambling 1-acre garden created with wildlife in mind. Mixed beds, borders, native trees, some unusual perennials. 3 ponds, stream, fruit and vegetables. Winner 1998 LTNC Wildlife Competition, 1999 Daily Mail National Garden Competition. *Adm £1 Acc chd free. Sun June 4 (11-4.30)*

Croft House, Ulceby ♿❀ (Mr & Mrs Peter Sandberg) *nr Brigg. At War Memorial from E turn L, from W turn R into Front St and then into Pitmoor Lane.* 2-acre garden set within a formal design filled with informal planting. Many old favourites alongside sought-after varieties. Mixed and herbaceous borders, bulbs, meadow, gravel bed, Victorian vinery. Refreshments by arrangement. *Adm £1.50 Chd free. By appt only, individual and group visits welcome, please* **Tel 01469 588330**

▲ **Doddington Hall, Lincoln** ♿✂ (Antony Jarvis Esq) *5m SW of Lincoln. From Lincoln via A46, turn W on to B1190 for Doddington. Free car park.* Superb walled gardens; thousands of spring bulbs; wild gardens; mature trees; Elizabethan mansion also open. TEAS, Coffee and snacks available. *Adm garden only £2.15 Chd £1.10 (ACNO to Lincolnshire Old Churches Trust and St Peter's Church Doddington). For NGS Sun May 14 (2-6)*

▲ **Grimsthorpe Castle, Bourne** ♿❀ (Grimsthorpe & Drummond Castle Trust) *8m E of A1 on the A151 from the Colsterworth junction, 4m W of Bourne.* 15 acres of formal and woodland gardens which incl bulbs and wild flowers. The formal gardens encompass fine topiary, roses, herbaceous borders and an unusual ornamental kitchen garden. TEAS and light meals. *Adm £3 OAP £2 Chd £1.50. Combined adm castle and garden £6.50 OAP £4.75 Chd £3.25 (ACNO to Grimsthorpe and Drummond Castle Trust). For NGS Sun April 16, Thurs June 15 (11-6)*

▲ **Gunby Hall, Burgh-le-Marsh** ❀ (Mr and Mrs J Wrisdale) *2½m NW of Burgh-le-Marsh; S of A158. Free parking.* 7 acres of formal and walled gardens; old roses, herbaceous borders; herb garden; kitchen garden with fruit trees and vegetables. Tennyson's 'Haunt of Ancient Peace'. House built by Sir William Massingberd 1700. Plant centre. TEAS. *Adm gardens £2.50 Chd £1. For NGS Sun July 2 (2-6) NT membership cards not valid*

Hall Farm, Harpswell ♿✂❀ (Pam & Mark Tatam) *7m E of Gainsborough on A631. 1½m W of Caenby Corner.* 1-acre garden with mixed borders of trees, shrubs, roses and unusual perennials. Over 100 - mainly old - varieties of rose. Sunken garden, pond, courtyard garden and recently constructed walled gravel garden. Short walk to old moat and woodland. Free seed collecting in garden Sept 3. TEAS. *Adm £1.50 Chd 50p. Sun Sept 3 (10-5.30). Garden open daily with collecting box (10-5); by appt in the evenings*
Tel 0142 7668412

Harrington Hall, Spilsby ✂❀ (Mr & Mrs David Price) *6m NW of Spilsby. Turn off A158 (Lincoln-Skegness) at Hagworthingham, 2m from Harrington.* Approx 5-acre Tudor and C18 walled gardens, incl recently designed kitchen garden; herbaceous borders, roses and other flowering shrubs. High terrace mentioned in Tennyson's 'Maud'. TEAS. *Adm £2 Chd under 14 free. Sun July 23 (2-5)*

25 High Street, Rippingale ♿✂❀ (Mr & Mrs R Beddington) *On A15 5m N of Bourne. Turn E at Xrds into Rippingale. No 25, Westcombe, is 5th house on R.* ½ acre village garden. Borders, island beds, ponds and vegetable garden. Yr-round interest. Hellebores and snowdrops in spring. TEA. *Adm £1 Acc chd free. Sat, Sun Feb 19, 20 (11-4)*

Holly House, Boston ♿✂❀ (Sally & David Grant) *Fishtoft Drove, nr Frithville. Fishtoft Drove is an unclassified rd approx 3m N of Boston and 1m S of Frithville on the W side of the West Fen Drain.* Approx 1-acre informal gardens with mixed borders, scree beds, old sinks with alpines and steps leading down to a large pond with cascade and stream. Softly curving beds are full of unusual and interesting herbaceous plants. *Adm £1.20 Chd free (ACNO to Pilgrim Heart and Lung Fund). Sun May 21 (2-5.30)*

NEW **The Holmes, Kirton Holme** ♿✂❀ (Mr & Mrs R G Tunnard) *On B1192 halfway between Hubberts Bridge and Kirton.* Small fenland garden of 1 acre with mixed borders of shrubs, roses and unusual herbaceous plants that can survive our cold winds and don't need staking. TEAS. *Adm £1.25 Chd free. Sun June 25 (2-6)*

Holton-le-Moor Hall, Holton-le-Moor ♿✂❀ (Mr & Mrs P H Gibbons) *6m N of Market Rasen off B1434 or A46.* 2½ acre well-established garden with spring bulbs, flowering trees and shrubs. Large kitchen garden and orchard. TEAS in aid of St Luke's Church. *Adm £1.50 Chd free. Sun April 30 (2-5.30)*

Houlton Lodge, Goxhill ♿✂❀ (Mr & Mrs M Dearden) *6m E of Barton-on-Humber. Follow signs to Goxhill, do not go into village centre but straight on over railway bridge and take 5th turning on R. Houlton Lodge is about 100yds from junction on LH-side. Park cars outside property.* A well-established very neat garden approx ¾ acre. Shrub rose and mixed borders; large island bed and rockery, conifer bed. Grass bed and water feature. TEAS in aid of Goxhill Methodist Church. *Adm £1 Chd free. Sun June 4 (2-6). Private visits welcome, please* **Tel 01469 531355**

NEW **Linden House, Wootton** ♿✂❀ (Norman & Pauline Jackson) *5m S of Barton on Humber on A1077. Garden situated in High Street.* Small village garden with unusual plants, herbaceous borders and pond. TEAS. *Combined adm £1.50 with* **Becklehon**. *Sun April 30 (2-5.30)*

Little Ponton Hall, Grantham ♿❀ (Mr & Mrs Alastair McCorquodale) *½m E of A1 at S end of Grantham bypass.* 3 to 4 acres garden. Spacious lawns with cedar tree over 200yrs old. Many varieties of old shrub roses and clematis; borders and young trees. Stream with spring garden; bulbs and river walk. Newly designed walled kitchen garden and listed dovecote. Adjacent is St Guthlacs Church which will be decorated and all visitors welcome. TEAS in aid of The Church. *Adm £2 Chd 50p. Sun June 18 (2-6)*

Manor Farm, Keisby ✂❀ (Mr & Mrs C A Richardson) *9m NW of Bourne, 10m E of Grantham, signed to Keisby from Lenton and Hawthorpe.* ½ acre plantsman's garden. Over 250 named snowdrops, hellebores and many other early flowering plants. *Adm £1 Chd free (ACNO to Stamford and Bourne MCR). Sat, Sun Feb 19, 20 (11-4)*

▲ **Marston Hall, nr Grantham** ♿❀ (The Reverend Henry Thorold) *6m N of Grantham. Turn off A1, 4½m N of Grantham; on 1½m to Marston. Station: Grantham.* Notable trees; wych elm and laburnum of exceptional size. House C16 continuously owned by the Thorold family. Interesting pictures and furniture. TEAS. *Adm house & garden £2.50 Chd £1 (ACNO to Marston Church). For NGS Sun June 25 (2-6)*

70 North Street, Winterton ♿✂❀ (Peter & Gail Phillips) *From Barton on Humber head W on the A1077. After approx 7m turn L into Winterton at the Winterton/Winteringham Xrds (B1207). House approx ½m on L.* ¼ acre plantaholic's garden with colour from April to September, with a 'feature' fish pond and two wildlife ponds (frogs and newts). Wildflower area, alpine bed, Japanese garden, tropical area and mini orchard. Our passion is unusual perennials which mingle around the garden with old favourites and cottage garden plants. TEAS in aid of The Lincolnshire Trust for Nature Conservation (under cover) all day. *Adm £1 Chd free. Suns May 21, Aug 20 (10-6) Private visits welcome by appt, please* **Tel 01724 733695**

NEW **The Old Farmhouse, Morton** ✂❀ (Mr & Mrs N Barnes) *2m N of Bourne.Turn R at Xrds (Kings Head PH), down High Street. House on L of church, behind Five Bells PH.* ⅓ acre garden created over the last years, divided into separate areas. Small walled garden in shadow of village church with formal pond and herbaceous borders. Island beds in other garden featuring a wide selection of plants. Courtyard area. TEAS. *Adm £1 Chd free. Weds April 19, May 10, June 21 (2-5)*

The Old Rectory, East Keal ❀ (John & Ruth Ward) *2m SW of Spilsby on A16. Turn into Church Lane by PO.* Beautifully situated, with fine views, a rambling cottage garden falling naturally into varied separate areas, with shrubs, roses, climbers, perennials and annuals. Small ponds and rock garden. TEA. TEAS June only. *Adm £1.20 Chd free. Suns April 16, June 11, Thurs March 16, May 11 (2-5). Private visits welcome every Thursday by appt, please* **Tel 01790 752477**

The Old Vicarage, Holbeach Hurn ✂❀ (Mrs Liz Dixon-Spain) *Turn off A17 N to Holbeach Hurn, past Post Box in the middle of village, 1st turn R into Low Rd. Old Vicarage on R approx 400 yds.* 2 acres of gardens incl mature trees, formal and informal areas, a croquet lawn surrounded by borders of shrubs, roses, herbaceous plants; pond, bog garden and wild flowers; shrub roses in old paddock area. *Combined adm with* **Old White House** *(see below) £2 Chd free (ACNO to St Matthews Housing Assoc). Sun June 11 (2-6). Private visits welcome, please* **Tel 01406 424148**

Old White House, Holbeach Hurn ♿✂ (Mr & Mrs A Worth) *Turn off A17 N to Holbeach Hurn, follow signs to village, go straight through, turn R after the Rose and Crown at Baileys Lane.* 1½ acres of mature garden, featuring herbaceous borders, roses, patterned garden, herb garden and wild garden with small pond. TEAS. *Combined adm with* **The Old Vicarage** *(see above) £2 Chd free (ACNO to St Matthews Housing Assoc). Sun June 11 (2-6)*

Park House Farm, Walcott ♿✂❀ (Mr & Mrs Geoffrey Grantham) *Walcott 16m S of Lincoln on B1189 between Billinghay and Methingham.* 1-acre plantsman's garden made within traditional farm buildings sheltering many half-hardy plants. A small knot garden with a formal pool is a new feature: 2 further acres of ornamental trees. *Adm £1.50 Chd free. Parties welcome by appt May to July, please* **Tel 01526 860409**

Park View, Holton-le-Moor ♿✂❀ (Mr & Mrs D Jackson) *6m N of Market Rasen Turn L off A46 onto B1436 to*

Holton-le-Moor village. 2-acre garden started approx 9 yrs ago. Mixed shrubs, trees and herbaceous borders. TEAS. *Combined adm with* **Cortaderia**£1.50. *Sun June 18 (1.30-5.30) Private and group visits welcome by appt, please* **Tel 01678 828444**

Pinefields, Bigby ✗❀ (Reg & Madeleine Hill) *Off A1084 between Caistor 5m and Brigg 4m. At top of Smithy Lane - junction with Main Street. 4th house from Church.* 3/4 acre plantsman's garden. Shrubs and herbaceous borders containing some unusual plants. Roses and clematis on pergolas and trellis. Gravelled alpine and hot area with adjoining seating. An established wildlife pond leading to a curved pergola and wildlife area. *Adm £1.20 Chd free. Group visits welcome by appt June/July, please* **Tel 01652 628327**

4 Ringwood Close, Birchwood ✗✗❀ (Mr & Mrs J Brown) *SW of Lincoln. From A46 by-pass take Skellingthorpe Rd (signed Birchwood) for ¼m; turn R at t-lights Rix garage, then 1st R then R again. Parking at Green Barrel PH.* ⅓ acre garden, bordered by mature woodland and created over 30yrs by enthusiastic plant collectors. Gravel bed with grasses, herbaceous borders featuring unusual plants. Blue garden completed 1999. Blue fenced contemplative garden with blue/yellow planting scheme. Vegetables in raised beds. TEAS in aid of St Luke's Church. *Adm £1.50 Chd free. Sun June 25 (11-5) Private visits welcome by appt, please* **Tel 01522 683960**

Saxby-all-Saints Gardens *Between South Ferriby and Brigg on the B1204 in the centre of Saxby-All-Saints Village.* TEAS. *Combined adm £1.50 Chd 50p. Sun June 11 (2-5.30)*
 The Chestnuts ❀ (Mr & Mrs P Blake) *50 Main St.* Mature garden set in approx ⅓-acre. Mature trees and shrubs, lawns, herbaceous borders, pond, water feature, summer house, hostas, ferns etc
 Rose Cottage ✗ (Mr & Mrs B Bearfield) A mature country garden of approx ⅓ acre to the rear of C17 cottage. Lawns, mature trees, old and modern roses. Variety of cottage garden shrubs and flowers in beds and borders. TEAS

2 School House, Stixwould ✗❀ (Andrew & Sheila Sankey) *1½m N of Woodhall Spa.* ¼ acre garden, redesigned in Oct 1994 in the cottage garden style, to incl front garden with unusual perennials and shrubs, herb garden, and small turf maze. Owners are garden designers. TEAS. *Adm £1 Chd free (ACNO to Sick Children's Trust). Suns May 7, July 30 (2-6). Private visits welcome May to Sept, please* **Tel 01526 352453**

2 School Lane, Stow ✗❀ (Alexander J Wyllie) *On B1241 midway Lincoln to Gainsborough. E along Ingham Lane, School Lane 1st L. No parking in Lane. Please park in village 2 min walk.* ¼ acre on edge of village, wander up the drive and round to the formal hedged fountain garden with mixed borders and small hot front garden. Return to the curved herbaceous walk leading to short woodland path and lawn. Return by brick path. Various small trees and shrubs. 12 yrs development still progressing. TEAS under cover in aid of St Mary's Church. *Adm £1.50 Chd 50p. Sun Oct 8 (11-5)*

Springtyme, Sibsey ✗✗❀ (Mr & Mrs J W Lynn) *Station Rd. 5m N of Boston. From A16 at Sibsey turn R onto B1184, towards Old Leake, garden on R in 400yds.* Approx ¼ acre informal garden with alpine house, scree beds, alpine troughs, densely planted mixed borders and pond. Featured in Garden Answers and on TV. *Adm £1 Chd free. Private visits welcome by appt only, please* **Tel 01205 750438**

NEW **Station House, Halton Holegate** ✗❀ (Mr & Mrs R Gill) *From Spilsby follow B1195 E to Halton Holegate, in village turn R into Station Rd, ½m, last house in village on R before bridge.* 4-acre plantsman's garden with large pond and woodland walks, rare trees and plants conservatory. *Adm £2. Sun June 4 (11-5)*

Sturton-by-Stow Gardens ✗✗❀ *Halfway between Lincoln and Gainsborough on B1241 and A1500 Xrds. Combined adm £2 Chd free. Sun July 9 (2-6)*
 73 Saxilby Road, Sturton by Stow ✗❀ (Charles & Tricia Elliott) *On B1241.* Small garden and hardy plant nursery in open aspect. Extensively cultivated beds and borders contain a wide range of perennial plants used with shrubs and ponds to give all year interest and colour. TEAS. *Garden and nursery open March - Oct, Fri-Mon (10-5) NGS collection box*
 NEW **3 Village Farm Drive** (Mr & Mrs M Dunn) *On A1500, 100yds from village centre parking.* Enclosed garden containing really attractive and interesting water and other related features. Approached by walled area with raised plants, continuing to patio with pergola surrounded by climbers, shrubs, tubs, baskets, hardy and tender perennials.

Sutton St Edmund Village Gardens ✗✗ *Peterborough 18m, Spalding 16m, Wisbech 8m.* TEAS. *Combined adm £1.50 Chd 50p (ACNO to Cystic Fibrosis Research Trust). Sun June 18 (12-6)*
 Holly Tree Farm ❀ (Mr & Mrs C Pate) *In Sutton St Edmund if facing S take R turn in village onto Chapel gate. Next L onto Hallgate, farm 1st house on R.* 1-acre family garden, 3 acre pasture for cows. Free range poultry. Island beds of perennials and shrubs, vegetables, fruit, scree, all in cottage garden style. Developed over the last 10yrs. Iris and alliums in May. Unusual herbaceous perennials for sale. TEAS
 Inley Drove Farm ❀ (Dr & Mrs F Pryor) *N of Sutton St Edmund, 2m straight on when rd swings R, 2nd turning on R into Inley Drove.* Garden 5 acres and wood 7½ acres still under construction. Double mixed borders, dry garden, herbs, natural pond, nut walk, roses, orchard and shrubs, all on land which was arable farmland until 1992

Toft House, Old Leake ✗✗❀ (Mr & Mrs Grant) *7m from Boston on A52 to Skegness, garden situated 1½m N of church in Fold Hill. Also 4m from Sibsey on B1184.* Approx 2-acre garden has evolved over 40yrs. Large informal beds with many unusual trees, shrubs and plants enhanced by a bowling green lawn. A formal potager with rose arches and box hedging. Tea. *Adm £1 Chd 50p. Sun May 14 (2-6)*

15 Vicarage Gardens, Scunthorpe ✗❀ (Chris & Jill Dyson) *In the centre of Scunthorpe, off Oswald Rd and*

adjacent to the museum. Parking in the rd and the museum car park. ⅓ acre town garden full of surprises; gravel garden, mixed borders, pergola, lawn and courtyard garden with pond. Wide collection of interesting shrubs and perennials. TEAS. *Adm £1.50 Chd free (ACNO to St Lawrence's Church). Sun May 28 (2-6)*

The Villa, South Somercotes ❀ (Michael & Judy Harry) *8m E of Louth on unclassified rd between S Cockerington and N Somercotes.* Plantsman's ¼ acre surrounds Victorian house and outbuildings: contains many unusual perennials, roses, herbs. Old orchard and livestock add to peaceful rural character. *Adm £1 Chd free. Individual and group visits welcome by appt only, refreshments by arrangement, please* **Tel 01507 358487**

Walnut Cottage, Careby ♿❀ (Mr & Mrs R L Grundy) *6m N of Stamford on B1176. 5m E of A1 at Stretton. Situated approx ⅓m at end of Main St on L.* ½ acre garden with interesting herbaceous borders. Herb garden, shade and gravel areas, water garden with S facing slope leading to small woodland garden with pond. Featured in 'The Garden' Sept 98. TEAS. *Adm £1.50 Chd free. Sun June 25 (11-5) Private visits welcome by appt only Tues and Sat, June and July (Tea available), please* **Tel 01780 410660**

The Herb Society

H orse chestnut (*Aesculus hippocastanum*) extracts are used to treat varicose veins.

E yebright (*Euphrasia officinalis*) was first used for eye problems because the flowers resemble bloodshot eyes.

R ose water, from various Rosa species, was the original ingredient for cold cream.

B alm, or lemon balm (*Melissa officinalis*) has undergone clinical trials as a cure for cold sores.

S aw palmetto (*Serenoa repens*) helps prevent prostate disease.

O regano (*Origanum vulgare*) means "joy of the mountains".

C araway (*Carum carvi*) a few seeds chewed is a safe remedy for indigestion.

I pecac (*Cephaelis ipecacuanha*) is a Brazilian rainforest herb used in cough mixtures.

E chinacea (*Echinacea* spp.) is an immune stimulant now endangered in the wild through over-collection.

T ea tree oil (from *Melaleuca alternifolia*) is a potent antifungal and antiseptic.

Y lang-ylang (*Cananga odorata*) yields an essential oil which has relaxant and aphrodisiac effects.

The Herb Society
Deddington Hill Farm, Warmington, Banbury OX17 1XB
Tel: 01295 692000
Events Hotline: 01295 692001
Email: email@herbsociety.co.uk
Website: www.herbsociety.co.uk

London (Greater London Area)

Hon County Organiser: Mrs Maurice Snell, Moleshill House, The Fairmile, Cobham, Surrey KT11 1BG Tel 01932 864532

Assistant Hon County Organisers: Alanna Wilson, 38 Ornan Road, London NW3 4QB Tel 020 7794 4071
Don Fuller Esq, 109 Halsbury Road East, Northolt Park, Middlesex UB5 4PY Tel 020 8422 7417
Mrs Catherine Horwood, 133 Haverstock Hill, London NW3 4RU Tel 020 7586 0908
Mrs Kathy Lynam, 26 Northchurch Road, London N1 4EH Tel 020 7254 8993
Mrs Nancye Nosworthy, 9 Eland Road, London SW11 5JX Tel 020 7228 1119
Mrs Joan Wall, Orchard Cottage, 3 Woodlands Road, Bickley, Kent BR1 2AD Tel 020 8467 4190
Mrs Lesley West, 11 Woodlands Road, Barnes, London SW13 0JZ Tel 020 8876 7030

ACO, Tours: Mrs Julia Hickman, Little Lodge, Watts Road, Thames Ditton Surrey Tel 020 8339 0931

ACO, Publicity: Mrs Sophie Dealtry, 38 Eland Road, London SW11 5JY Tel 020 7350 2347

Hon County Treasurer: Maurice Snell Esq, Moleshill House, The Fairmile, Cobham, Surrey KT11 1BG Tel 01932 864532

DATES OF OPENING

Regular openings
For details see garden description
Chelsea Physic Garden, SW3
Myddelton House Gardens, Enfield

February 27 Sunday
Myddelton House Gardens, Enfield

March 11 Saturday
The Elms, Kingston-on-Thames

March 12 Sunday
The Elms, Kingston-on-Thames

March 26 Sunday
7 The Grove, N6

April 2 Sunday
Chelsea Physic Garden, SW3
Eccleston Square, SW1
15 Lawrence Street, SW3

April 8 Saturday
The Elms, Kingston-on-Thames

April 9 Sunday
5 Burbage Road, SE24
The Elms, Kingston-on-Thames

April 15 Saturday
Trinity Hospice, SW4

April 16 Sunday
10 Chiltern Road, Pinner
9 Eland Road, SW11
29 Gilston Road, SW10
70 Gloucester Crescent, NW1
109 Halsbury Road East, Northolt Park
Ham House, Richmond
16 Hillcrest Road, E18
21a The Little Boltons, SW10
Natural History Museum Wildlife Garden, SW7
Trinity Hospice, SW4
7 Upper Phillimore Gardens, W8
47 Winn Road, SE12

April 30 Sunday
7 The Butts, Brentford
51 Cholmeley Crescent, N6
Elm Tree Cottage, S Croydon
1 Grange Park, W5
1 Hocroft Avenue, NW2
5 St Regis Close, N10
26 Thompson Road, SE22

May 1 Monday
1 Hocroft Avenue, NW2
11 Hocroft Road, NW2

May 6 Saturday
The Elms, Kingston-on-Thames
The Holme, NW1

May 7 Sunday
17 Church Lane, SW19
36 Downs Hill, Beckenham
The Elms, Kingston-on-Thames
Elmsdale Road Gardens, E17
51 Gloucester Road, Kew
109 Halsbury Road East, Northolt Park
The Holme, NW1
85 Merton Hall Road, SW19
2 Millfield Place, N6
17a Navarino Road, E8
7 St Albans Grove, W8
Seymour Buildings, W1
Waltham Forest Register Office, E17
The Watergardens, Kingston-on-Thames

May 11 Thursday
Flat 1, 1F Oval Road, NW1 (evening)

May 13 Saturday
Highwood Ash, NW7

May 14 Sunday
39 Arundel Gardens, N21
5 Burbage Road, SE24
Elm Tree Cottage, S Croydon
5 Greenaway Gardens, NW3
11 Hampstead Way, NW11
37 Heath Drive, NW3
Highwood Ash, NW7
38 Killieser Avenue, SW2
43 Penerley Road, SE6
11 Woodlands Road, SW13

May 17 Wednesday
12 Lansdowne Rd, W11

May 21 Sunday
9 Caroline Close, W Drayton
133 Crystal Palace Road, SE22
Culverden Road Gardens, SW12
5 Garden Close, SW15
Hall Grange, Croydon
109 Halsbury Road East, Northolt Park
767 Hertford Road, Enfield
10A Hoveden Road, NW2
Regents College's Botany Garden, NW1
64 Thornhill Road, E10
131 Upland Road, SE22

May 27 Saturday
Roots & Shoots, SE11

May 28 Sunday
48 Addison Road, E11
116 Hamilton Terrace, NW8

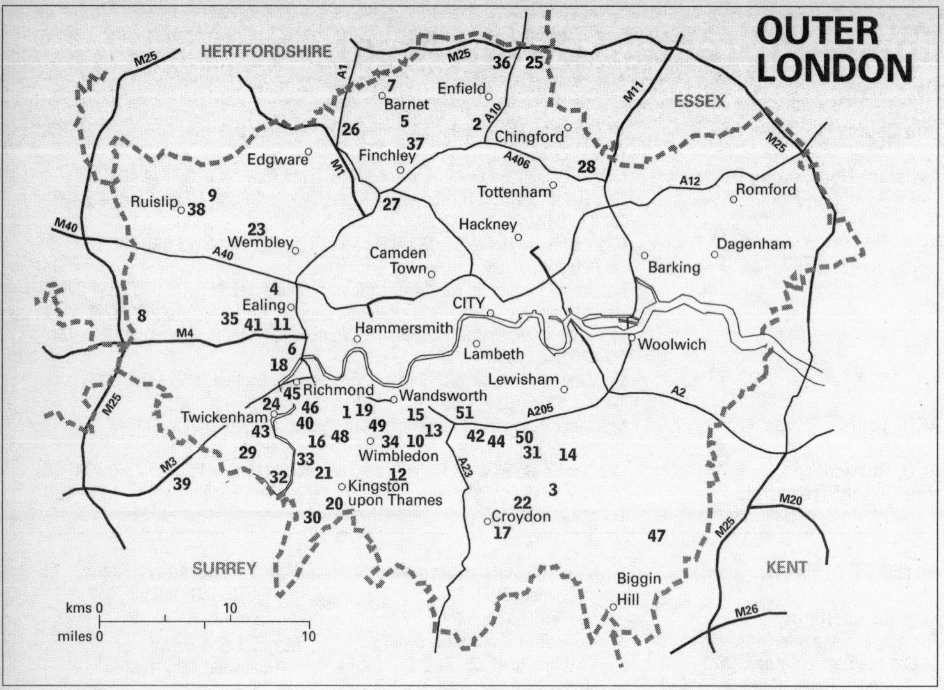

KEY TO OUTER LONDON

1 66 Alton Road
2 39 Arundel Gardens
3 1 Audrey Close
4 Azalea House
5 Barnet Gardens
6 7 The Butts
7 7 Byng Road
8 9 Caroline Close
9 10 Chiltern Road
10 17 Church Lane
11 26 Claygate Road
12 41 Cranleigh Road
13 Culverden Road
14 36 Downs Hill
15 20 Eatonville Road
16 The Elms
17 Elm Tree Cottage
18 The Ferry House
19 5 Garden Close
20 8 Grafton Park Road
21 114 Gloucester Road
22 Hall Grange
23 109 Halsbury Road East
24 Ham House
25 767 Hertford Road
26 Highwood Ash
27 5 Hillcrest Avenue
28 16 Hillcrest Road
29 Holly Cottage
30 239a Hook Road
31 26 Kenilworth Road
32 Little Lodge
33 9 Lower Teddington Road
34 85 Merton Hall Road
35 38 Minterne Avenue
36 Myddelton House Gardens
37 263 Nether Street
38 North Ruislip Gardens
39 80 Old Charlton Road
40 Ormeley Lodge
41 Osterley Park House
42 10A The Pavement
43 Pembridge Cottage
44 48 Rommany Road
45 7 St George's Road
46 St Michael's Convent
47 58 Warren Road
48 The Watergardens
49 Wimbledon Gardens
50 14A Wiverton Rd
51 66 Woodbourne Avenue

KEY TO INNER LONDON

1 29 Addison Avenue
2 48 Addison Road
3 51 Albert Bridge Road
4 Albion Square Gardens
5 33 Balmuir Gardens
6 Barnes Gardens
7 15a Buckland Crescent
8 5 Burbage Road
9 57 Breakspears Road
10 35 Camberwell Grove
11 Carlyle's House
12 11 Cavendish Ave
13 Chelsea Physic Garden
14 101 Cheyne Walk
15 Chiswick Mall
16 51 Cholmeley Crescent
17 Choumert Square
18 Chumleigh Multicultural Garden
19 13 College Cross
20 2 Cottesmore Gardens
21 24 Croom's Hill
22 133 Crystal Palace Road
23 De Beauvoir Gardens
24 Dulwich Gardens
25 Eccleston Square
26 9 Eland Road
27 Elmsdale Road Gardens
28 14 Farm Avenue
29 Fenton House
30 Flat 1, 1F Oval Road
31 73 Forest Drive East
32 22 Gayton Road
33 29 Gilston Road
34 70 Gloucester Crescent
35 51 Gloucester Road
36 Goldsborough Tudor Grange
37 1 Grange Park
38 5 Greenaway Gardens
39 7 The Grove
40 116 Hamilton Terrace,NW8

INNER LONDON

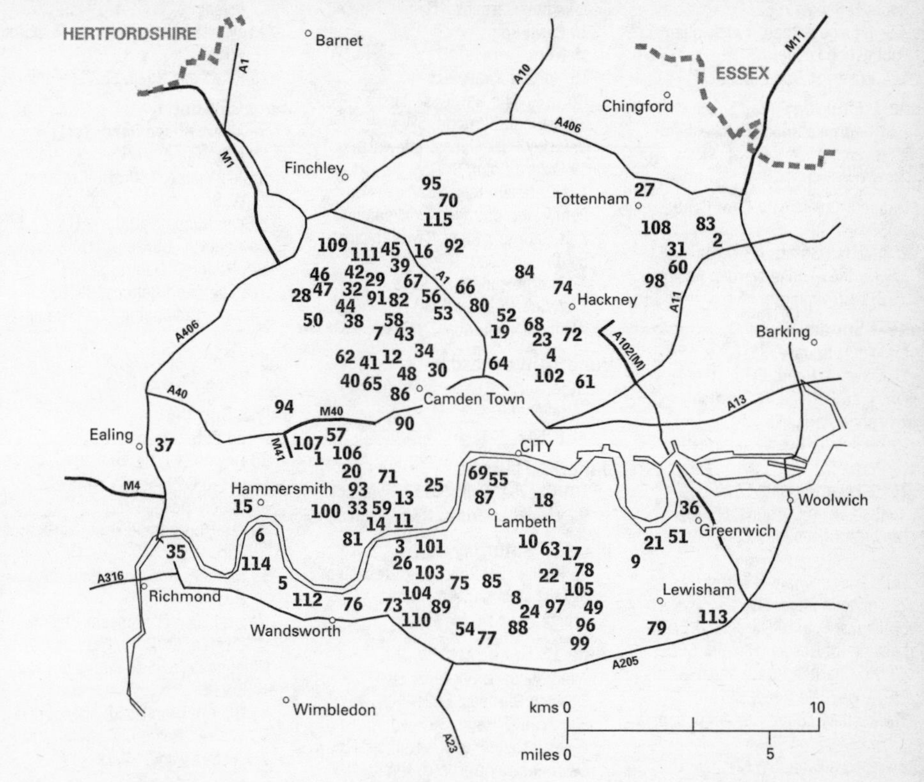

41 117 Hamilton Terrace,NW8
42 11 Hampstead Way
43 133 Haverstock Hill
44 37 Heath Drive
45 Highgate Village
46 1 Hocroft Avenue
47 11 Hocroft Road
48 The Holme
49 125 Honor Oak Park
50 10A Hoveden Road
51 Hyde Vale Gardens
52 Islington Gardens
53 Kentish Town Gardens
54 38 Killieser Avenue
55 Lambeth Community Care
56 15 Langbourne Avenue
57 12 Lansdowne Rd
58 10 Lawn Road
59 15 Lawrence Street
60 1 Lister Road
61 London Buddhist Centre
62 22 Loudoun Road
63 Lyndhurst Square Garden
64 Malvern Terrace
65 2 Melina Place
66 13 Mercers Road
67 2 Millfield Place
68 82a Mortimer Road
69 Museum of Garden History
70 Muswell Hill Gardens
71 Natural History Museum
72 17a Navarino Road
73 Nightingale
74 15 Norcott Rd
75 2 Northbourne Road
76 39 Oxford Road
77 71 Palace Road
78 174 Peckham Rye
79 43 Penerley Rd
80 Penn Road Gardens
81 35 Perrymead Street
82 1 Pond Street
83 46 Preston Drive
84 13 Queen Elizabeth's Walk
85 62 Rattray Road
86 Regents College's Botan
87 Roots & Shoots
88 167 Rosendale Road
89 35 Rudloe Road
90 Seymour Buildings
91 South End Road
92 Southwood Lodge
93 7 St Albans Grove
94 57 St Quintin Avenue
95 5 St Regis Close
96 Tewkesbury Lodge Garden
97 26 Thompson Road
98 64 Thornhill Road
99 27 Thorpewood Ave
100 21a The Little Boltons
101 Thrive,SW11
102 Thrive,E2
103 Trinity Hospice
104 103 Thurleigh Road
105 131 Upland Road
106 7 Upper Phillimore Gard
107 1 Vanderbilt Villas
108 Waltham Forest Register
109 3 Wellgarth Road
110 2 Western Lane
111 10 Wildwood Rd
112 35 Wincanton Rd
113 47 Winn Road
114 11 Woodlands Road
115 27 Wood Vale

117 Hamilton Terrace, NW8
Myddelton House Gardens, Enfield
Roots & Shoots, SE11
7 St George's Road, Twickenham
Southwood Lodge, N6
14A Wiverton Road, SE26

June 1 Thursday
7 St George's Road, Twickenham (evening)

June 3 Saturday
Lambeth Community Care Centre, SE11
263 Nether Street, N3 (evening)
Tewkesbury Lodge Garden Group, SE23 (evening)

June 4 Sunday
Choumert Square, SE15
26 Claygate Road, W13
Elm Tree Cottage, S Croydon
1 Grange Park, W5
109 Halsbury Road East, Northolt Park
26 Kenilworth Road, SE20
Kentish Town Gardens, NW5
Lambeth Community Care Centre, SE11
Little Lodge, Thames Ditton
22 Loudoun Road, NW8
Lyndhurst Square Gardens, SE15
Museum of Garden History, SE1
80 Old Charlton Road, Shepperton
167 Rosendale Road, SE21
Tewkesbury Lodge Garden Group, SE23
2 Western Lane, SW12

June 7 Wednesday
5 Burbage Road, SE24 (evening)

June 8 Thursday
Fenton House, NW3 (evening)
Flat 1, 1F Oval Road, NW1 (evening)

June 10 Saturday
The Ferry House, Old Isleworth
114 Gloucester Road, Kingston
Holly Cottage, 40 Station Road, Hampton
263 Nether Street, N3 (evening)
15 Norcott Road, N16

June 11 Sunday
33 Balmuir Gardens, SW15
Barnes Gardens, SW13
15a Buckland Crescent, NW3
35 Camberwell Grove, SE5
10 Chiltern Road, Pinner
Chiswick Mall, W4
The Ferry House, Old Isleworth
114 Gloucester Road, Kingston
7 The Grove, N6
133 Haverstock Hill, NW3
Highgate Village, N6
Holly Cottage, 40 Station Road, Hampton
Islington Gardens, N1
10 Lawn Road, NW3
Malvern Terrace, N1
15 Norcott Road, N16
North Ruislip Gardens, Ruislip
2 Northbourne Road, SW4
Osterley Park House, Isleworth
39 Oxford Road, SW15
174 Peckham Rye, SE22
Pembridge Cottage, Twickenham
7 St George's Road, Twickenham
South End Road, NW3
27 Thorpewood Ave, SE26
3 Wellgarth Road, NW11
Wimbledon Gardens, SW19

June 14 Wednesday
Little Lodge, Thames Ditton (evening)
71 Palace Road, SW2 (evening)

June 15 Thursday
101 Cheyne Walk, SW10 (evening)
9 Montpelier Grove, NW5 (evening)

June 17 Saturday
26 Kenilworth Road, SE20 (evening)
St Michael's Convent, Ham
Trinity Hospice, SW4

June 18 Sunday
Albion Square Gardens, E8
Dulwich Gardens, SE21
Elm Tree Cottage, S Croydon
Goldsborough Tudor Grange, SE3
5 Greenaway Gardens, NW3
5 Hillcrest Avenue, NW11
38 Killieser Avenue, SW2
Leyborne Park Gardens, Kew
London Buddhist Centre, 51 Roman Road, E2
38 Minterne Avenue, Southall
Ormeley Lodge, Richmond
71 Palace Road, SW2
43 Penerley Road, SE6
Penn Road Gardens, N7
1 Pond Street, NW3
Thrive, SW11
103 Thurleigh Road, SW12
Trinity Hospice, SW4
47 Winn Road, SE12
66 Woodbourne Avenue, SW16

June 21 Wednesday
133 Crystal Palace Road, SE22 (evening)
5 Hillcrest Avenue, NW11 (evening)
103 Thurleigh Road, SW12 (evening)

June 22 Thursday
Seymour Buildings, W1 (evening)
Southwood Lodge, N6 (evening)

June 24 Saturday
125 Honor Oak Park, SE23 (evening)
9 Lower Teddington Road, Hampton Wick
48 Rommany Road, SE27 (evening)

June 25 Sunday
51 Albert Bridge Road, SW11
66 Alton Road, SW15
Azalea House, 18 Royle Crescent, W13
7 Byng Road, High Barnet
De Beauvoir Gardens, N1
125 Honor Oak Park, SE23
21a The Little Boltons, SW10
9 Lower Teddington Road, Hampton Wick
82a Mortimer Road, N1
5 St Regis Close, N10

July 2 Sunday
7 The Butts, Brentford
36 Downs Hill, Beckenham
Elm Tree Cottage, S Croydon
5 Garden Close, SW15
109 Halsbury Road East, Northolt Park
13 Mercers Road and the Coach House, N19
Natural History Museum Wildlife Garden, SW7
Nightingale, 105 Nightingale Lane, SW12
80 Old Charlton Road, Shepperton
58 Warren Road, Chelsfield
2 Western Lane, SW12

July 5 Wednesday
1 Audrey Close, Beckenham
1 Audrey Close, Beckenham (evening)
8 Grafton Park Road, Worcester Park (evening)

July 8 Saturday
114 Gloucester Road, Kingston
48 Rommany Road, SE27 (evening)
Thrive, E2

July 9 Sunday
41 Cranleigh Road, SW19
20 Eatonville Road, SW17
14 Farm Avenue, NW2
22 Gayton Road, NW3
114 Gloucester Road, Kingston
8 Grafton Park Road, Worcester Park
Muswell Hill Gardens, N10
35 Perrymead Street, SW6
35 Rudloe Road, SW12
10 Wildwood Road, NW11
35 Wincanton Road, SW18

July 14 Friday
10A Hoveden Road, NW2 (evening)

July 16 Sunday
11 Cavendish Avenue, NW8
Chumleigh Multicultural Garden, SE5
24 Croom's Hill, SE10 (evening)
24 Croom's Hill, SE10
70 Gloucester Crescent, NW1
5 Greenaway Gardens, NW3
116 Hamilton Terrace, NW8
37 Heath Drive, NW3
Hyde Vale Gardens, SE10
15 Langbourne Avenue, N6
2 Melina Place, NW8
17a Navarino Road, E8
10A The Pavement, SE27
57 St Quintin Avenue, W10

July 20 Thursday
2 Millfield Place, N6 (evening)

July 22 Saturday
Carlyle's House, SW3
15 Lawrence Street, SW3
27 Wood Vale, N10

July 23 Sunday
Carlyle's House, SW3
13 College Cross, N1
117 Hamilton Terrace, NW8
Holly Cottage, 40 Station Road, Hampton
15 Lawrence Street, SW3
48 Rommany Road, SE27
5 St Regis Close, N10
27 Wood Vale, N10

July 29 Saturday
Trinity Hospice, SW4

July 30 Sunday
29 Addison Avenue, W11
Azalea House, 18 Royle Crescent, W13
Barnet Gardens, Barnet
Myddelton House Gardens, Enfield
57 St Quintin Avenue, W10
Trinity Hospice, SW4

August 6 Sunday
10 Chiltern Road, Pinner
2 Cottesmore Gardens, W8
133 Crystal Palace Road, SE22
239a Hook Road, Chessington
1 Lister Road, E11
13 Queen Elizabeth's Walk, N16
2 Western Lane, SW12

August 13 Sunday
73 Forest Drive East, E11
80 Old Charlton Road, Shepperton
64 Thornhill Road, E10
1 Vanderbilt Villas, Sterne Street, W12

August 19 Saturday
The Holme, NW1

August 20 Sunday
The Holme, NW1
62 Rattray Road, SW2

September 2 Saturday
Trinity Hospice, SW4

September 3 Sunday
57 Breakspears Road, SE4
Trinity Hospice, SW4

September 10 Sunday
48 Addison Road, E11
46 Preston Drive, E11

September 17 Sunday
51 Albert Bridge Road, SW11
26 Thompson Road, SE22

September 24 Sunday
7 The Grove, N6

October 8 Sunday
36 Downs Hill, Beckenham

October 15 Sunday
The Watergardens, Kingston-on-Thames

October 29 Sunday
Chelsea Physic Garden, SW3

2001

February 25 Sunday
Myddelton House Gardens, Enfield

DESCRIPTIONS OF GARDENS

29 Addison Avenue, W11 ✂ (Mr & Mrs D B Nicholson) *No entry for cars from Holland Park Avenue, approach via Norland Square and Queensdale Rd. Station: Holland Park. Bus 94.* Small garden packed with interesting plants, winner of many prizes and photographed over the last 10yrs for several gardening magazines. Lots of unusual wall shrubs, variegated plants and colourful perennials. Phlox paniculata (over 40 varieties) a special favourite. *Adm £1 Chd 50p (ACNO to the Museum of Garden History). Sun July 30 (2-6)*

48 Addison Road, E11 ✂ (Mrs Joan Mason) *Wanstead Central Line. Cross Cambridge Park Rd to N side, Addison Rd 2nd on R beside Catholic Church.* Town garden approx 20′ × 50′. Courtyard style with raised beds. Designed for privacy, with foliage suitable for flower arranging. TEA. *Adm £1. Suns May 28, Sept 10 (2-5)*

NEW **51 Albert Bridge Road, SW11** (Loretta & Ron Gerson) *From Albert Bridge Road go to no. 51 and enter the garden from side entrance in front garden. Nearest tube S. Kensington and Sloane Square.* Medium to small size tropical garden on 3 split levels. Original Anderson Bomb Shelter incorporated in the design. Sunny aspect, SW facing, many unusual plants. TEAS. *Adm £2 Chd £1 (ACNO to Shelter). Suns June 25 (12-7), Sept 17 (12-6)*

Albion Square Gardens, E8 *2m N of Liverpool St Station (BR & tube). 1m S of Dalston/Kingsland Station (BR). Buses 22, 67, 149, 243. By car approach from Queensbridge Rd northbound turning L into Albion Drive leading to Albion Square.* Homemade TEAS in award-winning leafy Central Gardens. *Combined adm £5 for 5 or £1.50 each, Chd £1.50 for 5 or 50p each. Sun June 18 (2-5.30)*

12 Albion Square ❀ (A Black) Victorian Gothic church provides backdrop to this 70′ L-shaped garden. Brick-paved herb garden and grassy walkway lead to yew hedge enclosed lawns and terraces. Planting is 8 years old. Features lifesize Minotaur sculpture and Children's Café. *(ACNO to The Peter Walker Trust)*

24 Albion Square (Mr David French) 80′ town garden designed to unfold as a series of views and focal points divided by a yew hedge. Emphasis on foliage plants rather than flowers. Secluded seating areas, fountain. Through shared summerhouse to No 25. *(ACNO to St Joseph's Hospice, Hackney)*

25 Albion Square (Sandy Maclennan) 80′ informal walled garden on two levels with pond featuring ornamental shrubs and trees creating interest in foliage, form and colour. *(ACNO to The Peter Walker Trust)*

252 Haggerston Road (Ms Heather Wilson) 60′ long, mid-terrace shady town garden. Informal, densely planted design with emphasis on unusual perennials and shrubs, incl peat bed, herbs, ferns, dry shade area, herbaceous border, fruit trees and (friendly) bee-hive. TEAS *(ACNO to St Joseph's Hospice, Hackney)*

NEW **56 Middleton Road** ❀ (Jan Bright) An 80′ secluded town garden combining sunlit borders with a small dappled woodland glade. The emphasis is on scented plants and foliage.

NEW **66 Alton Road, SW15** (Dr Margaret O'Connor) *Roehampton. From Roehampton Lane, Alton Rd opp Shell petrol station. From A3 lanes going into London, Alton Rd is slip road on L opp cemetery gates. House Victorian, with white tower and 2 fir trees opp Heathmere School, i.e. on SW side of Alton Rd.* About ⅓ acre of garden bordered on S by Charles II wall with extensive views of Richmond Park beyond. Lawn is flanked with a wild nature pond and a cascade, a gravel garden and 2 long borders of mixed herbaceous plants and shrubs. Accent is on colour and form of foliage. A bog garden with hemerocallis (varied colours), arum lilies and irises. Beds round greenhouse with pomegranate, pittisporum (variegated), yucca and callistemon. Trees include eucalyptus, robinia, malus, prunus, climbing roses and 15 clematis. TEAS. *Adm £1.50 Chd £1. Sun June 25 (2-6)*

39 Arundel Gardens, N21 (Julie Floyd) *From Winchmore Hill mainline station approx 7 mins walk, turn along Hoppers Rd, Arundel Gardens 3rd on L, 39 is 1st blue door on the R. The W9 Hoppa bus runs along Hoppers Rd. from Southgate Underground.* 100′ × 30′ town garden planted in an informal cottage style, unusual shrubs, climbers and herbaceous plants; over 30 clematis including 11 clematis alpina varieties; arbour, small water feature and conservatory with a collection of cacti and succulents. *Adm £1 Chd 50p (ACNO to E A Bowles of Myddelton House Society). Sun May 14 (2-5)*

1 Audrey Close, Beckenham (David Wyatt Esq) *2 mins from Eden Park station. By railway bridge in South Eden Park Road (where parking is available).* A ¼-acre garden - with the R Beck running through - having an oriental theme. The front has a Japanese rock garden, the back includes a pond, acers and bamboos. TEAS. *Adm £2 Chd £1. Wed July 5* **Afternoon Opening** *(2-5)* **Evening Opening** *(6-9) £3.50. Wine.*

NEW **Azalea House, 18 Royle Crescent, W13** (Teresa & Denis Daly) *Situated by Scotch Common and Cleveland Park. Train to Ealing Broadway (District and Central line). Bus 297, E2, E7 to Argyle Rd. From Greenford bus 297, E2, E7 to Scotch Common, Argyle Rd 5 mins walk from bus.* Colourful front garden, mixed shrubs, herbaceous borders, lilies, oleanders, hardy geraniums, obelisks with clematis. Back courtyard 40' x 30'. A profusion of pots, window boxes, hanging baskets, herb garden, hostas and anything that will grow in a pot. Water fountain. TEAS. *Adm £1 Chd free (ACNO to Shooting Star Children's Hospice). Suns June 25, July 30 (2-6)*

33 Balmuir Gardens, SW15 (Mrs Gay Wilson) *Putney. 5 mins walk from Putney mainline station. Off the Upper Richmond Rd on corner with Howards Lane. Bus 337, 74, 14.* A designer's garden completely re-landscaped in spring 1998, on a corner plot that is continually evolving. Secluded tiny mixed borders backed by stained beams. Slate and pebble mosaics, a formal pond with a waterfall through moose antlers and a still water lily pond. A passionate plantswoman who tries out different colour combinations. All crammed into 80′ × 38′ at widest only 16′ at narrowest. *Adm £2 Chd 50p (ACNO to Friends of the Earth). Sun June 11 (2-7)*

Barnes Gardens, SW13 *Adm £4 for 4 gardens or £1.50 each garden, OAP £3 for 4 gardens or £1 each garden, Chd free. Sun June 11 (2-6)*

25 Castelnau, SW13 (Dr & Mrs P W Adams) *Castelnau is on the main route from Hammersmith Bridge.* The garden is approx 120′ × 40′ designed in 1978 by Malcolm Hillier. Planned for ease of maintenance and family living. Wide variety of herbaceous plants, some attractive roses and a compact working vegetable area with screened swimming pool.Flowers and Pumpkin plants! Cream TEAS

26 Nassau Road (Mr & Mrs A Hallett) *26 Nassau Road lies midway between the Thames and Barnes Pond and is approached via Lonsdale Rd or Church Rd.* Long, slim, terraced garden with tall wisteria framed with weigela, philadelphus, pittosporum, chaenomeles, ceanothus. Borders of hebe, cistus, lilies, geranium, rose, phlox, potentilla and spiraea compete for colours, scents and shapes. Secret oasis behind box bay and lavender hide a sculpture, arouse the senses and dreams of a cottage garden - in Barnes.

8 Queen's Ride (H H Sir Frank & Lady White) *Train: Barnes Station, turn R down Rocks Lane, then L along Queen's Ride. Bus, 22 terminus at Putney Hospital; 3 minutes walk W along Queen's Ride. House is at the junction of Queen's Ride and St Mary's Grove.* ⅔-acre garden facing Barnes Common. Croquet lawn with herbaceous and mixed borders and a small history of the rose garden. Garden quiz. TEA

12 Westmoreland Road (Mr & Mrs Norman Moore) *From Hammersmith take Bus 209, 33, or 72 to the Red Lion. Briefly retrace steps along Castelnau turn L into Ferry Rd then L at Xrds.* Garden on two levels. Raised stone terrace planted with choisya, wisteria, jasmine and decorative herbs. Steps down to two lower lawns, flanked by densely planted borders of flowering shrubs, lavender, larkspur, paeony and hollyhocks, and divided by pretty gazebo, with honeysuckle, roses and clematis. Beyond lies a shady circular lawn with pool and fountain, pink and white hydrangeas, ferns and hostas. (ACNO to Viera Gray House)

NEW **Barnet Gardens, Barnet** *20 mins walk midway between High Barnet and Totteridge underground stations Northern Line. Buses 34, 234, 263 and 326, alight at the junction of the Great North Road - Cherry Hill and Lynsdown Avenue.* TEAS. *Combined adm £2 for 3 gardens. Sun 30 July (11-5)*

NEW **10 Cherry Hill** (Graham & Jean Shaddick) Small, modern, colourful front garden of terraced house. Back garden 60' x 18' immaculately maintained and planted for maximum colour impact.

NEW **40 Cherry Hill** (Ian & Margaret Cordery) Yr-round foliage interest in front garden. Back garden 110' x 26' on sloping site. Upper and lower patios, hard landscaping with geometric lines. Colour-themed beds featuring container plants. Sculptures and water feature.

NEW **45 Great North Road** (Ronald & Miriam Raymond) 50' x 50' cottage-style front garden. Extensive variety of unusual plants reflecting a plantsman's personal choice. The rear garden consists of tiered beds and a small pond and also features a large variety of well planted tubs.

NEW **57 Breakspears Road, SE4** (Biddy Bunzl) *Brockley station 5 mins walk. Lewisham station 15 mins walk. Buses 36, 21, 321 from Lewisham station alight at Lewisham College at Breakspears Rd.* 300 sq metres newly designed and planted. Subtropical forest to desert plants. Unusual grasses, perennials, bamboos, mixed planting. Recycled wooden structures. TEAS. *Adm £2 Chd free. Sun Sept 3 (12-7)*

15a Buckland Crescent, NW3 (Lady Barbirolli) *Swiss Cottage tube. Bus: 46, 13 (6 mins) or Hampstead Hoppa (request stop nearby).* ⅓-acre; interesting collection of shrubs and plants in well-designed garden. *Adm £2 Chd free (ACNO to RUKBA). Sun June 11 (2.30-6.30). Private visits welcome for parties of 25 and over, please* **Tel 020 7586 2464**

5 Burbage Road, SE24 (Mr & Mrs Crawford Lindsay) *Nr junction with Half Moon Lane. Herne Hill mainline station, 5 mins walk. Buses 2, 3, 37, 40, 68, 196.* Garden of member of The Society of Botanical Artists. 150′ × 40′ with large and varied range of plants, many propagated for sale. Herb garden, herbaceous borders for sun and shade, climbing plants, pots, terraces, lawns. Subject of several articles incl 'The Garden', 'The English Garden' and 'The Times'. TEAS (May 14 only) *Adm £1.50 Chd free. Suns April 9, May 14 (2-5)* **Evening Opening** *Wed June 7 (6-8.30) £2.50. Wine. Groups of 5 or more by appt, please* **Tel 020 7274 5610**

7 The Butts, Brentford (Ms Susan Sharkey) *A turning off Half Acre, buses E2 and E8. A short walk from Brentford High St, buses 267 and 235.* Garden designer's walled garden, 90′ × 45′. Divided into 3 rooms; the first a terrace next to house with raised beds and water feature. A pergola divides this from a box-edged lawn with deep borders. A pleached hedge and arch lead to a secret garden with a circular terrace and pond with further water feature. The planting is biased towards foliage featuring leaf shape, texture and colour for maximum impact and yr-round interest. TEAS. *Adm £1.50 Chd 50p (ACNO to Hounslow Extra Club). Suns April 30, July 2 (2-6)*

7 Byng Road, High Barnet (Mr & Mrs Julian Bishop) Jolly organic garden dominated by 3 large borders: two 'cool' borders with mainly perennials and roses and a vibrant 'hot' border incl day lilies, crocosmias and other unusual plants. Also a woodland area, fountain, vegetable patch, many pots and some unusual foxgloves and salvias. TEAS. *Adm £1.50 Chd free (ACNO to Barnet Hospital Special Care Baby Unit). Sun June 25 (2-5). Private visits welcome* **Tel 020 8440 2042**

35 Camberwell Grove, SE5 (Lynette Hemmant & Juri Gabriel) *From Camberwell Green go down Camberwell Church St. Turn R into Camberwell Grove. No 35 is on the L.* 120′ × 20′ London garden, backing onto St Giles Church. A typical cottage garden, a lot of colour, pots overflowing. Artist's studio a feature. *Adm £1 Chd 50p. Sun June 11 (2-7)*

Capel Manor Gardens Sun Oct 8 (10-5). See Hertfordshire

Carlyle's House, SW3 (The National Trust) *Off Chelsea Embankment between Albert and Battersea Bridges. NT sign on corner of Cheyne Row. Or via Kings Rd and Oakley St. NT sign on corner of Upper Cheyne Row. Tubes: Sloane Square and S Kensington. Buses: 11, 19, 22, 49, 239.* 70′ walled town garden with a lawn. Restored Victorian planting theme, reflecting Thomas Carlyle's lifetime. Mature walnut and fig trees create shade for ferns. Vines on the sunny wall. Herbaceous plants and shrubs. Box edged rectangular beds and paved courtyard. *Adm £1 Chd free. For NGS Sat, Sun July 22, 23 (1-5)*

9 Caroline Close, W Drayton (Mr & Mrs Edwin White) *From Station Rd turn into Swan Rd (next to Vauxhall car showrooms) and park on The Green. Walk up Old Farm Rd next to The Swan into Caroline Close (200m).* This contemporary garden (185′ × 35′), has been enthusiastically planted with a wide range of interesting shrubs, perennials and ornamental trees. The split-level format follows closely the contours of a former stream bed resulting in varied and contrasting perspectives of both plants and wildlife, especially butterflies and dragonflies. *Adm £1.50 Chd free. Sun May 21 (1.30-4). Private visits welcome,* **Tel 01895 447795**

11 Cavendish Avenue, NW8 (Dr & Mrs T Laub) *The house is situated behind Lords Cricket Ground off Wellington Rd. 5min walk from St John's Wood tube station.* Large secluded garden divided into 4 'rooms', each with its own distinct character. Cascading water into three ponds with huge Gunnera manicata partly shading bottom pond. Interesting urns and other features, as well as unusual plants: collection of ferns, camellias, acers and hostas. Garden of yr-round interest. TEAS. *Adm £2 Chd free. Sun July 16 (2-6)*

■ **Chelsea Physic Garden, SW3** *66 Royal Hospital Rd, Chelsea. Bus 239 (Mon-Sat). Station: Sloane Square (10 mins). Parking Battersea Park (charged). Entrance in Swan Walk (except wheelchairs).* 2nd oldest Botanic Garden in UK; 3.8 acres; medicinal and herb garden, perfumery border; family order beds; historical walk, glasshouses. TEAS. *Adm £4 Students/Chd £2. Suns April 2 to Oct 29 (2-6); Weds April 5 to Oct 25 (12-5); Winter Festival Suns Feb 6, 13 (11-3) Chelsea Flower Show week Mon-Fri May 22-26 and Chelsea Festival Week Mon-Fri June 19-23 (12-5). For NGS Suns April 2, Oct 29 (2-6)*

101 Cheyne Walk, SW10 (Malcolm Hillier Esq) *Situated to the W of Battersea Bridge.* Long and narrow, strongly layered with a structure of evergreen hedges and topiaries. A colonnaded Mediterranean terrace with many containers leads to a winding path set about with old roses and perennials. A romantic arbour surrounded and covered by perfumed plants surveys the whole length of the garden. **Evening Opening** *Thurs June 15 (6-8) £3.50. Wine and food. Private visits welcome for parties of 5 and over, please* **Tel 020 7352 9031**

10 Chiltern Road, Pinner (Mrs G & Mr D Cresswell) *Eastcote. Off Cheney St and Barnhill/Francis Rd which link Cuckoo Hill/Eastcote High Rd (B466) with Bridle Rd/Eastcote Rd. Please park in Francis Rd.* Plantswoman's garden ⅓-acre, mature trees, mixed shrubs and herbaceous plantings many propagated for sale. TEAS. *Adm £1.50 Chd free. Suns April 16, June 11, Aug 6 (2-5)*

Chiswick Mall, W4 *Station: Stamford Brook (District Line). Bus: 27, 267,391 and 190 to Young's Corner from Hammersmith through St Peter's Sq under A4 to river. By car A4 Westbound turn off at Eyot Gdns S, then R into Chiswick Mall. Sun June 11 (2-6)*

Eyot Cottage, W4 (Mr & Mrs Peter Trumper) Two interconnecting gardens, both with beautiful river frontage. One an old walled garden recently re-planted with many unusual white plants and shrubs. The other an upper terrace garden laid out by the owners with imaginative use of old stones and pavers. *Adm £1 Chd 50p.*

16 Eyot Gardens, W6 (Ms Dianne Farris) Small town garden. Front garden planted white, blue and yellow. The back shows what can be done with a small space, by using the walls for yr-round interest. Terrace, fountain and garden art. TEAS. *Adm £1 OAPS 50p Chd free.*

Lingard House, W4 (Rachel Austin) A walled garden divided into a brick courtyard and terrace with a huge acacia tree; a formal lawn with miniature pond and water-spout and unusual herbaceous planting. A wire-work pergola reveals a wild garden with ancient apple trees, climbing roses and beehive. *Adm £1 Chd free.*

Morton House, W4 (Mr & Mrs M Manser) A ⅓-acre walled garden with lawns, yew hedges and mixed planting. Much loved but belonging to people who are rather short of time and who have enthusiastically over-planted. *Adm £1 Chd 50p (ACNO to West London Action for Children).*

Swan House, W4 (Mr & Mrs George Nissen) An informal walled garden, considerably replanted 4yrs ago within an established framework. Herbaceous border, fruit trees, small vegetable garden. *Adm £1 Chd 50p.*

51 Cholmeley Crescent, N6 (Ernst & Janet Sondheimer) *Highgate. Between Highgate Hill and Archway Rd, off Cholmeley Park. Nearest tube Highgate.* Approx 1/6-acre garden with many alpines in screes, peat beds, tufa, troughs and greenhouse; shrubs, rhododendrons, camellias, magnolias, pieris, ceanothus etc. Clematis, bog plants, roses, primulas, treeferns. Water features. Alpines for sale. TEA. *Adm £1 Chd 50p. Sun April 30 (2-6). Private visits welcome, please* **Tel 020 8340 6607**

Choumert Square, SE15 *Via wrought iron gates off Choumert Grove. Peckham Rye station is visible from the gates, and buses galore (12, 36, 37, 171, 312, 78, 63, 345) less than 10 mins walk. Free car park 2 mins.* As seen on 'Gardeners' World'! About 46 mini gardens with maxi-planting in a Shangri-la situation that the media has described as a 'Floral Canyon', which leads to a small communal 'secret garden'. TEA. *Adm £2 Concessions £1.50 Chd 50p. Sun June 4 (2-6)*

Chumleigh Multicultural Garden, SE5 (Southwark Council) *Situated midway along Albany Rd which runs between Old Kent Rd and Camberwell Rd. Nearest tube Elephant & Castle; buses P3, 42.* Constructed around almshouses (erected in 1821 by the Friendly Female Soc) now a Parks Visitor Centre. Walled garden, nearly 1 acre divided into English, Oriental, African and Carribean, Islamic and Mediterranean styles. Many unusual plants incl tree fern, jelly palm, rice paper plant. Formal and informal water features. TEAS. *Adm £1. Sun July 16 (10-6)*

17 Church Lane, SW19 (Mr & Mrs P Kelly) *200yds S of the Kingston Rd, 10 mins walk from both Wimbledon (Main line and District line) and South Wimbledon (Northern line) stations.* A garden designer's own garden, this 50 × 10m suburban plot comes complete with well disguised air-raid shelter and is divided into a number of distinct sections: terrace with child safe water feature, oriental courtyard, lawn and borders, vegetable garden and children's play area. A strict geometry is softened by effusive planting. Soon to be featured in Sainsbury's magazine and on Gardeners' World. TEA. *Adm £2 Chd free. Sun May 7 (10-4)*

26 Claygate Road, W13 (Ms Sawyer & John Bishop Esq) *Easy walk from Northfields Station (Piccadilly Line). Buses E2 & E3. Situated between Northfield Ave and Boston Manor Rd. 5min drive from junction 2 of M4.* Colourful front garden leading to imaginative award winning (3 times winner in Ealing in Bloom competition) small (33′ × 21′) back garden which maximises space in unusual and quirky ways. An abundance of climbing roses interplanted with clematis. Fruit trees, miniature pond with goldfish, fountain, raised herb garden, a profusion of beautiful pots, window boxes, hanging baskets, small lawn and herbaceous borders. TEAS. *Adm £1 Chd free. Sun June 4 (2-6)*

13 College Cross, N1 (Diana & Stephen Yakeley) *Station: Highbury and Islington. Bus: 4,19,30,43,104,279 to Highbury Corner or Islington Town Hall. A1 runs through Canonbury Sq.* Prize-winning walled garden behind a Georgian terrace house, 5m x 17m, enclosed by evergreen climbers with bamboo, bay, box, olive and fig trees. Paved areas with architectural plants chosen for form and texture in shades of green. Large pots of white flowers incl lilies, oleander and brugmansia. Featured in 'The Garden' Sept 1998. *Adm £1.50 Chd 75p. Sun July 23 (2-6). Also open with* **Islington Gardens** *Sun June 11 (2-6)*

2 Cottesmore Gardens, W8 (The Marchioness of Bute) *From Kensington Rd turn into Victoria Rd. (Cottesmore Gardens on R after Stop St)* A wide range of trees, shrubs and plants concentrating on foliage shapes and unusual plant material. TEA. *Adm £2.50 Chd £1 (ACNO to Winter Garden Trust). Sun Aug 6 (2-5)*

NEW **41 Cranleigh Road, SW19** (Brian O'Reardon) *1¼m S of Wimbledon off B286 (Martin Way). Tube: Morden 10mins; rail S Merton 5mins; bus 164 to S Merton.* Paved terrace with pots of tender specimen plants. Steps leading to Mediterranean garden with large pond and hard landscaping flanked by deep borders full of shrubs and perennials. Leads to the English garden with old roses and colour co-ordinated beds around a circular lawn. This leads to the sheltered garden with fruit, herbs, camellias, ferns, a waterfall and wildlife pond. TEA. *Adm £1 Chd 50p. Sun July 9 (2-6)*

NEW **24 Croom's Hill, SE10** ✿ (Mrs Elizabeth Noble) *Croom's Hill runs down side of Royal Park. 5 mins walk Greenwich station BR Docklands Light Railway and buses 177, 180, 199. House is on pedestrian crossing near bottom of hill. Entrance in Gloucester Circus which runs LH-side of house via stables.* Formal walled C17 garden incorporating old stables separated by wrought iron railings, arched gate with steps down to lawn, brick and york stone patios. Half-moon shaped herbaceous border, very imaginatively planted to complement curved patios. Lots of topiary, flowering shrubs, ornamental trees. Beautiful large fountain. Labour saving innovations on view. Evergreens offset a mass of colour and are strictly shaped. Property Listed Grade II (not open). TEAS. *Adm £1.50 Chd 70p. Sun July 16 (2.30-6.30)* **Floodlit Opening** *(8.30-10.30) £2.50. Wine.*

133 Crystal Palace Road, SE22 ✿ (Sue Hillwood-Harris & David Hardy) *East Dulwich. Buses 176, 185, 12.* The addition of a pergola has subtly changed the character of this inspirational 17′ × 36′ Victorian garden created around a weathered brick terrace (once the garden wall). Roses, wisteria, clematis, shrubs, herbs, spectacular tree fern and shade-loving plants combine in formality tempered by wilful indiscipline. Featured by Gay Search, Express on Sunday, European and Japanese magazines. TEAS. *Adm £1 (ACNO to Amnesty). Suns May 21, Aug 6 (2-6).* **Evening Opening** *Wed June 21 (6.30-9) £2.50. Wine. Private visits welcome* **Tel 020 8693 3710**

Culverden Road Gardens, SW12 *Station: Balham and Tooting Bec.* No 68 designed and planted by two garden designer owners. TEAS. *Combined adm £3 Chd £1. Sun May 21 (2-6)*

68 Culverden Road (Back) (Nick Branwell) S facing, backing onto Tooting Bec Common, with terrace, summer house, and many unusual and architectural plants in beds and pots.

68 Culverden Road (Front) (Nick Ryan) A transformed parking space with raised brick beds, seating area, circular paving in granite setts and extensive use of trelliswork and architectural plants.

82 Culverden Road (E Powell) Long S facing garden which backs onto Tooting Bec Common. There are five areas in the garden: terrace and formal pond; lawn with mixed shrub and herbaceous borders; informal pond surrounded by a yew hedge; cottage garden area (herbaceous plants and vegetables); and an orchard and woodland area with large compost bins. Front garden in traditional style

De Beauvoir Gardens, N1 *Islington-Hackney border. Adm £1 Chd 50p per garden. Sun June 25 (2-6)*

132 Culford Road (Mr & Mrs J Ward) *Underground Victoria Line to Highbury & Islington. 30 and 277 bus from Highbury and Islington, bus stop in St Pauls Rd. 38 bus from Angel Islington. Alight at Alms Houses bus stop in Balls Pond Rd, cross over and walk down Culford Rd. 132 is near junction with Englefield Rd.* Garden is approx 100′ × 30′. Recently laid out in 'rooms'. Sunken area close to house shingled with many pots, sinks and scented plants. Pergola over paved area with clematis, vine and honeysuckle. Kitchen garden and raised bed at rear of garden. Emphasis on climbing plants and shrubs. Several areas for sitting, eating and dreaming.

158 Culford Road (G M Breen) *See above.* Small town garden (15′ × 85′) with country feel. Winding path with surrounding herbaceous borders, which include shrubs, small trees and wide variety of perennial plants.

51 Lawford Road (Mrs Carol Lee) *Lawford Rd (formerly called Culford Rd) is a cul-de-sac with entrance for cars from Downham Rd. Parking fairly restricted. Downham Rd runs between Kingsland and Southgate Rd. Buses Kingsland Rd 149, 243, 22A/B and 67, Southgate Rd 141 and 76.* A small garden 16′ × 45′ at rear of a typical Victorian terraced house. Bricked with different levels, lots of pots and a pond with waterfalls. Hostas, ferns and anything that will grow in a pot. TEAS. *(ACNO to National Deaf Children's Soc).*

68 Mortimer Road (Mr A Harman & Mr J Norton) *2m N of Liverpool St Station (mainline and tube). Buses 149 and 242. By car off Downham Rd.* A large town garden 90′ × 30′. A mix of formal and informal, created since 1994, lots of places to sit and enjoy different aspects. *Private visits welcome, please* **Tel 020 7923 0706**

26 Northchurch Road (Mrs Kathy Lynam) *Angel tube then Buses 38, 73, down Essex Rd, alight bus stop after Essex Rd Station just before Northchurch Rd. Cross over and proceed down Northchurch Rd (petrol stn on corner) to lower end near church. House on L.* Walled back garden, approx 70′ × 30′ with 2 old apple trees, greenhouse and lawn, mixed borders with clematis, roses and lots of perennials. Places to sit and ponder. TEA. *Private visits welcome, please* **Tel 020 7254 8993**

36 Downs Hill, Beckenham ✿❀ (Marc & Janet Berlin) *2 mins from Ravensbourne Station near top of Foxgrove Rd.* Long ⅔-acre E-facing garden sloping steeply away from the house. Ponds and waterfalls with patio garden. Over 100 pots. Wooded area. Greenhouses. Dense planting. Varied collection of trees, shrubs and flowers. *Adm £1 Chd free (ACNO to NSPCC). Suns May 7, July 2, Oct 8 (2.30-5)*

Dulwich Gardens, SE21 ✿❀ *Mainline trains to N and W Dulwich then 15mins walk, or tube to Brixton then P4 bus passes both gardens. Combined adm £3 Chd free. Sun June 18 (2-5)*

103 Dulwich Village ✿❀ (Mr & Mrs N Annesley) About ½-acre country-garden-in-London. Long herbaceous border, spacious lawn, ornamental pond, roses and many and varied other plants, plus vegetable patch. TEAS. Gate to next door garden

105 Dulwich Village (Mr & Mrs A Rutherford) About ½-acre, mostly herbaceous with lawns and lots of old-fashioned roses. Shrubbery, ornamental pond, water garden. A very pretty garden with many unusual plants

20 Eatonville Road, SW17 ❀ (Pamela Johnson & Gethyn Davies) *Tooting. 400yds from Tooting Bec tube (Northern Line). Bus stop Trinity Rd nr Police Station. Nos 249, 219, 349 or 155 and 355 on Balham High Rd at tube station.* Garden designer's own 42' x 23' S facing garden. Open again after a short break and a few changes. Many unusual and tender plants making the most of the city's micro-climate. A garden designed to be used as an outside room. TEAS with delicious homemade cakes. *Adm £1.50 Chd free. Sun July 9 (2-6)*

Eccleston Square, SW1 ♿✂❀ (Roger Phillips and the Residents) *Off Belgrave Rd near Victoria Station, parking allowed on Suns.* 3-acre square planned by Cubitt in 1828. The Garden Committee has worked over the last 18 years to see what can be created despite the inner city problems of drought, dust, fumes, shade and developers. The garden is sub-divided into mini-gardens incl camellia, iris, rose, fern, and container garden. A national collection of ceanothus incl more than 70 species and cultivars is held in the square. Featured on TV in 'The 3,000 Mile Garden'. TEAS. *Adm £2 Chd £1. Sun April 2 (2-5)*

9 Eland Road, SW11 ✂❀ (Mrs Nancye Nosworthy) *Battersea. Off Lavender Hill backing onto Battersea Arts Centre. G1, 345, 77 and 77a buses stop at top of st. Clapham Junction Station nearby and bus 137 Queenstown Rd.* 50' courtyard on slopes of Lavender Hill. Terraces with tender shrubs, woodland plants and spring bulbs; a pergola covered in vines and pool with fountain. *Adm £1 Chd free. Sun April 16 (2-5)*

Elm Tree Cottage, S Croydon ✂ (Ms Wendy Witherick & Michael Wilkinson Esq) *85 Croham Rd, off B275 from Croydon, off A2022 from Selsdon 64 Bus Route.* A gently sloping plantsperson's garden with fine views of Croham Hurst and Valley. The garden is full of unusual roses, perennials, climbers and shrubs. Pond and bog garden in pots. Unsuitable for those unsteady on their feet and pushchairs. Featured on BBC Gardeners' World. Newly designed front garden. *Adm £2 Chd free. Suns April 30, May 14, June 4, 18, July 2 (2-5). Private visits welcome, please* **Tel 020 8681 8622**

The Elms, Kingston-on-Thames ✂❀ (Prof & Mrs R Rawlings) *1m E Kingston on A308. Kingston Hospital and Norbiton mainline station 100yds. Enter via Manorgate Rd at foot of Kingston Hill.* 55' × 25' garden owned by 'plantaholic'! Trees, shrubs, climbers, herbaceous and ground cover plants, some rare. Pool, fruit trees and soft fruits. Roof garden not open on NGS public days. Featured on television and in many publications. TEAS. *Adm £1.50 Chd 50p (ACNO to Terence Higgins Trust/Home Farm Trust). Sats, Suns March 11, 12; April 8, 9; May 6, 7 (2-5). Private groups min 10 persons please* **Tel 020 8546 7624**

Elmsdale Road Gardens, E17 ✂❀ *Walthamstow Central underground (Victoria Line) and mainline station (from Liverpool Street). 10 mins walk via High Street and Erskine Rd. Buses include 2, 20, 34, 48, 58, 69, 212, 215, 251, 257, 275, 505, 551, W11, W15 to Walthamstow Central & 123 along Forest Rd. Parking permits not required on Sundays although spaces likely to be very limited. Free car park in Palmerston Rd.* A group of seven, evolving, informal East End gardens backing onto late Victorian houses with open aspects. Each garden has something different to offer including unusual plants and bulbs, shrubs, climbers, herbaceous plants, some grasses and old roses, a fruit tunnel and small water features. Home made TEAS. *Combined adm £2.50 Chd 50p. Sun May 7 (2-6)*

15 Elmsdale Road (Monica Scarfe)
17 Elmsdale Road (Cristina Franchi & Peter Argall)
18 Elmsdale Road (Kate & Don Gorman)
20 Elmsdale Road (Mel Watson)
38 Elmsdale Road (Valerie Allport)
NEW **55 Elmsdale Road** (Jean Duggelby)
NEW **48 Erskine Road** (Catherine Ross)

NEW **14 Farm Avenue, NW2** ✂ (Mrs Christine Winterburgh) *Buses 113, 13, 28, 82, 245, 260. Off Cricklewood Lane near Hendon Way (A41). Cricklewood station (Thameslink). Easy parking.* Informal garden planned for yr-round interest. Packed, colourful borders of shrubs and herbaceous perennials and terrace with pots. Interesting front garden with lavender hedge. TEAS. *Adm £1.50 Chd free. Sun July 9 (2-6)*

▲ **Fenton House, NW3** ✂❀ (The National Trust) *300yds from Hampstead Underground. Entrances: top of Holly Hill and Hampstead Grove.* Recently created timeless 1½-acre walled garden. Laid out on 3 levels, garden rooms contain imaginative plantings concealed by yew hedges. The herbaceous borders have been planned to give yr-round interest while the brick-paved sunken rose garden provides a sheltered hollow of scent and colour. The formal lawn area contrasts agreeably with the rustic charm of the kitchen garden and orchard, where a water-spout trickles tranquilly in the background. A new Vine House built in 1998. *For NGS* **Evening Opening** *Thurs June 8 (6.30-8.30). £3 Chd 50p. Wine*

The Ferry House, Old Isleworth ♿❀ (Lady Caroline Gilmour) *By car (coaches by prior arrangement) follow signs to Syon Park parking available inside gate on L. By bus 267 from Hammersmith, 37 from Richmond.* 3 acres of mature gardens. Terrace with urns and troughs filled with unusual plants. Old-fashioned roses, climbers, shrubs and perennials edge the lawn leading down to lovely views of the Thames. Adjacent garden with herbaceous borders, avenues, groups of shrubs with backdrop of fine old trees in Syon Park. Shaded sitting areas. Vegetable and fruit cage. Home made TEAS. *Adm £2.50 OAPs £1.50 Chd 50p. Sat, Sun June 10, 11 (2-6). Open in the Spring by appt only. Please* **Tel 020 8560 6769** *Groups at other times by appt only. Adm £4*

73 Forest Drive East, E11 ✂❀ (A J Wyllie Esq) *Leytonstone. Into Whipps Cross Rd, then SW into James Lane. 1st L into Clare Rd, 1st R into Forest Drive East. By bus to Whipps Cross Hospital or tube to Leytonstone and bus to James Lane.* 20' × 65' country garden in miniature, but with full-sized plants, behind a terraced house. Small lawn with mixed borders leading to a shrub and woodland area. 2 fountains and various unusual plants. Also 20' square front garden informally planted round formal paths and centrepiece. TEA. *Adm £1.50 Chd 50p (ACNO to The Margaret Centre, Whipps Cross Hospital). Sun Aug 13 (11-5)*

Frogmore Gardens, Windsor Tues May 16 (10.30-7 last adm 6). See Berkshire

5 Garden Close, SW15 ♿✂ (Mr & Mrs T Jestico) *off Portsmouth Rd, 7-10 mins walk from the Green Man Public House, via Wildcroft Rd Putney Hill.* ¼-acre walled garden which serves as a backdrop to architect's all glass house (not open). Oriental inspiration with black bamboos, and swathes of box, hebe, lavender and rhododendrons. Ponds and timber decks surround the house. *Adm £1.50. Suns May 21, July 2 (11-5)*

22 Gayton Road, NW3 ✂ (Mr & Mrs C Newman) *From Hampstead underground station turn L down Hampstead High St, Gayton Rd 1st on the L.* Small Victorian brick paved garden 60' x 20' with shrubs, roses, climbers, tiny pond, plants in containers. *Adm £1.50 Chd 50p. Sun July 9 (2-5)*

29 Gilston Road, SW10 ✂ (Margaret & James Macnair) *Gilston Rd leads N from Fulham Rd to the Boltons.* Small front garden and long back garden (85′ × 35′). Many spring bulbs, flowering currant, viburnum, early clematis and camellias. *Adm £1.50. Sun April 16 (2-5.30)*

70 Gloucester Crescent, NW1 ✂ (Lucy Gent & Malcolm Turner) *Nr junction Gloucester Crescent and Oval Rd 600yds SW of Camden Town tube station.* A square in front; a triangle at the side; a wedge at the back. Strong geometry on the ground plays off against extensive plant interest. *Adm £1.50 Chd 50p. Suns April 16, July 16 (11-3). Private visits welcome, please* **Tel 020 7485 6906**

51 Gloucester Road, Kew ✂❀ (Mrs Lindsay Smith) *10 mins walk from Kew Gardens tube station. Travel towards S Circular along Leybourne Park Rd, cross main rd, down Forest Rd 1st L into Gloucester Rd. House halfway down on R.* A small square cottage garden. Many interesting plants and shrubs. Wallflowers and bulbs in spring. TEA. *Adm £1.50 Chd 75p. Sun May 7 (2-5)*

114 Gloucester Road, Kingston ♿✂❀ (Mr R Knight) *1m E of Kingston off A308 (Kingston Hill): follow signs to Kingston Hospital, and garden is 400yds SW. Buses to Kingston Hospital: LT 213, 85, 57, K3, K5, K6, K8, K10 and 131 Wimbledon to Kingston stop 'Cambridge Flats'. 5 mins from Norbiton Station.* An 1/8-acre densely planted suburban garden, with some century-old trees. Re-designed by Gillian Temple to improve management, and to increase the habitats to include aquatic, bog, scree, rock, woodland, patio-container areas and trellises. Emphasis on form and foliage. Hardy geraniums, euphorbia and persicaria sp. and some rarer plants. Herbs, kitchen and fruit garden, greenhouse. TEAS. *Adm £1.50 Chd 50p (ACNO The New Masonic Samaritan Fund). Sats, Suns June 10, 11, July 8, 9 (2-6). Private visits welcome, please* **Tel 020 8286 8830**

Goldsborough Tudor Grange, SE3 ♿✂❀ *114 Westcombe Park Rd, Blackheath.Nearest mainline station Westcombe Park (10 mins walk) or Maze Hill (15 mins walk). Buses to the Standard from Central London and surrounding areas. Car parking available.* Community garden for close care and nursing home residents. Approx ½ acre of landscaped gardens, incl walkways of rose-covered pergolas; fish ponds; herbaceous borders and colourful annuals. A very sheltered and peaceful garden. TEAS available. *Adm £1 Chd 50p. Sun June 18 (2-5)*

NEW **8 Grafton Park Road, Worcester Park** ✂❀ (Robin Green & Ralph Cade) *Off A3. From A240 (Kingston to Epsom) take slip road signed Worcester Park. R at the Hogsmill Inn, L at next junction, Grafton Rd. Park in Grafton Rd. Grafton Park Rd is 1st on L.* California hits London suburbia. Situated on a steep slope 50' x 50'. Much use of gravel, railway sleepers and unusual garden features. Over 300 pots in many shapes and plantings. Inspired planting in hot and cool borders including many different and unusual plants. Tiny vegetable garden hides behind 'sun trap' deck and 'beach hut'. TEAS. *Adm £1.50 Chd 50p. Sun July 9 (1-5).* **Evening Opening** *Wed July 5 (6-9) £2.50. Wine and light refreshments*

1 Grange Park, W5 ♿✂ (David Rosewarne Esq & Ms Magie Gray) *Off Warwick Rd at the SW corner of Ealing Common.* Artists 100′ × 50′ woodland garden, relaxed planting giving a strong sense of design and form using textural surfaces and pattern making, creating a sense of magic and intimacy. Terraced, with fountain well, twigloo, a dingley dell, enchanters and spirit catchers. Organically gardened with an emphasis on drought tolerant planting and love. *Adm £2 Chd free. Suns April 30, June 4 (2-6)*

5 Greenaway Gardens, NW3 ✂ (Mrs Marcus) *Off Frognal Lane. Tube (½ mile) Hampstead or Finchley Rd stations. Buses: Finchley Rd, West End Lane stop, nos. 13, 82, 113.* A country garden in the heart of the city, combining formal and informal features on three levels: terrace with climbing plants; water feature and swimming pool; large lawn surrounded by herbaceous borders planted for yr-round interest in drifts of colour: mauve and silver, red, yellow, orange, pink and white. Hundreds of varieties of summer flowering herbaceous perennials, roses and shrubs including many traditional cottage garden plants. Partially suitable for wheelchairs. TEAS July 16 only. *Adm £1 Chd free. Suns May 14, June 18, July 16 (2-6)*

7 The Grove, N6 ♿✂ (Thomas Lyttelton Esq) *The Grove is between Highgate West Hill & Hampstead Lane. Stations: Archway or Highgate (Northern Line, Barnet trains) Bus: 210, 271, 143 to Highgate Village from Archway, 214 from Camden Town.* ½-acre designed for maximum all-yr interest with its variety of conifers and other trees, ground cover, water garden, vistas, 19 paths, surprises. TEAS. *Adm £1.50 OAPs/Chd £1. Suns March 26, June 11, Sept 24 (2-5.30). Private visits welcome, please* **Tel 020 8340 7205**

Hall Grange, Croydon ♿✂ (Methodist Homes) *Situated in Shirley Church Rd near to junction with Upper Shirley Rd. From N leave A232 at junction of Shirley Rd and Wickham Rd. From S leave A212 at junction of Gravel Hill and Shirley Hills Rd.* The garden, laid out circa 1913 by Rev W Wilks secretary to RHS, comprises 5 acres of natural heathland planted with azaleas, rhododendrons, heathers and shrubs and is unchanged. Parking nearby. TEA. *Adm £1.50 Chd free (ACNO to Methodist Homes). Sun May 21 (2-5)*

109 Halsbury Road East, Northolt Park ✂❀ (Don & Wendy Fuller) *Nearest underground Sudbury Hill. L out of station, first L Cavendish Avenue. Turn L at the end, over small bridge and first R.* Prize winning town garden (160′ × 40′). Herbaceous and mixed borders giving yr-round interest, particularly delightful in spring and summer. New white border and seating area. Over 100 hardy geraniums. Many unusual plants grown and propagated for sale. *Adm £1 Chd free (ACNO to Greater Ealing Old People's Home). Suns April 16, May 7, 21, June 4, July 2 (2-5)*

▲ Ham House, Richmond (The National Trust) *Mid-way between Richmond and Kingston W of A307 on the Surrey bank of the R Thames. Signposted with National Trust signs.* Restored C17 garden, gravel terrace, pots, paths dividing eight large grass plats; wilderness; parterre. Rose garden; C17 borders. TEAS. *Adm House and Garden £5 Chd £2.50 Family ticket £12.50 Garden only £1.50 Chd 75p. For NGS Sun April 16 (10.30-6)*

116 Hamilton Terrace, NW8 (Mr & Mrs I B Kathuria) *5mins walk from Maida Vale tube station, next to St Marks Church. Buses 16, 16a, 98.* Large formal front and back garden on different levels, yorkshire stone paving, large pots and containers, wide variety of flowering shrubs, climbers, clematis, iris, roses, hostas, hebes, lawn. Winner of Hampstead garden competition 1998 and 1999. TEAS. *Adm £2 Chd 50p (ACNO to St Marks Repair Appeal). Suns May 28, July 16 (2-6). Private visits welcome by appt please* **Tel 020 7625 6909**

117 Hamilton Terrace, NW8 (Mrs K Herbert & the Tenants Association) *Hamilton Terrace, where there is room for parking, is parallel with Maida Vale. Buses from Marble Arch 16, 98 go to Elgin Avenue which is near.* This is a large garden, part of the back is kept wild and there is a tiny garden in memory of Dame Anna Neagle, who lived in the house. Garden photographed by Channel 4, won a bronze medal from the London Gardens Society. TEA. *Adm £1.50 Chd 20p (ACNO to the SCOPE). Suns May 28, July 23 (2-6)*

11 Hampstead Way, NW11 (Mr & Mrs R L Bristow) *Nearest tube station Golders Green, 10 min walk up North End Rd, L into Wellgarth Road, R up Hampstead Way.* 1/4-acre prize winning garden on two levels, unusual plants around lawns in the front; at the back, woodland garden, lawn and large patio with water features and pots. TEAS. *Adm £1.50 Chd 50p. Sun May 14 (2.30-6)*

133 Haverstock Hill, NW3 (Mrs C Horwood) *Belsize Park tube station turn L out of station. Buses C11, C12, 168 (Haverstock Arms stop).* Prize-winning 120ft long narrow garden divided into rooms. Packed planting of old and English roses, clematis, cottage garden perennials from balconied terrace to 'secret garden'. Pond and pots with many unusual tender perennials and scented plants. Featured in 'Country Life' and 'Homes and Gardens'. *Adm £1.50 Chd 50p. Sun June 11 (2-5.30)*

37 Heath Drive, NW3 (C Caplin Esq) *Station: Finchley Rd; buses: 82, 13 & 113 Heath Drive.* Many uncommon plants; lawn; pond; rockery; bamboos; ferns. Large compost heap. Unusual treatment of fruit trees, greenhouse and conservatory. Unusual plants for sale incl bamboos. Eight times winner of Frankland Moore Cup. TEAS. *Adm £2 Chd 50p (ACNO to Royal Marsden). Suns May 14, July 16 (2.30-6)*

NEW **767 Hertford Road, Enfield** (Maria Miola & Cyril Cleary) *From London: Travel N on A1010 (Hertford Rd) towards Waltham Cross. House on RHS just before junction with Mandeville Rd and Gun & Magpie public house. From M25: exit 25 signposted A10 London. 1st L at traffic lights to Freezywater, onto Bullsmoor Lane. In 1m at traffic lights R into Hertford Rd. Buses: 310, 279 to Mandeville Rd.* A young, evolving town garden approx 90' x 20'. At the side there is a long, shady, raised border containing ferns, climbers etc. The main garden is lawn with mixed herbaceous borders, an arbour, small water feature and varied collection of plants in pots. An arched trellis leads to a vegetable plot with fig tree. TEAS. *Adm £1 Chd 50p. Sun May 21 (2-6)*

Highgate Village, N6 *The Grove is between Highgate West Hill and Hampstead Lane Stations: Archway or Highgate (Northern Line, Barnet trains). Bus: 210, 214, 271, 211 to Highgate Village.* TEAS at 5 The Grove. *Adm £3 for 3 gardens, £1.50 each garden Chd/OAP £2 for 3 gardens or £1 each garden. Sun June 11 (2-5)*

4 The Grove (Cob Stenham Esq) 2-tiered with formal upper garden; view across Heath; orchard in lower garden

5 The Grove (Mr & Mrs A J Hines) Garden on 2 levels. *(ACNO to local Scouts)*

7 The Grove See separate entry

Highwood Ash, NW7 (Mr & Mrs R Gluckstein) *Highwood Hill, Mill Hill. From London via A41 (Watford Way) to Mill Hill Circus; turn R up Lawrence St; at top bear L up Highwood Hill; house at top on R. Stations Totteridge and Whetstone or Edgware (Northern Line). Stanmore (Jubilee Line) Arnos Grove (Piccadilly Line). Bus 251 to door.* 3¼-acre incl rose garden, shrub and herbaceous borders, rhododendrons, azaleas, lake with waterfall, new terrace with raised herb garden, a mixture of formal and informal. TEAS. *Adm £1.50 Chd 50p (ACNO to The North London Hospice). Sat, Sun May 13, 14 (2-6)*

5 Hillcrest Avenue, NW11 (Mrs R M Rees) *Hillcrest Ave is off Bridge Lane. By bus to Temple Fortune, Buses 82, 102, 260. Nearest tube Golders Green or Finchley Central. Walk down Bridge Lane.* Small labour-saving colourful garden with many interesting features; rockery, fish pond, conservatory, tree fern. Secluded patio, auriculum theatre. Cypressus, Sempervirens. Prize-winning Mediterranean front garden. Photographed for Japanese magazines. TEAS. *Adm £1.50 Chd 50p (ACNO to ADS). Sun June 18 (2-6).* **Evening Opening** *Wed June 21 (6-9) £2.50. Wine. Private visits welcome, please* **Tel 020 8455 0419**

16 Hillcrest Road, E18 (S Killingback Esq) *N from London on A11 (Woodford High Rd) L into Hillcrest, last lamp on L. S from M25 or North Circular, R into Grove Hill R twice into Hillcrest. From South Woodford station (Central Line). Short walk W uphill.* Small suburban garden dedicated especially to the display of over 14,000 tulips in rows, over 300 different varieties. Featured in Garden Answers, the Oldie and the Independent. *Adm £1 Chd 50p (ACNO to Emma Killingback Memorial Fund). Sun April 16 (2-6)*

1 Hocroft Avenue, NW2 (Dr & Mrs Derek Bunn) *113, 245, 260, 82 and 13 buses. Cricklewood Thames Link*

station. *Easy parking.* Prize-winning garden with yr-round interest, especially in the Spring. Front garden shown on BBC Gardeners' World, in their Front Garden series. Mixed borders in the back garden with a wide variety of plants. Subject of an article by Tony Venison in Country Life focusing on plant sales in the NGS. Home made TEAS. *Adm £1.50 Chd free (ACNO to Hampstead Counselling Service). Sun, Mon April 30, May 1 (2.30-5.30)*

11 Hocroft Road, NW2 ✗ (Mr & Mrs R Graham) *2nd L off Hendon Way (A41) from Finchley Rd. Buses 113, 13, 28, 82, 245 & 260.* An organic ½-acre, formal garden on 3 levels, enclosed by tall yew hedges and designed for all-yr interest and easy maintenance. Large lawns bordered by roses, perennials and evergreens; long paths and architectural features create colourful vistas. Ornamental pond, small orchard and vegetable garden. Pergolas create a stunning clematis and rose walk. Cream TEAS. *Adm £2 Chd free (ACNO to Wednesday's Child). Mon May 1 (2.30-5.30)*

Holly Cottage, 40 Station Road, Hampton ✗ (Ms M Cartwright) *Buses 267 and 68 to Hampton Church. From river end 5 mins walk. Buses 111 and 216 pass the house. Alight Police Station 100yds. Hampton mainline station 5mins.* The long secluded front garden is planted for winter and spring interest and leads on to a pretty paved cottage garden (30′ × 25′). Densely planted, it contains many hardy geraniums, pond, separate water feature, and mistletoe grown on an old apple tree. TEA. *Adm £1 Chd 50p. Sat/Sun June 10, 11, Sun July 23 (2-5)*

The Holme, NW1 ♿✗ (Lessee of The Crown Commission) *Inner Circle, Regents Park opp Open Air Theatre. Nearest tube Regents Park or Baker St.* 4-acre garden filled with interesting and unusual plants. Sweeping lakeside lawns intersected by islands of herbaceous beds. Extensive rock garden with waterfall, stream and pool. Formal flower garden with unusual annual and half hardy plants, sunken lawn, fountain pool and arbour. *Adm £2.50 Chd £1. Sats, Suns May 6, 7, Aug 19, 20 (2.30-5.30)*

125 Honor Oak Park, SE23 ✗❀ (Mrs Heather West) *Near South Circular (A205) and Honor Oak Park rail station.* Multifarious, frothy plant collection on 2 levels: the lower a shady dell with informally planted box-edged parterre; the upper sunny with grass, pond, conservatory, verandah and pots flanked by even more pots on wide, stone steps. (Reviewed in Homes and Gardens July 1998). Strawberry cream TEAS (Sun only). *Adm £1.50 Chd 50p Sun June 25 (2-6).* **Evening Opening** *Sat June 24 (6.30-8.30) £2.50 incl wine*

239a Hook Road, Chessington ♿ (Mr & Mrs D St Romaine) *A3 from London, turn L at Hook underpass onto A243 Hook Rd Garden is approx 300yds on L. Parking opp in park. Bus 71, K4 from Kingston and Surbiton to North Star public house.* Garden photographer's garden. 1/4-acre developing garden divided into 2. The flower garden contains a specimen Albizia julibrissin, a Robinia hispida, and a good mix of herbaceous plants, shrubs and climbers. Also a gravel garden, rose tunnel and pond. The potager divided by paths into small beds has many vegetables, soft fruit, fruit trees,

and herbs all inter-planted with flowers. TEAS. *Adm £1.50 Chd 50p. Sun Aug 6 (2-6)*

NEW 10A Hoveden Road, NW2 ✗❀ (Ian Brownhill & Michael Hirschl) *Nearest tube stations are Kilburn and Willesden Green, then 15 min walk. Hoveden Rd is the 1st road on the RHS from the junction of Cricklewood Broadway and Walm Lane. Buses stop on Cricklewood Broadway: 16, 32, 189, 226, 245, 260, 266 and 316.* A small (70′ x 25′) intimate garden recently transformed from a concrete wasteland. Constructed around a box-edged circular lawn, deep beds are filled with a wide range of plants incl alliums, hydrangeas, roses, ornamental grasses, hardy geraniums, as well as other cottage garden favourites. Other features of the garden incl a long 'moat-like' pond, a gazebo, obelisks and many containers. *Adm £1.50 Chd 50p. Sun May 21 (2.30-6).* **Evening Opening** *Fri July 14 (6-9). £2.50. Wine*

Hyde Vale Gardens, SE10 *Greenwich. Parking is allowed at the top of Hyde Vale and in the Royal Hill car park. From Greenwich BR station turn L towards town centre. Turn R on Royal Hill just before Pelican crossing. Turn L at 4th street (Hyde Vale). No parking outside residences.* TEAS. *Combined adm £2.50. Sun July 16 (2-5)*

> **31 Hyde Vale** (Alison & John Taylor) Small semi-formal garden featuring sunny terrace with climbers, box and many pots.
>
> **51 Hyde Vale** (Jane Baker) Architect-designed Italianate N facing garden (20′ x 60′) behind terraced house. Very vertiginous steps requiring great care.

Islington Gardens, N1 ✗❀ *Station: Highbury and Islington, King's Cross. Bus: 4, 19, 30, 43, 104, 279 to Highbury Corner or Islington Town Hall. 17, 91, 259 to Caledonian Rd. A1 runs through Canonbury Sq. Combined adm £4 or £1.20 each garden Chd £2 or 60p each garden. Sun June 11 (2-6)*

> **37 Alwyne Rd** ♿✗❀ (Mr & Mrs J Lambert) *Buses 38, 56, 73, 171A up Essex Rd.* Bordering the New River and its recently restored gardens. Views over the river and the park would make you think you are in the country; an enclosed formal garden reminds you that you are in town. Old-fashioned roses, topiary, white and silver bed, hollies. TEAS
>
> **13 College Cross** See separate entry
>
> **4 Mountfort Crescent** ♿ (Ms Bridget Barker) *Off Barnsbury Square (unmade rd).* Garden landscaped in 1995, already surprisingly mature. 92′ × 41′. Evergreen and architectural plants give yr-round interest. Hybrid musk and English roses, box edging, topiary and cistus. Phormiums and euphorbias provide mixture of yellows and greens opposite terrace. Good ground cover planting. TEAS
>
> **36 Thornhill Square** (Mr & Mrs C McKane) Prize-winning 120′ long informal garden, with unusual herbaceous plants and shrubs in curved beds giving a country garden atmosphere. Clematis and old roses, incl a rambler covering the Wendy House. Unusual plants for sale. TEAS. *(ACNO to St Mary's Church).*

26 Kenilworth Road, SE20 ✗❀ (Mr & Mrs S Clutson) *Approx 1m from Beckenham or Crystal Palace. 5mins walk from Kenthouse mainline station. Buses go along Beckenham*

Rd Nos 227, 176, 194, 312 & 726. Access to garden via a passageway between Nos 20 and 22 Kenilworth Rd. Small 35′ × 18′ back garden on two levels, designed in 1985 by present owners with ease of maintenance and young family in mind. Circular paved and gravelled areas planted with many Mediterranean native shrubs, perennials and bulbs in a profusion of purple, pink and white. Garden featured on BBC Gardeners World May 1999. TEAS. *Adm £1 Chd free (ACNO to Brittle Bones Society). Sun June 4 (2-5.30).* **Evening Opening** *Sat June 17 (6-8.30) £2.50. Wine. Other times by appt* **Tel 020 8402 9035**

Kentish Town Gardens, NW5 *Kentish Town and Tufnell Park tube stations and buses C2, 135, 134, 214. Combined adm £1.50 Chd £1 or Adm each garden £1 Chd 70p (ACNO to Quaker Peace and Service). Sun June 4 (2-5.30)*

55 Falkland Road (Ms C Bateman) *By car approach from Lady Margaret Rd or Montpelier Grove.* Small walled garden 40′ × 20′ plus raised shade bed. A cottage-style garden crammed with plants

9 Montpelier Grove, NW5 (S Fielden & R Harper) *Off Lady Margaret Rd. Parking in street (no restrictions).* Narrow 60′ garden behind terrace house. Designed for use by family with working parents. Variety of plants for interest and backdrop of greenery. Colour co-ordination and combination of particular interest. **Evening Opening** *Thurs June 15 (6-9) £2.50. Wine*

38 Killieser Avenue, SW2 (Mrs Winkle Haworth) *5 min walk from Streatham Hill mainline station. Buses 159, 137, 133 to Telford Avenue. Killieser Ave 2nd turning L off Telford Ave.* Exuberantly planted, romantic, 90′ × 28′ garden featured in numerous Japanese books. Contains many unusual perennial plants, violas and viticella clematis. Classical rose arch, obelisk, Gothic arbour and water feature. Top terrace redesigned with parterre. TEAS. *Adm £1.50 Chd 50p. Sun May 14, June 18 (2-6). Private visits welcome for 5 or more, please* **Tel 020 8671 4196**

Lambeth Community Care Centre, SE11 *Monkton Street. Tube or buses to Elephant and Castle, cut behind Leisure Centre to Brook Drive. Turn into Sullivan Rd at Bakery, passage to Monkton St. Buses 3, 109, 159 or drive (ample parking) to Kennington Rd; at The Ship public house turn into Bishop's Terrace, 1st R to Monkton St.* ⅔-acre garden. Mixed shrubs, trees, small rose garden, herbs, interesting walkways and mixed borders. Prize winner in London Hospital Gardens Competition. TEAS. *Adm £1 OAP/Chd 50p (ACNO to Community Health, S London Charitable Fund). Sat, Sun June 3, 4 (2-5)*

15 Langbourne Avenue, N6 (R P St J Partridge) *Holly Lodge Estate. Off Highgate West Hill. Entrance by car via Swains Lane.* A steeply rising garden behind a semi-detached house, full of dramatic foliage and contrasting textures. Dicksonia antarctica, hardy palms, yuccas, tetrapanax, phormiums, ferns, bamboos and many exotic rarities create an impression of seclusion and mystery in a small area. *Adm £1.50. Sun July 16 (2.30-5.30). Private visits welcome* **Tel 020 8340 5806**

12 Lansdowne Rd, W11 (The Lady Amabel Lindsay) *Holland Park. Turn N off Holland Park Ave nr Holland Park station; or W off Ladbroke Grove ½-way along. Bus: 12, 88, GL 711, 715. Bus stop & station: Holland Park, 4 mins.* Medium-sized fairly wild garden; border, climbing roses, shrubs; mulberry tree 200 yrs old. *Adm £2 Chd £1. Wed May 17 (2-6)*

10 Lawn Road, NW3 (Mrs P Findlay) *Tube to Belsize Park or go up Haverstock Hill. Turn R at Haverstock Arms then L. House 200yds on R, with blue door.* Small garden with uniquely curvaceous design of intersecting circles, set in rectangular format. Organically cultured, very heavily stocked; many unusual and native species plants. *Adm £1.50 Chd 75p. Sun June 11 (2.30-6)*

15 Lawrence Street, SW3 (John Casson Esq) *Between King's Rd and the river parallel to Old Church St. Nearest tubes: Sloane Square and South Kensington. Buses 11, 19, 22, 211, 319, 49.* Prize-winning small Chelsea cottage garden (featured in Secret Garden Walks): 12 different camellias (April), clematis, roses, herbaceous perennials and shrubs; all-yr-round interest; some unusual plants. House (built c1790), not open except for access to garden. *Adm £1.50 Chd free (ACNO to Chelsea Physic Garden). Sun April 2, Sat July 22, Sun July 23 (2-6)*

Leyborne Park Gardens, Kew *2 min walk from Kew Gardens station. Take exit signposted Kew Gardens. On leaving station forecourt bear R past shops. Leyborne Park is 1st rd on R. Bus 391, R68 to Kew Gdns station. Bus 65 to Kew Gdns, Victoria Gate. Access by car is from Sandycombe Rd.* TEAS. *Combined adm £1.50 Chd free (ACNO to Arthritis and Rheumatism Council for Research). Sun June 18 (2-5.30)*

38 Leyborne Park (Ann & Alan Sandall) 120ft long garden; lawn with mixed borders; containers; long established vine; many unusual herbaceous plants; irises, peonies, bamboos; plants for the dry garden.

40 Leyborne Park (Debbie Pointon-Taylor) 120ft long garden; lawn and mixed borders; collection of herbaceous geraniums; clematis; mature shrubs; conifers; patio with containers.

1 Lister Road, E11 (Myles Challis Esq) *Leytonstone underground station (central line). 5 mins to High Rd Leytonstone. Hills garage marks corner of Lister Rd which is directly off High Rd.* Garden designer's unexpected, densely planted sub-tropical garden containing a mixture of tender plants such as daturas, gingers, cannas, tree ferns, bananas and hardy exotics incl gunneras, bamboos, cordylines, phormiums and large leaved perennials in a space unbelievably only 40′ × 20′. *Adm £1 Chd 50p. Sun Aug 6 (11-5)*

21a The Little Boltons, SW10 (Mrs D Capron) *Between Fulham and Old Brompton Rd off Tregunter Rd. Nearest tube Earls Court, buses C1, 14, 74.* Prize winning 70' x 40' herbaceous plant collection. Portrayed in House and Garden Magazine and Private Gardens of London. *Adm £1.50 Chd free. Suns April 16, June 25 (2-6)*

Little Lodge, Thames Ditton (Mr & Mrs P Hickman) *Watts Rd (Station 5 mins). A3 from London; after Hook underpass turn L to Esher; at Scilly Isles turn R towards Kingston; after 2nd railway bridge turn L to Thames Ditton village; house opp library after Giggs Hill Green.* A cottage-style informal garden. Many British native plants. An atmosphere of tranquillity, featuring plants with subtle colours and fragrance; small brick-pathed vegetable plot. TEAS. *Adm £1.50 Chd free (ACNO to Cancer Research). Sun June 4 (11.30-6).* **Evening Opening** *Wed June 14 (6.30-9) £2.50. Wine and light refreshments. Private visits welcome, please* **Tel 020 8339 0931**

London Buddhist Centre, 51 Roman Road, E2 *Bethnal Green tube, few minutes walk eastwards along Roman Rd at junction of Roman Rd and Globe Rd. Entrance on Globe Rd.* Courtyard and roof garden on two levels. Roses, lilies and other plants in containers. Steep steps unsuitable for those unsteady on feet. TEAS. *Adm £1 (ACNO to The Karuna Trust). Sun June 18 (2-6)*

22 Loudoun Road, NW8 (Mrs Ruth Barclay) *3 to 4 min walk to St. John's Wood tube station. Lies between Abbey Rd and Finchley Rd serviced by buses, a few mins from bus stop.* A strong emphasis on design; water; arbour garden within a garden. Back Italianate courtyard, romantic and mysterious. Interesting water features, incl grotto with water cascading down mussel shells surrounded by ferns and tree ferns. Prizewinner for 4 consecutive years. Featured in numerous books and voted one of 5 best town gardens in the UK by The Independent. TEAS. *Adm £2 Chd 50p. Sun June 4 (2-6)*

9 Lower Teddington Road, Hampton Wick (Mrs Elsa Day) *5 mins from mainline train (Waterloo) to Hampton Wick. Buses 281, 285, 111, 216, 411, 416 to High St. From A308 at roundabout take A310 (Twickenham) then R fork at 'Swan' public house. No 9 is 6th house on the L. Close to R Thames, Kingston and Hampton Court.* Small walled garden laid to gravel and brick on different levels, includes a water feature (rill) small bog area, herb bed, climbers, fruit and vegetables in containers as well as numerous perennials. Garden undergoing some changes this year. TEAS. *Adm £1.50 (ACNO to MIND). Sat, Sun June 24, 25 (2-6). Private visits welcome by appt, please* **Tel 020 8977 4786**

Lyndhurst Square Gardens, SE15 *5min walk NW from Peckham Rye station. Reduced service on Sunday. No 36 bus from Oval tube or no 171 from Waterloo. Park in nearby streets. Combined adm £2 Chd £1. Sun June 4 (2-5.30)*

1 Lyndhurst Square, SE15 (Ms Josephine Pickett-Baker) Recently designed, 80' x 40' walled garden. Formal layout with lawn, flower beds, mosaic, gravel and flagstones. Sunken terrace with herb garden in retaining wall. Plants in terracotta containers. Evergreen, slightly tropical looking structure to planting, with perennials planted through and around. More foliage than flowers. Many unusual plants. Sitting areas in sun or shade. TEAS

3 Lyndhurst Square, SE15 (Stephen Haines Esq) Sophisticated cottage garden approx 80' × 50' Old roses, herbaceous borders, many climbers on house and in garden, sunken garden with fountain and container planting, surrounded by mature trees

Malvern Terrace, N1 *Barnsbury. Approach from S via Pentonville Rd into Penton St, Barnsbury Rd; from N via Thornhill Rd opp Albion public house. Tube: Highbury & Islington. Bus: 19, 30 to Upper St Town Hall.* Unique London terrace of 1830's houses built on site of Thos Oldfield's dairy and cricket field. Cottage-style gardens in cobbled cul-de-sac. Victorian plant stall. Home-made TEAS. Music. *Combined adm £2 Chd free (ACNO to Alzheimers Disease Society) Sun June 11 (2-5.30)*

A selection of gardens in Malvern Terrace

NEW **2 Melina Place, NW8** (Mr & Mrs G A Yablon) *No parking in Melina Place which is just off Grove End Road, but on single yellow lines in nearby roads is permissible. St John's Wood tube station (Jubilee line) is 6 mins away and buses 139, 189, 82, 113, 16 all run nearby.* Walled town garden with country feel surrounding Regency house (not open). Also newly planted courtyard garden. Good selection of herbaceous, shrubs and climbers. Formal and informal planting. Homemade TEAS. *£1.50 Chd 50p. Sun July 16 (2.30-6)*

13 Mercers Road and the Coach House, N19 *Off Holloway Rd (A1) N of Odeon Cinema. Combined adm £2 Sun July 2 (2-6)*

The Coach House (Mr B Quinlan-West) . Situated at the rear of the main house, with a small ornamental garden pond housing around 100 gold fish and koi carp plus two large terrapins, a rockery area with a variety of seasonal plants provides colour all through the year

13 Mercers Road (Dr & Mrs N Millward) 30' × 15' front garden featuring whites, greys and greens. 30' × 20' rear garden on two levels. Profusion of pastel shades from April to Sept. Many small-flowered clematis, pink Schizophragma, Dregea sinensis and other interesting climbers and perennials. *Private visits welcome for small groups and individuals, please* **Tel 020 7281 2674**

NEW **85 Merton Hall Road, SW19** (Gay & Jonathan Gray) *200 yds N of Kingston Rd, 15 mins walk from Wimbledon (mainline and District line) and South Wimbledon (25 mins walk, Northern line). Buses 152, 163, 164 to Nelson Hospital at Kingston Rd end of road.* Totally redesigned and planted in 1998 by Gay Wilson this 9m x 28m garden has distinct areas; a terrace with solanum and wisteria planted arbour, a circular lawn edged with small overflowing borders, and a Mediterranean garden with pebble mosaic and child safe pool, all densely planted in peaceful, cool colours for yr-round interest within a strong structure. TEAS. *Adm £2 Chd 50p (ACNO to Sturts Farm Community of The Sheiling Trust). Sun May 7 (2-6)*

2 Millfield Place, N6 *Garden is off Highgate West Hill, E side of Hampstead Heath. Buses C2, C11, C12 or 214 to Parliament Hill Fields.* 1½-acre spring and summer garden with camellias, rhododendrons, many flowering shrubs and unusual plants. Spring bulbs; herbaceous borders; small orchard; spacious lawns. TEAS (May only). *Adm £2 Chd 50p, large family group £5 Sun May 7 (2-6).* **Evening Opening** *Thurs July 20 (5.30-9). Adm £2.50. Wine*

NEW **38 Minterne Avenue, Southall** (Iris Clarke) *From A40 follow signs for Greenford to Norwood Green. 2nd R off Tentelowe Lane. From A4 Windmill Lane from Gillette corner. Nearest tube Osterley but no bus direct from here. 120 bus runs from Hounslow to Shepherds Bush.* Pretty suburban garden 100ft x 40ft with mature trees, shrubs, climbing roses, over 50 clematis, terrace with pots; courtyard area; cottage garden feel. TEAS. *Adm £1.50 Chd free. Sun June 18 (2-5)*

Moleshill House Cobham Sun May 21 (2-5). See Surrey

NEW **82a Mortimer Road, N1** ♿ (Mrs Elizabeth Haines) *North London line BR station: Dalston. Nearest bus 76, next nearest those on Kingsland Rd and Southgate Rd.* 28yds x 14yds town garden - lawn, beds with shrubs, herbaceous and bedding plants, bulbs. Patio and small pond. TEAS. *Adm £1.50 Chd 50p. Sun June 25 (2.30-5.30)*

▲ **Museum of Garden History, SE1** ♿✲❀ *Lambeth Palace Rd. Bus: 507 Red Arrow from Victoria or Waterloo, (C10 only on Sundays) alight Lambeth Palace.* 7,450 sq ft. replica of C17 garden planted in churchyard with flowers known and grown by John Tradescant. Tombs of the Tradescants and Admiral Bligh of the 'Bounty' in the garden. Opened by HM the Queen Mother in 1983. Museum being established in St Mary-at-Lambeth. The new garden at The Ark, 220 Lambeth Road, also open. TEAS. *Adm £2 OAPs/Chd 50p for both gardens. (ACNO to Museum of Garden History). For NGS Sun June 4 (10.30-5)*

Muswell Hill Gardens, N10 ✲ *Combined adm £1.50 or £1 each garden Chd free. Sun July 9 (2-5)*

5 Cecil Road, N10 (Ben Loftus Esq) *Just off Alexander Park Rd between Muswell Hill and the North Circular Rd.* 70′ × 20′ garden designer's peaceful garden; old apple trees, roses, euphorbias, masses of lilies, paeonies, hellebores, ferns, bulbs and evergreens; many scented plants, rich and varied foliage, pond, decking, unusual plants in containers. Garden recently much altered. Featured by Gay Search in Sainsbury's magazine

83 Grove Avenue, N10 ❀ (Mr & Mrs M Williams) *Just off Alexandra Park Rd by library.* Previous grass and concrete 'garden' newly designed and planted 1997/98. Back 120′ × 25′, mixed flower borders incl old roses, clematis and penstemons, fruit and vegetables, pond, pergola and patios. Front 30′ × 25′, woodland planting for mainly spring/early summer interest. Gardened organically. TEAS.

■ **Myddelton House Gardens, Enfield** ♿✲❀ (Lee Valley Park) *Bulls Cross. Junction 25 (A10) off M25 S towards Enfield. 1st set traffic lights R into Bullsmoor Lane, L at end along Bulls Cross.* 4 acres of gardens created by E A Bowles. Gardens feature diverse and unusual plants incl national collection of award winning bearded irises. Large pond with terrace, two conservatories and interesting historical artefacts. TEAS and plants for sale on NGS days. *Adm £1.90 OAPs £1.30. Suns and Bank Hols April 23-Oct 29 (2-5). Open Mon-Fri (except Xmas hols) (10-4.30). For NGS Suns Feb 27, May 28, July 30 (Feb 25 2001)*

NEW **Natural History Museum Wildlife Garden, SW7** ♿✲ *Cromwell Road, S Kensington. 5mins walk from S Kensington tube station.* The Museum's garden was designed and created in 1995 to show a range of typical habitats found in lowland Britain. These incl deciduous woodland, meadow, chalk downland, fen and heathland. The areas are linked by meandering paths and 3 ponds provide a central focus. Despite its central London location the garden has already attracted an impressive and varied amount of wildlife, which is being monitored by Museum staff and volunteers. *Adm £2 Chd free. Suns April 16, July 2 (2-5)*

17a Navarino Road, E8 ✲ (John Tordoff Esq) *Situated between Dalston and Hackney and connects Graham Rd with Richmond Rd. Buses 38, 22A, 22B, 277, 30.* A formal Italian garden of clipped box and yew; rambler roses over arches and a pergola; Japanese garden, with a large informal pond, tea house, ornamental bridge, and miniature Mount Fuji. Plantings of azaleas, acers and bamboo *Adm £1.50 Chd 50p. Suns May 7, July 16 (12-5). Private visits of ten or more welcome, please* **Tel 020 7254 5622**

263 Nether Street, N3 ♿✲ (Mr & Mrs Malcolm Wiseman) *Turn L from W Finchley tube. House is on the L, 2mins along the rd. Parking in roads off Nether St. House is directly facing Penstemon Close.* A sculptor's garden, designed and planted as an outdoor gallery. Toes, noses and hands peep out unexpectedly between smaller plants whilst lush, dramatic foliage acts as a backdrop to life-size sculpture. Exciting water features are camouflaged to surprise unsuspecting visitors whilst mirrors and turf are used to extraordinary effect. A garden to delight and stimulate visitors, incorporating art, horticulture and a certain amount of irreverent fun and frivolity. Garden lit at dusk. Music. *Adm £4.50. Wine and food.* **Evening Opening** *Sats June 3, 10 (7-10)*

NEW **Nightingale, 105 Nightingale Lane, SW12** ♿✲❀ *7 mins walk from Clapham South tube station (Northern line) or 10 mins walk from Balham tube station. A 7 min walk from Wandsworth Common BR station. Also served by buses G1690 and G1689.* Beautifully designed and landscaped gardens at England's largest residential home for the elderly. Whilst still in the early stages of development, the gardens greatly enhance a superb Grade II Victorian listed building. Koi carp pond, rose gardens, 'safe' garden for the frail and a wide variety of plants and shrubs. This is a delightful environment for inspiration and to enjoy tea and cakes in a glorious setting. TEAS. *Adm £2 Chd £1. Sun July 2 (2.30-5.30)*

15 Norcott Road, N16 ✲❀ (Mr & Mrs J Welch) *Buses 73, 149, 76, 67, 243. Clapton, Stoke Newington, Rectory Rd stations (Rectory Rd closed Suns).* Largish (for Hackney) walled back garden. Pond, herbs, herbaceous plants especially irises, geraniums and campanulas. TEAS. *Adm £1 Chd 50p (ACNO to St Joseph's Hospice). Sat, Sun June 10, 11 (2-6)*

North Ruislip Gardens, Ruislip ✲❀ *Combined adm £2 Chd free Sun June 11 (2-5.30)*

235 Eastcote Road, Ruislip (T & J Hall) *From Ruislip High Street take the B466 (Eastcote Rd) nearest tube Ruislip Manor. Parking off Eastcote Rd in Evelyn Ave please.* Medium sized surburban garden 115′ × 80′. Contains a wide variety of unusual herbaceous perennials and shrubs. Grasses, hostas, ferns, many propagated from the garden for sale. A number of small 'garden rooms'. 2 small ponds, numerous containers.

Home made TEAS and preserves. *Private visits welcome, please* **Tel 01895 677925**

82 Evelyn Avenue, Ruislip ⊗ (Mr & Mrs Ken Morgan) *Nearest underground station Ruislip Manor. Turn R out of station. Continue up and over the hill; cross the Eastcote Rd and turn 1st R into Evelyn Ave.* Surburban garden 40′ × 170′. Curving borders and island beds planted with shrubs and herbaceous plants to give yr-round interest. Lawns and mature trees

2 Northbourne Road, SW4 ⊗ (Mr & Mrs A Holmes) *Clapham Common tube. Buses 137, 137A, 37.* W-facing, walled garden 36′ × 56′ with good architectural planting and rose pergola. Featured in Sainsbury's Magazine and Japanese home interest magazine. Sunken patio with interesting container planting, wall fountain and fire salamander mosaic. 'Knot' garden to front of house maturing nicely. Garden designed by Judith Sharpe. TEAS. *Adm £1.50 OAPs/Chd 75p (ACNO to the Foundation for the Study of Infant Deaths). Sun June 11 (2-6)*

NEW **80 Old Charlton Road, Shepperton** ⊗❀ (Mrs Marie-Elaine Houghton) *Old Charlton Rd is an extension of Shepperton High St. 5 mins walk from Shepperton station - regular trains from London Waterloo.* 150' x 20' long garden built in 1997 divided into colour-themed rooms incl small Mediterranean-style courtyard, patio garden with raised pond surrounded by gold borders, drought-tolerant gravel garden planted with ornamental grasses and silver-leaved plants, and fruit and vegetable garden. Featured in the Daily Telegraph. *Adm £2 Chd 50p (ACNO to RNLI). Suns June 4, July 2, Aug 13 (11-5). Private visits welcome, please* **Tel 01932 242216**

Orchard Cottage, Bickley Sun July 23 (2-5.30). See Kent

Ormeley Lodge, Richmond ⊗ (Lady Annabel Goldsmith) *Ham Gate Avenue. From Richmond Park, exit at Ham Gate into Ham Gate Ave. 1st house on R. From Richmond A307, 1½m past New Inn on R, first turning on L. House is last on L. Bus: 65.* Large walled garden in delightful rural setting on Ham Common. Newly designed formal garden, wide herbaceous borders, box hedges. Walk through to newly planted orchard with wild flowers. Vegetable garden. Secluded swimming pool area, trellised tennis court with roses and climbers. TEA. *Adm £2 Chd 50p. Sun June 18 (3-6)*

▲ **Osterley Park House, Isleworth** ♿❀ (National Trust) *Jersey Rd, Isleworth. Access is via Thornbury Rd on N side of A4 (Great West Rd) between Gillette Corner and Osterley tube station. Follow brown tourist signs. Nearest station Osterley (Piccadilly Line). Car Park £2.50 (NT Members free).* Park with Regency-style pleasure grounds, Adam semi-circular garden house undergoing restoration with attractive herbaceous plantings. Private walled nursery and cut-flower garden open, with a chance to meet the gardeners. Interesting specimen trees, serpentine lakes and meadows rich in bird life. TEAS. *Adm by donation. For NGS Sun June 11 (11-4)*

Flat 1, 1F Oval Road, NW1 ⊗ (Sheila Jackson) *Tube station Camden Town. Buses: any bus to Camden Town, C2 and 274 stop very near.* A small side garden approaches an illustrator's hidden back garden 20' x 24' abutting the Euston railway line. A variety of plants, mainly in pots, are banked to create interesting shapes, making use of a variety of levels. This garden is the subject of the book 'Blooming Small, a City Dwellers Garden'. *Adm £1 Chd 50p.* **Evening Openings** *Thurs May 11, June 8 (6-9) or private visits welcome, please* **Tel 020 7267 0655**

39 Oxford Road, SW15 ♿⊗ (Jennifer Adey) *3 mins walk from E Putney Tube, off Upper Richmond Rd. Buses 14, 74 and 37.* Unusual small walled garden 40' x 50'. Formal box-edged design, mainly foliage. Arched walk covered with hops, small cobbled planted areas. Interesting summerhouse and imaginative views through wrought iron gates. *Adm £1 Chd 50p. Sun June 11 (2-6)*

71 Palace Road, SW2 (Mr & Mrs J Nieboer) *Tulse Hill mainline, Brixton tube. Buses 2A, 2B. By car enter Palace Rd from Norwood High St or Hillside Rd.* 45′ × 40′ front garden, formal and enclosed on a theme of blue and white. 90′ × 45′ rear garden laid out with herbaceous borders. New gothic brick summerhouse with newly planted box parterre echoing the gothic theme. Featured in Home and Gardens and on Japanese television. Art gallery featuring Elizabeth Parsons' work. TEAS. *Adm £1.50 Chd 50p. Sun June 18 (1.30-6).* **Evening Opening** *Wed June 14 (6-8.30) £2.50. Wine. Chd 50p.*

10A The Pavement, SE27 ❀ (Brendan Byrne Esq) *Chapel Rd. Located off Ladas Rd down alleyway behind All Seasons Fish Bar. Buses 68 to Knights Hill alight at S London College. No. 2 to Norwood bus garage. Mainline W Norwood. Come out Knights Hill, turn L. Chapel Rd is 10 mins walk on L after passing bus garage.* Smallest garden in London. A hidden oasis behind houses and shops. Country type of garden, mostly in containers. Shrubs, herbaceous, bedding, rare plants and herbs continually changing. Featured in 'The Observer', Sainsbury's magazine and Country Life. *Adm £1 Acc chd free with adult (ACNO to Horses & Ponies Protection Assoc). Sun July 16 (10-12, 2-6)*

174 Peckham Rye, SE22 ♿❀ (Mr & Mrs Ian Bland) *The house overlooks Peckham Rye Common from the Dulwich side. Reached by an alley to the side of the house.* 100' x 30' rear garden originally designed (and frequently changed) by Judith Sharpe - a recent Chelsea medallist - the garden is easy-care and child-friendly while displaying a wide variety of contrasting foliage and yr-round interest. Best in early June when the pink and blue flowers predominate. TEAS. *Adm £1.50 Chd free. Sun June 11 (2.30-5.30)*

NEW **Pembridge Cottage, Twickenham** ⊗ (Ian & Lydia Sidaway) *10 Strawberry Hill Rd. 1m from Twickenham town centre. Close to Strawberry Hill railway station. Strawberry Hill Rd is approached from Cross Deep or Waldegrave Rd bus 33, R68 or Hampton Rd bus 110, 267, 281, 290, 490. Easy parking.* 140' x 20' constantly evolving artist's garden with studio building. Divided into several brick, gravel and wooden seating areas. Strong evergreen shrub structure providing yr-round interest. Many thin Italian cypress, maples, trimmed and shaped box, lonicera, lavender, santolina, laurels and viburnum. Euphorbias, bamboo, herbs, ferns and gunnera. A packed garden influenced by Mediterranean,

Japanese and northern European styles. TEA. *Adm £1 Chd 50p. Sun June 11 (2-6)*

43 Penerley Road, SE6 ♿✂❀ (Mr & Mrs E Thorp) *BR stations Catford. Catford Bridge (15 mins walk). Many bus routes to Catford. Off A21 just S of S Circular Rd.* Plant lover's shady garden 33' x 100', with lots of interesting and unusual plants, many propagated for sale. Formal lawns, informal planting, paved areas with ferns, hostas and other foliage plants in pots. *Adm £1.50 Acc chd free (ACNO to The Lovemore Trust). Suns May 14, June 18 (2-5.30)*

Penn Road Gardens, N7 *Caledonian Rd underground. Turn L out of station and continue N up Caledonian Rd for approx 700yds. Penn Rd is on LH-side. Buses 17, 91, 259 along Caledonian Rd; 29, 253 to nearby Nags Head.* TEA. *Adm £1 each garden Chd free. Sun June 18 (2-6)*

2a Penn Road ♿ (Mr & Mrs P Garvey) 100′ × 30′ walled garden, plus long side-entrance border and small front garden; colourful, well-stocked borders, mature trees, containers, arches, vegetable garden. Prizewinner in local garden competition

6a Penn Road ✂❀ (Victoria & Garry Trainer) 100' x 25' old family garden with 100-yr-old arch rose. Over 20 varieties of clematis. Decked area.

35 Perrymead Street, SW6 ✂ (Mr & Mrs R Chilton) *Fulham. New King's Rd W from Chelsea; 1st on L after Wandsworth Bridge Rd. Stations: Fulham Broadway or Parsons Green; bus 22 from Chelsea; 28 from Kensington.* Small paved garden with ornamental feature; surrounded by mature trees. Shrubs, climbers (especially clematis) interspersed with summer planting suitable for shade. *Adm £1.25 Chd 60p. Sun July 9 (2-6)*

NEW **1 Pond Street, NW3** ✂ (Mrs Barbara Frost) *Nearest tube Belsize Park. Turn R on exit. Buses C11, 24, 46, 168, 268.* Large, overflowing L-shaped garden, divided into 3, reached via a sheltered courtyard with colourful containers, lemon and fig trees, herb troughs and water feature. Circular lawn bordered by an old stone path. Subtle use of colour in the beds with many unusual shrubs and perennials, roses, honeysuckles, clematis and other climbers. TEAS. *Adm £1.50 Chd 50p. (ACNO to Wednesday's Child). Sun June 18 (2-5.30)*

46 Preston Drive, E11 ✂❀ (Ms Teresa Farnham) *Wanstead central line tube. Walk down A12 N side. Preston Drive 1st on L after footbridge. House opp cricket pitch.* Garden designer's town garden 80′ × 20′. Secluded position between cricket pitch and allotments although only 8m from Marble Arch. Constantly changing as owner experiments. Emphasis on foliage. Pond. Limited use of recycled materials. TEAS. *Adm £1 Chd 50p. Sun Sept 10 (2-5). Private visits welcome, please* **Tel 020 8530 6729**

13 Queen Elizabeth's Walk, N16 ✂ (Lucy Sommers) *From Manor House tube go S down Green Lanes, then take 2nd L off Lordship Park.* 100′ × 23′ plantsperson's romantic garden continually evolving as new ideas on colour and form come to fruition each year. Many interesting shrubs, climbers and perennials in both sunny, and over the years, increasingly shady woodland areas. *Adm £1.50 OAP/Chd 75p. Sun Aug 6 (2-6). Private visits for groups of 6 or more by arrangement, please* **Tel 020 8802 1662**

NEW **62 Rattray Road, SW2** ✂ (Elspeth Thompson) *Near Brixton tube and BR station (5mins walk).* Very small (20' x 20') contemporary town garden on several levels. Decking, climbers, bamboo, acanthus, herb garden and vegetables in pots. New purple front garden just begun. Planting mostly purple, bronze, lime, white. TEA. *Adm £1.50 Chd 50p. Sun Aug 20 (2.30-5.30)*

Regents College's Botany Garden, NW1 ❀ *Regents Park. Located at the junction of York Bridge and the Inner Circle. Baker Street tube is 5 mins walk. Buses: 13, 18, 27, 30, 74, 82, 113, 139, 159, 274. Enter main gate or Garden Gate adjacent to footbridge at Clarence Gate.* Described as a Secret Garden, this former Botanic Garden has been sympathetically developed so as to retain its intrinsic charm and relaxed, naturalistic atmosphere. Garden areas flow together and host a diverse selection of plants. TEA. *Adm £1.50 OAPs/Chd £1. Sun May 21 (12-5). Private visits welcome, please* **Tel 020 7487 7494**

48 Rommany Road, SE27 ✂ (Dr B Barnes & R Stuart-Moonlight Esq) *Gipsy Hill mainline station. Buses 3, 322. Easiest access to Rommany Rd via Gipsy Rd.* A luscious small 30′ × 20′ walled town garden created in 1995 by present owners. Ferns and hostas lead towards the York stone patio and herbaceous borders. A vine and rose covered pergola forms the entrance to the rear secret garden with fountain and trachelospermum arch. Featured in BBC Gardeners World 1998. For benefit of all, max 15 persons at any one time. TEAS. *Adm £1 Chd 50p (ACNO to RNLI). Sun July 23 (1-6).* **Evening Openings** *Sats June 24, July 8 (6-8.30) £2.50. Wine*

Roots & Shoots, SE11 ♿❀ (Roots & Shoots Training Scheme) *Vauxhall Centre, Walnut Tree Walk. Tube: Lambeth North; Buses 159, 109, 3. Just off Kennington Rd, 5 mins from War Museum.* Mixed borders, plant nursery, ½-acre wildlife garden, large summer meadow, superb walnut tree, acacia dealbata, shrub roses and other unusual shrubs. TEAS. *Adm £1 Chd 50p (ACNO to Roots & Shoots). Sat, Sun May 27, 28 (11-4)*

167 Rosendale Road, SE21 ✂❀ (Mr & Mrs A Pizzoferro) *House at junction of Rosendale Rd and Lovelace Rd. Station Tulse Hill.* Back garden 100′ long backing onto allotments, featuring a stream (which runs naturally in winter), wildlife pond and bog garden bordered by a timber deck. Small woodland area at end of plot. Gravel and cobbles form the central part of the garden, surrounded by generous borders which include grasses, bulbs and perennials. Many plants in pots, incl a large collection of hostas and hemerocallis. The 40′ front garden has a hotter colour theme with a range of euphorbias. Plants in shingle and cobbles. TEAS. *Adm £1.50 Chd 50p (ACNO to London Children's Flower Society). Sun June 4 (2-6)*

35 Rudloe Road, SW12 ✂ (Judith Sharpe) *Directly off Poynders Rd (South Circular Rd). Bus 255 from Clapham Common to Pollards Hill, 5 mins walk from Clapham South station.* Tiny paved gem of a garden (32′ × 17′) 20 yrs in the making. There are mature specimens of Eupatorium ligustrinum, Euphorbia mellifera, Fargesia nitida, Ceanothus 'Concha', Rosa banksia 'Lutea', phormiums, myrtle, pittosporums etc, making control essential. Interesting container planting incl clerodendron, hoheria, melianthus, yucca and trachycarpus. This is a garden to be enjoyed even in the depths of winter. TEAS. *Adm £1.50 Chd 50p. Sun July 9 (2-6)*

7 St Albans Grove, W8 (Mrs E Norman-Butler) *Stations: Kensington High St or Gloucester Rd. Bus Milestone for 9, 46, 52, 72; Gloucester Rd for 49, 74. From Gloucester Rd turn into Victoria Grove then into St Alban's Grove.* A country garden designed for all seasons and one pair of hands, which won the Brighter Kensington Back Garden Cup several times and the Rose Bowl in 1998. *Adm £1.50 Chd 50p. Sun May 7 (2.30-6.30)*

7 St George's Road, Twickenham ✿❀ (Mr & Mrs R Raworth) *St Margaret's. Off A316 between Twickenham Bridge and St Margaret's roundabout.* ½-acre maturing town garden backing onto private parkland. Garden divided into 'rooms'. Unusual shrubs, clematis and old English roses. Large conservatory with rare plants and climbers. Parterre, new water feature, pergola, paved garden. Mist propagated specimens and unusual plants for sale. Featured in Penelope Hobhouse's 'Garden Style' and 'The Conservatory Gardener' by Anne Swithinbank. TEAS. *Adm £2 Chd 50p. Suns May 28, June 11 (2-6).* **Evening Opening** *Thurs June 1 (6-8) £3.50. Wine. Private visits welcome, please* **Tel 020 8892 3713**

St Michael's Convent, Ham ✿❀ (Community of the Sisters of The Church) *56 Ham Common. From Richmond or Kingston, A307, turn onto the common at traffic lights nr the New Inn, 100yds on the R adjacent to Martingales Close. Mainline trains to Richmond (also district line) or Kingston, then No 65 bus from either to Ham Common.* 4-acre walled organic garden. Bible garden and circle garden of meditation. Extensive herbaceous borders, two orchards, wildlife areas, working kitchen garden, vinehouse and ancient mulberry tree. Wheelchairs with difficulty. TEAS. *Collection Box. Sat June 17 (11-3)*

57 St Quintin Avenue, W10 ✿❀ (H Groffman Esq) *1m from Ladbroke Grove/White City Underground. From Ladbroke Grove station, bus 7 to North Pole Rd.* 30′ × 40′ walled garden; wide selection of plant material. Patio; small pond; hanging baskets; special features. Regular prizewinner in garden competitions. Featured on TV and in horticultural press. Special floral display for commemoration of HM the Queen Mother's 100th birthday. TEAS. *Adm £1.50 Chd £1. Suns July 16, 30 (2-7). Private visits welcome for parties of 10 and over, please* **Tel 020 8969 8292**

5 St Regis Close, N10 ✿❀ (Ms S Bennett & E Hyde Esq) *Muswell Hill. 2nd L in Alexandra Park Rd from Colney Hatch Lane. Tube: Bounds Green/E Finchley then bus.* Maureen Lipman's favourite garden. 'Inspirational'. Constantly evolving combination of humour, trompe l'oeil and tranquility. Features baroque temple, pagodas, ponds, waterfalls, lawns and abundant borders. Oriental colourful RAKU-tiled mirrored enclosure created by artist owners in garden studio, provokes imaginative container planting and conceals plant nursery. International press coverage. BBC Gardeners World. TEAS. *Adm £1.50 Chd 50p. Suns April 30, June 25, July 23 (2-7). Private parties of 10 and over by arrangement.*

Seymour Buildings, W1 ✿ (Seymour Housing Co-operative) *153/155 Seymour Place. Tube Edgware Rd, Marylebone, Baker St, Marble Arch, Marylebone mainline and numerous buses.* 150′ × 95′ garden surrounded by 4-6 storey buildings, constructed by Westminster Council in 1982, but has since been replanted. The sheltered microclimate enables marginally hardy species to thrive. Large pool with waterfall, raised beds, rock garden. Dense plantings incl bamboo, ferns, 11 trees, musa, arbutus, yuccas, acacias, cordylines, melianthus, helleborus and euphorbia. Emphasis on evergreen shrubs and architectural plants. Stairlift for wheelchairs. TEAS. *Adm £1.50 Chd £1 (ACNO to Terence Higgins Trust). Sun May 7 (2-6).* **Evening Opening** *Thurs June 22 (6-9) £2.50. Wine*

South End Road, NW3 ♿✿ *Hampstead tube station, Hampstead High St, bottom of Downshire Hill, South End Rd facing 'Freemason's Arms' public house.* A delightful prizewinning row of cottage front gardens, facing Hampstead Heath. Also pretty walled back garden with flowers, vine, figs and other fruit trees at 101 South End Rd. *Combined adm £3 Chd £1. Sun June 11 (2-6)*

95 South End Road (Ms Deborah Moggach)
97 South End Road (Dr Edward Brett)
101 South End Road (Mr & Mrs Paul Lindsay)

Southwood Lodge, N6 ✿❀ (Mr & Mrs C Whittington) *33 Kingsley Place. Off Southwood Lane. Buses 210, 271, 143, 214. Tube Highgate.* A romantic, hidden garden laid out last century on a steeply sloping site, now densely planted with a wide variety of shrubs, bulbs, roses and perennials. Pond, waterfall, frogs. Many unusual plants are grown and propagated for sale. Featured in Gardens Illustrated and Sunday Express Colour Magazine. *Adm £1.50 Chd 50p. Sun May 28 (2-6).* **Evening Opening** *Thurs June 22 (6-8.30) £2.50. Wine. Private visits welcome, April to July please* **Tel 020 8348 2785**

NEW **Tewkesbury Lodge Garden Group, SE23** *Off South Circular (A205) behind Horniman Museum and Gardens. Nearest station Forest Hill mainline or buses 176, 185, 312, P4 (10 mins walk).* Wine (June 3); TEAS (June 4). *Combined adm £4 (June 3); £3 (June 4).* **Evening Opening** *Sat June 3 (6-9); Sun June 4 (2-6)*

NEW **The Coach House, 3 The Hermitage** ♿✿❀ (Pat Rae) Sculptor's mature courtyard garden. Previously shown in 1980's. Crammed full of unusual plants and sculptures. New water-feature. Vegetables and decorative plants in containers large and small changing with the seasons.

NEW **27 Horniman Drive** (Rose Agnew) Small, low maintenance, N-facing front garden with a variety of shrubs creating a tapestry of green. Constantly evolving back garden with an emphasis on harmony of colour using perennials, roses and shrubs. Vegetable areas, greenhouse, views over S London and N Downs.

NEW **53 Ringmore Rises** ♿ (Valerie Ward) Corner plot with spectacular views over London. Newly created front garden inspired by Beth Chatto's dry garden, with stunning borders in soft mauves, yellows and white.

More mature rear garden on three levels. Differently themed beds, some shaded, others sunny. Large pond; patio with pergola. Limited access for wheelchairs. NEW **27 Westwood Park** ✗ (Jean Lawrence) Behind this 1930's house (not open) you will find a long narrow garden with classical lines. Beautiful restrained planting adds to an air of peace and tranquility. Small sunken garden; raised beds made from York stone. NEW **30 Westwood Park** ✗ (Jackie McLaren) Garden designer's sloping creation, herb garden, water features, winding paths with modern elements, unusual plant combinations. Every step you take in this intimate garden reveals a new delight in terms of planting and design. Many unusual pots and hanging baskets link patio and garden.

26 Thompson Road, SE22 ✗ (A Noel Esq) *A205 South Circular from Clapham Common, L into Lordship Lane, R into Crystal Palace Rd, 1st L into Landcroft Rd, 1st R Thompson Rd*. Anthony Noel, author, garden designer and creator of the legendary 17 Fulham Park Gardens, has re-designed his Dulwich garden. After a brief flirtation with gravel and highly-coloured urns, he has returned to the gentle, romantic style of town gardening (but still with a theatrical twist) that has made him famous. *Adm £2 OAP £1. Suns April 30, Sept 17 (2.30-6)*

64 Thornhill Road, E10 ✗ (Mr P Minter & Mr M Weldon) *Off Oliver Rd, near Leyton Orient football ground. Leyton underground 10 mins walk*. A town garden 165' × 30' developed over the last 5 yrs. Densely planted mixed borders framed by mature fruit trees surrounding formal lawns. Small woodland area under development. Many unusual varieties, roses old and new, crocosmia, canna, day lilies, dwarf conifer collection, late spring bulbs, flowering shrubs and pots give genuine yr-round interest. TEAS. *Adm £1.50 Chd 50p. Suns May 21, Aug 13 (2-6)*

27 Thorpewood Ave, SE26 ✗✿ (Barbara & Gioni Nella) *Just off the S circular (A205) turning up Sydenham Hill nr Hornimans gardens or Dartmouth Rd from Forest Hill. BR Station Forest Hill. Bus stop Thorpewood Ave nos 312, 122*. Mature tree bordered ½-acre garden on a gently sloping site. Interesting mixed borders with lots of shrubs, perennials and climbers. There is a formal vegetable plot and a gravel slope growing Mediterranean and alpine plants. The lawns and patio provide peaceful sitting areas. TEAS. *Adm £2 Chd free (ACNO to NSPCC). Sun June 11 (2-5.30)*.

Thrive, E2 ✗✿ (Horticultural Therapy) *St Mary's Garden. At the junction with Appleby St*. Fully accessible garden with herb and vegetable beds, raised beds, containers, herbaceous areas, pergola, woodland and meadows. Horticultural Therapy staff on hand for advice and information on accessible gardening, tools, techniques and therapeutic gardening. TEAS. *Adm £1 Chd free (ACNO to Thrive). Sat July 8 (11-3)*

Thrive, SW11 ✗✿ *(formerly the Horticultural Therapy Demonstration Garden). East Carriage Drive, Battersea Park, between athletics track and tennis courts.* ⅓-acre, fully accessible garden with heated greenhouse, wildlife meadow and pond; vegetable and herb gardens, raised beds and containers, herbaceous beds, pergola, raised pond and

seaside garden. Horticultural Therapy staff on hand for advice and information on accessible gardening, tools, techniques and therapeutic gardening. TEAS. *Adm £1 Chd free (ACNO to Thrive). Sun June 18 (11-6)*

103 Thurleigh Road, SW12 ✗✿✿ (Mr & Mrs Charles MacKinnon) *Clapham S tube station (Northern Line) 5mins walk*. A 80' × 90' walled garden surrounded by limes. Formal courtyard with box and lavender balances deep herbaceous borders and secret areas with dixonia ferns. Careful planting to minimise upkeep and to balance my dreams of Sissinghurst with our children's footballs. TEAS. *Adm £1.50 Chd 50p. Sun June 18 (1-6)*. **Evening Opening** *Wed June 21 (6.30-9) £2.50. Wine and light refreshments (ACNO to Queen Mary's Clothing Guild)*

● **Trinity Hospice, SW4** ✗✿✿ *30 Clapham Common North Side. Tube: Clapham Common. Bus: 37, 137, 35 stop outside*. 2-acre park-like garden restored by Lanning Roper's friends as a memorial to him and designed by John Medhurst. Ricky's sculpture a feature. TEAS. *Adm £1 Chd free. Sats, Suns April 15, 16; June 17, 18; July 29, 30; Sept 2, 3 (2-5)*

131 Upland Road, SE22 ✗✿✿ (Glenys Payne & Peggy Harvey) *Nearest mainline E. Dulwich or Peckham Rye*. Unusual, semi-oriental style rear stone garden, designed for effect and low maintenance. Tranquil ponds and waterfalls in a lush evergreen setting. Winding path of paddle stones passes 2 dinosaur eggs shaded by miniature umbrella tree. Side garden with bamboo walkway flanked by container planting over trellis work of clematis and ivies cascading over walls and windows. Enclosed front garden informally laid out with random paving, evergreen shrubs and climbing plants over wrought iron gate and fence. TEAS. *Adm £1 Chd 25p. Sun May 21 (2-5.30)*

7 Upper Phillimore Gardens, W8 ✗ (Mr & Mrs B Ritchie) *From Kensington High St take either Phillimore Gdns or Campden Hill Rd; entrance Duchess of Bedford Walk*. 100' × 35' garden; rockery, sunken garden; Italian wall fountain, ground cover planting, pergola. TEA. *Adm £1 Chd 50p. Sun April 16 (2.30-6)*

1 Vanderbilt Villas, Sterne Street, W12 ✗ (Dr Tim Leunig & Ms Julia Cerutti) *2nd L off N side of Shepherd's Bush Green, then first R. Buses 49, 72, 94, 95, 207, 220, 237, 260, 283, 295 & Central line tube: N via alley at W side of tube, then L*. Jason Payne designed and planted L-shaped garden. Genuinely small (max 20' × 20'), but densely planted with palms, banana, magnolia, albizia, phormiums, canna lilies and lots of climbers, this exotic sub-tropical garden is mature within three years of planting. Patio and pond: almost a conservatory without a roof! As seen on TV. NB size means queueing may be necessary, and garden is ill-suited to children. TEAS. *Adm £1. Sun Aug 13 (2-7)*

NEW **Waltham Forest Register Office, E17** ✗ (Waltham Forest Council) *Situated on corner of Grove Rd and Fraser Rd. By bus to Lea Bridge Rd, Bakers Arms and 5min walk up Fraser Rd*. Front and rear gardens of former Victorian vicarage in Walthamstow. Despite adverse conditions, a garden has been created as a backdrop for wedding parties. A walkway, planted with roses and passion flowers, leads to a honeysuckle and clematis arbour. Mixed borders and newly planted oak. TEA. *Adm 75p Chd 25p. Sun May 7 (2-5)*

NEW **58 Warren Road, Chelsfield** ❀ (Mrs Margaret Coppard & Richard Coppard) *From Orpington town centre, travel S along Sevenoaks Rd towards Green St Green. Approx 1m. Old Warren Rd is on L immediately after the pedestrian crossing. From Chelsfield Station, approx ½m W down Warren Rd.* A small, mediterranean inspired garden with many interesting features including drought tolerant trees and shrubs designed around a central water feature. Informal woodland retreat to front. TEAS. *Adm £1 Chd 50p. Sun July 2 (11-5)*

The Watergardens, Kingston-on-Thames (The Residents' Association) *From Kingston take the A308 (Kingston Hill) towards London about ½m on R turn R into Warren Rd.* Japanese landscaped garden originally part of the Coombe Wood Nursery, approx 9 acres with water cascade features. *Adm £2.50 OAP £1.50 Chd 50p. Suns May 7, Oct 15 (2-5)*

3 Wellgarth Road, NW11 ❀ (Mrs A M Gear) *Hampstead Garden Suburb. Turning off the North End Rd. Golders Green tube 6 mins walk. Buses, 268, 210.* A walk all round the house, swathe of grass with long borders of bushes, trees and climbers. Close planting, herbaceous beds, roses, heathers, lavenders: herbs, mints, some uncommon plants. Paving, pots, and old oak tree; small pond with bubbling water. Winner in Hampstead Gardens Competition 1999. Home-made TEAS. *Adm £1.50 (ACNO to St John's Hospice at the Hospital of St John and St Elizabeth, London). Sun June 11 (2-6)*

2 Western Lane, SW12 (Ms Anne Birnhak) *Clapham South or Balham underground stations, Wandsworth Common train and walk along Nightingale Lane. The Nightingale public house is on the corner of Western Lane. Drivers please park in Nightingale Lane.* Enchanting walled patio garden (21′ square) bursting with plants (50 different clematis and 30 different roses). Professionally designed and landscaped. Pergola, fountain, obelisks and loads of interesting containers. *Adm £1. Suns June 4, July 2, Aug 6 (2-5)*

10 Wildwood Road, NW11 ♿ (Dr J W McLean) *Hampstead. Wildwood Rd is between Hampstead Golf Course and N end of Hampstead Heath. From North End Rd turn by Manor House Hospital into Hampstead Way, then fork R.* Garden planned and maintained by owner; one of finest herbaceous borders in North London, pond, HT roses; owner-grown prize-winning delphiniums and seedlings. TEA. *Adm £1.50 Chd free. Sun July 9 (2-6.30)*

Wimbledon Gardens, SW19 *Train: from mainline/underground station 10 minute walk to first 2 gardens. Bus: 93 to top of Wimbledon Hill and walk along Ridgway or, for Somerset Rd, alight on Parkside at Calonne Rd; route 200 alight on Ridgway at Murray Rd and walk downhill. Maps showing shortest route between gardens will be available. Combined adm £3 for 3 gardens or per garden see below. Chd free. Sun June 11 (2-6)*

2 Denmark Avenue (Gillian Quenzer) Town garden (60' x 27') designed for relaxation. Small lawn dominated by a 30 yr-old magnolia tree. Informal shrub and flower beds plus annuals in season with sculptures by owner emerging from the plants and hanging on the wall by the veranda. *Adm £1*

3 Murray Road ♿ (Michael & Juliet Waugh) *On small corner site opp St John's Church.* Continuous narrow lawn curves round 3 sides of house, bordered by informal cottage garden planting of small shrubs, fruit trees, climbers and easily grown herbaceous and ground cover plants that can withstand dry soil. 2 small ponds. TEAS. *Adm £1*

21 Somerset Road ♿❀ (John & Ella Perring) Early Victorian house (not open) behind beech hedge, formal front garden and drive; yr-round planting. Partly walled rear garden with 2 fine specimen cedars which pre-date the house, shrubs, herbaceous, ground cover, plants climbing over pergolas and a small herb feature around a lawn with lots of pine needles in it! TEAS served in the conservatory. *Adm £1.50*

35 Wincanton Road, SW18 ❀ (Miss Helen Faulls) *Off Wimbledon Park Rd, Southfields tube. Bus 39.* Sunny garden in a conservation area. Created by densely planting a wide variety of shrubs and herbaceous plants, incl many from the southern hemisphere, within a strong design. Colour, form and flowers yr-round. Terrace enclosed by mixed planting and fences clothed with shrubs and climbers to form a luxuriant setting for outdoor living. Featured in Sainsbury's magazine and European and Japanese publications. *Adm £1 Chd 50p (ACNO to International Spinal Research Trust). Sun July 9 (1-6).*

47 Winn Road, SE12 ♿❀ (Mr & Mrs G Smith) *Lee. 8m SE central London. 15mins walk from either Lee mainline station (Sidcup line to Dartford) or Grove Park (Orpington line) from Charing Cross. By car, ½m from A20 Sidcup bypass or A205 S Circular.* ⅓-acre mature plantsman's garden maintained by owners. Mixed borders, alpine beds, fruit and vegetables; 3 greenhouses featuring displays of pelargoniums, fuchsias, begonias, cacti and succulents. TEAS. *Adm £1.50 Chd free (ACNO to The Fifth Trust). Suns April 16, June 18 (2-5)*

14A Wiverton Road, SE26 ❀ (Eric Mole Esq) *Bus 75 or 194 to Newlands Pk, Penge East 5mins walk, train from Bromley South, or from Victoria 2 per hr to Penge E station.* Small established garden of 50′ × 18′ over 80 varieties of camellias, alpines, acers, some geraniums and a pool. Strictly limited numbers of people in the garden at any one time. TEA or coffee and biscuits. *Adm £1. Sun May 28 (2-5). Any day by appt March to May, please* **Tel 020 8778 9693**

27 Wood Vale, N10 ❀ (Mr & Mrs A W Dallman) *Muswell Hill 1m. A1 to Woodman public house; signed Muswell Hill; Muswell Hill Rd sharp R Wood Lane leading to Wood Vale; Highgate tube station.* ¾-acre garden with herbaceous borders; ponds; orchard and kitchen garden. Unusual layout full of surprises. Numerous shrubs, roses, trees and conifers; greenhouses. Special millenium features. Visitors may also wander in neighbouring gardens, all of which are of high standard. TEAS. *Adm £1.50 Chd 50p under*

5yrs free (ACNO to British Legion and Union Church). Sat, Sun July 22, 23 (1.30-6)

66 Woodbourne Avenue, SW16 (Bryan D'Alberg & Keith Simmonds) *Enter from Garrads Rd by Tooting Bec Common. Easy parking.* Garden designer's garden constantly evolving. Featured in Sainsbury's magazine and Tessa Everleigh's book the 'Decorated Garden Room'. Cottage style front garden 40′ × 60′ containing roses, irises and herbaceous plants. Rear garden approx 40′ × 80′ created over the last 9 yrs features shrubs, trees, gazebo and pool, creating a tranquil oasis in an urban setting. TEAS. *Adm £1.50 Chd 50p (ACNO to Terrence Higgins Trust). Sun June 18 (1-6)*

11 Woodlands Road, SW13 (Mr & Mrs Victor West) *Take Vine Rd off Upper Richmond Rd to find Woodlands Rd 2nd L.* A garden for all seasons with a variety of mature trees and shrubs forming the structure, and contrasting foliage and flowering perennials giving colour. A number of densely planted beds frequently changing to accommodate owners' desire for even more which, along with a pond and terraced area, are all confined within this medium-sized garden. Unusual plants for sale. Cream TEAS. *Adm £1.50 Chd 50p. Sun May 14 (2-6)*

Evening Opening (See also garden description)

1 Audrey Close, Beckenham	July 5
5 Burbage Road, SE24	June 7
101 Cheyne Walk, SW10	June 15
24 Croom's Hill, SE10	July 16
133 Crystal Palace Road, SE22	June 21
Fenton House, NW3	June 8
8 Grafton Park Road, Worcester Park	July 5
5 Hillcrest Avenue, NW11	June 21
125 Honor Oak Park, SE23	June 24
10A Hoveden Road, NW2	July 14
26 Kenilworth Road, SE20	June 17
Little Lodge, Thames Ditton	June 14
2 Millfield Place, N6	July 20
9 Montpelier Grove, NW5	June 15
263 Nether Street, N3	June 3 & 10
Flat 1, 1F Oval Road, NW1	May 11 & June 8
71 Palace Road, SW2	June 14
48 Rommany Road, SE27	June 24 & July 8
7 St George's Road, Twickenham	June 1
Seymour Buildings, W1	June 22
Southwood Lodge, N6	June 22
Tewkesbury Lodge Garden Group, SE23	June 3
103 Thurleigh Road, SW12	June 21

Gardeners' Royal Benevolent Society

Gardeners' Royal Benevolent Society has been helping retired gardeners, groundsmen, horticultural workers, nurserymen and seedsmen for 160 years.

Gardeners' Royal Benevolent Society
Bridge House, 139 Kingston Road,
Leatherhead, Surrey KT22 7NT

Tel: 01372 373962

SYON HOUSE AND GARDENS

SYON PARK, BRENTFORD, MIDDLESEX TW8 8JF
TELEPHONE: 020 8560 0883

A Gardener's Paradise

In 200 acres of Capability Brown's landscaped parkland can be found the Gardens, the Great Conservatory, a Rose Garden and over 200 species of rare trees. Syon House - with its magnificent Robert Adam interiors and the Garden Centre are also accessible.

Gardens open: Daily 10am - 5.30pm / dusk except Dec 25th, 26th

House Open: 15 Mar - 29 Oct, Weds, Thurs, Sunday and Bank Holidays 11am - 5pm

Close to Kew Gardens

GROUP VISITS WELCOME.

THE NATIONAL GARDENS SCHEME

Chelsea Week London Garden Tours

The National Gardens Scheme will be offering five exclusive tours of private London gardens during Chelsea Week. The tours include gardens not normally open to the public and are special private visits guided by the owners.

Monday 22nd May
Islington & Hackney Gardens
Five contrasting gardens in north and east London, including a prize winning oriental garden and a visit to the famous de Beauvoir area of Islington.

Tuesday 23rd May
Wimbledon, Putney & Barnes Gardens
Some of these gardens are not normally open through the NGS, but the owners have generously agreed to open for this tour.

Wednesday 24th May
Gardens in Dulwich, Peckham & SE London
Including a garden designer's innovative garden and an artist's garden.

Thursday 25th May
Gardens in Ealing, Brentford & SW London
Five gardens including a textile designer's imaginative garden and a garden designer's newly created garden.

Friday 26th May
Outer London Gardens
Visit to 4 private gardens, one of which is not normally open, including a unique Californian garden and a flower arranger's garden.

£45.00 per person per tour including all visits, transport, lunch and wine

For all visits meet at the Museum of Garden History at 9.30am for coffee and private visit. Transport by coach to all gardens. At the end of the tours, the coach will return to The Museum of Garden History which is on the south side of Lambeth Bridge next door to Lambeth Palace.

For more information please see the NGS website www.ngs.org.uk or contact Mrs Julia Hickman (44) (0) 181 339 0931

Norfolk

Hon County Organisers: Mrs Neil Foster, Lexham Hall, King's Lynn, Norfolk PE32 2QJ Tel 01328 701341
Mrs David McCosh, Baconsthorpe, Old Rectory, Holt, Norfolk NR25 6LU Tel 01263 577611

Assistant County Organisers: Mrs Michael Hart, Orchard House, 60 Docking Road, Ringstead, Norfolk PE36 5LA Tel 01485 525267
Lady Mann, Billingford Hall, Diss, Norfolk IP21 4HN Tel 01379 740314

Hon County Treasurer: Neil Foster Esq, Lexham Hall, King's Lynn, Norfolk PE32 2QJ Tel 01328 701288

DATES OF OPENING

Regular openings
For details see garden description
Alby Crafts Gardens, Erpingham
Bradenham Hall, Bradenham
Elsing Hall, Dereham
Gayton Hall, King's Lynn
Hoveton Hall Gardens, nr Wroxham
Mannington Hall, Norwich
Oak Tree House, Thorpe
The Old Vicarage, East Ruston
The Plantation Garden, Norwich
Raveningham Hall, Raveningham
Sandringham Grounds

By appointment only
For telephone numbers and other details see garden descriptions. Private visits welcomed
The Shrubbery, East Tuddenham

February 20 Sunday
Rainthorpe Hall, Tasburgh

April 9 Sunday
Gayton Hall, King's Lynn
The Old House, Ranworth

April 16 Sunday
Alby Crafts Gardens, Erpingham

April 23 Sunday
Bradenham Hall, Bradenham
Lake House, Brundall
Wretham Lodge, East Wretham

April 24 Monday
Lake House, Brundall
Wretham Lodge, East Wretham

April 30 Sunday
Clermont House, Lt Cressingham
Desert World, Thetford Road, Santon Downham
Mannington Hall, Norwich
The Old Vicarage, Carbrooke
The Plantation Garden, Norwich

May 5 Friday
The Old Vicarage, East Ruston

May 7 Sunday
Stody Lodge, Melton Constable

May 14 Sunday
Clermont House, Lt Cressingham
Elmham House, North Elmham
The Garden in an Orchard, Bergh Apton
How Hill Farm, Ludham
The Mowle, Ludham
Stody Lodge, Melton Constable
Stow Hall, Stow Bardolph

May 19 Friday
Hoveton Hall Gardens, nr Wroxham

May 21 Sunday
How Hill Farm, Ludham
Lexham Hall, nr Litcham
The Mowle, Ludham
Sheringham Park, Upper Sheringham
Stody Lodge, Melton Constable
Wretham Lodge, East Wretham

May 28 Sunday
Aylsham Gardens
Stody Lodge, Melton Constable

May 29 Monday
Baconsthorpe Old Rectory, Holt
Stody Lodge, Melton Constable

June 4 Sunday
Sheringham Park, Upper Sheringham

June 11 Sunday
Besthorpe Hall, Attleborough
Conifer Hill, Starston
The Old Vicarage, Carbrooke
Southacre Old Rectory

June 18 Sunday
Desert World, Thetford Road, Santon Downham
The Dutch House, Ludham
Elsing Hall, Dereham
Lexham Hall, nr Litcham
Oxburgh Hall Garden, Oxburgh
Stow Hall, Stow Bardolph
Wretham Lodge, East Wretham

June 24 Saturday
Lawn Farm, Holt

June 25 Sunday
The Harralds, Gissing
Hockering Nursery, nr Dereham
Hoveton House, nr Wroxham
Lawn Farm, Holt
Magpies, Mundford
Wicken House, Castle Acre

July 1 Saturday
Blickling Hall, Aylsham

July 9 Sunday
Easton Lodge, Easton
Gayton Hall, King's Lynn
Minns Cottage, Potter Heigham
Orchards, Raveningham
Raveningham Hall, Raveningham

July 16 Sunday
Felbrigg Hall, Roughton
Oxburgh Hall Garden, Oxburgh

July 23 Sunday
Bradenham Hall, Bradenham
The Harralds, Gissing

July 29 Saturday
Blickling Hall, Aylsham

August 5 Saturday
Hoveton Hall Gardens, nr Wroxham

August 6 Sunday
The Garden in an Orchard, Bergh Apton

August 20 Sunday
Oak Tree House, Thorpe

September 3 Sunday
The Plantation Garden, Norwich

September 10 Sunday
Minns Cottage, Potter Heigham

September 17 Sunday
Felbrigg Hall, Roughton

September 23 Saturday
The Garden in an Orchard, Bergh Apton

September 24 Sunday
Bradenham Hall, Bradenham
The Garden in an Orchard, Bergh Apton

October 1 Sunday
Mannington Hall, Norwich

October 6 Friday
The Old Vicarage, East Ruston

October 8 Sunday
Gayton Hall, King's Lynn

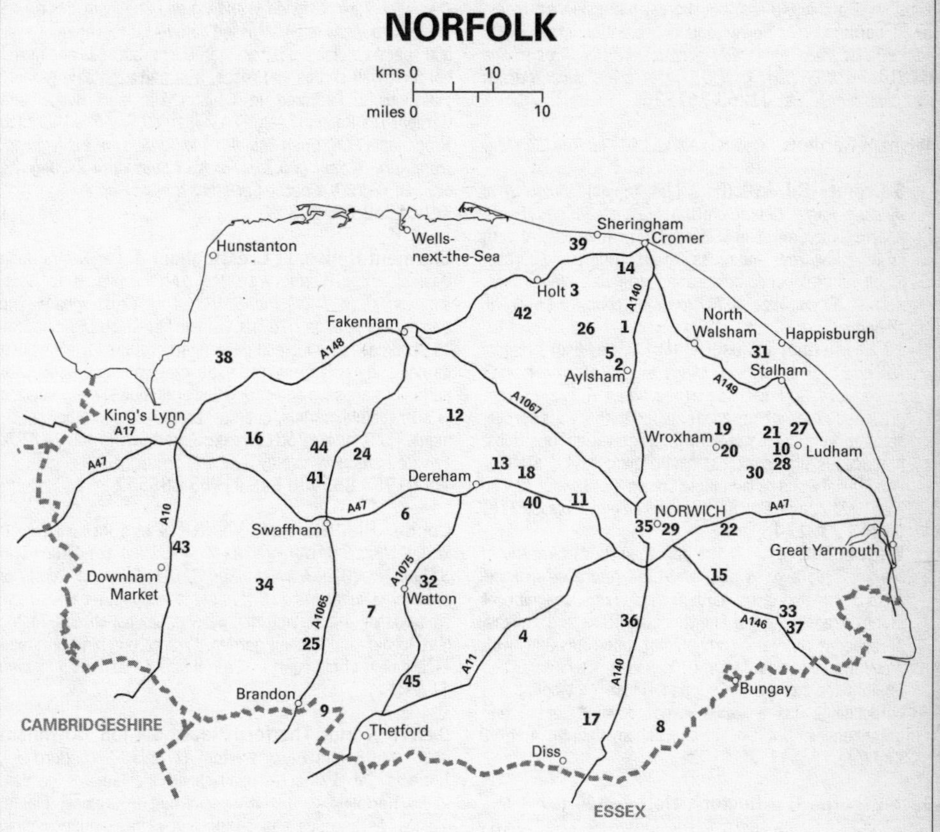

KEY

1 Alby Crafts Gardens
2 Aylsham Gardens
3 Baconsthorpe Old Rectory
4 Besthorpe Hall
5 Blickling Hall
6 Bradenham Hall
7 Clermont House
8 Conifer Hill
9 Desert World
10 The Dutch House
11 Easton Lodge
12 Elmham House
13 Elsing Hall
14 Felbrigg Hall
15 The Garden in an Orchard
16 Gayton Hall
17 The Harralds
18 Hockering Nursery
19 Hoveton Hall Gardens
20 Hoveton House
21 How Hill Farm
22 Lake House
23 Lawn Farm
24 Lexham Hall
25 Magpies
26 Mannington Hall
27 Minns Cottage
28 The Mowle
29 Oak Tree House
30 The Old House
31 The Old Vicarage, East Ruston
32 The Old Vicarage, Carbrooke
33 Orchards
34 Oxburgh Hall Garden
35 The Plantation Garden
36 Rainthorpe Hall
37 Raveningham Hall
38 Sandringham Grounds
39 Sheringham Park
40 The Shrubbery
41 Southacre Old Rectory
42 Stody Lodge
43 Stow Hall
44 Wicken House
45 Wretham Lodge

DESCRIPTIONS OF GARDENS

■ **Alby Crafts Gardens, Erpingham** ♿❀ (Mr & Mrs John Alston) *On A140 4m N of Aylsham. Park in Alby Crafts car park.* 4-acre garden with 4 ponds. Primroses, spring bulbs, wild orchids, irises, hellebores, old-fashioned roses, mixed borders, wild flower and conservation area. TEAS. *Adm £2 Chd free. Open mid-March to mid-Oct, Tues to Sun (11-5). For NGS Sun April 16, with plant sale. Parties welcome, please* **Tel 01263 761226**

Aylsham Gardens *Combined adm £3.50 Chd free. Sun May 28.*

5 Cromer Rd ♿❀ (Dr & Mrs James) *100yds N of Aylsham Parish Church down old Cromer Rd on LH-side.* Approx 1 acre of semi-wild garden nr town centre with large willow trees and grass. Mixed borders and shrubs. Small natural pond, hostas and primulas. Vegetables. *Adm £1.50 Chd free (ACNO to NCH Action for Children). (2-6pm)*

10 St Michael's Close ❀ (M I Davies Esq) *Aylsham NW on B1354 towards Blickling Hall; 500yds from market place, turn R, Rawlinsons Lane, then R again.* Front gravelled area with mixed shrub and herbaceous border; small rockery. Back garden with large variety of shrubs, herbaceous plants, bulbs, small lawn, roses, azaleas. Pond, aviary and guinea pigs. Cream TEAS. *Adm £1 Chd free. (11-6pm). Private visits welcome, please* **Tel 01263 732174**

West Lodge ♿ (Mr & Mrs Jonathan Hirst) *¼m NW of market square on N side of B1354 (entrance in Rawlinsons Lane).* 9-acre garden with lawns, magnificent mature trees, rose garden, rhododendrons and azaleas, herbaceous borders, ornamental pond planted with many primula and large C19 walled kitchen garden (maintained as such). Georgian House (not open) and outbuildings incl a well-stocked toolshed (open) and greenhouses. TEAS in aid of Aylsham Church. *Adm £2 Chd free. (2-5pm)*

Baconsthorpe Old Rectory, Holt ♿✗❀ (Mr & Mrs David McCosh) *Follow sign to Baconsthorpe from Holt bypass for 3m. Rectory is beside church at far end of village.* Continuing restoration of 3-acre garden. Extensive box hedges dividing kitchen garden and newly planted herbaceous borders. 30ft conservatory. Thatched summer house, rosebeds and mulberry trees; lawns and large trees; decorative outbuildings. TEAS. *Adm £2.50 Chd free (ACNO to St Mary's PCC). Bank Hol Mon May 29 (2-6). By appt May, June and July please* **Tel 01263 577611**

Besthorpe Hall, Attleborough ♿ (John Alston Esq) *1m E of Attleborough. On Attleborough-Bunwell Rd; adjacent to Besthorpe Church.* Garden with shrubs, trees and herbaceous borders within Tudor enclosures; walled kitchen garden; tilting ground. Coach parties by appt. TEAS. *Adm £2 Chd free (ACNO to Besthorpe Church). Sun June 11 (2-5). Also private visits welcome, please* **Tel 01953 452138**

▲ **Blickling Hall, Aylsham** ♿✗ (The National Trust) *1¼ miles NW of Aylsham on N side of B1354. 15m N of Norwich (A140).* Large garden, orangery, crescent lake, azaleas, rhododendrons, herbaceous borders. Historic Jacobean house. Wheelchairs available. Lunches and cream TEAS. *Adm £3.70 Chd £1.85 For NGS Sats July 1, 29 (10.30-5.30)*

■ **Bradenham Hall, Bradenham** ✗❀ (Mrs R C Allhusen) *Off A47 6m E of Swaffham, 5m W of East Dereham. Turn S signed Wendling and Longham. 1m turn S signed Bradenham, 2m.* Massed daffodils, arboretum of over 800 species all labelled. Rose garden, herbaceous and mixed borders, wall shrubs and roses, fruit and vegetable garden, glasshouses. Featured in Country Life and House and Garden. Tea Room. Cream TEAS. *Adm £3 Chd free (ACNO to Bradenham PCC) Open 2nd, 4th and 5th Suns of every month from April to Sept (2-5.30). For NGS Suns April 23, July 23, Sept 24 (2-5.30). Coaches at other times by appt*
Tel 01362 687243

Clermont House, Lt Cressingham ♿ (Mr & Mrs John Davies) *From Watton take the B1108 towards Lt Cressingham. Turn L off the B1108 at Lt Cressingham. The entrance is ½m on L.Toilets.* Established since 1984, approx 13 acres lawns, woodland garden, arboretum, formal walled garden and newly formed lake. Several woodland walks with daffodils, narcissus and spring flowering bulbs. Many species of acer, betula, sorbus, quercus, crataegus and other specimens. TEAS. *Adm £2.50 Chd free. Suns April 30, May 14 (2-5). Private visits welcome by appt*
Tel 01953 885900 Fax 01953 885557

Conifer Hill, Starston ♿❀ (Mr & Mrs Richard Lombe Taylor) *18m S of Norwich. A140 to Pulham Xrds. Turn L to B1134, 1m NW of Harleston, off B1134. Take Low Rd out of Starston. Conifer Hill on L ½m out of village. Steep bend and white gates.* 4-acre Victorian garden. Lawns, shrubs, roses, herbaceous and kitchen garden. ½ acre pinetum, on steep escarpment of old quarry. TEAS. *Adm £2 Chd free. Sun June 11 (2-6)*

Desert World, Thetford Road, Santon Downham ✗❀ (Mr & Mrs Barry Gayton) *On B1107. Thetford 4m, Brandon 2m.* 1¼ acres landscaped plantsman's garden. Radio Norfolk's gardener, specialising in tropical plants, alpines, herbaceous and spring bulbs, incl sempervivums. Glasshouses containing 12,500 cacti and succulents. Desert garden. 40 varieties passion flowers. Views on roof garden. Viewing of glasshouses by appt only. TEA. *Adm £2 Chd free. Suns April 30, June 18 (1-6). Private, group visits and gardening lectures by appt. Please* **Tel 01842 765861**

The Dutch House, Ludham ✗ (Mrs Peter Seymour) *B1062 Wroxham to Ludham 7m. Turn R by Ludham village church into Staithe Rd. Gardens ¼m from village.* Long, narrow garden designed and planted by the painter Edward Seago, leading through marsh to Womack Water. Approx 2½ acres. TEAS. *Adm £2 Chd free. Sun June 18 (2-5.30)*

Easton Lodge, Easton ❀ (J M Rampton Esq) *6m W Norwich. Cross the new Southern Norwich Bypass at the Easton Roundabout and take the Ringland Rd.* Large garden in magnificent setting above river, surrounded by fine trees. Walks amongst interesting shrubs, roses and plants. Herbaceous border, walled kitchen garden, wildflower meadow and lake. Late Georgian house with Jacobean centre portion (not open). TEAS. *Adm £2.50 Chd free. Sun July 9 (2.30-5.30).*

Elmham House, North Elmham ♿✂❀ (Mr & Mrs R S Don) *5m N of East Dereham, on B1110. Entrance opp Church.* Wild garden, C18 walled garden, view of park and lake. TEAS. *Adm £2.50 Chd free (ACNO to St Mary's Church N Elmham). Sun May 14 (2-6). Private visits by appt only, please* **Tel 01362 668363**

■ **Elsing Hall, Dereham** ❀ (Mrs D Cargill) *2m E of Dereham off A47. Sign to Elsing.* Medieval house (not open) surrounded by moat. Over 200 varieties of old-fashioned roses. Wild flower lawn, walled kitchen garden with roses, fruit trees and clematis. Many water plants by moat and fish stew. Rare and interesting trees in arboretum. Formal garden with clipped box, lavender, sage, santolina and thyme. Suitable wheelchairs in places. TEAS in aid of Elsing Church. *Adm £3 Chd free. Open Suns June to Sept (2-6). For NGS Sun June 18 (2-6). Coaches at other times by appt, please* **Tel 01362 637224**

▲ **Felbrigg Hall, Roughton** ♿✂ (The National Trust) *2½m SW of Cromer, S of A148; main entrance from B1436.* Large pleasure gardens; mainly lawns and shrubs; orangery with camellias; large walled garden restored and restocked as fruit, vegetable, herb and flower garden; vine house; dovecote; dahlias; National colchicum collection; wooded parks. 1 electric and 3 manual wheelchairs available. Lunches, pre-booking essential. TEAS. *Adm £2.20 Chd £1. For NGS Suns July 16, Sept 17 (11-5)*

The Garden House See Suffolk

The Garden in an Orchard, Bergh Apton ♿❀ (Mr & Mrs R W Boardman) *6m SE of Norwich off A146 at Hellington Corner signed to Bergh Apton. Down Mill Rd 300 yds.* 3½-acre garden set in old orchard. Many rare plants set out in an informal pattern of wandering paths. ½ acre of wild flower meadows, many bamboos, species roses and michaelmas daisies. 9 species of eucalyptus. A plantsman's garden. TEAS. *Adm £2 Chd free. Suns May 14, Aug 6, (11-6), Sept 24, Sat Sept 23 (11-5).* **Tel 01508 480322**

■ **Gayton Hall, King's Lynn** ♿❀ (Mr & Mrs Julian Marsham) *6m E of King's Lynn on B1145; R on B1153. R down Back St 1st entrance on L.* 20-acre water garden, with over 2m of paths. Lawns, woodland, lakes, streams and bridges. Many unusual trees and shrubs. Spring bulbs and autumn colour. Traditional and waterside borders. Primulas, astilbes, hostas, lysichitum, gunnera and many more. TEAS. *Adm £2.50 Chd free (ACNO to St John Ambulance, National Osteoporosis Society, NSPCC). Weds April to July (2-5). For NGS Suns April 9, July 9, Oct 8 (2-6). Groups and private visits welcome, please* **Tel 01553 636259**

NEW **The Harralds, Gissing** ✂❀ (Janet & Ronan Sleep) *4m NE of Diss and 1½m W of Tivetshall-St-Mary and A140. From Gissing church take Rectory Rd. Grove Rd next R.* 3/4 acre with garden rooms, of interest to plantsmen and designers. Themes incl colour control, architectural planting, foliage effects, see-through borders and climbers. Much use of allium, eryngium, euphorbia, kniphofia, verbascum, hedera, ilex and clematis. TEAS and plant sale in aid of St Mary's, Gissing. *Adm £2 OAPs £1.50 Chd free. Suns June 25, July 23 (12.30 - 5). Also private visits and groups welcome, please* **Tel 01379 677288**

NEW **Hockering Nursery, nr Dereham** ♿❀ (Ian Harris) *On main A47 8m from Norwich. 5m from Dereham.* Wholesale nursery garden of 5 acres divided into 12 separate areas incl ponds and sheltered sitting. Mainly planted with shrubs and small trees and incorporating many hard landscape features. Children's garden. Less formal garden under construction in newly acquired field . TEAS. *Adm £1.50 Chd free. Sun June 25 (11-5.30)*

■ **Hoveton Hall Gardens, nr Wroxham** ♿✂❀ (Mr & Mrs Andrew Buxton) *8m N of Norwich; 1m N of Wroxham Bridge on A1151 Stalham Rd.* 10-acre gardens and grounds featuring daffodils, azaleas, rhododendrons and hydrangeas in woodland. Mature, walled herbaceous garden. Water plants, lakeside walk and walled kitchen garden. Early C19 house (not open). TEAS. *Adm £3 Chd £1 under 5 free. Gardens open, every Wed, Fri, Sun and Bank Hols, Easter Sun to Sept 24 incl. For NGS Fri May 19, Sun Aug 5 (11.30-5.30) (ACNO to Multiple Sclerosis Society Research)*

Hoveton House, nr Wroxham ♿✂ (Sir John & Lady Blofeld) *9m N Norwich, ½m Wroxham on B1062, Horning-Ludham Rd.* Old-fashioned walled garden; magnificent herbaceous and other borders full of unusual plants and bulbs; rock garden. Rhododendron grove 100 yrs old and towering 30'. Kitchen garden. Park, lawns and walks with magnificent view. William & Mary House (not open). TEAS. *Adm £2.50 Chd free (ACNO to St John's Church). Sun June 25 (2-5.30)*

How Hill Farm, Ludham ❀ (P D S Boardman Esq) *2m W of Ludham on A1062; then follow signs to How Hill. Farm Garden S of How Hill.* Very pretty garden started in 1968 with three ponds, 3-acre Broad (dug as conservation project), water lilies and view over the R Ant to fine old mill. Paths through rare conifers. Unusual and rare rhododendrons with massed azaleas, ornamental trees, shrubs and some herbaceous plants. Collections of English holly, Ilex aquifolium (over 100 varieties) and 65 different bamboos. Partly suitable for wheelchairs. TEAS. *Adm £2 Chd under 12 free (ACNO to How Hill Trust). Suns May 14, 21 (2-5)*

Lake House, Brundall ❀ (Mr & Mrs Garry Muter) *Approx 5m E of Norwich on A47; take Brundall turn at Roundabout. Turn R into Postwick Lane at T-junction.* An acre of water gardens set among magnificent trees in a steep cleft in the river escarpment. Informal flower beds with interesting plants; a naturalist's paradise; unsuitable for young children or the infirm. Wellingtons advisable. Unusual plants for sale. TEAS. *Adm £2.50 Chd free (ACNO to Water Aid). Easter Sun & Mon April 23, 24 (11-6). Private parties by prior appt, please* **Tel 01603 712933**

Lawn Farm, Holt ♿✂❀ (Mrs G W Deterding) *Leave Holt on Cley Rd (opp. King's Head) 1m on R.* 6½-acre garden with ponds and mediaeval courtyard gardens. Interesting trees and spectacular roses. TEAS. *Adm £3 Chd free. Sat, Sun June 24, 25 (10-5). Open by appt April to July 31, please* **Tel 01263 713 484**

Lexham Hall, nr Litcham ♿✂❀ (Mr & Mrs Neil Foster) *2m W of Litcham off B1145.* Fine 17th/18th century Hall (not open). Parkland with lake and river walks. Formal garden with terraces, yew hedges, roses and mixed borders. Traditional kitchen garden with crinkle-crankle wall. 3-acre woodland garden with azaleas, rhododendrons, spring bulbs and rare trees. TEAS. *Adm £3 Chd free (ACNO to St Andrews Church, E. Lexham, May; All Saints Church, Litcham, June). Suns May 21, June 18 (2-6). Also groups (min 20) by appt May 1 to July 31 (weekdays only), please* **Tel 01328 701288**

Magpies, Mundford ♿✂❀ (Mr & Mrs Dennis Cooper) *From Mundford roundabout take A1065 to Swaffham. After ¼m turn L into Green Lane.* 1½-acre garden with island beds, intensively planted with unusual perennials, ornamental grasses and cottage garden plants. Paths lead to hidden gardens giving a cottage garden effect. A wilder margin encourages birds throughout the yr. Featured in 'Garden Answers'. Unusual plants available from adjoining nursery. *Adm £1.50 Chd free. Sun June 25 (12-6). Private visits welcome, please* **Tel 01842 878496**

■ **Mannington Hall, Norwich** ♿✂❀ (The Lord & Lady Walpole) *2m N of Saxthorpe; 18m NW of Norwich via B1149 towards Holt. At Saxthorpe (B1149 & B1354) turn NE signed Mannington.* 20 acres feature roses, shrubs, lake and trees. Daffodil lined drive. Extensive countryside walks and trails. Moated manor house (not open). Saxon church with C19 follies. Lunches and TEAS in aid of St Mary's Church. *Adm £3 OAPs/students £2.50 Chd free. Suns May to Sept, Weds, Thurs, Fris June to Aug. For NGS Suns April 30, Oct 1 (12-5)*

Minns Cottage, Potter Heigham ♿✂❀ (Mr and Mrs Derek Brown) *Chapel Rd. From Norwich take A1151 then A149 to Potter Heigham Xrds. Turn L into Station Rd on to T junction, turn L into School Rd, turning into Green Lane. At telephone box turn R into Chapel Rd.* Approx 1¼ acres winding lawns leading through pergolas to rose garden with old English roses and other small gardens with mixed borders. Recently planted woodland area with rhododendrons and bulbs. A garden to walk round peacefully at all seasons. TEAS. *Adm £2 Chd free. Suns July 9 (2-6), Sept 10 (2-5)*

The Mowle, Ludham ✂❀ (Mrs N N Green) *B1062 Wroxham to Ludham 7m. Turn R by Ludham village church into Staithe Rd. Gardens ¼m from village.* Approx 2½ acres running down to marshes. Interesting shrub borders, unusual trees incl tulip trees and a golden catalpa. TEAS. *Adm £2 Chd under 12 free. Suns May 14, 21 (1.30-5.30) and by appt, please.* **Tel 01692 678213**

■ **Oak Tree House, Thorpe** ✂❀ (Will Giles Esq) *6 Cotman Rd. E of Norwich off A47. New entrance and car park at side entrance of Alan Boswell Insurance on Thorpe Rd next to MAFF. ½m from Thorpe railway station.* Exotic city garden of ½ acre on S-facing hillside. Unusual plants incl palms, bananas, cannas, gingers, aroids and tree ferns. New water feature. Six exotic cats. Extensive media coverage. TEAS. *Adm £3 Chd free. Suns July 9, 23, Aug 6, Sept 3, 17. For NGS Sun Aug 20 (1.30-5.30). Parties by appt, please* **Tel 01603 623167**

The Old House, Ranworth ✂❀ (Mr Francis & The Hon Mrs Cator) *Nr S Walsham, below historic church.* Attractive linked and walled gardens alongside beautiful, peaceful Ranworth inner broad. Bulbs, shrubs, potager and mown rides through recently established arboretum where dogs may be walked on leads. Pond with many species of ducks and geese. ½m of woodland walk. TEA. *Adm £2 Chd free. Sun April 9 (2-5)*

The Old Vicarage, Carbrooke ✂❀ (Lesley Kant & Stephen Cunneen) *20m W of Norwich, 3m E of Watton, off Norwich-Watton Rd (B1108). Turn into Broadmoor Rd for 2m leading to village centre.* 2-acre country garden, developed and maintained by owners. Planting incl mixed and herbaceous borders, vegetable garden, white parterre, courtyard herb garden, rose garden and spring bulbs. Garden leads into small wood (2 acres) planted 14yrs ago by Woodland Trust. Featured in BBC2 Garden Stories and The English Garden. TEAS in aid of Carbrooke Village Millennium Green. *Adm £2 Chd free. Suns April 30, June 11 (2-5.30). Parties by appt* **Tel 01953 883245**

■ **The Old Vicarage, East Ruston** ♿✂❀ (Alan Gray & Graham Robeson) *3m N of Stalham on Stalham to Happisburgh/Walcott Rd (ignore all 3 signposts to East Ruston). Turn R 200yds just N of East Ruston Church.* 14-acre exotic coastal garden and grounds incl impressive herbaceous borders, autumn border, tropical border incl bananas and palms, sunken and walled gardens, Mediterranean garden and wild flower meadows and walks. TEAS. *Adm £3.50 Chd £1. Open every Wed, Fri and Sun from April 23 to Oct 29 incl. For NGS Fris May 5, Oct 6 (2-5.30)*

Orchards, Raveningham ♿ (Priscilla Lady Bacon) *14m SE of Norwich, 4m from Beccles off B1136.* ¼ acre plantsman's garden with exceptional collection of rare and unusual plants and shrubs. Mixed herbaceous and shrub borders. *Adm £2 Chd free (ACNO to DGAA Homelife). Sun July 9 (2-5). Private visits welcome, by arrangement, please* **Tel 01508 548 322**

▲ **Oxburgh Hall Garden, Oxburgh** ♿✂ (The National Trust) *7m SW of Swaffham, at Oxburgh on Stoke Ferry rd.* Hall and moat surrounded by lawns, fine trees, colourful borders; charming parterre garden of French design. Lunches. Cream TEAS. *Adm £2.60 Chd 1.30p. For NGS Suns June 18, July 16 (11-5)*

■ **The Plantation Garden, Norwich** ♿✂❀ (Plantation Garden Preservation Trust) *4 Earlham Rd. Entrance between Crofters and Beeches Hotels, nr St John's R C Cathedral.* 3-acre Victorian town garden created 1856-97 in former medieval chalk quarry. Undergoing restoration by volunteers. Remarkable architectural features include 60ft Italianate terrace, unique 30ft Gothic fountain and restored rustic bridge. Surrounded by mature trees. Beautifully tranquil atmosphere. *Adm £2 Chd free (ACNO to Plantation Garden Preservation Trust). Suns April 30 to mid Oct. For NGS Suns April 30, Sept 3 (2-5). Private visits welcome, please* **Tel 01603 621868**

Rainthorpe Hall, Tasburgh ♿❀ (Mr & Mrs Alastair Wilson) *Approx 8m S of Norwich, just off the A140 - turn by* *garage in Newton Flotman. On 1m to red brick pillars and gates on L.* Elizabethan/Victorian Country House (not open) prettily set in interesting variety of gardens, incl knot hedge (said to be as old as the house) and hazel coppice (said to be older). Fine trees, spring bulbs and collection of bamboos. TEAS. *Adm £2.50 OAPs £1.50 Chd free (ACNO to Countrywide Workshops Charitable Trust). Sun Feb 20 (1-4). Private visits welcome, please* **Tel 01508 470618**

■ **Raveningham Hall, Raveningham** ♿❀ (Sir Nicholas Bacon) *14m SE of Norwich, 4m from Beccles off B1136.* Large garden specialising in rare shrubs, herbaceous plants, especially euphorbia, agapanthus and snowdrops. Victorian conservatory and walled vegetable garden. Newly planted arboretum. *Adm £2 Chd free. Garden open every Sunday and Bank Hols from Easter to end of July (2-5). For NGS TEA. Sun July 9 (2-5).*

● **Sandringham Grounds** ♿✿❀ (Sandringham Grounds) By gracious permission of H.M. The Queen, the House, Museum and Grounds at Sandringham will be open. 60 acres of formal gardens, woodland and lakes, with rare plants and trees. Donations are given from the Estate to various charities. TEAS. *Adm House and Grounds £5.50 OAPs £4.50 Chd £3.50. Grounds only £4.50 OAPs £4 Chd £3. April 15 to Oct 8 daily. House closed July 19 to Aug 2 incl & Grounds closed Good Friday July 23 to Aug 2 incl. (Hours: House 11-4.45; Grounds 10.30-5)*

▲ **Sheringham Park, Upper Sheringham** ♿❀ (The National Trust) *2m SW of Sheringham. Access for cars off A148 Cromer to Holt Road, 5m W of Cromer, 6m E of Holt (signs in Sheringham Town).* 50 acres of species rhododendron, azalea and magnolia. Also numerous specimen trees incl handkerchief tree. Viewing towers, waymarked walks, sea and parkland views. Special walk way and WCs for disabled. Electric wheelchairs available. TEAS. *Adm £2.60 per car. For NGS Suns May 21, June 4 (dawn to dusk).*
Tel 01263 823778

The Shrubbery, East Tuddenham ✿❀ (Mrs Fane) *Take A47 from Norwich. Turn L at sign East Tuddenham, Mattishall, through village to village pump and telephone box on R. Common Rd on L. Yellow house on L. Small car park and parking is permitted on rd.* Small plantsman's garden incl 3 ponds, acid, gravel and shrub gardens. Divided into different rooms with yr round colour but particularly in spring and summer. Featured in 'Your Garden' and Eastern Daily Press. TEAS. *Adm £2 Chd free. By appt only, please* **Tel 01603 880238**

Southacre Old Rectory ♿❀ (Mr & Mrs C Hardcastle) *3m NW of Swaffham off A1065 opp Southacre Church.* 3-acre garden with splendid views of Castle Acre Priory. Mixed borders, shrubs, vineyard, herb garden, pool and old-fashioned rose garden. Interesting C13 church. Featured in English Garden Magazine. TEAS in aid of Southacre Church Restoration Fund. *Adm £2.50 Chd free. Sun June 11 (2-5.30). Private visits welcome May, June and July, please* **Tel 01760 755469**

● **Stody Lodge, Melton Constable** ♿❀ (Mr & Mrs Ian MacNicol) *Approx 16m NW of Norwich off B1354. Signed from Melton Constable on Holt Rd.* 15 acres of spectacular gardens having one of the largest concentration of rhododendrons and azaleas in E Anglia and incl a Japanese water garden and formal garden with stunning walks and vistas. TEAS. *Adm £3.50 Chd free. Suns May 7, 14, 21, 28, Mon May 29 (2-5). Parties by appt on weekdays during this period*
Tel 01263 860572

Stow Hall, Stow Bardolph ♿❀ (Lady Rose Hare) *2m N of Downham Market off A10.* Large garden with mature trees, small secluded areas with alpines, bulbs, irises and roses. High walls and cloisters planted with scented and tender climbers. Victorian kitchen garden containing old pear and apple trees and interesting varieties of potatoes and strawberries. Architectural features on site of former Stow Hall. Plants in aid of Holy Trinity Church. TEAS. *Adm £2.50 Chd free. Suns May 14, June 18 (2-6).*

Wicken House, Castle Acre ♿✿❀ (Lord & Lady Keith) *5m N of Swaffham off A1065. W at Newton to Castle Acre, then 2m N off the rd to Massingham.* Large walled garden planted in sections with many roses and unusual herbaceous plants; gravel paths and greenhouses; swimming pool garden; spring and wild gardens. Fine views. Approx 6 acres. Rare plants for sale. Home-made cream TEAS. *Adm £2.50 Chd free (ACNO to the Friends of Castle Acre Church). Sun June 25 (2-5)*

Wretham Lodge, East Wretham ♿✿❀ (Gordon Alexander Esq) *A11 E from Thetford, L up A1075, L by village sign, R at Xrds then bear L.* In spring masses of species tulips, hellebores, fritillaries, daffodils and narcissi; bluebell walk. In June hundreds of old roses. Walled garden, with fruit and interesting vegetable plots. Mixed borders and fine old trees. Wild flower meadows. Featured in Peter Beales' Vision of Roses, Country Life and House & Garden. *Adm £2.50 Chd free. Easter Sun April 23, Mon April 24 (11-6) Suns May 21, June 18 (2.30-5.30). Also private visits and coach parties welcome, please write.*

THORNCROFT CLEMATIS NURSERY

Our *garden* and *specialist clematis nursery* in the heart of Norfolk is open
1st March - 31st October 10.00am - 4.30pm
Closed Wednesdays (Nov - Feb by appointment)
Year round mail order

On B1135 exactly halfway between Wymondham & Dereham. We are NOT in the village!
For catalogue please send £1 (cheque/PO or stamps) to:

THORNCROFT CLEMATIS NURSERY
REYMERSTON, NORWICH, NR9 4QG
Tel: 01953 850407 Fax: 01953 851788
E-mail: sales@thorncroft.co.uk

Northamptonshire

Hon County Organiser: Mrs Annabel Smyth-Osbourne, Versions Farm, Brackley, Northants NN13 5JY 01280 702412

Assistant Hon County Organisers: Mrs Jean Bussens, Glebe Cottage, Titchmarsh, Kettering, Northants NN14 3DB 01832 732510
Mrs Ruth Dashwood, Farthinghoe Lodge, Brackley, Northants NN13 5NX
Mrs R Blake, Lodge Lawn, Fotheringhay, Peterborough PE8 5HZ

Hon County Treasurer: Mr R H N Dashwood, Farthinghoe Lodge, Brackley, Northants NN13 5NX 01295 710377

DATES OF OPENING

Regular openings
For details see garden description
Coton Manor, Guilsborough
Cottesbrooke Hall Gardens, nr Creaton
Kelmarsh Hall, Market Harborough
The Old Rectory, Sudborough
The Prebendal Manor House, Nassington
The Walnuts, King's Cliffe
Wisteria Cottage, Maidwell

By appointment only
For telephone numbers and other details see garden descriptions. Private visits welcomed
The Spring House, Chipping Warden

March 19 Sunday
4 Elmington Cottages, Elmington

March 26 Sunday
The Old Rectory, Sudborough

April 8 Saturday
Brock's Close, 14 Park Street, King's Cliffe
The Walnuts, King's Cliffe

April 9 Sunday
Brock's Close, 14 Park Street, King's Cliffe
Charlton, nr Banbury
The Nursery Gardens, Geddington
The Walnuts, King's Cliffe

April 20 Thursday
Kelmarsh Hall, Market Harborough

April 23 Sunday
Evenley Wood Garden, Brackley

April 24 Monday
Evenley Wood Garden, Brackley
Great Addington Manor, Great Addington

April 25 Tuesday
Irthlingborough, Wellingborough

April 30 Sunday
Evenley Wood Garden, Brackley
Titchmarsh House, Titchmarsh

May 1 Monday
Evenley Wood Garden, Brackley

May 7 Sunday
Cedar House, Thurning
Great Brington Gardens, Northampton

May 14 Sunday
Hollyberry Barn, Bulwick
Bulwick Rectory, Bulwick
Holdenby House, Garden and Falconry Centre

May 21 Sunday
Deene Park, nr Corby
Guilsborough and Hollowell Gardens
Irthlingborough, Wellingborough
Nortoft Grange, Guilsborough

May 28 Sunday
Castle Ashby Gardens
4 Elmington Cottages, Elmington
Evenley Wood Garden, Brackley
Lois Weedon House, Weedon Lois
The Old Barn, Weedon Lois

May 29 Monday
Evenley Wood Garden, Brackley
Glendon Hall, Kettering

June 3 Saturday
Canons Ashby House, Daventry

June 4 Sunday
Blackpitts House, Whittlebury
Litchborough Gardens, nr Towcester
Sholebroke Lodge, Whittlebury

June 6 Tuesday
Coton Manor, Guilsborough

June 8 Thursday
The Haddonstone Show Garden, East Haddon Manor, nr Northampton (evening)

June 11 Sunday
Evenley Gardens, Brackley
The Nursery Gardens, Geddington
Preston Capes Gardens
Spratton Gardens, Spratton
Stoke Park, Stoke Bruerne
Titchmarsh Gardens, nr Thrapston

June 13 Tuesday
Evenley Gardens, Brackley (evening)

June 14 Wednesday
Badby Gardens

June 17 Saturday
Flore Gardens, nr Northampton

June 18 Sunday
Badby Gardens
Bulwick Gardens, nr Corby
Cottesbrooke Hall Gardens, nr Creaton
Easton Neston, Towcester
Flore Gardens, nr Northampton
Gamekeepers Cottage, Cottesbrooke
Maidwell Gardens
The Old Rectory, Sudborough
Slapton Gardens, Slapton

June 20 Tuesday
Evenley Gardens, Brackley (evening)

June 21 Wednesday
Bradden House, Bradden
Maidwell Gardens
The Old Barn, Weedon Lois

June 22 Thursday
Kelmarsh Hall, Market Harborough

June 24 Saturday
Courteenhall, Northampton
The Prebendal Manor House, Nassington

June 25 Sunday
Cedar Farm, Desborough
Great Harrowden Gardens, nr Wellingborough
Harpole Gardens, Northampton
Kilsby Gardens, nr Rugby
The Menagerie, Horton

July 2 Sunday
Aynho Gardens, Banbury
Cranford Gardens, nr Kettering
Peters Farm, Helmdon
West Haddon Gardens

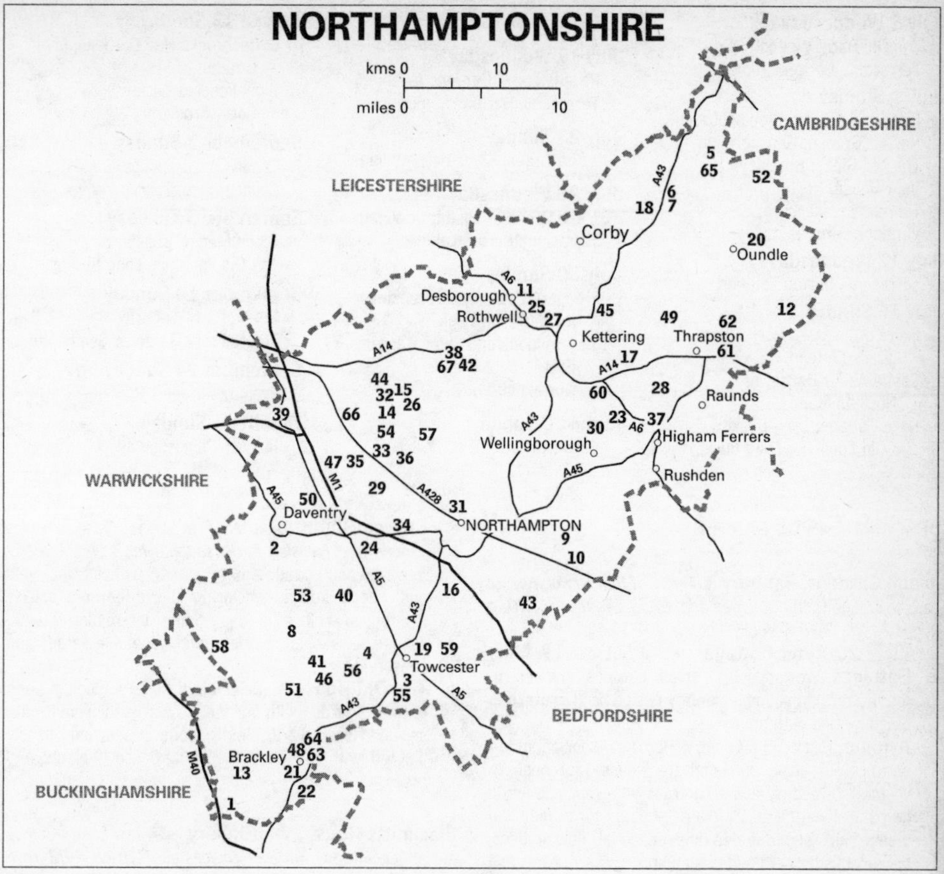

KEY

1 Aynho Gardens
2 Badby Gardens
3 Blackpitts House
4 Bradden House
5 Brock's Close
6 Bulwick Gardens
7 Bulwick Rectory
8 Canons Ashby House
9 Castle Ashby Gardens
10 Castle Ashby House
11 Cedar Farm
12 Cedar House
13 Charlton
14 Coton Manor
15 Cottesbrooke Hall Gardens
16 Courteenhall
17 Cranford Gardens
18 Deene Park
19 Easton Neston
20 4 Elmington Cottages
21 Evenley Gardens
22 Evenley Wood Garden
23 Finedon Gardens
24 Flore Gardens
25 Froggery Cottage
26 Gamekeepers Cottage
27 Glendon Hall
28 Great Addington Manor
29 Great Brington Gardens
30 Great Harrowden Gardens
31 1 The Green
32 Guilsborough and Hollowell Gardens
33 The Haddonstone Show Garden
34 Harpole Gardens
35 Haze Cottage
36 Holdenby House Garden and Falconry Centre
37 Irthlingborough
38 Kelmarsh Hall
39 Kilsby Gardens
40 Litchborough Gardens
41 Lois Weedon House
42 Maidwell Gardens
43 The Menagerie
44 Nortoft Grange
45 The Nursery Gardens
46 The Old Barn
47 The Old Fountain
48 The Old Glebe
49 The Old Rectory
50 Park House
51 Peters Farm
52 The Prebendal Manor House
53 Preston Capes Gardens
54 Ravensthorpe Gardens
55 Sholebroke Lodge
56 Slapton Gardens
57 Spratton Gardens
58 The Spring House
59 Stoke Park
60 Terracend
61 Titchmarsh Gardens
62 Titchmarsh House
63 Turweston Mill
64 Versions Farm
65 The Walnuts
66 West Haddon Gardens
67 Wisteria Cottage

July 5 Wednesday
The Old Barn, Weedon Lois
Terracend, Burton Latimer

July 9 Sunday
Finedon Gardens, Wellingborough
Nortoft Grange, Guilsborough
The Old Glebe, Brackley
Park House, Norton
Turweston Mill
Versions Farm, Brackley

July 12 Wednesday
Terracend, Burton Latimer

July 16 Sunday
Brock's Close, 14 Park Street,
King's Cliffe
Castle Ashby House, nr
Northampton
Haze Cottage, Long Buckby
The Old Fountain, Long Buckby

Ravensthorpe Gardens

July 19 Wednesday
Ravensthorpe Gardens (evening)
Terracend, Burton Latimer

July 23 Sunday
1 The Green, Kingsthorpe Village

July 26 Wednesday
1 The Green, Kingsthorpe Village
Terracend, Burton Latimer

July 30 Sunday
Froggery Cottage, 85 Breakleys
Road, Desborough
The Haddonstone Show Garden,
East Haddon Manor, nr
Northampton

August 6 Sunday
Bulwick Gardens, nr Corby

August 13 Sunday
Cottesbrooke Hall Gardens, nr
Creaton
Gamekeepers Cottage,
Cottesbrooke

September 3 Sunday
Canons Ashby House, Daventry
Cedar House, Thurning

September 5 Tuesday
Coton Manor, Guilsborough
The Old Fountain, Long Buckby

September 10 Sunday
Deene Park, nr Corby
The Nursery Gardens, Geddington

September 24 Sunday
Evenley Gardens, Brackley

October 1 Sunday
Bulwick Rectory, Bulwick

DESCRIPTIONS OF GARDENS

Aynho Gardens, Banbury & *6m SE of Banbury on B4100.* Teas in Village Hall. *Combined adm £2.50 Chd free (ACNO to Aynho Sports Field Assoc). Sun July 2 (2.30-6)*
NEW **20 Alms Cottages** (Mr J Russell) **19 Alms Cottages.** Two adjoining, small gardens planned to great effect with complementary designs and interesting planting. One with pond
Aynhoe Park ✗ (Country Houses Association) 14 acres of parkland surround the house (not open to visitors). Sweeping lawns, contrast with woodland left in its natural state to provide a rich habitat for wildlife and plants, incl small leafed ivy. Seasonal flower beds, herbaceous borders and graceful groupings of trees and limewalk
Catton House ✗ (Mrs C H Harmer) Well established small walled garden with mature trees, various shrubs and specialising in roses and clematis; sunken walled rose garden
Friar's Well (Mr & Mrs T R Sermon) 3-acre garden on top of hill with magnificent views; divided into sections with mixed hedges and stone wall; pleached limes and hornbeams, unusual shrubs and roses
Puente Sierra ✗ (Mr & Mrs R Sawbridge) 1 Cartwright Gardens. ½-acre walled garden with interesting mature evergreens, shrubberies and deciduous trees, bulbs, lilies, palms and hibiscus. Also fruit and vegetable area
NEW **Rambler Cottage** (Mr & Mrs G P Gibbs) Well established walled, cottage garden with unusual historic village pond as main feature
16 Roundtown (Miss A Bazin) Old-fashioned cottage garden with inner walled section, herbaceous borders, roses, shrubs and fruit trees

Badby Gardens *3m S of Daventry on E side of A361.* TEAS in aid of St Mary's Church. *Combined adm £2. Wed June 14, Sun June 18 (2-6)*

Church Hill ✗ (Dr & Mrs C M Cripps) *Close to Badby Woods and Fawsley Park (suitable for walks and picnics).* Medium-sized country garden with internal yew and beech hedges enclosing mixed borders thickly planted in colour groups. Some interesting plants, clipped yews, shady border, pond, vegetable garden and conservatory.
The Old House & (Dr & Mrs C Rose) A medium-sized enclosed garden with fine views over Badby woods with secluded court yard. Mostly stone raised beds densly planted with many traditional herbaceous plants and roses

Blackpitts House, Whittlebury &✿ (Mr & Mrs James Alexander-Sinclair) *3m S of Towcester. Turn off A413 Towcester end of Whittlebury village.* New walled garden. Innovative planting in borders and gravel. Slate parterre and 'bassin'. TEAS. *Combined adm with* **Sholebroke Lodge** *£2 Chd free. Sun June 4 (1-6)*

Bradden House, Bradden &✗✿ (Keith & Maggie Barwell) *5m W of Towcester.* 25 acres of garden with ornamental woodland and lake, the walled garden of Edwardian origin, the rest has been laid out by present owners since 1991. Good mixed borders with colour themes, long rose pergola and rose garden planted with new English roses around an ornamental pool, vegetable, herb and fruit gardens. Walk through newly planted park and flower meadow with ponds. TEAS. *Adm £2 Chd 50p (ACNO to The Royal National Rose Society). Wed June 21 (2-6)*

Brock's Close, 14 Park Street, King's Cliffe & (Dr Brian & Mrs Heather Cromie) *4m W of Wansford, at A1/A47 junction. Parking at village school Park Street, 50yds from Brock's Close.* 2 acres with small walled garden, rose beds, herbaceous borders and over 100 clematis. Broad sweeps of grass planted with trees and fine views. Teas at The Walnuts (April). Village Hall (July) *Combined Adm with* **The Walnuts** *£2.50 Chd free. Sat, Sun April 8, 9. Adm £1.50 Chd free. Sun*

July 16 (2-6). Private visits welcome £2 (minimum 6), please **Tel 01780 470754**

Bulwick Gardens, nr Corby *7m NE of Corby, 10m SW of Stamford, ½m off A43.* TEAS. *Combined adm £2 Chd free (ACNO to Multiple Sclerosis). Suns June 18, Aug 6 (2-5)*

Bulwick Hall ♿ (Mr & Mrs G T G Conant) Formal terraced 8-acre walled garden leading to river and island. 50 metre double herbaceous borders. 100 metre holly walk ending at attractive C17 wrought iron gates. C19 orangery and C17 arcade; large kitchen garden; fine mature trees; peacocks. TEAS

Hollyberry Barn, Bulwick ♿❀ (Colin McAlpine) A cottage garden with curved herbaceous borders; arches; raised vegetable beds; greenhouses; cold frames; gravelled area with alpine plants and pots. *Not open Aug 6. Sun May 14 with* **Bulwick Rectory**

The Shambles ✗ (Roger Glithero) Herbaceous plants, many containers, vegetable garden with fruit and an original village well. *Not open June 18*

Bulwick Rectory, Bulwick ♿✗❀ (The Reverend & Mrs Mervyn Wilson) *8m NE of Corby; 13m NE of Kettering; next to Bulwick Church.* Rectory garden with old dovecote and new folly. Shrubs, topiary notable collection of apple, pear and plum. Planted for beauty and utility. This is an unusual, self supporting garden developed and worked by the present rector to basic organic principles with vegetables, free range poultry and bees. TEAS (not Oct 1). *Adm £1.50 Chd free (ACNO to Bulwick Parish Church). Suns May 14 (combined adm with* **Hollyberry Barn** *), Oct 1 (2-5). Private visits welcome, please* **Tel 01780 450249**

▲ **Canons Ashby House, Daventry** ♿✗❀ (The National Trust) Formal gardens enclosed by walls. Gate piers from 1710; fine topiary; axial arrangement of paths and terraces; wild flowers, old varieties of fruit trees, newly planted gardens. Home of the Dryden family since C16, Manor House 1550 with contemporary wall paintings and Jacobean plasterwork. TEAS. *Adm £4 Chd £2 (includes house). Reduced party rate. For NGS Sat June 3, Sun Sept 3 (12-5.30)*

NEW **Castle Ashby Gardens** *8m E of Northampton off A428, 4m SW of Wellingborough off A45. Both signposted Castle Ashby.* TEAS. *Combined adm £2 Chd free. Sun May 28 (2-6)*

NEW **Castle Ashby Lodge** ✗ (Mr & Mrs Jonathan Pearson) *The Lodge entrance down drive ½m from A428.* Traditional farmyards converted to informal family gardens since 1977, herbaceous, shrub roses, shrubs, gravel and white garden. Walnut walk

NEW **The Menagerie** ❀ (Mr & Mrs Derrick Dunn) *House in park, signposted from Falcon Inn.* Garden and paddock approx 3½ acres, herbaceous borders, lawns and wild garden. Temple by Capability Brown overlooking the lake affording views of Castle Ashby House

▲ **Castle Ashby House, nr Northampton** ♿❀ (Earl Compton) *6m E of Northampton. 1½m N of A428; turn off between Denton and Yardley Hastings.* Parkland incl avenue planted at suggestion of William III in 1695; lakes etc by Capability Brown; Italian gardens with orangery; extensive lawns and trees. Nature trail. Elizabethan house (not open). TEA. *Adm £2.50 Chd/OAPs £1.50. For NGS Sun July 16 (11-5)*

NEW **Cedar Farm, Desborough** ♿✗ (Mr & Mrs R Tuffen) *6m N of Kettering, 5m S of Market Harborough on A6.* 2-acre garden with a further 8 acres of walks. Secret garden with roses and clematis. Orchard with many interesting trees. TEAS in aid of St Giles Church. *Adm £2 Chd over 5yrs 50p. Sun June 25 (2-6) Private visits welcome, please* **Tel 01536 763992**

NEW **Cedar House, Thurning** ✗ (Tony & Jenny Leeson) *5m S of Oundle. Off A605, through Barnwell. Last house in Thurning on rd to Luddington. From A14 take B660 N to Gt Gidding through Luddington to Thurning.* Informal 5-acre garden, paddocks and orchard. Large lawned areas, variety of conifers, deciduous trees, shrubs, roses and herbaceous plants. Large natural pond with a diversity of wildlife. TEAS. *Adm £2 Chd free. Suns May 7, Sept 3 (2-6)*

Charlton, nr Banbury ♿ *7m SE of Banbury, 5m W of Brackley. From A41 turn off N at Aynho; or from A422 turn off S at Farthinghoe.* Home-made TEAS The Cottage. *Combined adm £2 Chd £1 (ACNO to Charlton Playing Field). Sun April 9 (2-6)*

The Cottage (Lady Juliet Townsend) Flowering shrubs, spring bulbs, roses, lawns, woodland walk, stream and lakes. House in village street

Holly House (The Hon Nicholas Berry) Walled garden with beautiful views. C18 house (not open)

■ **Coton Manor, Guilsborough** ♿✗❀ (Mr & Mrs Ian Pasley-Tyler) *10m N of Northampton. 11m SE of Rugby nr Ravensthorpe Reservoir. From A428 & A5199 (formerly A50) follow Tourist signs.* C17 stone manor house with old yew and holly hedges, extensive herbaceous borders, rose garden, water garden, herb garden, woodland garden, famous bluebell wood (early May) and newly planted wildflower meadow. Home-made lunches and TEAS. *Adm £3.50 OAPs £3 Chd £2. Open daily Weds to Suns & Bank Hols Easter to end Sept. For NGS Tues June 6, Sept 5 (12-5.30). Private parties welcome, please* **Tel 01604 740219**

■ **Cottesbrooke Hall Gardens, nr Creaton** ♿✗❀ (Captain & Mrs J Macdonald-Buchanan) *10m N of Northampton, nr Creaton on A5199 and Brixworth on A508.* Notable gardens of great variety incl fine old cedars and specimen trees, herbaceous borders, water and wild gardens. Unusual plants - home grown. TEAS. *Adm House & Gardens £4 Gardens only £2.50 Chd half price. Open Easter to end Sept. House and Gardens open afternoons of Thursdays and Bank Hol Mons plus 1st Sun of each month May-Sept (2-5). Garden only also open on Tues, Wed, Fri afternoons. For NGS, Gardens only. Combined adm with* **Gamekeepers Cottage** *£2.50 Chd £1.25 (ACNO to All Saints Church). Suns June 18, Aug 13 (2-6).* **Tel 01604 505808**

NEW **Courteenhall, Northampton** ♿✗❀ (Charles & Joan Wake) *At junction 15 of M1 set milo meter to zero. Take A508 S signed Milton Keynes. Exactly 1m turn L immediately before pillar box. Follow signs down drive. NB Ignore signed rd to Courteenhall ½m S of M1 junction15.* Fine arboretum, formal gardens with extensive lawns and good herbaceous beds. Interesting walled garden. Georgian House (not open) by Samuel Saxon with traditional Repton Park. TEAS. *Adm £2 Chd free. Sat June 24 (2-5)*

Cranford Gardens, nr Kettering *4½m E of Kettering. A14 Kettering-Thrapston. Car parking available* TEAS. *Combined adm £2 Chd 50p (ACNO to Kettering Hospital Centenary Appeal). Sun July 2 (2-6)*

NEW **32 Church Lane** (Mr & Mrs D Bates) 1-acre of landscaped garden featuring trees, shrubs and herbaceous borders

16 Duck End (Margaret Thomson) Very small cottage garden . Borders of perennials and shrubs

45 High Street (Mr & Mrs M Naylor) A flower arranger's garden with many herbaceous plants, fernery, herb garden, pond

NEW **The Old Forge** (Cranford Arts) *From Cranford High St, turn into Grafton Rd (next to village hall).* An old forge garden with herbaceous borders, many containers TEAS.

Station House (Mr & Mrs A Bates) Garden created from the original railway station. Old platform now a walled patio with fishpond and rockery. Many varieties of trees, new planting of shrubs, herbaceous perennials. TEAS. **Also 2 small cottage gardens** - "Over the garden wall"

4 The Green (Mr & Mrs M Braines)

8 The Green (Mr I Wilson)

Deene Park, nr Corby (Edmund Brudenell Esq) *5m N of Corby on A43 Stamford-Kettering Rd.* Large garden; long mixed borders, old-fashioned roses, rare mature trees, shrubs, natural garden, large lake and waterside walks. Parterre designed by David Hicks echoing the C16 decoration on the porch stonework. Interesting Church and Brudenell Chapel with fine tombs and brasses. TEAS. *Adm £2 Chd 50p. Suns May 21, Sept 10 (2-5)*

Easton Neston, Towcester (The Lord & Lady Hesketh) *Entrance on Northampton Rd (old A43).* Hawksmoor's only private house (not open). Large formal garden; ornamental water, topiary; walled garden; woodland walk and C14 church (open in grounds). TEAS. *Adm £2.50 Chd 50p. Sun June 18 (2-6)*

4 Elmington Cottages, Elmington (Mr & Mrs D L Welman) *Proceed N along A605 from Oundle, garden ½m on R.* 4 acres started 1992. Herbaceous border, shrubbery, orchard, native and ornamental trees, kitchen garden, lavender and yew walks. *Adm £2 Chd free. Suns March 19, May 28 (2-6)*

Evenley Gardens, Brackley *From Brackley 1m S on A43.* Teas available. *Combined adm £2 Chd 50p. Suns June 11, Sept 24 (2-6).* **Evening Openings** *Tues June 13, 20 (5-9)*

15 Church Lane (Mr & Mrs K O'Regan) ⅓-acre garden with pond, mixed borders and vegetables. Terrace and herbs. Further orchard taken in 1998. Open all dates

33 The Green (Mr & Mrs A Bullock) A young garden, developing with a young family, with an accent on design. Open all dates

Hill Grounds (Mr & Mrs C F Cropley) Garden designer and lecturer's mainspring of inspiration. Plantsman's garden of 2 acres sheltered by 200yds C19 yew hedge. Many rare plants. *Open all dates*

Evenley Wood Garden, Brackley (R T Whiteley) *A43 3/4m S of Brackley, turn L to Evenley straight through village towards Mixbury 1st turning L.* A woodland garden spread over a 60-acre mature wood. Acid and alkaline soil. Magnolias, rhododenrons, azaleas, malus, quercus, acers, euonymus collection and many other species. A large collection of bulbous plants. TEAS. *Adm £2 Chd £1(ACNO to Mixbury Church). Suns, Mons April 23, 24, 30, May 1, 28, 29 (2-6) Private visits welcome, please Tel* **01280 703329**

Finedon Gardens, Wellingborough *2m NE of Wellingborough on the A510, 6m SE Kettering on the A6.* Teas in aid of Finedon Church, at Finedon Antique Centre. *Combined adm £1.50 Chd free Sun July 9 (2-6)*

1 Grove Way (Mr & Mrs P J Sibley) Small recently established plantsman's garden

4 Harrowden Lane (Mr & Mrs D J West) ½-acre garden on a steep slope, created since 1982 from waste land; lawns, flower beds; ornamental fish pond, aviary and greenhouses

67-69 High Street (Mr & Mrs S Hendry) ⅓-acre rear garden of a C17 cottage. Herbaceous perennials and many containers, vegetable plot

23 Regent Street (Mr & Mrs G Perkins) ½-acre garden, organically cultivated, 2 large ponds, aviaries and numerous pets. Large collection of containers

Flore Gardens, nr Northampton *7m W of Northampton, 5m E of Daventry on A45.* Flower Festival at All Saints Church and U.R Chapel. incl light lunches, Teas, plants, etc. *Combined adm £2.50 Chd free (ACNO to Flore Flower Festival). Sat, Sun June 17, 18 (11-6)*

Beech Hill (Dr & Mrs R B White) 1-acre facing S over Nene Valley. Mature trees, lawns and mixed borders, vegetable garden, orchard, alpine house and cool greenhouse containing orchids and carnivorous plants. Many varieties of clematis

24 Bliss Lane (John & Sally Miller) A small cottage garden with shrubs, perennials and herbs, summer house and vegetable patch

Bliss Lane Nursery (Chris Littlewood) An easily maintained informal garden opening out to a S facing nursery, surrounded by beech hedging and overlooking the Nene Valley

The Croft (John & Dorothy Boast) ⅓-acre cottage garden with mature trees, shrubs, lawns, interesting perennials, climbers and herbs

38 High Street (Mr & Mrs P Harrison) ¾-acre informal garden with views over the Nene valley. Incl mature trees, pond, vegetable garden and perennials

The Manor House (Richard & Wendy Amos) 1-acre garden with established lawns and herbaceous border surrounded by mature trees. Formal pond and walled kitchen garden

The Old Manor (Mr & Mrs Keith Boyd) Medium-sized garden of early C18 house (not open) comprising lawn, herbaceous border, rose garden, vegetables, fruit. Paddock with pond and shrubs

6 Thornton Close (Mr & Mrs D L Lobb) Medium-sized garden; trees, shrubs, herbaceous plants, conifers and alpines. 2 fish ponds

Froggery Cottage, 85 Breakleys Road, Desborough ❀ (Mr John Lee) *Signed off A6. 6m N of Kettering, 5m S of Market Harborough.* ½-acre plantsman's garden full of rare and unusual plants, special collection of over 225 varieties of penstemons incl dwarfs and species. Artefacts on display incl old ploughs and garden implements. Lunches and TEAS in aid of local charities. *Adm £1.50 Chd free. Sun July 30 (11.30-6)*

Gamekeepers Cottage, Cottesbrooke ♿✂❀ (Mr & Mrs D R Daw) *10m W of Northampton, nr Creaton on A50; nr Brixworth on A508.* Cottage garden featuring unusual herbaceous plants, flowers for drying, fruit, vegetables, native plants with a difference. Strictly organic. Featured on Ch4 Garden Club and in various publications. For NGS only. *Combined adm £2.50 Chd £1.25 with* **Cottesbrooke Hall**. *Suns June 18, Aug 13 (2-6)*

Glendon Hall, Kettering ♿✂❀ (Rosie Bose Jim & Sally Scott, Gary Proctor & Tracey Bottomly) *3m NW of Kettering. Take A6003 to Corby off roundabout W of Kettering, turn L onto Glendon Rd, signposted Rothwell, Desborough, Rushton. Entrance 1½m on L.* Approx 2 acres Victorian gardens. Mature specimen trees, topiary, box hedges, herbaceous borders stocked with many unusual plants, large walled kitchen gardens. TEAS. *Adm £2. Mon May 29 (2-6.30) Private visits welcome, please* **Tel 01536 711732**

Great Addington Manor, Great Addington (Mr & Mrs G E Groome) *7m SE of Kettering, 4m W Thrapston, A510 exit off A14 signed Finedon and Wellingborough. Turn 2nd L to the Addingtons.* 4½-acre manor gardens with lawns, mature trees, mulberry, yew hedges, pond and spinney. Spring daffodils. Teas in aid of Great Addington Church in Village Hall. *Adm £2 Chd over 5yrs 50p. Mon April 24 (2-5.30)*

Great Brington Gardens, Northampton ✂ *7m NW of Northampton off A428 Rugby rd. 1st L turn past main gates of Althorp.* Tickets/maps at church. Gardens signed in village. Parking facilities. Lunches, TEAS. Exhibition and plant stalls at various village venues in aid of St Mary's Church. *Combined adm £2 Chd free. Sun May 7 (11-5)*

Beard's Cottage ❀ (Captain & Mrs L G Bellamy) ½-acre of lawns, shrubs and herbaceous borders. Small vegetable garden

10 Bedford Cottages (Sue Paice & Phil Richardson) A wildlife garden designed to encourage wildflowers, butterflies, birds, bats and other mammals and insects. Ponds, feeding stations, hedgerows, nestboxes and a small meadow form part of this totally organic garden

Brington Lodge ♿❀ (Mr & Mrs P J Cooch) An old garden on the edge of the village, approx ¾ acre, partially walled with a number of spring flowering trees and shrubs. *Open every Wed in May and June or willingly by appointment.* **Tel 01604 770159**

30 Great Brington ♿ (Mr & Mrs John Kimbell) Interesting small garden attached to old stone cottage, well-stocked with shrubs, climbers and perennials. Small pond with bog area, secret garden

New Cross ♿ (Mr R J Kimbell) ½-acre old country garden surrounding a mellow Northamptonshire stone house. Mature trees and shrubs with many spring flowering bulbs

The Old Rectory ♿ (Mr & Mrs R Thomas) 3-acre garden with mature trees, yew hedging, formal rose garden, vegetable and small herb gardens. ½-acre orchard

Ridgway House (Mr & Mrs John Gale) 1½ acres with lawns, herbaceous borders and many spring-flowering shrubs and bulbs

Rose Cottage ♿ (Mr David Green) 3yr-old estate cottage garden designed, built and planted by owner. Variety of fan fruit trees, rockery and brick terrace with pagoda

Great Harrowden Gardens, nr Wellingborough *On A509 2m N of Wellingborough on the L. 5m S of Kettering on the R.* Cream TEAS. *Combined adm £2 Chd free. Sun June 25 (2-6)*

Dolphins ♿✂❀ (Mr & Mrs R C Handley) 2-acre country garden surrounding old stone house. Many old roses grown among interesting trees, shrubs and a wide range of hardy perennials

Great Harrowden Lodge ♿❀ (Mrs J & Mr R M Green) *Situated ¾m from Great Harrowden Church on the lane to Finedon.* 1¼-acre garden on a dry exposed site. Wide variety of herbaceous plants in long borders and island beds. Herb garden

1 The Green, Kingsthorpe Village ✂❀ (Mrs I Nightingale) *2m N of Northampton Town Centre. Turn off A508 into Mill Lane at Cock Hotel junction, taking 2nd turn R.* ⅓-acre welll-established garden on steep slope, partly terraced. Planned for yr-round interest with a variety of trees, shrubs, herbaceous and climbing plants; to be explored with many surprises. TEAS *Adm £1.20 Chd 50p Sun July 23 (12-5), Wed July 26 (2-6)*

Guilsborough and Hollowell Gardens *10m NW of Northampton between A5199 (formerly A50) - A428. 10m E of Rugby.* Cream TEAS at Dripwell House by Guilsborough WI. Teas at Hollowell Village Hall. *Combined adm £2.50 Chd free. Sun May 21 (2-6). Private visits welcome for parties of 12 and over*

Dripwell House, Guilsborough ✂❀ (Mr J W Langfield & Dr C Moss) 2½-acre mature garden; many fine trees and shrubs on partly terraced slope. Rock garden, herbaceous border, herb garden. Unusual shrubs, rhododendrons and azaleas in woodland garden. Cream TEAS in garden. **Tel 01604 740140**

Gower House ❀ (Peter & Ann Moss) Small garden evolving since 1991 on part of Dripwell vegetable garden. A plantsman's garden with herbaceous alpine, climbing plants and shrubs. **Tel 01604 740755**

NEW **Guilsborough House** ♿ (Mr & Mrs John McCall) *Southern extreme of Guilsborough on Hollowelll rd. Parking for Guilsborough Garden in field.* Country garden, terraces, lawns and hedges, mature trees

Rosemount, Hollowell ♿✂❀ (Mr & Mrs J Leatherland) *In centre of village, up hill behind bus shelter towards Church, entrance 100yds on R* ½-acre plantsman's garden, unusual plants and shrubs, alpine garden, fish pond, small collections of clematis, conifers, camellias, daphne and abutilons. Partly suitable for wheelchairs. Car parking and Teas at village hall behind Church, **Tel 01604 740354**

The Haddonstone Show Garden, East Haddon Manor, nr Northampton ♿✂❀ (Mrs R Barrow) *10m N of Northampton, 12m S of Rugby, from A428.* Walled garden on different levels, old shrub roses, ground cover plants, conifers, clematis and climbers; swimming pool surrounded by Haddonstone Colonnade, over 30 planted pots and containers. TEAS. *Adm £2.50 OAP £2 Chd free (ACNO to NSPCC).* **Evening Opening** *Thurs June 8 (5-9), Sun July 30 (2-6)*

Harpole Gardens, Northampton *4m W Northampton on A45 towards Weedon. Turn R at The Turnpike Hotel into Harpole.* TEAS and stalls at The Close. *Combined adm £2 Chd free. Sun June 25 (12-6)*

The Close ♿❀ (Mr and Mrs M Orton-Jones) *68 High St* Old-fashioned English country garden with large lawns, herbaceous borders and mature trees, stone house

The Cottage (Mr & Mrs J Roan) *23 Park Lane* An informal cottage garden transformed from a rubbish tip

47b High Street (Mr & Mrs Peter Rixon) An enclosed sixth of an acre garden consisting of cottage borders, a rockery, pond, rose and herb areas; a Japanese style feature and a large collection of cacti and succulents

74 Larkhall Lane (Mr & Mrs J Leahy) A medium-sized informal garden with a wide variety of plants, shrubs, some mature trees, climbers, alpines, pond and small vegetable plot. Becoming more established after many changes

19 Manor Close (Mr & Mrs E Kemshed) 40yds × 10yds flower arranger's garden on an estate, cultivated by present owners since 1975

Millers (Mr & Mrs M Still) *56 Upper High St* Old stone farmhouse with about an acre of lawns and mixed borders mainly shrubs; some mature trees; good views overlooking the farm and strawberry field

Thorpe House (Mr & Mrs R Fountain) A walled cottage garden with many unusual plants and sunken water feature created by the present owners

NEW **Haze Cottage, Long Buckby** ♿✂ (Ann & Peter Hartley) *On the B5385, ½m E from centre of village.* ⅓-acre country garden. Designed over the last 10yrs around an existing orchard. Cottage garden border to front. Mixed borders. Open views. *Combined adm with* **The Old Fountain** *£2 Chd free. Sun July 16 (1-6)*

▲ **Holdenby House, Garden and Falconry Centre** ❀ (Mr & Mrs James Lowther) *6m NW of Northampton. Signposted from A5199 and A428.* Impressive house and garden built from the Elizabethan remains of the largest house in England. Miniature Elizabethan garden by Rosemary Verey. Fragrant border replanted by Rupert Golby. Silver border and kitchen garden. Falconry centre and C17 farmstead bring this historical garden to life. Children's attractions, events and house open on bank hols. TEAS and shop. *Gardens and Falconry Adm £3 (groups of 25 or more £2.50) OAP £2.75 Chd £1.75. For NGS Sun May 14 (2-6)*

Irthlingborough, Wellingborough ♿✂❀ (Mr & Mrs D Ingall) *49 Finedon Rd. 5m E of Wellingborough, off the A6.* A garden of approx 1 acre full of interest and unusual plants, incl spring bulbs, herbaceous border, shrubs, pools, gravel bed and rock garden, wild and scented areas. Also fruit and vegetables. TEAS in aid of Barnardos. *Adm £1.50 Chd free. Tues April 25, Sun May 21 (2-5.30). Private visits welcome between Easter and end of July, please* **Tel 01933 650343**

■ **Kelmarsh Hall, Market Harborough** ♿❀ (Estate Preservation Trust) *5m S of Market Harborough, on A508 to Northampton. ½m N of junction of A508 with A14. Entrance at Top Lodge, on Xrds in Kelmarsh Village.* 1730 Palladian house by James Gibbs. C18 landscape with lake and woods. C20 garden by Nancy Lancaster. Spring bulbs, rose gardens, scented garden, herbaceous borders planted by Norah Lindsay, woodland walks. TEAS. *Adm £3.50 Chd £2. House and Garden open Suns and Bank Hol Mons Easter to end Aug (2.30-5). Garden only Tues, Thurs, April 4 to end Sept . Adm £2 Chd £1. For NGS Thurs April 20, June 22 (2-4.30)*

Kilsby Gardens, nr Rugby ❀ *5m SE of Rugby on A428 turn R on B4038 through village. 6m N of Daventry on A361.* Teas in village hall in aid of Village Hall funds. *Combined adm £2.50 Chd free. Sun June 25 (2-6)*

Carrillon (Mr & Mrs R Yabsley) Curves are the order for this small garden of approx 100sq m. The curved, raised, well stocked flower beds are complemented by the shaped path leading to a patio. Small fish pond set into a rock garden, The garden benefits from the mature trees in the adjacent garden which soften the high walls that surround it

Elms House (Mr & Mrs D Willis) Approx ½-acre developed over last 7yrs from derelict house and garden. Ponds, shrubs and herbaceous borders, grasses and vegetable garden

The Hollies ♿ (Mrs Ann Liddington) Garden developed within old farmyard. Herbaceous borders, roses, clematis, unusual plants and pond

NEW **Laurelcroft Cottage** (Miss G Mason) A small garden with some old fruit trees. Borders and beds with shrubs, perennials and annuals. Containers, greenhouse

Manor Cottage ✂ (Madam Cheng) A small partly stone walled cottage garden adjacent to a C17 thatched cottage. Borders designed for easy maintenance. Small vegetable plot and fruit trees, water feature utilising reclaimed natural materials

The Old Vicarage ♿✂ (Mr and Mrs P G B Jackson) *On A5 opp George Hotel.* 1-acre, lawns, mature trees, shrubs, herbaceous border, small water garden, vegetable garden

Pytchley House ♿✂ (Mr & Mrs T F Clay) *14 Main Rd* 1-acre mature garden still developing(!); lawns; trees; island beds; vegetables; new cottage garden; ponds; wild area

The Rickyard (Dr & Mrs N Gostick) A small walled garden in former farmyard. Some orginal features retained. Emphasis on 'vertical gardening' and containers to maximise space. Irrigation system reduces watering. Organic. Flower arrangers garden

The White House ♿ (John & Lesley Loader) *Chapel Street.* ½-acre partly walled garden with ponds and stream, heather bed, herbaceous border, vegetable garden and raised beds

Litchborough Gardens, nr Towcester ⚘ *Mid-way between Northampton and Banbury.* Teas in WI Hall. *Combined adm £2.50 Chd free (ACNO to St Martins Church). Sun June 4 (2-6)*

Bruyere Court ♿ (Mr R Martin) *Farthingstone Rd.* 4 acres of landscaped garden featuring lawns; 2 ornamental lakes with rock streams and fountain; shrub borders; rhododendron and azalea borders; herbaceous border; old-fashioned roses; ornamental trees and conifers

The Hall ♿ (Mr & Mrs A R Heygate) Large garden with open views of parkland; laid to lawns and borders with clipped hedges around the house; the extensive woodland garden has large numbers of specimen trees and shrubs; walks wind through this area and around the lakes

The House on the Green (Mr and Mrs K E Ellis) ¼-acre cottage garden which incls a well, summerhouse, water feature, rockery, variety of trees, shrubs, roses and bulbs, flowering plants, herb garden, soft fruit and fruit trees

NEW **The Old School** (Mr & Mrs S Burd) ¼-acre garden under further development from former school playground. Incls formal and informal gravel gardens, courtyard garden and a small wildflower area with a well. Oak and walnut trees amongst shrub and herbaceous borders

Orchard House ❀ (Mr & Mrs B Smith) *Banbury Rd* Landscape architects country garden designed for low maintenance; orchard, pools, conservatory and working pump. *Private visits welcome by parties of less than 5, please* **Tel 01327 830144**

Lois Weedon House, Weedon Lois (Sir John & Lady Greenaway) *7m from Towcester on the edge of village. Last entrance on R going E towards Wappenham.* Large garden with terraces and fine views; lawns; pergola; water garden; mature yew hedges; pond. TEAS. *Combined adm with* **The Old Barn** *£2 Chd free (ACNO to Lois Weedon PCC). Sun May 28 (2-6)*

Maidwell Gardens ⚘ *8m N of Northampton on A508, 6m S of Market Harborough.* **Wisteria Cottage** *also open.* TEAS. *Combined adm £2.50 Chd free. Sun June 18 (2-6), Wed June 21 (10-6)*

The Old Bake House (Ken & Angela Palmer) Small walled garden with herbaceous borders and shrubs

The Old Barn ♿❀ (Mr & Mrs John Groocock) 3/4-acre garden developed around an old stone barn. Mixed herbaceous and shrub borders, clematis and roses

School Farmhouse (Mr & Mrs D J Carter-Johnson) 3/4-acre walled cottage garden brimful of traditional mid-summer flowering perennials

■ **The Menagerie, Horton** ♿⚘❀ (Mr A Myers) *On B526, 6m S of Northampton, 1m S of Horton, turn E at lay-by, across field.* These newly developed gardens are set around an C18 folly, with 2 delightful thatched arbours. Most recently completed is the exotic bog garden to complement the native wetland garden. Also rose garden, shrubberies, herbaceous borders and wild flower areas. TEAS. *Adm £3.50 Chd £1.50. Mon & Thurs (2-5) April to Sept incl and last Sun of the month (2-6). House, garden and shell grotto open to parties by written appt. For NGS Sun June 25 (2-6)*

Nortoft Grange, Guilsborough ❀ (Sir John & Lady Lowther) *10m NW of Northampton, between A5199 (A50) and A428. On Naseby, Welford rd out of village.* 5-acre garden redeveloped over past 3 yrs. The herbaceous borders planted with a rich variety of shrubs and plants, many propogated by ourselves and will be on sale. Meadow where we are planting an interesting mixture of trees. Recently enlarged pond. We are struggling to establish a wild flower meadow on blue clay soil. TEAS. *Combined adm with* **Guilsborough and Hollowell** *£2.50 Chd free. Sun May 21 (2-6). Adm £1.50 Chd free (ACNO to Parkinson's Disease Society). Sun July 9 (2-5.30)*

The Nursery Gardens, Geddington ♿❀ (Christine Sturman) *3m N of Kettering on A43. Turn into village. Follow brown tourist signs for 'Boughton House'. Nursery gardens approx ½m on R.* 1-acre garden, set in 2½ acres which incl a spinney, paddock and nursery. Shrub and herbaceous borders, sunken garden, pergola walk and orchard. Featuring a cottage garden, mediterranean area and display beds. TEAS. *Adm £1.50 Chd free. Suns April 9, June 11, Sept10 (2-5) Group visits, evenings by appt, please* **Tel 01536 461020**

The Old Barn, Weedon Lois ⚘❀ (Mr & Mrs John Gregory) Plantsman's garden designed by the owners to compliment converted C18 barn; interesting selection of hardy perennials, incl collections of euphorbia, hardy geraniums and violas. Unusual plants for sale. TEAS. *Combined adm £2 with* **Lois Weedon House.** *Sun May 28. Adm £1.50. Weds June 21, July 5 (2-5)*

The Old Fountain, Long Buckby ♿⚘ (Ann & David Croston) *8m E of Northampton midway between the A428 and A5. Close to centre of village. Parking and toilet facilities at village square.* ⅓-acre partially walled garden. Interesting and varied perennials arranged in a series of colour themes set amongst mature shrubs, vegetable area, fruit cage and greenhouses. Garden under constant development. TEAS in aid of Long Buckby and District Gardening Club. *Combined adm with* **Haze Cottage** *£2 Chd free. Sun July 16. Adm £1 Chd free. Tues Sept 5 (1-6)*

The Old Glebe, Brackley ♿ (Richard Watson) *1½m N from Brackley town centre on the Radstone rd.* Garden developed from 6 acres of farmland over 8yrs. This is a blend of formal areas with herbaceous borders, semi tropical pond with island and stream /cascade. Mediterranean style 'hot' area is conceived for 2000. Teas at Versions Farm. *Combined Adm £2.50 with* **Turweston Mill** *and* **Versions Farm**. *Sun July 9 (2-6)*

■ **The Old Rectory, Sudborough** ♿⚘ (Mr & Mrs A Huntington) *exit 12 off A14. Village just off A6116 between Thrapston & Brigstock.* Classic 3-acre country garden with rare and unusual plants surrounding a fine Georgian Rectory (not open). Features incl mixed shrub and herbaceous borders; formal rose garden; newly planted pond area alongside Harper's Brook; woodland walk; spring bulbs and hellebore collection a specialty. Potager originally designed by Rosemary Verey and developed by the owners with Rupert Golby. Quantity of containers with emphasis on summer half-hardies. TEAS in aid of All Saints Church. *Adm £3 Chd free. Open every Tues April to Sept (10-4). For NGS Suns March 26, June 18 (2-6). Private visits welcome, please* **Tel 01832 733247**

Park House, Norton (Mr & Mrs J H Wareing Russell) *3½m N of Weedon (A5) 2nd Norton/Daventry turn on Loff A5. Garden entrance L before village.* Approx 5 acres. Lawns leading down to lakes. Large variety of trees and shrubs, herbaceous borders, heather beds, azalea, roses and ¼m lakeside walk. TEAS. *Adm £2 Chd free. Sun July 9 (2-6). Private visits welcome by appt, please* **Tel 01327 702455**

NEW **Peters Farm, Helmdon** (Sue Wallace) *5m N of Brackley. Follow B4525 W from A43 turn R to Helmdon (N). Bear L at war memorial to Sulgrave (W). 1m out of village.* The garden has developed over 15yrs from fields into 5 acres of formal borders and lawns with geometrical designs. Wildlife areas with meadow grasses, wild flowers, wooded area and pond. A mixture of shrubs, herbaceous perennials, grasses and annuals providing interest throughout the yr. Many plants have been propagated by myself. TEAS. *Adm £2 Chd free. Sun July 2 (2-6)*

■ **The Prebendal Manor House, Nassington** (Mrs J Baile) *Church Street, off c14 Wansford to Oundle Rd. 6m N of Oundle, 8m W of Peterborough, 6m S of Stamford.* 6-acres of recreated medieval gardens and wild flowers within the grounds of historic early C13 manor. House and gardens open on Sun and Wed May to Sept (2-5.30). Audio tours. TEAS. *Adm House and Garden £4 Chd £1.20 garden only £3 Chd £1.20. For NGS Sat June 24 (2-5.30). Please* **Tel 01780 782575**

Preston Capes Gardens *Approx 7m S of Daventry, 3m N of Canon's Ashby.* Ploughmans Lunch and Homemade TEAS at Old West Farm. Plants in aid of St Peter's & St Paul's Church. *Combined adm £2.50 Chd free. Sun June 11 (12-5)*

City Cottage (Mr & Mrs Gavin Cowen) A mature garden in the middle of an attractive village, with a walled herbaceous border, rose beds, flowering shrubs, wisteria

The Folly (Mr & Mrs A Carlisle) Approx ½-acre informal garden, with outstanding views. Lawns with specimen shrubs, herbaceous borders and ornamental fish pond. Sloping plot, with pond, marginal plants and berry-bearing trees and shrubs

Old West Farm (Mr & Mrs Gerard Hoare) *Little Preston* Maturing 2-acre garden. Woodland area underplanted with shrubs and bulbs. Roses and borders designed for yr-round interest

Ravensthorpe Gardens *Halfway between Rugby and Northampton. Signposted Ravensthope 1½m from the A428.* TEAS in aid of Guilsborough School PTA. *Combined adm £2 Chd free. Sun July 16 (2-6)* **Evening Opening** *£1.50, Wed July 19 (6.30-9)*

32 The High Street (Mr & Mrs J Patrick) Moderate size garden planted over the last 8yrs. Mostly perennials but some shrubs and roses; also greenhouses and vegetables

Ravensthorpe Nursery (Mr & Mrs Richard Wiseman) Approx 1-acre new show garden being developed to display plants; wide range of shrubs, trees and hardy perennials, incl shrub rose and mixed borders with fine views; also private ¼-acre owners' plantman's garden. **Tel 01604 770548**

Sholebroke Lodge, Whittlebury (A B X Fenwick Esq) *3m S of Towcester. Turn off A413 Towcester end of Whittlebury village.* 5-acre informal garden around attractive buildings. Grass walks through shrubs incl collection of viburnums and fine tree peonies. Wall plants and pond planting. Home-made TEAS. *Combined adm with* **Blackpitts** *House £2 Chd free. Sun June 4 (1-6)*

Slapton Gardens, Slapton *A tiny village 4m W of Towcester ¼m N of the Towcester to Wappenham Rd. Superb small 13/14th century village church, public footpath round village passing the Old Mill and stream. Car park by church.* Teas at Slapton Lodge. *Combined adm £2 Chd free. Sun June 18 (2-6)*

Boxes Farm (Mary & James Miller) Approx ¼-acre completely new garden created in 1997 around a rebuilt typical 'Grafton' farmhouse (not open). Garden had not been touched for over 30yrs. Small formal rose garden, herbaceous border surrounded by yews

NEW **Eaton Grey House** (Mrs P E Coats) Cottage garden, designed and planted in March 1997. Well stocked with roses, shrubs and some unusual plants. All-yr-round interest and a perfect example of what can be done with a small space in a short space of time

Fellyard (Mr & Mrs R Owen) Many changes to this mature 1½-acre garden since it was last open in 1997. New bog garden and stream, nuttery, wildflower meadow, and green/white and allium/iris borders. Herbaceous borders in progress, large kitchen garden and herb parterre, rose garden, espaliered fruit trees, orchards, and unusual specimen trees and plants in a rural setting. *Private visits welcome, please* **Tel 01327 860214**

The Old Royal Oak (Mrs David Mumford) An all-yr-round garden planted originally in 1989, matured trees and shrubs provide continuous colour heightened by herbaceous plants and bulbs. Scree bed provides extra interest in spring and early summer ½-acre - easy maintenance with some help

Spratton Gardens, Spratton *6½m NNW of Northampton off A5199. Turn R to Brixworth, L past Kings Head to car park.* Tickets/map at car park. Gardens signed in village. TEAS. *Combined adm £2 Chd free (ACNO to St Andrews Church, Spratton). Sun June 11 (2-6)*

NEW **Cotfield** (Roger & Joyce Rees) 1-acre walled Victorian garden featuring a mature tulip tree, border, rock garden and rose garden

NEW **9 Glebelands** (Mr & Mrs R Smith) Immaculate 80' x 25' garden with masses of colour, water feature and gravel rockery

NEW **Hunters Park** (Dr Angus Walker) 1½-acre garden with views over undulating farmland framed by mature ash trees. Attractive pond with waterfall, fish and conifer rockery

NEW The Stables (Mr & Mrs A Woods) 3/4-acre garden planted for all yr colour with shrubs, herbaceous borders, rockery, scree planting, ponds and pergola

NEW 6 Yew Tree Lane & (Mr & Mrs M Heaton) ½-acre part cottage style plus feature mulberry tree, lawns, herbaceous, rose and shrub borders, shady planting and water features

The Spring House, Chipping Warden ✗ (Mr & Mrs C Shepley-Cuthbert) *Mill Lane, on A361 between Banbury and Daventry.* Garden originally laid out by Miss Kitty Lloyd Jones in the thirties and now mature. Approx 3 acres app through a 16' tapestry hedge. April-May spring flowers, bulbs and blossom. June-Sept bog and water garden at its most colourful. Other times unconventional borders, shrub roses and specimen trees with many new plantings. Ploughmans lunches and Teas available for groups & clubs by arrangement. *Private visits welcome April to Oct, please* **Tel 01295 660261**

▲ **Stoke Park, Stoke Bruerne** & (A S Chancellor Esq) *Towcester. 1m off A508 between Northampton and Stony Stratford. Stoke Park is down a private road ¾m, 1st turning L, ¼m beyond village.* Approx 3 acres. Terraced lawn with ornamental basin, orchard, herb garden, shrub and other borders, as setting to two C17 pavillions and colonnade. TEA. *Adm £2 Chd £1. For NGS* Sun June 11 (2-6)

NEW Terracend, Burton Latimer (Bill & Daphne Frum) *3m S of Kettering approached from A14, A509 and A6.* Town garden 100' long with areas of special interest, a wealth of containers with hostas, lilies, fuchsias and clematis - over 60 varieties in diffferent situations. Many ferns, vegetables and fruit in raised beds. TEA. *Adm £1.50 Chd free.* Weds July 5, 12, 19, 26 (11-5)

Titchmarsh Gardens, nr Thrapston *2m N of Thrapston, 6m S of Oundle on A605, Titchmarsh signposted as turning to E.* TEAS in aid of St Mary's Church Titchmarsh *Combined adm £2 Chd free* Sun June 11 (2-6)

Glebe Cottage &✗ (Mrs J Bussens) ⅓ acre; NE aspect; informal herbaceous and shrub borders and beds. Clematis in a variety of situations

16 Polopit ✗ (Mr & Mrs C Millard) ½ acre. Developed since 1984; rockeries, ornamental and herbaceous borders; fruit decorative shrubs

Titchmarsh House &✗ (Mr & Mrs Ewan Harper) For description see separate entry below *Private visits welcome, please* **Tel 01832 732439**

Titchmarsh House, Titchmarsh & (Mr & Mrs Ewan Harper) *2m N of Thrapston, 6m of Oundle on A605, Titchmarsh signed as turning to E.* 4 acres extended and laid out since 1972; cherries, magnolias, herbaceous irises; shrubs roses, clematis, range of unusual shrubs, walled borders. TEA. *Adm £2 Chd free (ACNO to St Mary's Church). Special opening for Dryden Tercentenary.* Sun April 30 (2-5.30) *Private visits welcome, please* **Tel 01832 732439**

Turweston Mill &✗ (Mr & Mrs Harry Leventis) 5 acres, mill stream, water garden, lawns. TEAS at Versions Farm.

Open with **The Old Glebe** *and* **Versions Farm**. *Combined adm £2.50 Chd free.* Sun July 9 (2-6)

Versions Farm, Brackley &✗❀ (Mrs E T Smyth-Osbourne) *2m N of Brackley Town Hall take R turn to Turweston.* 3-acres plantsman's garden; wide-range of unusual plants; shrubs and trees; old stone walls; terraces; old-fashioned rose garden; pond. Conservatory. Cream TEAS in aid Whitfield Church. *Combined adm with* **The Old Glebe** *and* **Turweston Mill** *£2.50 Chd free.* Sun July 9 (2-6). *Parties welcome by appt May to July, please* **Tel 01280 702412**

■ **The Walnuts, King's Cliffe** (Mr & Mrs Martin Lawrence) *7m NE of Oundle, 7m SW of Stamford, 4m W of Wansford from A1 and A47; last house on L leaving King's Cliffe on rd to Apethorpe.* 2½-acre country garden with lawns, mature trees and hedges, mixed herbaceous and shrub borders, sunken rose garden. Mown pathway through meadow to pond, Willowbrook and woodland walk. Ornamental vegetable garden. TEAS in aid of All Saints Church. *Adm £1.50 Chd free. Every Wed April 5 to July 26. For NGS Combined adm with* **Brock's Close** *£2.50 Chd free.* Sat, Sun April 8, 9 (2-6). *Private visits welcome, please* **Tel 01780 470312**

The **National Gardens Scheme** (registered charity no. 279284) raises money for charities through the generosity of garden owners who open their fine gardens to the public on behalf of the Scheme.

HELP THE HOSPICES

Help the Hospices works with hospices to ensure that the best possible care is available for the terminally ill – people with advanced cancer, motor neurone disease, AIDS and other progressive, terminal illnesses

For further information on this charity, please contact: Help the Hospices, 34-44 Britannia Street, London WC1X 9JG.

Information is also available on the NGS website (www.ngs.org.uk)

West Haddon Gardens *The village is on the A428 between Rugby and Northampton and lies 4m E of M1 exit 18.* Teas in village hall and Baptist hall. *Combined adm £2.50 Chd free (ACNO to Parkinson's Disease and Human Communication International). Sun July 2 (2-6)*

Beech Trees ✂ (Gerald & Daphne Kennaird) Small partially walled garden with views over rolling Northamptonshire countryside. Terrace, lawns, mixed borders and small pond

Crystal House (Simon & Diana Cotton) ⅓ acre of walled garden with lawns, mixed borders, and an unusual summer house

Hardays House (Guy & Anne Ballantyne) 1½ acres, lawns and shrubbery on sloping ground with S-facing views, pond, vegetables and flower beds

Lime House ✂ (Lesley & David Roberts) ½-acre of walled garden with rockeries, herbaceous borders, walk-through shrubbery, rose beds; croquet lawn. Summer-house and patio with greenhouse

The Mews ✂ (Rob & Jane Dadley) ½-acre of secluded walled garden including lawns, secret garden, herbaceous border, formal and informal ponds, statuary and pergolas

Wesleyan Cottages (Stephanie & Paul Russell) Small walled garden with walkways and paved sitting areas. Colourful borders and containers and newly built pond and summer house

West Cottage (Geoff & Rosemary Sage) 1 acre of mixed borders and lawns; informal ponds; lawn tennis court; kitchen garden and greenhouses; many containers and baskets

Wisteria Cottage, Maidwell ✂❀ (Mr & Mrs P J Montgomery) *8m N of Northampton on A508. 6m S of Market Harborough.* A plantsman's cottage garden, approx ½-acre, originally farmland. Designed and planted by owners since 1989. Comprising a series of rooms in themed planting and structures. Featured in 'The English Garden'. TEAS. *Adm donations NGS. Daily April 23 to Sept 24 (2-6) also opening with* **Maidwell Gardens Tel 01604 686308**

Evening Opening (See also garden description)

Evenley Gardens, Brackley	June 13 & 20
The Haddonstone Show Garden, East Haddon Manor, nr Northampton	June 8
Ravensthorpe Gardens	July 19

Mediaeval Garden Ornaments
by Parva Classics
Duncote, Towcester
Tel: **01327 351824**

The Gardener's Companion

On 31 March a brand new 100 page glossy will arrive on news stands: *The Gardener's Companion* (£3.95) will make the perfect accompaniment to *The Yellow Book*, featuring brilliant ideas from a host of gardens that open for the NGS, and advice from their deeply knowledgeable owners. In its pages you will find garden design inspiration, winning plant combinations, propagating tips, and even the ultimate cake recipe, all accompanied by luscious pictures from some of the country's top photographers. Also in this annual publication will be our comprehensive review of the year's best in the world of gardening – top new garden products, show garden ideas and the most beautiful plants on the market.

Northumberland & Tyne and Wear

Hon County Organiser Mrs Susie White, Hexham Herbs, Chesters Walled Garden, Chollerford, Hexham NE46 4BQ Tel 01434 681483

Assistant Hon County Organisers Mrs T Sale, Ilderton Glebe, Alnwick, Northumberland NE66 4YD Tel 01668 217293

Mrs G Baker-Cresswell, Preston Tower, Chathill, Northumberland NE67 5DH Tel 01665 589210

Mrs Patricia Fleming, Wooperton Hall,Alnwick, Northumberland NE66 4XS Tel 01668 217009

Hon County Treasurer Mrs D Kinniment, Sike View, Kirkwhelpington, Northumberland NE19 2SA Tel 01830 540393

DATES OF OPENING

Regular openings

For details see garden description

Bradley Nursery & Gardens, Wylam
Ford Nursey, Ford

April 29 Saturday
Bide-a-Wee Cottage, Stanton

May 17 Wednesday
Loughbrow House, Hexham

May 28 Sunday
66 Darras Road, Ponteland

May 29 Monday
Berryburn, Ancroft

May 31 Wednesday
Wallington, Cambo

June 4 Sunday
Hexham Herbs, Chesters Walled Garden, Chollerford
Lilburn Tower, Alnwick

June 14 Wednesday
Bide-a-Wee Cottage, Stanton

June 15 Thursday
Herterton House, Hartington

June 18 Sunday
9 Grenville Court, Darras Hall

June 21 Wednesday
Loughbrow House, Hexham

June 25 Sunday
Mindrum, Cornhill on Tweed

July 2 Sunday
Ingram Cottage, West Woodburn
Ravenside, East Heddon

July 9 Sunday
Kirkwhelpington Village Gardens
Kiwi Cottage, Scremerston

July 13 Thursday
Herterton House, Hartington

July 16 Sunday
Cragside, Rothbury
4 Hamilton Terrace, West Boldon

July 19 Wednesday
Loughbrow House, Hexham

July 23 Sunday
Dilston Mill House, nr Corbridge
70a The Gables, Morpeth

August 3 Thursday
Herterton House, Hartington

August 6 Sunday
66 Darras Road, Ponteland

August 9 Wednesday
Bide-a-Wee Cottage, Stanton

August 13 Sunday
Wallington, Cambo

DESCRIPTIONS OF GARDENS

Berryburn, Ancroft ✿❀ (Mr & Mrs W J Rogers-Coltman) *5m S of Berwick. Take Ancroft Mill Rd off A1 for 1m; drive entrance 2nd turn on R beside council bridge.* 4 acres created from wilderness since 1981 and still being developed. Mixed borders; shrubs; roses; woodland walk alongside burn with collection of young, rare conifers. Partially suited for wheelchairs. TEA. *Adm £2 Chd free. Mon May 29 (2-5). Private visits welcome, please* **Tel 01289 387332**

Bide-a-Wee Cottage, Stanton ✿❀ (Mr M Robson) *7m NNW of Morpeth. Turn L off A192 out of Morpeth at Fairmoor. Stanton is 6m along this road.* Both a formal and informal garden developed out of a small stone quarry as well as some surrounding higher land, with natural rock, water and marsh areas. Garden contains mixed planting with a large number of perennial species and has been featured on BBC2 Gardeners World and in The RHS Garden Magazine. *Adm £2. Sat April 29 (1.30-4); Weds June 14; Aug 9 (1.30-5)*

● **Bradley Nursery & Gardens, Wylam** ❀ (Chris Potter) *Follow signs from A695 3m W of Blaydon, or 1m S of Wylam or from Wylam Station.* A 2-acre Victorian walled garden with replanted herbaceous borders, herb beds, wildflower walk and magnificent conservatory under restoration. Permanent garden sculpture exhibition with some work for sale, plus wide range of plants. *Donations for NGS. Daily March 1 to October 31 (9-5). Tours by arrangement, please* **Tel 01661 852176.** Sun June 18 2.30. Guided tour by artists £2

▲ **Cragside, Rothbury** ✿❀ (The National Trust) *13m SW of Alnwick (B6341); 15m NW of Morpeth (B6344).* Formal garden in the 'High Victorian' style created by the 1st Lord Armstrong. Fully restored orchard house, carpet bedding, dahlia walk and fernery. 3½ acres of rock garden. Extensive grounds of over 1000 acres famous for rhododendrons and beautiful lakes. Restaurant. Shop. Grounds, Power Circuit and Armstrong Energy Centre. TEAS. *Adm House, Garden & Grounds £6.50; Garden & Grounds £4 Chd £2. Family ticket House, Garden & Grounds (2 adults & 3 chd) £16. For NGS Sun July 16 (10.30- 6.30). Large parties by appt, please* **Tel 01669 620150/620333**

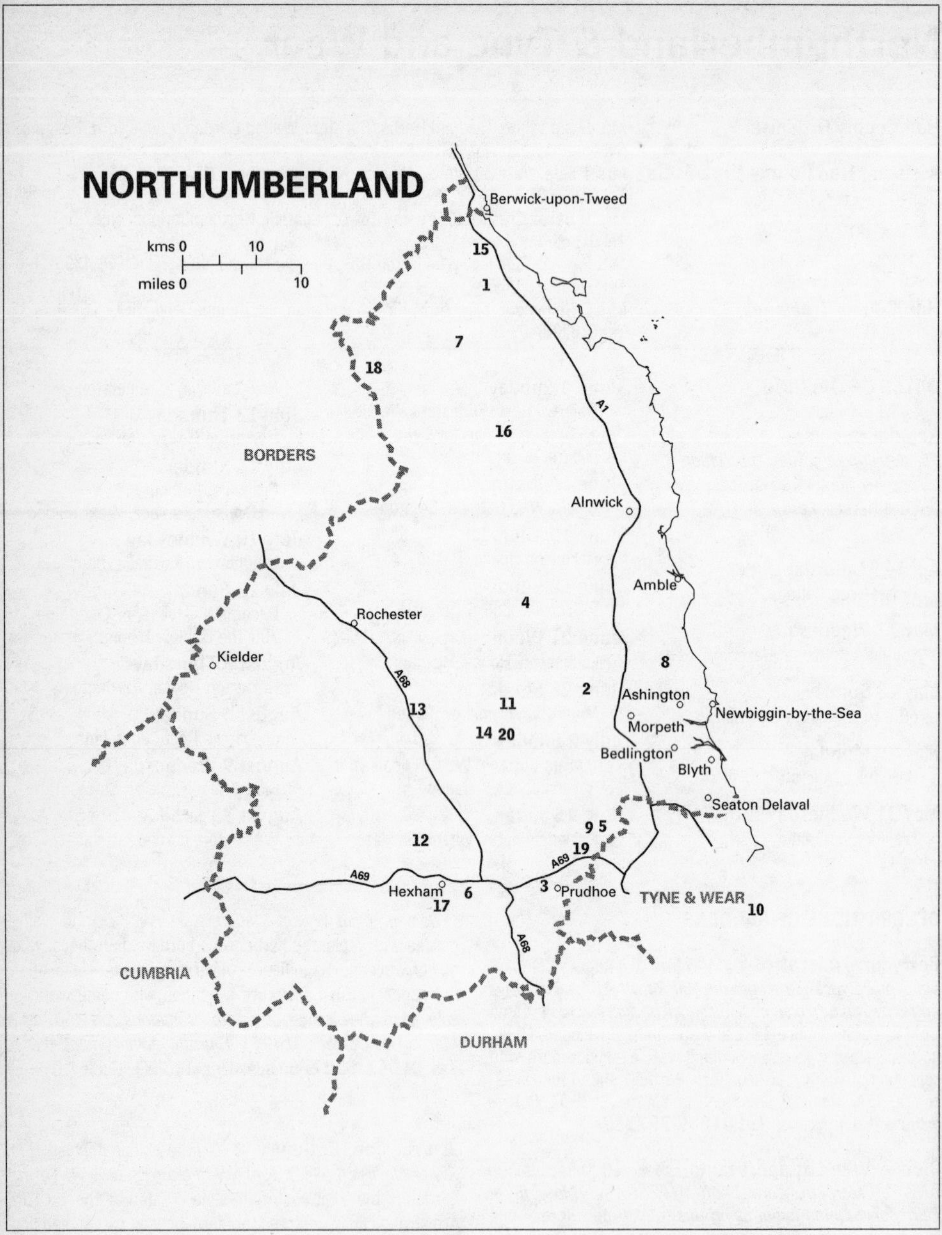

KEY

1 Berryburn
2 Bide-a-Wee Cottage
3 Bradley Nursery and Garden
4 Cragside
5 66 Darras Road
6 Dilston Mill House
7 Ford Nursery
8 70a The Gables
9 9 Grenville Court
10 4 Hamilton Terrace
11 Herterton House
12 Hexham Herbs, Chesters Walled Garden
13 Ingram Cottage
14 Kirkwhelpington Village Gardens
15 Kiwi Cottage
16 Lilburn Tower
17 Loughbrow House
18 Mindrum
19 Ravenside
20 Wallington

66 Darras Road, Ponteland ♿❀ (Mr & Mrs D J Goodchild) *SW of A696 at Ponteland. Turn L after crossing the R Pont. Travelling W, signposted Darras Hall. 1m on R.* Approx 1-acre garden, owner designed and maintained, with herbaceous and shrub borders incl unusual varieties. Conifers, kitchen garden, water garden, greenhouses and alpine troughs. Bulbs in spring. TEA. *Adm £2 Chd free. Suns May 28; Aug 6 (2-5.30)*

Dilston Mill House, nr Corbridge ✂ (Professors Elaine & Robert Perry) *Approx 1m W of Corbridge on A695.* Specialist cottage garden above the beautiful Devil's Water, with over 200 different medicinal plants and herbs (some poisonous) clearly labelled with their traditional uses. Bamboo walk and croquet lawn. Featured in 'The Northumbrian' Magazine 1998. Some steep steps. TEA. *Adm £2 Chd under 12 free (ACNO to Alzheimer's Disease Society). Sun July 23 (2-5)*

Ford Nursey, Ford ♿❀ (Chris Potter) *Berwick upon Tweed. Follow the flower signs on the brown Ford Etal Heritage signs to Ford Village, 10m N of Wooler off A697.* 2-acre walled garden incl display beds and growing areas. Recently replanted herbaceous borders. Teas available in village. *Donations for NGS Open all year Mon to Fri (8-6, or dusk), March to Oct Sat, Sun (10-6, or dusk)*

70a The Gables, Morpeth ✂❀ (Paul Robert Morrison) *7m from Ashington follow main E coast rd to sign Widdrington Station (not Widdrington village).* A 25-yr-olds award winning garden set in approx one fifth of an acre; owner designed and maintained. It is a surburban garden comprising a number of different areas for contemplation; crammed with many unusual plants in variety of settings, visitors will be able to experience some unusual plant associations of over 2000 plants. Come and find out for yourself what can be achieved in a small garden. TEAS. *Adm £1.50 Chd free (ACNO to Royal Gardeners Orphan Fund) Sun July 23 (12-5)*

NEW **9 Grenville Court, Darras Hall** ♿✂❀ (Mr & Mrs J C Scott) *SW of Ponteland A696, turn L after crossing river travelling N (signposted Darras Hall). At the end of Darras Rd turn R (Western Way) 2nd turning on the L.* ⅓-acre of mixed borders; a number of small gardens within the garden. Special interest in hardy geraniums (over 100) and hostas. TEAS. *Adm £2 Chd free. Sun June 18 (2-5.30)*

NEW **4 Hamilton Terrace, West Boldon** ♿✂❀ (Mrs Sue Jackson) *8m SE of Newcastle on A184. Turn at Bank Top Garage, WB, into Hylton Lane, then 1st L into Dipe Lane (following signs for Boldon Golf Club). Lane 2nd L 50yds.* A tranquil, hidden cottage garden created from an overgrown, derelict Lane. Still used for access, the lane has become a delightful community garden much used by residents for peaceful relaxation and social gatherings. A wide range of shrubs, perennials, herbs and annuals for foliage, texture and fragrance with emphasis on attracting insects and birds. Award winner Northumbria in Bloom 1999; featured on BBC 'Gardeners World' 1999. TEAS. *Adm £1.50 Chd free. Sun July 16 (12-5). Private visits welcome, please* **Tel 0191 5371928**

▲ **Herterton House, Hartington** ✂❀ (Mr Frank Lawley) *Cambo, Morpeth. 2m N of Cambo on the B6342 signposted to Hartington. (23m NW of Newcastle-on-Tyne).* 1 acre of formal garden in stone walls around a C16 farmhouse (not open). Incl small topiary garden; physic garden; flower garden; fancy garden; gazebo; and nursery garden. Planted since 1976. *Adm £2.20 Chd 5 - 15 £1. For NGS Thurs June 15, July 13, Aug 3 (1.30-5.30)*

Hexham Herbs, Chesters Walled Garden, Chollerford ♿✂❀ (Mr & Mrs K White) *6m N of Hexham, off the B6318. ½m W from Chollerford.* 2-acre walled garden containing a very extensive collection of herbs. Raised thyme bank, home to the National Thyme Collection. Roman garden; National Collection of Marjoram. Elizabethan-style knot garden, gold and silver garden and collection of dye plants. Herbaceous borders contain many unusual plants and old-fashioned roses. Woodland walk with wildflowers and pond. Featured on BBC2's Gardener's World in 1998. Shop sells herbal gifts and local honey. *Adm £1.50 Chd under 10 free. Sun June 4 (1-5)*

Ingram Cottage, West Woodburn ✂ (Mrs Mary Virden) *18m N of Corbridge on A68. In the village turn E behind the Bay Horse Inn for ½m along no-through rd.* 1-acre organic garden with panoramic views; divided into an informal, closely planted ornamental garden with emphasis on form and texture as well as colour-wide range of perennials, some unusual. Vegetable and fruit garden, wildlife priority garden being developed. Two ponds, poultry. Featured in Gardeners World TV 1998. TEAS. *Adm £2 Chd free (ACNO to Action Aid) Sun July 2 (2-5) Private visits welcome, please* **Tel 01434 270334**

Kirkwhelpington Village Gardens ✂ *On A696 approx 10m N of Belsay. Turn R into village.* A number of small gardens in an attractive village. Each garden entirely different with something of interest for everyone. Teas in village hall. *Combined adm £2 Chd free. Tickets at village hall (ACNO to Village Hall Fund). Sun July 9 (1.30-5.30)*

- **3 Albion Terrace** (Mr & Mrs R H Senior)
- **Cliff House** (Mr & Mrs I Elliot)
- **1 Meadowlands** (Mr & Mrs K Hodgson)
- **The School House** (Mr & Mrs F Young)
- **Sike View** (Professor & Mrs D Kinniment)
- **Welburn** (Professor D Wise)
- **West House** (Mr & Mrs C Scott)
- **Whitridge House** (Mr C & Dr J Keating)

Kiwi Cottage, Scremerston ♿✂❀ (Mrs D Smail) *Scremerston Village, about 2½m due S of Berwick-upon-Tweed. 1st house on the R hand side of the village, off the A1 coming from the S; last house on the L hand when travelling S from Berwick-upon-Tweed. Entrance through gateway next to War Memorial. Please drive in and do not park on the rd.* 3-acre garden with lawns, annuals, herbaceous plants, providing colour and interest throughout the year. Shrubs, orchard and medium vegetable garden. *Adm £2 Chd 50p. Sun July 9 (2.30-5)*

Lilburn Tower, Alnwick ✂❀ (Mr & Mrs D Davidson) *3m S of Wooler on A697.* 10 acres of walled and formal gardens incl conservatory and large glass house. About 30 acres of woodland with walks and pond garden. Rhododendrons and azaleas. Also ruins of Pele Tower, and C12 Church. TEAS. *Adm £2 Chd 50p under 8 free. Sun June 4 (2-6)*

Loughbrow House, Hexham ♿❀ (Mrs K A Clark) *Take B6303 from Hexham, signed Blanchland, after ¼m take R hand fork, after a further ¼m you come to another fork, the lodge gates are in intersection. Garden ½m up the drive.* A woodland garden with rhododendrons and azaleas. Bog garden with pond. Old-fashioned roses and a long bed of hybrid teas; 3 herbaceous borders; large area of lawns. An extensive kitchen garden and a paved courtyard. *Adm £2 Chd free. Weds May 17; June 21; July 19 (12-3)*

Mindrum, Cornhill on Tweed ❀ (Hon P J Fairfax) *On B6352, 4m from Yetholm, 5m from Cornhill on Tweed.* Old-fashioned roses; rock and water garden; shrub borders. Wonderful views along Bowmont Valley. Approx 3 acres. TEAS. *Adm £2 Chd 50p. Sun June 25 (2-6). Private visits welcome, please* **Tel 01890 850246**

Ravenside, East Heddon ❀ (Mrs Joan Barber) *9m from Newcastle on the A69 take the Heddon on the Wall B6528 turn off, at end of slip rd turn R under bridge then L to East Heddon. 3rd house on R.* 1 ⅓-acre plantswoman's garden filled with shrubs, shrub roses, herbaceous borders, alpines, many in troughs and pond with bog area. TEAS. *Adm £2 Chd free. Sun July 2 (2-5). Private visits welcome, please* **Tel 01661 825242**

▲ Wallington, Cambo ♿❀ (The National Trust) *From N 12m W of Morpeth (B6343); from S via A696 from Newcastle, 6m W of Belsay, B6342 to Cambo.* Walled, terraced garden with fine shrubs and species roses; conservatory with magnificent fuchsias; 100 acres woodland and lakes. House dates from 1688 but altered, interior greatly changed c.1740; exceptional rococo plasterwork by Francini brothers; fine porcelain, furniture, pictures, needlework, dolls' houses, museum, display of coaches. Tearoom. Shop. *Adm to Walled garden, garden and grounds £3.90 Chd £1.95. Last admission (5). For NGS Wed May31; Sun Aug 13 (10-7). Free guided walk at 2pm*

Gardeners' Royal Benevolent Society

Today the GBRS gives assistance to nearly 600 retired gardeners, and youger disabled gardeners and their partners, in the form of sheltered accommodation, quarterly payments, and special needs grants. Anyone who has earned his or her living in horticulture or gardening is eligible to apply for help from the GBRS

The Society also gives birthday and Christmas gifts, organises holidays and offers advice and support through the Casework Department.

The Society owns a range of properties in England and one in Scotland, from modern flats and bungalows to homes in rural setting. Between them they offer a variety of accommodation from residential/nursing care to indepenent self contained homes.

The Gardeners' Royal Benevolent Society
Bridge House, 139 Kingston Road, Leatherhead, Surrey KT22 7NT
Tel: 01372 373962

Nottinghamshire

Hon County Organisers: Mr & Mrs Tony Hill, The White House, Nicker Hill, Keyworth, Notts NG12 5EA Tel 0115 9372049

Assistant Hon County Organisers: Mr & Mrs J E Nicholson, 38 Green Lane, Lambley, Nottingham NG4 4QE Tel 0115 9312998

Mr & Mrs B H C Theobald, 37 Loughborough Road, Ruddington, Nottinghamshire NG11 6LL Tel 0115 9841152

Hon County Treasurer: Mr J A Gray, 43 Cliff Way, Radcliffe-on-Trent, Notts NG12 1AQ Tel 0115 9334272

DATES OF OPENING

Regular openings
For details see garden description
Felley Priory, Underwood
Hodsock Priory, Blyth

By appointment only
For telephone numbers and other details see garden descriptions. Private visits welcomed
Dumbleside, 17 Bridle Road
Roselea, Newark

March 19 Sunday
Hodsock Priory, Blyth

March 26 Sunday
Morton Hall, Retford
Woodpecker Cottage, Girton

March 29 Wednesday
Woodpecker Cottage, Girton

April 2 Sunday
7 Barratt Lane, Beeston

April 9 Sunday
Canal Turn, Retford
Felley Priory, Underwood
Netherthorpe House, Nr Worksop

April 23 Sunday
High Park, Eastwood
Netherthorpe House, Nr Worksop

April 30 Sunday
Elm House, Main St, Hickling

May 1 Monday
Mill Hill House, East Stoke

May 7 Sunday
Canal Turn, Retford
Netherthorpe House, Nr Worksop
14 Temple Drive, Nuthall

May 21 Sunday
Brackenhurst Campus, Southwell
37 Loughborough Road, Ruddington
Rose Cottage, 82 Main Rd, Underwood
Southwell, Bishops Manor

May 28 Sunday
Ashdene, Halam
Darby House, Nottingham
The White House, Keyworth

May 29 Monday
Holmes Villa, Walkeringham
Mill Hill House, East Stoke

May 31 Wednesday
The Beeches, Milton, Tuxford

June 3 Saturday
The Beeches, Milton, Tuxford

June 4 Sunday
Canal Turn, Retford
Epperstone Gardens
Holmes Villa, Walkeringham
The Manor House, Gonalston
Papplewick Hall, Papplewick
Park Farm, Normanton
32 Victoria Street, Hucknall

June 11 Sunday
Ashdene, Halam
Baxter Farm, Willoughby on the Wolds
Wolds Farm Bungalow, Wysall Lane
Woodbine Cottage, Granby

June 14 Wednesday
Mill Hill House, East Stoke

June 17 Saturday
Forge Cottage, School Lane, Kneesall
Stratford Cottage, Cropwell Butler

June 18 Sunday
Askham Gardens, Markham Moor
Forge Cottage, School Lane, Kneesall
1 Hilltop Cottage, Thurgarton
Rose Cottage, 82 Main Rd, Underwood
Stratford Cottage, Cropwell Butler

June 25 Sunday
Darby House, Nottingham
Laurel Farm, Stanton-on-the-Wolds
Norwell Gardens
136 Papplewick Lane, Hucknall
Park Farm, Normanton
Silks Cottage, Shelford

July 2 Sunday
Thrumpton Hall, Nottingham
Woodpecker Cottage, Girton

July 5 Wednesday
Woodpecker Cottage, Girton

July 9 Sunday
Brackenhurst Campus, Southwell
Canal Turn, Retford
12 Dunster Road, West Bridgford
14 Temple Drive, Nuthall

July 16 Sunday
Elm House, Main St, Hickling
136 Papplewick Lane, Hucknall
Rose Cottage, 82 Main Rd, Underwood

August 6 Sunday
Rose Cottage, 82 Main Rd, Underwood

August 27 Sunday
Mill Hill House, East Stoke

August 28 Monday
Mill Hill House, East Stoke

September 10 Sunday
Rose Cottage, 82 Main Rd, Underwood

September 20 Wednesday
Mill Hill House, East Stoke

October 15 Sunday
Morton Hall, Retford

By Appointment Gardens. These owners do not have a fixed opening day, usually because they cannot accommodate large numbers or have insuffucient parking space.

NOTTINGHAMSHIRE

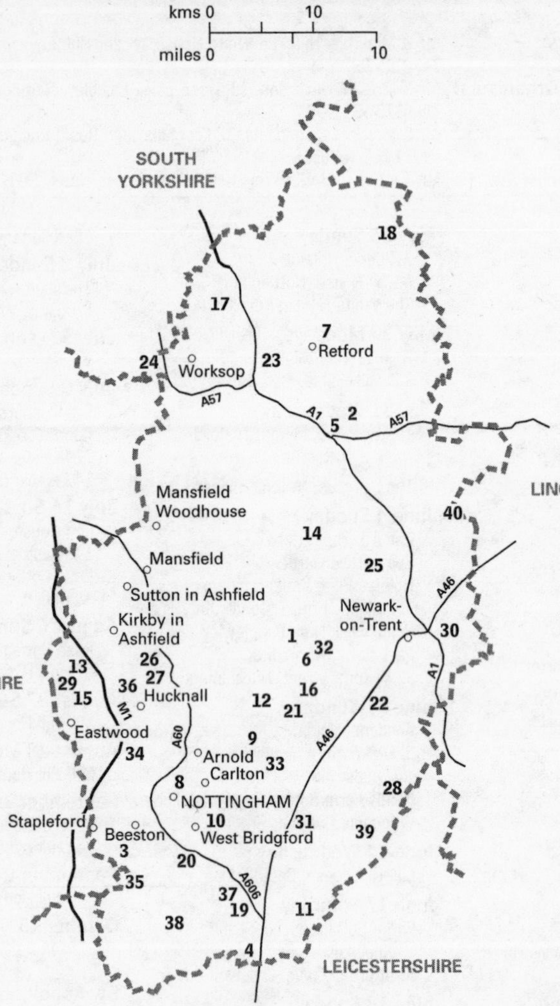

KEY

1 Ashdene
2 Askham Gardens
3 7 Barratt Lane
4 Baxter Farm
5 The Beeches
6 Brackenhurst Campus
7 Canal Turn
8 Darby House
9 Dumbleside
10 12 Dunster Road
11 Elm House
12 Epperstone Gardens
13 Felley Priory
14 Forge Cottage
15 High Park
16 1 Hilltop Cottage
17 Hodsock Priory
18 Holmes Villa
19 Laurel Farm
20 37 Loughborough Road
21 The Manor House
22 Mill Hill House
23 Morton Hall
24 Netherthorpe House
25 Norwell Gardens
26 Papplewick Hall
27 136 Papplewick Lane
28 Park Farm
29 Rose Cottage
30 Roselea
31 Silks Cottage
32 Southwell Bishops Manor
33 Stratford Cottage
34 14 Temple Drive
35 Thrumpton Hall
36 32 Victoria Street
37 The White House
38 Wolds Farm Bungalow
39 Woodbine Cottage
40 Woodpecker Cottage

DESCRIPTIONS OF GARDENS

Ashdene, Halam ❀ (David & Glenys Herbert) *Radley Road, W of Southwell. From B6386 in Halam village 300yds from Church.* Developed from orchard over 22yrs. Many mature trees incl 2 magnificent walnuts (200yrs), Paulownia (50yrs) and Mulberry. Japanese style garden with living architectural features incl mature spiral yew. Formal species rose, scented rose and woodland gardens. Many clematis, hebes. TEAS. *Adm £1.50. Suns May 28, June 11 (1-5)*

Askham Gardens, Markham Moor ♿ *On A638 between Markham Moor and Gamston, in Rockley village turn E to Askham.* Wide variety of pleasant English village gardens. TEAS at Manor Lodge. *Combined adm £2 Chd free (ACNO to Askham Church). Sun June 18 (2-6)*

Dovecote Cottage ♿ (Mr & Mrs D J Slack)
Manor Lodge (Mr & Mrs Kelly Bloom)
Nursery House (Mr & Mrs D Bird)
Stone Lea (Mr & Mrs J Kelly)
Villosa ❀ (Mr T Townrow)

7 Barratt Lane, Beeston ♿ (Mrs D Lucking & Mr & Mrs Hodkinson) *6m SW of Nottingham. Off A6005 nr Attenborough Station.* 3/4-acre established plantsman's garden. Mature trees, unusual flowering shrubs, miniature daffodils, fritillarias and hellebores. Children welcome. *Adm £1.20 Chd 40p (ACNO to St Mary's Church). Sun April 2 (11-6)*

Baxter Farm, Willoughby on the Wolds ♿❀ (Dr & Mrs Peter Tatham) *10m S of Nottingham, 12m N of Leicester. About ½m off A46 at the E end of Main St.* Old farmhouse and barns. 1-acre garden planted last 20 yrs. Conservatory, old cattle drinking pond now planted, herbaceous borders, informal plantings of old roses, irises, hardy geraniums and many climbers. Pergola in beech and yew hedged walks. Kitchen garden. TEAS. *Adm £1.20 Chd free. Sun June 11 (2-5)*

The Beeches, Milton, Tuxford ♿❀ (Margaret & Jim Swindin) *12m N of Newark. Off A1 at Markham Moor roundabout take Walesby sign into village (1m).* Garden for all seasons developed organically from a wilderness with wild life in mind. 1 acre with 2-acre hay meadow. Mature trees, shrubs, herbaceous, climbing and alpine plants. Pond, small woodland with bulbs and shade loving plants. Vegetables in raised beds and tunnel. Top and soft fruit. Adj Mausoleum grounds also open and Saxon Church in West Markham (walking distance). TEAS. *Adm £1.20 Chd free. Wed May 31, Sat June 3 (2-5.30)*

Brackenhurst Campus, Southwell ♿❀ (The Head of Department) *Brackenhurst 1m S of Southwell on A612.* Ornamental shrubs; lawns; rose, sunken, and walled gardens, glasshouses, views. Organic vegetable plot. Wheelchair users please notify in advance. TEAS. *Adm £1.50 Chd 50p. Suns May 21 (12-4.30) July 9 (12-5)*

Canal Turn, Retford ♿❀ (Mr & Mrs H M Healey) *Welham Rd. A620 Retford to Gainsborough Rd, nearly opp 'Hop Pole' public house 1m Retford roundabout.* True plantsman's garden 3¼ acres. Developing arboretum 1,000 trees, shrubs, many rare/unusual. Several water features incl large wildlife pond. Shrubberies, rockeries, herb, rose and conifer beds. Gazebo, pergola, trellis; many honeysuckle, clematis, grasses, bamboo. Large Japanese garden and recently planted shady stumpery. *Adm £1.50 Chd 50p. Suns April 9, May 7, June 4, July 9 (2-5). Private visits welcome, please* **Tel 01777 711449**

Darby House, Nottingham (Jed Brignal) *10 The Grove. ¾m NE of city centre. From city centre take A610, turn R into Forest Rd first L into Southey St.* Unusual city garden designed and developed by artist owner (whose work can be viewed on request) is a tranquil oasis in unlikely location. Victorian walled garden with ponds, waterfall, gazebos and a fairy-tale shady area surrounded by mature trees. House (1849) and garden provide temporary home and sanctuary for actors, writers, dancers and other creative visitors. *Adm £1.50 Chd free. Suns May 28, June 25 (2-6)*

Dumbleside, 17 Bridle Road ♿❀ (Mr & Mrs P Bates) *In Burton Joyce turn N off A612, Nottingham to Southwell Rd, into Lambley Lane. Bridle Rd ½m on R, an impassable looking rd.* 1-acre mixed borders, woodland slopes, stream and water garden wth naturalised ferns, primulas, hostas and moisture loving plants. Terrace and orchard with spring and summer bulbs. *Adm £1.50 Chd 50p By appt only, please* **Tel 0115 9313725**

12 Dunster Road, West Bridgford ❀ (Mr & Mrs M Jones) *Approx 2m S of Nottingham. From Trent Bridge follow A606 Melton Rd. Approx 1m turn L into Burleigh Rd, 40yds turn 4th R into Dunster Rd.* 90′ × 30′ garden developed since 1989. Mixed borders incorporating an archway with varied trees, shrubs and perennials, especially penstemons, hardy geraniums and climbers. Small woodland bed, patio and summerhouse. Wildlife pond, bog area and numerous containers. *Adm £1.20 Chd 30p (ACNO to Alzheimer's Disease Society). Sun July 9 (2-5)*

Elm House, Main St, Hickling ❀ (Mr & Mrs D Chambers) *10m SE of Nottingham. From junction of A46 and A606 head for Melton Mowbray. At Hickling Pastures turn L Hickling (2m) In village turn R for Elm House.* A 10yr-old 2-acre garden with open views. Lawn, flowering shrubs, herbaceous borders, pond vegetables and fruit. Also seaside, chess and railway themed gardens. Many magnolias and bulbs in spring, bedding and herbaceous in summer. TEAS. *Adm £1.50 Chd 50p. Suns April 30, July 16 (2-6)*

Epperstone Gardens *8m NE Nottingham off A6097 between Lowdham and Oxton. Combined adm £1.50 Chd free (ACNO to Epperstone Church Fabric Fund). Sun June 4 (2-6)*

Hazelwych (Mr P J Clark) ½-acre, trees, shrubbery pond and alpine terrace

The Old Rectory ❀ (Mr and Mrs Cedric Coates) Enter from churchyard. Approx 2 acres mature garden in superb setting incl lawns, borders, herbaceous, mature yews forming 'The Dark Walk'. Lovely sculptured large box hedge. New enclosed herb and salad garden and tree house.

■ **Felley Priory, Underwood** ♿❀ (The Hon Mrs Chaworth Musters) *8m SW Mansfield, off A608 ½m W M1 junction 27* Old-fashioned garden round Elizabethan house. Orchard of daffodils, herbaceous borders, pond. Topiary, rose garden. Unusual plants and shrubs for sale. Refreshments. TEAS in aid of Marie Curie Cancer Care. *Adm £1.50 Chd free. Weds March 8, 22, April 12, 26, May 10, 24, June 14, 28, July 12, 26, Aug 9, 23, Sept 13, 27, Oct 11, 25 (9-4): Suns March 19, April 16, May 21, June 18, July 16, Aug 20, Sept 17, Oct 15 (11-4). For NGS Sun April 9 (11-4). For information please* **Tel 01773 810230**

NEW **Forge Cottage, School Lane, Kneesall** (Ralph & Audrey King) *Off A616 at Kneesall church 10m. N of Newark. Garden within 200yds.* 3/4 acre closely planted during last 13yrs with a miscellany of trees, hardy shrubs, heather beds and perennials (some less usual). Secluded paths, raised beds, pond and moist area plus small enclosed courtyard. TEA (Sun only). Plant stall in aid of British Diabetic Assoc Research Fund. *Adm £1.50 Chd free. Sat, Sun June 17, 18 (2-6)*

NEW **High Park, Eastwood** (Mr & Mrs Charles Nott) *Adjacent to B600 and Moor Green Reservoir. 3m from junction 27 of M1, 1m N of Moor Green. Follow yellow signs for Wood.* 45 acres of magnificent mature oak woodland, blanketed with bluebells, rich in birdlife and other wild flowers. Enjoy up to 2miles of forest paths through the heart of DH Lawrence country. Waterproof footwear recommended. Picnic site available. Teas in aid of Foremarke Trust. *Adm £1.50 Chd free. Sun April 23 (11-4)*

1 Hilltop Cottage, Thurgarton ⊘❀ (Zoe & Gary Richmond-Dixon) *Situated approx 3m S of Southwell on the main A612 Nottingham-Southwell rd.* Long, narrow, exuberant cottage-style garden, many unusual and interesting plants. Distinctively divided into different areas to create peaceful retreat. Ornamental and individual in design incl small sculpture, topiary and willow archway. TEAS. Plants in aid of Dr Hadwen Trust. *Adm £1.50 Chd free. Sun June 18 (2-6)*

■ **Hodsock Priory, Blyth** ♿⊘ (Sir Andrew & Lady Buchanan) *Off B6045, Blyth-Worksop rd approx 2m from A1.* Share the beauty and peace of a traditional 5-acre private garden on the historic Domesday site. Sensational snowdrops, massed daffodils, fine trees, ponds. Hot refreshments *Adm £3 Chd 6-16 yr-olds 50p. Visitors in wheelchairs free. Open daily for 4 weeks for snowdrops Feb/March (10-4). Dates depend on weather, check by tel first. For NGS Sun March 19 (10-4). All enquiries to Lady Buchanan* **Tel 01909 591204**

Holmes Villa, Walkeringham ♿⊘❀ (Mr & Mrs Peter Clark) *Holmes Lane. NE Retford and within 4m Gainsborough, take A620 from Retford or A631 from Bawtry/Gainsborough and A161 to Walkeringham then towards Misterton. Turn at sign R Trent and follow signs for last mile.* Interesting flower arranger's and plantsman's garden; created and maintained by owners with rare, unusual perennials and shrubs. Many new features incl bank with evergreen shrubs. 4 ponds, ornamental ducks, scarecrows. Featured BBC Todays The Day and garden magazines. TEAS in aid of League of Friends of Bassetlaw Hospital. *Adm £1 Chd free. Mon May 29, Sun June 4 (1-5). Private visits welcome* **Tel 01427 890233**

Laurel Farm, Stanton-on-the-Wolds ⊘❀ (Mrs Val Moffat) *Browns Lane. Approx 7m SE of Nottingham. From A606 turn at Fina Garage onto Browns Lane; ½m on RHS.* Peaceful country garden of about ⅔ acre. Re-developed over last 5yrs. Informal and formal water features, bog, gravel areas and raised beds. Many rare and unusual shrubs and plants incl large and growing collection ceanothus; other new plants/beds since last year. Courtyard area. TEA in aid of Riding for the Disabled. *Adm £1.20 Chd free. Sun June 25 (2-5)*

37 Loughborough Road, Ruddington ⊘ (Mr & Mrs B H C Theobald) *4m S of Nottingham via A60 Loughborough Rd, cross A52 Ring Rd at Nottingham Knight. Take 1st L 400yds beyond roundabout and immed L again up Old Loughborough Rd.* 1-acre garden with many unusual varieties of spring bulbs, perennials, shrubs and trees in borders, island beds, shady walk and walled patio, formal pool and fountain. *Adm £1.80 Chd free. Sun May 21 (2-5). Private visits welcome by appt, please* **Tel 0115 984 1152**

The Manor House, Gonalston ♿❀ (Mr & Mrs John Langford) *Eighth mile on the N-side of A612 between Lowdham and Southwell.* Walled C17 farmhouse in centre of village. ¾-acre garden made from farmyard over past 25yrs by present owners. Pergolas, terraces, obelisks, Irish yews, box hedges, ponds used to give formality and to divide garden into separate areas. Enthusiasm for herbaceous plants, climbers, shrubs and their propagation. Plant stall for Sight Savers International. *Adm £1.50 Chd 50p. Sun June 4 (2-5)*

Mill Hill House, East Stoke ❀ (Mr and Mrs R J Gregory) *Elston Lane. 5m S of Newark on A46 turn to Elston. Garden ½m on R. Entrance through nursery car park.* ½-acre country garden close to the site of the Battle of East Stoke (1487). A series of small gardens closely planted with many unusual hardy/half hardy plants provide yr-round interest and a tranquil atmosphere. Featured on TV and in w/weekly. Teas in Newark. *Adm £1.50 Chd free. Weds June 14, Sept 20, Mons May 1, May 29, Aug 28, Sun Aug 27 (10-6). Private visits welcome (not Tues), please* **Tel 01636 525460**

Morton Hall, Retford ♿❀ (Lady Mason) *4m W of Retford. Entrance on Link Rd from A620 to S bound A1.* Spring woodland garden, flowering shrubs, rhododendrons, azaleas, specimen trees; pinetum in park, cedars and cypresses. Bulbs, autumn colour. Picnics. Partly suitable for wheelchairs. TEAS in aid of Ranby Church. *Adm £2.50 per car or £1.50 per person whichever is least. Suns March 26, Oct 15 (2-6). Also groups by appt, please* **Tel 01777 701142**

Netherthorpe House, Nr Worksop (Dr & Mrs G Drown) *Near N end of Worksop bypass take turn for Shireoaks. Through village and at church keep straight on signed Thorpe Salvin. Exactly 1m turn L, then 150yds on L. Park in farm next to airfield.* 2-acre garden developed over 30yrs by owner with many rare and unusual trees/shrubs some now reaching maturity. Fascinating garden; unmanicured, secluded and secretive. Spring bulbs. Children welcome to explore. *Adm £1.50 Chd free. Suns April 9, 23, May 7, (2-6). Private visits welcome by appt* **Tel 01909 475869**

Norwell Gardens ♿✂ *6m N of Newark off A1 at Cromwell turning.* Variety of gardens incorporating colourful planting schemes, herb garden, wildlife area, plantsman's garden, well stocked ponds, colour themed beds, interesting herbaceous. Vintage bus between gardens. TEAS in aid of Beaumond House Hospice. *Combined adm £2 Chd free. Sun June 25 (2-5.30)*

1 Marston Cottage (Mr & Mrs B Shaw)
Cornerways (Margaret & Les Corbett)
Southview Cottage (Jan Davies)
Norwell Nurseries ❀ (Andrew Ward)

Papplewick Hall, Papplewick (Dr & Mrs R B Godwin-Austen) *North end of Papplewick Village on B683, 7m N of Nottingham off the A60. Parking at Hall.* Woodland garden of approx 8 acres underplanted with rhododendrons; spring bulbs and hostas. *Adm £3 Chd £1 (ACNO to St James Church, Papplewick) Sun June 4 (2-5)*

136 Papplewick Lane, Hucknall ✂❀ (Mr & Mrs J Smith) *From Nottingham on A611, turn R at Byron Cinema. Turn L at mini island. Garden approx 400yds on R.* ¼-acre long garden with view, herbaceous borders and ornamental trees and shrubs. Two ponds, patio areas with a variety of basket and container plants. A wide variety of interesting and unusual plants. Greenhouses. *Adm £1.25 Chd free (ACNO to Neurodegenerative Support Group). Suns June 25, July 16 (1.30-5)*

Park Farm, Normanton (Mr and Mrs John E Rose) *Half way between Bottesford and Long Bennington on A1 side of Normanton village on old Normanton Airfield.* 3-acre garden, developed since 1987; formal and mixed borders; natural and formal ponds; small lakes seeded with wild flowers, scree gardens and small woodland area. Mature trees moved to flat open field prior to the creation of garden. Large scented, colour co-ordinated garden. Thatched summer house built to mark the millennium. Cream TEAS. *Adm £1.50 Chd free. Suns June 4, 25 (12-6)*

Rose Cottage, 82 Main Rd, Underwood ✂❀ (Mr & Mrs Allan Lowe) *1½m from junction 27 M1. Take B608 to Heanor. Join B600; after about 200-300yds turn R into Main Rd by large sign for 'the Hole in the Wall' Inn.* Flower arranger's cottage garden with ponds; shrubs; small secret garden. Rear garden of approx 1,000 sq yds with surprise features, partly developed from a field over last few years; goats and other animals. Various flowers for showing; greenhouses; aviary. TEAS. *Adm £1.20 Chd free. Suns May 21, June 18, July 16, Aug 6, Sept 10 (2-6)*

Roselea, Newark ✂❀ (Bruce and Marian Richmond) *Old Newark Road, Coddington. 1½m E of Newark. Leave A1 signed Coddington. 100yds from junction N; 300yds from junction S.* Medium-sized cottage style closely planted plantsman's garden. Colour all year round. Many unusual plants, esp clematis, 150 hardy geraniums. Pots and alpines. *Adm £1.20 Chd free. By appt only, please* **Tel 01636 676737**

Silks Cottage, Shelford ✂❀ (Mr and Mrs M J S Pearson) *8m E of Nottingham off A52, nr Radcliffe-on-Trent. 10m S of Newark, turn off A46 onto A6097, turn L at Gunthorpe Bridge.* 3/4-acre mature country cottage garden. Mixed borders. *Adm £1.50 Chd free. Sun June 25 (2-6)*

Southwell, Bishops Manor ♿ (The Rt Rev the Lord Bishop of Southwell) *End of Bishops Drive on S side of Minster.* The house is built into a part of the old medieval Palace of the Archbishops of York. The ruins form a delightful enclosed garden, lawns, 4 seasons tree garden, orchard and vegetable garden. Rockery, attractive borders in an unusual setting. Herb knot garden and other features under development. TEAS in aid of Southwell Care Trust. *Adm £1.50 Chd free. Sun May 21 (2-5)*

Stratford Cottage, Cropwell Butler ♿✂❀ (Mrs Jill Brereton) *9m E of Nottingham. 1m E of A46. From Cropwell Butler 600 yds on RHS on rd to Cropwell Bishop.* Medium-sized country garden, with panoramic views. Closely planted beds. Very big and spectacular pond, with bridge over, fish and waterside planting. Cream TEAS in aid of Hayward House Hospice. *Adm £1.20 Chd 50p. Sat, Sun June 17, 18 (2-5.30)*

14 Temple Drive, Nuthall ♿❀ (Mr & Mrs T Leafe) *4m NW of Nottingham. From M1 leave at junction 26, A610 towards Nottingham. Circle 1st roundabout in A6002 then Nottm Rd lane, leave on minor rd. From Nottingham take A610, turning off at Broxtowe Inn, Cinderhill. Parking restricted, use Nottingham rd.* ⅓-acre garden with herbaceous borders and island beds with interesting plants; flowering shrubs; troughs; old-fashioned roses; collections of hardy geraniums and clematis. Fruit and vegetable garden. TEAS and cake stall in aid of The Cats Protection League. *Adm £1.20 Chd 50p. Suns May 7, July 9 (2-5). For private visits* **Tel 0115 9271118**

Thrumpton Hall, Nottingham ♿❀ (The Hon Mrs Rosemary Seymour) *8m SW of Nottingham. W of A453; 3m from M1 at Exit 24.* Large lawns; massive yew hedges; rare shrubs; C17 larches, cedars, planted to commemorate historic events since George III. Lake. Early Jacobean house shown. NO DOGS in house. TEA. *Adm to Garden £2 Chd 50p; House £2 extra Chd £1 (ACNO to Museum of Garden History). Sun July 2 (2.30-6)*

32 Victoria Street, Hucknall ❀ (Perri Morton) *Approx 1m N of Hucknall market place on A611 Annesley Rd turn opp Jet Service Station into Victoria St.* Interesting 80' long narrow garden, with pebble sun design, packed planting showing ways of making full use of available space. Ponds, variety of climbers, unusual plants. *Adm £1.20 Chd free. Sun June 4 (2-5)*

The White House, Keyworth ✂❀ (Mr & Mrs A R Hill) *Nicker Hill. Approx 8m SE Nottingham. From A606 at Stanton-on-the-Wolds, by Fina Garage, turn into Browns Lane; follow rd into Nicker Hill.* ¾-acre overlooking fields. Attractive walled area incl formal pond; many pots. Brick pergola, water/bog. Many different vistas formed by informal rich colour coordinated planting; trees, shrubs, climbers, herbaceous, (many rare/unusual), propagated for large plant stall. Tender plants many unexpectedly thriving outside in E midlands. Featured on BBC TV Gardener' World Feb 1999. *Adm £1.50 Chd free Sun May 28 (2-5). Also private visits welcome, please* **Tel 0115 9372049**

NEW **Wolds Farm Bungalow, Wysall Lane** (Mrs Brenda Allsopp) *1½ miles between Rempstone and Wysall on a single track lane. 4m from Loughborough. 10m from Nottingham.* Approx ⅓ acre plant enthusiast's garden. Unusual perennials, shrub borders, pond, bog, orchard, wonderful panoramic views of surrounding countryside. *Adm £1.20 Chd free. Sun June 11 (2-5)*

Woodbine Cottage, Granby (Erika and Stuart Humphreys) *14m E of Nottingham on A52 Nottingham-Grantham. Turn S 1m E of Bingham signed Granby 2½m.* Small, traditional cottage garden, closely planted, unusual plants. *Adm £1.20 Chd free. Sun June 11 (1.30-5.30)*

Woodpecker Cottage, Girton (Mr & Mrs Roy Hill) *6m N of Newark W off A1133. 1st cottage on R in village.* Approx 1 acre interestingly designed and developed by owners, many unusual plants, trees, shrubs, water garden. Delphiniums and roses feature in summer, gravel and grass paths lead to secluded areas. French potage garden, field with indigenous trees, wild flowers. TEAS in aid of St Cecilia's Church, Girton. *Adm £1.50 Chd free. Suns, Weds March 26, 29 July 2, 5 (2-5.30). Private group visits welcome, please* **Tel 01522 778759**

ONE CHANCE ONLY!

The White House
Keyworth
Sunday, May 28th 2000
2-5pm

One chance only to buy some of the unusual plants featured in the BBC Gardeners World '99 Programme. Propagated from plants in the garden at The White House.

Marie Curie Cancer Care

Marie Curie Nurses help ease the burdens on patients' families and friends and help cancer patients remain at home. Last year, Marie Curie Nurses cared for more than half the people who died of cancer at home. For more information about Marie Curie Cancer Care, ring 0800 716 146 or visit our web site at www.mariecurie.org.uk

Oxfordshire

Hon County Organisers: Col & Mrs J C M Baker, Hartford Greys, Sandy Lane, Boars Hill, Oxford OX1 5HN Tel 01865 739360

Assistant Hon County Organisers:

Vale of White Horse & SW Oxon (Abingdon, Bampton, Faringdon & Wantage areas) Mrs R Whitworth, Abbey Farm, Goosey, Faringdon, Oxfordshire SN7 8PA Tel 01367 710252

N Oxon (Banbury, Charlbury and Chipping Norton areas) Mr & Mrs J G Ainley, South Newington House, South Newington, Nr Banbury OX15 4JW Tel 01295 721207

S Oxon (Didcot, Goring, Henley & Wallingford areas) Mr & Mrs R J Baldwin, Northfield Cottage, High Street, Long Wittenham, Oxon OX14 4QJ Tel 01865 407258

E Oxon (Headington, Iffley, Bicester, Kidlington, Steeple Aston & Thames areas) Mr & Mrs J Lankester, Park Wall, Otmoor Lane, Beckley, Oxford OX3 9TB 01865 351312

W Oxon (Witney, Burford & Woodstock areas), Central Oxford & Colleges Mr & Mrs G M Davies, Hampden House, 18 The Green, Sutton Courtenay, Oxfordshire OX14 4AE Tel 01235 848397

Editor & Advertising Manager: Mrs Catherine Pinney, Pond House, Pyrton, Watlington OX9 5AP 01491-612638

Hon County Treasurer: Col J C M Baker, Hartford Greys, Sandy Lane, Boars Hill, Oxford OX1 5HN

DATES OF OPENING

Regular openings

For details see garden description

Brook Cottage, Alkerton
Clock House, Coleshill
Kingston Bagpuize House, nr Abingdon
Old Church House, Wantage
Stanton Harcourt Manor, Stanton Harcourt
Waterperry Gardens

By appointment only

For telephone numbers and other details see garden descriptions. Private visits welcomed

7A Blandford Avenue, Oxford
Clematis Corner, Shillingford
4 Northfield Cottages, Water Eaton
The Old Rectory, Brightwell Baldwin
Small's House, Mackney
Stansfield, Stanford-in-the-Vale
Tadmarton Manor, Tadmarton
Wardington Manor, Wardington
Yeomans, Tadmarton

February 20 Sunday
Waterperry Gardens

February 27 Sunday
Broadwell House, nr Lechlade
Lime Close, Drayton

March 19 Sunday
Ashbrook House, Blewbury
Magdalen College, Fellows' Garden & President's Garden, Oxford
Wadham College, Oxford

April 2 Sunday
Home Close, Garsington
Shotover House, Wheatley

April 8 Saturday
Blenheim Palace, Woodstock

April 9 Sunday
Blenheim Palace, Woodstock
Broughton Poggs & Filkins Gardens
Buckland, nr Faringdon
Epwell Mill, nr Banbury
Kingston Bagpuize House, nr Abingdon
The Mill House, Sutton Courtenay
Holywell Manor, Oxford
Merton College Fellows' Garden, Oxford
Trinity College, President's Garden, Oxford
Pettifers, Lower Wardington
Shellingford House, Faringdon
Tadmarton Gardens

April 16 Sunday
The Mill House, Stadhampton
25 Newfield Road, Sonning Common
The Old Rectory, Coleshill

April 23 Sunday
The Manor House, Clifton Hampden

April 24 Monday
Broadwell House, nr Lechlade
Brook Cottage, Alkerton
Kencot Gardens, nr Lechlade

April 30 Sunday
Adderbury Gardens
Garsington Manor, nr Oxford
Sibford Ferris Gardens
Stanton Harcourt Manor, Stanton Harcourt
Wick Hall & Nurseries, Radley

May 1 Monday
Brook Cottage, Alkerton

May 7 Sunday
Town Farm Cottage, Kingston Blount

May 13 Saturday
Hearns House, Gallows Tree Common
Troy, Ewelme

May 14 Sunday
Headington Gardens
Hearns House, Gallows Tree Common
The Manor House, Sutton Courtenay
Pettifers, Lower Wardington
Waterperry Gardens
Wood Croft, Boars Hill

May 17 Wednesday
Towersey Manor, Towersey

May 20 Saturday
Greys Court, Rotherfield Greys
Partway House, Swalcliffe

May 21 Sunday
Balscote Gardens, nr Banbury
Clock House, Coleshill
Partway House, Swalcliffe
Salford Gardens, nr Chipping Norton
Steeple & Middle Aston Gardens

May 27 Saturday
Nutford Lodge, Longcot

May 28 Sunday
Barton Abbey, Steeple Barton
Bellevue, Hornton

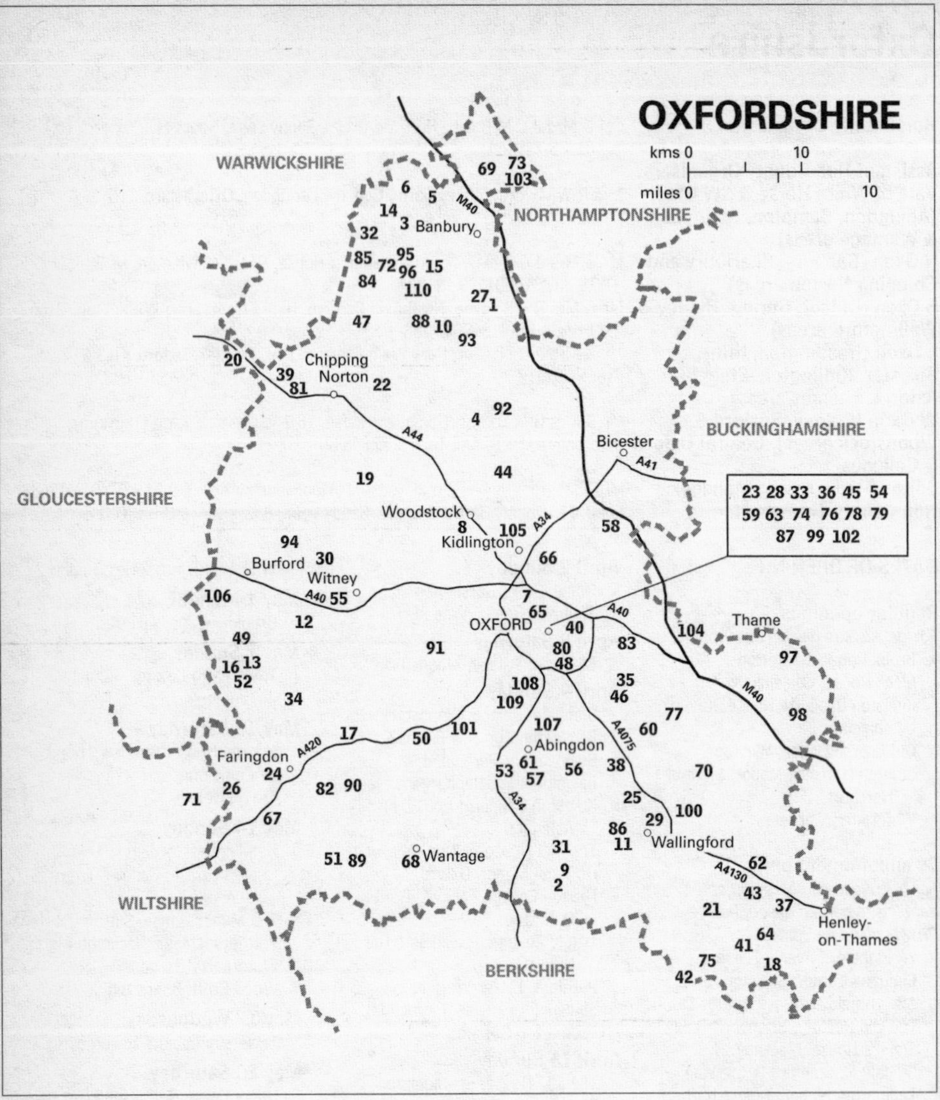

KEY

1 Adderbury Gardens
2 Ashbrook House
3 Balscote Gardens
4 Barton Abbey
5 Beech Court
6 Bellevue
7 7A Blandford Avenue
8 Blenheim Palace
9 Blewbury Gardens
10 Bloxham Gardens
11 Brightwell-cum-Sotwell
12 Brize Norton Gardens
13 Broadwell House
14 Brook Cottage
15 Broughton Castle
16 Broughton Poggs & Filkins Gardens
17 Buckland
18 Chalkhouse Green Farm
19 Charlbury Gardens
20 Chastleton Glebe
21 Checkendon Court
22 Chivel Farm
23 Christ Church Masters Garden
24 Claytons
25 Clematis Corner
26 Clock House
27 Colegrave Seeds Ltd
28 Corpus Christi
29 The Cuckoo Pen Nursery
30 Dundon House
31 East Hagbourne Gardens
32 Epwell Mill
33 Exeter College
34 Friars Court
35 Garsington Manor
36 Green College
37 Greys Court
38 Harcourt Arboretum
39 Haughton House

40 Headington Gardens
41 Hearns House
42 Heron's Reach
43 Highmoor Hall
44 Hill Court
45 Holywell Manor
46 Home Close
47 Hook Norton Manor
48 Iffley Gardens
49 Kencot Gardens
50 Kingston Bagpuize House
51 Kingstone Lisle Park
52 Langford Gardens
53 Lime Close
54 Magdalen College
55 Manor Farm
56 The Manor House,Clifton Hampden
57 The Manor House,Sutton Courtenay
58 Maryland
59 Merton College Fellows' Garden
60 The Mill House, Stadhampton
61 The Mill House, Sutton Courtenay
62 Nettlebed Gardens
63 New College
64 25 Newfield Road
65 North Oxford Gardens
66 4 Northfield Cottages
67 Nutford Lodge
68 Old Church House
69 The Old Manor, Cropredy
70 The Old Rectory, Brightwell Baldwin
71 The Old Rectory, Coleshill
72 Partway House
73 Pettifers
74 The Queen's College
75 Querns
76 Rewley House
77 Rofford Manor
78 St Anne's College
79 St Hilda's College
80 St John's Home
81 Salford Gardens
82 Shellingford House
83 Shotover House
84 Sibford Ferris Gardens
85 Sibford Gower Gardens
86 Small's House
87 Somerville College
88 South Newington House
89 Sparsholt Manor
90 Stansfield
91 Stanton Harcourt Manor
92 Steeple & Middle Aston Gardens
93 Stonewalls
94 Swinbrook House
95 Tadmarton Gardens
96 Tadmarton Manor
97 Towersey Manor
98 Town Farm Cottage
99 Trinity College, President's Garden
100 Troy
101 Tubney Gardens
102 Wadham College
103 Wardington Manor
104 Waterperry Gardens
105 Wayside
106 Westwell Manor
107 Wick Hall & Nurseries
108 Wood Croft
109 Wootton Hill
110 Yeomans

Charlbury Gardens, Charlbury
The Cuckoo Pen Nursery, Benson
Dundon House, Minster Lovell
Nettlebed Gardens
Nutford Lodge, Longcot
Wayside, Kidlington

May 29 Monday

Brook Cottage, Alkerton
Charlbury Gardens, Charlbury
The Cuckoo Pen Nursery, Benson
Epwell Mill, nr Banbury
Nutford Lodge, Longcot
Sparsholt Manor, nr Wantage

May 30 to June 2 Tuesday to Friday

Nutford Lodge, Longcot

June 3 Saturday

Nutford Lodge, Longcot

June 4 Sunday

Checkendon Court, Checkendon
Lime Close, Drayton
Nutford Lodge, Longcot
Harcourt Arboretum, Nuneham Courtenay
St John's Home, Oxford

June 10 Saturday

Hill Court, Tackley

June 11 Sunday

Bloxham Gardens, nr Banbury
Brightwell-cum-Sotwell Gardens, nr Wallingford
Brize Norton Gardens
Friars Court, Clanfield
Hill Court, Tackley
Kingstone Lisle Park, nr Wantage
Maryland, Fencott
The Mill House, Sutton Courtenay
Sibford Gower Gardens
Westwell Manor, nr Burford

June 14 Wednesday

Sibford Gower Gardens

June 17 Saturday

South Newington House, South Newington

June 18 Sunday

Clock House, Coleshill
Iffley Gardens, S Oxford
Langford Gardens, nr Lechlade
North Oxford Gardens
Green College, Oxford
St Hilda's College, Oxford
South Newington House, South Newington
Town Farm Cottage, Kingston Blount

June 21 Wednesday

Towersey Manor, Towersey

June 24 Saturday

East Hagbourne Gardens
Manor Farm, Old Minster Lovell

June 25 Sunday

Blewbury Gardens
Broughton Castle, nr Banbury
The Cuckoo Pen Nursery, Benson
Kencot House, nr Lechlade
Kiddington Hall, Woodstock
The Old Manor, Cropredy
Querns, Goring Heath
Rofford Manor, Little Milton
Stonewalls, Hempton
Tubney Gardens, Tubney

July 2 Sunday

Heron's Reach, Whitchurch-on-Thames
Exeter College, Rector's Lodgings, Oxford
New College, Oxford

July 9 Sunday

Beech Court, Horley
Claytons, Gt Coxwell, nr Faringdon
Sibford Gower Gardens
Stanton Harcourt Manor, Stanton Harcourt

July 15 Saturday

Highmoor Hall, Highmoor

July 16 Sunday

Ashbrook House, Blewbury
Chastleton Glebe, nr Moreton-in-Marsh
Cote House, nr Bampton
Headington Gardens
25 Newfield Road, Sonning Common
The Queen's College, Provost's,

Fellows' & Nuns' Gardens, Oxford
Rewley House, Oxford
St Anne's College, Oxford
Somerville College, Oxford
Wadham College, Oxford
Swinbrook House, nr Burford
Wayside, Kidlington

July 23 Sunday
Cote House, nr Bampton
Kingston Bagpuize House, nr Abingdon

July 30 Sunday
Broughton Castle, nr Banbury
The Cuckoo Pen Nursery, Benson
Trinity College, President's Garden, Oxford
Shotover House, Wheatley

August 6 Sunday
Colegrave Seeds Ltd, West Adderbury
Christ Church Masters Garden, Oxford
Corpus Christi, Oxford
Merton College Fellows' Garden, Oxford

August 13 Sunday
Beech Court, Horley
Chalkhouse Green Farm, Kidmore End
Headington Gardens

August 20 Sunday
Friars Court, Clanfield

August 27 Sunday
The Cuckoo Pen Nursery, Benson
Hearns House, Gallows Tree Common
Salford Gardens, nr Chipping Norton
Wootton Hill, Boars Hill

August 28 Monday
Brook Cottage, Alkerton
Hearns House, Gallows Tree Common
Kencot Gardens, nr Lechlade

September 3 Sunday
Chivel Farm, Heythrop

September 10 Sunday
Clock House, Coleshill
Haughton House, Churchill
The Old Rectory, Coleshill
Rofford Manor, Little Milton

September 17 Sunday
Epwell Mill, nr Banbury

September 24 Sunday
The Cuckoo Pen Nursery, Benson
Kingston Bagpuize House, nr Abingdon
The Mill House, Sutton Courtenay

October 1 Sunday
Garsington Manor, nr Oxford
Hook Norton Manor, Banbury
Pettifers, Lower Wardington
Waterperry Gardens

October 8 Sunday
Clock House, Coleshill

DESCRIPTIONS OF GARDENS

Adderbury Gardens *J10 M40 S off A423 on A4260, 3m S of Banbury* A large village with many quaint lanes and a beautiful church. TEAS at Institute, The Green. *Combined adm £2.50 Chd free. Sun April 30 (2-6)*

Berry Hill House ♿✂❀ (Mr & Mrs J P Pollard) *Berry Hill Rd, off A4260 signed Milton, Bloxham, W Adderbury* 2 acres; mature trees; lawns; shrubbery; mixed herbaceous and shrub borders. Kitchen garden

Home Farm House ♿ (Mr & Mrs J V Harper) 2 acres; lawns, mature trees and shrubs, newly landscaped paddock, pond

The Old Vicarage ♿❀ (Mr & Mrs Peter Job) Georgian House(not open), in 2 acres of mature gardens and meadows. Newly created lake beyond

NEW **Placketts** ✂ (Dr & Mrs D J White) *Nr Church.* Queen Anne cottage (not open) in 0.12 acres; old walled garden undergoing restoration. Guide Dogs.

Ashbrook House, Blewbury ♿❀ (Mr & Mrs S A Barrett) *4m SE of Didcot on A417.* 3½-acre chalk garden with small lake, stream, spring bulbs and herbaceous borders. TEAS. *Adm £1.50 Chd free. Suns March 19, July 16 (2-6)*

Balscote Gardens, nr Banbury Pretty hill village. *½m off A422 5m W of Banbury.* TEAS in Balscote in aid of Church (C14 St Mary Magdalene). *Combined adm (2 gdns) £2.50 Chd free. Sun May 21 (2-5.30)*

Home Farm ♿❀ (Mr & Mrs Godfrey Royle) C17 house and barn (not open), with attractive views from ½-acre plant lovers peaceful garden designed for yr-round interest with unusual plants, coloured foliage, flowering shrubs, bulbs and perennials. Featured in A Guide to Garden Visits '99, Gardener's World April '99 & Women's Weekly 'Gardening Special '99. Now a member of the Quiet Gardens Trust. *Adm £2. Private visits also welcome by appt, please* **Tel 01295 738194**

Manor Cottage (Mrs P M Jesson) A sloping garden terraced for ease of maintenance using a variety of materials incl stone, treated wood and sleepers. Many interesting plants and features built into the garden; 3/4 acre field planted under a local government scheme using broad leafed indigenous trees. Set in a delightful valley in this conservation village having extensive views over surrounding countryside

Barton Abbey, Steeple Barton ♿❀ (Mrs R Fleming) *On B4030; 1m Middle Barton; ½m from junction of A4260 and B4030.* 15-acre garden currently undergoing a complete reinterpretation following recontouring of terraces and lawns around house (not open). Replanted borders of yr-round interest; new hedges and evergreens. Views of St Mary's Church across 3 acre lake. Rock garden under renovation; streamside walk through woodland garden. Redesigned working walled garden with colour themed, herbaceous borders and working glasshouses. Plants and home produce stall. TEAS. *Adm £2 Chd free. Sun May 28 (2-5)*

Beech Court, Horley ♿✂ (Mr & Mrs V Hillman) *From Warwick Rd, Stratford Rd into Horley take rd to church. Signposted from there; ample parking.* About ¾ acre; lawns, mixed flower borders, herbaceous borders, rose bed. Lots of pots and baskets incl many fuchsias; goldfish ponds. Interesting walk ways, well stocked vegetable garden; all within a walled area. TEAS. *Adm £1.50 Chd free. Suns July 9; 13 Aug (2-6)*

Bellevue, Hornton ✂❀ (Mr & Mrs E W Turner) *Bell St. 6m NW of Banbury. Between A422 and B4100.* Approx 1½-acre; hillside garden of many aspects. Bordered walks; a 'surprise' garden leading to water falling to pools; flower

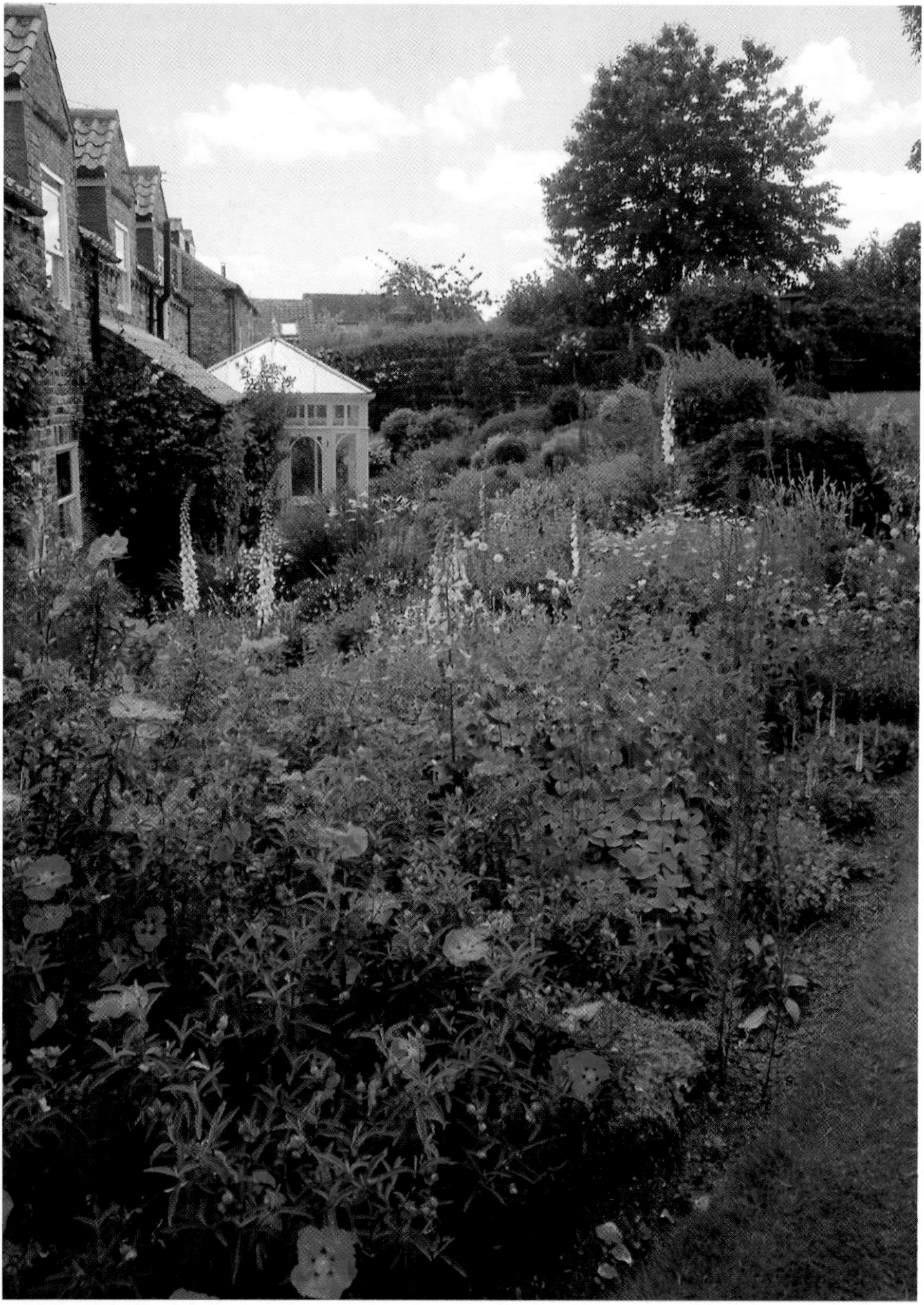

Ash Tree House, Yorkshire

The steep slope in this 0.2-acre garden has been stunningly transformed into a 'hanging garden' with *Cistus* x *purpureus*, the hardy *Geranium* 'Johnson's Blue', *G. psilostemon* and *G. oxonanium* 'Wargrave Pink', digitalis and veronica. Ash Tree is one of the Whixley gardens, which open as a group.

Photograph by Brian Chapple

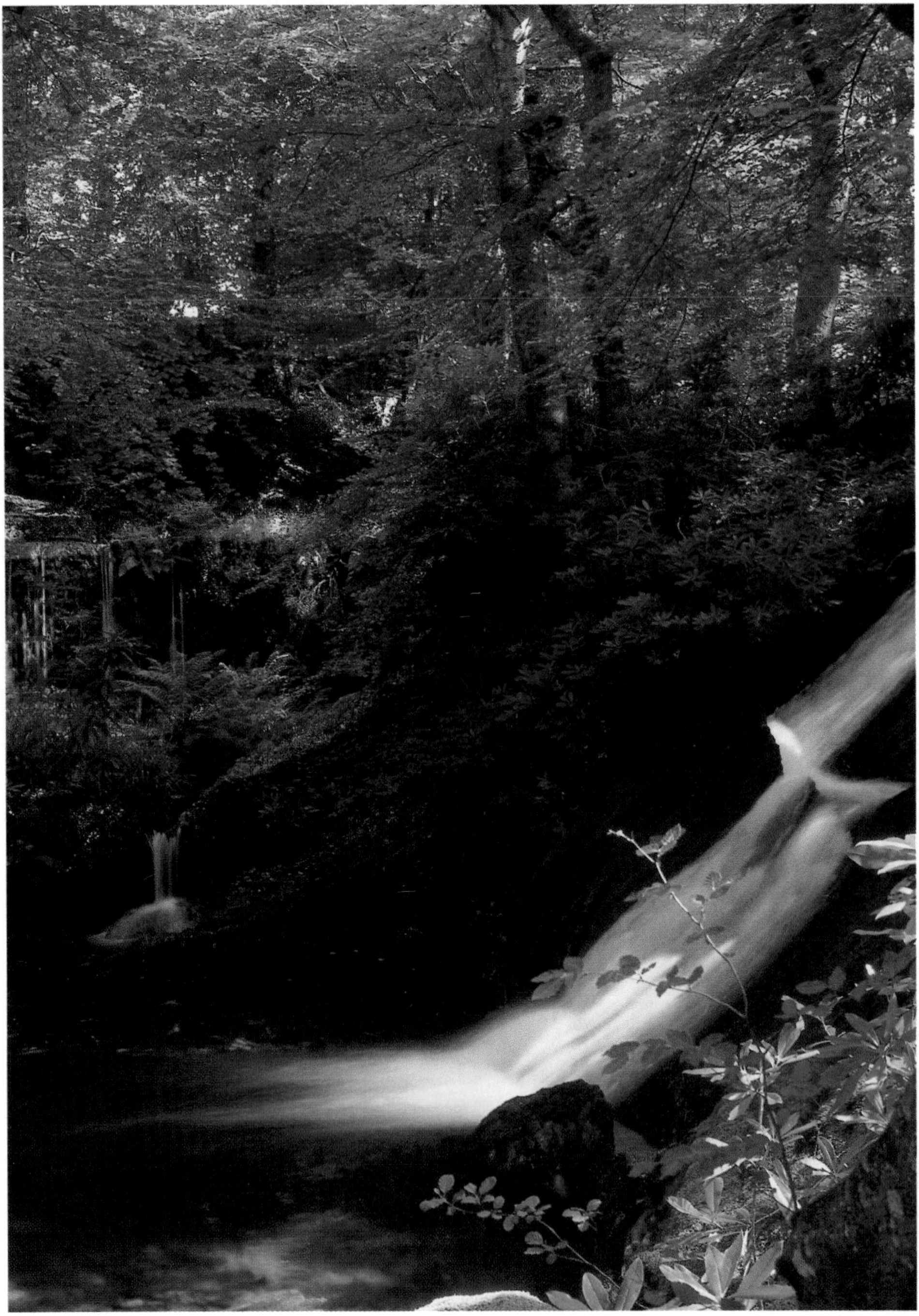

The Mill House, Ceredigion
An enchanting garden on the site of a former watermill, where visitors can enjoy the tranquility of the large mill pond. In spring, the reflections of the colourful azaleas and water plants create a beautiful space.
Photograph by Alex Ramsay

Holt Farm, Somerset
Blagdon Church floats in the distance on a purple wave of *Verbena bonariensis*.
Photograph by Mark Bolton

Below: **Dalemain, Cumbria**
Even the weeding is done in style at Dalemain. Old favourites like *Geranium* x *oxonianum* 'Wargrave Pink', cosmos, *Rosa glauca*, *Delphinium* 'Black Knight', combined with *Meconopsis grandis*, *Cynara cardunculus*, and *Crambe cordifolia* in an unblemished border. A pot of agapanthus on the left completes the picture.
Photograph by Val Corbett

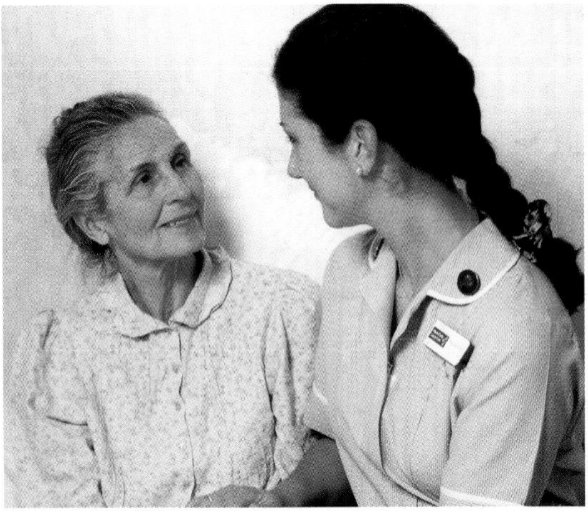

Marie Curie Cancer Care is one of the charities supported by gardens which open for the National Gardens Scheme. It has thousands of nurses nationwide who care for people with cancer in the comfort of their own homes, throughout the day or overnight, at no cost to the patient.
Photograph courtesy of Marie Curie Cancer Care

Below: **Hill House, Suffolk**
Rosa 'Gypsy Boy', *Penstemon* 'Garnet', *Euphorbia palustris*, campanulas, osteospermums, delphiniums, epilobiums and *Veronica teucrium* make a pretty picture in this 1-acre country garden.
Photograph by Alan Munson/Photos Horticultural

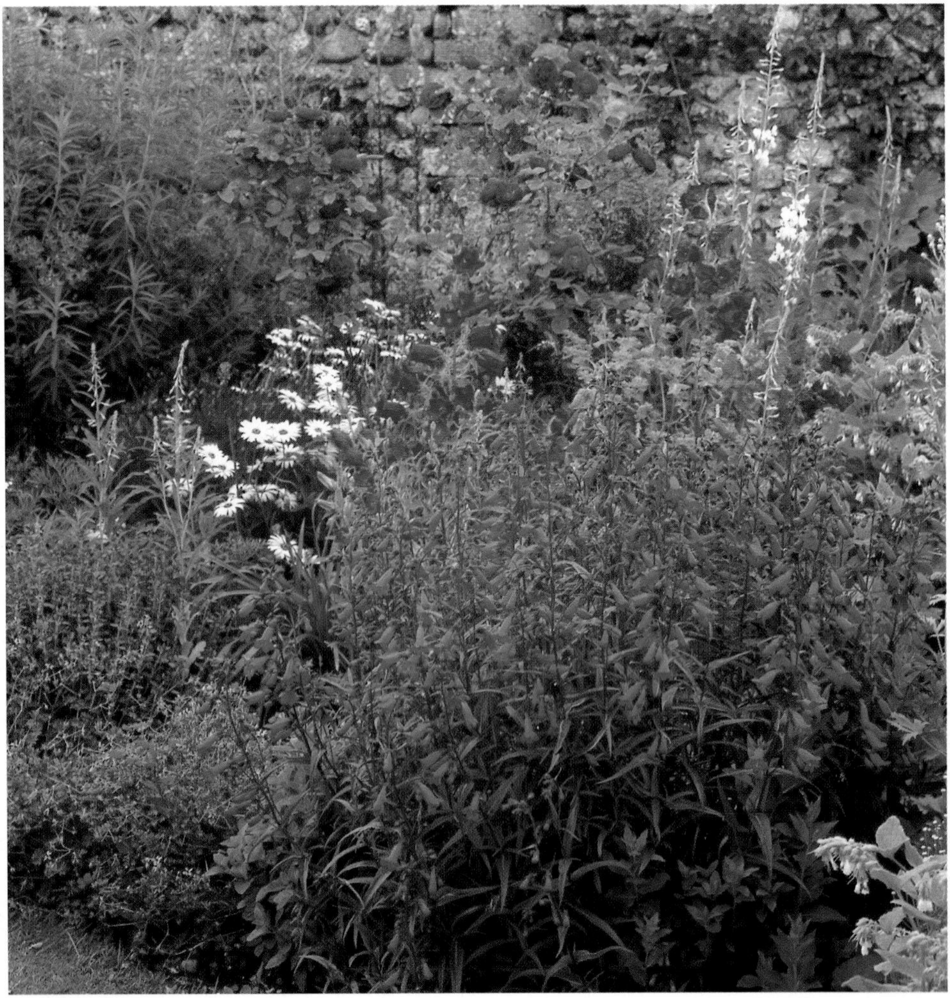

beds; kitchen garden and the finest views of Hornton Village. Miniature windmill ⅓ scale of original at Hornton, start of a model village. TEAS in aid of Cubs and Brownies. *Adm £2 Chd free. Sun May 28 (2-6). Private group visits welcome, please* **Tel 01295 670304**

7A Blandford Avenue, Oxford ♿✂ (Julie & Chris Elliott) *Off the Woodstock Rd, within the ring rd.* ½-acre plot redeveloped since 1996; strong design and imaginative planting. Gravel garden with pond, lawn with sun and shade borders, pergola, sinuous mounds, Japanese corner, mini spring meadow and wild walk. Ecological planting selected for form, foliage and colour with some unusual plants and grasses. Tea by arrangement. *Adm £1.50. Open by appt only May, June, July. Groups welcome, please* **Tel 01865 556369**

▲ **Blenheim Palace, Woodstock** ♿✂ (His Grace the Duke of Marlborough) *8m N of Oxford. Bus: 20 Oxford-Chipping Norton - Stratford, alight Woodstock.* Original grounds and garden plan by Henry Wise. Park landscaped and lake created by 'Capability' Brown in late C18. Maze; lavender and herb garden; formal gardens by Achille Duchêne; Butterfly house. Restaurant, Cafeteria. Adventure Play Area. *Adm charge not available on going to press. For NGS Sat, Sun April 8, 9 (10.30-4.45)*

Blewbury Gardens ♿✂❀ *Located on A417 between Streatley and Wantage.* 6 gardens in a charming downland village, the majority of which are cottage gardens surrounding beautiful old properties. Lime tolerant, unusual and climbing plants are much in evidence. Colour co-ordinated herbaceous borders stocked with perennials for all yr-round interest. A village opening for plantsman, artists and browsers. TEAS. *Combined adm £3 Acc chd free. Sun June 25 (2-6)*

Carpenters (Nick & Melanie Longhurst)
NEW **Church End House** (Loraine Fergusson)
Green Bushes ❀ (Phil & Rhon Rogers)
Hall Barn (Malcolm & Deirdre Cochrane)
Nottyngham Fee House (Patricia Weaver) Teas in aid of Westminster Childrens Hospital
Stocks ✂ (Richard & Norma Bird)

Bloxham Gardens, nr Banbury ✂ *A large village near Banbury on A361 to Chipping Norton.* Has a fine church with a 198ft spire. TEAS in village by WI. *Combined adm £2 Chd free. Sun June 11 (2-6)*

71 Courtington Lane (Mr Peter Sheasby) About ¼ acre with herbaceous borders, shrubs, rockeries and small peat beds; small pond and a series of alpine troughs; greenhouse contains cacti and a large succulent collection especially Lithops, Haworthia and Echeveria; a wide range of herbaceous species are grown

113 Courtington Lane (Mr& Mrs P C Bury) Sheltered garden with emphasis on herbaceous borders, shrubs and tubs. Winding paths giving attractive rural views

Frog Lane Cottage (Mr & Mrs R Owen) An artist's and a plantsman's garden. Steeply terraced on many levels, extending to the brook. Mixture of shrubs, herbaceous plants, and mature trees, wonderful views across valley (approx ⅔ acre)

Brightwell-cum-Sotwell Gardens, nr Wallingford *Off A4130 between Didcot (4m) and Wallingford (2m).* Ancient village with many timber-framed cottages (not open). Parking in village centre. TEAS at Sotwell House. *Combined adm £2 Chd free. Sun June 11 (2-6)*

NEW **The Barn** ♿✂ (Mr & Mrs A E Lascelles) S facing garden behind C16 thatched cottage (not open); herbaceous beds, colourful patio and fine views

NEW **Lucksall Cottage** ✂ (Miss P Gierson) Plantaholic's cottage garden of ⅓ acre.

The Priory ♿✂ (Mr & Mrs Cedric Scroggs) Walled garden, C16 farmhouse (not open), 200 plantings in shrubbery; herbaceous border and rose bed. Brick paved vegetable garden

Sotwell House ♿✂ (Mr & Mrs David Dobbin) 3-acre mature garden set in the centre of the village surrounded by moat which provides an ideal habitat for water fowl. The borders consist mainly of roses and herbaceous plants with a few specimen trees

Spring Cottage ✂ (Mr & Mrs M C Dix) Small pretty cottage (not open), featuring shrubs, roses, clematis and perennials

NEW **Stewarts Cottage** ✂ (Miss S Armstrong) C17 thatched cottage (not open) with cottage style front & rear garden

Sunnyside ♿ (Mr D Batten) 1-acre garden featuring annuals, mixed borders and 2 fishponds

Brize Norton Gardens ♿❀ *All in Manor Road in Brize Norton village, S of A40 between Witney and Burford.* TEAS. *Combined adm £3 Chd free. Sun June 11 (2-6)*

Barnstable House (Mrs J Butcher) Delightful small garden full of flowers; wishing well

NEW **Lingermans** (Mrs E Dobson) *Approx 2m from village.* 1-acre secluded garden areas; sunken garden with pergola. Old trees of note: 100yr old walnut, holly and white heart cherry.

NEW **The Long Barn** (Mr & Mrs K Gillians) Medium sized garden, mixed borders with less known plants and grasses; sunken patio with pots

The Manor House (Mrs Becky Broomfield) Walled garden, 1¼ acres of mature trees. 60′ pergola with roses, clematis, jasmine and wisteria, 200-yr-old Georgian privy in grounds. Garden presently being restored. House dates from C14. Grade II listed (not open)

NEW **Montrose** (Mrs J Whelan) Medium-sized garden; formal and relaxed areas under development

Ramshead Cottage (Mrs A Elsmore) Pretty little garden facing the Manor House

Broadwell House, nr Lechlade ♿✂❀ (Mrs Charles Cox) *5m NE Lechlade off A361.* In delightful Cotswold village with interesting church. Mature 2 acres, garden planted for colour throughout the year. Many interesting trees and shrubs incl wellingtonia, ginkgo, acers, aralias, salix, clematis. Topiary, rare plants, many golden, silver and variegated; unusual grasses, penstemons and osteospermums; many hardy geraniums. Listed house and old barn (not open). *Adm £1.50. Snowdrop Opening Sun Feb 27 (2-4); Combined adm with Kencot Gardens £3. Mon April 24 (2-6). Private parties and gardening clubs welcome by prior arrangement*

● **Brook Cottage, Alkerton** ❀ (Mrs David Hodges) *Well Lane. 6m W of Banbury. ¾m off A422. Follow signs in village.* 4-acre hillside garden formed since 1964. Wide variety of trees, shrubs and perennials in areas of differing character. Water garden; alpine scree; one-colour borders. Over 200 shrubs and climbing roses. Many clematis; interesting throughout season. DIY Tea & Coffee. Refreshments for groups by arrangement. *Adm £2.50 OAPs £2 Chd free. Mon to Fri incl Bank Hols (9-6) 24 April to 31 Oct. Evenings, weekends and all group visits by appt* **Tel 01295 670303 or 670590**

▲ **Broughton Castle, nr Banbury** ♿❀ (The Lord Saye & Sele) *2½m W of Banbury on Shipston-on-Stour rd (B4035).* 1 acre; shrubs, herbaceous borders, walled garden, roses, climbers seen against background of C14-C16 castle surrounded by moat in open parkland. House also open, extra charge. TEAS. *Adm Garden only £2 Chd £1. For NGS Suns June 25; July 30 (2-5)*

Broughton Poggs & Filkins Gardens ♿❀ *Enchanting limestone villages between Burford and Lechlade, just E of A361.* TEAS. *Combined adm £2 Chd free. Tickets from* **The Court House, Broughton Hall or Little Peacocks** *(ACNO to Broughton & Filkins Church Funds). Sun April 9 (2-5.30)*

Broughton Hall, Broughton Poggs ❀ (Mr & Mrs C B S Dobson) 5-acre garden with lawns; topiary; ponds and fountains; mature trees; borders; pergola; walled garden and many spring bulbs

NEW **Broughton Poggs Mill** (Mr & Mrs S Dewbury) Stream garden

Corner Cottage, Broughton Poggs (Mr & Mrs E Stephenson) Cottage garden with many interesting shrubs

NEW **The Cotswold Woollen Mill, Filkins** (R Martin Esq) Office garden with old flagstones, roses and water feature

The Court House, Broughton Poggs (Richard Burls Esq) Many interesting trees; shurbs and bulbs; lawns and a secret garden

The Garden Cottage, Broughton Poggs (Mr & Mrs R Chennells) Cottage garden

Little Peacocks, Filkins ❀ (Colvin & Moggridge, Landscape Consultants)

Manor Farm Cottage, Broughton Poggs (Mr & Mrs E R Venn) Cottage with water feature

NEW **The Old Rectory** (Mr & Mrs M Chevaux) Large garden of lawn, shrubs and mature trees

Rose Cottage, Broughton Poggs (R Groves Esq) Interesting shrubs; trees; flowers; bulbs; vegetables and a water feature

St Peter's House, Filkins (Mr John Cambridge) Large garden with many interesting shrubs; mature trees; lawns and sunken garden

Buckland, nr Faringdon ❀ (Mrs Richard Wellesley) *Signposted to Buckland off A420, lane between two churches.* Beautiful lakeside walk; fine trees; daffodils; shrubs. Norman church adjoins garden. TEAS. *Adm £3 Chd free (ACNO to Richard Wellesley Memorial Transport Fund). Sun April 9 (2-7). Private visits welcome Tues and Thurs, please* **Tel 01367 870235**

Chalkhouse Green Farm, Kidmore End ♿❀ (Mr & Mrs J Hall) *Situated 2m N of Reading between A4074 and B481. Approx 1.5m SE of Kidmore End.* 1-acre garden and traditional farmstead (not open). Herbaceous borders, herb garden, shrubs, old-fashioned roses, trees incl medlar, quince and mulberries. Farm animals incl an ancient breed of British White cattle, donkey, pigs, piglets, chickens, ducks and turkeys. Farm trail and donkey rides, vintage tractor trailer rides. Cream TEAS and swimming in covered pool in aid of Soundabout 'Music for disabled children appeal'. *Adm £2 Chd under 16 and wheelchairs free. Sun Aug 13 (2-6)*

Charlbury Gardens, Charlbury ♿❀ *Large historic village on B4022 Witney-Enstone.* Teas at the Church. *Combined adm £2 Chd 50p (ACNO to Wytham Hall Sick Bay for Homeless, Medical Care). Sun, Mon May 28, 29 (2-6)*

Gothic House (Mr & Mrs Andrew Lawson) *Nr Bell Hotel.* ⅓-acre walled garden, planted for sculpture display and colour association. False perspective, pleached lime walk with bulbs, trellis, alpine pyramid, terrace pots

The Priory (Dr D El Kabir & Colleagues) *Adjacent Church.* Formal terraced topiary gardens with Italianate features; foliage colour schemes, parterres, specimen trees and shrubs, water features and over 3 acres of recently planted arboretum

Chastleton Glebe, nr Moreton-in-Marsh (Prue Leith) *3m SE of Moreton-in-Marsh and W of Chipping Norton off A44.* 5 acres, old trees, terraces (one all red); small lake, island; Chinese-style bridge, pagoda; formal vegetable garden; views; rose tunnel. TEAS in aid of Chastleton Church. *Adm £2.50 Chd free. Sun July 16 (2-6)*

Checkendon Court, Checkendon ♿✗ (The Broackes Family) *NW of Reading. 2m NE of Woodcote off A4074 nr Checkendon Church.* 15 acres, attractively laid out with yew hedges, herbaceous borders, roses, kitchen garden. New rhododendrons and azalea planting and new laburnum pergola walk now complete. Teas in Checkendon Village Hall in aid of Checkendon School Assoc. *Adm £2.50 Chd free. Sun June 4 (2-5)*

Chivel Farm, Heythrop ♿✗❀ (Mr & Mrs J D Sword) *4m E of Chipping Norton, off A44 or A361.* High and open to extensive view, medium-sized garden designed for continuous interest. Colour schemed borders with many unusual shrubs, roses, herbaceous plants; small formal white garden, conservatory. TEAS in aid of St Nicholas Church, Heythrop. *Adm £2 Chd free. Sun Sept 3 (2-6)*

Christ Church, Oxford see Oxford University Gardens

Claytons, Gt Coxwell, nr Faringdon ♿✗❀ (Mr & Mrs Randal Pakeman) *Off A420 Swindon to Oxford 1m S of Faringdon.* 1¼-acre garden on gentle slope to small stream, facing W with rural outlook; many interesting and unusual plants, shrubs, scree bed, greenhouse. TEAS in aid of St Giles Church, Gt Coxwell. *Adm £2 Chd free. Sun July 9 (2-6)*

Clematis Corner, Shillingford ♿ (Mike & Dorothy Brown) *15 Plough Close. At Shillingford roundabout (10m S of Oxford on A4074), take A329 towards Warborough and*

Thame. Clematis Corner is 200yds from roundabout, 1st on L inside Plough Close, just round sharp L bend. ¼ acre garden specialising in clematis (over 300 varieties) grown in a variety of ways, within mixed flower beds, incl NCCPG National Collection of herbaceous clematis. TEAS. *Adm £2 (£1.50 for groups of 10 or more) Chd 50p (ACNO to ICRF). Private visits welcome by appt April 1 to Aug 31, please* **Tel 01865 858721**

Clock House, Coleshill ♿✂❀ (Denny Wickham & Peter Fox) *3½m SW of Faringdon on B4019.* Garden at top of village. Planted around site of Coleshill House, burnt down in the 50s. The main floor plan laid out and planted as a memorial to this famous house. Walled garden in old laundry drying ground; big greenhouse; unusual plants with emphasis on foliage, vegetables and herbs; good views across Vale of the White Horse and parkland. Toilets not suitable disabled. TEAS. *Adm £1.50 Chd free. Open every Thurs April to Oct (2-5) open late till 8pm on Thurs in June. Suns May 21, June 18, Sept 10, Oct 8 (2-6). Private visits welcome, please* **Tel 01793 762476**

Colegrave Seeds Ltd, West Adderbury ♿✂ (Mr John Whitehead) *Milton Rd. Off A4260 Banbury-Oxford rd. From M40 travelling S leave at junction 11: travelling N leave at junction 10. In Adderbury head for Milton and Bloxham. Trial grounds ½m on R.* Seed trial grounds and patio display gardens containing thousands of summer flowering annuals and perennials. Many new items in trial prior to introduction. A festival of colour unique in Oxfordshire. Covered display. TEAS. *Adm £2.50 Chd £1 (ACNO to The David Colegrave Foundation). Sun Aug 6 (10-5)*

Corpus Christi, Oxford See Oxford University Gardens

NEW **Cote House, nr Bampton** ♿✂❀ (Mrs David Anderson) *Hamlet situated off Standlake/Aston Rds. B4449 nr Bampton.* Large garden surrounding old manor house (not open); formal, secret, knot and herb gardens; long ornamental pond and rill. Hot and cool beds; many mature trees; espalier fruits; well stocked vegetable and soft fruit garden. *Adm £2 Chd £1 (ACNO to Oxford Bach Choir). Suns July 16, 23 (2-6)*

NEW **The Cuckoo Pen Nursery, Benson** ❀ (Mr & Mrs Ian Burles) *30 metres SW of the church turn L into St Helens Ave. The Nursery is approx 300m along on the R; (park on avenue along the hedge side).* Built on boggy allotment land the garden and nursery is bordered by drainage ditches and a chalk stream planted with moisture loving plants. Mounds of rubble have been contoured and planted with drought tolerant perennials. Features, a marsh wilderness area, mini wildflower meadow and cottage garden. Tea Room by R Thames 100 metres. *Adm £1.50 Chd under 12 free. Sun, Mon May 28, 29; Suns June 25; July 30; Aug 27; Sept 24 (2-6)*

Dundon House, Minster Lovell ♿✂❀ (Mr & Mrs W Pack) *Off B4047 opp White Hart, sign to Minster Lovell Hall and Leafield. First drive on R. Parking in field on L. Disabled parking at house.* Mainly C16 house (not open), 4 acres part terraced rebuilt on old quarry site in 1930s. Views across Windrush valley. Flower, shrub rose and wild gardens enclosed by yew hedges and stone walls, created in 1980s. Newly planted woodland. TEAS by WI. *Adm £2 OAPs £1.50 Chd free. Sun May 28 (2-6)*

East Hagbourne Gardens ♿❀ *1½m SE of Didcot.* 4 gardens and probably others together with award winning wildflower garden attached to the cemetery. An exceptionally pretty village which in '99 won the Oxfordfshire best kept village award and the regional competition of Britain in Bloom. Flower Festival in C11-12 Church. Renowned Bell-Ringers viewable (3-5). Art Galleries. TEAS & Plant Sales at **Manor Farm & Kingsholme**. *Combined adm £3 Chd free. Sat June 24 (2-6)*

1 Church Close ❀ (Mrs P Linklater) ¼-acre cottage garden, Elzabethan house (not open). Plants sale in aid of BBONT

Kingsholme (Mr & Mrs J Lawson) Partly Elizabethan, partly C17 house with mediaeval origins (not open). 3/4-acre garden with fine topiary in Box and Yew. Herbaceous and shrub borders; water garden; rockery

Lime Tree Cottage (Mr & Mrs R K Evans) ¼-acre old cottage garden, with stream

Manor Farm (Mr & Mrs R W Harries) 2-acre garden, water surrounds the main house (not open) in the form of a moat and full use has been made of this feature. TEAS in aid of Church & Village Hall.

Epwell Mill, nr Banbury ♿❀ (Mrs William Graham & Mrs David Long) *Epwell, 7m W of Banbury, between Shutford and Epwell.* Medium-sized garden, interestingly landscaped in open country, based on former water-mill; terraced pools; bulbs; azaleas. New white double border. TEAS. *Adm £1.50 Chd free (ACNO to Epwell Parochial Church Council). Suns April 9; Sept 17; Mon May 29 (2-6)*

Exeter College, Oxford see Oxford University Gardens

Friars Court, Clanfield ♿❀ (Mr J M Willmer) *On A4095 Faringdon to Witney, S of Clanfield [OS 285009].* C16 part moated farmhouse (not open). New/mature gardens, woodland walks and nature trail. Working displays on alternative energy, museum and shop. TEAS. *Adm £2 Chd under 12 free. Suns June 11, Aug 20 (2-6). Gardens open at other times by appt only,* **Tel 01367 810206**

Garsington Manor, nr Oxford ♿❀ (Mr & Mrs L V Ingrams) *SE of Oxford N of B480.* House C17 of architectural interest (not open). Monastic fish ponds, water garden, dovecot c.1700; flower parterre and Italian garden laid out by Philip and Lady Ottoline Morrell; fine trees and yew hedges. Free car park. TEAS in aid of local churches. *Adm £2 Chd free. Suns April 30; Oct 1 (2-5)*

Green College, Oxford see Oxford University Gardens

▲ **Greys Court, Rotherfield Greys** ✂❀ (Lady Brunner) *W of Henley-on-Thames on rd to Peppard.* 8 acres amongst which are the ruined walls and buildings of original fortified manor. Rose, cherry, wisteria and white gardens; lawns; kitchen garden; ice house; Archbishop's maze. Tudor house open with C18 alterations on site of original C13 house fortified by Lord Grey in C14. Donkey wheel and tower. A band plays during the afternoon; children's drawing competition. TEAS. *Adm garden £3 Chd £1.50 House & Garden £4 Chd £2. For NGS Sat May 20 (2-5.30)*

Harcourt Arboretum, Oxford see Oxford University Gardens

Haughton House, Churchill ♿ (Mr & Mrs A D Loehnis) *3m SW of Chipping Norton on B4450. From Burford, W for Churchill via A361.* 2 acre garden with areas of different interest. Herbaceous border; meadow; wonderful views. TEAS in aid of church. *Adm £2 Chd free. Sun Sept 10 (2-6)*

Headington Gardens *East Oxford, off London Road, ¾m inside ring road.* Teas in Parish Hall, Dunstan Rd in aid of WI and Friends of St Andrews. *Combined adm £2 Chd free. Suns May 14, July 16, Aug 13 (2-6)*

2 Fortnam Close ❀ (Mr & Mrs D Holt) *Off Headley Way, follow signs to John Radcliffe Hospital.* Multi-award winner, featured on TV and radio. ¼ acre garden on 3 levels, trees, shrubs, heathers, azaleas and a large wisteria. Roses, bearded iris and other herbaceous plants in a planned layout which incl a pond and pergola. Watercolour paintings and pressed flower arrangements to view if you wish

40 Osler Road ✗ (Mr & Mrs N Coote) *After traffic lights in centre of Headington shopping centre, 2nd turn on R opp Royal Standard public house.* Spacious 23-yr-old town garden ⅔-acre with mature specimens of exotics. Passion for design and planting, use of decorative pots, mosiac paths, whitewashed walls, shutters: Mediterranean fantasy in a cold climate. See Country Life 27 Aug 1998. *Private visits for groups welcome by appointment, please* **Fax 01865 767922 or Tel 01865 767680 (after gardening hours)** or e-mail: nicholas@coote100.freeserve.co.uk

Pumpkin Cottage ♿✗ (Mr & Mrs M Davis) *6 St Andrew's Lane, Old Headington, off St Andrew's Rd, nr to Church.* Small garden, 20m × 16m, enclosed within stone walls situated at rear of Grade II listed cottage (not open). Small pools; mixed planting; paved areas with container grown plants. Small cobble-paved front garden. Wheelchair access possible by arrangement

1 Stoke Place ✗ (Mr & Mrs M C Carrington) *Off St Andrew's Rd.* Just short of an acre shaped by a network of old stone walls which have survived in the area. Trees and stonework provide a framework for a linked series of paths and flower beds which gives an atmosphere of seclusion. Small pools and many contrasting shrubs and plants. *Open May 14 only (ACNO to RSPCA)*

Hearns House, Gallows Tree Common ♿❀ (Mr & Mrs John Pumfrey) *5m N of Reading, 5m W of Henley. From A4074 turn E at The Fox, Cane End.* Architects house (not open), in 2-acre garden in woodland setting. Designed for maintenance by two people with full time careers. Emphasis on design, good foliage and single colour areas with paved courtyards and shady walks. Redesigned and much expanded water feature. Wide variety of hardy plants incl for example 40 named Euphorbia. TEAS or coffee in aid of Oxfam. *Adm £2 Chd free. Sat, Sun May 13, 14; Sun, Mon Aug 27, 28 (10-12; 2-5)*

Heron's Reach, Whitchurch-on-Thames ❀ (Mr Bernard Vorhaus) *Eastfield Lane. From Pangbourne take Tollbridge rd over Thames to Whitchurch-on-Thames. At The Greyhound turn R into Eastfield Lane.* 1 acre in beautiful Thames-side setting with views to the Chilterns; woodland garden with pond, stream, shrubs and herbaceous borders. Tallest climbing rose in Britain. TEAS. *Adm £2 Chd free. Sun July 2 (2-6). Private visits also welcome in July, please* **Tel 01189 843140 or 0171 722 145**

Highmoor Hall, Highmoor ♿✗❀ (Mr & Mrs P D Persson) *1m S of Nettlebed on B481 to Reading.* 6-acre garden in a peaceful setting: open views across ha-ha; secluded areas; mature trees; water garden; walled kitchen garden; shrubberies and herbaceous borders with an accent on colour blending. New gravel garden and border of grasses and perennials. Arts Centre within the grounds with exhibition and sale of arts and crafts. TEAS. *Adm £2 Chd free (ACNO to TEAR Fund). Sat July 15 (2-6)*

Hill Court, Tackley ♿✗❀ (Mr & Mrs Andrew C Peake) *9m N of Oxford. Turn off A4260 at Sturdy's Castle.* Walled garden of 2 acres with yew cones at top of terrace as a design feature by Russell Page in the 1960s. Terraces incl silver, pink and blue plantings, white garden, herbaceous borders, shrubberies, orangery. Many rare and unusual plants. Entry incl History Trail with unique geometric fishponds (1620), C17 stables, pigeon house, C18 lakes, icehouse etc (stroll of 1hr (not suitable for wheelchairs)). TEAS to village charities. Pied Pipers recorder group (Sun only) *Adm £2 Chd free Sat, Sun June 10, 11 (2-6)*

Holywell Manor, Oxford see Oxford University Gardens

Home Close, Garsington ✗❀ (Dr P Giangrande & Miss M Waud) *Southend. SE of Oxford, N of B480.* 2-acre garden with listed house (not open) and granary. Interesting trees, shrubs and perennials planted for all-yr-interest. Terraces, walls and hedges divide the garden into ten distinct areas. *Adm £1.50 Chd free. Sun April 2 (2-6). Private visits welcome April 1 to Sept 30, please* **Tel 01865 361394**

Home Farm, Balscote see Balscote Gardens

Hook Norton Manor, Banbury ❀ (Mr & Mrs Nicholas Holmes) *SW of Banbury. From A361, 1m from Chipping Norton turn N and follow signs.* 2½-acres terraced lawns leading down to streams; trees, shrubs and bog garden. TEAS in aid of St Peter's Church. *Adm £1.50 Chd free. Sun Oct 1 (2-5.30)*

Iffley Gardens, S Oxford ✗❀ *Secluded old village within Oxford's ring road, off A4158 from Magdalen Bridge to Littlemore roundabout.* Renowned Norman church, featured on cover of Pevsner's Oxon guide. Short footpath from Mill Lane leads to scenic Iffley Lock, and Sandford to Oxford towpath. Teas from 3-5 at thatched village hall, Church Way. Two plant stalls, one in aid of NGS, the other for The White House Nursery *Combined adm £2 OAPs £1.50 Chd free Sun June 18 (2-6)*

8 Abberbury Road (F S Tordoff Esq) *Off Church Way.* ½-acre plantsman's garden developed since 1971. Mature trees, shrubs, coloured and variegated foliage, many old and modern shrub roses and large climbers. *Private visits welcome, please* **Tel 01865 778644**

24 Abberbury Road ♿ (Mr & Mrs E Townsend-Coles) ½-acre family garden with fruit, flowers and vegetables

65 Church Way ❀ (Mrs J Woodfill) Small cottage garden planted with shrubs, perennials and herbs, many of them grown for their historical associations. *Private visits welcome, please* **Tel 01865 770537**

71 Church Way (Mrs M L Harrison) A small, low maintenance, professionally designed, front garden with mixed shrubs and herbaceous plantings. *Private visits welcome, please* **Tel 01865 718224**

122 Church Way (Sir John & Lady Elliott) Small secluded cottage style garden with trees, shrubs, roses and herbaceous plants behind listed house (not open) with view of church tower

11 Iffley Turn ♿ (Lisa, Ann & Matthew Ellett) A well established garden of ½-acre containing many mature trees, a vegetable plot, herbaceous borders and a pond

The Mill House (Dr P A Lawrence) *30 Mill Lane.* A terraced garden dropping westwards to the river at the old mill-race

Rosedale ❀ (Mrs T Bennett) *Mill Lane, off Church Way.* ½-acre garden on different levels, hidden behind walls. A mixture of trees, shrubs, roses and herbaceous plants with a large rockery and tiny woodland garden. *Private visits welcome, please* **Tel 01865 714151**

Kencot Gardens, nr Lechlade *5m NE of Lechlade, E of A361 to Burford.* A most charming Cotswold village with interesting church. TEAS *Combined adm £3 Chd free. Mon April 24(incl* **Broadwell House***) Mon Aug 28 (2-6). Also* **Kencot House** *only open Sun June 25. Adm £2 Chd free (2-6).*

De Rougemont ♿ (Mr & Mrs D Portergill) ½ acre garden with very varied planting: over 350 named plants; beds for perennials, conifers, fuchsias, herbs and roses; spring bulbs; vegetables and fruit trees; soft fruit cage; greenhouse with vine; well

The Gardens ♿ (Lt Colonel & Mrs John Barstow) ¼ acre garden featuring spring bulbs, iris, roses, herbaceous, rock plants, old apple trees and a well

Ivy Nook (Mr & Mrs W Gasson) Cottage garden; rockeries, lawns, mixed borders.

Kencot Cottage (Mrs Molly Foster) Very small garden with spring bulbs and bedding, also bonsai trees

Kencot House, nr Lechlade ❀ (Mr & Mrs Andrew Patrick) 2-acre garden with lawns, trees, borders; quantities of daffodils and other spring bulbs; roses and over 50 different clematis; notable ginkgo tree. Interesting carved C13 archway. *Also open Sun June 25*

Manor Farm (Mr & Mrs J R Fyson) 2-acre garden with lawns and herbaceous borders; naturalised spring bulbs, incl long-established fritillaries; clipped yew, pleached lime walk, pergola with rambling and gallica roses. Mature orchards. C17 listed farmhouse (not open).

NEW **Pinnocks** (Mr & Mrs Coxeter) 1-acre garden. Spring bulbs, herbaceous borders, shrubs and a variety of trees incl Robinia and Tulip Tree

Kiddington Hall, Woodstock ❀ (The Hon Maurice & Mrs Robson) *4m NW of Woodstock. From A44 Oxford-Stratford, R at Xrds in Kiddington and down hill; entrance on L.* Partly suitable for wheelchairs. Large grounds with lake, parkland designed by Capability Brown; terraced rose garden and orangery beside house designed by Sir Charles Barry (not open); C12 church, C16 dovecote and large walled kitchen garden. Plant Stall & Cream TEAS in aid of St Nicholas Church, Kiddington. *Adm £2 Chd free. Sun June 25 (2-6)*

■ **Kingston Bagpuize House, nr Abingdon** ♿❀ (Mr & Mrs Francis Grant) Notable collection of unusual trees, shrubs, perennials and bulbs. House not suitable for wheelchairs. TEAS *Adm garden only £1.50. House and garden £3.50 OAP's £3 Chd £2.50 (under 5's free to garden, not admitted to the house) (ACNO to Michael Sobell House). Open Bank Hol weekends Sat, Sun, Mon, also March 12, 26; April 8, 9; May 13, 14; June 10, 11, 25; July 8, 9, 22, 23; Aug 9, 12, 13; and Sept 6, 9, 10, 23, 24; Oct 8, 22 (2-5.30) last adm 5pm. For NGS Suns April 9; July 23; Sept 24. Groups welcome all year by written appt, please* **Tel 01865 820259**

▲ **Kingstone Lisle Park, nr Wantage** ♿ (Mr & Mrs James Lonsdale) *5m W of Wantage along B4507.* 12 acres of gardens incl a shrubbery, pleached limes, an avenue leading up to an ornamental pond. 3 acres of lakes. TEAS. *Adm for NGS garden only £3 Chd free (ACNO to St John the Baptist Church, Kingstone Lisle). Sun June 11 (2-5)*

Langford Gardens, nr Lechlade ♿❀ *E of A361 Burford - Lechlade; W of A409 Burford - Faringdon.* Mixture of cottage and formal gardens in old limestone village which makes a feature of roses. Saxon church, known for saxon carvings (Langford Rood), decorated with flowers. TEAS in aid of St Matthew's church. *Combined adm £3 Chd free. Sun June 18 (2-6)*

Bakery Cottage (Miss R Amies)
The Barn (Mr & Mrs D E Range)
2 Church Lane (Mr & Mrs A Keating)
5 Church Lane (Mr D Carden)
1 Cooks Farm Cottages (Mr H Davies)
Cotswold Bungalow (Mr & Mrs J Dudley)
Dunford House (Mr & Mrs H Catling)
26 The Elms (Mr R Stacey)
Lime Tree Cottage (Dr & Mrs M G Schultz)
Lockey House (Alison Kemp, Nigel & Kate Gardener, Richard & Denise Kemp)
Lower Farm (Mr & Mrs T Brown)
Moss Cottage (Mr Mark Thomas)
The Old School & Barn (Sir Hardy Amies) Collection of 60 old English roses
The Old Vicarage (Mr & Mrs A Radcliffe)
Peevish Corner (Mr & Mrs D Kirby)
Rectory Farm (Mr& Mrs R J Kirby)
Rosefern Cottage (Mr & Mrs J Lowden)
Stonecroft (David Apperley & Christine Romanek)
Threeways (Mrs M Wilson)
Wellbank (Mr & Mrs Booth)

Lime Close, Drayton ♿❀ (M C de Laubarede) *35 Henleys Lane. 2m S of Abingdon.* 3-acre mature garden with very rare trees, shrubs, perennials and bulbs. Featured in Vogue, Harpers and Queen and Elle Décor. Magnificent early spring display of snowdrops, crocus, hellebores and early flowering shrubs. Ornamental potager, alpines, unusual topiary and shade borders. Herb garden designed by Rosemary Verey.

Listed C16 house (not open). Unusual plants for sale from Green Farm Plants. TEAS. *Adm £2 Chd free (ACNO to Hearing Dogs for the Deaf). Suns Feb 27 (2-5), June 4 (2-6). Parties of 10 or more welcome on other days by appt in writing to 35 Henleys Lane, Oxon OX14 4HU*

Magdalen College, Oxford see Oxford University Gardens

NEW **Manor Farm, Old Minster Lovell** ♿❀ (Sir Peter & Lady Parker) *Off B4047 rd between Witney/Burford, 1½m from Witney. Follow sign opp White Hart down to R Windrush, 100yds over bridge turn R at Old Swan and up village street. Manor Farm is last house on R before continuing to Crawley. Parking. Enter at end of 1st field towards Crawley if approaching from village. Drive back across field to enter close to garden.* No Parking in village. 6-acre garden of C15 farmhouse (not open) adjoining Minster Lovell Hall ruin. Old shrub and climbing roses, fish ponds, herbaceous and lawns. Old barns within garden area. TEAS. *Adm £2 Chd free (ACNO to British False Memory Society). Sat June 24 (2-5)*

The Manor House, Clifton Hampden ♿❀ (Mr C Gibbs) *4m E of Abingdon on A415.* 4-acre romantic C19 garden above R Thames with far-reaching views; long pergola, lime tunnel, herbaceous borders, bulbs, wild riverside walks, much new planting in progress. TEAS in aid of St Michael and All Angels Church. *Adm £2 Chd free. Sun April 23 (2.30-5.30). Parties welcome, please* **Tel 01865 407720**

The Manor House, Sutton Courtenay ♿⊘❀ (The Hon F D L Astor) *4m S of Abingdon. Out of Abingdon on the A415. Turn off to Culham -Sutton Courtenay. From A34 going N come into Milton Village take last rd on R to Sutton Courtenay.* 10 acres of garden approx 35 acres of land. ½m R Thames Bank. TEAS. *Adm £1.50 Chd 50p. Sun May 14 (2-6)*

NEW **Maryland, Fencott** ♿ (Mr & Mrs M Warner) *10m NE of Oxford M40 junction 9 A34 turn to Islip. Turn L to Charlton on Otmoor (4m) to Fencott.* 2½ acres newly established garden; ponds, shrubs, herbaceous & mixed borders, grasses in gravel bed all arranged in separate areas, incl kite garden and new yew walk. *Adm £2 Chd 50p (ACNO to Charlton on Otmoor School Association). Sun June 11 (2-6)*

Merton College See Oxford University Gardens

The Mill House, Stadhampton ♿❀ (Mr & Mrs F A Peet) *A329/B480, 8m SE of Oxford.* 1-acre family garden with old mill and stream. Mill not working but machinery largely intact and wheel turning with pumped water. Parking on green; parking for disabled only at house. TEAS in aid of Stadhampton Church Restoration Fund. *Adm £1 Chd free. Sun April 16 (2-5.30)*

The Mill House, Sutton Courtenay ♿⊘❀ (Mrs Jane Stevens) *Abingdon, Oxon, OX14 4NH* Approx 8½ acres; R Thames runs through garden which is on several islands with mill pond and old paper mill. TEAS *Adm £2 Chd £1, under 4 free Suns April 9, June 11, Sept 24 (2-6). Parties of 10 and over also welcome on other days by appt in writing*

Nettlebed Gardens *On A4130, some 5m NW of Henley-on-Thames. Take B481 towards Reading and after 200yds turn R into Sue Ryder Home where there is ample parking.* Teas and Plant sales in aid of Sue Ryder Home. *Combined adm £2 Chd free Sun May 28 (2-5.30)*

Red Lion House ♿⊘ (Mr & Mrs G Freeman) Small garden with rare and unusual plants

Sue Ryder Home ♿⊘❀ (The Sue Ryder Foundation) 26-acre garden surrounding large Edwardian house (not open). Fine rhododendrons and rare trees. Large lawns, pond and Italian terrace, dell and secret garden, large flower borders

New College, Oxford see Oxford University Gardens

25 Newfield Road, Sonning Common ♿⊘ (Joyce & David Brewer) *5m N of Reading on B481 Nettlebed Rd, on leaving village turn L past Catholic Church, Shiplake Bottom then immed L into Newfield Rd. Free parking available behind village hall Wood Lane. Garden 5 mins walk N.* Small interesting garden of ¼ acre. In excess of 180 varieties of clematis; shrubs, spring bulbs, annuals and containers; mature trees and vegetable garden. Fishpond, waterfall, bantams and miniature ducks. Featured in Womens Weekly Gardens to Visit June 99. TEAS. *Adm £1.50 Chd under 16 free (ACNO to Action Against Breast Cancer) Suns April 16, July 16 (2-6). Private visits welcome, please* **Tel 0118 9723611**

NEW **North Oxford Gardens** *Approx 3/4m N of Oxford City Centre, off Banbury Rd, two gardens of houses forming part of the early C20 extension of the North Oxford Victorian suburb, together with the modern garden at Wolfson College (award winning building designed by Powell & Moya (not open)).* TEAS at Wolfson College. *Combined adm £2 Chd free. Sun June 18 (2-6)*

NEW **6 Charlbury Road** ♿⊘ (John & Josephine Peach) *Charlbury Rd is parallel to Banbury Rd, off Bardwell or Linton Rds.* Walled ¼-acre town garden on two levels with mixed borders and plants in containers especially hostas. *(2-5)*

NEW **9 Rawlinson Road** ⊘ (Rani Lall) *Rawlinson Rd runs between Banbury and Woodstock Rds midway between Oxford City Centre and Summertown shops.* Small town garden with structured disarray of roses. Terrace of stone inlaid with brick and enclosed by Chinese fretwork balustrade, chunky brick and oak pergola covered with roses, wisteria and clematis; potted topiary. *Private visits welcome by appt only, please* **Tel 01865 559614**

Wolfson College ♿❀ (Prof W P Bradshaw) *End of Linton Rd, off Banbury Rd.* 9 acres by R Cherwell developed in recent years with comprehensive plant collection tolerant of alkaline soils, grown in interesting and varied habitats around a framework of fine mature trees

4 Northfield Cottages, Water Eaton ♿⊘❀ (Miss S E Bedwell) *nr Kidlington. From Sainsbury Roundabout S of Kidlington on A4260 take exit for A34 N. Take 1st R Water Eaton lane opp Kings Arms. Then 1st L following signs for Northfield Farm. Over 2nd bridge to 4th cottage on L.* Approx ¼ acre containing unusual herbaceous plants, bulbs, fruit, vegetables and greenhouse now extending into two further gardens. *Adm £1.50 Private visits for individuals and groups welcome all year, please* **Tel 01865 378910**

Nutford Lodge, Longcot ♿❀ (Mr & Mrs K Elmore) *In Longcot Village next to The King & Queen public house. S of A420 between Faringdon and Shrivenham.* 1½-acre sculpture garden with accent on fragrance, for the blind. Ponds, rockeries, colour schemed borders, potager, views to White Horse; indoor gallery and vintage motorbikes. *Adm £1 Chd free (ACNO to Headway in Oxford). Sat May 27 to Sun June 4 inclusive daily. Also private visits welcome, please* **Tel 01793 782258**

Old Church House, Wantage ♿ (Dr & Mrs Dick Squires) *Situated next to Parish Church nr the Wantage market square* An unusual town garden running down to the Letcombe brook. Much interest with different levels, follies, water, mature trees and many special plants. Tickets and teas at Vale & Downland Museum close by in Church St. *Adm £1 Chd free (ACNO to Vale & Downland Trust). Tues to Sat. Private visits also welcome, please* **Tel 01235 762785**

NEW **The Old Manor, Cropredy** ♿✗❀ (John & Liz Atkins) *4m NE of Banbury between A361 & A423.* 3 acres of formal and informal planting bordering the Oxford Canal. Many island beds of unusual herbaceous planting; old roses; shrubs; ditch garden; gravel garden (in progress). An ornamental kitchen garden and long herbaceous border lead to a newly planted woodland. A mediaeval moat and established spinneys provide a natural habitiat to wildlife. Many stitting areas for quiet contemplation. Cream TEAS. *Adm £2.50 Chd free (ACNO to Bekind). Sun June 25 (2-6)*

The Old Rectory, Brightwell Baldwin ♿ (Mr & Mrs Donald Chilvers) *2m W of Watlington via Cuxham (B480).* 1½-acre garden and parkland surrounding beautiful Georgian rectory (not open). Open views to S over ha-ha. Formal garden layout with herb, rose and herbaceous beds, terracing and walls. Designed by owners and planted 1990 yet mature; rare breed of sheep. *Adm £2 Chd free. Private visits welcome June 1 to Aug 31 by appt only, please* **Tel 01491 612432**

The Old Rectory, Coleshill ♿ (Sir George & Lady Martin) *Coleshill (NT village) is on B4019 midway between Faringdon and Highworth.* Medium-sized garden; lawns and informal shrub beds; wide variety shrubs, incl old-fashioned roses, 40-yr-old standard wisteria. Distant views of Berkshire and Wiltshire Downs. House dates from late C14 (not open). TEAS. *Adm £1 Chd free. Suns April 16 (2-6), Sept 10 (2-5)*

Oxford University Gardens

Christ Church Masters Garden, Oxford ✗ (The Treasurer) *Entrance on Christ Church Meadow (through War Memorial garden on St Aldate's).* Created in 1926, has herbaceous borders and a new border with some unusual shrubs. A walk through the newly designed and replanted Pocock's Garden, past Pocock's Plane, an oriental plane planted in 1636, leads to the Cathedral Garden. *Adm £1 Chd free. Combined adm with* **Corpus Christi** *and* **Merton Gardens**. *Sun Aug 6 (2-5)*

Corpus Christi, Oxford ♿✗ (C Holmes Esq, Domestic Bursar) *Entrance from Merton St or* **Christ Church Fellows' Garden**. Several small gardens and courtyards overlooking Christchurch meadows. Fellows' private garden not normally open to the public. TEAS in aid of Amnesty International *Adm £1. Combined adm £2.50 with* **Christ Church** *and* **Merton College**. *Sun Aug 6 (2-5)*

Exeter College, Rector's Lodgings, Oxford ✗ (Professor M Butler, Rector's Lodgings) *The Turl, between High & Broad Sts.* Small enclosed garden, herbaceous and shrubs, especially clematis. Fellows' Garden and Chapel also open. *Combined adm with* **New College** *£1.50 Chd free. Sun July 2 (2-5)*

Green College, Oxford ♿✗ (Mr M Kettlewell) *Woodstock Rd, next to Radcliffe Infirmary.* 3 acres; lawns, herbaceous borders, medicinal garden with notes on traditional usage of plants. Radcliffe Observatory (Tower of the Winds) open for views of Oxford. TEAS. *Adm £1 Chd free (incl Observatory). Sun June 18 (2-6)*

Harcourt Arboretum, Nuneham Courtenay ♿✗❀ (Mr T Walker) *6m S of Oxford on A4074 (formerly A423), 400yds S of Nuneham Courtenay.* 80 acres incl informal rhododendron walks, camellia, bamboo and acer collections, natural woodland and oak woodland, meadow with pond and associated aquatics and marginals; fine collection of mature conifers; many 150 yrs old. Staff available to answer queries. Plant stall in aid of Oxford University Botanic Garden. *Adm £1 Chd under 12 free. Sun June 4 (2-5)*

Holywell Manor, Oxford ✗❀ (Dr P A Bulloch, Garden Master) *Central Oxford at corner of Manor Rd & St Cross Rd on L of St Cross Church opp law library.* College garden of about 1 acre, not normally open to the public. Imaginatively laid out 50 yrs ago around horse chestnut to give formal and informal areas. Mature ginkgo avenue, spinney with spring flowers and bulbs. *Adm £1 Chd free Sun April 9 (2-6). Private visits welcome, please* **Tel 01865 271501**

Magdalen College, Fellows' Garden & President's Garden, Oxford ♿✗ (President & Fellows) *Entrance in High St.* 60 acres incl deer park, college lawns, numerous trees 150-200 yrs old, notable herbaceous and shrub plantings; Magdalen Meadows are surrounded by Addison's Walk, a tree-lined circuit by the R Cherwell developed since the late C18. An ancient herd of 40 deer is located in the grounds. Light lunch and TEAS. *Adm £2 Chd £1. Sun March 19 (1-5)*

Merton College Fellows' Garden, Oxford ♿✗ (Warden & Fellows) *Merton St, parallel to High St.* Ancient mulberry said to have associations with James 1; specimen trees incl sorbus and malus vars; long mixed border; recently established herbaceous bed; view of Christ Church meadow. *Adm £1 Chd free. Sun April 9 (2-5). Combined adm £2.50 with* **Christ Church** *and* **Corpus Christi**. *Sun Aug 6 (2-5)*

New College, Oxford ♿✗ (The Warden's Garden only) *Entered from New College Lane, off Catte St.* Secret walled garden, replanted 1988 with interesting mix of herbaceous and shrubs. *Adm £1 Acc chd free. Combined adm with* **Exeter College** *£1.50 Sun July 2 (2-5)*

The Queen's College, Provost's, Fellows' & Nuns' Gardens, Oxford ✗ (The Garden Master) *High*

Street. ½ acre with splendid herbaceous borders, rose garden, high old stone walls; large ilex tree. Magnificent statues set in wall of Hawksmoor's library (viewed from Provost's garden). *Combined adm with* **Wadham College** *£1.50. Sun July 16 (2-5)*

Rewley House, Oxford ♿✗ (Dr S Ott, Dept for Continuing Education) *Wellington Sq., St John Street.* Courtyard gardens, originally planted by townscaper, Jeanne Bliss, with variegated shrubs, climbers, trailing plants in mobile boxes on wheels. Landscaped gardens designed and maintained by Walter Sawyer, head of the University Parks. TEA. *Adm £1 Chd free. Sun July 16 (2-5). Private visits welcome, please* **Tel 01865 270375**

St Anne's College, Oxford ♿❀ (Simon Horwood Esq) *Woodstock Rd, opp the Radcliffe Observatory.* 5 acres of formal lawns, mature trees, annual and mixed borders, fellow's garden. TEAS. *Combined adm with* **Somerville College** *£2.00 Chd free (ACNO to Luther Street Medical Centre). Sun July 16 (2-6)*

St Hilda's College, Oxford ♿✗❀ (R C Needle, Clerk of Works) *Approx 15 mins walk E from city centre. Cross Magdalen Bridge and turn R at roundabout into Cowley Place. College Lodge at end on R. Or park in public car park at St Clements.* Approx 5 acres laid to lawns and flower beds with flood plain meadow containing interesting wild flowers. TEAS. *Adm £1 Chd under 12 free. Sun June 18 (2-5)*

NEW **Somerville College, Oxford** ♿✗ (Garden Committee) *Central Oxford. Enter from the Woodstock Rd, S of the Radcliffe Infirmary.* Approx 2 acres, robust college garden planted for yr-round interest. Formal bedding, colour, themed and old-fashioned mixed herbaceous borders. TEA. *Combined with* **St Anne's College** *£2 Chd free (ACNO to Oxford Botanic Garden Eucation Officer Appeal). Sun July 16 (2-6)*

Trinity College, President's Garden, Oxford ♿✗❀ (Dr C R Prior, Garden Master) *Entrance in Broad St.* Surrounded by high old stone walls, has mixed borders of herbaceous, shrubs and statuary. Historic Main College Gardens with specimen trees incl 250-yr-old forked catalpa, spring bulbs, fine long herbaceous border and handsome garden quad originally designed by Wren. **Fellows' Garden** Small walled terrace, herbaceous borders; water feature formed by Jacobean stone heraldic beasts. TEAS in aid of Sobell House Hospice Charity. *Adm £1.50 Chd free. Suns April 9; July 30 (2-5)*

Wadham College, Oxford ♿✗ (The Warden & Fellows) *Parks Rd.* 5 acres, best known for trees and herbaceous borders. In Fellows' main garden, fine ginkgo and Magnolia acuminata, etc; in Back Quadrangle very large Tilia tomentosa 'Petiolaris'; in Mallam Court white scented garden est 1994; in Warden's garden an ancient tulip tree; in Fellows' private garden Civil War embankment with period fruit tree cultivars, recently established shrubbery with unusual trees and ground cover amongst older plantings. *Adm £1 Chd free (ACNO to Sobell House Hospice). Sun March 19. Combined adm with* **The Queen's College** *£1.50. Sun July 16 (2-5)*

Wolfson College see North Oxfordshire Gardens

Partway House, Swalcliffe ♿✗❀ (Mr & Mrs M Brown) *nr Banbury. ¾m from Swalcliffe on Shipston Rd at the Sibford Ferris fork.* 2 acres of mature shrubs and herbaceous plants;distant views. Exceptional for the area is acid soil conditions, azaleas and rhododendrons. TEAS. *Adm £2 Chd free. Sat, Sun May 20, 21 (2-6)*

Pettifers, Lower Wardington ♿✗❀ (Mr J & the Hon Mrs Price) *5m NE of Banbury.* C17 village house (not open). 15 yr-old 1½ acre plantsman's garden frames an exceptional view of sheep pastures and wooded hills. Autumn border, with some areas reaching maturity. Unusual plants for sale. TEAS. *Adm £2 Chd free. Suns April 9; May 14; Oct 1 (2-6). Private visits welcome by appt, please* **Tel 01295 750232**

The Queen's College, Oxford See Oxford University Gardens

Querns, Goring Heath ♿✗❀ (Mr Michael & The Hon Mrs Whitfeld) *3m NE of Pangbourne. Take B4526 from A4074 Reading-Oxford Rd. After ½m follow signs.* 2 acres; shrub and herbaceous borders, rose garden, shrub rose garden, courtyard and formal pond. Listed house dating from early C16 with large thatched C17 barn (not open). *Adm £2 Chd free. Sun June 25 (2-6)*

Rewley College see Oxford University Gardens

Rofford Manor, Little Milton ♿✗❀ (Mr & Mrs J L Mogford) *10m SE of Oxford. 1m from Little Milton on Chalgrove Rd. Signposted Rofford only.* 2 acres, within old walls laid out since 1985. Vegetable, herb, rose and swimming pool garden; box garden with raised pool. Yew hedges and pleached limes; twin herbaceous borders planted Autumn 1989 flanking lawn leading to recently constructed ha-ha. TEAS in aid of St James' Church, Little Milton *Adm £2 Chd free Suns June 25, Sept 10 (2-6). Private visits welcome following written application, for periods June 19-24; Sept 4-9*

St Anne's College, Oxford See Oxford University Gardens

St Hilda's College, Oxford see Oxford University Gardens

St John's Home, Oxford ♿✗❀ *St Mary's Rd, off Leopold St S of Cowley Rd. 1m E from the Plain. Limited parking.* 3-acre grounds of All Saints Convent and St John's Home for the Elderly. Mature trees, lawns, secluded prayer garden and vegetable garden. Comper chapel open. TEAS. *Adm £1.50 OAPS £1 Chd free (ACNO to Society of All Saints Sisters of the Poor). Sun June 4 (2-5)*

Salford Gardens, nr Chipping Norton ✗ *2m W of Chipping Norton. Off A44 Oxford-Worcester.* TEAS. *Combined adm £2 Chd free. Suns May 21; Aug 27 (2-6)*

NEW **Manor Farm** ♿✗ (Mrs P G Caldin) Small mature well-stocked garden

Old Rectory ♿❀ (Mr & Mrs N M Chambers) 1½ acres mainly enclosed by walls. Yr-round interest, with unusual plants in mixed borders, many old roses, orchard and vegetable garden

Willow Tree Cottage ♿✂❀ (Mr & Mrs J Shapley) Small walled twin gardens; one created by owners since 1979 with shrub and herbaceous borders, many clematis; other created 1985 from old farmyard with large alpine garden. Featured in 'Successful Gardening'.

Shellingford House, Faringdon ♿ (Mr & Mrs Nicholas Johnston) *In Shellingford village off Faringdon to Wantage rd.* 2 acres with eccentric features, stream, fritillaries, spring flowers and bulbs. Orchard, gnome garden and childrens entertainments. TEAS. *Adm £2 Chd 50p (ACNO to Shellingford Church). Sun April 9 (2-6)*

Shotover House, Wheatley ♿❀ (Lt Col Sir John Miller GCVO MC DSO) *6m E of Oxford on A40. Bus: Oxford to Thame or Oxford to High Wycombe to London; alight Islip turn.* Large unaltered C18 landscape garden and park with lakes, ornamental temples, lawns and specimen trees; daffodils and other bulbs in Spring, shady walks in Summer. Also small collections of rare cattle, sheep and birds. TEAS. *Adm £1.50 Chd free. Suns April 2; July 30 (2-6)*

Sibford Ferris Gardens ✂ *Nr the Warwickshire border, S of B4035 (Banbury 6½m, Shipston-on-Stour 7½m).* TEAS in aid of Sibford Primary School PTA. *Combined adm £2 Chd free. Sun April 30 (2-6)*

Back Acre ❀ (Mr & Mrs F A Lamb) Almost an acre, much of which is wild woodland and rough grass with wild flowers; rockery and pond, constructed about 100 years ago and restored over the last few years

Home Close (Mr & Mrs P A Randall) Cotswold stone house (not open) fronting formal 1¼-acre garden designed by Baillie-Scott in 1911, under restoration. Courtyard with ornamental fountain and roman-style stone recesses. Terraced garden, large variety of shrubs incl rare species

Maria's House ♿ (Mr & Mrs B R Mills) ¼-acre old cottage garden, surrounded and subdivided by low stone walling. Features incl box hedge porch, small pond, rockeries and herbaceous borders

NEW **Pettiphers Piece** (Mr & Mrs J John) A small sloping country garden, newly formed but full of colour

Sibford Gower Gardens *Nr the Warwickshire border, S of B4035 Banbury 7m, Shipston-on-Stour 7m.* Superlative views and numerous intriguing tucked away lanes are features of this village. TEAS in aid of Sibford Primary School. **Handy Water Farm & Meadow Cottage**. *Combined adm for 2 gardens £2 Chd free. Sun, Wed June 11, 14;* **The Manor House, Temple Close, Meadow Cottage** *and* **Carters Yard.** Combined adm for 4 gardens £2.50 Acc chd free. Sun July 9 (2-6)

Carters Yard (Mr & Mrs H Tengvall) *Next to Wykeham Arms.* ⅓ acre very private cottage garden. Various beds and rockeries

Handywater Farm ✂❀ (Mr & Mrs W B Colquhoun) *½m N of Sibford Gower on rd to Epwell;* 1½-acre family garden in process of creation since 1980. Lovely setting in open rolling countryside. Westerly sloping lawns, stream and ponds, shrub and herbaceous beds

The Manor House ♿ (Mr & Mrs Martyn Booth) *Opp Wykeham Arms.* Completely reconstructed May 1989, the gardens (under 1 acre) are already well established and compliment the romantic atmosphere of this recently renovated rambling thatched manor house (not open)

Meadow Cottage ♿✂❀ (Mr & Mrs Roger Powell) *6 The Colony. At S end of village.* A 1.3-acre garden started from a field in 1988. Large 'shrubaceous' borders; over 1300 different plants; many unusual. Also conifers; and many shrub roses; budding arboretum and series of waterfalls leading to stream. Now maturing well; views. *Private parties welcome, please* **Tel 01295 780525**

Temple Close ♿❀ (Mrs Vera Jones) *E of Wykham Arms.* 1¼ acres with rockery; various beds of shrubs, roses, perennials and herbs; paved stream-side walk running through extensive water garden between two ponds with fountains; pets paddock; good view

Small's House, Mackney ✂ (Bruce & Sarah Balmer) *At the Red Lion public house in the centre of Brightwell-cum-Sotwell go down Mackney Lane, (no through rd), for ½m. Fork R at the bottom, Small's House is the last on the L.* Tudor H-shaped Manor house (not open) is set off by a series of garden rooms, the walls of which are mature yew hedges. Features incl unique topiary faces (carved by an American sculptor) spring bulb garden, chess garden, thatched tree house and mediaeval barn (2 acres in all). *Adm £2 Chd 50p. Open all yr-round. By appointment only, please* **Tel 01491 839167**

Somerville College, Oxford See Oxford University Gardens

NEW **South Newington House, South Newington** ✂❀ (Mr & Mrs John Ainley) *6m SW of Banbury. South Newington is between Banbury & Chipping Norton, on A361; take the lane signed The Barfords, 200yds turn L.* Garden designed for yr-round interest; many unusual trees; shrubs; roses herbaceous borders; spring bulbs; orchard; wildlife pond; organic kitchen; garden conservatory. TEAS in Village Hall. *Adm £2 Chd free. Sat, Sun June 17, 18 (2-6). Private visits welcome, please* **Tel 01295 721207**

Sparsholt Manor, nr Wantage (Sir Adrian & Lady Judith Swire) *Off B4507 Ashbury Rd 3 ½m W of Wantage.* Summer borders, lakes and wilderness. Teas in village hall in aid of Sparsholt Church. *Adm £1.50 Chd free (ACNO to St John Ambulance, Wantage Division). Mon May 29 (2-6)*

Stansfield, Stanford-in-the-Vale ✂❀ (Mr & Mrs David Keeble) *49 High St. 3½m SE of Faringdon. Park in street.* 1¼-acre garden on alkaline soil, evolved since 1979. Great variety of plants, many uncommon, shown in appropriate scree, trough, damp, shade or woodland situations and mostly for sale seasonally. Yr-round interest. TEAS. *Adm £1.50 Acc chd free. Garden clubs and private visits welcome (incl evenings). April-September. For appointment, please* **Tel 01367 710340**

■ **Stanton Harcourt Manor, Stanton Harcourt** ♿❀ (The Hon Mrs Gascoigne) *W of Oxford on B4449.* Picturesque stone manor house with unique C15 Great Kitchen, Chapel and Pope's Tower. Formal gardens leading to woodland area with remains of moat and medieval stew ponds. TEAS *Adm House and garden £5 Chd/OAP's £3. Garden only £3 Chd/OAP's £2 Thurs May 11, 25, June 8, 22, July 6, 20,; Aug*

3, 17, 24, Sept 7, 21, Suns April 23, May 14, 28, June 11, 25, July 23, Aug 6, 20, 27, Sept 10, 24, Bank hol Mons April 24, May 1, 29, Aug 28. For NGS Suns April 30, July 9 (2-6)

Steeple & Middle Aston Gardens *Midway between Oxford & Banbury, ½m off A4260.* Beautiful stone villages bordering Cherwell valley; interesting church and winding lanes with a variety of charming stone houses and cottages. Map available at all gardens. TEAS in Village Hall *Combined adm £2.50 Chd free Sun May 21 (1-6)*

Canterbury House (Mr & Mrs M G Norris) Former rectory (not open) in 2-acre garden with mature trees and intersected by walls. The garden is continually being redeveloped for ease of maintenance, interest and attraction of wildlife. *(ACNO to Specialcare Baby Unit, John Radcliffe)*

Home Farm House (Mr & Mrs T J G Parsons) *¾m N of Steeple Aston, opp Middle Aston House.* 1-acre informal garden surrounding C17 farmhouse (not open), fine view. Mixed planting, incl unusual perennials, shrubs and roses

Kralingen (Mr & Mrs Roderick Nicholson) 2-acre informal garden designed for low maintenance without professional help. Great variety of interesting trees and shrubs. Water garden and wild flower area

The Longbyre (Mr & Mrs Vaughan Billings) Hornton stone house (not open) in ¼ acre. Garden constructed out of old orchard. Water feature, mixed perennials, shrubs, tubs on different levels

Oak Ridge, Steeple Aston (Mr & Mrs M J Simmonds) Small, redeveloped cottage garden designed for low maintenance, botanical interest and quiet relaxation

NEW **Payne's Hill House** (Tim & Caroline Edwards) Old-established walled garden opens out to views across the middle of the village. 1½-acres. Includes a coppice and orchard, vegetables and fruit. Contains newly-replanted herbaceous borders, some unusual shrubs and trees, a large collection of hostas in the shade of a stone wall. A bog garden and water feature are under construction. Access to **Wickhams** is through this garden only

Rowans (Mr & Mrs M J Clist) *The Dickredge, opp White Lion* An acre of orchard and mixed garden, incl shrubs, herbaceous borders, alpines, vegetables and butterfly area

NEW **Wickhams** (Mrs C Owen-Lloyd) Partially terraced cottage garden with mature fruit trees and herbaceous borders. Also features small vegetable and herb beds.Access via Paynes Hill House garden

Stonewalls, Hempton (Mr & Mrs B Shafighian) *1½m W of Deddington on B4031.* A plantsman's garden of 1½ acres divided into many interesting areas, incl shrubbery, herbaceous border, conifer and heather bed, nearly 200 clematis and climbers. Sunken pool. TEAS in aid of St John's Church, Hempton. *Adm £1.50 Chd free. Sun June 25 (2-6)*

Swinbrook House, nr Burford (Mrs J D Mackinnon) *1½m N of Swinbrook on Shipton-under-Wychwood Rd.* Large garden; herbaceous border; shrubs; shrub roses; large kitchen garden; fine views. Picnics allowed. TEA. *Adm £1.50 Chd free. Sun July 16 (2-6)*

Tadmarton Gardens *5m SW of Banbury on B4035.* TEAS in village hall in aid of St Nicholas Church, Tadmarton. *Combined adm £2.50 Chd free. Sun April 9 (1.30-5)*

The Arches (Mr & Mrs J Bolland) 1/5-acre garden designed and created by present owners since 1983. Formal front garden with heather and ornamental grass beds. A series of garden rooms at rear in various themes, linked by a wheelchair friendly path. A garden for sitting in. *Also open by appt on weekdays, April to Sept. Adm £1.* **Tel 01295 788264**

Buxton House (Mr & Mrs J Steele) Small garden created in last 15 yrs incl a waterfall and two fountains

NEW **4 Old Glebe** (Dr & Mrs S R Smith) Small garden with water feature

Tile Cottage (Mr & Mrs D Woodward) Traditional country garden. Flowers, vegetables and orchard

Tadmarton Manor, Tadmarton (Mr & Mrs R K Asser) *5m SW of Banbury on B4035.* Old established 2½ acre garden; beautiful views of unspoilt countryside; fine trees, great variety of perennial plants and shrubs; tunnel arbour; C15 barn and C18 dovecote. *Adm £2. Group visits by appt May & June welcome, please* **Tel 01295 780212**

Towersey Manor, Towersey (Mr & Mrs U D Barnett) *1½m SE of Thame, 300yds down Manor Rd from Xrds in middle of village.* Behind the house lies 2 acres of secret gardens created from scratch by present owners in 1973. This once open lawn has been transformed by large formal hornbeam hedges that frame smaller informal areas incorporating a nuttery; many trees; shrubs; modern and old-fashioned roses. A vista now invites visitors to the 'Mound Meander' - stroll along mown paths or climb up for a fine view of the Chilterns - all newly established 1999. Plenty of shade in garden and seating for picnic teas. *Adm £1.50 Chd free. Weds May 17, June 21 (2-6). Private visits welcome on weekdays May, June, July, please* **Tel 01844 212077**

Town Farm Cottage, Kingston Blount (Mr & Mrs J Clark) *4m S of Thame. 1½m NE of junction 6, M40 on B4009 towards Prices Risborough.* 1¼-acre garden, featured on Gardener's World, April '99, with many unusual plants (many labelled and for sale). Developed over last 12 yrs by present 'plantaholic' owners. Large rockery, with new water feature, planted for all yr colour. Herbaceous borders; scree and ornamental grass beds; a shrubbery; wildflower area; new in 99 waterfall on rockery and new woodland area. Rare English black poplar trees by a lake, full of fish. Red Kites frequently seen overhead. TEAS June only. *Adm £1.50 Chd under 14 free. Suns May 7; June 18 (2-6). Private visits and Garden Clubs welcome, please* **Tel 01844 352152**

Trinity College, Oxford see Oxford University Gardens

Troy, Ewelme (Mr & Mrs D Ruck Keene) *3m NE of Wallingford. From roundabout on A4074/A4130 take exit signed Ewelme, RAF Benson (Clacks Lane). Approx 1½m turn R at T-junction towards Henley.* 1½-acre garden featuring grey and herb gardens, summer houses used by Jerome K Jerome (former owner). Small flock of Jacob sheep with lambs. TEAS in aid of Marie Curie Foundation. *Adm £2 Chd free. Sun May 13 (2-6)*

NEW **Tubney Gardens, Tubney** ♿✂❀ *Off A420 near Fifield (6m from Oxford). All gardens in Abingdon Rd in Tubney village.* TEAS in aid Tubney Church *Combined adm £2 Chd free Sun June 25 (2-6)*

NEW **Kirkstone** (Mr & Mrs Hadland) ⅓ acre. Informal with rockery and pool; small shrubbery. Mainly lawn. TEAS.

NEW **Linkside Cottage** (Mr & Mrs Durrands) Designed in 1996 to be a low maintenance, child friendly garden. S facing, backing onto the golf course, a mixture of fruit and ornamental trees, and plants which thrive in dry conditions

NEW **Little Court** (Mr & Mrs Jones) Entrance courtyard with water feature; shady woodland garden; lawn with herbaceous borders

NEW **Mandalay** (Mr & Mrs Scopes) Informal shady garden surrounded by woodland

NEW **Stone Court** (Ms Veillet-Lavallee) 2-acre garden presently being redesigned, unusual perennials, herbaceous borders, life-size horse made of branches

NEW **1 Thatch Farm Cottages** (Mr & Mrs Halliday) Partly cottage style, another part divided from orchard by wisteria

NEW **Tubney Farmhouse** (Mr & Mrs Goss) Large garden, shrub and herbaceous borders

Wadham College, Oxford see Oxford University Gardens

Wardington Manor, Wardington ♿ (The Lord Wardington) *5m NE of Banbury.* 5-acre garden with topiary, rock garden, flowering shrub walk to pond. Carolean manor house 1665 (not open). *Adm £4. Private visits by parties welcome, please* **Tel 01295 750202**

■ **Waterperry Gardens** ♿❀ (Mrs P Maxwell, Secretary) *2½m from Wheatley M40 Junction 8 from London. Junction 8 from Birmingham. 9m E of Oxford. Gardens well signed locally with Tourist Board 'rose' symbol.* 20-acre ornamental gardens with many interesting plants; shrub, herbaceous and alpine nurseries; glasshouses and comprehensive fruit section. High quality plant centre, garden shop (Tel 01844 339226). TEA SHOP. Saxon church with famous glasses and brasses in grounds. Guided tours by 'Friends of Waterperry' available on NGS open days. *Adm Gardens & Nurseries £3.40 OAPs £2.90 Chd £1.90 under 10 free. OPEN DAILY except Christmas and New Year hols and July 20 to 23. Coach parties by appt only Tel 01844 339254. For NGS (ACNO to NCCPG). Suns Feb 20, May 14, Oct 1 (9-5)*

NEW **Wayside, Kidlington** (Margaret & Alister Urquhart) *82 Banbury Rd. On the RH-side of A4260 travelling N through Kidlington.* ¼ acre garden with wide variety of plants and mature trees; hardy geraniums, fuschias, clematis and bulbs. Conservatory and greenhouse with tender plants; pergola leading to woodland garden; rhododendrons, tree ferns and extensive collection of hardy ferns. TEAS. *Adm £1.50 Chd free. (ACNO to E.D.S. Support Group). Suns May 28, July 16 (2-6). Private visit welcome from May to Sept, please* **Tel 01865 373687**

Westwell Manor, nr Burford ✂❀ (Mr & Mrs T H Gibson) *2m SW of Burford, from A40 Burford-Cheltenham, turn L after ½m on narrow rd signposted Westwell. Unspoilt hamlet with delightful church.* 6 acres surrounding old Cotswold manor house (not open), knot garden, potager, shrub roses, herbaceous borders, topiary, moonlight garden, rills and water garden. *Adm £3 Chd 50p (ACNO to St Mary's Church Westwell). Sun June 11 (2-6.30)*

Wick Hall & Nurseries, Radley ♿✂❀ (Mr & Mrs P Drysdale) *Between Abingdon & Radley on Audlett Drive. Parking for disabled at house, some off-street parking.* Approx 10 acres lawns and wild garden; topiary; pond garden; rockeries; walled garden enclosing knot garden; young arboretum. Early C18 house (not open), barn and greenhouses, large display of old horticultural and agricultural tools. TEAS in aid of Radley WI. *Adm £1.50 Chd free. Sun April 30 (2-5)*

Wood Croft, Boars Hill ❀ (Ms Maureen Doherty, Bursar) *Foxcombe Lane, S of Oxford. From ring rd follow signs to Wootton and Boars Hill. From junction at top Hinksey Hill, house 1st on L.* 1½ acres designed and planted by the late Prof G E Blackman FRS. Rhododendrons, camellias, azaleas, many varieties primula in woodland and surrounding natural pond; fine trees. TEA. *Adm £1 Chd free (ACNO to Royal Marsden Hospital Development Appeal). Sun May 14 (2-6)*

Wootton Hill, Boars Hill ♿❀ (A C & S Ellis) *From B4017 to Abingdon. Take 1st L 50 yds after Bystander Public House (Wootton Village).* Colourful 7 acres with large herbaceous border; extensive lawns; pond and natural woodland. TEAS. *Adm £2.50 Chd 50p. Sun Aug 27 (2-5)*

Yeomans, Tadmarton ❀ (Mrs M E Pedder) *5m SW of Banbury on B4035.* Small garden on 4 levels, featured in 'Easy Plants for Difficult Places' by Geoffrey Smith; C16 thatched cottage (not open). Colourful from spring to autumn; wide variety annuals, perennials, shrubs; many climbers incl roses, clematis; shrub roses with hips. *Adm £1 Chd free (ACNO to Katharine House Hospice Trust). Private visits welcome for 2 and over, by appt, please. April to Sept* **Tel 01295 780285**

Mediaeval Garden Ornaments
by Parva Classics
Duncote, Towcester
Tel: **01327 351824**

Powys

See separate Welsh section on page 427

Shropshire

Hon County Organiser: Mrs Sarah Stafford, The Old Rectory, Fitz, Shrewsbury, Shropshire SY4 3AS Tel 01743 850555
Hon Assistant County Organisers: Mr J Goodall, Rectory Cottage, Chetton, Bridgnorth, Shropshire WV16 6UF
Mrs Ann Cooke, Harnage Farm, Cound, Shropshire SY5 6EJ
Hon County Treasurer: Mrs Ann Trevor-Jones, Preen Manor, Church Preen, Church Stretton, Shropshire SY6 7LQ

DATES OF OPENING

Regular openings
For details see garden description
Burford House Gardens, Tenbury Wells
Hodnet Hall Gardens, nr Market Drayton
Weston Park, Shifnal
Wollerton Old Hall, Wollerton

By appointment only
For telephone numbers and other details see garden descriptions. Private visits welcomed
The Bungalow, Garmston
Farley House, Much Wenlock
Swallow Hayes, Albrighton

March 18 Saturday
Attingham Park, nr Shrewsbury

March 19 Sunday
Attingham Park, nr Shrewsbury

April 2 Sunday
Badger Farmhouse, Badger

April 4 Tuesday
Radnor Cottage, Clun

April 16 Sunday
Brownhill House, Ruyton XI Towns
Morville Hall Gardens, nr Bridgnorth
Oteley, Ellesmere

April 29 Saturday
Field House, Clee St Margaret

April 30 Sunday
Bitterley Court, Ludlow
Field House, Clee St Margaret
Jinlye Guest House, All Stretton
Moortown, nr Wellington

May 1 Monday
Millichope Park, Munslow

May 2 Tuesday
Radnor Cottage, Clun

May 5 Friday
Wollerton Old Hall, Wollerton

May 7 Sunday
Preen Manor, Church Preen

May 8 Monday
Mawley Hall, Cleobury Mortimer

May 12 Friday
Wollerton Old Hall, Wollerton

May 14 Sunday
Brownhill House, Ruyton XI Towns
Gate Cottage, nr Ellesmere

May 16 Tuesday
Radnor Cottage, Clun

May 19 Friday
Wollerton Old Hall, Wollerton

May 21 Sunday
Cricklewood Cottage, Plox Green
Cruckfield House, Ford
Hatton Grange, Shifnal
Rowan Cottage, St Martins
Stanley Hall, Bridgnorth
Thornfield, Twmpath, Gobowen

May 26 Friday
Wollerton Old Hall, Wollerton

May 28 Sunday
Jinlye Guest House, All Stretton
Peplow Hall, Hodnet
Walcot Hall, Lydbury North

May 29 Monday
Brownhill House, Ruyton XI Towns (evening)
Dudmaston, Quatt
Oteley, Ellesmere
Walcot Hall, Lydbury North

May 30 Tuesday
Radnor Cottage, Clun

June 3 Saturday
Hartshill Gardens, Oakengates

June 4 Sunday
Adcote School, Little Ness
Bitterley Court, Ludlow
Gate Cottage, nr Ellesmere
Hartshill Gardens, Oakengates
The Old Rectory, Fitz
The Patch, Acton Pigot

June 5 Monday
Brownhill House, Ruyton XI Towns (evening)

June 8 Thursday
Preen Manor, Church Preen

June 9 Friday
Cruckfield House, Ford

June 10 Saturday
Chyknell, Bridgnorth

June 11 Sunday
Adcote School, Little Ness
Brownhill House, Ruyton XI Towns
Limeburners, Ironbridge
Madeley New Gardens, Telford
Morville Hall Gardens, nr Bridgnorth
Ruthall Manor, Ditton Priors
Triscombe, Roslyn Rd, Wellington

June 12 Monday
Mawley Hall, Cleobury Mortimer

June 13 Tuesday
Radnor Cottage, Clun

June 17 Saturday
Whittington Village Gardens, nr Oswestry

June 18 Sunday
Harnage Farm, Cound
Lower Hall, Worfield
Whittington Village Gardens, nr Oswestry

June 22 Thursday
Preen Manor, Church Preen

June 25 Sunday
Acton Round, Morville
Brownhill House, Ruyton XI Towns
David Austin Roses, Albrighton
Glazeley Old Rectory, nr Bridgnorth
Millichope Park, Munslow
The Old Farmhouse, Boningale
The Old Rectory, Rodington

June 26 Monday
Acton Round, Morville

June 28 Wednesday
Nordybank Nurseries, Clee St Margaret

July 2 Sunday
Cricklewood Cottage, Plox Green
Jinlye Guest House, All Stretton
The Mill Cottage, Cound
The Patch, Acton Pigot

July 5 Wednesday
Burford House Gardens, Tenbury Wells

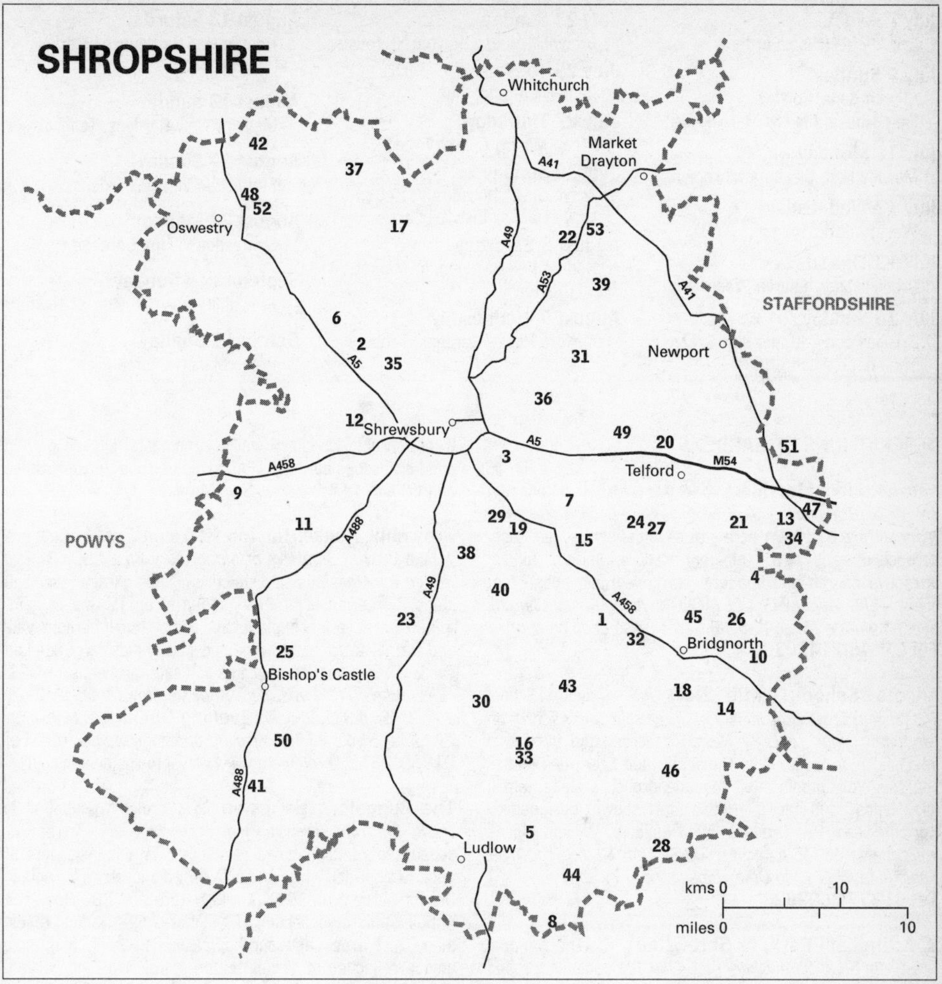

KEY

1. Acton Round
2. Adcote School
3. Attingham Park
4. Badger Farmhouse
5. Bitterley Court
6. Brownhill House
7. The Bungalow
8. Burford House Gardens
9. Church Bank
10. Chyknell
11. Cricklewood Cottage
12. Cruckfield House
13. David Austin Roses
14. Dudmaston
15. Farley House
16. Field House
17. Gate Cottage
18. Glazeley Old Rectory
19. Harnage Farm
20. Hartshill Gardens
21. Hatton Grange
22. Hodnet Hall Gardens
23. Jinlye Guest House
24. Limeburners
25. Linley Hall
26. Lower Hall
27. Madeley New Gardens
28. Mawley Hall
29. The Mill Cottage
30. Millichope Park
31. Moortown
32. Morville Hall Gardens
33. Nordybank Nurseries
34. The Old Farmhouse
35. The Old Rectory, Fitz
36. The Old Rectory, Rodington
37. Oteley
38. The Patch
39. Peplow Hall
40. Preen Manor
41. Radnor Cottage
42. Rowan Cottage
43. Ruthall Manor
44. The Shear
45. Stanley Hall
46. Stottesdon Village Gardens
47. Swallow Hayes
48. Thornfield
49. Triscombe
50. Walcot Hall
51. Weston Park
52. Whittington Village Gardens
53. Wollerton Old Hall

July 7 Friday
Cruckfield House, Ford

July 9 Sunday
Church Bank, Rowley
Field House, Clee St Margaret

July 10 Monday
Mawley Hall, Cleobury Mortimer

July 12 Wednesday
Weston Park, Shifnal

July 13 Thursday
Preen Manor, Church Preen

July 16 Sunday
Cricklewood Cottage, Plox Green
The Shear, Nash

July 23 Sunday
Brownhill House, Ruyton XI Towns

July 25 Tuesday
Radnor Cottage, Clun

July 27 Thursday
Preen Manor, Church Preen

July 30 Sunday
Jinlye Guest House, All Stretton
Linley Hall, nr Bishops Castle

August 5 Saturday
Hodnet Hall Gardens, nr Market Drayton

August 9 Wednesday
Burford House Gardens, Tenbury Wells

August 12 Saturday
Hodnet Hall Gardens, nr Market Drayton

August 13 Sunday
Madeley New Gardens, Telford

August 27 Sunday
Stottesdon Village Gardens

August 28 Monday
Stottesdon Village Gardens

September 3 Sunday
Brownhill House, Ruyton XI Towns

October 1 Sunday
Preen Manor, Church Preen

DESCRIPTIONS OF GARDENS

Acton Round, Morville ♿✇❀ (Mr & Mrs Hew Kennedy) *6m W of Bridgnorth. A458 Morville-Shrewsbury, 2m after Morville turn L (W).* 1½-acre garden with yew hedges; rose, herbaceous and newly planted borders; various follies; attractive church and beautiful early Georgian house (not open). TEAS. *Adm £2 Chd £1 (ACNO to Acton Round Church). Sun, Mon June 25, 26 (2-6.30) Garden also open by appt* **Tel 01746 714203**

Adcote School, Little Ness ✇ (Adcote School Educational Trust Ltd) *8m NW of Shrewsbury via A5, turn off NE follow signs to Little Ness.* 26 acres; fine trees incl beeches, tulip trees, oaks (American and Evergreen); atlas cedars, Wellingtonia etc; rhododendrons, azaleas; small lake; landscaped garden. House (part shown) designed by Norman Shaw RA; Grade 1 listed building; William Morris wallpapers; de Morgan tiles. TEAS. *Adm £2 Acc chd free. Suns June 4, 11 (2-5) Other times strictly by appt only* **Tel 01939 260202**

▲ Attingham Park, nr Shrewsbury ✇ (The National Trust) *4m SE of Shrewsbury on B4380.* Parkland landscaped by Leggett and Repton, offering choice of walks. Swathes of naturalised narcissi along the river bank. Tearoom (2-4). Park open (12-5). House closed. *Adm £1.80 Chd 90p (NT members, donations gratefully received). For NGS Sat, Sun March 18,19 (12-5)*

Badger Farmhouse, Badger ♿✇❀ (Mr & Mrs C J Walker) *From A464 Shifnal to Wolverhampton Rd turn S to Burnhill Green. In Burnhill Green turn W to Beckbury. At T junction in Beckbury turn S, ¾m on R.* 3-acre garden. Over 300 varieties of daffodils and narcissi in a mature setting. Mainly in three orchards, one of apple, one pear and plum, and one of cherry. Also fine trees, shrubs and roses. TEAS *Adm £1.50 Chd free (ACNO to Compton Hospice). Sun April 2 (2-6). Private visits welcome, please* **Tel 01746 783222**

Bitterley Court, Ludlow ♿❀ (Mr & Mrs J V T Wheeler) *Next to Bitterley Church. Follow A4117 E from Ludlow and turn off to Bitterley after about 2m. 5m from Ludlow altogether.* A 6-acre garden featuring specimen and rare trees, shrubs, woodland walks, ornamental kitchen garden and herbaceous borders. TEAS in aid of Hope House Hospice and WI. *Adm £2 Chd free. Suns April 30, June 4 (2-6)*

Brownhill House, Ruyton XI Towns ✇❀ (Roger & Yoland Brown) *10m NW of Shrewsbury on B4397. Park at Bridge Inn.* Unusual and distinctive hillside garden (over 500 steps) bordering River Perry featured on TV and in magazines. Great variety of plants and styles from laburnum walk and formal terraces to woodland paths, plus large kitchen garden. 200 varieties of plants for sale, proceeds to NGS. TEAS. *Adm £2 Chd free. Suns April 16, May 14; June 11, 25, July 23, Sept 3 (1.30-5.30).* **Evening Openings**. *Mons May 29, June 5 (6.30-8.30). Also by appt May-Aug please* **Tel 01939 261121** Website www.eleventowns.demon.co.uk

The Bungalow, Garmston ✇ (Carolyn C Hubble) *On B4380 6m from Shrewsbury on Ironbridge rd.* ⅔-acre, four seasons garden, featured on number TV channels, lots of publications incl introduction by Roy Lancaster (A Fantasy Dream Garden), in 1999 (Art in Nature and BBC Homes & Antiques). Large collection of hellebores 50+; bulbs, roses, many rare trees and shrubs; clear fish pool; fountains, unique collection of garden features, prize winning garden. *Adm £2.50. By appt only March 18 to Oct 15 (painters, journalists, photographers always welcome). Private visits, small groups, coach parties. For NGS, please* **Tel 01952 510714**

■ Burford House Gardens, Tenbury Wells ♿✇❀ (Treasures of Tenbury) *1m W of Tenbury Wells on A456.* 4 acres of sweeping lawns and serpentine borders, set in beautiful surroundings in the Teme Valley, around an elegant Georgian house (not open). National Clematis Collection and over 2,000 other kinds of plants in wonderful combinations of colours and textures. Nursery offers over 200 varieties of clematis and comprehensive range of usual and unusual plants. Fine church, gallery and gift shop. DOGS on lead, nursery only. TEAS. *Adm £3.50 Chd £1. Open every day, all yr-round 10-5. For NGS Weds July 5, Aug 9 (10-5)*

Church Bank, Rowley ✇❀ (Mr & Mrs B P Kavanagh) *12m SW of Shrewsbury on B4386 Montgomery Rd continuing through Westbury. After ⅓m turn R for Rowley. After 3½m*

turn L at Xrds for Brockton. Church Bank is on L after 120yds. A S-facing, steeply sloping garden; packed with interesting and unusual plants, predominantly perennial, with a large area of young woodland and 'natural' planting which incl 2 pools - one newly made - and a bog garden. Picnic area. *Adm £2 Chd free (ACNO to Action Aid). Sun July 9 (2-6); also private visits welcome May to Sept, please* **Tel 01743 891661**

Chyknell, Bridgnorth (Mr & Mrs W S R Kenyon-Slaney) *5m E of Bridgnorth between Claverley and Worfield. Signed off A454 and A458.* 5-acre rose and herbaceous garden; interesting shrubs and fine trees in tranquil park setting. TEAS. *Adm £2 Chd 50p. Sat June 10 (2-6)*

Cricklewood Cottage, Plox Green (Paul Costello) *On A488 1m SW of Minsterley. Park on grass verges, not on rd.* Delightful ⅓-acre cottage garden in attractive setting. Mature borders packed with shrubs and perennials, walks alongside trout stream, waterfalls, flourishing bog garden. Imaginative use of long narrow garden with a surprise round every corner. Featured in books and magazines. Teas at Holy Trinity. *Adm £2 Chd free (ACNO to Holy Trinity Church Minsterley). Suns May 21; July 2, 16 (2-6)*

Cruckfield House, Ford (Mr & Mrs G M Cobley) *5m W of Shrewsbury A458, turn L towards Cruckton.* 4-acre garden with backdrop of mature trees. The romantic S garden, formally designed, is informally and intensively planted with an extensive range of unusual herbaceous plants. Nick's garden, with many species trees and shrubs, surrounds a large pond with bog and moisture loving plants. Ornamental kitchen garden with pretty outbuildings. Rose and peony walk. TEAS. *Adm £2.50 Chd £1. Sun May 21; Fris June 9; July 7 (2-6) private visits welcome, min 25, by appt, please* **Tel 01743 850222**

▲ David Austin Roses, Albrighton (Mr & Mrs David Austin) *Bowling Green Lane, 8m NW of Wolverhampton. 4m from Shifnal (A464) L into Bowling Green Lane; or junction 3, M54 to Albrighton, R at sign 'Roses & Shrubs', Bowling Green Lane 2nd R.* Breeders of the famous English roses. Gardens; 900 varieties old roses, shrub, species and climbing roses. Semi-wild private garden, trees and water garden with many plants. Variety of plants for sale. Sculpture by Pat Austin. TEAS. *Adm £2.50 Chd free. For NGS Sun June 25 (2-6)*

▲ Dudmaston, Quatt (The National Trust) *4m SE of Bridgnorth on A442. Bus stop at gates ½m.* 8 acres with fine trees, shrubs; lovely views over Dudmaston Pool and surrounding country. Dingle walk. TEAS. *Adm £2.75 Chd £1. For NGS Mon May 29 (2-6)*

Farley House, Much Wenlock (Mr & Mrs R W Collingwood) *From A458 at Much Wenlock turn N on to A4169 signed Ironbridge; house 1m on L.* 1 acre garden on Wenlock Edge with pleasant views across the countryside; 5 species of wild orchids grow in grass with other wild flowers. Informal beds of unusual plants with contrasts of form and colour giving interest all-yr; roses, many growing up trees, alpines and tufa features. TEA and biscuits by arrangement. *Adm £2 Chd free. Open by appt April to Oct, coach parties welcome, please* **Tel 01952 727017**

Field House, Clee St Margaret (Dr & Mrs John Bell) *8m NE of Ludlow. Turning to Stoke St Milborough and Clee St Margaret, 5m from Ludlow, 10m from Bridgnorth along B4364. Through Stoke St Milborough to Clee St Margaret. Ignore R turn to Clee Village. Field House on L. Parking.* 1-acre garden created since 1982 for yr-round interest. Mixed borders; rose walk; pool garden; herbaceous borders; spring bulbs and autumn colours. TEAS in aid of Village Hall Fund. *Adm £2 Chd 50p. Sat April 29, Suns April 30; July 9 (12-6). Private visits welcome, please* **Tel 01584 823242**

Gate Cottage, nr Ellesmere (G W Nicholson & Kevin Gunnell) *10m N of Shrewsbury on A528. At village of Cockshutt take rd signposted English Frankton. Garden is 1m on R. Parking in adjacent field.* A developing garden at present about 2 acres. Informal mixed plantings of trees, shrubs, herbaceous, of interest to flower arrangers and plantsmen. Pool and rock garden; informal pools. Large collection of hostas; old orchard with roses. Constant alerations being made to incl items of unsual growth or colour. TEA in aid of WI. *Adm £1.50 Chd 50p Suns May 14, June 4 (1-5). Parties by appt at other times, please* **Tel 01939 270606**

Glazeley Old Rectory, nr Bridgnorth (Mr & Mrs R Arbuthnott) *3m S of Bridgnorth on B4363 Bridgnorth-Cleobury Mortimer rd.* 2-acre garden in beautiful natural setting. Herbaceous borders, bulbs, alpines, old fashioned roses. Shrubs and trees. Paved, heather and bog gardens. TEAS. *Adm £2 Chd 50p. Sun June 25 (2-6)*

Harnage Farm, Cound (Mr & Mrs Ken Cooke) *8m SE of Shrewsbury on A458. Turn to Cound 1m S of Cross Houses. Harnage Farm 1m, bearing L past church.* ½-acre farmhouse garden; well stocked with herbaceous plants, shrubs and climbers and a collection of old roses. Extensive views over beautiful Severn Valley. TEAS. *Adm £3 (ACNO to Ward 21 Nurses Fund, Shrewsbury Hospital) Sun June 18 (12-6)*

Hartshill Gardens, Oakengates *E of Shrewsbury. Once within the Telford/Wrekin district, follow local signs to Oakengates.* TEAS. *Combined adm £1.50 Chd free. Sat, Sun June 3, 4 (2-5.30)*

Longmede (Mr & Mrs D J Steele) *13 Hartshill Road.* Approx ½-acre ornamental garden with specimen trees, shrubs and raised alpine beds. Yr-round interest. Very easy access for the disabled. *Private visits welcome (April-Oct), please* **Tel 01952 612710**

Northcote (Mr & Mrs R A Woolley) *15 Hartshill Road.* ¼-acre garden with vegetables, flowers and shrubs. *Private visits welcome (April-Oct), please* **Tel 01952 613644**

Hatton Grange, Shifnal (Mrs Peter Afia) *Lodge gate entrance on A464, 2m S of Shifnal. 1m up drive.* Large dingle with pools, rhododendrons, azaleas, fine old trees; shrubbery; roses; lily pond garden. TEAS. *Adm £2 Chd free (ACNO* *to BACUP). Sun May 21 (2-7). Parties by appt, please* **Tel 01952 460415**

■ **Hodnet Hall Gardens, nr Market Drayton** ♿❀ (Mr & The Hon Mrs Heber-Percy) *5½m SW of Market Drayton; 12m NE Shrewsbury; at junc of A53 and A442.* 60-acre landscaped garden with series of lakes and pools; magnificent forest trees, great variety of flowers, shrubs providing colour throughout season; featured on TV and Radio. Unique collection of big-game trophies in C17 tearooms. Gift shop and kitchen garden. Teas and light lunches. Free parking. *Adm £3.25 OAP £2.75 Chd £1.20. April to end of Sept (Tues to Sun & Bank Hols 12-5). Reduced rates for organised parties of 25 or over* **Tel 01630 685 202.** For NGS Sats Aug 5, 12 (12-5)

Jinlye Guest House, All Stretton ✂❀ (Mrs Janet Tory) *Situated 1m out of All Stretton village. Turn off B4370 at red telephone box in All Stretton, following signs to Jinlye Guest House.* 1-acre garden created by present owner, situated at 1400′ above sea level immed adjoining the Long Mynd Hills. Magnificent views. The garden abounds with rare and interesting plants; herbaceous borders; alpine scree beds; large alpine house. Yr-round interest; lovely walks in 15 acres of grounds. TEAS in aid of Cats Protection League & Autistic Society. *Adm £2 Chd £1. Suns April 30; May 28; July 2, 30 (1-5). Private visits welcomed at any time by arrangement, please* **Tel 01694 723243**

Limeburners, Ironbridge ♿✂❀ (Mr & Mrs J E Derry) *Lincoln Hill. On outskirts of Ironbridge, Telford. From Traffic Island in Ironbridge take Church Hill and proceed up hill for ½m, garden on L 300yds below Lincoln Grange.* Prize-winning garden formerly site of a rubbish tip, developed by owners as a Nature garden to attract wildlife. Many unusual shrubs giving yr-round interest; water feature and pool. TEAS in aid of Ironbridge and Coalbrookdale Churches. *Adm £2 Chd free. Sun June 11 (2-6). Private visits also welcome April to Sept, please* **Tel 01952 433715**

Linley Hall, nr Bishops Castle ♿❀ (Justin Coldwell Esq) *3m NE of Bishops Castle. Turn E off A488 nr Lydham.* Parkland; lawns, walled kitchen garden; lake; temple. Plants and produce for sale. TEAS. *Adm £2 Chd free. Sun July 30 (2-6)*

Lower Hall, Worfield ♿❀ (Mr & Mrs C F Dumbell) *E of Bridgnorth. ½m N of A454 in village centre.* 4 acres on R Worfe. Garden developed by present owners. Courtyard with fountain, walled garden with old-fashioned roses, clematis and mixed borders. Water garden with pool, primula island and rock garden. Woodland garden incl rare magnolias and paper bark trees. Plant sales to local church. TEAS in aid of WI. *Adm £2.50 Chd free. Sun June 18 (2-6). Private visits welcome. Coach and evening parties by appt, Adm £3 local catering can be arranged* **Tel 01746 716607**

Madeley New Gardens, Telford ✂❀ (c/o Dr & Mrs G Richards) *From Ironbridge up steep hill towards Madeley (B4373) R at roundabout into Glendinning Way.* Group of gardens of various sizes up to 1¼ acres. Differing styles and planting incl water features, herbaceous borders and vegetables. Woodland walk. TEAS. *Adm £2 Chd 50p. Suns June 11, Aug 13 (2-6)* **Tel 01952 587417**

Mawley Hall, Cleobury Mortimer ♿❀ (Mr & Mrs R A Galliers-Pratt) *2m NE of Cleobury Mortimer. On A4117 Bewdley-Ludlow Rd. Bus: X92, alight at gate.* A natural garden in beautiful country with magnificent views; designed for wandering amongst roses, herbs, flowering shrubs; fine old trees. TEAS. *Adm £2 OAPs £1.50 Chd under 14, 50p. Mons May 8; June 12; July 10 (2-6)*

The Mill Cottage, Cound ♿✂❀ (Mrs A J Wisden & Miss J M Hawkes) *8m SE of Shrewsbury on A458. Turn to Cound 1m S of Cross Houses. Mill Cottage 300yds on L.* ¼-acre cottage garden. Unusual and lovely herbaceous plants. Good and varied collection of ferns and a variety of clematis, plus a collection of plants in pots, conservatory and outdoor. TEAS. *Adm £2 Chd 50p (ACNO to Shrewsbury League of Friends). Sun July 2 (2-6)*

Millichope Park, Munslow (Mr & Mrs L Bury) *8m NE of Craven Arms. From Ludlow (11m) turn L off B4368, ¾m out of Munslow.* 13-acre garden with lakes; woodland walks; fine specimen trees; wild flowers; herbaceous borders. TEAS in aid of local church. *Adm £2 Chd 50p. Mon May 1; Sun June 25 (2-6). Group visits welcome, please* **Tel 01584 841234**

Moortown, nr Wellington ✂❀ (David Bromley Esq) *5m N of Wellington. Take B5062 signed Moortown 1m between High Ercall and Crudgington.* Approx 1-acre plantsman's garden. Here may be found the old-fashioned, the unusual and even the oddities of plant life, in mixed borders of 'controlled' confusion. *Adm £2 Chd 50p. Sun April 30 (2-5.30)*

Morville Hall Gardens, nr Bridgnorth ♿❀ *3m NW of Bridgnorth on A458 at junction with B4368.* Nine gardens in and around Morville Hall. TEAS and plants in aid of Morville Church. *Combined adm £3 Chd £1. Suns April 16; June 11 (2-5).*

The Cottage (Mr & Mrs Begg) Pretty walled garden with good climbers

The Dower House (Dr Katherine Swift) 1½-acre sequence of gardens in various historical styles, incl turf maze, medieval garden, Elizabethan knot garden, formal veg garden, C17 canal garden, wild garden

Nos 1 & 2 Gatehouse (Mr & Mrs Rowe & Mrs B Chappuis) Two colourful cottage gardens, with woodland and formal areas

Morville Hall (Dr & Mrs J C Douglas) 4-acre garden in fine setting, incl box parterre, mature shrub borders, pond garden, medieval stewpond

Poplar Cottage Farm (Elizabeth Bacon) *¾m N of Morville on A458.* ⅓-acre flower arranger's garden; yr-round interest, many unusual plants

South Pavilion (Mr & Mrs B Jenkinson) Stylish formal courtyard garden

Top Pool Barn (Mrs J I Bolton) ⅓-acre family garden, begun 1992, built to survive children and dogs. *(not open June 11)*

The Vineyard (Mr I J S Rowe) Prize-winning small vineyard

Nordybank Nurseries, Clee St Margaret ❀ (P Bolton) *7½m NE of Ludlow. Turning to Stoke St Milborough and Clee St Margaret 5m from Ludlow, 10m from Bridgnorth along B4364, through Stoke St Milborough on the Lane to Clee St Margaret.* 1-acre garden on sloping site. Informal plantings of trees, shrubs and unusual herbaceous, incl herbs and wildflowers. Woodland plantings and splendid views; a permaculture cottage garden. TEAS in aid of Animal Rescue. *Adm £2 Chd free Wed June 28 (12-6)*

The Old Farmhouse, Boningale ❀ (Dipika & Nick Price) *1m S of Albrighton off the A464. 7m NW of Wolverhampton.* ⅓-acre. Family cottage garden around C17 timber framed house in rural hamlet (not open). Mixed herbaceous borders, old and English roses, lavenders, pinks and hardy geraniums. Traditional style cobbled yard and paths. Ample parking. TEAS in aid of Sargent Cancer Care. *Adm £2 Chd free. Sun June 25 (2-6). Private visits also welcome by appt May 1 to Aug 31* **Tel 01902 372 433**

The Old Rectory, Fitz ❀ (Mrs J H M Stafford) *A5 NW of Shrewsbury; turn off at Montford Bridge, follow signs; from B5067 turn off at Leaton, follow signs.* 1¼-acre botantist's garden; shrubs, vegetables; water garden. Partially suitable for wheelchairs. TEAS in aid of WI. *Adm £2 Chd 50p. Sun June 4 (12-5)*

NEW **The Old Rectory, Rodington** ❀ (Mr & Mrs R A Hurlow) *6m E of Shrewsbury. B5062 to Roden. Turn R in Roden to Rodington 1m. Turn L ½m and L again, follow signs.* Newly established 1-acre garden, pergola walk with clematis and roses. Courtyard; herbaceous borders; lily pond; evergreen beds; kitchen garden. Wild flower areas with new and old trees. TEAS. *Adm £2 Chd 50p. Sun June 25 (2-6)*

Oteley, Ellesmere ❀ (Mr & Mrs R K Mainwaring) *Entrance out of Ellesmere past Mere, opp Convent nr to A528/495 junction.* 10 acres running down to Mere, incl walled kitchen garden; architectural features; many interesting trees, rhododendrons and azaleas, views across Mere to Ellesmere Church. Wheelchairs only if dry. TEAS in aid of Guide Dogs for the Blind April 16 and NSPCC May 29. *Adm £2 Chd 50p. Sun, April 16, Mon May 29 (2-6). Private visits also welcome, please* **Tel 01691 622514**

The Patch, Acton Pigot ♿❀ (Mrs J G Owen) *8m SE of Shrewsbury between A49 and A458. Take Cressage Rd from Acton Burnell. Turn L after ½m, signpost Acton Pigot.* A garden for the plant connoisseur in excess of ½ acre. June early herbaceous; shrubs and trees. July; later herbaceous and lilies. Plants in aid of St. Anthony's Cheshire Home. TEAS. *Adm £1.50 Chd free Suns June 4, July 2 (2-6). Coach parties welcome by arrangement, please* **Tel 01743 362139**

Peplow Hall, Hodnet ♿❀ (The Lord & Lady Newborough) *3m S of Hodnet via A442; turn off E.* 10-acre garden with lawns, azaleas, rhododendrons, etc; roses, herbaceous borders; walled kitchen garden; 7-acre lake. TEAS. *Adm £3 Chd 50p. Sun May 28 (2-5.30)*

Preen Manor, Church Preen ❀ (Mr & Mrs Philip Trevor-Jones) *6m W of Much Wenlock; signposted from B4371 Much Wenlock-Church Stretton rd.* 6-acre garden on site of Cluniac monastery and Norman Shaw mansion (not open). Kitchen; chess; water and wild gardens. Fine trees in park; woodland walks. Replanning still in progress. Not suitable for wheelchairs. TEAS. *Adm £2.50 Chd 50p. Sun May 7; Thurs June 8, 22; July 13, 27 (2-6); Sun Oct 1 (2-5) 4.30 Harvest Thanksgiving. Private visits and coach parties by appt June & July only (min 15)* **Tel 01694 771207**

Radnor Cottage, Clun ❀ (Pam & David Pittwood) *8m W of Craven Arms, 1m E of Clun on B4368 midway between Clunton and Clun.* 2 acres S-facing slope, overlooking Clun Valley. Developed since 1988 for all-year-round interest. Daffodils; cottage garden borders; dry stone wall and terracing with herbs and alpines; stream and bog garden with willow collection; native trees, orchard, wild flower meadow. TEAS. *Adm £2 Chd 50p (ACNO to Shropshire & Mid Wales Hospice). Tues April 4, May 2, 16, 30; June 13; July 25 (2-6). Private visits welcome, please* **Tel 01588 640451**

Rowan Cottage, St Martins ♿❀ (Mr & Mrs P B Wilson) *A5 N from Oswestry, A483 S from Wrexham to join A5 at Chirk. At Gledrid roundabout take B5096 for St Martins, at mini roundabout bear L (Stan's Shop on L). Approx 150 metres, white house on R next to Woodcocks Newsagents. Limited rd parking, otherwise at Stan's Shop.* The garden has been created since 1997. Although immature, the garden of approx ⅓ acre has many established features, incl patio, pond, shady garden. It is a plantsman's garden with many unusual trees, shrubs and perennials, incl over 120 hardy geraniums. TEAS. *Adm £1.50 Chd 50p. Sun May 21 (12-5). By appt any evening or w/e,* **Tel 01691 773130**

Ruthall Manor, Ditton Priors ♿ (Mr & Mrs G T Clarke) *Bridgnorth. Ruthall Rd signed nr garage.* 1-acre garden with ha-ha and old horse pond planted with water and bog plants. Rare specimen trees. Designed for easy maintenance with lots of ground-covering and unusual plants. New features being developed. TEAS in aid of Village Hall by Committee. *Adm £2 Chd free. Sun June 11 (2-6.30). Parties welcome April to Sept, please* **Tel 01746 712608**

NEW **The Shear, Nash** ❀ (Mr & Mrs R M Knowles) *6m E of Ludlow, 3m N of Tenbury Wells off B4214. Tenbury Wells/Clee Hill Rd.* 1¼-acres around C15 farmhouse (not open), with glorious views. Clematis and other climbers; herbaceous borders; alpines; trees; shrubs. Rose walk with new sunken rose garden; vegetables and lawns. TEA. *Adm £2 Chd free. Sun July 16 (2-6)*

Stanley Hall, Bridgnorth ♿ (Mr & Mrs M J Thompson) *N of Bridgnorth. Leave Bridgnorth by N Gate; B4373; turn R at Stanley Lane.* Drive ¾m with rhododendrons, azaleas fine trees and chain of pools. TEAS in aid of Astley Abbotts Church. *Adm £2 Chd free. Sun May 21 (2-6)*

Stottesdon Village Gardens ♿❀ (Stottesdon Garden Committee) *7m from Bridgnorth on B4363 turn R 3m. From Kidderminster 11m on A4117 turn R 4m.* A village community in unspoilt countryside. A variety of gardens, new and old; cottage flowers; unusual plants; vegetables; bedding displays. TEAS in aid of St Mary's Church. *Combined adm £3 Chd £1. Sun, Mon Aug 27, 28 (2-6)*

Swallow Hayes, Albrighton ♿❀ (Mrs P Edwards) *Rectory Road WV7, 7m NW of Wolverhampton. M54 exit 3 Rectory Rd 1m towards Wolverhampton off A41 just past Wyevale Garden Centre.* 2 acres planted since 1968 with emphasis on all-yr interest and ease of maintenance. National collection of Hamamellis and Russell Lupins. Nearly 3000 different plants, most labelled. TEA. *Adm £2 Chd 10p (ACNO to Compton Hospice). By appt, groups £2.50 per head incl Tea & Biscuits, please* **Tel 01902 372624**

Thornfield, Twmpath, Gobowen ♿✗❀ (Mr & Mrs Paul Walker) *About 2m N of Oswestry. Turn off the A5 (Oswestry by-pass) at the Gobowen roundabout towards the Orthopaedic Hospital. 2nd R just over the railway bridge opp hospital car park.* Garden of approx 2 acres. Large borders informally planted with a mixture of trees, shrubs and herbaceous plants to provide interest and colour over many months. Pool containing goldfish and planted with waterlilies. TEAS. *Adm £2 Chd 50p. Sun May 21 (2-6)*

Triscombe, Roslyn Rd, Wellington ✗❀ (Dr & Mrs J Calvert) *Roslyn Rd is close to Wrekin College which is well signposted.* Approx $\frac{3}{4}$-acre town garden with access via steps. Features well stocked herbaceous and shrub borders, pond and bog garden, pergolas, rockery and container plants. TEAS in aid of Shropshire & Mid Wales Hospice, Telford Day Centre. *Adm £2 Chd 50p. Sun June 11 (1.30-5)*

Walcot Hall, Lydbury North ♿❀ (The Hon Mrs E C Parish) *Bishops Castle 3m. B4385 Craven Arms to Bishops Castle, turn L by Powis Arms, in Lydbury North.* Arboretum planted by Lord Clive of India's son. Cascades of rhododendrons, azaleas amongst specimen trees and pools. Fine views of Sir William Chambers' Clock Towers, with lake and hills beyond. TEAS. *Adm £2 Chd 15 and under free. Sun, Mon May 28, 29 (2-6). Also by appt for parties, please* **Tel 0171 581 2782**

■ **Weston Park, Shifnal** ♿ (The Weston Park Foundation) *7m E of Telford on the A5 at Weston-under-Lizard. Access junction 12 M6 and junction 3 M54. Free car/coach park.* Capability Brown landscaped gardens and parkland, incl fine collection, rhododendrons and azaleas. Formal gardens restored to original C19 design, rose garden and long border together with colourful adjacent Broderie Garden. TEAS and light meals available in The Old Stables restaurant. Park and garden. *Adm £4 OAP's £3, Chd £2.50, reduced rates for parties of 20 or more. Open Easter to September (enquiries for dates and times),* **Tel 01952 852100.** For NGS Wed July 12 (11-5)

Whittington Village Gardens, nr Oswestry ♿❀ *Daisy Lane, Whittington. $2\frac{1}{2}$m NE of Oswestry. Turn off B5009 150yds NW of church into Top St then into Daisy Lane. Car parking at Whittington Castle and Top St.* A group of 10 gardens, close to the church and Norman Castle. The owners are 'hands on' gardeners; several have kitchen gardens, supplying the family with organically grown fruit and vegetables. 6 have water features, and one cottage garden has been newly landscaped. For plant interest a collection of hardy geraniums and grasses, plants in hanging baskets and tubs; interesting wall plants and something special for the millennium. TEAS at The Bramleys; Top St in aid of Whittington Community Centre. *Adm £2.50 Chd free. Sat, Sun June 17, 18 (1-5.30)*

■ **Wollerton Old Hall, Wollerton** ♿✗❀ (Mr & Mrs J D Jenkins) *Nr Market Drayton on A53 between Hodnet and A53/A41 junction. Follow brown signs.* Award-winning 3-acre garden created around C16 house (not open). Featured on BBC2, Granada TV, various publications. A combination of formal design and intensive cultivation of perennials and clematis. A painter's garden using planting combinations with an emphasis on colour and form. Lunches, TEAS. *Adm £3 Chd £1. Every Fri and Sun May 1 to Aug 28 and Bank Hols (12-5). For NGS, every Fri in May. Parties, min 25, by appt, please* **Tel 01630 685760**

Evening Opening (See also garden description)

Brownhill House, Ruyton XI Towns — May 29 & June 5

Jinlye Guest House

Castle Hill, All Stretton, Shropshire SY6 6JP

01694 723243 www.jinlye.co.uk

Award winning Country House immediately adjoining the Long-Mynd Hills and 6000 acres of National Trust land. Furnished in period decor and offering luxurious and peaceful accomodation, all the spacious en-suite rooms have magnificent views. There is over an acre of cottage gardens which abound with rare and interesting plants for year round interest - scree beds and raised alpine beds to delight the connoisseur. We are renowned for our home from home atmosphere and you are assured of a warm welcome. Self Catering also available. Please send for our Colour Brochure.

ETC 5 DIAMONDS GOLD AWARD **AA 5 DIAMONDS**

Somerset

Hon County Organisers: Miss Patricia Davies-Gilbert, Coombe Quarry, West Monkton, Taunton, Somerset TA2 8RE Tel 01823 412187

Assistant Hon County Organisers: Miss Glenda Bryan, Blagdon House Lodge, Blagdon, North Somerset BS40 7TD Tel 01761 462121

Mrs Betty Hudspith, Rookwood, West Street, Hinton St George, North Somerset TA17 8SA Tel 01460 73450

Mrs Judy Kendall, Barle House, 17 High Street, Chew Magna, Somerset BS40 8PR Tel 01275 332459

Mrs Shirley Gyles, Rose Cottage, Flax Bourton, North Somerset BS48 3QE Tel 01275 462680

Somerset Leaflet: Richard Armitage Esq, Dormers, Park Lane, Carhampton, Somerset TA24 6NM Tel 01643 821327

Tour Advisor and Talks: Mrs Lynn Spencer-Mills, Hooper's Holding, Hinton St George, Somerset TA17 8SE Tel 01460 76389

Treasurer: John Spurrier Esq, Tudor Cottage, 19 Comeytrowe Lane, Taunton, Somerset TA1 5PA Tel 01823 333827

Publicity: Mrs Alison Kelly, The Mount, West Hill, Wincanton, Somerset BA9 9BY Tel 01963 32487

DATES OF OPENING

Regular openings

For details see garden description

Cothay Manor, Greenham
Elworthy Cottage, Elworthy
Gants Mill, Bruton
Gaulden Manor, Tolland
Glencot House, Wookey Hole
Greencombe, Porlock
Hadspen Garden, Castle Cary
Hatch Court, Hatch Beauchamp
Hestercombe Gardens, Cheddon Fitzpaine
Little Garth, Dowlish Wake
Lower Severalls, Crewkerne
Milton Lodge, Wells
The Time-Trail of Roses, Wells
Windmill Cottage, Backwell

By appointment only

For telephone numbers and other details see garden descriptions. Private visits welcomed

Benchmark, Wells
Bourne House, Burrington
Church Farm, Stanton Prior
Littlecourt, West Bagborough
The Mill, Wookey
Oare Manor Cottage, Oare
Sunnyside, Wells
Walnut Farm, Yarley

March 12 Sunday

Elworthy Cottage, Elworthy
Langford Court, Langford

March 14 Tuesday

Hestercombe Gardens, Cheddon Fitzpaine

March 23 Thursday

Elworthy Cottage, Elworthy

March 26 Sunday

Elworthy Cottage, Elworthy

April 2 Sunday

Coley Court & Widcombe Lodge, South Widcombe. East Harptree
Fairfield, Stogursey
Glencot House, Wookey Hole
Hangeridge Farm, Wrangway
Smocombe House, Enmore
Willow House, Bathampton

April 6 Thursday

Elworthy Cottage, Elworthy
Little Garth, Dowlish Wake

April 8 Saturday

Stowleys, Porlock

April 9 Sunday

Elworthy Cottage, Elworthy
Greencombe, Porlock
Montys Court, Norton Fitzwarren
The Mount, Chelston
Wayford Manor, Crewkerne

April 10 Monday

Montys Court, Norton Fitzwarren

April 13 Thursday

Little Garth, Dowlish Wake
Tone Dale House, Wellington

April 16 Sunday

Barrington Court, Ilminster
Cleeve Nursery, Cleeve
Congresbury Gardens
Crowe Hall, Widcombe
Holt Farm, Blagdon

April 19 Wednesday

Kingsdon, Somerton

April 20 Thursday

Elworthy Cottage, Elworthy
Little Garth, Dowlish Wake

April 21 Friday

Beryl, Wells

April 23 Sunday

The Mount, Wincanton

April 24 Monday

The Mount, Wincanton

April 26 Wednesday

Kingsdon, Somerton

April 27 Thursday

Little Garth, Dowlish Wake
The Mount, Wincanton

April 29 Saturday

The Spinney, Brockley

April 30 Sunday

Ilminster Gardens
Pear Tree Cottage, Stapley
The Spinney, Brockley
Wayford Manor, Crewkerne

May 1 Monday

Ilminster Gardens (evening)
Pear Tree Cottage, Stapley
The Spinney, Brockley

May 3 Wednesday

Kingsdon, Somerton

May 4 Thursday

Little Garth, Dowlish Wake

May 7 Sunday

Cannington College Gardens
Forge House, Oake

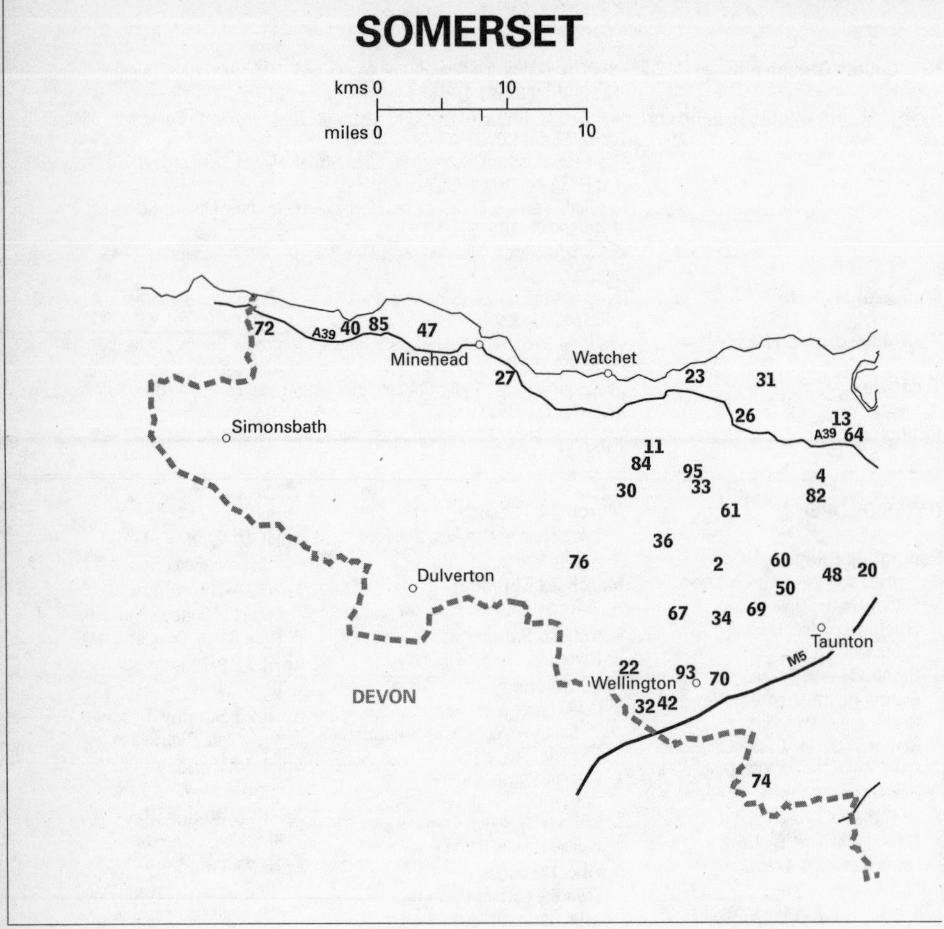

KEY

1 Abbey Farm
2 Ashmead
3 Babbs Farm
4 Barford Park
5 Barrington Court
6 Barrow Court
7 Benchmark
8 Beryl
9 Blackwithies
10 Bourne House
11 Braglands Barn
12 Brent Knoll Gardens
13 Cannington College Gardens
14 Cherry Bolberry Farm
15 Chinnock House
16 Church Farm and The Gables
17 Cleeve Nursery
18 Coley Court & Widcombe Lodge
19 Congresbury Gardens
20 Coombe Gardens
21 Coombe House
22 Cothay Manor
23 Court House
24 Crowe Hall
25 Dial House
26 Dodington Hall
27 Dunster Castle
28 East Horrington Gardens
29 East Lambrook Manor Gardens
30 Elworthy Cottage
31 Fairfield
32 Fernhill
33 Flaxpool House
34 Forge House
35 Gants Mill
36 Gaulden Manor
37 Glencot House
38 Goblin Combe
39 190 Goldcroft
40 Greencombe
41 Hadspen Garden
42 Hangeridge Farm
43 Hapsford House
44 Harptree Court
45 Hatch Beauchamp Gardens
46 Heale House
47 Heatherbank & Uplanda at Glebelands
48 Hestercombe Gardens
49 Higher Holbrook
50 Higher Yarde Farm
51 Hinton St George Gardens
52 Holt Farm
53 Ilminster Gardens
54 Kingsdon

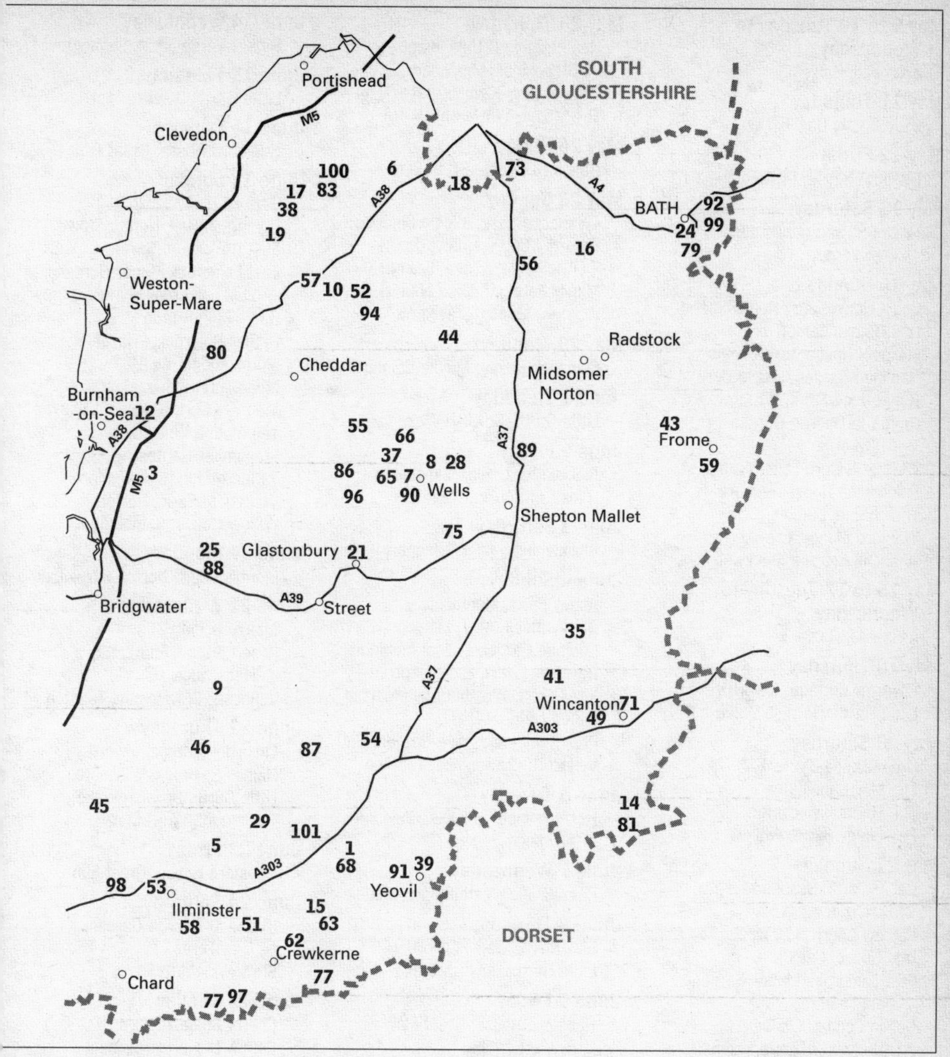

55 Kites Croft
56 Lady Farm
57 Langford Court
58 Little Garth
59 7 Little Keyford Lane
60 Little Yarford Farmhouse
61 Littlecourt
62 Lower Severalls
63 Manor Farm
64 The Mill, Cannington
65 The Mill, Wookey
66 Milton Lodge
67 Milverton Gardens
68 Montacute House
69 Montys Court
70 The Mount, Chelston
71 The Mount, Wincanton
72 Oare Manor Cottage
73 Parsonage Farm
74 Pear Tree Cottage
75 Perridge House
76 Pitt Farmhouse
77 Pondarosa
78 Popinjays & Little Norton Mill
79 Prior Park Landscape Garden
80 Rackley House
81 Rose Cottage
82 Smocombe House
83 The Spinney
84 Stogumber Gardens
85 Stowleys
86 Sunnyside
87 Sutton Hosey Manor
88 Thatch End
89 The Dower House & Darkey Pang TSO Gang
90 The Time-Trail of Roses
91 Tintinhull House
92 Tithe Cottage
93 Tone Dale House
94 Ubley Hill Farm House
95 Vellacott
96 Walnut Farm
97 Wayford Manor
98 Whitegate Farm
99 Willow House
100 Windmill Cottage
101 Yews Farm

May 9 to 10 Tuesday to Wednesday
Ashmead, Halse

May 11 Thursday
Little Garth, Dowlish Wake

May 12 Friday
Flaxpool House, Crowcombe

May 13 Saturday
Hinton St George Gardens, Crewkerne

May 14 Sunday
Court House, East Quantoxhead
Dial House, Catcott
Flaxpool House, Crowcombe
Hadspen Garden, Castle Cary
Hangeridge Farm, Wrangway
Hinton St George Gardens, Crewkerne
7 Little Keyford Lane, Frome
Smocombe House, Enmore
Thatch End, Catcott
Wayford Manor, Crewkerne
Windmill Cottage, Backwell

May 16 to 17 Tuesday to Wednesday
Ashmead, Halse

May 18 Thursday
Elworthy Cottage, Elworthy
Little Garth, Dowlish Wake

May 20 Saturday
Greencombe, Porlock
The Mill, Cannington
The Mount, Wincanton
Parsonage Farm, Publow

May 21 Sunday
Babbs Farm, Basonbridge, nr Highbridge
Barrow Court, Barrow Gurney
Dial House, Catcott
East Lambrook Manor Gardens, East Lambrook
Goblin Combe, Cleeve
7 Little Keyford Lane, Frome
The Mill, Cannington
Milton Lodge, Wells
The Mount, Chelston
The Mount, Wincanton
Parsonage Farm, Publow
Perridge House, Pilton
Pitt Farmhouse, Huish Champflower
Thatch End, Catcott
The Time-Trail of Roses, Wells
Whitegate Farm, Horton

May 23 to 24 Tuesday to Wednesday
Ashmead, Halse

May 24 Wednesday
Heatherbank & Uplands at Glebelands, Minehead

May 25 Thursday
Heatherbank & Uplands at Glebelands, Minehead
Little Garth, Dowlish Wake
The Mount, Wincanton

May 26 Friday
Hapsford House, Great Elm

May 28 Sunday
Chinnock House, Middle Chinnock
Elworthy Cottage, Elworthy
7 Little Keyford Lane, Frome
Manor Farm, Middle Chinnock
Wayford Manor, Crewkerne

May 29 Monday
Chinnock House, Middle Chinnock

June 1 Thursday
Little Garth, Dowlish Wake

June 2 Friday
Blackwithies, Aller, Langport
Hapsford House, Great Elm

June 3 Saturday
Blackwithies, Aller, Langport

June 4 Sunday
Abbey Farm, Montacute
Blackwithies, Aller, Langport
Coombe Gardens, West Monkton
Harptree Court, East Harptree
Kites Croft, Westbury-sub-Mendip
Milton Lodge, Wells
Prior Park Landscape Garden, Bath
Vellacott, Crowcombe, Taunton

June 6 Tuesday
Hestercombe Gardens, Cheddon Fitzpaine

June 7 Wednesday
Kites Croft, Westbury-sub-Mendip

June 8 Thursday
Elworthy Cottage, Elworthy
Little Garth, Dowlish Wake

June 9 Friday
Hapsford House, Great Elm

June 10 Saturday
190 Goldcroft, Yeovil
Higher Yarde Farm, Staplegrove
Rackley House, Compton Bishop

June 11 Sunday
Cleeve Nursery, Cleeve
Crowe Hall, Widcombe
Dial House, Catcott
Elworthy Cottage, Elworthy
190 Goldcroft, Yeovil
Hatch Beauchamp Gardens
Milverton Gardens
Rackley House, Compton Bishop
The Spinney, Brockley
Thatch End, Catcott
The Time-Trail of Roses, Wells
Windmill Cottage, Backwell

June 14 Wednesday
Higher Yarde Farm, Staplegrove

June 15 Thursday
Little Garth, Dowlish Wake

June 16 Friday
Hapsford House, Great Elm

June 18 Sunday
Barford Park, Spaxton
Dodington Hall, Nether Stowey
East Horrington Gardens, Wells
East Lambrook Manor Gardens, East Lambrook
Gants Mill, Bruton
Higher Holbrook, Wincanton
Milton Lodge, Wells
Montacute House, Montacute
Montys Court, Norton Fitzwarren
The Mount, Wincanton
Stogumber Gardens
Tithe Cottage, Bathampton
Whitegate Farm, Horton
Willow House, Bathampton

June 19 Monday
Montys Court, Norton Fitzwarren

June 21 Wednesday
Cherry Bolberry Farm
Rose Cottage, Church St, Henstridge
Vellacott, Crowcombe, Taunton

June 22 Thursday
Elworthy Cottage, Elworthy
Higher Holbrook, Wincanton
Little Garth, Dowlish Wake
The Mount, Wincanton

June 23 Friday
Hapsford House, Great Elm

June 24 Saturday
Hinton St George Gardens, Crewkerne
Stowleys, Porlock

June 25 Sunday
Cherry Bolberry Farm
Cothay Manor, Greenham
Greencombe, Porlock
Hinton St George Gardens, Crewkerne
Holt Farm, Blagdon
Pitt Farmhouse, Huish Champflower
Pondarosa, Wayford
Rose Cottage, Church St, Henstridge
Ubley Hill Farm House, Blagdon

June 28 Wednesday
Heatherbank & Uplands at Glebelands, Minehead

June 29 Thursday
Heatherbank & Uplands at Glebelands, Minehead
Little Garth, Dowlish Wake

June 30 Friday
Hapsford House, Great Elm

July 2 Sunday
Church Farm and The Gables
Fernhill, nr Wellington
Gaulden Manor, Tolland
Hangeridge Farm, Wrangway

July 5 Wednesday
Fernhill, nr Wellington
Vellacott, Crowcombe, Taunton

July 6 Thursday
Little Garth, Dowlish Wake

July 9 Sunday
Barrington Court, Ilminster
Milton Lodge, Wells
Pear Tree Cottage, Stapley
Popinjays & Little Norton Mill, Little Norton
Windmill Cottage, Backwell

July 10 Monday
Popinjays & Little Norton Mill, Little Norton (evening)

July 11 Tuesday
Congresbury Gardens

July 13 Thursday
Elworthy Cottage, Elworthy
Little Garth, Dowlish Wake

July 16 Sunday
Brent Knoll Gardens, Highbridge
7 Little Keyford Lane, Frome
Tintinhull, Yeovil
Yews Farm, Martock

July 19 Wednesday
Heatherbank & Uplands at Glebelands, Minehead

July 20 Thursday
Elworthy Cottage, Elworthy
Heatherbank & Uplands at Glebelands, Minehead
Little Garth, Dowlish Wake

July 22 Saturday
Greencombe, Porlock

July 23 Sunday
Braglands Barn, Stogumber
The Dower House & Darkey Pang Tso Gang, Oakhill
Elworthy Cottage, Elworthy
Heale House, Langport
7 Little Keyford Lane, Frome
Whitegate Farm, Horton

July 26 Wednesday
Vellacott, Crowcombe, Taunton

July 27 Thursday
Little Garth, Dowlish Wake

July 29 Saturday
The Mill, Cannington

July 30 Sunday
Cothay Manor, Greenham
Hangeridge Farm, Wrangway
Heale House, Langport
7 Little Keyford Lane, Frome
The Mill, Cannington
Sutton Hosey Manor, Long Sutton
Vellacott, Crowcombe, Taunton

August 3 Thursday
Dunster Castle, Dunster
Little Garth, Dowlish Wake

August 4 Friday
Little Yarford Farmhouse, Kingston St Mary

August 5 Saturday
Little Yarford Farmhouse, Kingston St Mary

August 6 Sunday
Coombe House, Bove Town
Fernhill, nr Wellington
Little Yarford Farmhouse, Kingston St Mary
Windmill Cottage, Backwell

August 9 Wednesday
Fernhill, nr Wellington

August 10 Thursday
Little Garth, Dowlish Wake

August 13 Sunday
Lady Farm, Chelwood
Vellacott, Crowcombe, Taunton

August 16 Wednesday
Vellacott, Crowcombe, Taunton

August 17 Thursday
Little Garth, Dowlish Wake

August 20 Sunday
Whitegate Farm, Horton

August 24 Thursday
Little Garth, Dowlish Wake

August 27 Sunday
Kites Croft, Westbury-sub-Mendip

August 28 Monday
Beryl, Wells

August 30 Wednesday
Kites Croft, Westbury-sub-Mendip

August 31 Thursday
Little Garth, Dowlish Wake

September 3 Sunday
Fernhill, nr Wellington
Vellacott, Crowcombe, Taunton

September 6 Wednesday
Fernhill, nr Wellington
Vellacott, Crowcombe, Taunton

September 7 Thursday
Little Garth, Dowlish Wake

September 10 Sunday
Braglands Barn, Stogumber

September 14 Thursday
Elworthy Cottage, Elworthy
Little Garth, Dowlish Wake

September 17 Sunday
Cleeve Nursery, Cleeve
Elworthy Cottage, Elworthy
Windmill Cottage, Backwell

September 21 Thursday
Little Garth, Dowlish Wake

September 24 Sunday
The Mount, Wincanton

September 28 Thursday
Little Garth, Dowlish Wake
The Mount, Wincanton

October 8 Sunday
Elworthy Cottage, Elworthy

October 12 Thursday
Elworthy Cottage, Elworthy

October 22 Sunday
Holt Farm, Blagdon

Regular Openings. Open throughout the year. They are listed at the beginning of the Diary Section.

By Appointment Gardens. These owners do not have a fixed opening day, usually because they cannot accommodate large numbers or have insuffucient parking space.

DESCRIPTIONS OF GARDENS

Abbey Farm, Montacute ♿❀ (Mr & Mrs G Jenkins) *4m from Yeovil follow A3088, take slip road to Montacute, turn L at T-junction into village. Turn R between Church and Kings Arms (no through Rd).* 2½-acre of mainly walled gardens on sloping site provide setting for mediaeval Priory gatehouse. Roses; shrubs, herbaceous borders. Clematis, white garden. Parking available. TEAS in aid of all Saints Primary School. *Adm £2 Chd free. Sun June 4 (2-5.30). Private visits welcome, please* **Tel 01935 823572**

Ashmead, Halse ♿✂❀ (Mr & Mrs O D West) *Approx 7m W of Taunton off A358, about 1m SW Bishop's Lydeard and W Somerset Railway Station. Follow signs to Halse. On LH-side before reaching village.* Approx 1½ acres informal country garden developed over the past 11yrs, with wildlife, especially birds, in mind. Mixed borders, large rockery, stream, pond, bog gardens and wild garden. *Adm £1.50 Chd 50p. Tues, Weds May 9 to May 24 incl (2-5). Private visits by arrangement, please* **Tel 01823 433041**

Babbs Farm, Basonbridge, nr Highbridge ❀ (Sue & Richard O'Brien) *2.5 km E of Highbridge and 2.5 km SSE of M5 exit 22, situated in Westhill Lane off B3141 (Church Rd), 100yds S of where it joins B3139 (Wells-Highbridge rd).* ¾-acre partly walled plantsman's garden adjoining old Somerset farmhouse and overlooking fields. Started in 1990 and still being developed. Herbaceous borders with many unusual plants, water features and bog plants, conservatory with tropical plants, further wild areas and field. TEAS. *Adm £2 Chd free. Sun May 21 (2-6)*

Barford Park, Spaxton ♿ (Mr & Mrs Michael Stancomb) *4½m W of Bridgwater, midway between Enmore and Spaxton.* 10 acres including woodland walk. Formal garden, wild garden and water garden, surrounding a Queen Anne house (not open) with park. and ha ha. TEAS. *Adm £2 Chd free (ACNO to Somerset Garden Trust). Sun June 18 (2-5.30)*

▲ **Barrington Court, Ilminster** ♿✂❀ (The National Trust) *NE of Ilminster.* Well known garden constructed in 1920 by Col Arthur Lyle from derelict farmland (the C19 cattle stalls still exist). Gertrude Jekyll suggested planting schemes for the layout; paved paths with walled rose and iris, white and lily gardens, large kitchen garden. Licensed restaurant, plant sales and garden shop. Lunches and TEAS. *Adm £4.20 Chd £2.10. Suns April 16, July 9 (11-5.30)*

Barrow Court, Barrow Gurney (Mrs Jo Collins (Organiser)) *From the A370 Weston-Super-Mare, Bristol Rd. Turn off onto A3130 to Barrow Gurney. Turn immed R into Barrow Court Lane. ½m up lane turn R into Barrow Court.* Barrow Court has an early C20 listed Italianate garden, designed by Inigo Thomas. Formal areas are set on 3 levels and incl parterres, fish pond, balustrades, gazeboes and exhedra. There is also a small arboretum and wild spinney. TEAS. *Adm £1.50 Chd 50p (ACNO to Barrow Gurney Church). Sun May 21 (2-6)*

Benchmark, Wells ✂❀ (Mr & Mrs T Whitman) *99 Portway. On A371 Cheddar Rd out of Wells, ½m from city centre on L.* ¾-acre mature garden with an orchard, productive potager, sundial garden and densely planted borders growing many unusual perennials incl more than 100 varieties of penstemon. *Adm £1 By appt, please* **Tel 01749 677155**

Beryl, Wells ♿❀ (Mr and Mrs E Nowell) *1m N of Wells off B3139 to Bath. Directions to The Horringtons & 'H' for hospital. L at Hawkers Lane opp BP garage.* Victorian park created in 1842. Walled vegetable garden broken into quadrangles with box hedging and double flower picking borders. More recent planting of trees and shrubs and creation of walks and vistas. Morning coffee and TEAS. *Adm £1 OAP/Chd 50p Fri April 21, Mon Aug 28 (11-5.30)* **Tel 01749 678738**

Blackwithies, Aller, Langport ❀ (Mr & Mrs Jack Ward) *2½m NW of Langport on A372 between villages of Aller and Othery. ½m N of Aller. Parking.* A developing 1¼-acre garden with extensive views of the levels and ancient woodlands. Plantings designed to provide vistas and hidden places with yr-round form and colour. Wide borders; large pond, canals, water lilies, marginal plants; long curving pergola, summer house; copse with specimen trees and apiary; vegetable, fruit garden; incl espaliers; greenhouses. Partly suitable for wheelchairs. TEAS and Plants in aid of St Andrew's Aller PCC for bells restoration fund). *Adm £2 Chd £1. Fri, Sat, Sun June 2, 3, 4 (11-5)*

Bourne House, Burrington ♿✂❀ (Mr & Mrs C Thomas) *12m S Bristol. N of Burrington. Turning off A38 signposted Blagdon-Burrington; 2nd turning L.* 4 acres, and 2 paddocks. Stream with waterfalls & lily pond; pergola; mature trees, and shrubs. Large area Autumn cyclamen. Mixed borders; new rose bed. *Adm £2 Chd free. Open by appt, please* **Tel 01761 462494**

Braglands Barn, Stogumber ♿✂❀ (Simon and Sue Youell) *12m NW of Taunton. Follow A358 towards Minehead. Turn L towards Stogumber, just past Bee World turn R, parking in field* 1-acre garden started in 1995. Mixed herbaceous and shrub borders with many unusual plants, rose bed, pond and bog garden. Planted to provide a succession of colour through the summer. Additional 1-acre field with trees. Teas available at Bee World *Adm £1.50 Chd free Suns July 23, Sept 10 (2-6)*

Brent Knoll Gardens, Highbridge ❀ *Off A38 2m N of Highbridge and M5 exit 22.* Two colourful country gardens. TEAS at Copse Hall in aid of Parish Hall. *Combined adm £3 Chd free. Sun July 16 (2-6)*

Copse Hall ❀ (Mrs S Boss & A J Hill Esq) Several acres incl terraced gardens, crinkle crankle kitchen garden wall, ponds, shrubs, beechwood and soay sheep. Partly suitable for wheelchairs. Private visits welcome, please Tel 01278 760301 evenings

Orchard (Roger & Lyn Brafield) The garden has matured since last open. Mixed planting with clematis roses etc

▲ **Cannington College Gardens** ♿✂❀ *Cannington, 3m NW of Bridgwater. On A39 Bridgwater-Minehead Rd.* Old College: Benedictine Priory 1138; fine Elizabethan W front; 7

old sandstone walled gardens. *Adm £2, OAP's & Chd (5-6 yrs) £1. Guided tours £25 per hour. For NGS Sun May 7 (2-5)*

Cherry Bolberry Farm ♿❀ (Mr & Mrs C Raymond) *Henstridge. From Henstridge T-lights continue on A357 through Henstridge towards Stalbridge. In centre of Henstridge turn R at small Xrds signed Furge Lane. Farm at end of lane. 5m E of Sherborne. 7m S of Wincanton.* 1 acre owner-designed garden planted for yr-round interest. Nature ponds, new fish pond, colour themed island beds. Extensive views. Sun June 25 (TEAS), Wed June 21 (TEA). *Combined adm with Rose Cottage £2 Chd free. Wed June 21, Sun June 25 (2-5.30)*

Chiffchaffs See Dorset

Chinnock House, Middle Chinnock ✂❀ (Mr & Mrs Guy Smith) *Off A30 between Crewkerne and Yeovil.* 2-acre walled gardens, scented and herbaceous. TEAS. *Adm £1.50 Chd free. Sun May 28, with Manor Farm adm £2.50, Mon 29 (2-6). Private visits welcome for parties of 2 or over, please* **Tel 01935 881229**

Church Farm and The Gables ♿✂❀ *6m from Bath on A 39 Wells Rd; at Marksbury turn L to Stanton Prior; gardens set in beautiful countryside in unspoilt village.* Ploughman's lunches & cream teas, in aid of St Lawrence Church. *Combined adm £2 Chd free. For NGS Sun July 2 (11-6)*

Church Farm, Stanton Prior (Mr & Mrs L Hardwick) Herbaceous borders, rock garden, scree garden; shrub roses, many unusual plants, wild area with ¼-acre pond. *Open by appt all yr, please* **Tel 01761 470384**

The Gables (Mr & Mrs Alistair Hardwick) Cottage garden open for NGS day only

Cleeve Nursery, Cleeve ❀ (Alan & Felicity Down) *Midway between Backwell and Congresbury (2m) on the A370 in the village of Cleeve.* Established 1 acre garden where the owners film HTV's 'Garden Calendar' programme each week. Primarily a cottage garden, features incl a dry border, walled garden, small fruit, veg and herb garden, planted containers and large range of less hardy perennials. TEA. *Adm £1.50 Chd free. Suns April 16, June 11, Sept 17 (2-4.30)*

Coley Court & Widcombe Lodge, South Widcombe. East Harptree *Combined adm £1.50 Chd free. Sun April 2 (2-6)*

Coley Court (Mrs M J Hill) *East Harptree, 8m N of Wells from A39 at Chewton Mendip take B3114 for 2m. Well before East Harptree turn R at sign Coley and Hinton Blewitt.* 1-acre garden, stone walls, spring bulbs; 1-acre old mixed orchard. Early Jacobean house (not open)

Widcombe Lodge (Mr & Mrs P M Walker) *From W Harptree take B3114 (Chewton Mendip rd), turn L at East Harptree Xrds for about 1m. Garden on R* Old walled garden, mature shrubs and massed bulbs

NEW **Congresbury Gardens** ✂ *Congresbury is approx 8 m N of Weston-super-Mare and 13ml S of Bristol on the A370. At traffic lights on the A370 in Congresbury head E signed Churchill/Cheddar and after approx 500yds turn R into Silver Street. Please park in Silver Street. For Fernbank park at Village car park at Ship and Castle.* TEAS (Sun), TEA (Tues) in aid of St Andrews PTA. *Combined Adm £1.50 Chd free. Sun April 16, Tues July 11 (10.30-6)*

NEW **Fernbank** (Simon & Julia Thyer) Wisteria clad Victorian house (not open) with approx ⅓ acre. 2 ponds, herbaceous borders, patio, vegtable garden, greenhouse and potting shed. Arbour with well pump, conservatory. Funny rare bantams and 2 ducks who 'cultivate' the garden. Approx 300 plants in containers

NEW **Meadowcroft, 3 Silver Mead** ❀ (Terry & Geraldine Holden) Just under ⅓ acre of shrub borders and trees, developed over the past 13 years from farmland. Two 'hot' Mediterranean type patios, one with a water feature and one shaded by a wisteria covered pergola. Many interesting features incl an abundance of pots and a lavender walk through a clematis/passion flower clad pergola. Great unrestricted views to the Mendips

Coombe Gardens, West Monkton *A38 between Taunton & Bridgwater. Well signed. Ample parking available. Picnics welcome.* TEAS. *Combined adm £2 Chd free. Sun June 4 (2-6)*

Coombe Mill ✂ (Mr & Mrs Hugh Pollard) Newly created gardens situated around a C17 Mill in an area of outstanding natural beauty. The total area of approx 2 acres incl a newly planted lime walk, an avenue of ornamental pears set in the formal section of the garden and a woodland walk through the quarry from which stone was obtained for the Mill and other buildings in the area. The latest project is a water garden now in its 4th yr.

Coombe Quarry, West Monkton (Miss Patricia Davies-Gilbert) Cottage garden with quarry walk. Roses and other shrubs, vegetables and animals.

Coombe House, Bove Town (Colin Wells-Brown & Alan Gloak) *Bove Town is a steep hill above Glastonbury High St. The house is about ¼m from the town. Very limited parking nearby, so please park in central town car park and take the 'Tor Bus' from St Dunstans car park or walk.* It is an old house with a young garden beginning to show architectural maturity. Walled formal, herbaceous and romantic shrub garden. Elegant grass garden. Delightful views and ambience. In all about 2 acres. Some tender and unusual plants. Vegetable garden, orchards, nut walk, water features and pergolas. NEW for 2000 a Bastion, with a view to a green elysium! TEAS. *Adm £2 Chd 50p (ACNO to Aled Richards Trust). Sun Aug 6 (2-6)*

■ **Cothay Manor, Greenham** ♿✂❀ (Mr & Mrs Alastair Robb) *Approx 4m from junction 26 or 27 on M5. On A38 take direction Greenham. As you descend hill into Greenham, on sharp LH-bend turn R. Follow lane always L. Carpark 1m.* Laid out in the 1920s by Reginald Cooper, Harold Nicholson of Sissinghurst's oldest friend, this jewel of a garden completely restored over the last 5 yrs. Plantsman's paradise, yew walk, courtyards, garden rooms, bog garden, river. Medieval house open to groups. Cream TEAS *Adm £3 Chd free Wed, Thur, Sun, Bank Hols, May to Sept incl groups by appt. NGS Suns June 25, July 30 (2-6)*

Court House, East Quantoxhead ♿❀ (Sir Walter & Lady Luttrell) *12m W of Bridgwater off A39; house at end of village past duck pond.* Lovely 5-acre garden; trees, shrubs, roses and herbaceous and woodland garden started 1992. Views to sea and Quantocks. Partly suitable for wheelchairs. Teas in Village Hall. *Adm £2 Chd free. Sun May 14 (2-5.00)*

▲ **Crowe Hall, Widcombe** ♿ (John Barratt Esq) *1m SE of Bath. L up Widcombe Hill, off A36, leaving White Hart on R.* Large varied garden; fine trees, lawns, spring bulbs, series of enclosed gardens cascading down steep hillside. Italianate terracing and Gothic Victorian grotto contrast with park-like upper garden. Dramatic setting, with spectacular views of Bath. Trellis and water garden created in 1995. Dogs welcome. TEAS. *Adm £2 Chd £1 For NGS Suns April 16, June 11 (2-6)* **Tel 01225 310322**

NEW **Cucumber Cottage** See Dorset

Dial House, Catcott ♿✗ (Mrs Peter Strallen) *Turn N off A39 between Bridgwater (8m) and Street to Catcott. Continue straight into village. Turn L at T junction. Fork R at War Memorial and immed L at cul de sac sign. No parking at house, please follow signs to school carpark.* Informal partly walled garden surrounding C14 house (not open) wisteria, rambling roses, herbaceous borders. Catcott is a regular winner of Britain in Bloom. *Combined adm with Thatch End £2.50 Chd 50p. Suns May 14, 21, June 11 (2-6). Private visits welcome by appt in May and June, please* **Tel 01278 722008**

Dodington Hall, Nether Stowey ✗❀ (Grania & Paul Quinn) *A39 Bridgwater-Minehead. 2m W of Nether Stowey turn at signpost opp Castle of Comfort. ¼m turn R. Entrance through churchyard.* Reclaimed 1½-acre terrace garden; clematis, shrub roses, bulbs; Tudor house (part open). TEAS in aid of LIFE. *Adm £2 Chd free. Sun June 18 (2.30-5.30).* **Tel 01278 741400**

NEW **The Dower House & Darkey Pang Tso Gang, Oakhill** ❀ TEAS. *Combined adm £2.50 Chd 50p. Sun July 23 (2-6)*

Darkey Pang Tso Gang, Oakhill ✗❀ (Graham & Chrissy Price) *3m N of Shepton Mallet off A367 in Oakhill High St opp converted chapel.* ¾-acre. Creatively designed and landscaped by owners since 1981. Crammed with trees, shrubs, herbaceous and climbers, with a lushness of greens and leaf combinations. Winding paths link wild and cultivated areas with grotto, pergola, wildlife pond and bog garden. New features annually. *Private visits welcome by arrangement £2 June to Sept, please* **Tel 01749 840795**

NEW **The Dower House, Oakhill** ♿✗❀ (Mrs Rebecca Edwards) *3m N of Shepton Mallett off A367, turn up Zion Hill off Oakhill High Street. Park in the village hall car park. Unmade lane directly opp entrance to village hall leads to The Dower House.* ½ acre garden and courtyard, both surrounded by high stone walls. Gravel courtyard features climbing roses and clematis. The main garden has a mix of mature shrubs and trees with beds planted in cottage style. Small pond full of water lilies. The garden at the front of the Queen Ann house (not open) has an attractive semi-circular stone wall full of self sown wild strawberries, ferns, poppies and aquilegia.

▲ **Dunster Castle, Dunster** ♿✗ (Mr M Marshall, The National Trust) *3m SE of Minehead. NT car park approached direct from A39.* Terraces of sub-tropical plants, shrubs and camellias surrounding the fortified home of the Luttrell family for 600 yrs; fine views. Self-drive battery operated car available. Teas in village. *Adm Garden Only £3 Chd £1.30. Family ticket £7.30. For NGS Thurs Aug 3 (10-5)*

East Horrington Gardens, Wells *2m E of Wells off B3139 leaving Wells golf course on R. Seven mixed gardens, large and small.* TEAS. *Combined adm £2.50 Chd free. Sun June 18 (2-6)*

Ashmount (Mr and Mrs Gordon Cox) 4 acres of garden created by present owners over 25 yrs featuring many varieties of trees and shrubs. Fishponds, extensive lawns and vistas - a garden to stroll in.

NEW **Goose House** ✗ (Dr & Mrs I Capstick) 13 yr-old garden originally part of Manor Farm, East Horrington. 1/5 acre, the layout completed 3 yrs ago; progressively easy maintenance being essential in plan. Mediterranean gravel planting; perennials and shrubs in the borders. Variety of sitting out areas together with pieces of mendip stone

NEW **Henley Cottage** ♿ (Mr & Mrs Johnson) Small country garden with patios and water features, shrubs, bulbs and summer flowers

NEW **Hill Farm Bungalow** (Mr & Mrs R Eastment) Interesting collection of flowering shrubs and plants in rock garden settings, all in labour-saving gravelled surrounds

NEW **Manor Farm** ♿ (Mr & Mrs Fridd) Old farmhouse walled garden with many old and unusual plants and trees; vegetable garden, walled courtyard and lawns

NEW **The Old Post Office** (Mr & Mrs J I Harris) *On site of former village shop/post office, at x-rds at East Horrington, opp the former church of St. John's.* 3 gardens at different levels at the front, side and at the rear, the latter the larger, elevated and enclosed by high stone wall. Spring and summer bedding, flowering and foliage shrubs, trees, small water rockery and conservatory. About ⅓ acre. Emphasis on colour, mainly through flowers. Specialising in begonias, early chrysanthemums and dahlias grown for pleasure and for exhibition in local, regional and national shows

NEW **Swallow Barn** (Hazel & Eric Willmott) A 5 yr-old garden of mixed herbaceous perennials and shrubs. Interesting water feature from stone found on site

NEW **East Lambrook Manor Gardens, East Lambrook** ❀ (Robert & Marianne Williams) *Off A303, 2m N of South Petherton.* One of Englands best loved privately owned gardens created by the late Margery Fish and made famous through her many books and lectures. Intriguing cottage-style garden with important collection of plants, many of which she saved from virtual extinction. The informality of this grade I listed garden creates delightful feeling of peace and old world tranquility. New owners have launched extensive restoration programme which will help improve many historicaly important areas. From Easter to Sept the C17 Malthouse has ongoing exhibitions by well known West

Country Artists. New plant sales area now available, with restored display of the National Collection of Geraniums. TEAS in the Malthouse. *Adm £2.50 Chd 50p. Suns May 21, June 18 (11-5)*

■ **Elworthy Cottage, Elworthy** ✗✿ (Mike and Jenny Spiller) *12m NW of Taunton on B3188.* 1-acre garden. Many unusual herbaceous plants. Large collection of hardy geraniums (over 200 varieties); hellebores, pulmonarias, campanulas, penstemons, violas, grasses and plants for foliage effect. Wide selection of plants from the garden for sale. *Adm £1.50 Chd free (ACNO to CLIC). Nursery and Garden open Tues, Thurs and Fri (10-4) mid March to mid Oct. For NGS Suns March 12, 26, April 9, May 28, Jun 11, July 23, Sept 17, Oct 8, Thurs March 23, April 6, 20, May 18, June 8, 22, July 13, 20, Sept 14, Thurs Oct 12 (1.30-5). Coaches and groups welcome, by appt Tel 01984 656427*

Fairfield, Stogursey &✗ (Lady Gass) *11m NW of Bridgwater 7m E of Williton. From A39 Bridgwater-Minehead turn N; garden 1½m W of Stogursey.* Woodland garden with bulbs and shrubs; paved maze. Views of Quantocks. Dogs in park and field only. TEA. *Adm £2 Chd free (ACNO to Stogursey Church). Sun April 2 (2-5.30)*

Fernhill, nr Wellington ✗✿ (Peter & Audrey Bowler) *White Ball Hill. W on A38 from Wellington. Past Beam Bridge Hotel and at top of Hill follow signs on L into garden and car park.* Mature wooded garden in approx 2 acres with rose, herbaceous, shrub, and mixed borders all unique in colour and content. Interesting octagonal pergola; alpine and bog garden with waterfalls and pools leading to shady arbour. TEAS on terrace with fine views over ha-ha to Black Downs and Mendips. Good plant collection. *Adm £2 Chd free. Suns, Weds July 2, 5, Aug 6, 9, Sept 3, 6 (2-6). Private visits welcome Tel 01823 672423*

Flaxpool House, Crowcombe & (Lady Clark) *House situated on Main Rd from Cross Keys (outside Taunton) to Minehead 8m.* House in trees beside the Flaxpool Garage. Plenty of parking space inside. Spring garden, azaleas, rhododendrons, camellias. Fishpond, swimming pool. 1 acre, area where dogs can run. TEAS. *Adm £1.50 Chd 50p. Fri May 12, Sun 14 (3-6)*

Forge House, Oake &✗✿ (Peter & Eloise McGregor) *On A38 midway between Taunton & Wellington. Take signpost for Oake. 1st house on R entering village. Please park in village or village hall car park.* A level 1-acre informal country garden with emphasis on colour, bee and butterfly plants and fragrance. Unmanaged wildlife area and pond, wildflowers are encouraged, new ideas in progress. Ideal for elderly and disabled. TEA if fine. *Adm £2 Chd 50p. Sun May 7 (2-6). Disabled & parties welcome week-ends April to June Tel 01823 461500 after 7*

NEW **Gants Mill, Bruton** (Alison & Brian Shingler) *W out of Bruton centre on the Yeovil Rd, A359, under railway bridge 100yds uphill, fork R down Gants Mil Lane.* ½ acre garden created in the last 4yrs to a garden designer plan. Clematis, rose arches and pergolas; streams, ponds, bog garden, brick circle, grasses in gravel; colour themed planting with many oriental poppies, delphiniums, daylilies, waterlilies, pen-

stemons and dahlias. Kitchen garden. TEAS. *Adm £2 Chd £1. Garden and watermill open Thurs, 2nd & 4th Suns June 1 - Sept 28. For NGS Sun June 18 (2-5) www.gantsmill.co.uk*

Gaulden Manor, Tolland &✗✿ (Mr & Mrs J Le G Starkie) *Nr Lydeard St Lawrence. 9m NW Taunton off A358.* Medium-sized garden made by owners. Herb; bog; scent and butterfly gardens. Bog plants, primulas and scented geraniums. Partly suitable for wheelchairs. Cream TEAS. *Adm house & garden £4.20, garden only £3, Chd £1. Sun July 2 (2-5)*

Glencot House, Wookey Hole ✗✿ (Mrs Jenny Attia) *½m SW of Wells. From Wells follow the signs to Wookey Hole. Through the village, past the Wookey Hole Caves and take 1st turning L into Titlands Lane. Proceed for approx ½m and the entrance to Glencot Cricket field is on LH-side. Drive across field and park. 1½m SW of Wells.* 18 acres of parkland of which approx 4 acres are formal gardens with frontage to R Axe. Herbaceous borders, rose walk and terraced walk with water features. TEAS. *Adm £2 Chd 50p. Sun April 2 (2-5) also open Weds (11-5)*

Goblin Combe, Cleeve ✗✿ (Mrs H R Burn) *10m S of Bristol on A370, turn L onto Cleeve Hill Rd just before Lord Nelson Inn. After 300 yds turn L onto Plunder St, first drive on R. Car parking near the bottom of the drive just beyond the Plunder St turning.* 2 acre terraced garden with interesting collection of trees, shrubs and borders, surrounded by orchards, fields and woodlands. Magnificent views. TEAS. *Adm £1.50 Chd free (ACNO to The Music Space Trust) Sun May 21 (2-5.30). Private visits welcome, please Tel 01934 838599*

190 Goldcroft, Yeovil &✗✿ (Eric & Katrina Crate) *Take A359 from roundabout by Yeovil College, then 1st R. ¼-acre.* Colour-themed shrub and herbaceous borders and island beds, rose garden, raised ponds, vegetable garden designed for the visually impaired. As seen on BBC 2 Gardeners' World. TEAS in aid of Yeovil Visually Impaired Bowls Club. *Adm £2 Chd 50p Sat, Sun June 10, 11 (2-5). Groups welcome by appt Tel 01935 475535*

■ **Greencombe, Porlock** &✗✿ (Miss Joan Loraine) *½m W of Porlock, L off road to Porlock Weir* 54yr-old garden on edge of ancient woodland, overlooking Porlock Bay. Choice rhododendrons, azaleas, camellias, maples, roses, hydrangeas, ferns, small woodland plants and clematis. National collections of Polystichum, (the 'thumbs up' fern), Erythronium (dog's tooth violets), Vaccinium (blue-berries) and Gaultheria. Completely organic, with compost heaps on show. TEA. *Adm £3 Chd (under 16) 50p Sats, Suns, Mons, Tues, Weds, April, May, June, July (2-6); For NGS Sats, Suns, April 9, May 20, June 25, July 22 (2-6) private visits, please Tel 01643 862363*

● **Hadspen Garden, Castle Cary** &✗✿ (N & S Pope) *2m SE of Castle Cary on A371 to Wincanton.* 5-acre Edwardian garden featuring a 2-acre curved walled garden with extensive colourist borders of shrub roses and choice herbaceous plants; woodland of fine specimen trees. National Rodgersia Collection. Lunches, TEAS. *Adm £3 Chd 50p (ACNO to Friends of the Earth). Garden and Nursery open Thurs, Fri,*

Sat, Sun & Bank Hol Mon (10-5); private visits welcome, March 2 to Sept 30 (10-5) For NGS Sun May 14 (10-5) please **Tel 01749 813707 (after 6pm).**

Hangeridge Farm, Wrangway ♿✂❀ (Mrs J M Chave) *Wellington, 1m off A38 bypass signposted Wrangway. 1st L towards Wellington Monument over motorway bridge 1st R.* 1-acre garden, herbaceous borders, flowering shrubs and heathers, raised rockeries, spring bulbs. Lovely setting under Blackdown Hills. Selection of plants available from garden. TEAS. *Adm £1 Chd free. Suns April 2, May 14, July 2, 30 (2-6). Parties by appt* **Tel 01823 662339**

Hapsford House, Great Elm ✂ (Mr & Mrs R Enthoven) *½m out of Frome on A362 to Radstock. 1st rd on L to Great Elm, Hapsford and Mells.* Approx ½m house on L 9-acre C19 Grade II listed garden runs from Regency house (not open) to island on River Mells. Woodland, riverside and meadow walks. Extensive laburnum walk to main house. Sensitive restoration since 1990 and replanting incl many species and shrub roses. Unsuitable for children. *Adm £2.50 Chd £1.50. Fris from May 26 to June 30 (11-6). Parties by appt* **Tel 01373 452820**

Harptree Court, East Harptree ♿❀ (Mr & Mrs Richard Hill) *8m N of Wells via A39 Bristol Rd to Chewton Mendip, then B3114 to East Harptree, gates on L. From Bath via A368 Weston-super-Mare Rd to West Harptree.* This spacious garden was designed when the house was built in 1797. 2 ponds are linked by a romantic waterfall and a stream, flanked by large trees. Herbaceous borders a lily pond and a formal garden are amongst the other features. TEAS. *Adm £1.50 Chd free. Sun June 4 (2-6)*

Hatch Beauchamp Gardens *5m SE of Taunton (M5 junction 25) off A358 to Ilminster. Turn L in village of Hatch Beauchamp at Hatch Inn. Parking at Hatch Court.* TEAS. *Combined adm £2.50 Chd £1 under 12 free. Sun June 11 (2-5.30)*

● **Hatch Court, Hatch Beauchamp** ♿✂❀ (Dr & Mrs Robin Odgers) 5-acre garden with 30 acres of parkland and deer park surrounding a perfect 1750 Palladian mansion. Extensive, recent and continuing restoration redesign and replanting. Magnificent walled kitchen garden, fine display of roses, shrubs, clematis and many young trees. Glorious views and a lovely setting. 1995 Historic Garden Restoration Award. *Adm £3.50 House open Thurs (2.30-5.30). June 15-Sept 7. Adm £2.50 Garden open daily April 1-Sept 30 (10-5.30). For NGS Sun June 11 (2-5.30)*

Hatch Court Farm ♿✂ (John Townson Esq) ⅓-acre walled garden with mixed borders created over recent yrs from derelict farm buildings. Also wild area with mediaeval pond surrounded by wood and parkland. Woodland walk

NEW **Heale House, Langport** ♿✂ (Mr & Mrs S O'Malley) *½m W of Currey Rivel Church off Water Street.* 2 acre level garden with large box parterre and 70yd double herbaceous border (colour-themed). TEAS in aid of Somerset St John's Ambulance. *Adm £1.50 Chd free. Suns July 23, 30 (2-6) Private visits welcome by appt, please* **Tel 01458 251220**

NEW **Heatherbank & Uplands at Glebelands, Minehead** ❀ *Centre of Minehead Wellington Square turn L into Park St signed Porlock. 2nd turning on the R, Western Lane and at top turn L. Glebelands sign is straight ahead. Please park in the road. Combined adm £2 Chd free. Weds, Thurs May 24, 25, June 28, 29, July 19, 20 (11-5)*

NEW **Heatherbank** (M D & J M Medland) ⅓ acre once part of the Vicarage Glebe, extends up hill through lawns and shrub borders to a terraced pond and rockery, giving wide views over the bay to the distant Quantocks. Specialist plants incl rhododendrons and azaleas in spring, herbaceous borders in season, hollies and maples in late summer.

NEW **Uplands** (Margaret & Malcolm Scott) ¼ acre gently sloping garden with fine views. Variety of small trees and shrubs surround colour themed herbaceous beds, with lilies, delphiniums and roses. Clematis and honeysuckles on trellises. Low retaining walls with unusual dwarf plants. Narrow paths and steps, unsuitable for pushchairs. *Also by appt, please* **Tel 01643 704185**

Hestercombe Gardens, Cheddon Fitzpaine ❀ (Mr P White) *4m N of Taunton. Follow Tourist Information 'Daisy' symbol.* Encompasses over 3 centuries of garden history in 50 acres of formal gardens and parkland. Famous Edwardian gardens designed by Lutyens and Jekyll created in 1904-6. Landscape Garden 1st opened in 1997 in 125 yrs designed by Coplestone Warre Bampfylde in the 1750's. Georgian pleasure grounds comprise 40 acres of lakes, temples and woodland walks. TEAS. *Adm £3.60 Chd £1 under 5 free (ACNO to Hestercombe Gardens Trust) Open every day (10-5). For NGS Tues March 14, June 6 (10-5)*

NEW **Higher Holbrook, Wincanton** ❀ (Mrs John Smythies) *On A371, 2½m between Wincanton and Castle Cary. Follow NGS signs.* Approx 2 acres with expansive views, winding paths to reveal hidden features. Trees covered by roses, vines and clematis. Three water features, wild flower meadow and other areas being developed. TEAS. *Adm £2 Chd free. Sun, Thurs June 18, 22 (11-5)*

NEW **Higher Yarde Farm, Staplegrove** ♿❀ (Tom & Anita Harris) *2m NW of Taunton town centre, off A358; at Staplegrove village, L turn past church. 3/4m at T-junction turn R. 100yds L turn. 600yds entrance on R. [ST193 Grid ref 206277].* 2 acre informal country cottage garden with herbaceous, rose and shrub borders. Stream divides more formal area from wild flower meadow, wildlife pond and developing woodlands. TEAS. *Adm £2 Chd free. Sat, Wed, June 10, 14 (2-6)*

Hinton St George Gardens, Crewkerne *2m NW of Crewkerne. N of A30 Crewkerne-Chard; S of A303 Ilminster Town Rd, at roundabout signed Lopen & Merriott, then R to one of Somerset's prettiest villages.* TEAS in aid of Cats Protection League, dog park provided at Hooper's Holding. *Combined adm £3 Chd free. Sats, Suns, May 13, 14, Jun 24, 25 (2-6)*

NEW **Church View** (Mrs S Hardy) ¼ acre - lots of tulips in spring fronting a collection of shrubs and herbaceous perennials. Excellent productive vegetable and fruit plot. *Sat, Sun, May 13, 14 (only)*

End House & (Helen Ford) Old walls protect informal plantings of trees, shrubs, climbers and herbaceous plants in this $\frac{1}{2}$ acre. Two large pergolas emphasize a courtyard garden. *Sats, Suns May 13, 14, Jun 24, 25 (2-6)*

Fig Tree Cottage &✗ (Mr & Mrs Whitworth) Old walled cottage garden and courtyard of stables made from kitchen garden of neighbouring rectory, over the past 19 years by owners inspired by Margery Fish. Ground cover, shrubs, old-fashioned roses. Three giant fig trees, all perennials. *Sat, Sun May 13, 14 (only), Private visits welcome, please* **Tel 01460 73548**

Hooper's Holding &❀ (Ken & Lyn Spencer-Mills) $\frac{1}{3}$-acre garden, in colour compartments; lily pool; dwarf conifers, rare herbaceous and shrubby plants; NCCPG National Collection of Hedychiums; pedigree cats (sometimes kittens on view). (Hedychiums flowering Sept and Oct). *Adm £1.50. Sat, Sun May 13, 14 (only), Private visits welcome, please* **Tel 01460 76389**

NEW **The Old Post Office** (Gillian & Derek Esp) Walled terraced garden on three levels. Small water feature TEAS in aid of St George's Church. *Sat, Sun June 24, 25 (2-6) (only)*

Rookwood (Ian & Betty Hudspith) 1/4-acre, modern garden, herbaceous borders, pond, greenhouse, vegetable garden and fruit cage, fountain and obelisks *Combined adm with Springfield House, The Firs, The Old Post Office and The End House £3 Chd free. Sat, Sun, June 24, 25 (2-6) (only)*

Springfield House &❀ (Captain & Mrs T Hardy) $1\frac{1}{2}$-acres; semi-wild wooded dell, mature trees framing view to Mendips, shrubs, herbaceous plants, bulbs. *Sat, Sun, June 24, 25 (only) (2-6)*

The Firs (Mr & Mrs E Cable) Mixed garden of 3/4 acre incl trees, shrubs and herbaceous borders leading to kitchen garden at far end. *Sat, Sun June 24, 25 (2-6) (only)*

Holt Farm, Blagdon ✗❀ (Mrs Sarah Mead) *Approx 12m S of Bristol, located off the A368 Weston-Super-Mare to Bath Rd, between the villages of Blagdon and Ubley. The entrance to Holt Farm is approx $\frac{1}{2}$m outside Blagdon, on the L-hand side.* A developing farmhouse garden bordering Blagdon lake with wild flower meadow, stream, woodland walk and sunken walled garden and potager. Spring bulbs, herbaceous summer planting and late summer autumn colour throughout the 3 acre site. Cream TEAS. *Adm £1.50 Chd free (ACNO to St Andrews Appeal). Suns April 16, June 25, Oct 22 (2-6).*

Ilminster Gardens ✗❀ TEA. *Combined adm £2.50 Chd free. Sun April 30, (2-5) Mon May 1 (5.30-7.30)*

5 Summerlands Park Avenue (Katherine Crouch) *BBC Gardener of the year 1999. Not suitable for wheelchairs.* 90' long sloping suburban back garden, designed and built by owner from bare plot since 1990. Railway sleeper and gravel terraces, shrubs, tulips, alliums, aquilegias, camomile walk, salad bed

Hermitage &✗❀ (Mr & Mrs E B Phillips) *On B3168 (old A303) on W side of Ilminster, next to Shrubbery Hotel.* 2-acres garden with mixed borders on various levels. Rockeries, ponds, vegetable garden. TEAS in aid of St Mary's Parish Hall Fund (ACNO to Action for ME)

15 Summerlands Park Ave (Christine Akhurst) Wedge shaped, cottage style garden, 85' long. Slopes towards the S with heavy clay soil. Interesting shrubs bulbs and perennials, mature fruit trees and a particularly fine quince. *(ACNO to Children's Hospice of the SW)*

Kingsdon, Somerton &✗❀ (Mrs Charles Marrow) *2m SE of Somerton off B3151 Ilchester Rd. From Ilchester roundabout on A303 follow NT signs to Lytes Cary; left opp gates $\frac{1}{2}$m to Kingsdon.* 2-acre plantsman's garden and nursery garden. Over 500 varieties of unusual plants for sale. Teas in Village Hall. *Adm £2 Chd free. Weds April 19, 26 May 3 (2-7). Private visits welcome, please* **Tel 01935 840232**

Kites Croft, Westbury-sub-Mendip ✗❀ (Dr & Mrs W I Stanton) *5m NW of Wells. On A371 follow signs from Westbury Cross.* 2-acre garden planted for colour throughout season with fine views to Glastonbury Tor. Cypress-like columnars and yuccas, lend a Mediterranean air. Winding paths lead down to lawn, ponds, rockery, herbaceous borders, shrubs and wood. Some unusual plants from garden for sale. *Adm £1.50 Chd free Suns, Weds, June 4, 7, Aug 27, 30 (2-5). Private visits and groups welcome, please* **Tel 01749 870328**

Lady Farm, Chelwood ❀ (Mr & Mrs M Pearce) *On the A368 $\frac{1}{2}$m E of Chelwood roundabout (A37 & A368) 8m S of Bristol and 8m W of Bath.* Garden commenced 9yrs ago encompassing 6 acres incl: spring fed watercourse flowing into 2 lakes with adjacent large rock features. New formal garden with colour themed perennials. Rambling roses, hosta and alluim walk. Large area of new style 'prairie' and 'steppe' planting as shown on HTV 'All Gardens Great and Small' 98. Featured in English Garden Magazine and Telegraph 1999. Not recommended for children under 14. Loos and parking facilities. TEAS in aid of Chelwood Church. *Adm £3 Chd free. Sun Aug 13 (2-6) Private parties always welcome, please* **Tel 01761 490770**

Langford Court, Langford &✗❀ (Jane Lady Wills) *150yds S of A38 Bristol-Bridgwater rd. $11\frac{1}{2}$m S of Bristol. $1\frac{1}{2}$m N of Churchill traffic lights. Signpost marked Upper Langford.* $3\frac{1}{2}$ acres. Lawns and trees, good display of daffodil and crocus. Topiary. Pleasant setting and outlook. Water garden and woodland walk. TEAS in aid of Somerset St John Ambulance. *Adm £2 Chd free Sun March 12 (2-5.30)*

NEW **Little Garth, Dowlish Wake** ✗❀ (Roger & Marion Pollard) *2m S of Ilminster. Turn R off Ilminster/Crewkerne Rd. At Kingstone Cross, then L follow Dowlish Wake sign. Turn L at Glebe Cottage (white cottage) before reaching church. Turn R following signs.* $\frac{1}{2}$ acre plantsman's garden for all seasons with many interesting and unusual perennials. Although essentially 'cottage style' emphasis is placed on the artistic arrangement of plants, using foliage, grasses and colour-themes. Speke Hall car park in front of the nearby church may be used if necessary. *Adm £1.50 Chd free. Thurs April 1 to Oct 1 (10.5.30). Private visits welcome, please* **Tel 01460 52594**

7 Little Keyford Lane, Frome ✗❀ (Duncan Skene) *Approach Frome on B3092. Take 1st L on outskirts.* Plant enthusiast's garden full of colour, surprise and unusual plants, including many which cannot be seen elsewhere in

the UK. Recently reatured in 'English Garden' and 'Woman and Home' magazines. Special collections: siberian irises (May); 'spider', 'variant' and 'unusual form' daylilies (July). Unsuitable for wheelchairs, regrettably. Refreshments. *Adm £1.50 Chd free (ACNO to Amnesty International) Suns May 14, 21, 28, July 16, 23, 30, (2.30-5.30). Private visits welcome,* **Tel 01373 472879**

NEW **Little Yarford Farmhouse, Kingston St Mary** &✿ *(Brian Bradley) 3½m N out of Taunton on Kingston St Mary rd. At 30mph sign turn L down Parsonage Lane. Continue 1¼m due W ignore turn R to Yarford. Continue 100yds. Turn R up concrete rd. Park on L.* Creative landscaping around C17 farmhouse (not open). Interesting and specimen trees including pendular and variegated forms esp beech. 3 ponds, aquatic and bog plants, climbers, herbaceous and grasses. A plantsmans garden. TEAS in aid of St Mary's and All Saints Church Broomfield. *Adm £2 Chd free. Fri Aug 4 (11-4), Sat, Sun Aug 5, 6 (2-6)*

Littlecourt, West Bagborough &✗ *(Jane Kimber & John Clothier) 7m N of Taunton off A358.* 6-acre garden in fine setting with woodland and water; spectacular new borders, interesting and extensive planting; wonderful views. *Adm £2. Private visits very welcome any time, please* **Tel 01823 432281**

● **Lower Severalls, Crewkerne** &✗✿ *(Howard & Audrey Pring) 1½m NE of Crewkerne. Turning for Merriott off A30; or Haselbury from A356.* 2½-acre plantsman's garden beside early Ham stone farmhouse. Herbaceous borders and island beds with collections of unusual plants, shrubs and interesting features. Herb gardens. Garden and nursery. Nursery sells herbs, herbaceous plants and half-hardy conservatory plants. Suitable for children *Adm £2 Chd free. (open daily March 1 to Oct 20 (10-5), Suns 2-5. Closed Thurs & Sun except Sun (2-5) in May & June). Coaches and groups welcome by appt* **Tel 01460 73234**

Manor Farm, Middle Chinnock ✗ *(Simon & Antonia Johnson) Off A30 between Crewkerne and Yeovil.* Garden of 'rooms', created over the last nine years; incl formal areas, mixed borders, pond garden, herb garden, vegetable and cutting garden, and orchard. *Combined Adm with* **Chinnock House** *£2.50 Chd free. Sun May 28 (2-6). Groups by appt,* **Tel 01935 881895**

The Mill, Cannington ✗✿ *(Mr and Mrs J E Hudson) 21 Mill Lane. 4m W of Bridgwater on A39. Turn opposite Rose & Crown.* ¼-acre cottage type plantsman's garden with waterfall and pond, over 100 clematis, National Collection of Clematis texensis hybrids and National Caltha Collection. TEA in aid of Cannington W.I. *Adm £2 Chd free (ACNO to NCCPG). Sats May 20, July 29 (2-5), Suns May 21, July 30 (11-5). Private visits welcome by appt, please* **Tel 01278 652304**

The Mill, Wookey &✗✿ *(Peter & Sally Gregson) 2m W from Wells off A371. Turn L into Henley Lane, driveway 50yds on L.* 2½ acres beside R Axe. Traditional and unusual cottage plants informally planted in formal beds with roses, grasses, pergola, lawns and shady 'folly garden'. Ornamental kitchen garden. Wide selection of plants seen in garden for sale in

nursery. TEA for pre-arranged groups. *Adm £1 Chd free. Please* **Tel 01749 676966**

Milton Lodge, Wells ✗✿ *(D C Tudway Quilter) ½m N of Wells. From A39 Bristol-Wells, turn N up Old Bristol Rd; car park first gate on L.* Mature Grade II listed terraced garden with outstanding views of Wells Cathedral and Vale of Avalon. Mixed borders, roses, fine trees. Separate 7-acre arboretum. TEAS *Adm £2.50 Chd under 14 free Open daily (2-5) ex Sats, Good Friday to end Oct; parties by arrangement. For NGS Suns May 21, June 4, 18, July 9 (2-5). Private visits welcome, please* **Tel 01749 672168**

Milverton Gardens ✗ *7m W of Taunton on B3227. L at Milverton roundabout.* TEAS in aid of Methodist Church Refurbishment Fund. *Combined adm £3 Chd free. Sun June 11 (2-5.30)*

　NEW **Brendon** *(Mr & Mrs B Skittrall)* ½ acre walled garden on two levels. Herbaceous border, garden with pond; productive fruit and vegetable garden. Outside WC
　Cobbleside *(Mr & Mrs C Pine)* 3/4-acre walled garden incl herb garden and potager and new wildlife pond. Completely redesigned, before and after photographs and plans on display. *Group private visits by appt please* **Tel 01823 400404**
　New Halls *(Mr M Priscott)* A Victorian walled garden developed as a market garden; vegetables fruit and flowers. Outside WC. *Private visits by appt please,* **Tel 01823 400018**

▲ **Montacute House, Montacute** &✗✿ *(The National Trust) NT signs off A3088 4m W of Yeovil and A303.* Magnificent Elizabethan House with contemporary garden layout. Fine stonework provides setting for informally planted mixed borders and old roses; range of garden features illustrates its long history. LUNCH and TEAS. *Adm Garden only £3.10 Chd £1.30. For NGS Sun June 18 (11-5.30)*

Montys Court, Norton Fitzwarren &✗✿ *(Major & Mrs A Mitford-Slade) 4m W of Taunton on B3227. 1m W of Norton Fitzwarren on LH side.* 2-acre garden in parkland setting with views to the Quantock and Blackdown Hills. Formal rose garden filled with tulips in spring. Numerous shrubs, mature trees, extensive lawns and herbaceous border. TEAS (Sun only). *Adm £2 Chd free Sun, Mon, April 9, 10 (2-5), Sun, Mon June 18, 19 (2-5.30)*

The Mount, Chelston ✗✿ *(Jim & Gilly Tilden) Off M5 1m NW of junction 26. At A38 Chelston roundabout take Wellington rd. After 200yds turn R to Chelston. 1st house on R.* Enclosed garden with herbaceous borders and shrubs, trees, ericaceous area, more shrubs, many roses and small bog garden outside. 1 acre altogether. TEAS in aid of Wellington Stroke Club. *Adm £1.50 Chd free. Suns April 9, May 21 (2-5.30). Private visits also welcome, please* **Tel 01823 666237**

The Mount, Wincanton ✗✿ *(Alison & Peter Kelly) Follow one-way system round lower half of town, bear L at signposted Castle Cary, on up hill, house on L. 1¼-acre.* Plantswoman's garden with hidden surprises. Speciality an alpine lawn and garden, half terraced shrub borders, gravel bed, rock garden and pond. TEA and biscuits, donation to

NGS. *Adm £2 Chd free. Sun, Mon April 23, 24, Thurs 27, Sat, Sun, May 20, 21, Thurs, 25, Sun June 18, Thurs 22, Sun Sept 24, Thurs 28 (2-5.30)*

Oare Manor Cottage, Oare ✿ (Mr & Mrs J Greenaway) *6m W of Porlock off A39. 50yds from Oare Church immortalized in R D Blackmore's 'Lorna Doone'.* Sheltered cottage garden in the romantic Oare Valley. Old-fashioned herbaceous borders, tall hedges. Featured on ITV West Country. Fine views of the moor. Parking in lower field. *Adm £1.50 Chd 50p (Share to Anti-Slavery International). Coaches welcome. Private visits welcome during June & July, please* **Tel 01598 741242**

2 Old Tarnwell, Upper Stanton Drew see Bristol & South Gloucestershire

Parsonage Farm, Publow ✿❀ (Mr & Mrs Andrew Reid) *9m S of Bristol. A37 Bristol-Wells; at top of Pensford Hill, almost opp B3130 to Chew Magna, take lane which runs down side of row of houses. 250yds on R.* 3½-acre woodland garden with large collection of trees and shrubs incl rhododendrons, azaleas and conifers; tuffastone rockery. Partly suitable for wheelchairs. TEAS in aid of All Saints, Publow. *Adm £1.50 Chd free. Sat, Sun May 20, 21 (2-5)*

Pear Tree Cottage, Stapley ❀ (Mr & Mrs Colvin Parry) *9m S of Taunton nr Churchinford.* Charming cottage garden leading to 2½-acre newly made park; well planted with interesting trees and shrubs leading to old leat and mill pond. Cream TEAS. *Adm £1.50 Chd 50p. Sun, Mon April 30, May 1, Sun July 9 (2-6)*

Perridge House, Pilton ✿ (Richard and Jennifer Sheldon) *Shepton Mallet 3m. Pilton ½m to E. Coming from Shepton Mallet turn R off B3136 (Pilton shop on R) for N Wootton. ½m to 1st turning L. 200yds to 1st entrance on L.* Grounds are approx 20 acres of which ½ is Beech Wood and garden (3 acres). S facing slope offering a wide range of trees and shrubs many of which are unusual. The best time of year is May. TEAS in aid of Pilton Church. *Adm £2 Chd 50p. Sun May 21 (2-5.30)*

Pitt Farmhouse, Huish Champflower ✿❀ (Mr & Mrs J C Boyd) *3½m NW of Wiveliscombe from Wiveliscombe town square turn R at White Hart Hotel follow same rd for 3½m to Huish Champflower then follow signs to garden.* 1½ acre plantsman's garden on the S-side of Hill. Home to a wide collection of interesting plants. TEAS in aid of St Peters Church Huish Champflower. *Adm £1.50 Chd free. Suns May 21, June 25 (2-6). Private visits welcome, please* **Tel 01984 623145**

Pondarosa, Wayford ✿❀ (Mr & Mrs Gordon Brown) *Approx 2½m S of Crewkerne off the B3165 Lyme Regis Rd Dunsham Lane.* Approx 2-acre garden being transformed from field. Water garden. Mixed borders. Collection of ornamental water fowl. TEA. *Adm £1.50 Chd free. Sun June 25 (2-6)*

Popinjays & Little Norton Mill, Little Norton *6m W of Yeovil. From A303 take A356. L to Norton-sub-Hamdon. Through village and follow signs. Combined adm £2.50 Chd free. Sun, July 9 (2-6)* **Evening Opening** *Mon July 10 (6-8)*

Little Norton Mill (Mr & Mrs T Hart) 3 acres of landscaped gardens, meadow and orchard. Mill pond, ornamental ponds, marsh garden. Many mature rare trees and shrubs. *Private group visits welcome by arrangement,* **Tel 01935 881679 or 881337**

Popinjays (Mr & Mrs Eric Dunkley) Hamstone house with courtyard and 1-acre sloping garden. Herbaceous planting, water features, seating areas; fruit, vegetables and orchard, plus paddock with views from Ham Hill treeline across Little Norton valley and beyond. No parking: use field as for Little Norton Mill.

▲ Prior Park Landscape Garden, Bath ✿ (Mathew Ward) *1m S of Bath City centre. Visitors are advised to use public transport as there is no parking at Prior Park or nearby. For leaflet explaining how to reach the garden phone 01225 833422. Buses Badgerline 2 and 4, Bath bus company S1. Disabled drivers may reserve a parking place.* Beautiful and intimate C18 landscape garden created by Bath entrepreneur Ralph Allen (1693-1764) with advice from the poet Alexander Pope and 'Capability' Brown. Sweeping valley with magnificent views of the city, Palladian bridge and lakes. Major restoraton of the garden continues. Prior Park College, a co-educational school, not open. *Adm £3.80 Chd £1.90. Sun June 4 (11-5.30). National Trust members free £1 voucher to use towards guide book or in NT shop. £1 off admission with a valid bus or train ticket.* **Tel 01225 833422**

Rackley House, Compton Bishop ♿❀ (R & J Matthews) *2m W of Axbridge and 7m E of Weston-Super-Mare. Leave A38 at Cross and take the rd to Loxton, Bleadon. Rackley Lane is about 1½m from Cross, and Rackley House is the only house on the RH-side at the end of the Lane. Parking in field just past the house.* ½-acre garden on S slope with light alkaline soil. Features incl iris garden, rockery and scree, small knot garden, pond and terrace. Some unusual plants and variety of cyclamen, snowdrops and old-fashioned roses. TEA. *Adm £1.50 Chd free. Sat, Sun June 10, 11 (2-6). Private visits welcome* **Tel 01934 732311**

Rose Cottage, Church St, Henstridge ♿❀ (Mr & Mrs J A Perrett) *Approx 7m between Sherborne and Shaftesbury on A30. Turn into village at traffic lights and take second R into Church St and Rose Cottage is on R.* ¼-acre cottage garden, edged by stream, planted to create a romantic mood full of evocative scents, in threads of gentle colour combinations. TEAS at Cherry Bolberry Farm in aid of British Red Cross. *Combined adm with Cherry Bolberry Farm £2 Chd free. Wed June 21, Sun June 25 (2-5.30)*

Sherborne Garden, Litton see Bristol & South Gloucestershire

Smocombe House, Enmore ✿❀ (Mr and Mrs D Wellesley Wesley) *4m W of Bridgwater take Enmore Rd, 3rd L after Tynte Arms.* 5-acres S facing in Quantock Hills. The late Arthur Hellyer wrote a glowing article for 'Country Life' about this lovely woodland garden; views down to stream and pool; waterside stocked with interesting plants for spring/summer display; arboretum designed by Roy Lancaster; charming old kitchen garden. Garden not really suitable for wheelchairs or those who have difficulty in walking. TEAS in aid of Enmore Parish Church. *Adm £2 Chd free. Suns April 2, May 14 (2-6)*

Snape Cottage see Dorset

The Spinney, Brockley ♿❀ (John and Felicity Ford) *9m SW of Bristol on the A370. Follow signs from Brockley X-rds.* A peaceful 3 acre garden set in the middle of a small wood with an abundance of bluebells in spring. A woodland feel whilst incorporating more modern trends of water, gravel, grasses, bold foliage, climbers and lots of perennials. TEAS and Plant stall in aid of Project Trust. *Adm £1.50 Chd free. Sat, Sun April 29, 30, Mon May 1, Sun June 11 (2-5)*

Stogumber Gardens ❀ *358 NW from Taunton for 11m. Sign to Stogumber W near Crowcombe.* Five delightful gardens of interest to plantsmen in lovely village at edge of Quantocks. TEAS. *Combined adm £2.50 Chd free. Sun June 18 (2-6)*

Brook Cottage ♿✂ (Mrs M Field) Good plants incl lilies in a lovely setting; small pond for added interest

Butts Cottage (Mr & Mrs J A Morrison) Cottage garden with old roses, old-fashioned perennials, alpines, pond, small vine house and organic vegetable garden

Cridlands Steep (Mrs A M Leitch) Large and interesting garden with collection of trees and wildlife pond. Plant Stall

Hill Farm (Mr & Mrs A Jeans) A large garden on three levels with herbaceous plants, shrubs and roses

Pitts Cottage (Mr & Mrs B Young) Pretty cottage garden with interesting herbaceous plants. Redeveloped rear garden with vegetables and herb bed

Stowleys, Porlock ♿❀ (Rev R L Hancock) *Bossington Lane. NE of Porlock off A39. 6m W of Minehead.* Medium-size garden, approx 2 acres with magnificent views across Porlock Bay and Bristol Channel. Daffodils, roses, unusual tender plants incl leptospermum, drimys and embothrium. Parking in paddock next door to garden. TEAS. *Adm £1.50 Chd free Sats April 8, June 24; Plants June only (2-6)*

Sunnyside, Wells ✂❀ (Nigel Cox & Patsy Koeb) *W from Wells (2m) along B3139 to Wedmore Rd. After Pheasant Inn at Wookey reach village sign for Yarley 100yds beyond turn L up Yarley Hill, house 200yds on L.* ½-acre cottage garden with large variety of plants, some rare. Organic vegetable plot. Large collection of asiatic and oriental lilies and also many varieties of salvia. *Combined adm by appointment with Walnut Farm £2 Chd 50p*

Sutton Hosey Manor, Long Sutton ♿✂❀ (Roger Bramble) *On A372 just E of Long Sutton.* 2-acres; ornamental kitchen garden, lily pond, pleached limes leading to amelanchier walk past duck pond; rose and juniper walk from Italian terrace; Judas tree avenue; new ptelea walk. TEA. *Adm £2 Chd over 3 yrs 50p. Sun July 30 (2.30-6)*

Thatch End, Catcott ♿✂❀ (Mrs Rita Williams) *Turn N off A39 between Bridgwater and Street to Catcott. Continue straight into village turn L at T junction. Fork R at War Memorial and immed L at cul de sac sign. No parking at house. Please follow signs to school car park.* Typical small cottage garden. Wide variety of plants and vegetable garden on three levels. Wheelchairs lowest level only. TEAS. *Combined adm with Dial House £2.50 Chd 50p. Suns May 14, 21, June 11 (2-6). Private visits also welcome by appt in May and June,* **Tel 01278 722 327**

■ **The Time-Trail of Roses, Wells** ✂ (Mrs Susan Lee) *No on-site parking. Use car park in Tucker St and walk to entrance at top of Westfield Rd.* Magnificent collection of 1500 different roses, planted in ½-acre garden in date order of their introduction to show their beauty, diversity and evolution. NCCPG collection. Millennium Display of Conservation Scheme. Also many spring bulbs, lilies, fruit and herbs. *Adm £2.50 May, June, July. From Aug £1.50 Chd free. May to July, open Wed to Sun. Closed Aug. Sept to mid Oct, open Suns only (2-6). For NGS Suns May 21 (species roses), June 11 (old roses) Parties by appt* **Tel 01749 674677**

▲ **Tintinhull, Yeovil** ✂ (The National Trust) *NW of Yeovil. Tintinhull Village, Yeovil. Signs on A303, W of Ilchester.* Famous 2-acre garden in compartments, developed 1900-1960, influenced by Gertrude Jekyll and Hidcote; many good and uncommon plants. C17 & C18 house (not open). TEAS in aid of St Margaret's Church. *Adm £3.70 Chd £1.80. For NGS Sun July 16 (12-6)*

NEW **Tithe Cottage, Bathampton** ✂ (Mr & Mrs G Atkinson) *2m E of Bath, between A4 and A36, in centre of Bathampton Village, opposite Post Office. Limited parking in High Street. Ample parking and good lunches in George public house by canal.* A truly tiny terraced garden recently developed into interesting areas each with a different character, planned with retirement, enjoyment and ease of maintenance in mind! Plants selected for long term value are closely planted and colour co-ordinated for effect. Paved areas are packed with containers, many with permanent subjects. *Combined adm with Willow House £2.50 Chd free. Sun June 18 (2-5)*

Tone Dale House, Wellington ✂ (Mr & Mrs Ben Fox) *Just outside Wellington on the Milverton to Wellington Rd.* 3-acre garden first planned in early C18 beside a millstream. Many interesting trees and various plantings. Parking limited. Cream TEA. *Adm £2 Chd free. Thurs April 13 (11-6)*

Ubley Hill Farm House, Blagdon ❀ (Peter & Jeanne Gilraine) *6m NE of Cheddar. Situated off the B3134, Burrington Coombe rd, above Ubley. Ubley Drove is a no-through rd.* 1 acre on N escarpment of the Mendip Hills with views across Chew Valley and the Severn Estuary. Built onto a rock outcrop so the surrounding garden is mainly on 2 levels linked by rock garden terraces with pond and waterfall. A kitchen garden, bog garden, lawn and mainly informal beds with perennials and shrubs. Tea served in courtyard garden. Peter a specialist grower and breeder of slipper orchids available to view on request. TEAS. *Adm £2 Chd free (ACNO to Action on Child Exploitation). Sun June 25 (12-6)*

Vellacott, Crowcombe, Taunton ✂❀ (Kevin and Pat Chittenden) *Off A358 9m NW of Taunton signed Lawford.* ½-acre garden on S-facing slope with splendid views. Profusely stocked with a very wide range of plants and trees. Ponds, fruit garden and potager. TEAS. *Adm £2 Chd free. Suns,*

Weds June 4, 21, July 5, 26, 30, Aug 13, 16, Sept 3, 6 (2-5.30). Small groups and private visits welcome by appt, please **Tel 01984 618249**

Walnut Farm, Yarley ✿❀ (Angela & John Marsh) *3m W of Wells. On B3139 turn L at Yarley Cross. Island site 200yds up Yarley Hill.* ⅔-acre garden with many unusual perennials planted amongst shrubs, roses and climbers. 2 ponds and bog garden. Yr-round interest. Splendid views of Mendips. Conservatory. Small conservation area in adjoining field. TEAS for pre-arranged groups together with plants in aid of Help the Hospices. *Combined adm with Sunnyside £2 Chd 50p. Private visits and groups welcome, by appt, please* **Tel 01749 676942**

Wayford Manor, Crewkerne ❀ (Mr & Mrs Robin Goffe) *SW of Crewkerne. Turning on B3165 at Clapton; or on A30 Chard-Crewkerne.* 3 acres, noted for magnolias and acers. Bulbs, flowering trees, shrubs, rhododendrons. Garden redesigned by Harold Peto in 1902. Fine Elizabethan manor house (not open). TEAS in aid of local charities. *Adm £2 Chd 50p. Suns April 9, 30, May 14, 28 (2-6); also private parties welcome, but please* **Tel 01460 73253**

Weston House See Dorset

NEW **Whitegate Farm, Horton** (Lin & Trevor Lant) *2½m W of Ilminster. From Ilminster roundabout take A303 towards Honiton, for approx 2m turn 1st R signed Horton and Whitegate Farm is 1st on the R.* 1 acre garden with lovely views of surrounding hills. A garden in the making having been created in 1999 from fields surrounding farmhouse. There are long sweeping borders with a wealth of perennial planting. An orchard and vegetable patch. TEAS in aid of Horton Churches. *Adm £1.50 Chd free. Suns May 21, June 18, July 23, Aug 20 (2-6) Private visits and groups wlcome, please* **Tel 01460 52419**

Willow House, Bathampton ♿✿ (Simon and Jill Downs) *2m E of Bath between A4 and A36 in centre of Bathampton Village. House up lane at end of Kennet Park. Parking in Kennet Park.* ⅓-acre canalside garden developed over past 4 yrs by owners to withstand roaring westerly and icy easterly winds. Wild flower canalside area, spring bulbs, summer shrubs and perennials. Visitors on April 2 will have a chance to see at close hand renovation work to drained canal. TEAS. *Suns April 2 Adm £1.50, Chd free. Sun June 18 combined with Tithe Cottage Adm £2.50 (2-5) (ACNO to Kennet and Avon Canal Trust)*

■ **Windmill Cottage, Backwell** ✿❀ (Mr & Mrs A Harwood) *Hillside Rd. 8m SW of Bristol. Take A370 Backwell. Parking available in Backwell and New Inn (10 min walk). Hillside Rd is single track lane with no parking (unless for special reasons)* You can scramble up scree, walk on the wild side. Parade through a pergola, wander by water, there is scent; there is colour; and clematis that clings; these are few of our favourite things. TEAS. *Adm £2 Chd free. Suns May 14, June 11, July 9, Aug 6, Sept 17 (2-5.30). Also open Weds June 14, July 12, Aug 16 (2-5.30) (not for NGS). Groups welcome by appt, please* **Tel 01275 463492**

Yews Farm, Martock ✿❀ (Louise & Fergus Dowding) *In East Street, between Post Office and Nag's Head.* 1 acre of theatrical planting. Big plants in the Jungle garden, foxtail lilies, bananas, giant Echium. Also spiky grassy, thistly borders; a cat mint and delphinium walk; a clipped bay and rosemary avenue; topiary birds and live hens. Abundant flora and fauna within organic kitchen garden, trained fruits and flowers for cutting. The best home-made TEAS. *Adm £2 Chd free. (ACNO to Guardians of Martock Church). Sun July 16 (2-6)*

Evening Opening (See also garden description)

Ilminster Gardens	May 1
Popinjays & Little Norton Mill, Little Norton	July 10

Crossroads Caring For Carers

Crossroads is the leading national charity providing support to carers; giving them a regular break from their caring responsibilities.

For more information, please contact:
Crossroads,
10 Regent Place, Rugby CV21 2PN

Information is also available on the NGS website (www.ngs.org.uk)

This elegantly furnished Victorian Mansion set in 18 acres of gardens and parkland with river frontage offers a high class accommodation, good food and friendly service. Special Breaks available.

The gardens of Glencot will be open every Wednesday from 11am to 5pm. Light lunches, refreshments and plants available. Gardening Party or Group visits welcome by prior arrangement.

Glencot Lane, Wookey Hole, Near Wells, Somerset BA5 1BH
Tel: 01749 677160 Fax: 01749 670210
Email: glencot@ukonline.co.uk Web: ukonline.co.uk/glencot

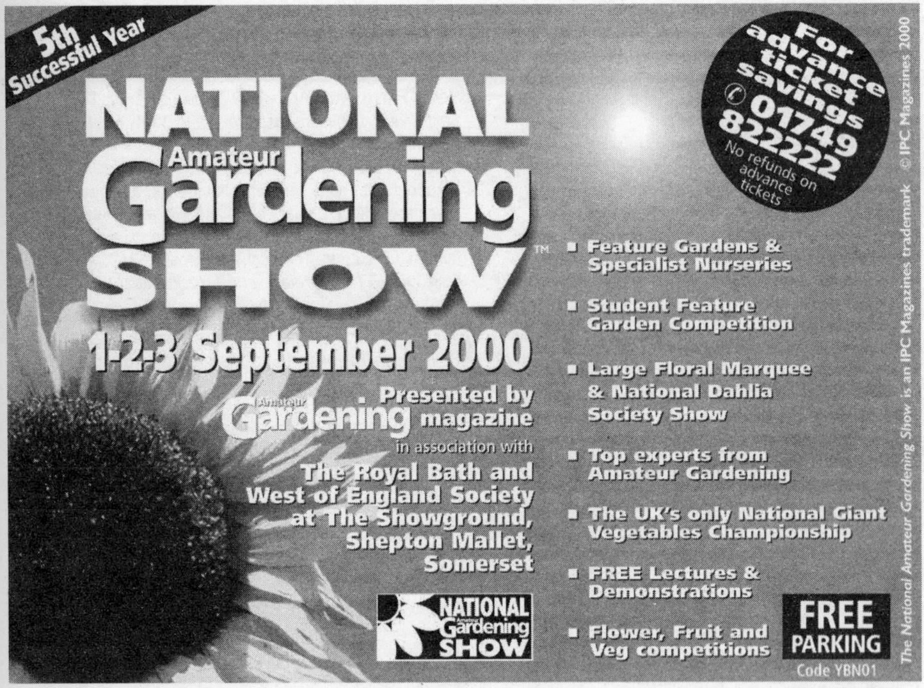

Macmillan Cancer Relief

Macmillan Cancer Relief Information Line: 0845 601 6161
Macmillan Cancer Relief Website: www.macmillan.org.uk

Staffordshire & part of West Midlands

Hon County Organisers: Mr & Mrs David Hewitt, Arbour Cottage, Napley, Market Drayton, Shrops TF9 4AJ Tel & Fax 01630 672852

Assistant Hon County Organisers Mr & Mrs Leslie Standeven Tel 07808 227309

DATES OF OPENING

Regular openings
For details see garden description
Manor Cottage, Chapel Chorlton

March 26 Sunday
Stanley House Farm, Milwich

April 14 Friday
Arbour Cottage, Napley

April 21 Friday
Arbour Cottage, Napley

April 28 Friday
Arbour Cottage, Napley

April 29 Saturday
7 Beech Tree Road, Walsall Wood

April 30 Sunday
7 Beech Tree Road, Walsall Wood

May 5 Friday
Arbour Cottage, Napley

May 6 Saturday
Heath House, nr Eccleshall

May 17 Wednesday
Elvendell, 4 Partridge Ride The Burntwood, Loggerheads

May 19 Friday
Arbour Cottage, Napley

May 21 Sunday
The Beeches, Rocester
Edgewood House, Stourton
Little Onn Hall, Church Eaton
Stanley House Farm, Milwich
Westward Ho, Kingsley Wood Rd. Rugeley

May 28 Sunday
26 Lapley Avenue, Stafford
Woodside House, Barton-under-Needwood

June 2 Friday
Arbour Cottage, Napley

June 3 Saturday
The Old Doctors House, Loggerheads

June 4 Sunday
Flashbrook Lodge, Flashbrook
The Garth, Milford
The Wombourne Wodehouse, Wolverhampton

June 7 Wednesday
Thornfold, Leek

June 10 Saturday
Elvendell, 4 Partridge Ride The Burntwood, Loggerheads

June 11 Sunday
The Hollies Farm, Pattingham
Thornfold, Leek
Woodside House, Barton-under-Needwood

June 16 Friday
Arbour Cottage, Napley

June 17 Saturday
Birch Trees, Eccleshall

June 18 Sunday
Bankcroft Farm, Tatenhill, Burton-on-Trent
26 Lapley Avenue, Stafford
Stanley House Farm, Milwich
Strawberry Fields, Hill Ridware

June 20 Tuesday
Heath House, nr Eccleshall

June 21 Wednesday
12 Darges Lane, Great Wyrley (evening)

June 24 Saturday
The Old Doctors House, Loggerheads

June 25 Sunday
Biddulph Grange Garden, Biddulph
43 Broad Lane, Bradmore, Wolverhampton
Flashbrook Lodge, Flashbrook
The Garth, Milford
The Old Doctors House, Loggerheads
Pinfold Cottage, Shenstone

June 30 Friday
Arbour Cottage, Napley
Grafton Cottage, Barton-under-Needwood

July 2 Sunday
Bankcroft Farm, Tatenhill, Burton-on-Trent
The Beeches, Rocester
43 Broad Lane, Bradmore, Wolverhampton
Grafton Cottage, Barton-under-Needwood

Chelsea Week – London Garden Tours

The National Gardens Scheme will be offering five exclusive tours of private London gardens during Chelsea Week. The tours include gardens not normally open to the public.

For more information please see the NGS website www.ngs.org.uk or contact Mrs Julia Hickman (44) (0) 181 339 0931.

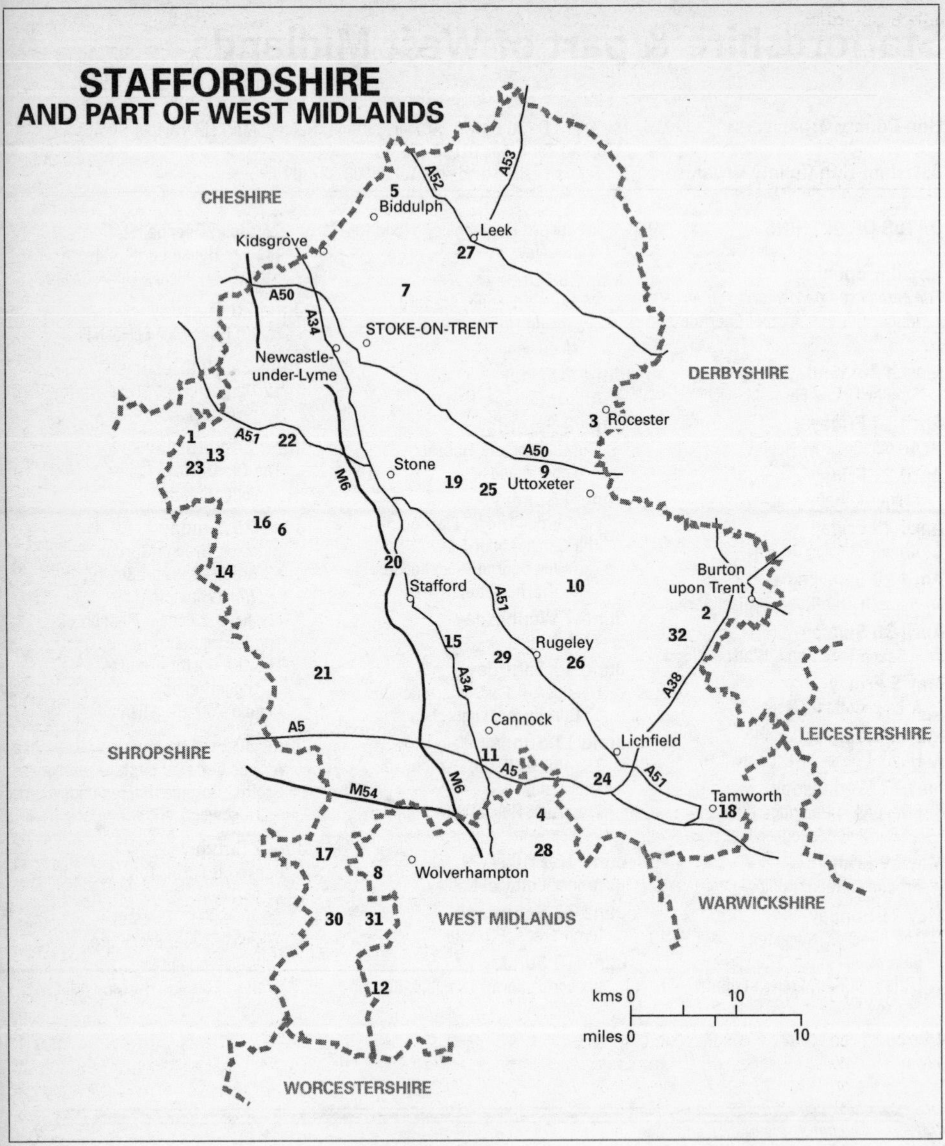

KEY

1 Arbour Cottage
2 Bankcroft Farm
3 The Beeches
4 7 Beech Tree Road
5 Biddulph Grange Garden
6 Birch Trees
7 Bleak House
8 43 Broad Lane
9 Brook House Farm
10 Brookside
11 12 Darges Lane
12 Edgewood House
13 Elvendell
14 Flashbrook Lodge
15 The Garth
16 Heath House
17 The Hollies Farm
18 Inglenook
19 Ivy Cottage
20 26 Lapley Avenue
21 Little Onn Hall
22 Manor Cottage
23 The Old Doctors House
24 Pinfold Cottage
25 Stanley House Farm
26 Strawberry Fields
27 Thornfold
28 98 Walsall Road
29 Westward Ho
30 The Willows
31 The Wombourne Wodehouse
32 Woodside House

July 8 Saturday
Ivy Cottage, Garshall Green
The Old Doctors House, Loggerheads

July 9 Sunday
Brook House Farm, Dagdale, Bramshall
Ivy Cottage, Garshall Green
98 Walsall Road, Aldridge
Woodside House, Barton-under-Needwood

July 15 Saturday
Heath House, nr Eccleshall

July 16 Sunday
Bankcroft Farm, Tatenhill, Burton-on-Trent
Bleak House, Bagnall
Brookside, Abbots Bromley
Inglenook, Tamworth
26 Lapley Avenue, Stafford
Strawberry Fields, Hill Ridware

July 21 Friday
Elvendell, 4 Partridge Ride The Burntwood, Loggerheads

July 23 Sunday
The Willows, Trysull

July 26 Wednesday
Strawberry Fields, Hill Ridware

July 30 Sunday
43 Broad Lane, Bradmore, Wolverhampton
Woodside House, Barton-under-Needwood

August 2 Wednesday
Inglenook, Tamworth

August 5 Saturday
Westward Ho, Kingsley Wood Rd. Rugeley

August 6 Sunday
43 Broad Lane, Bradmore, Wolverhampton
Brookside, Abbots Bromley
Grafton Cottage, Barton-under-Needwood
Westward Ho, Kingsley Wood Rd. Rugeley

August 25 Friday
Birch Trees, Eccleshall

August 30 Wednesday
Inglenook, Tamworth

September 10 Sunday
12 Darges Lane, Great Wyrley

September 17 Sunday
Arbour Cottage, Napley

September 24 Sunday
Biddulph Grange Garden, Biddulph

DESCRIPTIONS OF GARDENS

Arbour Cottage, Napley ♿✄❀ (Mr & Mrs David Hewitt) *4m N of Market Drayton on Staffs/Shrops border. Take A53 then B5415 signed Woore, turn L 1¾m at telephone box.* Country garden 2 acres with alpine screes, mixed perennials, shrub roses and many paeonias, bamboos etc. Colour all yr from shrubs and trees of many species. Cream TEAS. *Adm £2 Chd free. Fris April 14, 21, 28, May 5, 19, June 2, 16, 30, Sept 17 (2-5). Private visits welcome April, May and June, please* **Tel 01630 672852**

Bankcroft Farm, Tatenhill, Burton-on-Trent ✄❀ (Mrs Penelope Adkins) *Branston Rd. Take Tatenhill rd off A38 Burton/Branston flyover. 1m, 1st house on left approaching village. Parking on farm.* 1 acre organic country garden with shrubs and trees. Herbaceous borders, ponds, large fruit and vegetable garden, extensive woodland and wildlife area. TEAS in aid of Burton Cats Protection League. *Adm £1.50. Suns June 18, July 2, 16 (1-5). Private visits welcome by appt June and July* **Tel 01283 546715**

7 Beech Tree Road, Walsall Wood ✄❀ (Mr & Mrs B Davis) *A461 Walsall/Lichfield Rd. 3m from Walsall. 6m from Lichfield. From Walsall turn R and immed R again just past the church in Walsall Wood. From Lichfield turn L and immed R just before church.* Plantsman's garden approx 60′ × 30′. Rockeries and pool. No grass. 1st class collection of alpines and primulas. Dwarf conifers, some very rare species. Many miniature ferns. Primarily small plants underplanted with many unusual bulbs. Fences covered with mainly evergreen climbers. Paths narrow. Car park 50yds. *Adm £1.50 Chd free Sat, Sun April 29, 30 (11-5). Private visits welcome by appt Feb to end of May, please* **Tel 01543 820921** (evenings)

The Beeches, Rocester ♿✄❀ (Mr & Mrs K Sutton) *Mill Street 5m N of Uttoxeter on B5030, turn right into village by J.C.B. factory. By Red Lion public house take road for Marston Montgomery.* A plant lover's garden of about ¾ acre, herbaceous borders, box garden, many varieties of shrubs, rhododendrons and azaleas. Pools, roses, fruit trees, climbing plants, an all year round garden. 3 times winner of East Staffs Borough in Bloom competition. TEA. *Adm £2 Chd free. Suns May 21, July 2 (2-5)*

▲ **Biddulph Grange Garden, Biddulph** ✄❀ (Mr Andrew Humphris, National Trust) *3½m SE of Congleton, 7m N of Stoke-on-Trent on A527.* An exciting and rare survival of a high Victorian garden extensively restored since 1988. Conceived by James Bateman, the 15 acres are divided into a number of smaller gardens designed to house specimens from his extensive plant collection. An Egyptian Court; Chinese Pagoda, Willow Pattern Bridge; Pinetum and Arboretum combine to make the garden a miniature tour of the world. TEAS. *Adm £4.30 Chd £2.20 Family £10.70. March 25 to Oct 29, Wed to Fri (12-6), Sat to Sun (11-6). For NGS Suns June 25, Sept 24 (11-6)* **Tel 01782 517999**

Birch Trees, Eccleshall ✄❀ (Susan & John Weston) *1½m W of Eccleshall on B5026, turn L at junction signposted Copmere End. After ½m straight across Xrds by Star Inn. House ¼m up hill.* Tranquil ½-acre country garden with unusual plants and shrubs. Herbaceous borders, peat bed, water features and veg garden. TEAS. *Adm £2 Chd 50p. Sat June 17, Fri Aug 25 (1.30-5.30). Also private visits, please* **Tel 01785 850448**

Bleak House, Bagnall ✄❀ (Mr & Mrs J H Beynon) *A5009 to Milton Xrds turn for Bagnall. 2m up hill past golf course to corner opp Highlands Hospital.* 1-acre plantswoman's garden on 3 levels with roses, herbaceous borders. Terraces leading to informal garden incl stone quarry with pool and waterfall. TEAS. *Adm £2 Chd free. Sun July 16 (1-6). Parties welcome, please* **Tel 01782 534713**

NEW **43 Broad Lane, Bradmore, Wolverhampton** ✄❀ (Robert Parker) *1½m from town centre on SW side. Follow signs for Bantock House. Adjacent to Bantock Park. Broad Lane is part of B4161. 200yds from Bradmore Arms traffic lights.* A small, shady Victorian walled and hedge garden cunningly designed to deceive the eye, full of curves, both horizontal and vertical. A series of small gardens. One passes through an opening to find a contrasting sunny, rectangular herb garden and small vinery, several water features and many objets trouvés. Featured BBC Gardeners' World summer 1999. TEA. *Adm £1.50 Chd free. Suns June 25, July 2, 30, Aug 6 (2-6)*

NEW **Brook House Farm, Dagdale, Bramshall** ♿✗❀ (Jim & Zoe Barker) *Bramshall lies approx 2m W of Uttoxeter on the B5027 Stone Rd. In Bramshall turn into Church Lane go through village turn 1st L past the Robin Hood public house. ½m down the lane house stands behind a triangular green.* A 2½ acre prize winning country garden, hardy perennials and shrubs, formal rose garden with fountain. Parterre, grass garden. Double 'Hot' border, Mediterranean garden, natural stream, shrubberies, orchard. TEAS in aid of MENCAP. *Adm £2 Chd free. Sun July 9 (2-5) Groups by appt (min 10) May - July* **Tel 01889 562110**

Brookside, Abbots Bromley ✗ (Mrs M Harvey) *Approach village from Uttoxeter or Rugeley via B5013; from Burton via B5017. Turn opp Bagot Arms Inn situated in the main st.* Village garden comprising shrubs, herbaceous and bedding plants, rose and herb gardens, water features with brook running along the northern boundary. TEAS in nearby C17 hall. *Adm £1.50 Chd free. Suns July 16, Aug 6 (1.30-5.30)*

12 Darges Lane, Great Wyrley ✗❀ (Mrs A Hackett) *From A5 take A34 towards Walsall. Darges Lane is 1st turning on R (over brow of hill). House on R on corner of Cherrington Drive.* ¼-acre well stocked plantsman's and flower arranger's garden. Foliage plants a special feature. Mixed borders incl trees, shrubs and rare plants giving yr-round interest. Features constantly changing. National collection of lamiums. TEAS. *Adm £1.50 Chd 50p.* **Evening Opening** *Wed June 21 (6-9) Sun Sept 10 (2-6). Also private visits welcome, please* **Tel 01922 415064**

Edgewood House, Stourton ❀ (Mr & Mrs G E Fletcher) *4m W of Stourbridge 11m E of Bridgnorth. Take A458 from Stew Poney Junction off A449 (Wolverhampton/Kidderminster) towards Bridgnorth. 1st lane on R (Greensforge Lane). ¾m along lane on L.* 17 acres of woodland with winding paths and cultivated natural garden with small pools. Rhododendrons and azaleas. Cream TEAS. *Adm £2 Chd free. Sun May 21 (1-5)*

NEW **Elvendell, 4 Partridge Ride The Burntwood, Loggerheads** ✗ (Mr & Mrs John Hainsworth) *On Staffordshire/Shropshire borders. Turn off A53 Newcastle-Market Drayton Rd onto Kestrel Drive nr Loggerheads Xrds and adjacent hotel. Please park with consideration - cars can be parked at Loggerheads Hotel if needed.* ½ acre woodland idyll. A designers garden in development with creative hard landscaping. Grove of mature tree ferns (6 species) plus many other ferns, rhododendrons (50 + varieties), pools, waterfall, bog gardens (incl carnivorous plants) and mixed borders. TEAS in aid of Staffordshire Wildlife Trust. *Adm £1.50 Chd 50p. Wed May 17, Sat June 10, Fri July 21 (1-5)*

Flashbrook Lodge, Flashbrook ✗ (Mrs Minnie Mansell) *On A41 4m N of Newport, take rd signed Knighton.* A garden established in 1992 from green field site of approx 1 acre. Features large pool, rockery, waterfall, pergola, gazebo, arbour, trees, shrubs, old-fashioned shrub roses and herbaceous perennials with all yr interest. TEAS. *Adm £2 Chd 50p (ACNO St Michael and All Angels Church, Adbaston). Suns June 4, 25 (2-6). Private visits welcome,* **Tel 01952 550005**

The Garth, Milford ❀ (Mr and Mrs David Wright) *2 Broc Hill Way, 4½m SE of Stafford. A513 Stafford-Rugeley Rd; at Barley Mow turn R (S) to Brocton; L after ½m* ½-acre; shrubs, rhododendrons, azaleas, mixed herbaceous borders, naturalized bulbs; plants of interest to flower arrangers. Rock hewn caves. Fine landscape setting. Coach parties by appt. Cream TEAS. *Adm £2 Chd free. Suns June 4, 25 (2-6). Private parties welcome, please* **Tel 01785 661182**

■ **Grafton Cottage, Barton-under-Needwood** ✗❀ (Mr & Mrs Peter Hargreaves) *Leave A38 for Catholme south of Barton follow sign to Barton Green, ¼m on L.* There is a secret behind every corner in this ¼-acre traditional cottage garden created and maintained by the owners. Emphasis is on scent, colour theme borders, unusual perennials, old roses with many varieties of clematis. A meandering stream adds delight. Featured on BBC2 and in the English Garden and other publications. TEAS. *Adm £2 Chd free. For NGS Fri June 30, Suns July 2, Aug 6 (1.30-5.30). Groups welcome,* **Tel 01283 713639**

Heath House, nr Eccleshall ✗❀ (Dr D W Eyre-Walker) *3m W of Eccleshall. Take B5026 towards Woore. At Sugnall turn L, after 1½m turn R immediately by stone garden wall. After 1m straight across Xrds.* 1½-acre garden. Borders, bog garden, woodland garden, peat bed and alpine bed. Many unusual plants. TEAS. *Adm £2 Chd free (ACNO Parish Church). Sat May 6 (2-5.30) Tues June 20 (2-8) Sat, July 15 (2-5.30). Private visits welcome, please* **Tel 01785 280318**

The Hollies Farm, Pattingham ✗❀ (Mr & Mrs J Shanks) *From Wolverhampton A454 W, follow signs to Pattingham. Cross t-lights at Perton, 1½m R for Hollies Lane. From Pattingham take Wolverhampton Rd 1m turn L to Hollies Lane.* 2-acre plantsman's landscaped garden with interesting trees and shrubs in lovely countryside setting. Unusual perenials, very good plants for sale. TEAS in aid of NSPCC. *Adm £2 Chd free. Sun June 11 (2-6)*

Inglenook, Tamworth ♿✗❀ (Mr & Mrs J Sippitts) *25 Clifford St, Glascote. From new A5 bypass, take B5440 signed Glascote to B5000 approx ½m. Follow sign for town centre at roundabout for 300yds. Clifford St 1st R opp Glascote WMC. Extra parking opp WMC.* ¼-acre garden of mixed borders, shrubs and trees; wildlife pond, ornamental pond. Arbours and gazebo. Major award winning garden, incl many at local level. Changes made for the yr 2000. TEAS. *Adm £1.25 Chd free. Suns July 16, Aug 30, Wed Aug 2 (2-6)*

NEW **Ivy Cottage, Garshall Green** ♿ (Andrew & Helen Adams) *Situated 1m N of Milwich which is on the B5027 Stone to Uttoxetr Rd. Garshall Green is signposted by Milwich Village Hall.* Varied Country Garden with herbaceous border, rockeries, roses, delphiniums, clematis and vegetable garden in secluded countryside. TEAS. *Adm £1.50 Chd 50p. Sat, Sun July 8, 9 (2-5)*

26 Lapley Avenue, Stafford (Mrs D Parker) *2m NW of Stafford Town. Off junction 14 on M6. On to Eccleshall Rd towards Stafford. First right into Creswell Farm Drive. Straight on to end of road to car park and signed short walk to 26 Lapley Ave.* Small town garden completely landscaped by owners since 1990. With a few surprises! Pond with a bridge, pergola, specimen trees although young, wide variety of plants. TEA. *Adm £1.50 Chd free. Suns May 28, June 18, July 16 (2-5.30)*

Little Onn Hall, Church Eaton (Mrs A Kidson) *6m SW of Stafford. A449 Wolverhampton-Stafford; at Gailey roundabout turn W on to A5 for 1¼m; turn R to Stretton; 200yds turn L for Church Eaton; or Bradford Arms-Wheaton Aston and Marston 1¼m.* 6-acre garden; herbaceous lined drive; abundance of rhododendrons; formal paved rose garden with pavilions at front; large lawns with lily pond around house; old moat garden with fish tanks and small ruin; fine trees; walkways. Paddock open for picnics. TEAS. *Adm £3 Chd 50p. Sun May 21 (2-6). Private visits welcome, by appt* **Tel 01785 840154**

Manor Cottage, Chapel Chorlton (Mrs Joyce Heywood) *6m S of Newcastle-U-Lyme. On A51 Nantwich to Stone Rd turn behind Cock Inn at Stableford; white house on village green.* Good garden design with emphasis on plant association and outstanding collections of ferns, euphorbias, geraniums and unusual plants. TEAS. *Adm £1.50 Chd 50p. Every Mon April 17 to Aug 28 (2-5). Also private visits welcome, please* **Tel 01782 680206**

The Old Doctors House, Loggerheads (Mr & Mrs David Ainsworth) *The Burntwood. On Staffs/Shrops border. Turn off A53 Newcastle to Market Drayton rd onto Kestrel Drive/The Burntwood nr Loggerheads Xrds, adjacent hotel.* ¾-acre garden with a strong sense of peace and tranquility. Woodland plantings of ferns, meconopsis, hostas complemented by mixed beds of penstemon, geraniums, euphorbia, salvia etc. Pool, waterfall, bog area. Featured in Central TV 1999. TEAS in aid of Shropshire Hospice. *Adm £2 Chd 50p. Sats, June 3, 24, July 8, Sun June 25 (1-5). Groups welcome, please* **Tel 01630 673363**

Pinfold Cottage, Shenstone (Mrs Cherry Scobie) *Shenstone is 6m N of Sutton Coldfield and 3m S of Lichfield on the A5127. For Pinfold Hill turn L at the small island on the A5127 if approaching from Sutton, or R if approaching from Lichfield. No 6 is an early C19 cottage set at right angles to the rd on the L, but proceed another 80yds to park at The Plough & Harrow public house.* An enchanting cottage garden of approx ¼-acre which has been developed over the last 15yrs to include a pond, rockery, some interesting trees and shrubs and hidden corners, which has been the work of its enthusiastic lady owner. *Adm £1.50 Chd free. Sun June 25 (2-5)*

Stanley House Farm, Milwich (Mr & Mrs J Lockwood) *On B5027 between Milwich and Uttoxeter approx 2m Milwich and 4m Uttoxeter.* A new garden of 3 acres started from scratch in 1994. Features include a wild flower orchard; bog garden; walled garden; laburnum tunnel; ponds; shrubs; trees and herbaceous borders. Trees are a special feature and an arboretum is being planted. *Adm £2 Chd free. For hellebores and TEA Sun March 26 (1-4) and TEAS Suns May 21, June 18 (1-5)*

Strawberry Fields, Hill Ridware (Tom & Margaret Adams) *5m N of Lichfield. B5014 Lichfield/Abbots Bromley. At Hill Ridware turn into Church Lane by Royal Oak Inn, then 1st R. Please park at Royal Oak Inn.* A surprise round every cornerof this delightful ⅓-acre award winning garden. Water trail leading through rooms of colour-themed herbaceous beds, pergolas, arbours, small bog garden, interesting shrubs and trees, unusual climbers. Pleasing country views. Cream TEAS. *Adm £2 Chd free. Suns June 18, July 16, Weds July 26, (11-5). Group visits welcome, please* **Tel 01543 490516**

Thornfold, Leek (Mrs P Machin) *A523. 1m from Leek. L at hospital Moorland Rd, 2nd R Thornfield Ave, Arden Close on R. Please park with consideration in the Avenue.* A small cottage garden, yr-round colour from mixed herbaceous borders, trellises with roses and clematis. Pond, unusual plants. TEA. *Adm £1.50 Chd free. Wed June 7, Sun June 11 (1.30-5)*

98 Walsall Road, Aldridge (Mr & Mrs T Atkins) *3m NW of Walsall on A454, 300yds past White House Inn.* ⅓-acre well stocked small town garden, created over 25yrs, a tranquil haven behind a main rd. Mostly shrubs and perennials with informal pond. TEAS in aid of St Giles Hospice. *Adm £2 Chd 50p. Sun July 9 (1-5.30)*

Westward Ho, Kingsley Wood Rd. Rugeley (Mr & Mrs A Hargreaves) *From N: Proceed from junction A513 and A51 towards Rugeley. After 1m turn R into Bower Lane, after 1.8m turn R into Kingsley Wood Rd. From S: At large island in Rugeley take A51 to Stone/Stafford. After 300 yds turn L at t-lights towards Penkridge after 1.7m turn R into Stafford Brook Rd. 1st L into Kingsley Wood Rd. Large car park at rear.* Large garden in heart of Cannock Chase with places to sit and enjoy herbaceous beds, shrubs, trees, pool, pagoda, vegetable garden and woodland walk. TEAS in aid of Chadsmoor Methodist Church. *Adm £2 Chd free. Suns May 21, Aug 6, Sat Aug 5 (2-5)*

■ **The Willows, Trysull** (Mr and Mrs Nigel Hanson) *7m SW of Wolverhampton. From A449 at Himley B4176 towards Bridgnorth, 2¼m turn R to Trysull. ¾m on L.* 2-acre plant lover's garden created and maintained by garden designers Nigel and Jane since 1981. Natural pool, hostas, gunnera etc. Shrub rose garden, tropical beds with dramatic flowers and foliage. Colour theme borders with an extensive range of interesting and unusual plants. TEAS. *Adm £2 Chd free. Every Sat June 10 to Sept 16 incl. For NGS Sun July 23 (2-6). Groups welcome, please* **Tel 01902 897557**

The Wombourne Wodehouse, Wolverhampton (Mr and Mrs J Phillips) *4m S of Wolverhampton just off A449 on A463 to Sedgley.* 18-acre garden laid out in 1750. Mainly rhododendrons, herbaceous and iris border, woodland walk, water garden. TEAS. *Adm £2.50 Chd free. Sun*

June 4 (2-5.30); also private visits welcome in May, June, July, please **Tel 01902 892202**

Woodside House, Barton-under-Needwood (Mr & Mrs R C Webster) *Barton Gate. Take B5016 out of Barton-under-Needwood. Turn R at Top Bell public house, 300yds turn R.* 1-acre garden of rare and unusual plants, incl 120 varieties of salvias and 100 delphiniums; Japanese garden with stream, waterfalls and pond; rose walk with many varieties of old roses; cottage garden. Large Koi pond with rockery and waterfall. Featured in BBC TV 'Gardeners World' BBC 'Real Rooms' and various principal gardening magazines during 1998/9. Cream TEAS. *Adm £2 Chd free (ACNO St Giles Hospice). Suns May 28, June 11, July 9, 30 (1.30-6). Private visits welcome, please* **Tel 01283 716046**

Evening Opening (See also garden description)

12 Darges Lane, Great Wyrley	June 21

The National Trust Careership Scheme

In 1999, five more individuals commenced a three-year National Trust apprenticeship in gardening with a bursary from the The National Gardens Scheme. Ten apprentices, at different Trust gardens throughout England and Wales, now receive support from the NGS. The apprentices range from school leavers to mature applicants seeking a career change. The National Trust's apprenticeship, known as Careership, combines day-to-day practical experience under the guidance of a head gardener with periods of residential training and study at Bicton College in Devon.

Applications for places are available from January 2000, and the three-year course commences in September 2000.

For more information on Careership and vacancies in 2000 contact, John McKennall, 01208 74281 or fill in the coupon below.

National Trust Careership Scheme
An apprenticeship in horticulture with the National Trust

If you are interested in receiving more information about Careership, the National Trust's apprenticeship scheme in gardening, please complete this coupon and send to: John McKennall, The National Trust, Training Section Office, Lanhydrock Park, Cornwall PL30 4DE, enclosing a SAE.

PRINT

NAME..

ADRESS..

....

....

(NGS)

Suffolk

Hon County Organiser: (East)	Mrs Robert Stone, Washbrook Grange, Washbrook, Ipswich IP8 3HQ Tel 01473 730244
Hon County Organiser (West)	Mrs Elizabeth Seiffer, Garden House Farm, Rattlesdon Road, Drinkstone, Bury St Edmunds IP30 9TN Tel 01449 736434
Assistant Hon County Organisers (East)	Mrs Derek Brightwell, Bucklesham Hall, Bucklesham IP10 0AY Tel 01473 659263
	Mrs T W Ingram, Orchard House, Chattishall Lane, Hintlesham IP8 3NW Tel 01473 652282
	Mrs R I Johnson, 13 Trinity St, Bungay NR35 1EH Tel 01986 895226
(West)	Mrs Maureen Ridge, Treaclebenders, Drinkstone, Bury St Edmunds IP30 9TP Tel 01449 736226
Hon County Treasurer: (West)	Mr Hans Seiffer, The Garden House, Rattlesden Road, Drinkstone, Bury St Edmunds IP30 9TN Tel 01449 736434

DATES OF OPENING

Regular openings

For details see garden description

Blakenham Woodland Garden, Little Blakenham
Euston Hall, Thetford
Rumah Kita, Bedfield
Somerleyton Hall, Lowestoft
Woottens, Wenhaston

By appointment only

For telephone numbers and other details see garden descriptions. Private visits welcomed

Battlies House, Bury St Edmunds
Grundisburgh Hall, Woodbridge
Thrift Farm, Cowlinge

February 13 Sunday
Gable House, Redisham

March 26 Sunday
Barham Hall, Barham
The Beeches, Walsham-le-Willows
East Bergholt Place, East Bergholt

April 2 Sunday
Bresworth House, Cotton

April 9 Sunday
Great Thurlow Hall, Haverhill

April 16 Sunday
Tollemache Hall, Offton

April 24 Monday
East Bergholt Place, East Bergholt
Garden House Farm, Drinkstone

May 1 Monday
Rosemary, Rectory Hill

May 7 Sunday
Bucklesham Hall, Bucklesham
Somerleyton Hall, Lowestoft

May 14 Sunday
18 The Avenue, Ipswich
Blakenham Woodland Garden, Little Blakenham
The Old Hall, Barsham
St Stephens Cottage, Spexhall
Treaclebenders, Drinkstone

May 17 Wednesday
Blakenham Woodland Garden, Little Blakenham

May 21 Sunday
Folly Farm, Lindsey
The Priory, nr Stoke-by-Nayland
Rosedale, Bures
Windmill Cottage, Capel St Mary

May 28 Sunday
Aldeburgh Gardens, Aldeburgh
2 Brook Farm Cottage, Walsham-Le-Willows
Elmsett Manor, Elmsett, Ipswich
The Lawn, Walsham-L-Willows
Windmill Cottage, Capel St Mary

May 29 Monday
Home Farm House, Rushbrooke
Rosemary, Rectory Hill

June 1 Thursday
Euston Hall, Thetford

June 3 Saturday
Brook Hall, Crowfield
Washbrook Grange, Washbrook (evening)

June 4 Sunday
Brook Hall, Crowfield
Bucklesham Hall, Bucklesham
The Rookery, Eyke
Washbrook Grange, Washbrook

June 10 Saturday
Mildenhall Gardens
Wyken Hall, Stanton

June 11 Sunday
Bedfield Hall, nr Framlingham
12 Borrow Road, Oulton Broad
Holly Cottage, Long Melford
Mildenhall Gardens
Rosemary, Rectory Hill
Rumah Kita, Bedfield

June 17 Saturday
Ely House, Long Melford
Magnolia House, Yoxford
Sun House, Long Melford

June 18 Sunday
Barton Mere, Gt Barton
Ely House, Long Melford
Magnolia House, Yoxford
Newe House, Pakenham
Reydon Grove House, Reydon, Nr Southwold
Sun House, Long Melford

June 24 Saturday
18 The Avenue, Ipswich (evening)

June 25 Sunday
Euston Hall, Thetford
The Garden House, Bungay
Garden House Farm, Drinkstone
Hall Farm, Weston, Beccles
North Cove Hall, Beccles

July 1 Saturday
Brook Hall, Crowfield

July 2 Sunday
Brook Hall, Crowfield
Hengrave Hall, Hengrave
The Hill House, Glemsford
The Old Hall, Barsham
Rosedale, Bures

July 8 Saturday
Thumbit, Walsham-le-Willows

July 9 Sunday
Highfields Farm, Bures
Redisham Hall, Beccles
Shelley Hall, Ipswich
Thumbit, Walsham-le-Willows

July 16 Sunday
Bresworth House, Cotton

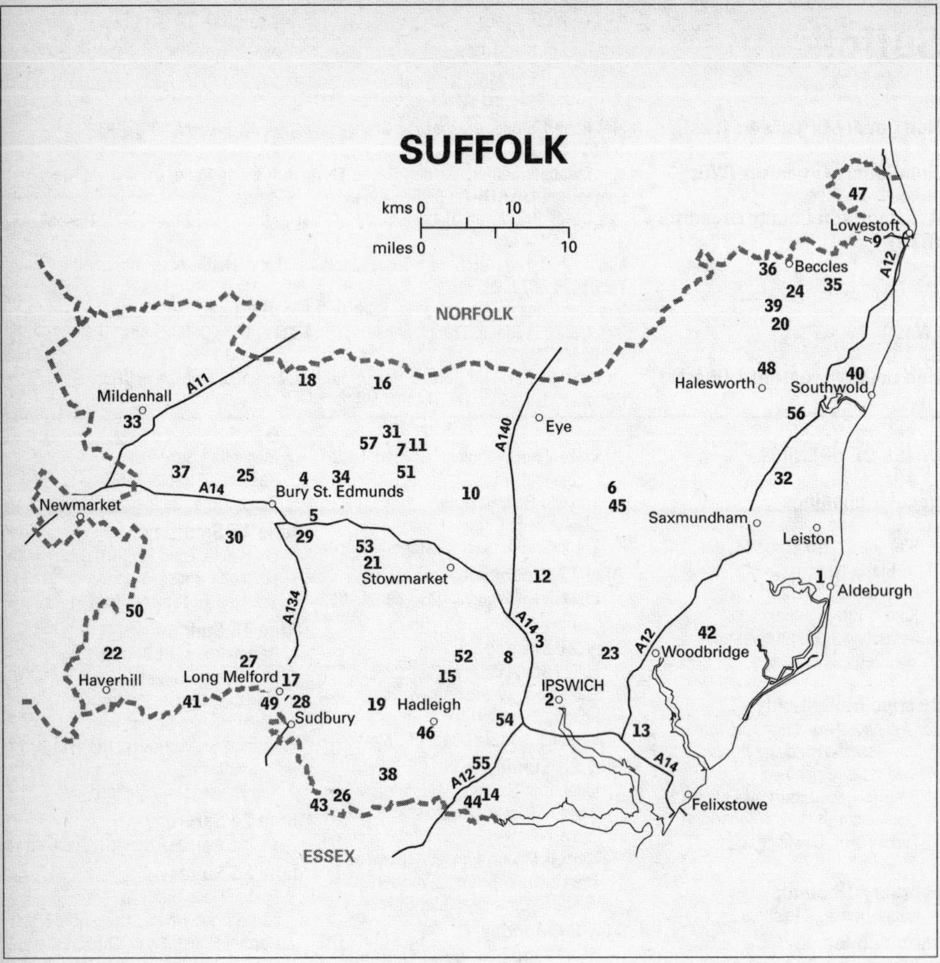

KEY

1 Aldeburgh Gardens
2 18 The Avenue
3 Barham Hall
4 Barton Mere
5 Battlies House
6 Bedfield Hall
7 The Beeches
8 Blakenham Woodland Garden
9 12 Borrow Road
10 Bresworth House
11 2 Brook Farm Cottage
12 Brook Hall
13 Bucklesham Hall
14 East Bergholt Place
15 Elmsett Manor
16 Elvezia
17 Ely House
18 Euston Hall
19 Folly Farm
20 Gable House
21 Garden House Farm
22 Great Thurlow Hall
23 Grundisburgh Hall
24 Hall Farm
25 Hengrave Hall
26 Highfields Farm
27 The Hill House
28 Holly Cottage
29 Home Farm House
30 Ickworth House
31 The Lawn
32 Magnolia House
33 Mildenhall Gardens
34 Newe House
35 North Cove Hall
36 The Old Hall
37 Porters Lodge
38 The Priory
39 Redisham Hall
40 Reydon Grove House
41 Riverside House
42 The Rookery
43 Rosedale
44 Rosemary
45 Rumah Kita
46 Shelley Hall
47 Somerleyton Hall
48 St Stephens Cottage
49 Sun House
50 Thrift Farm
51 Thumbit
52 Tollemache Hall
53 Treaclebenders
54 Washbrook Grange
55 Windmill Cottage
56 Woottens
57 Wyken Hall

Elvezia, Barningham
Riverside House, Clare, Sudbury
Treaclebenders, Drinkstone

July 19 Wednesday
Highfields Farm, Bures

July 23 Sunday
Highfields Farm, Bures

July 30 Sunday
Porters Lodge, Cavenham
Rosedale, Bures

August 6 Sunday
Gable House, Redisham

August 27 Sunday
Rosedale, Bures

September 3 Sunday
Euston Hall, Thetford
Hall Farm, Weston, Beccles
St Stephens Cottage, Spexhall

September 10 Sunday
Ickworth House, Park & Gardens, Horringer
The Old Hall, Barsham

September 28 Thursday
Euston Hall, Thetford

October 15 Sunday
East Bergholt Place, East Bergholt

DESCRIPTIONS OF GARDENS

Aldeburgh Gardens, Aldeburgh ❀ *From A12 take A1094 to Aldeburgh. On approach to town go over 1st roundabout then almost immed R into Park Rd. At tennis courts on the R turn R into Priors Hill Rd.* TEAS and tickets at Stanford House. *Combined adm £3 Chd free; Single garden £2. Sun May 28 (2-5.30)*

Heron House ✗ (Mr & Mrs J H Hale) 2 acres with views over coastline, river and marshes. Unusual trees, herbaceous beds, many shrubs, ponds and a waterfall in a large rock garden

Stanford House (Lady Cave) 1½ acres of terraced garden with waterfall, water garden and wide variety of rare plants and specimen shrubs luxuriating in a mild maritime climate. Beautiful views over river marsh and sea

NEW **18 The Avenue, Ipswich** ♿❀ (Mr M S Parson and Mr R A Burlinson) *Northern end of Christchurch Park. Along Henley Rd at Marlborough Hotel turn into Ellesmere Rd. No 18 is at the T-junction at the far end.* Bungalow in approx ½ acre enclosed site N of town centre. Front rock and gravel garden contains large specimen magnolia grandiflora, pomegranate, dwarf confiers, alpines and grasses. To the rear, mixed borders, trees, grass rather than lawn, a pond, raised vegetable beds, greenhouse and a summerhouse. Planting is in a relaxed style which allows for self sown wildflowers. No chemicals used. Garden maintained by the owners. Plant stall in aid of Suffolk Wildlife Trust. TEAS. *Adm £1.50 Chd free. Sun May 14 (2-6)* **Evening opening** *Sat June 24 (6-9) Wine. Adm £3 Private visits welcome* **Tel 01473 255245**

Barham Hall, Barham ♿✗❀ (Mr & Mrs Richard Burrows) *From Ipswich A14 W. 4m sign Great Blakenham to roundabout. Leave by 3rd turning to Claydon. Through Claydon, (after decontrolled signs) turn R up Church Lane to Barham Green. ½m up Church Lane.* 7 acres of undulating gardens. 3 herbaceous borders, lake surrounded by azaleas and bog plants, woodland shrub garden full of spring flowers; very considerable collection of victorian roses set in well kept lawns with mature trees; a water garden and many other interesting features. Church with famous Henry Moore sculpture open. TEA. *Adm £2 OAPs £1.50 Chd 25p (ACNO to St Mary's & St Peter's Church Barham). Sun March 26 (2-5)*

NEW **Barton Mere, Gt Barton** ♿❀ (Mr & Mrs C O Stenderup) *4m NE of Bury St Edmunds. Take A143 towards Ixworth. After Gt Barton turn R at Bunbury Arms public house. Continue straight on past the turnings to Pakenham and Barton Hamlet (TBS). Entrance to drive 100yds after Barton Hamlet (TBS) on L.* C16 house (not open) with later Georgian façade, set in parkland overlooking lake 'The Mere'. Mainly walled gardens with roses, herbaceous borders, shrubs, large vegetable garden and conservatory. Plants for sale in aid of the church. TEAS at Newe House. *Adm £2 Chd £1. Open with Newe House Sun June 18 (2-6)*

Battlies House, Bury St Edmunds ♿✗ (Mr & Mrs John Barrell) *Turn N off A14 at GT Barton and Rougham industrial estate turning, 3m E of Bury St Edmunds. In ½m turn R by lodge.* 8-acre garden; lawn; shrubberies, woodland walk with a variety of old trees; rhododendrons; elms and conifers. *Adm £2 Chd free. Private visits welcome, please* **Tel 01284 787397**

Bedfield Hall, nr Framlingham (Timothy & Christine Easton) *Bedfield is 2½m NW of the A1120 on secondary rd turning between Earl Soham and Saxtead Green.* 2-acre moated gardens around C15-C17 house (not open). Formal yew hedges and topiary with potager. Shrub roses, iris beds, woodland area. Timothy Easton cards. *Combined adm £3.50 with Rumah Kita. Sun June 11 (2-5)*

The Beeches, Walsham-le-Willows ♿ (Dr & Mrs A J Russell) *10m NE of Bury St Edmunds; signed Walsham-le-Willows off A143. At Xrds in village pass Church on L, after 50yds turn L along Grove Rd. Pink house behind Church.* 3 acres; lawns, herbaceous border, mature and newly-planted trees. Potager, thatched summer house with ornamental pond, gazebo, and wild garden by stream. TEAS. *Adm £2 Chd under 14 free (ACNO to St Mary's Church, Walsham-le-Willows) Sun March 26 (2-5.30)*

■ **Blakenham Woodland Garden, Little Blakenham** ✗ (Blakenham Woodland Garden) *4m NW of Ipswich. Follow signs from 'The Beeches' at Lt Blakenham, 1m off the old A1100, now called B1113.* 5-acre bluebell wood densely planted with fine collection of trees and shrubs; camellias, magnolias, cornus, azaleas, rhododendrons, roses, hydrangeas. *Adm £1 Chd £1. Open daily (1-5) except Sats, March 1 to June 30. For NGS Sun Wed May 14, 17 (1-5). Parties welcome by appt, please* **Tel 01473 833249**

12 Borrow Road, Oulton Broad (Mrs Jenny Wiltshire) *Oulton Broad is to the W of Lowestoft. On the A1117 through Oulton Broad turn off at the roundabout between the Wherry Hotel and the chemists. L into Caldecott Rd then 1st R.* Large garden on a N-facing slope with sandy soil. Island beds containing perennials, shrubs and trees. Pond, vegetable garden and many planted containers. Arches over the path and trellis work. TEA. *Adm £1.50 Chd free. Sun June 11 (1-5.30)*

NEW **Bresworth House, Cotton** ♿✂❀ (Keith & Ann Bullock) *6m N of Stowmarket between B1113 and A140 close to Cotton Church.* Developing 1-acre garden planted and designed by owners on site surrounded and sheltered by mature indigenous trees. Island beds, mixed border, unique water feature and recycled farm iron. TEAS. *Adm £2 Chd free (ACNO to Cotton Church & Village Hall) Suns April 2 (2-5) July 16 (2.5.30)*

2 Brook Farm Cottage, Walsham-Le-Willows ♿ (Mr & Mrs J Folkard) *11m E of Bury St Edmunds. ½m on Ixworth Rd from Walsham Le Willows. Thatched House opp The Lawn on R. Next to Brook Farm.* ⅓ acre Cottage garden, vegetables, herbs. Two greenhouses and small fish pond. TEAS at the Lawn. *Combined adm £3 with The Lawn. Sun May 28 (2.30-6)*

NEW **Brook Hall, Crowfield** ♿✂❀ (Mr & Mrs D S Pumfrey) *3m N of Coddenham and 2m S of Stonham Aspal and Pettaugh A1120. Brook Hall is reached down a farm drive.* 1½ acres of mixed herbaceous borders with over 80 roses; gravel garden; kitchen garden; natural pond and wild life area. TEAS. *Adm £2 Chd free. Sats, Suns June 3, 4 July 1, 2 (11-5)*

Bucklesham Hall, Bucklesham ✂ (Mr and Mrs D Brightwell) *6m SE of Ipswich, 1m E of village opp to Bucklesham School.* 7 acres created by previous owners in 1973 and maintained by present owners since 1994. Unusual plants, shrubs and trees. Shrub/rose garden, water and woodland gardens. Partly suitable for wheelchairs. TEAS in aid of Bucklesham Village School. *Adm £2 Chd £1. Suns May 7, June 4 (2-6). Private visits welcome by parties of 4 or more, please* **Tel 01473 659263**

East Bergholt Place, East Bergholt ♿✂❀ (Mr and Mrs Rupert Eley) *On the B1070 towards Manningtree, 2m E of A12.* 15-acre garden originally laid out at the beginning of the century by the present owner's great Grandfather. Full of many fine trees and shrubs some of which are rarely seen in East Anglia. Particularly beautiful in spring when the rhododendrons, magnolias and camellias are in full flower, and in Autumn, with newly cut topiary and Autumn colours. TEAS. *Adm £2 Chd free. Sun March 26, Mon April 24 (2-5.30) Sun Oct 15 (1-5)*

Elmsett Manor, Elmsett, Ipswich ❀ (Mr & Mrs O Cooper) *Situated 1m N of the village in Manor Rd.* 2.5 acres. Won Strutt and Parker Garden Award for Suffolk. Several distinct areas: Mediterranean walled swimming pool area; orchard and wild area; informal water garden; lily pond and kitchen garden. Linked by brick paths, Victorian arches smothered in roses with yew and lavender walks. Exuberant use of cottage style on a large scale. Garden 'romps and rambles with glorious enthusiasm'. TEAS. *Adm £2 Chd free. Sun May 28 (2-6)*

NEW **Elvezia, Barningham** (Kate & Len Lucas) *10m NE of Bury St Edmunds. Take A143 from Bury, at Stanton turn L on B1111. Pass Barningham village sign turn L then 1st R. Garden 4th on the R.* Small front and rear garden which, while both different, combine the exotic, the classic and traditional. Designed and built around some 600 choice species and varities for yr-round colour and interest. TEA. *Adm £2 Chd free. Sun July 16 (2-6)*

Ely House, Long Melford ♿ (Miss Jean Clark) *Church Walk N end of village opp top green. 3½m N of Sudbury on A134.* Interesting small-walled garden with mixed borders. Home of potter making fountains and garden pots. Adjacent orchard. *Combined adm with Sun House £3. Sat, Sun June 17, 18 (2-6)*

● **Euston Hall, Thetford** ✂ (His Grace The Duke of Grafton) *On the A1088 12m N of Bury St Edmunds, 3m S of Thetford.* Terraced lawns, herbaceous borders, rose garden, C17 pleasure grounds, lake and watermill. C18 house open; famous collection of paintings. C17 church; temple by William Kent. Craft shop. Wheelchair access to gardens, tea-room and shop only. TEAS in Old Kitchen. *Adm house & garden £3 OAPs £2.50 Chd 50p Parties of 12 or more £2.50 per head. Thurs June 1 to Sept 28; Suns June 25 & Sept 3 (2.30-5)*

NEW **Folly Farm, Lindsey** (Mr & Mrs Michael Moore) *4m SE of Lavenham. 2m W of Kersey. Follow signs for St James' chapel, Ancient Monument. Then go 600yds W to farm on N-side of rd.* Linear garden of nearly 3 acres created since 1989 comprising formal rose garden, many herbaceous borders, knot garden, five hedges, laburnum and wisteria, pergola and kitchen garden, all in an old farmyard and courtyard setting. TEAS. *£2 Chd under 12 free (ACNO Save the Children Fund). Sun May 21 (2-6)*

Gable House, Redisham ♿✂❀ (Mr and Mrs John Foster) *3½m S of Beccles. Mid-way between Beccles and Halesworth on Ringsfield-Ilketshall St Lawrence Rd.* 1-acre garden containing wide range of interesting plants, alpines and bulbs in newly created scree and woodland area. Greenhouses with many unusual plants. Home-made TEAS. *Adm £2 (ACNO to St Peters Church Redisham). Snowdrop day Sun Feb 13 (11-4); Sun Aug 6 (2-6)*

The Garden House, Bungay ♿ (Mr & Mrs David Mitchell) *Within the town of Bungay, situated at the joining of Upper Olland Street and Flixton Road.* Town garden, architectural in design with mixed planting of herbaceous plants, shrubs, climbers, with pleached hedging on light sandy soil. *Adm £2 Chd free. (ACNO to Association of Friends of All Hallows Hospital). Sun June 25 (2-5.30)*

Garden House Farm, Drinkstone ✂❀ (Mrs Seiffer) *A14 turn off at Woolpit, village centre turn L follow signs to Drinkstone, then Drinkstone Green, past village hall, then 1st L, Rattlesden Rd. After ¾m turn L down lane. 3m from Woolpit.* 11 acre garden. Lake, woodland gardens with rare trees and shrubs. Summer borders, winter garden. Colour and interest all yr-round. TEAS. *Adm £2 Chd free. Easter Mon April 24. Sun June 25 (2-5.30). Private visits welcome, please* **Tel 01449 736434**

Great Thurlow Hall, Haverhill ♿ (Mr & Mrs George Vestey) *N of Haverhill. Great Thurlow village on B1061 from*

Newmarket; 3½m N of junction with A143 Haverhill-Bury St Edmunds rd. 20 acres. River walk and trout lake with extensive and impressive display of daffodils and blossom. Spacious lawns, shrubberies and roses. Walled kitchen garden. TEA. *Adm £2 Chd free. Sun April 9 (2-5)*

Grundisburgh Hall, Woodbridge ♿✗ (Lady Cranworth) *3m W of Woodbridge on B1079, ¼m S of Grundisburgh on Grundisburgh to Ipswich Rd.* Approx 5 acres: walled garden with yew hedges; wisteria walk and mixed borders. Old rose garden; lawns and ponds. *Adm £2.50 Chd free (ACNO to St Marys Grundisburgh, St Botolphs Culpho). Private visits welcome May 20 to July 20, please* **Tel 01473 735 485**

Hall Farm, Weston, Beccles (Mr & Mrs Peter Seppings) *1½m S of Beccles on A145. The entrance is the same as for Winter Flora, continue 300yds along the drive to the private house.* 1½ acre comprising cottage garden type planting of shrub roses and perennials within a formal design. The terrace overlooks a large pond surrounded by naturalistic planting, lawns and shrubs. Many unusual annuals and perennials here and in the Winter Flora garden at the entrance which is carefully colour themed with herb garden, gravel garden and willow structures. TEAS on terrace or in conservatory. *Adm £2 Chd free. Collection box in flower shop when private garden is not open. Suns June 25, Sept 3 (2-6)*

Hengrave Hall, Hengrave ♿✗❀ (Mr Peter Scrivener) *3½m NW Bury St Edmunds on A1101. Tudor mansion (tours available).* Lake and woodland path. 5-acre formal garden with spacious lawns. Mixed borders with some unusual plants. Organic kitchen garden. TEAS in aid of Hengrave Bursary Fund. *Adm £2 OAPs £1 Chd free. Sun July 2 (2-6)*

Highfields Farm, Bures ♿✗❀ (Mr & Mrs John Ineson) *6m SE of Sudbury. From Bures Church take Nayland Rd. In 2m turn L signposted Assington. Take 1st R Tarmac Drive. From other directions take Assington-Wormingford rd.* Approx 1½-acre plantsman's garden started in 1984 with mixed borders, shrubs, chamomile lawn and herbaceous beds. Various flint features and lily pond. Selection of ornamental fowls. Winner BBC Radio Suffolk/East Anglian Daily Times Garden of the Year Competition 1998. TEAS. *Adm £2 Chd free. Suns July 9, 23, Wed July 19 (2-6). Private visits welcome in July and August, please* **Tel 01787 227136**

The Hill House, Glemsford ♿✗ (Sir John & Lady Mowbray) *100yds N of village of Glemsford on the back rd to Hawkedon and Boxted.* Pretty country garden of 1 acre with interesting mixed borders, conservatory and kitchen garden. *Adm £2 Chd free. Sun July 2 (2-6)*

Holly Cottage, Long Melford ✗❀ (Mrs Barbara Segall) *Coming from Sudbury roundabout take A134 travelling N towards Bury St Edmunds. Take 1st R turn off A134 Long Melford bypass. 4th house on L 250yds along rd, Mills Lane.* Garden writer's ½-acre country garden features long, mixed herbaceous borders, vegetables and herb gardens with unusual vegetables. Old roses, small bog garden, shade garden and arbours. Good spring colour as well as summer and autumn interest. TEAS. *Adm £2 Chd free. Sun June 11 (2-6)*

Home Farm House, Rushbrooke ♿✗❀ (Anita Rothschild) *3m SE Bury St Edmunds. From A14 Bury St Edmunds East/Sudbury exit, proceed towards town centre, after 50yds 1st exit from roundabout and immed turn R. Proceed ¾m to T-junction, turn L, follow rd for 2m. Rushbrooke church on L, turn R into paddock railed drive.* 3-acres: walled garden, mixed borders, roses, lawns, incl 1¼ acre kitchen garden (potager) and glasshouses with stone fruit, figs, vinery, orchids, general propagation. Further 5 acres parkland and orchard, moat garden. Ornamental wattle and thatched summerhouse. TEAS. *Adm £2.50 Chd free. Mon May 29 (2-5). Also private visits by arrangement with head gardener,* **Tel 01284 386276**

▲ Ickworth House, Park & Gardens, Horringer ♿✗ (The National Trust) *Ickworth is 2m SW of Bury St Edmunds, in the village of Horringer on the A143 Bury to Haverhill Rd.* 70 acres of garden. South gardens restored to stylized Italian landscape to reflect extraordinary design of the house. Fine orangery, agapanthus, geraniums and fatsias. North gardens informal wild flower lawns with wooded walk; the Buxus collection, great variety of evergreens and Victorian stumpery. New planting of cedars. The Albana Wood, a C18 feature, initially laid out by Capability Brown, incorporates a fine circular walk. Restaurant TEAS. *Adm £5.50 (house, park and garden) Chd £2.40. £2.40 (park and garden) Chd 80p. For NGS Sun Sept 10 (10-5.30). Pre-booked visits of 15 and over welcome, please* **Tel 01284 735270**

The Lawn, Walsham-L-Willows ♿ (Mr and Mrs R Martineau) *NE from Bury St Edmunds on A143 about 6m to Ixworth bypass R at 2nd roundabout signposted Walsham-Le-Willows. 3½m house on R. ½m short of village.* About 3½ acres of lawns, herbaceous borders and shrubs overlooking parkland. Woodland walk around 8 acre wood. TEAS. *Combined adm £3 with 2 Brook Farm Cottages. Sun May 28 (2.30-6).*

Magnolia House, Yoxford ✗ (Mr Mark Rumary) *On A1120 in centre of Yoxford.* Small, completely walled village garden. Mixed borders with flowering trees, shrubs, climbers, bulbs, hardy and tender plants. Featured in UK and foreign gardening books and magazines. TEA *Adm £2 Chd free Sat, Sun June 17, 18 (2-6)*

Mildenhall Gardens ❀ *From Fiveways roundabout at Barton Mills on A11 follow signs to Mildenhall. The gardens are all within a five minute walk from town centre car parks.* TEAS. *Combined adm £2.50. Sat, Sun June 10, 11 (2-5)*

6a Church Walk ✗ (Mr & Mrs D G Reeve) Walled garden surrounding modern bungalow. Sunken paved area, raised bed with pond and waterfall. Patio with water feature, established rockery, many herbaceous plants and shrubs incl over 50 varieties of Hemerocallis (DayLily). *Private visit also wlcome by appointment, please* **Tel 01638 715289**

15 Mill Street (Mr & Mrs J Child) An elegant walled garden, approx ½ acre, landscaped over the past 4 yrs, but looking well established. River frontage with pergolas, a pond and perennial borders. Large walled vegetable garden. **Tel 01638 510418**

Tiggywinkle Cottage, Wamil Way (Mrs Marion Turner) A small secluded cottage garden contains pillar,

shrub and patio roses, flowering shrubs and many unusual perennials and alpines. A newly created brick courtyard has replaced a small lawn area. Statues and containers complement the borders.
Tel 01638 715827

Newe House, Pakenham (Mr Spicer) *5m NE of Bury St Edmunds. Take A143 towards Ixworth. After Gt Barton turn R at Bunbury Arms then immed L, marked Pakenham. At end of village turn L drive on R just after thatched cottage.* Red brick Jacobean house (not open) with fine façade and 3 dutch gables. Grounds containing walled garden, specimen trees, rosewalk, fountain and unusual collection of sculpture. TEAS. *Adm £2 Chd free. Open with Barton Mere Sun June 18 (2-6)*

North Cove Hall, Beccles ♿❀ (Mr & Mrs B Blower) *Just off A146 3½m E of Beccles on Lowestoft Rd. Take sign to North Cove.* 5 acres of garden; large pond; new water feature; mature and interesting young trees. Walled kitchen garden; shrub roses; herbaceous borders; woodland walks. Home-made TEAS. *Adm £2 Chd free Sun June 25 (2-5.30)*

The Old Hall, Barsham ♿❀ (Maurice & Jane Elliott) *Off B1062 1½m W of Beccles.* Recently restored C16 Hall, (not open) Civic Trust Award 1994. Young garden, many unusual trees, shrubs and climbers. 85 clematis, recently enlarged herb garden (over 600 different grown); greenhouse. Small nursery specialising in herbs. TEAS. *Adm £2 Chd free. Suns May 14, July 2, Sept 10 (2-5). Private visits welcome, please* **Tel 01502 717475**

Porters Lodge, Cavenham ♿ (Mr Craig Wyncoll) *5m W of Bury St Edmunds; 1m SW of Cavenham on the rd to Kentford.* Surrounded by a mature wood in which 2 acres of walks and glades encircle and are linked into the inner garden formed from an acre of semi-formal lawns and mixed borders. An unusual and interesting garden designed as a series of interlocked spaces which are enlivened by fountains and ponds, statuary and architectural 'follies' culminating in a pavilion which houses unique water organ playing music by Haydn. TEAS. *Adm £2 Chd free. Sun July 30 (2-6)*

The Priory, nr Stoke-by-Nayland ♿❀ (Mr and Mrs H F A Engleheart) *8m N of Colchester, entrance on B1068 rd to Sudbury.* Interesting 9-acre garden with fine views over Constable countryside; lawns sloping down to small lakes & water garden; fine trees, rhododendrons & azaleas; walled garden; mixed borders & ornamental greenhouse. Wide variety of plants; peafowl. Home-made TEAS. *Adm £2.50 Chd free. Sun May 21 (2-6)*

Redisham Hall, Beccles ♿🚫 (Mr Palgrave Brown) *From A145 1½m S of Beccles, turn W on to Ringsfield-Bungay Rd. Beccles, Halesworth or Bungay, all within 6m.* 5 acres; parkland and woods 400 acres. Georgian house C18 (not open). Safari rides. TEAS. *Adm £2 Chd free (ACNO to East Suffolk Macmillan Nurses & Marie Curie Cancer Care Suffolk Branch). Sun July 9 (2-6)*

Reydon Grove House, Reydon, Nr Southwold ♿❀ (Cmdr & Mrs J Swinley) *Situated ½m N of Reydon Church. Turnings off the Wangford-Southwold rd.* 1½-acre mature garden. Large collection of herbaceous plants and shrubs, many interesting and unusual ones. Old-fashioned roses. Vegetable garden. TEAS in aid of Reydon Church. *Adm £2 Chd free. Sun June 18 (2-5.30). Private visits welcome June to Aug, please* **Tel 01502 723655**

Riverside House, Clare, Sudbury 🚫 (Mr & Mrs A C W Bone) *On the A1092 leading out of Clare towards Haverhill.* A peaceful walled country garden leading down to the river Stour. Fine lawns, trees, shrubs and mixed herbaceous beds. A splash of summer annuals completes the picture. *Adm £2 Chd free. Sun July 16 (2-5.30)*

The Rookery, Eyke ♿🚫❀ (Capt & Mrs Sheepshanks) *5m E of Woodbridge turn N off B1084 Woodbridge-Orford Rd where sign says Rendlesham.* 10-acre garden. Many rare specimen trees and shrubs; landscaped on differing levels, providing views and vistas; the visitor's curiosity is constantly aroused by what is round the next corner; ponds, Japanese garden, rhododendrons, roses, bulbs, borders as well as Staverton vineyard. Wine tastings at farm shop. Home-made TEAS. *Adm £2.50 Chd 50p. Sun June 4 (2-5.30). Private visits welcome for parties of 10 and over, please* **Tel 01394 460271**

Rosedale, Bures 🚫❀ (Mr & Mrs Colin Lorking) *40 Colchester Rd. 9m NW of Colchester on B1508. As you enter the village of Bures, garden is on the L. 5m SE of Sudbury on B1508, follow signs through village towards Colchester, garden is on the R as you leave village.* Approx ⅓-acre, plantsman's garden; many unusual plants, herbaceous borders, pond, woodland area. Featured in Daily Mail Weekend Magazine, Womans Weekly and winner of BBC Suffolk Garden of the Year competition 1999. TEAS. *Adm £2 Acc chd free. Suns May 21, July 2, 30, Aug 27 (12-5.30). Private visits welcome, please* **Tel 01787 227619**

Rosemary, Rectory Hill ♿🚫❀ (Mrs N E M Finch) *Turn off the A12 at East Bergholt and follow rd round to church. Rosemary is 100yds down from the church on L.* Mature 1-acre garden adapted over 30yrs from an old orchard loosely divided into several smaller gardens; mixed borders; herb garden; over 100 old roses, good trees, unusual plants. TEAS. *Adm £2 Chd free Mons May 1, 29, Sun June 11 (1.30-5) and private visits welcome June and July, please* **Tel 01206 298241**

Rumah Kita, Bedfield ♿ (Mr & Mrs I R Dickings) *2½m NW of the A1120 on secondary rd turning between Earl Soham and Saxtead Green.* 1½-acre garden designed and planted by owners; mixed borders of many unusual plants incl paeonia rocks variety, emonopteris henryii, sequoiadendron giganteum pendulum. Parterre, scree, peat and raised alpine beds. TEAS. *Combined adm £3.50 Chd free with Bedfield Hall. Sun June 11 (2-6) Also open every Thurs from June 11 to Sept 14. Adm £2 Chd free. Private visits welcome, individual or parties, please* **Tel 01728 628401**

St Stephens Cottage, Spexhall 🚫❀ (Martin Wilson) *2m from Halesworth off A144 Halesworth to Bungay Rd take signposted lane to Spexhall Church.* 1-acre cottage garden with island beds surrounding mature trees, natural pond, unusual plants. New 3 acres which incl formal scented garden, rosary, potager and newly planted arboretum. Featured in national journals. TEAS. *Adm £2 Chd free. Suns May 14, Sept 3 (2-5)*

NEW **Shelley Hall, Ipswich** (Mr & Mrs Andrew Scott) *A12 take B1070 to Hadleigh L end of Holton St Mary signed Shelley. Follow road 2m down steep hill. T junction then R next L over bridge drive on L.* Fascinating mediaeval garden recreated in just 5 days by Channel 4 Lost Gardens according to early C16 plan, on original moated site. Hyssop maze, raised herb beds and stew ponds. Walled garden with interesting borders complementing the Tudor Manor house (not open) all encompassed in lovely parkland. TEAS. *Adm £2.50 Chd free. Sun July 9 (2-6)*

■ **Somerleyton Hall, Lowestoft** (The Lord & Lady Somerleyton) *5m NW of Lowestoft. Off B1074.* Large garden; famous maze, beautiful trees and borders. Glasshouses and ornamentation. House C17 lavishly remodelled in 1840's by Sir Morton Peto. Grinling Gibbons' carving, library, tapestries. Mentioned in Domesday Book. Light lunches & TEAS. *Adm £5, OAP's £4.80, Chd £2.50 Family £14.20. House open 1-5 Gardens 12.30-5.30: Easter Sun to end Sept, Thurs, Suns, Bank Hol Mons; in addition Tues, Weds, July and Aug; For NGS Sun May 7. Group private visits welcome by prior arrangement (Min 20)*

Sun House, Long Melford (Mr & Mrs John Thompson) *Centre of village, 3½m N of Sudbury on A134 opp Cock & Bell Inn.* 2 attractive adjacent walled gardens with roses, shrubs, hostas, ferns and many rare herbaceous plants. Over 100 clematis, water and architectural features, folly and paved courtyards. Winner Best Garden in East Anglia - Look East TV - BBC Gardeners World. *Combined adm with Ely House £3 Chd free (ACNO 10 per cent to St Nicholas Hospice). Sat, Sun June 17, 18 (2-6)*

Thrift Farm, Cowlinge (Mrs J M Oddy) *7m SE of Newmarket, centrally between Cowlinge, Kirtling and Gt Bradley. On the Gt Bradley rd from Kirtling.* Picturesque thatched house (not open) set in a cottage style garden extending to approx 1½ acres. Forever changing island beds filled with herbaceous plants amongst shrubs and ornamental trees in great variety, also orchard. A garden which encourages you to walk round. Owner maintained. TEA. *Adm £2. By appt from April to October. Private visits welcome please* **Tel 01440 783274**

Thumbit, Walsham-le-Willows (Mrs Ann James) *10m NE of Bury St Edmunds. Leave A143 at Walsham-le-Willows sign and continue through Xrds by church on Badwell Rd to outskirts of village (½m).* House is part of thatched C16 one-time inn (not open). Shared driveway - (please do not drive in). Small informal garden with emphasis on design and plant association. Pergola, pool, topiary. 500 choice plants, shrubs, roses and climbers. 'Strutt and Parker' award winner and featured on ITV. TEA, lunches by arrangement. *Adm £2 Chd free. Sat, Sun July 8, 9 (2-6). Private visits welcome, please* **Tel 01359 259 414**

Tollemache Hall, Offton (Mr & Mrs M Tollemache) *Nr Ipswich S of the B1078 opp the Ringshall turning.* 4 acres of recently renovated garden in a lovely rural setting. Shrubs, rose and knot gardens. A large walled garden with interesting herbaceous borders. Also woodland walk planted with many conifer species. Suffolk Punches. TEAS. *Adm £2 Chd free. Sun April 16 (2-6)*

Treaclebenders, Drinkstone (Mrs Maureen Ridge) *10m E of Bury St Edmunds. Leave A14 at Woolpit, L at village pump, R opp Plough public house. R at T junction with grass triangle, L beside railings at Xrds into Drinkstone. After 1m turn L opp phone box into Rattlesden Road. 200yds and L into Cross St. Garden on R of lane. Park in Rattlesden Rd.* Plantsman's garden of about 1 acre surrounding thatched Tudor cottage (not open). All yr colour, incl many winter and spring bulbs and autumn and winter cyclamen. Plant stall in aid of ARC. TEAS. *Adm £2 Chd free (ACNO to The Arthritis Research Campaign). Suns May 14, July 16 (11-6). Private visits welcome, please* **Tel 01449 736 226**

Washbrook Grange, Washbrook (Mr & Mrs Robert Stone) *From Ipswich take A1071 to Hadleigh. L at 1st roundabout and then 1st R to Chattisham.* 5 acres surrounding rambling C16 house (not open) with lawns sloping to small lake and river. Formal minimalist canal garden and informal river and woodland walks. Herbaceous borders, shrubberies and arboretum all packed with plants both old and new. Maple walk and ornamental vegetable garden. TEAS. *Adm £2.50 Chd free. Sun June 4 (2-6).* **Evening opening** *Wine. Adm £3. Sat June 3 (6-8.30). Private visits welcome, please* **Tel 01473 730244**

Windmill Cottage, Capel St Mary (Mr & Mrs G A Cox) *Approx 3m S of Ipswich. Turn off at Capel St Mary. At far end of village on R after 1.2m.* ½-acre plantsman's cottage style garden. Island beds, pergolas with clematis and other climbers. Many trees and shrubs, iris bed, ponds and vegetable area. One of the finalists in the BBC Radio Suffolk Garden of the Year. TEAS. *Adm £2 Chd free. Suns May 21, 28 (2-6)*

Woottens, Wenhaston (Mr M Loftus) *Blackheath Rd. Woottens is between A12 and B1123 follow signposts to Wenhaston.* Small romantic garden with attached plantsman nursery, in all about 1-acre; scented leafed pelargoniums, violas, cranesbills, lilies, salvias, penstemons primulas, etc. Featured in Gardens Illustrated and RHS Journal. *Adm £1.50 OAPs 50p Chd 20p. Weds May to Sept (9.30-3)*

Wyken Hall, Stanton (Sir Kenneth & Lady Carlisle) *9m NE from Bury St Edmunds along A143. Follow signs to Wyken vineyards on A143 between Ixworth and Stanton.* 4-acre garden much developed recently; knot and herb garden; old-fashioned rose garden, wild garden, nuttery, pond, gazebo and maze; herbaceous borders and old orchard. Woodland walk, vineyard. Wine and Refreshments. *Adm £2.50 OAPs £2 Chd free. Sat June 10 (10-6)*

Evening Opening (See also garden description)

18 The Avenue, Ipswich	June 24
Washbrook Grange, Washbrook	June 3

Surrey

Hon County Organiser: Mrs Eileen Pearcy, Far End, Pilgrims Way, Guildford GU4 8AD 01483 563093

Assistant Hon County Organisers: Miss Christine Collins, Knightsmead, Rickman Hill Road, Chipstead CR5 3LB 01737 551694

Mrs Daphne Foulsham, Vale End, Albury, Guildford GU5 9BE 01483 202296

Mrs Norma Kent, Compton Lodge, 4 Compton Way, Moor Park, Farnham GU10 1QZ 01252 782076

Mrs Gayle Leader, Stuart Cottage, East Clandon GU4 7SF Tel 01483 222689

Mr Keith Lewis (Leaflets), 41 Shelvers Way, Tadworth KT20 5QJ 01737 210707

Mrs Caroline Norman, Spring Cottage, Mannings Hill, Cranleigh GU6 8QN 01483 272620

Mrs Jeanette Simpson (Publicity), Kingcups, The Green, Pirbright GU24 0JT 01483 474901

Mrs Averil Trott, Odstock, Castle Square, Bletchingley RH1 4LB 01883 743100

Mr Fred Wood, Pathside, 70 York Road, Cheam, Surrey SM2 6HJ 020 8642 4260

Hon County Treasurer: Mr Ken Kent, Compton Lodge, 4 Compton Way, Moor Park, Farnham GU10 1QZ 01252 782076

DATES OF OPENING

Regular openings

For details see garden description

Crosswater Farm, Churt
Loseley Park, Guildford
Painshill Landscape Garden, nr Cobham
Ramster, Chiddingfold
Titsey Place Gardens, Oxted
Walton Poor, Ranmore

By appointment only

For telephone numbers and other details see garden descriptions. Private visits welcomed

Chauffeur's Flat, Tandridge
Hookwood Farmhouse, West Horsley
Knightsmead, Chipstead
Pinewood House, Woking
Unicorns, Farnham
87 Upland Road, Sutton

Evening Opening (See also garden description)

66 Avenue Road, Belmont July 6
Chilworth Manor, Guildford June 8 & July 6
The Copse Lodge, Burgh Heath June 7
Culverkeys, Ewell July 12
Four Aces, Pirbright July 2
Heathfield, Albury Heath July 12
Red Oaks, Redhill July 14
RHS Garden Wisley June 28 & August 22
Shepherds Lane Gardens June 28 & July 12
Stuart Cottage, East Clandon August 3
Tanyard Farmhouse, Langshott, Horley July 8 & 12
Vale End, Albury August 2
Walnut House, Reigate July 13
Woodbury Cottage, Reigate July 5

February 27 Sunday
9 Raymead Close, Fetcham

March 12 Sunday
Tanyard Farmhouse, Langshott, Horley

March 19 Sunday
Albury Park, Albury

April 2 Sunday
Vann, Hambledon

April 3 Monday
Vann, Hambledon

April 4 to 7 Tuesday to Friday
Vann, Hambledon

April 8 Saturday
Chilworth Manor, Guildford
Vann, Hambledon

April 9 Sunday
Chilworth Manor, Guildford
Vann, Hambledon

April 10 Monday
Chilworth Manor, Guildford

April 11 to 12 Tuesday to Wednesday
Chilworth Manor, Guildford

April 16 Sunday
Lodkin, Hascombe
Munstead Wood, Godalming
41 Shelvers Way, Tadworth
Winkworth Arboretum, Hascombe
Woodcote Park Nursery, Send

April 19 Wednesday
Long Barton, Guildford
41 Shelvers Way, Tadworth

April 23 Sunday
Coverwood Lakes, Ewhurst
High Meadow, Churt

April 24 Monday
High Meadow, Churt

April 30 Sunday
Coverwood Lakes, Ewhurst
22 Knoll Road, Dorking
Nuthatch, Haslemere
The Old Croft, South Holmwood

May 1 Monday
Crosswater Farm, Churt
The Old Croft, South Holmwood
Vann, Hambledon
Walton Poor, Ranmore

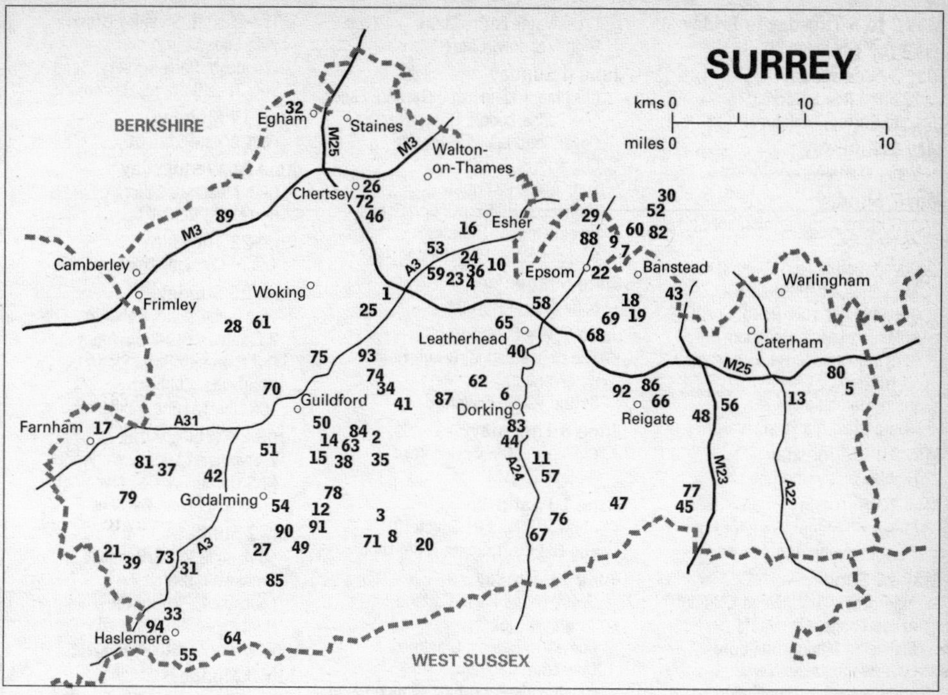

KEY

1 RHS Garden
2 Albury Park
3 Alderbrook
4 April Cottage
5 Arden Lodge
6 Ashcombe Cottage
7 66 Avenue Road
8 Barhatch Farm
9 Bethany
10 Beverstone
11 Brook Lodge Farm Cottage
12 Brookwell
13 Chauffeur's Flat
14 Chilworth Manor
15 2 Chinthurst Lodge
16 Claremont Landscape Garden
17 Compton Lodge
18 The Copse Lodge
19 Copt Hill Shaw
20 Coverwood Lakes
21 Crosswater Farm
22 Culverkeys
23 Dorset Cottage
24 Dovecote
25 Dunsborough Park
26 105 Fairway
27 Feathercombe
28 Four Aces
29 10 The Glade
30 72 Green Wrythe Lane
31 Halnacker Hill
32 47 Harvest Road
33 Haslehurst
34 Hatchlands Park
35 Heathfield
36 Heathside
37 Hethersett
38 High Hazard
39 High Meadow
40 Highlands
41 Hookwood Farmhouse
42 Huntsmore
43 Knightsmead
44 22 Knoll Road
45 Langshott Manor
46 106 Liberty Lane
47 Little Mynthurst Farm
48 Little Priory
49 Lodkin
50 Long Barton
51 Loseley Park
52 50 Milton Avenue
53 Moleshill House
54 Munstead Wood
55 Nuthatch
56 Odstock
57 The Old Croft
58 73 Ottways Lane
59 Painshill Landscape Garden
60 Pathside
61 Pinewood House
62 Polesden Lacey
63 Postford House
64 Ramster
65 9 Raymead Close
66 Red Oaks
67 Redland House
68 Ridings
69 41 Shelvers Way
70 Shepherds Lane Gardens
71 Spring Cottage
72 69 Station Road
73 Street House
74 Stuart Cottage
75 Sutton Place
76 Tanhouse Farm
77 Tanyard Farmhouse
78 Thanescroft
79 Tilford Cottage
80 Titsey Place Gardens
81 Unicorns
82 87 Upland Road
83 6 Upper Rose Hill
84 Vale End
85 Vann
86 Walnut House
87 Walton Poor
88 41 West Street
89 Windlesham Park
90 Winkworth Arboretum
91 Wintershall Manor
92 Woodbury Cottage
93 Woodcote Park Nursery
94 Yew Tree Cottage

May 2 to 5 Tuesday to Friday
Vann, Hambledon

May 3 Wednesday
22 Knoll Road, Dorking
Long Barton, Guildford

May 6 Saturday
Vann, Hambledon

May 7 Sunday
Ashcombe Cottage, Ranmore Common
Coverwood Lakes, Ewhurst
Highlands, Leatherhead
Pathside, 70 York Road, Cheam
Polesden Lacey, Bookham
Tanyard Farmhouse, Langshott, Horley
Vann, Hambledon
Wintershall Manor, Bramley

May 10 Wednesday
Highlands, Leatherhead

May 13 Saturday
Chilworth Manor, Guildford
Feathercombe, Hambledon

May 14 Sunday
Alderbrook, Smithwood Common
Arden Lodge, Limpsfield
Chilworth Manor, Guildford
Coverwood Lakes, Ewhurst
Feathercombe, Hambledon
Hethersett, Littleworth Cross
Ridings, Tadworth
Windlesham Park, nr Bagshot

May 15 Monday
Chilworth Manor, Guildford

May 16 to 17 Tuesday to Wednesday
Chilworth Manor, Guildford

May 20 Saturday
Feathercombe, Hambledon
The Old Croft, South Holmwood

May 21 Sunday
Coverwood Lakes, Ewhurst
Dunsborough Park, Ripley
Feathercombe, Hambledon
Lodkin, Hascombe
Moleshill House, Cobham
Munstead Wood, Godalming
The Old Croft, South Holmwood
Postford House, Chilworth
Walton Poor, Ranmore

May 28 Sunday
Compton Lodge, Farnham
Copt Hill Shaw, Kingswood, Tadworth
Coverwood Lakes, Ewhurst
Crosswater Farm, Churt
High Meadow, Churt
Postford House, Chilworth

May 29 Monday
Compton Lodge, Farnham
Crosswater Farm, Churt
High Meadow, Churt

June 4 Sunday
Claremont Landscape Garden, Esher
The Copse Lodge, Burgh Heath
Coverwood Lakes, Ewhurst
Culverkeys, Ewell
Four Aces, Pirbright
Halnacker Hill, Bowlhead Green
Street House, Thursley
6 Upper Rose Hill, Dorking

June 5 Monday
Four Aces, Pirbright

June 7 Wednesday
The Copse Lodge, Burgh Heath (evening)
Sutton Place, Guildford

June 8 Thursday
Chilworth Manor, Guildford (evening)

June 10 Saturday
Chilworth Manor, Guildford
The Old Croft, South Holmwood

June 11 Sunday
Brook Lodge Farm Cottage, Blackbrook
Chilworth Manor, Guildford
Dovecote, Cobham
Hatchlands Park, East Clandon
High Hazard, Blackheath
The Old Croft, South Holmwood
Ridings, Tadworth
41 West Street, Ewell

June 12 Monday
Chilworth Manor, Guildford
High Hazard, Blackheath

June 13 to 14 Tuesday to Wednesday
Chilworth Manor, Guildford

June 14 to 15 Wednesday to Thursday
Barhatch Farm, Cranleigh

June 14 Wednesday
Brook Lodge Farm Cottage, Blackbrook
Shepherds Lane Gardens
Spring Cottage, Cranleigh

June 17 Saturday
69 Station Road, Chertsey
Thanescroft, Shamley Green

June 18 Sunday
April Cottage, 36 Knowle Park, Cobham
Dorset Cottage, Cobham
Four Aces, Pirbright
Haslehurst, Haslemere
Little Priory, South Nutfield
Red Oaks, Redhill
Redland House, Capel
Spring Cottage, Cranleigh
Thanescroft, Shamley Green
Vale End, Albury
Woodcote Park Nursery, Send
Yew Tree Cottage, Haslemere

June 19 Monday
Four Aces, Pirbright

June 21 Wednesday
High Meadow, Churt
Red Oaks, Redhill

June 22 Thursday
Tilford Cottage, Tilford

June 25 Sunday
66 Avenue Road, Belmont
2 Chinthurst Lodge, Wonersh
Dunsborough Park, Ripley
Heathside, Cobham
106 Liberty Lane, Addlestone

June 28 Wednesday
2 Chinthurst Lodge, Wonersh
RHS Garden Wisley (evening)
Shepherds Lane Gardens

July 2 Sunday
66 Avenue Road, Belmont
Brookwell, Bramley
Four Aces, Pirbright (evening)
Huntsmore, Shackleford
Woodbury Cottage, Reigate

July 3 Monday
Four Aces, Pirbright
Huntsmore, Shackleford

July 5 Wednesday
Woodbury Cottage, Reigate (evening)

July 6 Thursday
66 Avenue Road, Belmont (evening)
Chilworth Manor, Guildford (evening)
Huntsmore, Shackleford

July 8 Saturday
Chilworth Manor, Guildford
Little Mynthurst Farm, Norwood Hill
Stuart Cottage, East Clandon
Tanyard Farmhouse, Langshott, Horley (evening)

July 9 Sunday
Arden Lodge, Limpsfield
Chilworth Manor, Guildford
47 Harvest Road, Englefield Green
Heathfield, Albury Heath
Little Mynthurst Farm, Norwood Hill
41 Shelvers Way, Tadworth
Stuart Cottage, East Clandon

July 10 Monday
Chilworth Manor, Guildford

July 11 to 12 Tuesday to Wednesday
Chilworth Manor, Guildford

July 12 Wednesday
Culverkeys, Ewell (evening)

Heathfield, Albury Heath (evening)
41 Shelvers Way, Tadworth
Shepherds Lane Gardens
Tanyard Farmhouse, Langshott, Horley (evening)

July 13 Thursday
Walnut House, Reigate (evening)

July 14 Friday
Red Oaks, Redhill (evening)

July 16 Sunday
Beverstone, Oxshott
Brook Lodge Farm Cottage, Blackbrook
Munstead Wood, Godalming
Red Oaks, Redhill
Walnut House, Reigate

July 19 Wednesday
Brook Lodge Farm Cottage, Blackbrook
Long Barton, Guildford

July 23 Sunday
Heathfield, Albury Heath
50 Milton Avenue, Sutton
73 Ottways Lane, Ashtead
Tanhouse Farm, Newdigate
Walton Poor, Ranmore
91 West Hill Avenue, Epsom

July 26 Wednesday
High Meadow, Churt
Long Barton, Guildford

July 27 Thursday
73 Ottways Lane, Ashtead

July 29 Saturday
Street House, Thursley

July 30 Sunday
72 Green Wrythe Lane, Carshalton
47 Harvest Road, Englefield Green
Nuthatch, Haslemere
Vale End, Albury

August 2 Wednesday
Vale End, Albury (evening)

August 3 Thursday
Stuart Cottage, East Clandon (evening)

August 5 Saturday
The Old Croft, South Holmwood

August 6 Sunday
10 The Glade, Stoneleigh
Odstock, Bletchingley
The Old Croft, South Holmwood

August 12 Saturday
Bethany, 87 Sandy Lane, Cheam
69 Station Road, Chertsey

August 13 Sunday
Bethany, 87 Sandy Lane, Cheam
Brook Lodge Farm Cottage, Blackbrook
105 Fairway, Chertsey

August 16 Wednesday
Brook Lodge Farm Cottage, Blackbrook

August 19 Saturday
Langshott Manor, Horley

August 20 Sunday
Langshott Manor, Horley

August 22 Tuesday
RHS Garden Wisley (evening)

August 27 Sunday
Haslehurst, Haslemere
High Meadow, Churt
Yew Tree Cottage, Haslemere

August 28 Monday
High Meadow, Churt

September 3 Sunday
Woodbury Cottage, Reigate

September 6 Wednesday
Brook Lodge Farm Cottage, Blackbrook

September 10 Sunday
Woodcote Park Nursery, Send

September 17 Sunday
Claremont Landscape Garden, Esher

October 1 Sunday
Albury Park, Albury

October 15 Sunday
9 Raymead Close, Fetcham
Walton Poor, Ranmore
Winkworth Arboretum, Hascombe

October 22 Sunday
Coverwood Lakes, Ewhurst

2001

February 25 Sunday
9 Raymead Close, Fetcham

DESCRIPTIONS OF GARDENS

Albury Park, Albury ♿✂❀ (Trustees of Albury Estate) *5m SE of Guildford. From A25 take A248 towards Albury for 1/4m, then up New Rd, entrance to Albury Park immed on L.* 14-acre pleasure grounds laid out in 1670s by John Evelyn for Henry Howard, later 6th Duke of Norfolk. ¼m terraces, fine collection of trees, lake and river. The gardens of Albury Park Mansion also open (by kind permission of Country Houses Association Ltd) (house not incl, separate charge). TEAS in aid of GUTS & Albury Trust. *Adm £2 Chd 50p. Suns March 19, Oct 1 (2-5)*

Alderbrook, Smithwood Common (Mr Peter Van Den Bergh) *Cranleigh. A281 from Guildford turn L 1m out of Bramley. Turn R at roundabout then immediately L. Drive on L just beyond far end of Smithwood Common.* Approx 8 acres of woodland walks with azaleas and rhododendrons. Rock garden with large pools linked by a stream filled with bog plants which is flanked by bamboo and Japanese maples. Terraces with magnificent views to S Downs. TEAS. *Adm £2.50 Chd free. Sun May 14 (2-6)*

April Cottage, 36 Knowle Park, Cobham ♿✂❀ (Peter & Angela Orr Ewing) *1¼m SE of Cobham centre. Off A245 Stoke Rd. Knowle Park is the 5th on the L after Esso garage.* 50′ × 156′. Photos of development in last 7yrs. Many hardy plants, some colour theming, arches, obelisks and trellis. Gazebo with cordon trained fruit trees. Potager style vegetable garden, greenhouse and fruit cage. Wall fountain. Much grown from seed and cuttings. Peat free and virtually organic. Views to open fields. *Adm £1.50 Chd free (ACNO to Stoke d'Abernon Village Hall). Sun June 18 (2-6)*

Arden Lodge, Limpsfield ♿✂ (Mr & Mrs C Bruce-Jones) *1m E of Oxted. From A25 take B269 Edenbridge rd for 200 yds. R down Brick Kiln Lane. Pastens rd 2nd turning L, house at end of road.* 2-acre greensand garden with extensive views of Weald. Herbaceous border; rhododendrons, azaleas and much formal and informal mixed planting with interesting trees, shrubs, roses and containers. TEAS. *Adm £2 Chd free. Suns May 14, July 9 (2-6)*

Ashcombe Cottage, Ranmore Common ♿✂❀ (Mrs B Davis) *2m NW of Dorking. From Dorking turn R at the top of Ranmore Hill signed Bookham, Westhumble. Pass Parish Church. In ½m go straight ahead down private drive. Cottage is at end of lane.* ¾-acre garden of old gamekeeper's cottage. Mixed beds of shrubs, perennials and annuals. Many unusual plants. Interesting water feature. Greenhouse. Small nursery selling hardy perennial plants. Home-madeTEAS. *Adm £1.50 Chd 50p. Sun May 7 (10-5).*

Private parties welcome by arrangement, please **Tel 01306 881599**

66 Avenue Road, Belmont ✲❀ (Messrs Church,Varela & Rosso-Rossi) *Sutton. Corner house on the junction with Dorset Rd. Avenue Rd runs parallel to the A217 (Belmont Rise). Turn off the A217 into Dorset Rd, Avenue Rd is 200yds ahead. Ample parking.* An artistic plantsman's front and rear garden, designed built and maintained by present owners, approx 100′ × 50′. Comprising well stocked herbaceous beds; unusual shrubs; informal water gardens; decorative patios and a countersunk lawn. Unusual garden features. Use of mirrors, metal sculptures, railway sleepers and telegraph poles. *Adm £1.50 Chd 75p. Sun June 25, July 2 (12-5),* **Evening Opening** *Thurs July 6 £2.50. Wine (5.30-8)*

NEW **Barhatch Farm, Cranleigh** ✲❀ (Mr & Mrs P M Grol) *A281 from Guildford, L at B2128 to Cranleigh through village, take Ewhurst Rd for 1m, turn L into Barhatch Rd which becomes Barhatch Lane. Garden 1st on R after Fernfell Golf Club.* A rambling garden of 6 acres, surrounding a Tudor farmhouse. Herbaceous borders, an abundance of old roses, walled pond, newly planted rose arbour and ornamental pond. Wildflower meadow and sunken garden. TEA. *Adm £2 Chd free. Wed, Thurs June 14, 15 (11.30-5.30)*

Bethany, 87 Sandy Lane, Cheam ✲❀ (Mr & Mrs B West & Mr & Mrs L West) *Situated approx 1m S of Cheam village.* ⅓-acre plantsmans garden featuring sub-tropical plants, incl palm trees, several tree ferns, bananas, agaves, bamboos and acers. Large collection of cannas; rockery with small water feature. Fruit trees, dahlias, vegetable garden and three greenhouses. TEAS. *Adm £1.50 Chd 50p. Sat, Sun Aug 12, 13 (1-5)*

NEW **Beverstone, Oxshott** ✲ (Derek & Brenda Carver) *Immediately off the A244 and adjacent to the Q8 Filling Station in Oxshott Village. Free public car park opp.* 2-acre garden comprising shrub borders, gravel and dry stream-bed garden. Specialist collections of iris and hemerocallis. The open day coincides with daylily flowering. Over 500 modern cultivars are represented making it one of Europe's most important hemerocallis collections. Partially suitable for wheelchairs. TEA. *Adm £2 Chd free. Sun July 16 (10.30-6) Private visits welcome by appt, please* **Tel 01372 842448**

Brook Lodge Farm Cottage, Blackbrook ♿✲❀ (Mrs Basil Kingham) *3m S of Dorking. Take L-hand turning for Blackbrook off A24, 1m S of Dorking 500yds past Plough Inn.* 3½-acre 50-yr-old plantsman's garden made by present owner. Hardy and tender plants, especially flowering shrubs, herbaceous, shrub roses, climbers, conifers and bulbs. Emphasis on foliage and plant association. Large kitchen garden and fruit cage, attractive herb garden and large heated greenhouse leading to smaller gardener's cottage garden. Featured in various magazines. TEAS. *Adm £2 Chd free (ACNO to St Catherine's Hospice, Crawley). Suns June 11, July 16, Aug 13, Weds June 14, July 19, Aug 16, Sept 6 (2-5). Private visits welcome if pre-booked*

Brookwell, Bramley ♿✲❀ (Mr & Mrs P R Styles) *1½m S of Bramley on A281; turn R into private road-bridleway in Birtley Green.* 2-acre garden, lake, and woodland. Mixed borders, sunken garden and knot garden planted with scented flowers and herbs. Collection of old roses, fruit tunnel, small vegetable and soft fruit garden; greenhouses and conservatory. TEAS. *Adm £2 Chd 25p. Sun July 2 (2-6). Private visits welcome by appointment. June and July , please* **Tel 01483 893423** (evenings)

Chauffeur's Flat, Tandridge ✲ (Mr & Mrs Richins) *Turn off A25 for Tandridge. Take drive on L past church. Follow arrows to circular courtyard.* Enter 1-acre tapestry of magical secret gardens with magnificent views. The surefooted visitor may explore the many surprises on this exuberant escape from reality. Imaginative use of recycled materials creates an inspired variety of ideas, while wild and specimen plants reveal an ecological haven. *Adm £2 Chd 25p. Sat to Fri May 20 to 26 Mon to Sun June 19 to 25. By appt only, please* **Tel 01883 715937**

Chilworth Manor, Guildford ♿✲ (Lady Heald CBE) *3½m SE of Guildford. From A248, in centre of Chilworth village, turn up Blacksmith Lane.* House C17 with C18 wing on site of C11 monastery recorded in Domesday Book; monastic stewponds in garden. C18 walled garden added by Sarah, Duchess of Marlborough; spring flowers; flowering shrubs; herbaceous border. House also open Sats and Suns. Attractive car park open from 12.30 for picnicking. TEAS (Sat, Sun, only). *Adm to garden £2 Chd free. Adm to house £1.50 Sat & Sun only (ACNO to Marie Curie). Open Sats to Weds April 8 to 12, May 13 to 17, June 10 to 14, July 8 to 12 (2-6).* **Evening Openings** *Thurs June 8, July 6 (6-8) Adm £2.50. Wine, also private visits welcome, please* **Tel 01483 561414**

2 Chinthurst Lodge, Wonersh ♿✲❀ (Mr & Mrs M R Goodridge) *4m S Guildford, A281. At Shalford turn E onto B2128 towards Wonersh. Just after Wonersh rd sign, before village, garden on R.* 1-acre yr-round garden, herbaceous borders, white garden, large variety specimen trees and shrubs; kitchen garden; fruit cage; two wells; ornamental pond, millennium parterre garden. TEAS. *Adm £2 Chd free (ACNO to Guildford Branch, Alzheimer's Society). Sun June 25 (12-6), Wed June 28 (2-6)*

▲ **Claremont Landscape Garden, Esher** ♿ (The National Trust) *1m SE of Esher; on E side of A307 (No access from A3 by-pass). Station: Esher. Bus GL 415, alight at entrance gates.* One of the earliest surviving English landscape gardens; begun by Vanbrugh and Bridgeman before 1720; extended and naturalized by Kent; lake; island with pavilion; grotto and turf amphitheatre; viewpoints and avenues. TEAS 11-5. *Adm £3.20 Chd £1.60 family £8. For NGS Suns June 4, Sept 17 (10-7)*

Compton Lodge, Farnham (Mr & Mrs K J Kent) *2m E of Farnham along A31 Hogs Back (new rd) follow signs to Runfold. Turn S down Crooksbury Rd at Barfield School signposted Milford/ Elstead. 1m on R Compton Way, Compton Lodge 2nd house on R.* 1¼-acre S-facing sloping garden. Exciting mixed planting of shrubs, herbaceous perennials, grasses and hostas planted for year round colour. Mature rhododendrons, azelea and heather beds. 2 ponds. Interesting aspects and views from all parts of the garden. TEAS. *Adm £2 Chd 50p. Sun, Mon May 28, 29 (11-5)*

The Copse Lodge, Burgh Heath ♿✂❀ (Mr & Mrs E Wallbank) *6m S of Sutton on A217 dual carriageway. Heathside Hotel car park 200yds on L from traffic lights at junction A217 with Reigate Rd. Please park in overflow car park at rear of hotel (our thanks to Heathside Hotel). Garden 60yds on L from hotel.* ¾-acre architectural garden featuring yuccas, palms and grasses; large tender specimens in pots; Japanese garden with bamboos, acers and Tea House; ornamental pond with waterfalls, rock garden; conservatory with specimen palms. Featured in the Daily Mail. TEAS. *Adm £2 Chd free. Sun June 4 (11-5.30).* **Evening Opening** *Wed June 7 (7-9)*

Copt Hill Shaw, Kingswood, Tadworth ♿✂❀ (Mr & Mrs Malcolm Barlow) *Alcocks Lane 6m S of Sutton off the A217. 1st turn on L after Burgh Heath traffic lights, Waterhouse Lane. Alcocks Lane 1st on L. Parking in Furze Hill, courtesy of Legal and General.* A formal garden of 1½ acres laid out in 1906. Fine yew hedges and topiary with azaleas, mature trees and pergola of old roses and clematis. Spring bulbs, alliums, small collection of unusual plants. Vegetable garden. TEAS. *Adm £2 Chd free (ACNO toThe Childrens Trust). Sun May 28 (2-5.30)*

● **Coverwood Lakes, Ewhurst** ♿✂❀ (Mrs C G Metson) *Peaslake Rd. 7m SW of Dorking. From A25 follow signs for Peaslake; garden ½m beyond Peaslake.* Landscaped water, bog garden and cottage gardens (in lovely setting between Holmbury Hill and Pitch Hill); with rhododendrons, azaleas, primulas, fine trees. 3½-acre Arboretum planted March 1990. Featured in NGS video 1. Marked farm trail to see pedigree cattle and flock of sheep. (Mr & Mrs Nigel Metson). Home-made TEAS. *Adm £2.50 Chd £1 car park and Chd under 5 free (Share to NGS). Suns April 23, 30 May 7, 14, 21, 28, June 4 (2-6); Sun Oct 22 hot soup and sandwiches (11-4.30). Also private visits welcome, please* **Tel 01306 731103/1**

■ **Crosswater Farm, Churt** ♿✂❀ (Mr & Mrs E G Millais) *Farnham and Haslemere 6m, from A287 turn E into Jumps Road ½m N of Churt village centre. After ¼m turn acute L into Crosswater Lane and follow signs for Millais Nurseries.* Idyllic 6-acre woodland garden. With plantsman's collection of rhododendrons, azaleas and sorbus, incl rare species collected in the Himalayas, and hybrids raised by the owners. Ponds, stream and companion plantings. Specialist Rhododendron nursery also open. TEAS on NGS days only. *Adm £2 Chd free. Daily May 1 to June 9. For NGS Mon May 1, Sun, Mon May 28, 29 (10-5). Private parties welcome, please* **Tel 01252 792698**

Culverkeys, Ewell ✂❀ (Anne & Geoff Salt) *20a Longdown Lane North. [OS 187 22.5608]. 1m E of Epsom (A24). 1m S of Ewell Village. Leave Ewell by-pass by Reigate Rd (A240) to pass Nescot on L. Turn R in ¼m.* A well-stocked garden, 50′ × 180′, designed for all-yr interest with many unusual plants and interesting associations, focusing on foliage, perennials and climbers (especially clematis). Of particular interest to plant enthusiasts and flower arrangers. TEAS in aid of Epsom Gardens Flower Club. *Adm £1.50 Chd 50p. Sun June 4 (2-5.30)* **Evening Opening** *£2.50. Wine. Wed July 12 (6-9)*

Dorset Cottage, Cobham ♿ (Mrs V Ellis) *1m E of Cobham off A245 Cobham to Leatherhead Rd. From Cobham, turn 2nd L after passing the Esso garage, into Oak Rd, Dorset Cottage is at the end of this cul-de-sac. Please park carefully in rd.* ⅓-acre garden with some original Victorian outhouses and walls, covered with unusual climbers. A romantic garden with sunken area and formal pond. Box hedges enclose the flower beds. There is an indoor swimming pool with palms and tender perennials. *Adm £1.50 Chd free (ACNO to Stoke D'Abernon Village Hall Building Fund). Sun June 18 (2-6)*

Dovecote, Cobham ✂❀ (Mr & Mrs R Stanley) *Off A307 Esher to Cobham rd near A3 bridge. Turn R from Cobham, L from Esher into Fairmile Lane. Then 4th L into Green Lane* ⅓-acre plot surrounding extended bothy. Secluded plant lovers yr-round garden with natural boundaries of mature trees, shrubs and hedges developed by present owners to incl many hardy plants on light sandy soil. TEAS. *Adm £1.50 Chd free. Sun June 11 (10.30-5.30)*

Dunsborough Park, Ripley ✂❀ (A J H Baron Sweerts de Landas Wyborgh) *Entrance across Ripley Green. Bus GL 715 alight Ripley village.* Extensive walled gardens redesigned by Penelope Hobhouse; herbaceous borders; 70ft gingko hedge, ancient mulberry tree, water garden. Edwardian wooden glasshouses (under restoration). Part suitable for wheelchairs. TEAS in aid of charities. *Adm £2.50 Chd £1.25. Suns July 9, Sept 10 (11-5). For NGS Suns May 21, June 25 (11-5). Private visitors welcome by appt,* **Tel 01483 225366**

Elm Tree Cottage South Croydon, see London

The Elms see London

105 Fairway, Chertsey ✂❀ (Mr Tony Keating) *Junction 11 M25 to Chertsey. Off Free Prae Rd. Opp. RC School.* Subtropical garden containing palms, bananas, tree ferns, cannas, cacti, hardy exotics, passion flowers in a front and rear garden of semi-detached house. TEA. *Adm £1 Chd 50p. Sun Aug 13 (11-5)*

Feathercombe, Hambledon ❀ (Mrs M E Campbell) *S of Godalming. 2m from Milford Station off Hambledon Rd, between Hydestile Xrds and Merry Harriers.* 12-acre garden of mature rhododendrons, azaleas, shrubs and topiary. Fine views of Blackdown, Hindhead and Hogs Back. House by Ernest Newton. Garden designed and made from 1910 by Surrey author and journalist Eric Parker and his wife Ruth (neé Messel) of Nymans. Now maintained by his grandchildren. *Adm £2.50 Chd 50p (ACNO to St Peter's Church, Hambledon). Sats, Suns, May 13, 14, 20, 21 (2-6)*

Four Aces, Pirbright ✂❀ (Mr & Mrs R V St John Wright) *5m NW of Guildford on A322 Bagshot Road. Just before Brookwood arch, opp West Hill Golf Club, L into Cemetery Pales. After village sign sharp L into Chapel Lane. Four Aces 100yds on R. Overflow parking in village green car park, 250yds.* ⅔-acre plantsmans garden with herb garden, 2 ponds, terraces with pergolas, loggias and pots. Mixed borders overflowing with shrubs, old-fashioned and other roses, perennials, all planted in informal cottage garden style. TEAS. *Adm £2 Chd free. Suns, Mons June 4, 5, 18, 19,*

July 3 (11-5). **Day and Evening Opening** *Sun July 2 (11-8). Private visits welcome by appt May to July, please* **Tel 01483 476226**

NEW 10 The Glade, Stoneleigh ✂ (Pam & John Stevens) *2m E of Epsom A24, leave Ewell By Pass at Organ Inn lights turning R into London Rd, 4th L at Briarwood 1st R into Chadacre Rd, 1st L into The Glade No 10 is on L. From A3 leave at Tolworth roundabout into Kingston Rd, 3m to Organ Inn lights turn L then as above.* A small garden aprox 90' x 30' on 2 levels, patio area with colourful pots and raised beds, gravel area with a dry river bed. Good yr-round foliage colour. Many alpines and acers. TEAS. *Adm £1.50 Chd free (ACNO to National Osteoporosis Society). Sun Aug 6 (11-5)*

NEW 72 Green Wrythe Lane, Carshalton ✂❀ (Mrs G Cooling) *From Carshalton Ponds turn N across ponds into North St. Continue to Wrythe Green, then 1st R into Green Wrythe Lane.* 150' x 70' cottage style garden incl raised rockeries, herbaceous borders, woodland area, wildlife pond, containers. Almost organic. Small needlework exhibition and craft sale. *Adm £1.50 (ACNO to Children's Cancer Unit, Royal Marsden Hospital). Sun July 30 (10.30-4.30)*

Hall Grange Croydon, see London

Halnacker Hill, Bowlhead Green ✂❀ (Mr & Mrs C N Daubeny) *From A3 southbound turn L signposted Bowlhead Green (opp Thursley exit); at Xrds turn R and go 0.7m. From A286 turn off just S of Brook into Park Lane; after 2m turn R signposted Bowlhead Green.* 6 acres of gardens and woodlands. Terraced country garden, designed as series of informal plantsman's gardens, with large variety of trees, shrubs, perennials, old roses, many tender and less common plants. Woodland garden and walks, with fine views. TEAS. *Adm £2 Chd free. Sun June 4 (2-5.30)*

47 Harvest Road, Englefield Green ✂ (Joan & Tony Faulkner) *Directly opp Royal Holloway College on A30. Nearest BR station is Egham. Car parking facilities are a short walk away in Victoria Street.* Small cottage garden, shrubs, mixed borders and ornamental trees; gazebo and small pond. Now features a Japanese style garden. TEAS. *Adm £1 Chd free. Suns July 9, 30 (2-6)*

Haslehurst, Haslemere ✂❀ (Mrs W H Whitbread) *Bunch Lane. Turn off High St into Church Lane, leave church on L, carry on to T-junction, turn R, Hazelhurst 2nd on L.* 2½ acres; lawns, superb trees, rhododendrons, azaleas; various shrubs; paved rose garden, double herbaceous border; woodland rockery & waterfall. C15 Barn. TEAS. *Adm £1.50 Chd 50p (ACNO to Queen Mary's Clothing Guild). (also* **Yew Tree Cottage***) Suns June 18, Aug 27 (2-6). Private visits welcome, please* **Tel 01428 643471**

▲ Hatchlands Park, East Clandon ♿✂ (The National Trust) *Situated near East Clandon, off A246. If using A3 from London direction, follow signposts to Ripley to join A247 and proceed via West Clandon to A246. If coming from Guildford take A25 and then A246 towards Leatherhead at West Clandon.* The garden and park were designed by Repton in 1800 and there are 3 newly restored walks in the park. On the S side of the house is a small parterre designed by Gertrude Jekyll in 1913 to flower in early June. The house is open to the public on this day. Restaurant. *Adm £1.80 Chd 90p gardens only. For NGS Sun June 11 (11.30-5.30)*

Heathfield, Albury Heath ❀ (Mr & Mrs M Demetriadi) *5½m SE of Guildford and 1m SE of Albury. From Albury take A248 E for ¼m and turn 1st R up New Road. Follow signs to car park in Heath Lane.* 1-acre plantsman's garden, larger part of which was landscaped by Mrs Demetriadi in 1996. It now contains a number of rooms with many unusual plants. Running water/bog garden and rockery, herb, vegetable and fruit gardens, Mediterranean garden, mixed borders and attractive courtyard. Coffee/TEAS in aid of Royal Surrey County Hospital's Abracadabra Appeal. *Adm £2.50 Chd free. Suns July 9, 23 (10-5).* **Evening Opening** *£3. Wine. Wed July 12 (6-8.30) Private visits welcome, please* **Tel 01483 202139**

NEW Heathside, Cobham ✂❀ (Miss M A Arnott & Mr T K Bartholomew) *1½m E of Cobham, off A245 Cobham to Leatherhead Rd. From Cobham take 4th turning L after Esso Garage into Fairmile Lane. Straight on at mini-roundabout into Water Lane for ½m. Links Green Way is 3rd turning on L.* Terraced ¼-acre plantsperson's garden on sandy soil; formal area with pergola and sundial; 50 different roses; many clematis. Ornamental fish pond, wildlife pond plus 2 other water features, urns and obelisks. Small courtyard area as seen on BBC's Gardener of the Year 99. TEAS. *Adm £1.50 Chd free. Sun June 25 (11-5)*

Hethersett, Littleworth Cross ❀ (Lady Adam Gordon) *S of Hog's Back (A31) 1½m from Seale Church on Elstead rd or 1m N from B3001 (Milford-Farnham rd) on Seale Rd.* A unique opportunity to enjoy this historic woodland garden created at the end of C19 by H J Mangles, an early hybridiser of rhododendrons. In the 25-acre wood are many mature trees and shrubs incl many of his hybrids, species from the earliest expeditions to the Himalayas, as well as large drifts of azaleas. Dogs on leads. *Adm £2 Chd under 12 free. Sun May 14 (2-6)*

High Hazard, Blackheath ♿✂❀ (Mr & Mrs P C Venning) *4½m SE of Guildford on A281, at Shalford turn E on B2128 to Wonersh, then turn L into Blackheath Lane, straight on at Xrds in village. Garden is 300yds on R. Heath car park a further 150yds up lane.* ½-acre garden designed and laid out by the present owners. Herbaceous and mixed borders containing interesting and some unusual herbaceous perennial plants, a large number of which are for sale on the premises. TEAS in aid of St Martin's Church, Blackheath. *Adm £2 Chd free. Sun, Mon June 11, 12 (2-6)*

High Meadow, Churt ✂❀ (Mrs J Humphries) *Tilford Rd. From Hindhead A3 Xrds A287 signposted Farnham. After ½m R fork to Tilford. 1.9m to Avalon PYO. Toilets. Park here, short walk to garden. Disabled park in drive.* Approx 1 acre maintained by owners. Rare and unusual plants attractively planted to provide all-year interest; large collection of old and David Austin roses, pergola walk, sunken garden with pond, colour co-ordinated borders, alpines and troughs; featured in Channel 4 Garden Party. TEAS, Bank Hols only. *Adm £2 Chd free (ACNO to GUTS. at Royal Surrey County Hospital). Bank Hols Suns, Mons April 23, 24, May 28, 29, Aug*

27, 28, Weds June 21, July 26 (2-5). Groups of more than 10 welcome, please **Tel 01428 606129**

Highlands, Leatherhead ✂❀ (Mr & Mrs R B McDaniel) *Givons Grove. From Leatherhead bypass (A24) at roundabout by Texaco garage 1m S of Leatherhead turn into Givons Grove and proceed up hill (The Downs) for ¾m, ignoring side turnings. Highlands is on the R.* Chalk garden of 1 acre on a steep slope. Large rock garden; mixed borders; pond, fruit and vegetable garden. Fine views over Mole Valley. TEAS in aid of Cystic Fibrosis. *Adm £1.50 Chd free. Sun, Wed, May 7, 10 (2-5.30)*

Hookwood Farmhouse, West Horsley ♿✂❀ (Sarah & Eric Mason) *From Guildford A246 turn R into Staple Lane (signposted Shere). At top turn L then first L into Shere Rd and first L into Fullers Fm Rd. From Leatherhead turn L into Greendene, after approx 2.5 miles turn R into Shere Rd then first L.* The 1.5 acre garden made by the owners is on S facing slope of N Downs. Wide range of plants and large collection of hardy Geraniums. Walled garden in old farmyard. *Adm £2 Chd free. Private visits welcome by app April-June, please* **Tel 01483 284760**

NEW **Huntsmore, Shackleford** ♿✂❀ (The Dowager Viscountess Leathers) *5m SW of Guildford, 1m W of A3. In village of Shackleford next to The Cider House Inn.* S-facing semi-shady garden approx ½-acre. Mixed borders incl clematis and roses surrounding C16 cottage (not open). Rose pergola and sitting places. Disabled parking please Tel 01483 810359. TEAS (2.30-4.30). *Adm £2 Chd 25p (ACNO to Mission to Seamen). Sun July 2 (12-5), Mon, Thurs July 3, 6 (2-5)*

Knightsmead, Chipstead ✂❀ (Mrs Jones & Miss Collins) *Rickman Hill Rd, Chipstead. From A23 in Coulsdon turn W onto B2032. Through traffic lights, L fork into Portnalls Rd. Top of hill at Xrds, R into Holymead Rd. R into Lissoms Rd. R into Bouverie Rd.* ½-acre plantsman's garden, owner designed and maintained. Wide variety of shrubs, perennials for yr-round interest; hellebores, spring bulbs, woodland plants; pond; scented roses; raised alpine and peat beds, clematis, hardy geraniums etc. *Adm £2 Chd 50p. Private visits welcome, please* **Tel 01737 551694**

22 Knoll Road, Dorking ♿✂❀ (David & Anne Drummond) *From one-way system after May's Garage turn L up the Horsham Rd (A2003 which runs to N Holmwood roundabout A24). Knoll Road is on R just beyond The Bush Inn.* ⅓-acre town garden, interesting and unusual plants and artefacts, mixed borders, raised beds, sinks, mini-meadow and peat bed, fern alley and some fruit and vegetables, a surprising front garden; conservatory. (Mostly suitable for wheelchairs if driven to front door.) Refreshments in aid of Amnesty. *Adm £1.50 Chd free. Sun April 30, Wed May 3 (10.30-5.30). Private visits and groups welcome, please* **Tel 01306 883280**

NEW **Langshott Manor, Horley** ♿❀ *N of Horley. Off the A23 at the Chequers roundabout. 3/4m down Ladbroke Rd on the R.* 3 acres of garden around a C16 Manor house (not open). Beautifully split by walls and hornbeam arches. Numerous borders and kitchen garden, small lake. TEAS. *Adm £2 Chd £1. Sat, Sun Aug 19, 20 (9-5)*

106 Liberty Lane, Addlestone ✂❀ (Mrs Ann Masters) *5m NE of Woking off B3121. From junction 11 of M25 take A320 signposted Woking then L into B3121 or A317 signposted Weybridge and R into B3121 and follow yellow signs.* 100′ × 30′ suburban garden belonging to self confessed 'plantaholic' containing an interesting mix of shrubs, grasses, hardy perennials, climbers and hardy geraniums, a pond and some rare and unusual plants. Special interest in propagation. Light snacks and TEAS in aid of St Paul's Church. *Adm £1 Chd free. Sun June 25 (11-5). Private visits welcome, please* **Tel 01932 851593**

Little Lodge Thames Ditton (see London)

Little Mynthurst Farm, Norwood Hill ♿✂❀ (Mr & Mrs G Chilton) *Between Leigh (2m) and Charlwood (3m); from Reigate take A217 to Horley; after 2m turn R just after river bridge at Sidlowbridge; 1st R signed Dean Oak Lane; then L at T junction.* 12-acre garden; walled, old-fashioned roses, herbaceous borders and shrubs around old farm house (not open), rose beds and lake setting; Tudor courtyard and orchard; bird and butterfly garden; rose walk, newly planted with David Austin's English roses. Kitchen garden with greenhouses and secret garden. TEAS in aid of Leigh and District Cottage Garden Society and NGS. *Adm £2 Chd free. Sat, Sun July 8, 9 (12-5). Coach parties welcome on NGS days only by prior arrangement please contact Head Gardener Mark Dobell* **Tel 01293 862639 or 863318**

NEW **Little Priory, South Nutfield** ❀ (Liz & Richard Ramsay) *Nutfield, on A25, 1.5m E of Redhill. Turn into Mid St, following sign for South Nutfield. 1st R after 40mtres Sandy Lane . Garden ⅓m on R.* Rambling 5-acre country garden, richly planted for colour and drama through the yr. Magnificent views. Victorian walled garden, ponds, wild flower areas, fruit and vegetable gardens. Restored greenhouses, incl 1860's pit greenhouse. Partly suitable for wheelchairs. Cream TEAS in aid of Winged Fellowship Trust. *Adm £2 Chd free. Sun June 18 (1-5)*

Lodkin, Hascombe ❀ (Mr & Mrs W N Bolt) *Lodkin Hill. 3m S of Godalming. Just off B2130 Godalming-Cranleigh, on outskirts of Hascombe; take narrow lane signposted to garden.* Country garden of about 5½ acres. Woodland, stream, restored Victorian greenhouses in full use. Kitchen garden and flower borders. Spring bulbs in profusion. Steep slopes but in part suitable for wheelchairs. TEAS. *Adm £1.50 Chd 20p. Suns April 16, May 21 (2-5.30). Private visits welcome, please* **Tel 01483 208323**

NEW **Long Barton, Guildford** (Harry Herbert Stokes) *Situated 1m E of Guildford centre. A246 (Epsom Rd) from Guildford, after approx ½m turn R into Tangier Rd. At top turn L into Warren Rd which becomes One Tree Hill. At Xrds turn sharp R into Longdown Rd - Long Barton last house on R.* Approx 2-acre S-facing hillside garden. Formal pond, knot garden, Japanese maples, specimen trees and many spring flowers. Decorative wrought iron and stone work. Paintings and prints of garden available. TEA. *Adm £1.50 Chd free (ACNO to St Martha's Church). Weds April 19, May 3, July 19, 26 (10-12 - 2-5)*

● Loseley Park, Guildford ♿✂❀ (Mr & Mrs M G More-Molyneux) *Leave A3 at Compton, S of Guildford, on B3000 for 2m. Signposted. Guildford Station 2m, Godalming Station 3m.* Charming 2½-acre walled garden. Featuring award-winning rose garden, with over 1,000 bushes, mainly old-fashioned varieties. Herb garden with sections for culinary, medicinal, ornamental and dye plants. Flower, vegetable and fountain gardens. Moat walk, terrace, herbaceous borders, ancient wisteria. Magnificent vine walk. TEAS *Adm £2.50 Chd £1.50 concession £2. Open May 1 to Sept 30, Weds, Thurs, Fris, Sats, Bank Hol Mons, Suns in June, July, Aug (11-5)* **Tel 01483 304440**

50 Milton Avenue, Sutton ✂❀ (Chris & David Wright) *1m E of Sutton Stn, off Westmead Rd. 154 bus to Westmead Rd/Ringstead Rd. At bottom of Ringstead Rd turn into Kingsley Ave, 1st R, then 1st L. Or bus to Wrythe Green, turn into Brookfield Ave, then 2nd turn on L.* Award winning Sutton and London in bloom front garden planted with special theme. Small rear garden 30′ × 80′, planted to capacity with hardy and tender perennials, shrubs with interesting foliage, gravel border with succulents, grasses and hostas around a small pond, patio with baskets and fuchsias. Display of antique garden tools. *Adm £1.30 Chd 50p. Sun July 23 (11-5)*

Moleshill House, Cobham ♿✂❀ (Mr & Mrs M Snell) *House is on A307 Esher to Cobham Rd next to free car park by A3 bridge.* Flower arranger's romantic walled garden. Topiary and garlanded cisterns around house; circular lawn surrounded by newly planted borders designed for drought tolerance; gravel bed; dovecote; bee alcoves; sorbus lutescens avenue, bog garden, paving and pots. TEAS. *Adm £2 Chd free. Sun May 21 (2-5) Private visits welcome by appt for 10 or more, please* **Tel 01932 864532**

Munstead Wood, Godalming ♿❀ (Sir Robert & Lady Clark) *Take B2130 Brighton Rd out of Godalming towards Horsham. After 1m church on R, Heath Lane just thereafter on L. 400yds on R is entrance to Munstead Wood. Parking on L of Heath Lane.* 10 acres of rhododendrons, azaleas, woods and shrub and flower beds. The house (not open) was designed by Edwin Lutyens and was the home of Gertrude Jekyll until her death. TEAS. *Adm £3 OAPs £1.50 Chd free (ACNO to CHASE Children's Hospice Service). Suns April 16, May 21, July 16 (2-6)*

Nuthatch, Haslemere ✂❀ (Mr & Mrs S Vaughan) *Tennysons Lane. From S end of Haslemere High St, turn L on B2131. 2nd R into Haste Hill. Straight on at Xrds, then L into Tennysons Lane. Garden 1m on L. Park in NT Blackdown car park (short walk).* 1.7 acre sloping wooded garden, developed since 1994. Herbaceous and mixed borders. Woodland areas linked by narrow (sometimes steep) paths. Unusual woodland plantings. New spring opening with many bulbs camellias and magnolias. Tropical and tender plantings in summer. Blackdown walks close by. TEAS. *Adm £1.50 Chd 50p. Suns April 30, July 30 (11-5)*

Odstock, Bletchingley (Averil & John Trott) *Between Godstone (2m) and Redhill (3m) on A25, at top of village nr Red Lion PH. Parking in village, no parking in Castle Square.* ⅔-acre plantsman's garden maintained by owners and developed for all-yr interest. Special interest in grasses and climbers, 76 at last count. Japanese features; dahlias. No-dig, low-maintenance vegetable garden. TEAS. *Adm £2 Chd free (ACNO to St Mary's Church, Bletchingley). Sun Aug 6 (1-5.30). (Disabled welcome - please telephone first* **01883 743100**)

The Old Croft, South Holmwood (David & Virginia Lardner-Burke) *3m S of Dorking. From Dorking take A24 S for 3m. Turn L at sign to Leigh-Brockham into Mill Road. ¾m on L, 2 free car parks in NT Holmwood Common. Follow signs for 500yds along woodland walk.* 5-acre parkland garden with lake, stream, ponds, woodland, wild and formal areas, herb garden, wide variety of specimen trees and shrubs; more new developments. Garden designed by owner. TEAS. *Adm £2 Chd free (ACNO to St Catherine's Hospice, Crawley). Sun, Mon April 30, May 1, Sats, Suns May 20, 21, June 10, 11, Aug 5, 6 (2-6). Access for disabled, please* **Tel 01306 888224**

73 Ottways Lane, Ashtead ♿✂❀ (Mr & Mrs Peter Gray) *From A24 Ashtead to Leatherhead rd turn into Ottways Lane just S of Ashtead Village or into Grange Rd at traffic lights N of M25 by Downsend School.* Approx ⅓-acre. Large herbaceous border, shrubs and fuchsias. Patio with pergola, hanging baskets, troughs and water feature. TEAS and extensive plant sale (share to NGS) in aid of Family Focus. *Adm £2 Chd free. Sun July 23 (11-5.30), Thurs July 27 (2-5.30)*

● Painshill Landscape Garden, nr Cobham ♿✂ (The Director) *Signed from A3. ½m W Cobham on A245. Entrance in Between Streets.* C18 lanscape garden. Restored ornamental pleasure grounds and shrubberies, 14-acre lake fed from river by immense waterwheel; grotto, ruined Abbey, Temple, Chinese Bridge, castellated Tower, Mausoleum, Turkish tent and newly planted vineyard. TEAS. *Adm £3.80, disabled, students and OAPS £3 chd 5-16 £1.50 Acc chd under 5 free. Open April to Oct, Tues to Sun and B/hols (10.30-6) (last entry 4.30); Nov to March, Tues to Thurs, Sats and Suns (11-4) or dusk if earlier (last entry 3). Closed Christmas Day and Boxing Day, open New Years Day. Pre-booked private groups of 10 and over £3 P.P., please* **Tel 01932 868113**

Pathside, 70 York Road, Cheam ✂❀ (Mr & Mrs F Wood) *York Rd runs between Cheam Rd and towards Dorset Rd which is a turning off the traffic light junction with Belmont Rise (A217).* Comparatively small but mature sub-urban garden with good range of trees, shrubs, herbaceous plants, lawn, ponds etc. A footpath pattern has been laid round the garden forming views, vistas and planted 'rooms' with landscaping. Interesting sunken dell garden, which has been rebuilt, featuring stone walls, arches and raised beds. Exhibition of paintings. TEAS in aid of 1st Cheam Brownies. *Adm £1. Sun May 7 (10-4). Groups welcome by appt, please* **Tel 0208 642 4260**

Pinewood House, Woking ♿✂ (Mrs R Van Zwanenberg) *Heath House Rd. 3m Woking, 5m Guildford off A322 opp Brookwood Cemetery Wall.* 4 acres. Walled garden and arboretum; water garden; bulbs in April. Interesting house finished in Dec '86 with indoor plants. TEAS if requested. *Adm house & gardens £3. Private visits welcome for parties of 2-30 April to Oct, please* **Tel 01483 473241**

▲ Polesden Lacey, Bookham ♿❀ (The National Trust) *nr Dorking. 1½m S of Great Bookham off A246 Leatherhead-Guildford rd.* 30 acres formal gardens; walled rose garden, winter garden, lavender garden, iris garden, lawns; magnificent views. Regency villa dating early 1820's, remodelled after 1906 by the Hon Mrs Ronald Greville. King George VI and Queen Elizabeth (now the Queen Mother) spent part of their honeymoon here. For wheelchair details Tel 01372 452048. Plants in aid of NT. Lunch and TEAS in licensed tearoom in grounds. *Adm garden and grounds £3, Chd £1.50; family ticket £7.50. For NGS garden only Sun May 7 (10-6)*

Postford House, Chilworth ♿❀ (Mrs R Litler-Jones) *4m SE Guildford A248 Route Bus LC 425 Guildford-Dorking alight nr entrance.* 25 acres woodland; bog garden; stream; rose garden; vegetable garden; rhododendrons, azaleas and shrubs; swimming pool open. Morning coffee; home-made TEAS in aid of RSPCA. *Adm £2 Chd free. Suns May 21, 28 (11-5). Private visits welcome, please* **Tel 01483 202657**

● Ramster, Chiddingfold ♿❀ (Mr & Mrs Paul Gunn) *On A283, 1½m S of Chiddingfold; large iron gates on R.* Mature 20-acre woodland garden of exceptional interest with lakes, ponds and woodland walks. Laid out by Gauntlett Nurseries of Chiddingfold in early 1900s. Fine rhododendrons, azaleas, camellias, magnolias, trees and shrubs. New bog garden. Picnic area. TEAS daily in May. *Adm £3 Chd under 16 free (Share to NGS). Daily from April 16 to July 9 (11-5). Parties welcome, please* **Tel 01428 654167**

9 Raymead Close, Fetcham ✗❀ (Mrs Susan Kirkby) *Take A245 out of Cobham, through Stoke D'Abernon on Cobham rd over motorway, through Fetcham, then L at Raymead Way, then 2nd L. From B2122 Gt Bookham to Leatherhead rd, turn L into Cobham Rd, R into Raymead Way then 2nd L.* ⅓-acre plantsman's garden of unusual design with narrow paths, small sunken garden, ponds and cosy secluded corners. Trees, shrubs, perennials and annuals with an emphasis on yr-round colour. Also interesting berries and winter bark. TEAS. *Adm £1.50 Chd £1. Sun Feb 27, Sun Oct 15 (1-4), Sun Feb 25 2001, or* **Tel 01372 373728**

Red Oaks, Redhill ✗❀ (Brian & Prue Moray) *A25 from Reigate E towards Redhill, after 1m turn R at war memorial (just after Toyota garage) into Hatchlands Rd. Then immed L for 25yds, cross Whitepost Hill junction into Blackstone Hill and park hereabouts. Walk up hill to Red Oaks following signs, approx 300yds.* This ⅔-acre pleasant garden incl cobbled courtyard, pond, conservatory, sunken garden, wide lawn with mixed borders and a view to Reigate Hill. Developed and maintained by the owners. Light lunches, TEAS. *Adm £2 Chd free. Suns June 18, July 16 (11-5). Wed June 21 (2-6)* **Evening Opening** *£3. Wine, Fri July 14 (6-9) Private visits welcome between open dates please,* **Tel 01737 764425**

Redlands House, Capel ♿✗❀ (Mr & Mrs P Jefferys) *A24 S of Dorking for 6m. Take turn to Capel village. On R before church. Park on roadside or village hall car park.* 1.5 acres of varied planting with colour themed herbaceous borders, shrubs, ornamental gazebo, pergola walk, wildlife pond and copse. Homemade teas at Capel Church. *Adm £2 Chd free. Sun June 18 (2-5)*

▲ RHS Garden Wisley ♿✗ (Royal Horticultural Society) *1m from Ripley, W of London on A3 and M25 (Junction 10). Follow signs with flower logo.* The primary garden of the RHS and centre of its scientific and educational activities. Arboretum, alpine and wild garden, rock garden, mixed borders, model gardens, model fruit and vegetable garden, rose garden, glasshouses, orchard and trial grounds. *Ticket prices (incl RHS members): £3.50 (ACNO to RHS Wisley Garden). For NGS* **Special Evening Openings** *with music, Wed June 28 (6.30-9.30),Tues Aug 22 (6-9)*

Ridings, Tadworth ♿✗❀ (Mr & Mrs K Dutton) *A217 to large roundabout 6m S of Sutton and 3m N of junction 8 on M25, take B2220 sign posted Tadworth. Take 2nd R into Tadorne Rd; L into Cross Rd. House on corner of Epsom Lane S.* 3/4-acre informal garden planted by present owners over 24yrs. Unusual trees, shrubs and herbaceous plants with emphasis on foliage and colour harmony. New water feature. Vegetable plot. TEAS. *Adm £2 Chd free. Suns May 14, June 11 (2-5.30) Private visits welcome (May to July), please* **Tel 01737 813962**

41 Shelvers Way, Tadworth ✗❀ (Mr & Mrs K G Lewis) *6m S of Sutton off the A217. 1st turning on R after Burgh Heath traffic lights heading S. 400yds down Shelvers Way on L.* ⅓-acre plantsman's garden with attractive cobbled and shingle area (unsuitable for wheelchairs) leading to a wide variety of herbaceous and other plants. Many spring bulbs followed by azaleas and old roses. Designed and developed by owners. Coffee and TEAS. *Adm £1.50 Chd free. Weds April 19, July 12. Suns April 16, July 9 (10.30-5) Groups welcome by appt, please* **Tel 01737 210707**

Shepherds Lane Gardens ✗❀ *From Guildford, 1m W from A3 on A322 Worplesdon Rd. Turn L at traffic lights at Emmanuel Church, Stoughton into Shepherds Lane. Gardens are L on brow of hill. Alternatively, via A323 Aldershot Rd and Rydes Hill Rd, Shepherds Lane is 2nd R.* TEAS. *Combined adm £1.50 Chd free (ACNO to Abbeyfield). Weds June 14 (1.30-5), June 28, July 12 (2-5) and (7-9)* **Evening Opening**.

67 Shepherds Lane (Mr & Mrs C Graham) ¼-acre suburban garden with mixed borders, lawn, gravel bed, white garden, specimen trees, pond, alpine bed, fruit garden with dwarf trees. *Private visits welcome, please* **Tel 01483 566445**

69 Shepherds Lane ♿ (Mrs J Hall) Suburban garden 35′ × 100′. Newly created in 1996 on circular theme. All seasons garden with mixed shrubs, herbaceous and tree planting in silver, pink and blue shades. Linked by ornamental gates with No 67 to appear as one garden

Spring Cottage, Cranleigh ♿✗❀ (Mr & Mrs D E Norman) *A281 from Guildford turn L 1m out of Bramley. Turn R at roundabout then immed L, into Smithwood Common Rd; garden 1m on R just N of Cranleigh School. Easy parking.* 1-acre garden with lovely view; cottage garden; small woodland garden; old roses, pond and new brick pergola. Ploughman's lunches and TEAS. *Adm £2 Chd free. Wed, Sun June 14, 18 (11.30-5.30); private visits of 12 or more welcome, please* **Tel 01483 272620**

69 Station Road, Chertsey ✗ (Steven Leon & Stephanie Grimshaw) *Junction 11 M25 to A317, L at roundabout, L*

Eastworth Rd. 1st L Highfield Rd into Station Rd. Green house on R, ¼ down Station Rd. Small garden with informal planting of unusual shrubs and trees. With gazebos, pond, folly and hidden surprises. *Adm £1.50 Chd free. Sats June 17, Aug 12 (12-4). Private visits welcome, please* **Tel 01932 567725**

Street House, Thursley ♿❀ (Mr & Mrs B M Francis) *From London take A3. 8m past Guildford turn R at sign Thursley/Churt/Frensham, 50yds past Three Horseshoes inn, bear L at fork signed The Street and NoThrough Road. Garden ahead. From Portsmouth/Petersfield turn L from A3 into Thursley village. Parking on recreation ground 100yds past house. Please park carefully in wet weather.* Street House (not open), a listed Regency building and childhood home of Sir Edwin Lutyens where he first met Gertrude Jekyll. Garden of 1¼ acres divided into three. Astrological garden. Specimen cornus kousa; rare old roses; special rhododendrons and camellias; rubus tridel. Home-made TEAS. *Adm £2 Chd 50p. Sun June 4, Sat July 29 (2-6). Private visits welcome by appt* **Tel 01252 703216**

Stuart Cottage, East Clandon ♿❀ (Mr & Mrs J M Leader) *4m E of Guildford on A246 or from Ripley - Rose Lane, follow yellow signs.* ½-acre partly walled garden surrounding C16 cottage (not open). A formal structure with informal harmonious planting. Rose/clematis walk, water features, and wisteria walk. Brick paths edged with lavender and rosemary, along with Victorian chimney pots used as planters add to the charm of this cottage garden. Also floral celebration in church. Ploughmans lunches and homemade TEAS, share to Cherry Trees and Church Fund. *Adm £2 Chd free. Sat, Sun July 8, 9 (12-5)* **Evening Opening** *Thurs Aug 3 £2.50. Wine and Music, 7-onwards) Groups welcome by appt, please* **Tel 01483 222689**

▲ Sutton Place, Guildford ♿✗ (Sutton Place Foundation) *From A320 (Guildford-Woking) turn into Clay Lane. At Xrds take Blanchards Hill towards Sutton Green. Lodge gates approx ¼m on R.* 60 acres, around Tudor Manor House (not open). A series of individual gardens each with its own theme and interest. A woodland garden which runs down to the R Wey. Many of the gardens were designed by Sir Geoffrey Jellicoe and the more recently established gardens were designed by Patrick Bowe. Light lunches and TEAS. *Adm £5 Chd £2. For NGS Wed June 7 (10-4) Suitable for wheelchairs in parts. NO COACH PARTIES ON JUNE7. Private visits welcome by prior appt. for parties of 12-40 please* **Tel 01483 504455**

Tanhouse Farm, Newdigate ♿✗ (Mr & Mrs N Fries) *Midway between Dorking and Horsham. On A24 turn L at roundabout at Beare Green. R at T junction in Newdigate 1st farm on R approx ⅔m.* C16 listed farmhouse (not open) in informal 1-acre garden developing since 1987. With herbaceous borders, collection of fuchsias and pelargonium, rose garden, small lake, stream, lily ponds, short farm walk, picnic area. Cream TEAS. *Adm £2 Chd free. Sun July 23 (2-6)*

Tanyard Farmhouse, Langshott, Horley ♿❀ (Mr & Mrs E Epson) *N of Horley on A23. From Redhill turn L into Ladbroke Rd at Shell roundabout. Garden ½m.* ⅓-acre garden owner designed and planted around a C15/17 Wealdon farmhouse (not open). Now being developed for all yr. interest; hellebores, pulmonaries, spring bulbs, fern and hosta bed; roses, clematis, hardy geraniums, white garden and pond, many perennials. Featured in Gardening Which July 1999. TEA in aid of St Catherines Hospice. *Adm £1.50 Chd 50p. Suns March 12, May 7 (12-4)* **Evening Opening** *£3. Wine. Chd £1 (incl soft drink). Sat, Wed July 8, 12 (6-8.30)*

Thanescroft, Shamley Green ♿✗❀ (Mr & Mrs Peter Talbot-Willcox) *5m S of Guildford, A281 Guildford-Horsham rd, at Shalford turn E onto B2128 to Wonersh and Shamley Green. At Shamley Green Village sign turn R to Lord's Hill, ¾m on L.* 4acres. Pool garden with shrubberies and rowan avenue. Lower level kitchen garden integrated with roses, mixed borders, yew and box hedges. Orchard with shrub roses. Lawns and fine old trees. Rhododendrons and primula walk. Ice house. TEAS. *Adm £2 Chd free. Sat, Sun June 17, 18 (2-6)*

Tilford Cottage, Tilford ✗❀ (Mr & Mrs R Burn) *3m from Farnham station along the Tilford Rd. Tilford Cottage is opp Tilford house. Parking on village green.* Approx 2 acres created during the past 10yrs by Rodney Burn in an area of outstanding natural beauty. Mediterranean terrace and conservatory with pot plants, many running water features, wildlife water meadow with 15 species of butterflies noted last year, bog garden with dragonflies, orchard, topiary garden, river walk, herb garden, knot garden, dove cote, heather bed, carp pond. Victorian style glass house, fruit and vegetable garden, formal lawns, gravel garden, fruit arches, plenty of garden seats to sit and rest. TEAS. *Adm £2.50 Chd free. Thurs June 22 (10-4). Groups by appt May 1 Sept 30* **Tel 01252 795423**

● Titsey Place Gardens, Oxted ✗ (The Trustees of the Titsey Foundation) *A25 between Oxted and Westerham, turn L into Limpsfield Village down High St, turn L (on sharp bend) into Bluehouse Lane and R into Water Lane. Follow road under M25 through park to walled garden car park.* Gresham ancestral home since 1534. Walled kitchen gardens, lakes and fountains in 15 acres. *Adm £4.50 House and garden; £2, Chd £1 (under 16) garden only. Weds and Suns May 17 to end Sept and Bank Holiday Mons (1-5). Easter Mon (garden only). Private visits welcome if pre-booked, please* **Tel 01273 407056** Infinite capacity for garden. Restricted numbers on house tours

Unicorns, Farnham ✗ (Mr & Mrs Eric Roberts) *Long Hill, The Sands. Approx 4½m E of Farnham take A31 towards Guildford. 1st slip rd to Runfold turn R, then L into Crooksbury Rd through 's' bend then L turn to The Sands through village past Barley Mow public house on R. Park tactfully in Littleworth Rd. Long Hill 1st turning on R.* Partly woodland garden on a sloping site, rhododendrons, azaleas, ferns, plants for ground cover and many other interesting and unusual plants and shrubs. *Adm £1.50 Chd free. Private visits welcome from mid April to end of July, please* **Tel 01252 782778, after 6pm**

87 Upland Road, Sutton ♿✗ (Mr & Mrs David Nunn) *50yds S Carshalton Beeches station into Waverley Way, at shops into Downside Rd, then 1st on L.* 0.4-acre secluded suburban plantsman's garden overlaying chalk. Shrubs; herbaceous; orchard; fruit and vegetable garden. Developed and maintained by owners. Display of botanical watercolour paintings. *Adm £2. By appt only May-June (not Weds), please* **Tel 020 8643 1427**

6 Upper Rose Hill, Dorking (Peter & Julia Williams) *From roundabout at A24/A25 junction follow signs to town centre and Horsham. ½m S of town centre turn L after Pizza Piazza and 2nd R at top of hill. Parking available in rd and in large car park behind Sainsbury's (5 min walk).* ½-acre informal plantman's terraced garden on dry sand. Planted for yr round interest of foliage and form; fruit and vegetables, gravel bed and alpine troughs, some unusual plants. Autumn colour, grasses attractive into Oct. Featured in Amateur Gardening Nov 98. TEAS in aid of Mole Valley Crossroads. *Adm £1.50 Chd free Sun June 4 (2-6). Private visits welcome, please* **Tel 01306 881315**

Vale End, Albury (Mr & Mrs John Foulsham) *4m SE of Guildford. From Albury take A248 W for ¼m.* 1-acre walled garden in beautiful setting overlooking mill pond and woods beyond. Borders range from hot and dry to cool and shaded with wide range of roses, annuals and perennials. Clipped yew walk with rope swag, attractive courtyard, fruit, vegetable and herb garden. Morning coffee and home-made TEAS in aid of Crossroads. *Adm £2 Chd free. Suns June 18, July 30 (10-5).* **Evening Opening** *£3. Wine. Wed Aug 2 (6-8.30) Groups welcome by prior arrangement, please* **Tel 01483 202296**

Vann, Hambledon (Mrs M Caroe) *6m S of Godalming. A283 to Wormley. Follow yellow 'Vann' signs for 2m.* An English Heritage registered garden of 4½ acres surrounding Tudor/William & Mary house (not open) with later additions and alterations by W D Caröe. Old cottage garden, pergola, ¼-acre pond, Gertrude Jekyll water garden 1911, azaleas, spring bulbs and woodland. New South End and double vegetable garden borders. Featured on TV, Great English Gardens, and many magazines. Maintained by family with 2 days help per week. Private groups and guided garden tours welcome April until end June. Lunches, home-made teas, and refreshments for groups by prior arrangement Tel or Fax 01428 683413. WC. *Adm £3 Chd 50p (ACNO to Hambledon Village Hall). Sun April 2 to Sat April 9 (10-6), Bank Hol Mon May 1 (2-6). TEAS. Tues May 2 to Sun May 7 (10-6)*

NEW **Walnut House, Reigate** (Inger & Dirk Laan) *Gatton Rd. 1m N of Reigate. M25 junction 8, A217 (signed Reigate) . Immed after Esso Garage turn L into Raglan Rd, at 1st X-rds (after0.4m) turn L into Gatton Rd. After approx 500yds Gatton Close on L. Please park carefully in Gatton Rd, no parking in Gatton Close.* Owner designed pleasure garden of ⅓-acre with comfortable seating areas enjoying varied vistas of the garden and views beyond to Reigate Hill. A garden with changing atmospheres from intimate fernery under tree canopy to large water garden with strong architectural features under open skies, leading to a romantic flower garden with unusual plants mixed with old favourites. Pergola, greenhouse, small terraced potager. TEAS Sun. *Adm £2 Chd free (ACNO to RNIB). Sun July 16 (11-5).* **Evening Opening** *£3.50 Chd free. Wine /nibbles, Thurs July 13 (5.30-9)*

■ **Walton Poor, Ranmore** (Mr & Mrs Nicholas Calvert) *4m W of Ranmore. From N and W off A246 on outskirts of East Horsley turn R to Greendene, 1st fork L Crocknorth Rd. From Dorking take Ranmore Rd to E Horsley.* Approx 3 acres; tranquil, rather secret garden; paths winding between areas of ornamental shrubs. Special features are a dell, a pond set in borders, herb garden. Autumn colour. Specialist range of herbs and other plants for sale. TEAS (May and July). *Adm £2 Chd 50p. For NGS Mon May 1, Suns May 21, July 23 (11-6) Sun Oct 15 (11-5). Private visits of 10 and over welcome to herb and main gardens by appt, please* **Tel 01483 282273**

NEW **41 West Street, Ewell** (Mr & Mrs Wrate) *1m NE of Epsom, turn L at sign for Ewell Village (Epsom Rd), then L again at telephone box into The Kingsway. Take 2nd turning on R into The Rise and R again at T-junction with West St, house at tip of incline, on RH-side.* Flower beds and fun beds - beds of grass and beds with glass - stems and stones. 2 small areas which have plants and shrubs, and where animals, insects and birds can be found. *Adm £1 Chd free. Sun June 11 (1-5)*

Windlesham Park, nr Bagshot (Mr & Mrs Peter Dimmock) *Woodlands Lane. 2m E of Bagshot. S of Sunningdale, NW of Chobham; from Windlesham Church S to T-junction, turn L into Thorndown Lane becoming Woodlands Lane over M3; entrance 100yds on R, white pillars.* 9-acre parkland setting with many and varied well established azaleas and rhododendrons. A fine cedar and mature trees; wet areas. WC. Not suitable for wheelchairs. TEAS. *Adm £2 Chd 50p (ACNO to St John the Baptist Church). Sun May 14 (2-6)*

▲ **Winkworth Arboretum, Hascombe** (The National Trust) *Godalming. Entrance with car parks - 3m SE of Godalming on E side of B2130. Coaches (by written arrangement). Station: Godalming 3m.* 95 acres of hillside planted with rare trees and shrubs; 2 lakes; many wild birds; view over N Downs. In spring magnolias and bluebells bring superb displays of colour, matched by the dramatic reds and golds of autumn. Tours on both days with Eric Barrs, Head of Arboretum from kiosk 2.30pm; £2 extra, chd free. Limited suitability for wheelchairs. Disabled visitors use lower car park. Disabled WC. TEAS 11-5.30. *Adm £3 Chd 5-16 £1.50 Family ticket £7. All NT members donation please. For NGS Suns April 16, Oct 15 (daylight hrs)*

Wintershall Manor, Bramley (Mr & Mrs Peter Hutley) *3m S of Bramley Village on A281 turn R, then next R. Wintershall drive next on L. Bus: AV33 Guildford-Horsham; alight Palmers Cross, 1m.* 2-acre garden and 200 acres of park and woodland; bluebell walks in spring; wild daffodils; rhododendrons; specimen trees; lakes and flight ponds; superb views. Chapel of St Mary, Stations of Cross, Rosary Walk and St Francis Chapel. June 2000 'Life of Christ' (rehearsals may be in progress on NGS day). Partially suitable for wheelchairs. TEAS. *Adm £2.50 OAPs £1.50 Chd 4-14 50p (ACNO to Wintershall Charitable Trust). Sun May 7 (2-5.30). Private parties welcome, please* **Tel 01483 892167**

RHS Garden Wisley see RHS Garden Wisley

Woodbury Cottage, Reigate (Mr & Mrs R Stoneley) *Colley Lane 1m W of Reigate. M25 junction 8, A217 (direction Reigate). Immed before level Xing turn R into Somers Rd., cont as Manor Rd. At very end turn R into Coppice Lane and follow signs to car park. Garden is 300yds walk from car park.* Cottage garden just under ¼-acre made and maintained by owners. The garden is stepped on a slope with mixed harmonious planting, enhanced by its setting under Colley Hill. Still attractive in September. TEAS. *Adm £2 Chd free. Suns July 2, Sept 3 (10-5).* **Evening Opening** *£3. Wine. Wed July 5 (5-8). Private visits welcome, please* **Tel 017372 44235**

NEW **Woodcote Park Nursery, Send** (Mr & Mrs David Gibbison) *4m E of Guildford on the A246. Turn L, through E Clandon and continue on Ripley rd - Nursery is opp HM Prison. From A3, turn L in Ripley, Rose Lane, then take 2nd R for 1m.* 4 acres wholesale nursery and small private garden. Specialising in clematis - 180 varieties grown also other climbers and plants. Many interesting plants in garden. TEA. *Adm £2 Chd free. Suns April 16, June 18, Sept 10 (10-4)*

Yew Tree Cottage, Haslemere (Mr & Mrs E E Bowyer) *Bunch Lane. Turn off High St into Church Lane, leave church on L, carry on to T junction, turn L, 1st house on L.* 2-acre garden created by owners since 1976 on hillside. Large variety of trees and shrubs, water garden, kitchen garden, Jacob and Shetland sheep, rare breed poultry, Shetland pony in paddock beyond garden. Partially suitable wheelchairs. See **Haslehurst**. Teas at Haslehurst. Plants sales at Yew Tree Cottage. *Adm £1.50 Chd 50p. Suns June 18, Aug 27 (2-6). Coach parties by prior arrangement. Private visits welcome, please* **Tel 01428 644130**

Nurses Welfare Service

A nurse in charge of a night shift is attacked and tied up by robbers.
Who is there to pick up the pieces?
The Nurses Welfare Service. Tel 0171 222 1563.

The Queen's Nursing Institute

The Queen's Nursing Institute was established in 1887 as a professional organisation with charitable status. Today it promotes the highest standards of nursing for the best possible community health care.

More information is available on the NGS website www.ngs.org.uk

The *National Gardens Scheme* is pleased to invite you to special Evening Openings at

The Royal Horticultural Society's Garden at

Wisley

on the occasion of the Wisley Flower Shows

Wednesday June 28th
6:30–9pm

Tuesday August 22nd
6–9pm

The delights of an evening stroll through the renowned gardens at Wisley will be enhanced on both occasions by musical entertainment. The Wisley Flower Show marquee will be open on both evenings with plant sales by show exhibitors.

Admission: £3.50 (excluding refreshments)
in aid of the National Gardens Scheme
(admission fee also applies to RHS members)

Coach parties must pre-book two weeks in advance
Telephone (01483) 224234

The Terrace Restaurant will be open for pre-booked dinner reservations on
Telephone (01483) 225329

The Conservatory Cafe will be open for drinks and self-service buffet

RHS Garden, Wisley is located near the A3/M25 intersection at Junction 10

Sussex

Hon County Organisers:	
(East & Mid Sussex)	Mrs Janet Goldsmith, Sunnymead, Tapsells Lane, Wadhurst TN5 6RS Tel 01892 783264
(West Sussex)	Mrs Consie Dunn, Wildham, Stoughton, Chichester, Sussex West PO18 9JG 01243 535202
Assistant Hon County Organisers:	
(East & Mid-Sussex)	Mrs Julia Ball, Turf Lodge, Sheep Plain, Crowborough TN6 3ST
	Mrs Miriam Book, Appledore, 50 Hill Drive, Hove BN3 6QL
	Mrs Rosemary Collins, Windwhistle, Faircrouch Lane, Wadhurst TN5 6PP
	Mrs Judy Emrich, Old Mill Barn, Argos Hill, Rotherfield TN6 3QF
	Mrs June Henderson, The Oast, Fletching Street, Mayfield TN20 6TN
	Mr & Mrs Richard Holmes, Beauchamps, Float Lane, Udimore TN31 6BY
	Mrs Incya Humphreys, Witherenden Mill, Station Road, Stonegate, Sussex TN5 7EU
	Mrs Sophie Neal, Legsheath Farm, nr East Grinstead RH19 4JN
	Mrs Jan Newman, Graywood House, Graywood, East Hoathly BN8 6QP
	Mrs Carolyn Steel, Beeches, Cuckfield Lane, Warninglid RH17 5UB
(West Sussex)	Mrs Angela Azis, Coke's Barn, West Burton, Pulborough RH20 1HD
	Mrs Jane Burton, Church Farmhouse, Ford Water Road, Lavant, Chichester PO18 0AL
	Mrs Judith Dean, 8 Wimblehurst Road, Horsham, W Sussex RH12 2ED
	Mrs Jennifer Woodall, Nyewood House, Nyewood, Petersfield, Hants GU31 5JL
Hon County Treasurers:	
(East & Mid Sussex)	Mr David Goldsmith, Sunnymead, Tapsells Lane, Wadhurst TN5 6RS
(West Sussex)	Mr Peter Edwards, River House, Church Lane, Bury, Pulborough RH20 1PB

DATES OF OPENING

Regular openings

For details see garden description

Bates Green, Arlington
Borde Hill Garden, Haywards Heath
Cabbages & Kings, Hadlow Down
Great Dixter, Northiam
High Beeches
Merriments Gardens, Hurst Green
Moorlands, Friar's Gate, nr Crowborough
Orchards, Rowfant

By appointment only

For telephone numbers and other details see garden descriptions. Private visits welcomed

Ketleys, Flimwell
Little Thakeham, Storrington
The Old Chalk Pit, Hove
The Old Rectory, Newtimber
Spur Point, Kingsley Green
Trotton Old Rectory, Petersfield
Whitehouse Cottage, Staplefield
Yew Tree Cottage, Crawley Down

March 12 Sunday
Champs Hill, Coldwaltham

March 15 Wednesday
Champs Hill, Coldwaltham

March 19 Sunday
Champs Hill, Coldwaltham
Penns in the Rocks, Groombridge

March 22 Wednesday
Champs Hill, Coldwaltham

March 25 Saturday
The Manor of Dean, Tillington
Rymans, Apuldram

March 26 Sunday
Berri Court, Yapton
Champs Hill, Coldwaltham
Cooke's House, West Burton
Denmans, Fontwell
The Manor of Dean, Tillington
Woodstock, Chichester

March 27 Monday
Berri Court, Yapton
Cooke's House, West Burton
The Manor of Dean, Tillington
Woodstock, Chichester

March 28 Tuesday
Cooke's House, West Burton

March 29 Wednesday
Champs Hill, Coldwaltham

April 2 Sunday
Champs Hill, Coldwaltham
Cooke's House, West Burton
New Grove, Petworth

April 3 Monday
Cooke's House, West Burton
Northwood Farmhouse, Pulborough

April 4 Tuesday
Cooke's House, West Burton
Northwood Farmhouse, Pulborough

April 6 Thursday
Borde Hill Garden, Haywards Heath

April 9 Sunday
Chidmere House, Chidham

April 10 Monday
Chidmere House, Chidham

April 14 Friday
Ashdown Park Hotel, Wych Cross

April 15 Saturday
King Edward VII Hospital, Midhurst
The Manor of Dean, Tillington

April 16 Sunday
Ghyll Farm, Sweethaws Lane
The Manor of Dean, Tillington
Newtimber Place, Newtimber

April 17 Monday
The Manor of Dean, Tillington
46 Westup Farm Cottages, Balcombe

April 21 Friday
Five Oaks Cottage, West Burton

April 22 Saturday
Five Oaks Cottage, West Burton

Hampton Cottage, Fittleworth

April 23 Sunday
Bignor Park, Pulborough
Five Oaks Cottage, West Burton
Hampton Cottage, Fittleworth
Warren House, Crowborough

April 24 Monday
Bignor Park, Pulborough
Five Oaks Cottage, West Burton

April 26 to 27 Wednesday to Thursday
Little Dene, Chelwood Gate

April 27 Thursday
Five Oaks Cottage, West Burton

April 29 Saturday
Down Place, South Harting
Duckyls, Sharpthorne

April 30 Sunday
Cooksbridge, Fernhurst
Down Place, South Harting
Duckyls, Sharpthorne
Five Oaks Cottage, West Burton
High Beeches
64 Old Shoreham Road, Hove
The Patched Gloves, Broad Oak

May 1 Monday
Ashburnham Place, Battle
Cooksbridge, Fernhurst
Coombland, Coneyhurst
Five Oaks Cottage, West Burton
Highdown, Goring-by-Sea
New Grove, Petworth
Stonehurst, Ardingly
Warren House, Crowborough

May 3 Wednesday
Champs Hill, Coldwaltham
Nyewood House, Nyewood

May 5 Friday
Stone Cross House, Crowborough

May 7 Sunday
Berri Court, Yapton
Champs Hill, Coldwaltham
Chidmere House, Chidham
Framfield Grange, Uckfield
Hammerwood House, Iping
New Grove, Petworth
Offham House, Offham
Selehurst, Lower Beeding
Stone Cross House, Crowborough
Three Oaks, West Broyle, Chichester

May 8 Monday
Berri Court, Yapton
Chidmere House, Chidham
46 Westup Farm Cottages, Balcombe

May 9 Tuesday
Three Oaks, West Broyle, Chichester

May 10 Wednesday
Champs Hill, Coldwaltham

May 11 to 12 Thursday to Friday
Coke's Barn, West Burton

May 11 Thursday
Sheffield Park Garden, Sheffield Park (evening)

May 13 Saturday
Alcheringa, West Chiltington
Coke's Barn, West Burton
Five Oaks Cottage, West Burton
The Manor of Dean, Tillington
Standen, East Grinstead

May 14 Sunday
Alcheringa, West Chiltington
Ansty Gardens
Cobblers, Crowborough
Coke's Barn, West Burton
Five Oaks Cottage, West Burton
Ghyll Farm, Sweethaws Lane
Hammerwood House, Iping
The Manor of Dean, Tillington
Mountfield Court, nr Robertsbridge
The Old Farm House, Shoreham by Sea
Warren House, Crowborough

May 15 Monday
The Manor of Dean, Tillington
Mountfield Court, nr Robertsbridge

May 17 Wednesday
Champs Hill, Coldwaltham

May 18 to 19 Thursday to Friday
Five Oaks Cottage, West Burton

May 20 Saturday
Gaywood Farm, nr Pulborough
Hampton Cottage, Fittleworth
Rymans, Apuldram

May 21 Sunday
Cowbeech Farm, Cowbeech
Cowdray Park Gardens, Midhurst
Fittleworth House, Fittleworth
Gaywood Farm, nr Pulborough
Hampton Cottage, Fittleworth
6 Holbrook Park, Old Holbrook
Legsheath Farm, nr Forest Row
Moorlands, Friar's Gate, nr Crowborough
New Barn, Egdean
Sennicotts, Chichester
Warren House, Crowborough
93 Wayland Avenue, Brighton

May 22 Monday
New Barn, Egdean
46 Westup Farm Cottages, Balcombe

May 23 Tuesday
New Barn, Egdean

May 24 to 25 Wednesday to Thursday
Little Dene, Chelwood Gate

May 27 Saturday
Five Oaks Cottage, West Burton
The White Magpie, Lamberhurst

May 28 Sunday
Baker's Farm, Shipley
Cookscroft, Earnley
Cowbeech Farm, Cowbeech
Duckyls, Sharpthorne
Fishers Farm, Etchingham
Five Oaks Cottage, West Burton
Ghyll Farm, Sweethaws Lane
72 Grand Avenue, Worthing
High Beeches
Manvilles Field, Fittleworth
Maybanks Manor, Rudgwick
Nymans Garden, Handcross
Rose Cottage, Hadlow Down
The White Magpie, Lamberhurst

May 29 Monday
Cobblers, Crowborough
Cookscroft, Earnley
Coombland, Coneyhurst
Five Oaks Cottage, West Burton
Highdown, Goring-by-Sea
Manvilles Field, Fittleworth
Sienna Wood, East Grinstead
Stonehurst, Ardingly
Warren House, Crowborough

May 31 Wednesday
Maybanks Manor, Rudgwick

June 3 Saturday
Coombland, Coneyhurst
Hampton Cottage, Fittleworth
Hoathly Hill, W Hoathly
Hobbs Barton, Framfield
King John's Lodge, Etchingham
Neptune House, Cutmill (evening)

June 4 Sunday
Fitzhall, Midhurst
Hailsham Grange, Hailsham
Hampton Cottage, Fittleworth
Hobbs Barton, Framfield
King John's Lodge, Etchingham
Neptune House, Cutmill (evening)
Nyewood House, Nyewood
Pembury, Clayton

June 7 Wednesday
Nyewood House, Nyewood
West Dean Gardens

June 8 Thursday
Uppark, South Harting

June 10 Saturday
Chantry Green House, Steyning
Somerset Lodge, Petworth

June 11 Sunday
Box Cottage, Sutton
Chantry Green House, Steyning
Clinton Lodge, Fletching
Cobblers, Crowborough

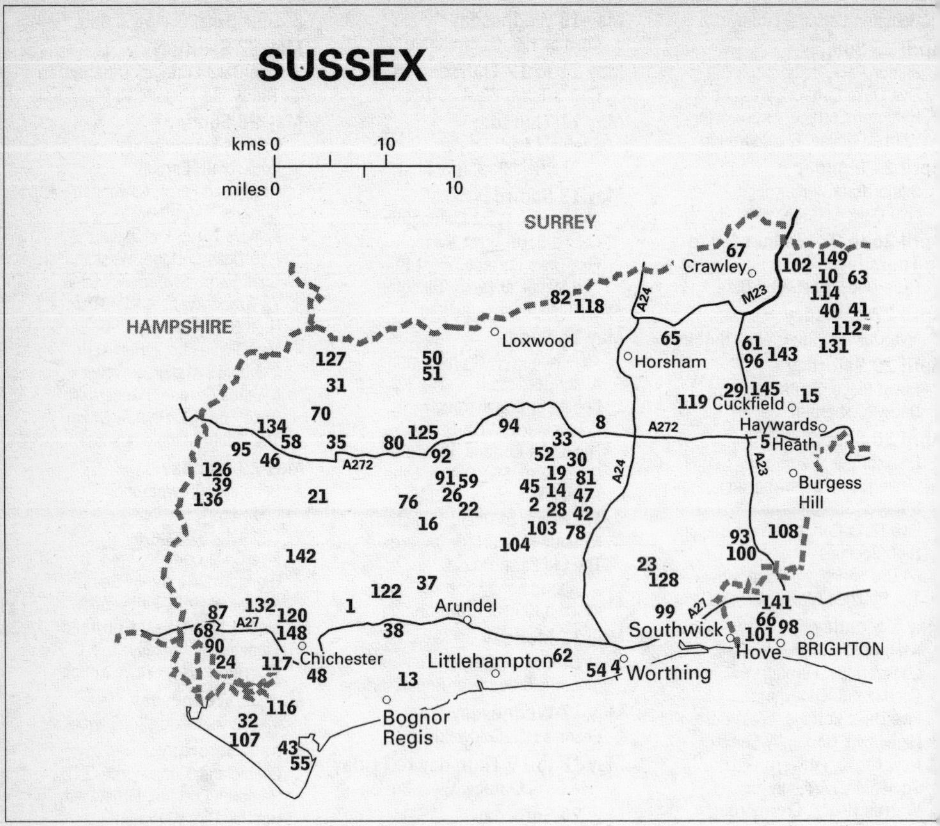

KEY

1 2 Adelaide Cottages
2 Alcheringa
3 Alfriston Clergy House
4 Ambrose Place Back Gardens
5 Ansty Gardens
6 Ashburnham Place
7 Ashdown Park Hotel
8 Baker's Farm
9 Banks Farm
10 Bankton Cottage
11 Bateman's
12 Bates Green
13 Berri Court
14 Bignor Park
15 Borde Hill Garden
16 Box Cottage
17 Brickwall House
18 Buckhurst Park
19 Bumble Cottage
20 Wilderness Farm
21 Casters Brook
22 Champs Hill
23 Chantry Green House
24 Chidmere House
25 Clinton Lodge
26 Coates Manor
27 Cobblers
28 Coke's Barn
29 Colwood House
30 Cooke's House
31 Cooksbridge
32 Cookscroft
33 Coombland
34 Cowbeech Farm
35 Cowdray Park Gardens
36 Crown House
37 Dale Park House
38 Denmans
39 Down Place
40 Duckyls, Sharpthorne
41 Duckyls Holt, West Hoathly
42 Ebbsworth
43 Fieldings
44 Fishers Farm
45 Fittleworth House
46 Fitzhall
47 Five Oaks Cottage
48 Footpath Nursery
49 Framfield Grange
50 Frith Hill
51 Frith Lodge
52 Gaywood Farm
53 Ghyll Farm
54 72 Grand Avenue
55 The Grange
56 Great Dixter
57 Hailsham Grange
58 Hammerwood House
59 Hampton Cottage
60 Hankham Hall Cottage
61 High Beeches
62 Highdown
63 Hoathly Hill
64 Hobbs Barton
65 6 Holbrook Park
66 Hove Gardens
67 Ifield Gardens
68 Jacaranda
69 Ketley
70 King Edward VII Hospital
71 King John's Lodge
72 Kings Hill House
73 Knabb's Farmhouse
74 Latchetts
75 Legsheath Farm
76 Lilac Cottage

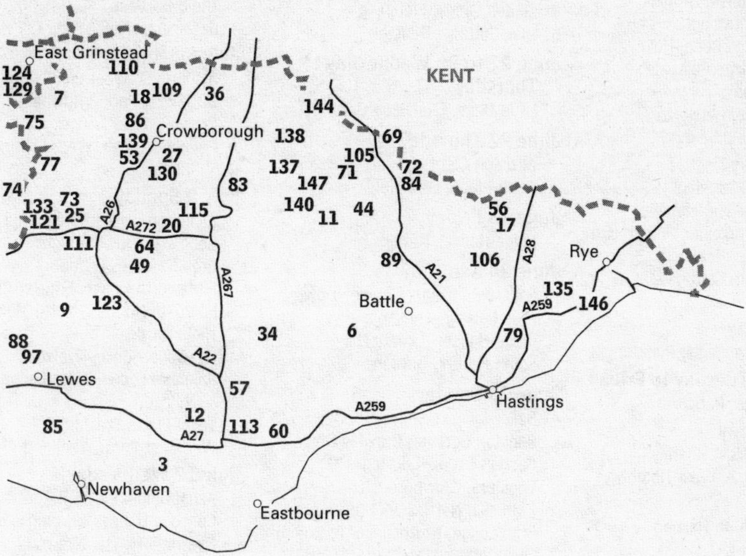

77	Little Dene
78	Little Thakeham
79	The Lodge Garden
80	The Manor of Dean
81	Manvilles Field
82	Maybanks Manor
83	Mayfield Gardens
84	Merriments Gardens
85	Monk's House
86	Moorlands
87	Morning Flight
88	Mount Harry House
89	Mountfield Court
90	Neptune House
91	New Barn
92	New Grove
93	Newtimber Place
94	Northwood Farmhouse
95	Nyewood House
96	Nymans Garden
97	Offham House
98	The Old Chalk Pit
99	The Old Farm House
100	The Old Rectory
101	64 Old Shoreham Road
102	Orchards
103	Palmer's Lodge
104	Parham Gardens
105	Pashley Manor Gardens
106	The Patched Gloves
107	33 Peerley Road
108	Pembury
109	Penns in the Rocks
110	Perryhill
111	Pheasants Hatch
112	The Priest House
113	Priesthawes Farm
114	Ridge House
115	Rose Cottage
116	Rosecroft
117	Rymans
118	Sands
119	Selehurst
120	Sennicotts
121	Sheffield Park Garden
122	Sherburne House
123	Shortgate Manor Farm
124	Sienna Wood
125	Somerset Lodge
126	South Harting Gardens
127	Spur Point
128	St Mary's House
129	Standen
130	Stone Cross House
131	Stonehurst
132	Three Oaks
133	Town Place
134	Trotton Old Rectory
135	Udimore Gardens
136	Uppark
137	Wadhurst Park
138	Wadhurst Village Gardens
139	Warren House
140	Waterloo Farm
141	93 Wayland Avenue
142	West Dean Gardens
143	46 Westup Farm Cottages
144	The White Magpie
145	Whitehouse Cottage
146	Winchelsea's Secret Gardens
147	Witherenden Mill
148	Woodstock
149	Yew Tree Cottage

Dale Park House, Madehurst
Frith Hill, Northchapel (evening)
Frith Lodge, Northchapel (evening)
Hankham Hall Cottage, Hankham, nr Pevensey
Hove Gardens
Knabb's Farmhouse, Fletching
Mayfield Gardens
Mount Harry House, Offham
Offham House, Offham
64 Old Shoreham Road, Hove
Priesthawes Farm, Polegate
Sands, Warnham
Somerset Lodge, Petworth
Town Place, Freshfield

June 12 Monday
Clinton Lodge, Fletching
Knabb's Farmhouse, Fletching
Northwood Farmhouse, Pulborough
Somerset Lodge, Petworth
46 Westup Farm Cottages, Balcombe

June 13 Tuesday
Northwood Farmhouse, Pulborough

June 13 to 16 Tuesday to Friday
Somerset Lodge, Petworth

June 15 Thursday
Duckyls Holt, West Hoathly
The Priest House, West Hoathly

June 16 Friday
Down Place, South Harting

June 17 Saturday
Coombland, Coneyhurst
Down Place, South Harting
Gaywood Farm, nr Pulborough
The Manor of Dean, Tillington
Somerset Lodge, Petworth
Town Place, Freshfield
Winchelsea's Secret Gardens

June 18 Sunday
Ambrose Place Back Gardens, Richmond Rd
Banks Farm, Barcombe
Berri Court, Yapton
Cowbeech Farm, Cowbeech
Down Place, South Harting
Fieldings, Church Norton
Frith Hill, Northchapel (evening)
Frith Lodge, Northchapel (evening)
Gaywood Farm, nr Pulborough
72 Grand Avenue, Worthing
The Grange, Church Norton
The Lodge Garden, Westfield
The Manor of Dean, Tillington
The Patched Gloves, Broad Oak
Perryhill, Hartfield
Rose Cottage, Hadlow Down
Sherburne House, Eartham
Somerset Lodge, Petworth
Udimore Gardens, Rye
93 Wayland Avenue, Brighton

June 19 Monday
Berri Court, Yapton
Fieldings, Church Norton
The Grange, Church Norton
The Lodge Garden, Westfield
The Manor of Dean, Tillington

June 21 Wednesday
Bateman's, Burwash
Clinton Lodge, Fletching
Lilac Cottage, Duncton

June 21 to 22 Wednesday to Thursday
Little Dene, Chelwood Gate

June 22 Thursday
Alfriston Clergy House, Alfriston
Town Place, Freshfield

June 23 Friday
Ridge House, Turners Hill

June 24 Saturday
Bankton Cottage, Crawley Down
Lilac Cottage, Duncton
Ridge House, Turners Hill
South Harting Gardens

June 25 Sunday
Baker's Farm, Shipley
Bankton Cottage, Crawley Down
Casters Brook, Cocking
Cobblers, Crowborough
Frith Hill, Northchapel (evening)
Frith Lodge, Northchapel (evening)
Lilac Cottage, Duncton
Mayfield Gardens
Pheasants Hatch, Piltdown
Shortgate Manor Farm, Halland
South Harting Gardens

June 26 Monday
Pheasants Hatch, Piltdown
Shortgate Manor Farm, Halland
46 Westup Farm Cottages, Balcombe

June 28 to 29 Wednesday to Thursday
Parham Gardens

June 28 Wednesday
Sands, Warnham (evening)

June 30 Friday
Cowbeech Farm, Cowbeech (evening)

July 1 Saturday
Wadhurst Village Gardens

July 2 Sunday
Casters Brook, Cocking
Hailsham Grange, Hailsham
Jacaranda, Nutbourne
Kings Hill House, Hurst Green
Morning Flight, Hambrook
Town Place, Freshfield
Wadhurst Village Gardens

July 5 Wednesday
Clinton Lodge, Fletching
Cowbeech Farm, Cowbeech (evening)
72 Grand Avenue, Worthing (evening)
Morning Flight, Hambrook

July 7 Friday
Ifield Gardens
Jacaranda, Nutbourne

July 8 Saturday
Alcheringa, West Chiltington
Buckhurst Park, Withyham
Crown House, Eridge
Palmer's Lodge, West Chiltington Village

July 9 Sunday
Alcheringa, West Chiltington
Cobblers, Crowborough
Crown House, Eridge
Fittleworth House, Fittleworth
Footpath Nursery, North Mundham
Ifield Gardens
Nyewood House, Nyewood
Palmer's Lodge, West Chiltington Village
Town Place, Freshfield
Wadhurst Park, Wadhurst

July 12 Wednesday
Ashburnham Place, Battle
Colwood House, Warninglid
Nyewood House, Nyewood

July 14 Friday
Berri Court, Yapton (evening)
Pashley Manor Gardens, Ticehurst

July 15 Saturday
Bumble Cottage, West Chiltington
The Manor of Dean, Tillington
Palmer's Lodge, West Chiltington Village

July 16 Sunday
Ansty Gardens
Bumble Cottage, West Chiltington
Colwood House, Warninglid
The Manor of Dean, Tillington
Moorlands, Friar's Gate, nr Crowborough
Nymans Garden, Handcross
Palmer's Lodge, West Chiltington Village
33 Peerley Road, East Wittering
Witherenden Mill, Stonegate

July 17 Monday
The Manor of Dean, Tillington

July 19 Wednesday
Rosecroft, Sidlesham

July 20 Thursday
Duckyls Holt, West Hoathly

July 20 to 21 Thursday to Friday
Ebbsworth, Nutbourne

July 20 Thursday
Monk's House, Rodmell nr Lewes
The Priest House, West Hoathly

July 22 Saturday
Bumble Cottage, West Chiltington
Sennicotts, Chichester (evening)

July 23 Sunday
Brickwall House, Northiam
Bumble Cottage, West Chiltington
Cobblers, Crowborough
72 Grand Avenue, Worthing
64 Old Shoreham Road, Hove
Rosecroft, Sidlesham

July 29 Saturday
Neptune House, Cutmill (evening)

July 30 Sunday
Neptune House, Cutmill (evening)

August 2 Wednesday
Clinton Lodge, Fletching

August 4 Friday
St Mary's House, Bramber

August 5 Saturday
Rymans, Apuldram (evening)
St Mary's House, Bramber

August 6 Sunday
Champs Hill, Coldwaltham
Cobblers, Crowborough
The Lodge Garden, Westfield

August 7 Monday
The Lodge Garden, Westfield

August 9 Wednesday
Champs Hill, Coldwaltham

August 12 Saturday
Bignor Park, Pulborough

August 13 Sunday
2 Adelaide Cottages, Halnaker
Bignor Park, Pulborough
Champs Hill, Coldwaltham
Waterloo Farm, Burwash Common

August 16 Wednesday
Ashdown Park Hotel, Wych Cross
Champs Hill, Coldwaltham

August 18 Friday
Latchetts, Freshfield Lane, Danehill

August 19 Saturday
Latchetts, Freshfield Lane, Danehill
The Manor of Dean, Tillington

August 20 Sunday
Champs Hill, Coldwaltham
Cobblers, Crowborough
The Manor of Dean, Tillington
33 Peerley Road, East Wittering
Perryhill, Hartfield

August 21 Monday
The Manor of Dean, Tillington

August 23 to 24 Wednesday to Thursday
Little Dene, Chelwood Gate

August 26 Saturday
Ashburnham Place, Battle

August 27 Sunday
Chidmere House, Chidham
Newtimber Place, Newtimber
Penns in the Rocks, Groombridge
Warren House, Crowborough

August 28 Monday
Chidmere House, Chidham
Highdown, Goring-by-Sea
New Barn, Egdean

September 2 Saturday
Alcheringa, West Chiltington
Bumble Cottage, West Chiltington

September 3 Sunday
Alcheringa, West Chiltington
Bumble Cottage, West Chiltington
Cobblers, Crowborough
Hankham Hall Cottage, Hankham, nr Pevensey

September 9 Saturday
Gaywood Farm, nr Pulborough
Hampton Cottage, Fittleworth
Standen, East Grinstead

September 10 Sunday
Cobblers, Crowborough
Gaywood Farm, nr Pulborough
Hampton Cottage, Fittleworth
The Old Farm House, Shoreham by Sea

September 16 Saturday
The Manor of Dean, Tillington

September 17 Sunday
The Manor of Dean, Tillington

September 18 Monday
The Manor of Dean, Tillington

September 24 Sunday
Cowbeech Farm, Cowbeech
Denmans, Fontwell

October 7 Saturday
The Manor of Dean, Tillington

October 8 Sunday
The Manor of Dean, Tillington

October 9 Monday
The Manor of Dean, Tillington

October 15 Sunday
Coates Manor, Fittleworth

October 17 Tuesday
Sheffield Park Garden, Sheffield Park

October 18 Wednesday
Ashburnham Place, Battle

October 29 Sunday
Berri Court, Yapton

October 30 Monday
Berri Court, Yapton

DESCRIPTIONS OF GARDENS

2 Adelaide Cottages, Halnaker ♿❀ (Mrs Joan Mezulis) *3½m NE of Chichester on A285. 200yds on L after Anglesey Arms PH. Off street parking.* An unexpected, hidden garden of ½ acre at the end of a path. A blaze of summer colour in herbaceous borders; vegetables from unusual seeds brought from Latvia. Wide variety of trees and shrubs. TEAS. *Adm £1.50 Chd 50p. Sun Aug 13 (2-6). Small parties welcome from May, please* **Tel 01243 773685**

NEW **Alcheringa, West Chiltington** ❀ (Trevor & Ksenia Watts) *3m E of Pulborough, 3m N of Storrington. From Pulborough turn off A283 into West Chiltington Rd then R into Monkmead Lane, L into Nytimber Lane then 1st L into Silver Wood. B2139 from Storrington L into Greenhurst Lane, R at T-junction, L into Monkmead Lane, then R into Nytimber Lane. Car park opp Nytimber Lane.* Mature woodland garden within 3/4 acre site with a framework of rare and unusual trees and shrubs, providing a sheltered environment for many tender species. Some outstanding specimen plants, herb, vegetable and fruit gardens under development. TEA. *Adm £1.50 Chd free. Sats, Suns May 13, 14, July 8, 9, Sept 2, 3 (2-6)*

NEW **Alfriston Clergy House, Alfriston** (The National Trust) *4m NE of Seaford, just E of B2108, in Alfriston village, adjoining The Tye and St Andrews Church [189: TQ521.029] Bus: RDH 125 from Lewes, Autopoint 126 from Eastbourne and Seaford.* Step back into the Middle Ages with a visit to this C14 thatched Wealden 'Hall House'. Trace the history of this magnificent building - the first to be acquired by the National Trust in 1896. Discover why the chalk floor is soaked in sour milk, and see wattle and daub restoration work in progress. Explore the delightful cottage garden and savour the idyllic setting beside Afriston's famous parish church, with stunning views across the meandering R Cuckmere. *Adm £2.50 Chd £1.25. Thurs June 22 (10-5)*

Ambrose Place Back Gardens, Richmond Rd ✂❀ *Worthing. Take Broadwater Rd into town centre, turn R at traffic lights into Richmond Rd opp Library; small town gardens with entrances on left; parking in rds.* TEAS. *Adm £1.50 Chd 50 (ACNO to Christ Church and St Paul's Worthing). Sun June 18 (11-1, 2-5)*

1 Ambrose Place (Mrs M M Rosenberg) Walled garden; shrubs, pond, climbing plants

3 Ambrose Place (Mr & Mrs M Smyth) Paved garden with climbing plants, lawn and pond

4 Ambrose Place (Mrs J Green) Paved garden, raised herbaceous borders, lawn and flowering summer plants

5 Ambrose Place (Mr & Mrs P Owen) Paved with borders

6 Ambrose Place (Mrs Lesley Roberts) Attractive garden with conservatory

7 Ambrose Place (Mark & Susan Frost) Patio garden, with conservatory

NEW **9 Ambrose Place** (Mr & Mrs D Irvine) Small town garden with courtyard greenhouse and interesting water feature

11 Ambrose Place (Mrs M Stewart) Roses, summerhouse, flowering plants

13 Ambrose Place (Linda Gamble) Discrete courtyard with design studio

14 Ambrose Place (Mr & Mrs A H P Humphrey) Roses, flowering plants, greenhouse and bonsai collection

Ambrose Villa (Mrs J Leocadi) Secluded town garden, pond, statues, shrubs and perennials

Ansty Gardens ✂❀ *On A272. 3m W of Haywards Heath. 1m E of A23. Start in car park signposted in Ansty village.* Coffee, Ploughmans, TEAS & plants in aid of Riding for the Disabled, St Catherines Hospice, St James & St Peters Hospice, Ansty Village Hall Trust. *Combined adm £2.50 Chd free. Suns May 14, July 16 (11-6)*

Apple Tree Cottage (Mr & Mrs G J Longfield) Cottage garden, herbaceous borders, mature trees

Brenfield (Dr & Mrs A Mace) Major private collection of cacti and succulents

Greenacre (Mr & Mrs V Owen) 2½-acre mixed garden

Netherby (Mr & Mrs R Gilbert) Cottage garden *May 14 only*

Whydown Cottage (Mrs R Gibson) 1-acre woodland garden

Ashburnham Place, Battle ♿✂❀ (Mr Graham Wood - Ashburnham Christian Trust) *5m W of Battle on A271 (formerly B2204).* 220 acres of beautifully landscaped gardens with glorious views over 3 lakes designed by George Dance and Capability Brown. Recent restoration work includes scented Prayer Garden and kitchen gardens within the 4-acre walled garden. Work in progress on C19 winter garden. Peaceful woodland walks. Features from several centuries. Light Lunches July 12 and Aug 26, Cream TEAS in C18 orangery. *Adm £2.50 Chd 50p (ACNO to Ashburnham Christian Trust). Mon May 1 (2-5), Wed July 12, Sat Aug 26 (11-5), Wed Oct 18 (2-5)*

Ashdown Park Hotel, Wych Cross ✂ (Mr Kevin Sweet) *6m S of E Grinstead. Take A22, 3m S of Forest Row turn L at Wych Cross by garage, 1m on R. From M25 take M23 S and leave at junction 10 taking A264 to E Grinstead. Approach from S on A22, turn R at Wych Cross.* 186 acres surrounding Ashdown Park Hotel. Parkland setting, mixture of woodland walks, water gardens and walled garden with glasshouse. Fine mature specimen trees, terraced lawns leading to carp filled lake. Restored 'Secret Garden'. A peaceful oasis in the heart of Ashdown Forest. Gardens and grounds under 7yr restoration plan. TEA. *Adm £2.50 Chd free. Fri April 14, Wed Aug 16 (2-6)*

Baker's Farm, Shipley ✂❀ (Mr & Mrs Mark Burrell) *5m S of Horsham. Take A24 then A272 W, 2nd turn to Dragon's Green, L at George and Dragon then 300yds on L.* Large Wealden garden, lake, laburnum tunnel, shrubs, trees, rose walks of old-fashioned roses; scented knot garden and bog gardens. TEAS. *Adm £2 Chd free (ACNO to St Mary the Virgin, Shipley). Suns May 28, June 25 (2-6). Parties by appt, please* **Tel 01403 741215**

Banks Farm, Barcombe ♿✂❀ (Mr M R Warren) *5m NE Lewes. Take A26 Uckfield rd, approx 3m turn L to Barcombe. At Xrds (2m) turn R, signed Newick. ¼m turn R. Approach from A275, 2½m N of Lewes take Barcombe turn at Rainbow Inn.* This 9-acre garden has glorious views across to S Downs. Created from 'nothing' over 40yrs by present owner. Wide variety of trees and shrubs with many unusual species demonstrates owner's gardening passion. Roses, 3 large ponds with fish and waterside planting, sweeping lawns. TEAS. *Adm £2.50 Chd free. Sun June 18 (2-6)*

Bankton Cottage, Crawley Down ♿✂❀ (Mr & Mrs Robin Lloyd) *4m W of East Grinstead. 2½m E of M23 (J.10). On B2028 1m N of Turners Hill Xrds.* 3½-acre partially walled cottage garden; herbaceous borders, shrub and climbing roses, small lake and pond with bog gardens. Enormous number of terracotta pots planted up. Private garden of the owners of Pots and Pithoi. TEAS in aid of Cheshire Homes. *Adm £2 Chd free. Sat, Sun June 24, 25 (2-6). Large parties welcome by appt only May to July, please* **Tel 01342 718907 or 714793**

▲ **Bateman's, Burwash** ♿✂ (Miss Jan Wallwork Wright) *½m S (A265). From rd leading S from W end of village.* Home of Rudyard Kipling from 1902-1936. Garden laid out before he lived in house and planted yew hedges, rose garden, laid paths and made pond. Bridge to mill which grinds local wheat into flour. LUNCHES and TEAS. *Adm £5 Groups 15 or more £4.25 Chd £2.50 For NGS Wed June 21 (11-5.30) last entry 4.30. Parties welcome by appt on open days, please* **Tel 01435 882302, Fax 882811**

Bates Green, Arlington ♿✂❀ (Mr & Mrs J R McCutchan) *2½m SW of A22 at Hailsham, 2m S Michelham Priory, Upper Dicker, and 2½m from Wilmington on A27 [TQ 5507].* Plantsman's tranquil garden of over 1½ acres; extensive refurbished rockery, natural pond, mixed borders with colour themes, shaded foliage garden giving yr-round interest from spring bulbs to autumn cyclamen. TEA self service. *Adm £2 Chd free. Every Mon April to Sept 10.30-6. Private visits welcome, please* **Tel 01323 482039**

Berri Court, Yapton ♿❀ (Mr & Mrs J C Turner) *5m SW of Arundel. In centre of village between PO & Black Dog PH.*

A2024 Littlehampton-Chichester rd passes. Intensely planted 2-acre garden of wide interest; trees, flowering shrubs, heathers, eucalyptus, daffodils, shrub roses, hydrangeas and lily pond. TEA June 18 and 19 for afternoon opening. *Adm £1.50 Chd free. Suns, Mons March 26, 27, May 7, 8, June 18, 19, (2-5); Sun, Mon Oct 29, 30 (12-4.30).* **Evening Opening** *Fri July 14. Wine. (6-8.30) Private visits welcome for 4 and more, please* **Tel 01243 551663**

Bignor Park, Pulborough ❀ (The Viscount & Viscountess Mersey) *5m S of Petworth on West Burton rd. Nearest village Sutton (Sussex).* 11 acres of trees, shrubs, flowers and magnificent views of the South Downs, from Chanctonbury Ring to Bignor Hill. New pond in the shrubbery. Outdoor exhibition of Aeolian harps. Bring a picnic. TEAS. *Adm £2.50 Chd free. Easter Sun, Mon April 23, 24 Sat, Sun Aug 12, 13 (12-5)*

■ **Borde Hill Garden, Haywards Heath** ♿❀ (Andrewjohn Stephenson Clarke Esq) *1½m N of Haywards Heath on Balcombe Rd.* Visitor attraction of the year 1999 SEETB.'One of the country's truly great gardens' - Country Life. 200 acres of garden and parkland; wide diversity of species from rhododendrons, camellias and magnolias to herbaceous borders, English roses, autumn bulbs and shrubs. Largest number of *champion* trees in private ownership. Extensive restoration with National Lottery grant. TEAS. *Adm £4.50 Chd £1.75 Family day £11, Season £27.50. Open daily all year round. For NGS Thurs April 6 (10-6)* **Tel 01444 450326, Fax 01444 440427** www.bordehill.co.uk

NEW **Box Cottage, Sutton** ♿ (Anthea Pratt) *4½m S of Petworth turn L to Sutton and Bignor proceed 2m turn R to Sutton at 1st Xrds. Enter Sutton Street and Box Cottage is on the R just before the White Horse PH. Steep drive.* Small cottage garden with beautiful views of the downs; undulating ground, informal planting, plenty of roses and small herbaceous borders. *Adm £2 Chd under 16 free. Sun June 11 (2-5)*

Brickwall House, Northiam ♿ (Frewen Charitable Trust) *8m NW of Rye on B2088.* Tudor home of Frewen family since 1666. Featured in the filming of 'Cold Comfort Farm'. Gardens and walls built and laid out by Jane Frewen c1680; chess and knot gardens; arboretum. TEAS in aid of Marie Curie Cancer Care. *Adm £2 Chd £1 under 10 free. Sun July 23 (2-5). Parties welcome of 30 to 50, please* **Tel 01797 223329**

Buckhurst Park, Withyham ✂ (Earl & Countess De La Warr) *On B2110 between Hartfield and Groombridge. Drive adjacent to Dorset Arms PH.* Historic garden undergoing complete restoration. Repton park, large lake with woodland walk and ornamental waterfall and rocks created by James Pulham. Terraces, lily pond and pergolas designed by Lutyens and originally planted by Jekyll. Shetland pony stud. TEAS. *Adm £4 Chd £2 (ACNO to Sussex Historic Churches). Sat July 8 (2-5.30). Private visits for groups sometimes possible, please* **Tel 01892 770790 or 770220**

Bumble Cottage, West Chiltington ✂ (Mr & Mrs D Salisbury-Jones) *From Storrington take B2139 Coolham Rd, then 1st L into Fryern Rd signed roundabout. 1m fork L into Monkmead Lane. Nr Roundabout Hotel.* Charming 'all seasons' garden of 1-acre created from a sandy slope. Wide variety of trees, shrubs and herbaceous borders, ponds and water features all set off by immaculate lawns. Cream Teas at Roundabout Hotel adjacent. *Adm £2 Chd 25p. Sats, Suns July 15, 16, 22, 23, Sept 2, 3 (2-6)*

■ **Cabbages & Kings, Hadlow Down** ✂❀ (Mr & Mrs Andrew Nowell) *Wilderness Farm. ½m S of A272 centre Hadlow Down.* In his guide Patrick Taylor writes 'There is no other garden like this. It offers valuable inspiration for gardeners.' Designed by Ryl Nowell. Intimate spaces richly planted and detailed, lead out to meadow paths in spectacular countryside. Adjoining farm buildings house a permanent exhibition explaining the principles of garden design. TEAS. *Adm £3 OAPs £2.50. Open Thurs, Fri, Sat, Sun, Mon Easter- end Oct (10.30-5.30). Group visits welcome by appt, please* **Tel 01825 830552**

Casters Brook, Cocking ♿✂ (Marion & John Whitehorn) *3m S of Midhurst at Cocking PO on A286 take sharp turn E; garden is 100yds to right.* Ponds, with islands, fountains, trout and a small bridge distinguish this 2-acre site, sloping past lawns and rose beds down to the ponds with a gunnera under a huge plane tree. Near the house are a fig court, potager and herb garden; by the churchyard a secret garden and a shady walk. Dramatic sculptures by Philip Jackson on loan add the finishing touch. TEAS. *Adm £2 Chd free (ACNO to Cocking Church). Suns June 25, July 2 (2-6). Private visits welcome, please* **Tel 01730 813537**

Champs Hill, Coldwaltham ♿✂❀ (Mr & Mrs David Bowerman) *S of Pulborough. on A29, turn R to Fittleworth; garden 400yds.* 27 acres of acid-loving plants around sand pits and woodland. Superb views. TEAS. *Adm £2.50 Chd free. Suns, Weds March 12, 15, 19, 22, 26 29, April 2, May 3, 7, 10, 17, Aug 6, 9, 13, 16, 20 Suns (2-6), Weds (11-4). Private visits welcome for parties of 10 and over, please* **Tel 01798 831868**

Chantry Green House, Steyning ✂❀ (Mr R S Forrow & Mrs J B McNeil) *5m N of Worthing, 10m NW of Brighton off A283. Turn into Church St from High St opp White Horse Inn. Garden 150yds down on LH-side. Parking on Fletchers Croft car park, entrance opp church.* An interesting 1-acre garden, recently redesigned by Jack Grant White. Features incl a wall fountain, herbaceous borders and extensive shrub borders with a predominance of colourful evergreens providing interest throughout the year. Small arboretum; rock and water garden. *Adm £2 Chd 50p. Sat, Sun June 10, 11 (2-5)*

Chidmere House, Chidham ♿ (Mr Thomas Baxendale) *6m W of Chichester. A259 1m Bus: SD276/200 Chichester-Emsworth.* Interesting garden, open for NGS since 1935; subject of article in 'Country Life' and other magazines; yew and hornbeam hedges; bulbs, and flowering shrubs bounded by large mere, now a private nature reserve. C16 house (not open). TEAS Suns only. *Adm £2 Chd free under 12 (ACNO to Chidham Parish Church). Suns, Mons April 9, 10, May 7, 8 (2-6) Aug 27, 28 (2-7). Parties welcome, please* **Tel 01243 572287 or 573096**

Clinton Lodge, Fletching ♿✂ (Mr & Mrs H Collum) *4m NW of Uckfield; from A272 turn N at Piltdown for Fletching,*

1½m. 6-acre formal and romantic garden, overlooking parkland, with old roses, double herbaceous borders, yew hedges, pleached lime walks, copy of C17 scented herb garden, medieval-style potager, vine and rose allee, wild flower garden. Carolean and Georgian house (not open). TEAS. *Adm £3 Chd £2 (ACNO to Fletching Church Fabric Fund). Sun June 11, Mon June 12, Weds June 21, July 5, Aug 2 (2-5.30). Parties over 20 welcome by appt, please* **Tel 01825 722952**

Coates Manor, Fittleworth ✄❀ (Mrs G H Thorp) *½m S of Fittleworth; turn off B2138 at signpost marked 'Coates.'* 1-acre, mainly shrubs and foliage of special interest, surrounding Elizabethen house (not open). Flowing design punctuated by clipped shrubs and specimen trees. Newly paved walled garden with interesting perennials, clematis, scented climbers and smaller treasures. Cyclamen, nerines, amaryllis, berries and coloured foliage give late season interest. Featured in UK and foreign garden magazines. TEAS in aid of Children's Society. *Adm £1.50 Chd 20p. Sun Oct 15 (11-5). Private visits welcome, please* **Tel 01798 865356**

Cobblers, Crowborough ♿✄❀ (Mr & Mrs Martin Furniss) *Mount Pleasant, Crowborough. A26, at Crowborough Cross take B2100 towards Crowborough Station. At 2nd Xrds turn into Tollwood Rd.* 2-acre sloping site designed by present owners to display great range of herbaceous and shrub species. Famous water garden. Colour all season. A good example of the cottage style advocated by William Robinson and Gertrude Jekyll in 1900. 10 different, unique, owner-made garden seats. Subject of many articles and TV programmes. *Adm (incl home-made TEAS) £4 Chd £1. Suns May 14, June 11, 25, July 9, 23, Aug 6, 20, Sept 3, 10, Mon May 29 (2.30-5.30). Groups welcome by appt, please* **Tel 01892 655969**

Coke's Barn, West Burton ✄ (Mr & Mrs Nigel Azis) *5m SW of Pulborough-Petworth. At foot of Bury Hill turn W off A29 to West Burton for 1m then follow signs.* Just under 1-acre garden around converted barn 1670 (not open) which divides into 2 natural spaces. The yard a sheltered enclosure with gravelled areas, mixed shrubs, roses and other traditional cottage perennials; walls covered in decorative ivies, vines, roses and clematis. 2nd part of garden subdivided by hedges. Planting follows gentle contours; at far end 2 small pools surrounded by damp loving plants. Conservatory on S side of barn. TEAS. *Adm £2 Chd 50p. Thurs, Fri, Sat, Sun May 11, 12, 13, 14 (2-5). Private visits for parties of 4 and over Adm £2.50 please,* **Tel/Fax 01798 831636**

Colwood House, Warninglid ♿ (Mr & Mrs Patrick Brenan) *⅓ ⅓m W of A23 on B2115 at E end of Warninglid village.* 6½ acres with mature and specimen trees from the last century. Rolling lawns and woodland edge, 100ft terrace and herbaceous border overlooking flower-rimmed croquet lawn. New parterre garden, herb and rose gardens. Cut turf labyrinth and forsythia tunnel. Fountains; ornaments; gazebos and pavilions. Pets' cemetery and gypsy caravan. TEAS. *Adm £2 Chd 20p (ACNO to Action Research). Wed, Sun July 12, 16 (2-6)*

Cooke's House, West Burton ♿✄ (Miss J B Courtauld) *5m SW of Pulborough. Turn off A29 at The Squire and Horse, Bury, ¾m.* Old garden with views of the Downs; Elizabethan house (not open); varied interest, spring flowers, topiary, herbaceous borders, herbs. TEA. *Adm £1.50 Chd free under 14. Suns, Mons, Tues March 26, 27, 28, April 2, 3, 4 (1-5). Private visits welcome,* **please Tel 01798 831353/ 831371**

Cooksbridge, Fernhurst ✄ (Mr & Mrs N Tonkin) *On A286 between Haslemere and Midhurst, ¾m S of Fernhurst Xrds.* 6 acres, and adjoining bluebell wood beside the R Lodd. This is a plantsman's garden for all seasons. Herbaceous border; vine and ornamental plant houses; lily pond and lake with waterfowl. TEAS. *Adm £2 Chd 50p 5 and under free (ACNO to Sussex Wildlife Trust). Sun April 30, Mon May 1 (2-6)*

Cookscroft, Earnley ♿❀ (Mr & Mrs J Williams) *6m S of Chichester. At end of Birdham Straight take L fork to E Wittering. 1m on, before sharp bend turn L into Bookers Lane. 2nd house on L .* 5-acre garden started from fields 10yrs ago. Many trees grown from provenance seeds or liners. Collections of eucalyptus, birch, snake bark maples and unusual shrubs. 3 ponds with waterfalls. Cottage garden and Japanese garden. An interesting and developing garden, incl a woodland area. TEAS in aid of St Wilfrids Hospice. *Adm £1.50 Chd free. Sun, Mon May 28, 29 (2-6). Private visits welcome by appt, please* **Tel 01243 513671**

Coombland, Coneyhurst ✄❀ (Neville Lee Esq) *In Billingshurst turn off A29 onto A272 to Haywards Heath approx 2m. In Coneyhurst, turn R for further ¾m.* This is not a tidy, predictable garden but full of peace and tranquility. 6 acres undulating clay site. Old roses with interesting underplantings. Bluebell wood and copse; large pond with water wheel; wild flowering meadow. Designed by Graham Stuart Thomas. National Collection Hardy Geraniums. TEAS and Lunches on terrace. *Adm £2 Chd 50p (ACNO to NCCPG June 3 only). Mons May 1, 29, Sats June 3, 17 (10-5)), please* **Tel 01403 741727**

Cowbeech Farm, Cowbeech ✄❀ (Lady Shawcross) *4m NE of Hailsham. A271 to Amberstone, turn off N for Cowbeech.* 5-acre garden with knot herb garden and water feature. Bog garden with many unusual plants, Japanese garden with bridge, moongate and waterfall, carp and koi carp. Beautiful colours in spring and autumn. Yellow and red borders. Farmhouse. TEAS Suns only. *Adm £3 Chd £1.25. Suns May 21, 28 (2-5) June 18 (2-6), Sept 24 (2-5).* **Evening Opening** *Fri June 30, Wed July 5 (5.30-8.30) Wine. Private visits welcome by appt May to Oct, please* **Tel 01323 832134**

Cowdray Park Gardens, Midhurst ✄ (The Viscount & Viscountess Cowdray) *S of A272. 1m E of Midhurst. Entrance by East Front.* Avenue of Wellingtonias; rhododendrons, azaleas; lakes; large variety of trees and shrubs, herb parterre; chequerboard topiary garden; Lebanon cedar 300 yrs old; pleasure garden surrounded by ha-ha, new themed herbaceous border; laburnum tunnel and cherry avenue. TEAS *Adm £2 Chd free Sun May 21 (2-6)*

Crown House, Eridge ♿✄❀ (Major L Cave (Retd)) *3m SW of Tunbridge Wells. A26 Tunbridge Wells-Crowborough* *rd (229, 729 bus route); in Eridge take Rotherfield turn S, then take 1st R, house 1st on L, short walk from bus stop.* 1½ acres with pools; rose garden and rose walk; herbaceous border; herb garden. Full size croquet lawn. Panoramic views. Prize winner in Sunday Express garden of the year competition. Plant and produce stalls. TEAS. *Adm £2 Chd under 14 free (ACNO to Multiple Sclerosis). Sat, Sun July 8, 9 (2-6). Private visits and groups welcome May to Oct, please* **Tel 01892 864389 or 864605**

Dale Park House, Madehurst (Robert & Jane Green) *Take A27 E from Chichester, or A27 W from Arundel, then A29 (London) for 2m, turn L to Madehurst and follow red arrows.* Set in parkland on the S downs with magnificent views to the sea. Large walled garden with 200' herbaceous border, mixed borders, roses. Rose and clematis arches, interesting collection of hostas, foliage plants and shrubs, orchard and kitchen garden. TEAS in aid of Madehurst Church. *Adm £2 Chd free. Sun June 11 (2-5)*

▲ **Denmans, Fontwell** ♿✂❀ (John Brookes Esq) *Chichester and Arundel 5m. Turn S on A27 at Denmans Lane, W of Fontwell Racecourse.* Renowned gardens extravagantly planted for overall, all-year interest in form, colour and texture; areas of glass for tender species. TEAS. *Adm £2.90 OAPs £2.60 Chd £1.60 child rate 4-16yrs. For NGS Suns March 26, Sept 24 (9-5)* **Tel 01243 542808**

Down Place, South Harting ✂❀ (Mr & Mrs D M Thistleton-Smith) *1m E of South Harting. B2124 to Chichester, turn L down unmarked lane below top of hill.* 7-acre hillside, chalk garden on the N side of S Downs. Extensive herbaceous, shrubs and rose borders on different levels merge into a natural wild flower meadow renowned for its collection of native orchids. Interesting walks through newly regenerated woods. Fully stocked vegetable garden and greenhouses. Spring flowers. CREAM TEAS. *Adm £2 Chd 50p (ACNO to Friends of Harting Parish Church). Sat, Sun April 29, 30 to incl exhibition of small botanical and landscape paintings. Fri, Sat, Sun June 16, 17, 18 (2-6). Private visits welcome by appt, April-July, please* **Tel 01730 825374**

Duckyls, Sharpthorne ❀ (Lady Taylor) *4m SW of E Grinstead. 6m E of Crawley. At Turners Hill take B2028 S 1m fork left to W Hoathly, turn L signed Gravetye Manor.* Interesting old 12-acre woodland garden. Partly suitable for wheelchairs. TEAS. *Adm £3 Chd £1 (ACNO to Elizabeth Fitzroy Homes). Sat, Sun April 29, 30, Sun May 28 (2-6)*

Duckyls Holt, West Hoathly ❀ (Mr & Mrs Kenneth Hill) *4m SW of E Grinstead. 6m E of Crawley. At Turners Hill take B2028 S 1m fork left to W Hoathly, 2m on R.* A surprisingly intimate cottage garden of about 2 acres on many different levels. Small herb garden, formal and informal plantings. Herbaceous borders, rose border and new formal rose garden. Heated swimming pool, which visitors are welcome to use. TEAS. Also open within walking distance The Priest House. *Combined adm £2.50 Chd free. Thurs June 15, July 20 (11-5.30)*

Ebbsworth, Nutbourne ✂❀ (Mrs F Lambert) *nr Pulborough. Take A283 E from junction with A29 (Swan Corner) 2m with 2 L forks signposted Nutbourne. Pass Rising Sun and follow signs to garden.* Charming, well-planted, owner maintained cottage garden, surrounding old cottage. Roses and lilies, together with herbaceous borders. Man-made stream and ponds planted with water plants. TEAS. *Adm £2 Chd free. Thurs, Fri July 20, 21 (2-5)*

NEW **Fieldings, Church Norton** ✂❀ (Peter & Susan Maguire) *From A27 Chichester by pass take B2145 to Selsey through Hurston and Sidlesham. On s-bend turn L to Church Norton, 150yds on turn R down Grange Lane, house 3rd on R. Or take A286 after approx 200yds turn L onto B2201 at Shell garage via Donnington and Sidlesham.* Organic garden approx 1-acre adjoining farmland within sound of the sea. Created lovingly almost from scratch since 1989, now full of flowers, trees, shrubs, fruit, ponds, lawns, wild garden and greenhouses. Outstanding vegetable area. Founders of Chichester Organic Gardening Society (COGS) in 1992 affiliated to the Henry Doubleday Research Association and Soil Association. TEAS at The Grange. *Adm £1.50 Chd 50p. Sun, Mon June 18, 19 (2-5)*

Fishers Farm, Etchingham ♿✂ (Mr & Mrs David Pettman) *Take A265 to Etchingham from A21 at Hurst Green. 1st turning L after level crossing. After ½m turn R into Fontridge Lane, continue for 1m.* 3 acres incl walled garden, pond with golden orfe, formal rose garden and mixed borders with azaleas, acers and old-fashioned shrub roses. TEAS. *Adm £2.50 Chd free. Sun May 28 (2-6)*

Fittleworth House, Fittleworth ♿✂❀ (Edward & Isabel Braham) *On Bedham Rd, just off A283.* Approx 3 acres. In Spring, bulbs, bedding, azaleas, wisteria, herbaceous borders, early vegetables. By Summer, walled vegetable garden at peak, bedding, tubs and urns, old/modern roses etc in borders, shade under magnificent cedar. Fountain. Georgian House (not open). Garden for all seasons. TEAS, plants and visitors' guide in aid of NSPCC/Village School. *Adm £1.50 Chd free and welcome. Suns May 21, July 9 (1-6). Parties welcome by arrangement (Mark Saunders), please* **Tel 01798 865074**

▲ **Fitzhall, Midhurst** ✂❀ (Mr & Mrs G F Bridger) *Iping, 3m W of Midhurst. 1m off A272, signposted Harting Elsted.* 9 acres; incl herb garden; herbaceous and shrub borders; vegetable garden, woodland walks. Farm adjoining. House (not open) originally built 1550. TEAS. *Adm £2 Chd £1. For NGS Sun June 4 (2-6)* **Tel 01730 813634**

Five Oaks Cottage, West Burton ✂❀ (Jean & Steve Jackman) *From the A29 4m S of Pulborough, take the B2138 signposted to Fittleworth and Petworth. Turn immediately L and L again at the T-junction. 1m on the L.* An artist's garden where wild and cultivated flowers compete to attract insects and birds. Many uncommon plants and quirky touches. Organic vegetable plot and exhibition of paintings inspired by the garden. A 'no smoking' garden. Unsuitable for children due to small pond and poisonous plants. Small nursery with herbaceous plants for sale. *Adm £1.50. Fris, Sats, Suns, Mons, Thurs April 21, 22, 23, 24, 27, 30, May 1, 13, 14, 18, 19, 27, 28, 29 (2-5)*

NEW **Footpath Nursery, North Mundham** ♿❀ (Noel & Jenny Bettridge) *1m SE of Chichester. Take A259 Chi-*

chester to Bognor Regis Rd. Follow signs to North Mundham. Take Church Rd opp school. Post Office Lane 2nd turning on L. Owner maintained 1-acre garden built from field over last 10yrs. Box, phormium, grasses, pond, willow figures and sculptures. 1-acre commercial greenhouse nursery growing alstromeria for cut flower market. TEAS in aid of St Stephans Church. *Adm £1.50 Chd free. Sun July 9 (2-6)*

Framfield Grange, Uckfield ♿❀ (Mr & Mrs J T Gore) *On B2102 2½m E of Uckfield or from Framfield ¼m East.* 10 acres of garden with shrub borders, wild flower meadow and lakes. Woodland walks with a variety of hybrid and species rhododendrons and azaleas. Beautifully kept walled kitchen garden. TEAS in aid of Macmillan Cancer Relief. *Adm £2 Chd free. Sun May 7 (2-6)*

Frith Hill, Northchapel ✗❀ (Mr & Mrs Peter Warne) *7m N of Petworth on A283 turn E in centre of Northchapel into Pipers Lane. ¾m on L.* 1 acre. Walled gardens with herbaceous border; shrubbery; old-fashioned roses; water and architectural features; herb garden leading to white garden with gazebo, new feature natural pond facing outstanding views of Sussex Weald. **Evening Opening** *Adm £2.50 Chd free. Wine (ACNO to 1st Northchapel Scouts). Suns June 11, 18, 25 (5-8)*

Frith Lodge, Northchapel (Mr & Mrs Geoffrey Cridland) *7m N of Petworth on A283 turn E in centre of Northchapel into Pipers Lane ¾m into bridleway.* 1-acre cottage style garden created around pair of converted Victorian gamekeepers cottages (not open). Undulating ground with spectacular roses, informal planting with paved and hedged areas; outstanding views of Sussex Weald. The English Garden 1998, Country Homes and Interiors 1999. **Evening Opening** *Adm £2.50 Chd £1. Suns June 11, 18, 25 (5-8). Parties welcome by appt only, please write to Frith Lodge, Northchapel, W Sussex, GU28 9JE*

Gaywood Farm, nr Pulborough ♿✗ (Mrs Anthony Charles) *3m S of Billingshurst turn L off A29 into Gay Street Lane. After railway bridge at 2nd junction fork L and at T junction turn L signed 'no through rd'.* 3-acre garden, surrounding ancient farm house (not open), built between C14 and C18. Fine weeping Ash, black Mulberry, Irish yews and extravagantly planted borders with interesting plant assoc. Large pond surrounded by good planting. Small gravel garden becoming established and a second, larger, now being planted. TEAS. *Adm £2 Chd free. Sats, Suns May 20, 21, June 17, 18, Sept 9, 10 (2-5). Group visits welcome, please* **Tel 01798 812223**

Ghyll Farm, Sweethaws Lane ❀ (Mr & Mrs I Ball) *Crowborough. 1m S of Crowborough centre on A26. L into Sheep Plain Lane immed R Sweethaws Lane ½m.* 'The Permissive Garden' planted by the late Lady Pearce. 1-acre. Azaleas, camellias, woodland bluebell walk; spectacular views. TEAS. *Adm £2 Chd 50p Suns April 16, May 14, 28 (2-5.30) Private visits welcome by appt, please* **Tel 01892 655505**

72 Grand Avenue, Worthing ✗ (Mr & Mrs D E Marshall) *10m W of Brighton, 6m E of Littlehampton, off A259. From Brighton follow signs for Worthing town centre then A259 at traffic lights (Richmond Rd). Continue for approx 1m to traffic lights/junction with Heene Rd. Carry straight on and take 5th turning on L for Grand Avenue.* Charming walled garden. Clematis, roses, perennials, alpines, decorative foliage trees and shrubs. Attractive range of pots. Courtyard area. *Adm £1.50 Chd free. Suns May 28, June 18, July 23 (2-5).* **Evening Opening** *Wed July 5 (5.30-8)*

NEW **The Grange, Church Norton** ♿✗ (Roger Bunn & David Haynes) *From A27 Chichester by pass take B2145 to Selsey through Hunston and Sidlesham after 6m signed Church Norton turn L, approx 150yds turn R down Grange Lane.* C17/18 farmhouse (not open) restored 15yrs ago set in 7 acres. 2 walled gardens, one planted with herbaceous plants, the other interesting shrubs and trees. Restored C18 octagonal summer house. 2500 trees have been planted to create 3 'long walks'. TEAS and Refreshments in aid of Selsey Health Centre. *Adm £1.50 Chd 50p. Sun, Mon June 18, 19 (2-5)*

● **Great Dixter, Northiam** ✗❀ (Christopher Lloyd Esq) *½m N of Northiam, off A28 8m NW of Rye.* The gardens are the hallmark of gardening writer Christopher Lloyd where the variety of clipped topiary, carpets of wild flowers, the ever changing tapestry of mixed borders (incl the famous Long Border), dreamy ponds and a startlingly exuberant exotic garden, all surrounding a late C15 medieval manor house, can be seen to astonish and inspire. *Adm house and gardens £6 Chd £1.50 gardens only £4.50 Chd £1. April to Oct daily (2-5) except Mons but open on Bank Hol Mons*

Hailsham Grange, Hailsham ♿✗❀ (Noel Thompson Esq) *Turn off Hailsham High St into Vicarage Rd, park in public car park.* Formal garden designed and planted since 1988 in grounds of former early C18 Vicarage (not open). A series of garden areas representing a modern interpretation of C18 formality; Gothic summerhouse; pleached hedges; herbaceous borders, romantic planting in separate garden compartments. Featured in Country Living and Grass Roots. TEAS in adjacent church in aid of The Childrens Society. *Adm £2 Chd free. Suns June 4, July 2 (2-5.30)*

Hammerwood House, Iping ♿❀ (The Hon Mrs J Lakin) *1m N of A272 Midhurst to Petersfield Rd. Approx 3m W of Midhurst. Well signposted.* Large informal garden; fine trees, rhododendrons, azaleas, acers, cornus, magnolias; wild garden (¼m away), bluebells, stream. TEAS. *Adm £2 Chd free (ACNO to King Edward VII Hospital, Midhurst). Suns May 7, 14 (2-5.30)*

Hampton Cottage, Fittleworth ❀ (Nick & Louise Elliott) *Off the A283 between Pulborough (2m) and Petworth (3m) School Lane is equi-distant between A283 and B2138. Hampton Cottage is behind former police house. Parking in rd or at village hall a short walk away.* A picturesque cottage garden packed with interesting and unusual plants collected by a plantaholic! Old summerhouse and garden memorabilia creating a nostalgic feel. *Adm £1.50 Chd free. Sat, Sun April 22, 23, May 20, 21, June 3, 4, Sept 9, 10 (2-5)*

NEW **Hankham Hall Cottage, Hankham, nr Pevensey** ♿❀ (Mr & Mrs Simon Buller) *4m N Eastbourne, 3m S Hailsham. From A27 take exit signed Stonecross. Turn*

N on B2104 signed Hailsham. R immediately after A27 overpass into Hankham Rd. Fork R into Foords Lane. At T-junction turn R. 200yds on R. Plantsman's 2-acre informal country garden, providing interest and colour in every month. Wide variety of trees, shrubs and perennials; natural pond and young spinney encouraging wildlife. Plougmans lunches and TEAS in aid of Break through Breast Cancer Research. *Adm £2. Suns June 11, Sept 3 (12-5)*

■ **High Beeches** (High Beeches Gardens Conservation Trust) *Situated on B2110 1m E of A23 at Handcross.* 20-acres of enchanting landscaped woodland and water gardens; spring daffodils; bluebells and azalea walks; many rare and beautiful plants; wild flower meadows; glorious autumn colours. Picnic area. Car Park. TEAS (WI Stall). *Adm £3.50 Acc chd free. Daily April, May, June Sept, Oct (1-5) closed on Weds. In July & Aug Mons & Tues only. For NGS Suns April 30, May 28 (1-5). Also by appt for organised groups at any time, please* **Tel 01444 400589**

▲ **Highdown, Goring-by-Sea** (Worthing Borough Council) *Littlehampton Rd (A259), 3m W of Worthing. Station: Goring-by-Sea, 1m.* Famous garden created by Sir F Stern situated in chalk pit and downland area containing a wide collection of plants. Spring bulbs, paeonies, shrubs and trees. Many plants were raised from seed brought from China by great collectors like Wilson, Farrer and Kingdon-Ward. *Collecting box. For NGS Mons May 1, 29, Aug 28 (10-6). Parties by appt, please* **Tel 01903 239999 ext 2544**

Hoathly Hill, W Hoathly ♿❀ (Hoathly Hill Community) *4m SW of E Grinstead. 6m E of Crawley. At Turners Hill Xrds take B2028 S, 1m fork L to W Hoathly, 2m turn R at Vinol's Cross Inn. Follow car park signs.* 5 acres resident managed organic gardens. Display herb garden with 200 medicinal and culinary varieties. Walled garden with lawn and herbaceous borders. Large vegetable and soft fruit garden. Pond with water feature. Mature trees. Extensive views to S Downs. Sculpture workshop and exhibits. TEAS. *Adm £2 Chd free. Sat June 3 (2-5.30)*

Hobbs Barton, Framfield ♿✂❀ (Mr & Mrs Jeremy Clark) *From Uckfield take B2102 E to Framfield. Approaching from S leave A22 at Pear Tree junction S end of Uckfield by pass. At T-junction by church continue ¼m along The Street, L into Gatehouse Lane for ½m, L down lane past mill.* 2½ acres of informal gardens with undulating lawns, mixed borders, shrubberies, roses etc; specimen trees incl fine Metasequoia glyptostroboides; several water features; part walled vegetable and fruit garden. Featured on Meridian TV 1999. TEAS in aid of Macmillan Cancer Relief in splendid C17 barn room. *Adm £2.50 Chd 25p. Sat, Sun June 3, 4 (2-6)*

6 Holbrook Park, Old Holbrook ♿✂❀ (John Pollard Esq) *From Horsham take A24 Dorking direction. At roundabout take A264 signposted Gatwick. Follow dual carriageway then 2nd lane on L marked Old Holbrook.* 2 acres Victorian parkland garden with fine trees, azaleas and rhododendrons. Informal areas provide colour and interest throughout the year; shrub and herbaceous walk, two ponds, conservatory, pergola, recently planted Bamboo walk. TEAS. *Adm £2 Chd free. Sun May 21 (2-6)*

Hove Gardens ✂❀ *On A27T Brighton bypass take A2038 Hove exit. At Devil's Dyke roundabout take exit into Dyke Road Ave. ⅔m R into Tongdean Rd, L into Tongdean Ave.* TEAS. *Combined adm £2 Chd 50p. Sun June 11 (12-6)*

- NEW **18 Tongdean Avenue** (Drs Howard & Caroline Carter) Situated on a hill with panoramic sea views across to Worthing, Isle of Wight and Brighton. S facing chalk garden with herbaceous borders and old shrub roses. Vegetable patch under restoration - plans available for potager and new greenhouse
- NEW **20 Tongdean Avenue** (Mr & Mrs Ian Dodds) Landscaped and designed in falling areas on hillside with views of sea to the S. Beautiful old Wych elm and pond feature. Mixed shrub and herbaceous border

Ifield Gardens ✂❀ *Approx 1m NW of Crawley. Take Ifield exit off Ifield-West Green roundabout on A23 Crawley by-pass. Follow Ifield Avenue and take 3rd turn on L. Ifield Green. Follow signs.* TEA. *Combined adm £2 Chd 50p. Fri July 7 (11-4) Sun July 9 (2-5)*

- **27 Strathmore Road** (Marcelle & Brian Newsom) Pretty compact, varied and colourful back garden
- **31 Strathmore Road** (Pat & Bill Higginbotham) Mixed planting with several ornamental features
- **37 Strathmore Road** (Majorie Tomlin) Attractively divided back garden with mixed planting
- NEW **54 Strathmore Road** (Mr & Mrs S Armitt) Small garden, approx 75' x 35'. L shaped with mixed flower beds, fruit trees, lawn and patio at each end. Small pond
- NEW **The Tweed** (Mrs Sue Gilbert) Cottage garden surrounging the old (and current !) Ifield workhouse

Jacaranda, Nutbourne ♿✂ (Mr & Mrs Ian Corteen) *On A259, 4m W of Chichester, 2m E of Emsworth, close to Barleycorn PH. Parking St Wilfrid's church hall 100yds on R in Broad Rd opp Barleycorn.* In an area of one-seventh of an acre there are shrubs, hanging baskets, containers, herbaceous borders and show quality vegetables all meticulously maintained by an enthusiast. TEAS (Sun only) at St Wilfrid's in aid of St Mary's, Chidham Fabric Fund. *Adm £1.50 Chd free. Sun July 2, Wed July 5 (2-6)*

Ketleys, Flimwell ✂ (Helen Yemm & Chris Craib) *Rosemary Lane. Approx 12m SE of Tunbridge Wells between A21 and B2087.* Airy 2½-acre garden on several levels with oblique views over Bewl Water and surrounding farmland, in its 3rd yr of extensive reshaping and replanting. Gravel garden, small vegetable garden, formal pond, lawns shrinking before advancing borders, wild pond and bog garden and bits that are even wilder. Opened for the first time last year. *Adm £3 Chd (on leads!) 50p. No open day this year, small groups welcome by appt from May onwards, please* **Tel 01580 879 300**

King Edward VII Hospital, Midhurst ♿ (The Facilities Director) *3m NW of Midhurst.* Hospital built early this century, stands in grounds of 152 acres in elevated position of great natural beauty; extensive views across Downs. Gardens by Gertrude Jekyll. Aspect over gardens and pine woods little changed. TEAS. *Collecting box. Sat April 15 (10-4)*

King John's Lodge, Etchingham ♿✂❀ (Mr & Mrs R A Cunningham) *Burwash to Etchingham on the A265 turn L* *before Etchingham Church into Church Lane which leads into Sheepstreet Lane after ½m. L after 1m.* 3-acre romantic garden surrounding a listed house (not open). Formal garden with water features, wild garden, rose walk, large herbaceous borders, old shrub roses and secret garden. Garden statuary for sale. TEAS. *Adm £2.50 Chd free. Sat June 3 (2-6), Sun June 4 (11-6). Also private visits welcome, please* **Tel 01580 819232**

Kings Hill House, Hurst Green (Mr & Mrs M Marceau) *Take A229 signposted Hawkhurst E off A21 (Coopers Corner). ⅓m R into Merriments Lane.* A mature garden of approx 4 acres set in 25 acres of rolling countryside on the border of East Sussex and Kent. Originally laid out in 1930 this nicely balanced garden features roses, herbaceous borders, rhododendrons, herb garden and pond. Additional walks; avenue of specimen trees and old woodland copse. TEAS. *Adm £2 Chd free (ACNO to Hawkhurst Cottage Hospital League of Friends). Sun July 2 (2-5.30)*

Knabb's Farmhouse, Fletching (Mrs W G Graham) *4m NW of Uckfield; from A272 turn N at Piltdown for Fletching, 1½m. Garden at N end of village and farm.* ½ acre informal garden; mixed beds and borders; shrubs, roses, perennials, foliage plants. Good views over ha-ha. TEAS. *Adm £1.50 Chd 20p. Sun, Mon June 11, 12 (2-6)*

Latchetts, Freshfield Lane, Danehill (Mr & Mrs Laurence Hardy) *5m NE Haywards Heath. SW off A275. In Danehill turn into Freshfield Lane at War Memorial. 1m on R. Parking in mown field.* Beautiful 3-4 acre country garden with over 500 trees, shrubs and plants, interesting features throughout. Water garden, wild area, colourful borders, ducks on pond beyond ha-ha. Vegetable and cutting garden, brick and stone walls, paving. Genuine well, terraces, pergolas, arches and long rose bank. Delicious home made cream TEAS. *Adm £2.50 Chd free. Fri, Sat Aug 18, 19 (2-5.30). Group visits by appt, please* **Tel 01825 790237**

Legsheath Farm, nr Forest Row (Mr & Mrs M Neal) *Legsheath Lane. 2m W of Forest Row, 1m S of Weirwood Reservoir.* Panoramic views over reservoir. Exciting 10-acre garden with woodland walks, water gardens and formal borders. Of particular interest, clumps of wild orchids, a fine davidia, acers, eucryphia and rhododendrons. TEAS. *Adm £2 Chd free. Sun May 21 (2-6)*

Lilac Cottage, Duncton (Mr & Mrs R F J Withers) *Willett Close. 3m S of Petworth on the W side of A285 opp gates Burton Park. Park in Close.* ¼ acre village garden in 5 separate areas with shrubs, small trees, herbaceous beds and approx 100 varieties of mostly shrub roses; herb garden, secret garden, ferns, alpines and cacti. TEAS. *Adm £1.50. Wed, Sat, Sun June 21, 24, 25 (2-6)*

Little Dene, Chelwood Gate (Professor & Mrs D Anderson) *8m S of East Grinstead. Take A275 off A22 at Wych Cross, then 1st L and 2nd R.* Plantsman's garden yr-round interest. Many unusual shrubs and climbers, over 100 clematis, raised alpine bed. Wheelchairs if dry. TEAS by arrangement. *Adm £1.50. Weds, Thurs April 26, 27, May 24, 25, June 21, 22, Aug 23, 24 (11-4.30). Also evening visits. Private visits and parties welcome, please* **Tel 01825 740657**

Little Thakeham, Storrington (Mr & Mrs T Ractliff) *From Storrington take B2139 to Thakeham. After 1m turn R into Merrywood Lane and garden is 400yds on L.* 4-acre garden with paved walks, rose pergola, flowering shrubs, specimen trees, herbaceous borders and carpets of daffodils in spring. The garden laid out to the basic design of Sir Edward Lutyens in 1902 and planted by his client Ernest Blackburn. Partially suitable for wheelchairs. *Adm £7 to incl tea. Garden and House viewable by prior arrangement for parties of 10 or over,* **Tel Pauline Ractliff 01903 744416**

▲ The Lodge Garden, Westfield (Sandra Worley & Danny Butler) *Between Westfield & Sedlescombe. From Hastings take A28 Ashford Rd to Westfield Village. Just past car showroom turn L into Cottage Lane past post office approx 2m on L adjacent to Westfield Place.* Redesigned over the last 8yrs into a plantsman's cottage style garden with pond, arches, gazebo and 1860 working hand pump. Small Japanese style garden. Boasting wide range of unusual herbaceous plants and shrubs surrounded by deciduous woodland. Owners nursery. TEAS. *Adm £1.50. Suns, Mons June 18, 19, Aug 6, 7 (11.30-4.30). Parties welcome by appt, please* **Tel 01424 870186**

The Manor of Dean, Tillington (Miss S M Mitford) *2m W of Petworth. Turn off A272 N at NGS sign.* Flowers, shrubs, specimen trees, bulbs in all seasons. 2 pigmy goats, Vietnamese pigs, tame lambs. House (not open) 1400-1613. TEA 50p. *Adm £1 Chd over 5 50p. Sats, Suns, Mons March 25, 26, 27, April 15, 16, 17, May 13, 14, 15, June 17, 18, 19, July 15, 16, 17, Aug 19, 20, 21, Sept 16, 17, 18, Oct 7, 8, 9 (2-5). Private visits welcome, please* **Tel 01798 861247**

Manvilles Field, Fittleworth (Mrs P J Aschan & Mrs J M Wilson) *2m W of Pulborough take A283 to Fittleworth, turn R on sharp L-hand bend.* 2 acres of garden with orchard, many interesting shrubs, clematis, roses, other herbaceous plants. Beautiful views surrounding garden. TEAS. *Adm £1.50 Chd free. Sun, Mon May 28, 29 (2-6)*

Maybanks Manor, Rudgwick (Mr & Mrs John Beckwith-Smith) *N end of Rudgwick at Cox Green. 1m from A281. Horsham 9m, Guildford 14m, Cranleigh 4m.* Approx 7 acres. Partially planned by the late Lanning Roper for the present owners in 1961. This garden has many interesting plants and features. With a 'Blue' garden a ruby wedding border and a large greenhouse full of tender plants. In a lovely setting with wonderful views. TEAS in aid of West Sussex Assoc for the Disabled, Horsham branch. *Adm £2.50 Chd free. Sun, Wed May 28, 31 (2-6)*

Mayfield Gardens *8m S of Tunbrigde Wells off A267.* Light refreshments. *Combined adm £2 Chd 20p. Suns June 11, 25 (2-5.30)*

NEW **May Cottage** (Mr & Mrs I A D Lyle) *At E end of High St turn down Fletching St by Marchants Garage signed Witherenden. ¼ on L at bottom of hill.* ¼ acre cottage garden in course of redevelopment. Paved areas, raised flower beds, small pond, wooded area, many interesting herbaceous plants

NEW **Woodnorton** ❀ (Ken & Janet Wood) *Approaching Mayfield from W turn off A267 at roundabout. ¼m on L at West St/Newick Lane junction.* Combined efforts of plantswoman wife and landscaping husband over the last 7yrs have turned this sloping ½ acre heavy clay plot into an interesting variety of gardens. Incls small stream garden, area of woodland planting, kitchen garden, terraced potager as well as a wealth of climbing roses, perennials and shrubs

● **Merriments Gardens, Hurst Green** ♿ (Mr & Mrs M Buchele, Mr David Weeks) *Hawkhurst Rd. Situated between Hawkhurst & Hurst Green.* 4-acre garden with richly planted mixed borders in country setting. Ponds, streams and rare plants give beautiful display all season. 'A unique experiment in colour composition'. TEAS. *Adm £2.50 Chd £1. Open daily April 1 to end Sept (9.30-5.30) Suns (10.30-5.30). Parties welcome by appt, please* **Tel 01580 860666**

Monk's House, Rodmell nr Lewes ✗ (The National Trust) *4m S of Lewes. From A27 to Brighton turn L at roundabout signposted Kingston. 1¼m turn R at T junction signed to Newhaven. In Rodmell turn L. ½m near church. (No access from A26). [198:TQ421.064].* A cottage garden planted in the manner of Leonard Woolf, with bold colours, bordering on the exotic. Four contrasting sections – formal walled area, orchard, large open lawn and kitchen garden. The lawn is the Woolfs' bowls lawn and the kitchen garden is currently let to the local allotments association. Garden only open. *Adm £1.50 Chd 75p. Thurs July 20 (2-5)*

Moorlands, Friar's Gate, nr Crowborough ❀ (Dr & Mrs Steven Smith) *2m N of Crowborough. St Johns Rd to Friar's Gate. Or turn L off B2188 at Friar's Gate.* 4 acres set in lush valley adjoining Ashdown Forest; water garden with ponds and streams; primulas, rhododendrons, azaleas, many unusual trees and shrubs. New river walk. Rockery restored to original 1929 design. Appearing in GRBS Calender 2000 'Gardens to Remember'. TEAS. *Adm £2.50 Chd free. Every Wed April 1 to Oct 1 (11-5). Suns May 21, July 16 (2-6)*

Morning Flight, Hambrook ✗❀ (Gillian & George Harris) *Midway between Chichester and Havant on A259 turn N opp Barleycorn PH signed Hambrook, garden 1m on R opp post office. Parking in rd.* Artist's garden. About one seventh of an acre, but packed with interest and colour. Water gardens, Bonsai, design features, herbaceous and grasses. *Adm £1.50 Chd free. Sun, Wed July 2, 5 (2-6)*

Mount Harry House, Offham ♿ (Lord & Lady Renton of Mount Harry) & **Mount Harry Lodge** *(Mr & Mrs A K Stewart-Roberts) (2 adjoining gardens). 2m NW of Lewes on S side of Ditchling Road B2116, ½m W of A275. Coach parking.* 7-acre and 1-acre terraced gardens on chalk; herbaceous and shrubbery borders, wild flower walk, specimen trees, laburnum walks, walled garden, dell garden, conservatory, ornamental tree nursery.In beautiful downland setting. *Combined adm £3.50, Chd free. (ACNO Sussex Housing and Care, formerly SHAA). Sun June 11 (2-6)*

Mountfield Court, nr Robertsbridge ✗ (Mr & Mrs Simon Fraser) *2m S of Robertsbridge. On A21 London-Hastings; ½m from Johns Cross.* 3-acre wild woodland garden; walkways through exceptional rhododendrons, azaleas, camellias and other flowering shrubs; fine trees and outstanding views. Small herb garden. Homemade TEAS. *Adm £2 Chd free (ACNO to All Saints Church Mountfield). Sun, Mon May 14, 15 (2-5)*

Neptune House, Cutmill ✗❀ (The Hon Robin & Mrs Borwick) *From Chichester take A259 straight over Bosham roundabout towards Emsworth , after ½m R into Newells Lane. 150yds turn L.* 6-acre garden incl a lake. Gravel beds, wildflower meadow, Italian courtyard with tender and unusual plants. Bring a picnic, plenty of tables and chairs available; sit and enjoy the atmosphere of this peaceful and magical garden. *Adm £2.50 Chd £1. Sats, Suns June 3, 4, July 29, 30 (2-8) with live classical music.* **Afternoon and Evening Openings**. *Private visits and coach tours are welcome from April 1 to Sept 30 by prior appt. Please* **Tel 01243 576900 or Fax 01243 575541**

New Barn, Egdean ♿✗❀ (Mr & Mrs A Tuck) *1m S of Petworth turn L off A285, at 2nd Xrds turn R into lane. Or 1m W of Fittleworth take L fork to Midhurst off A283. 200yds turn L.* 2 acres, owner maintained all yr-round garden. Converted C18 barn (not open) in beautiful peaceful farmland setting. Large natural pond and stream, water irises, roses, shrubs and herbaceous, many interesting trees. Seats in garden, picnic area, 2 swings. Autumn colour. Refreshments. *Adm £2 Chd 20p. Sun, Mon, Tues May 21, 22, 23; Bank Hol Mon Aug 28 (11-5.30). Private visits welcome all yr, min 4 visitors, please* **Tel 01798 865502**

New Grove, Petworth ♿✗❀ (Mr & Mrs Robert de Pass) *1m S of Petworth turn L off A285 and take next L. Follow signs. From the N at Xrds in Petworth straight across into Middle Street then L into High Street follow signs.* A mature garden of about 3 acres. Mainly shrubs with all year interest incl box parterres; magnolias, camellias, azaleas, cornus, roses etc. lovely views to the South Downs. TEAS in aid of King Edward VII Hospital, Midhurst. *Adm £2 Chd free. Sun April 2, Bank Hol Mon May 1, Sun May 7 (2-6). Groups welcome by arrangement min 10 people April to June,* **Tel 01798 342203**

Newtimber Place, Newtimber ♿❀ (Andrew Clay Esq) *7m N of Brighton off A281 between Poynings and Pyecombe.* Beautiful C17 moated house (not open). Gardens and woods full of bulbs and wild flowers in spring. In summer, roses, herbaceous border and lawns. Moat flanked by water plants. Mature trees. Wild garden; ducks, chickens and fish. TEAS in aid of Newtimber Church. *Adm £2 Chd 50p. Suns April 16, Aug 27 (2-5.30)*

Northwood Farmhouse, Pulborough ♿✗ (Mrs P Hill) *1m N of Pulborough on A29. turn NW into Blackgate Lane and follow lane for 2m then follow the signs.* Cottage garden with bulbs, roses, pasture with wild flowers and pond; all on Wealden clay, surrounding Sussex farmhouse (not open) dating from 1420. TEA. *Adm £2 Chd £1. Mons, Tues April 3, 4, June 12, 13 (2-6)*

Nyewood House, Nyewood ♿❀ (Mr & Mrs Timothy Woodall) *From A272 at Rogate take rd signposted Nyewood, S for approx 1¼m. At 40 mph sign on outskirts of Nyewood, turn L signposted Trotton. Garden approx 500yds on R.* 3-acre S facing garden recently renovated; colour planted borders, 100 varieties of roses, knot garden, pleaching, rose walk, water feature, and potager. TEAS. *Adm £2 Chd free. Weds May 3, June 7, July 12, Suns June 4, July 9 (2-5.30)*

▲ **Nymans Garden, Handcross** ♿✂❀ (Ms Julianne Davis) *On B2114 at Handcross signposted off M23/A23 London-Brighton rd, SE of Handcross. Bus: 137 from Crawley & Haywards Heath [TQ 265 294].* One of the great gardens of the Sussex Weald. Walled garden with fountain, hidden sunken garden, rose garden, romantic ruins and woodland walks. A few rooms in Nymans House are open. Bring your own picnic and enjoy the garden. Tearoom (11-5), shop and plant centre (11-6). *Adm £5 Chd £2.50. For NGS Suns May 28, July 16 (11-6)*

Offham House, Offham ♿❀ (Mr & Mrs H N A Goodman & Mr & Mrs P Carminger) *2m N of Lewes on A275. Cooksbridge station ½m.* Fountains; flowering trees; double herbaceous border; long paeony bed. Queen Anne house (not open) 1676 with well-knapped flint facade. Herb garden. Walled kitchen garden with glasshouses. Featured in George Plumptre's Guide to 200 Gardens in Britain. Home-made TEAS. *Adm £2 Chd 25p (ACNO to Lewes Victoria Hospital). Suns May 7, June 11 (1-5)*

The Old Chalk Pit, Hove ♿✂❀ (Mr & Mrs Hugo Martin) *27 Old Shoreham Road, Hove, E Sussex BN3 6NR. On A270.* Unexpected, romantic oasis for chalk loving plants; old roses and climbers forming different informal areas incl white garden, ponds, wildlife and shady spots. TEA by arrangement. *Adm £1.50 Chd 50p. Private and group visits welcome, please* **Tel 01273 564807**

NEW **The Old Farm House, Shoreham by Sea** ❀ (Mr & Mrs Peter Tinniswood) *2m NW of Shoreham by Sea. Coming from E of A27, turn R at T-lights after crossing R Adur. Take immediate L turn into Lancing College.* A wild, rambling old garden slowly being redeveloped with many less common flowers and shrubs mainly grown from seeds and cuttings. Emphasis on plants which suit chalky soil and dry conditions without watering once established. Contrast between the flint-walled garden round the house (not open), with overflowing beds and self sown plants, and the serener grassy dell with mature trees. The college chapel will be open. TEAS. *Adm £1.50 Chd 50p (ACNO to Friends of Lancing Chapel). Suns May 14, Sept 10 (12-5)*

The Old Rectory, Newtimber ♿ (Mr & Mrs Lambert Coles) *7m N of Brighton off A281 between Poynings and Pyecombe.* 2 acres with views of South Downs and Newtimber Church. Pond garden, fine tulip tree, perennial borders; combined kitchen and flower garden. *Adm £1.50 Chd 50p. Parties welcome any day April-July by appt, please* **Tel 01273 857288**

64 Old Shoreham Road, Hove ♿✂ (Brian & Muriel Bailey) *A270. (Opp No. 21).* Mainly walled, S facing garden 12.6 metres by 33.6 metres on flint and chalk, designed and built by owners. Many features. Automatic watering for 124 containers. Over 900 different varieties of plants incl over 100 clematis. - all labelled. TEAS. *Adm £1.50 Chd 50p. Suns April 30, June 11, July 23 (2-5) Group visits welcome, please* **Tel 01273 889247**

Orchards, Rowfant ✂❀ (Mrs Penelope Hellyer) *From Turners Hill Xrds N on B2028 for 1½m, L into Wallage Lane, or from A264 turn S at Duke's Head roundabout for 2m, R into Wallage lane - ½m turn R into farm lane.* 7-acre woodland garden created by the late renowned horticulturists Arthur and Gay Hellyer. Rhododendrons, camellias, snowdrops, hellebores, herbaceous and mixed borders, orchards, bluebell wood, wild orchid meadow, heather/conifer garden, woodland walks. Autumn colour. Continuing restoration by daughter and husband. Yr round interest. Featured in A Guide to Garden Visits by Judith Hitching and by local television. Owner's nursery. Self-service TEA. *Adm £2 Acc chd free. Weds to Sats March to Oct (12-4)* **Tel 01342 718280** Penelope.Hellyer@Hellyers.co.uk

Palmer's Lodge, West Chiltington Village ✂ (R Hodgson Esq) *At Xrds in centre of West Chiltington Village opp Queens Head. 2m E of Pulborough 3m N Storrington.* A charming plantsman's ½-acre garden with herbaceous and shrub borders. TEAS, Sunday only in aid of Motor Neurone. *Adm £1.50 Chd free. Sats, Suns July 8, 9, 15, 16 (2-6). Private visits welcome following written application (July only)*

▲ **Parham Gardens** ♿✂❀ (home of Lady Emma & Mr James Barnard) *4m SE of Pulborough on A283 Pulborough-Storrington Rd.* In heart of ancient deer park, below the South Downs. 4 acres of walled garden; 7 acres C18 Pleasure Grounds with lake. 'Veronica's Maze' brick and turf maze designed with the young visitor in mind. Picnic area. Suitable for wheelchairs on dry days. Light lunches and Cream TEAS. *Adm £3 Chd 50p garden only. For NGS Wed, Thurs June 28, 29 (12-6)* **Tel 01903 744888/742021** parham@dial.pipex.com www.parhaminsussex.co.uk

▲ **Pashley Manor Gardens, Ticehurst** ✂❀ (Mr & Mrs James Sellick) *On B2099 between A21 and Ticehurst.* Sumptuous blend of romantic landscaping, imaginative plantings and fine old trees; fountains, springs and large ponds. This is a quintessentially English Garden of a very individual character with exceptional views to surrounding valleyed fields. Many eras of English history are reflected here, typifying the tradition of the English Country House and its garden. *Adm £5 OAPs £4.50. For NGS Fri July 14 (11-5)*
Tel 01580 200888

The Patched Gloves, Broad Oak ♿✂❀ (Mr Howard Norton) *Nr Rye. On Chitcombe Road B2089, 4m E of A21, ¾m W of A28.* 3-acres with extensive collection of interesting plants in 4 contrasting areas. Mediterranean garden; traditional garden; semi-wild pond garden and reclaimed field with Jekyll-style herbaceous border, roses and specimen trees. TEAS (June only). *Adm £2 Chd free. Suns April 30, June 18 (2-6)*

33 Peerley Road, East Wittering ✂❀ (Paul & Trudi Harrison) *From A286 take B2198 to Bracklesham turn R into*

Stocks Lane then L at Royal British Legion into Legion Way and follow rd round to Peerley Rd ½ way along. Small garden 80′ × 40′ 100yds from sea packed full of ideas and unusual plants using every inch of space to create unusual rooms and places for adults and children to play. A must for anyone attempting to garden by the sea. *Adm £1. Suns July 16, Aug 20 (2-6) Private visits welcome by appt, please* **Tel 01243 673215**

Pembury, Clayton ♿❀ (Nick & Jane Baker) *Nr Hassocks. 6m N of Brighton. On B2112, 100yds from A273. Parking on village green; disabled parking only at garden.* Owner maintained 2-acre garden on clay soil. Winding paths give the visitor a choice of walks through mixed borders, paved areas and woodland, with views to the South Downs and surrounding countryside. Jack and Jill windmills (Jill open pm), Saxon church with restored wall paintings and children's play area nearby. Light refreshments in village hall in aid of Clayton Church Fund. *Adm £2 Chd free. Sun June 4 (11-6)* www.users.zetnet.co.uk/pembury

Penns in the Rocks, Groombridge ♿✿❀ (Lord & Lady Gibson) *7m SW of Tunbridge Wells on Groombridge-Crowborough Rd just S of Plumeyfeather corner.* Large wild garden with rocks; lake; C18 temple; old walled garden with herbaceous, roses and shrubs. House (not open) part C18. Dogs under control in park only (no shade in car park). TEAS. *Adm £2.50 Up to two chd 50p each, further chd free. Suns March 19, Aug 27 (2.30-5.30). Parties welcome, please* **Tel 01892 864244**

Perryhill, Hartfield ♿✿ (Mr John Whitmore & Family) *Midway between East Grinstead and Tunbridge Wells. 1m N of Hartfield on B2026. Turn into unmade lane just S of Perryhill Nurseries.* 1½ acres, set below C15 Hall house (not open), with stunning views onto Ashdown Forest. Mixed borders, formal rose garden, ornamental shrubs and trees, parterre, water garden and fruit. TEAS. *Adm £2 Chd 50p. Suns June 18, Aug 20 (2-6)*

Pheasants Hatch, Piltdown ♿❀ (Mrs G E Thubron) *3m NW of Uckfield on A272.* 2 acres; rose gardens with ponds and fountains; beautiful herbaceous borders; foliage; wild garden; peacocks. TEAS. *Adm £1.50 Chd free. Sun, Mon June 25, 26 (2-6.30). Parties welcome June to July, please* **Tel 01825 722960**

▲ The Priest House, West Hoathly ❀ (Sussex Archaeological Society) *4m SW of East Grinstead, 6m E Crawley. At Turners Hill take B2028 S, 1m fork L to West Hoathly, 2m S turn R into North Lane.* C15 timber-framed house with small cottage garden. Large selection of herbs in formal garden plus mixed herbaceous borders with long established yew topiary, box hedges and espalier fruit trees. Also open within walking distance Duckyls Holt. *Combined Adm £2.50 Chd free. For NGS Thurs June 15, July 20 (11-5.30)* **Tel 01342 810479**

Priesthawes Farm, Polegate ♿✿❀ (Mr & Mrs A Wadman) *On B2104 2½m S Hailsham 4m N Eastbourne. 1m N of Stone Cross.* C15 listed house of historical interest (not open) surrounded by 2½ acres. Walls used to full advantage with large clematis collection, climbers, old roses, herbaceous borders and pergola. Mainly replanted in the last 15 yrs. Lovely views over farmland. TEAS in aid of St Mary's Westham & NGS. *Adm £2 Chd free (ACNO to St Wilfreds Hospice). Sun June 11 (10.30-12 & 2-5). Private visits also welcome mid May to July, please* **Tel 01323 763228**

NEW **Ridge House, Turners Hill** (Mr & Mr Nicholas Daniels) *On B2110 4m SW of East Grinstead. 3m E of Crawley, 5m SE junction 10 of M23. Via A264 and B2028. 30yds E of Crown PH on Turners Hill Xrds. Parking in recreation ground E of Ridge House and across B2028 in school playground.* 1-acre garden with extensive views. Mixed borders, large vegetable garden, Victorian greenhouse, specimen trees; dell with pond. Interesting terrace. TEAS. *Adm 2 Chd free. Fri, Sat June 23, 24 (2-6)*

Rose Cottage, Hadlow Down ✿❀ (Ken & Heather Mines) *6m NE of Uckfield on A272 turn L past New Inn PH to village hall.* Created from ½ acre of wilderness since 1994. Shoestring budget requires imaginative use of reclaimed materials to satisfy confirmed plantaholic's passion for unusual plants. Tiny woodland and gravel gardens, ponds, mouldering carvings from a demolished Victorian church. Organic 'Heritage' HDRA vegetable plants for sale. TEAS. *Adm £1.50 Chd 50p. Suns May 28, June 18 (2-6) Also by appt, please* **Tel 01825 830314**

NEW **Rosecroft, Sidlesham** ♿❀ (Mr & Mrs Charles Roe) *4m N of Selsey, from Chichester turn R off B2145 opp The Anchor PH. Fletchers Lane is the 2nd on the R.* 1½-acre photographers garden. Vistas and settings rather than 'rooms'. Luxuriant, colourful, and vibrant. Lawns, palms, cannas, cascade pelargoniums and water feature. TEA. *Adm £2 Chd 50p. Wed, Sun July 19, 23 (2-6)*

Rymans, Apuldram ♿ (Mrs Michael Gayford) *Take Witterings Rd out of Chichester; at 1½m SW turn R signposted Apuldram; garden down rd on L.* Walled and other gardens surrounding lovely C15 stone house (not open); bulbs, flowering shrubs, roses. New water feature. Sandwiches and drinks in aid of Leukemia Research Fund. *Adm £2 Chd 50p. Sats March 25, May 20 (12-4).* **Evening Opening** *Sat Aug 5. Wine and music (6-9)*

Sands, Warnham ♿✿ (Professor & Mrs R P Dales) *3½m NW of Horsham. From A24 enter Warnham and follow signposts to Northlands and Ockley.* Country garden of approx 1 acre on Wealden clay, surrounding C15 farmhouse (not open). Various areas from grassy orchard to pond, kitchen garden and herb garden are separated by hedges. Borders and beds contain mainly shrubs and herbaceous perennials; collection of hardy geraniums. TEAS. *Adm £1.50 Chd free. Sun June 11 (2-5.30).* **Evening Opening** *£2.50 Chd free. Wine, Wed June 28 (6-8). Some visits possible in April/May by appt, please* **Tel 01403 254843**

Selehurst, Lower Beeding ✿❀ (Mr & Mrs M Prideaux) *4½m S of Horsham on A281 opp Leonardslee.* Woodland garden in romantic valley. Sham-Gothic tower on the skyline above a pebblework waterfall, chain of five ponds, further waterfalls, pretty bridge. Fine trees, tree-like rhododendrons, eucryphias, azaleas, camellias, stewartias. Formal features incl walled garden with borders, semi-circular arbour of cytissus battandieri, 60′ rose and laburnum tunnel underplanted with ferns, artichokes, grasses and hostas. Newly planted box and herb parterre. Fine views of the South Downs. TEAS. *Adm £2 Chd free (ACNO to St. John's Church, Coolhurst). Sun May 7 (1-5)*

Sennicotts, Chichester ♿❀ (John Rank Esq) *Fron Chichester take B2178 signed Funtington for 2m. Entrance on R. Long drive ample parking nr house. From Fishbourne turn N marked Roman Palace then straight on until T junction. Entrance opp.* 6-acre mature garden with intriguing spaces; lawns, rhododendrons and azaleas. Large walled kitchen garden and cutting garden; greenhouses and orchards. TEAS. *Adm £2 Chd free. Sun May 21 (2-6).* **Evening Opening** *£3. Sat July 22 (5-8). Wine, Music and Sausages, chairs available. Bring your picnic.*

▲ **Sheffield Park Garden, Sheffield Park** ♿✗ (The National Trust) *Midway between E Grinstead and Lewes, 5m NW of Uckfield; E of A275.* Magnificent 120 acres (40 hectares) landscaped garden laid out in the C18 by 'Capability' Brown and Humphry Repton. Further development in early years of this century by its owner Arthur G Soames. Centrepiece is original lakes, linked by cascades and waterfalls with many rare trees and shrubs. Beautiful at all times of the year. Teas at Oak Hall (Not NT). *Adm £4.50 Chd £2.25. For NGS* **Evening Opening** *Thurs May 11 (6.30-8.30) Tues Oct 17 (10.30-6 last adm 5)*

Sherburne House, Eartham ♿✗❀ (Mr & Mrs Angus Hewat) *6m NE of Chichester, approach from A27 Chichester-Arundel Rd or A285 Chichester-Petworth Rd, nr centre of village, 200yds S of church.* Chalk garden of about 2 acres facing SW. Shrub and climbing roses, lime-tolerant shrubs, herbaceous, grey-leaved and foliage plants, pots, water feature, small herb garden, kitchen garden potager and conservatory. TEAS. *Adm £2 Chd 50p Sun June 18 (2-6) By appt in month of June, please* **Tel 01243 814261**

NEW **Shortgate Manor Farm, Halland** ♿✗❀ (David & Ethel Walters) *N from Lewes on A26 fork R onto B2192. At Ringmer roundabout keep L on B2192. Approx 2½m on R. From A22 Eastbourne - Uckfield rd turn S at Halland Forge roundabout. 1m on L.* 2 acre cottage garden created from 'an area of grass' by owners over 18yrs. Approached by an avenue of poplars festooned with rambling roses. Barns and pergolas covered in clematis, honeysuckle and roses. Beds and borders constantly being expanded to provide space for increasingly wide variety of plants, incl. new hot border. Colourfully planted containers. TEAS. *Adm £2 Chd free. Sun, Mon June 25, 26 (2-5)*

NEW **Sienna Wood, East Grinstead** ✗❀ (Michael & Alison Brown) *From East Grinstead 1½m SW on B2110. Turn L into Coombe Hill Road. ¼m on L (7 humps).* 8-acre garden of great variety; formal borders surrounding summer croquet lawn; rose garden and orchard; potager; long wisteria walk; sheltered garden with wild orchids and stream. Extensive rhododendron plantings. ½ acre lake with bluebell woods behind (suitable footwear recommended). The gardens, under new ownership (formerly Middle Coombe) are beginning an era of transition, with interesting new plantings. TEAS in aid of MCR. *Adm £3. Mon May 29 (11-5)*

Somerset Lodge, Petworth (Mr & Mrs R Harris) *North St. On A283 and A272 100yds N of church. Parking in town car park.* Charming ½ acre town garden with ponds and walled kitchen garden, small collection of old roses and wildflower garden. Cleverly landscaped on slope with beautiful views. TEAS in aid of Petworth Cottage Hospital. *Adm £1.50 Chd 50p. Sats, Suns, Mon, Tues, Wed, Thurs, Fri June 10, 11, 12, 13, 14, 15, 16, 17, 18, (12-6). Parties by appt, please* **Tel 01798 343842**

South Harting Gardens ✗❀ *4m SE of Petersfield on B2146.* Cream TEAS at Pyramids. *Combined adm £2 Chd free. Sat, Sun June 24, 25 (2.5.30)*

Ivy House ♿ (Mr & Mrs D Summerhayes) *At S end of village opp Harting Church on B2136.* 1½-acre terraced village garden, sloping down to brook with orchard and paddock beyond. Specimen trees, shrubs and roses. Views to Harting Down

Pyramids, South Harting ♿❀ (Mrs Stephanie Morgan) *200yds on R up North Lane.* ½ acre with mainly chalk-loving plants; old-fashioned roses, rose arbour; pool; uniquely shaped old apple trees. Interesting modern house (designed 1965 by Stout & Lichfield (not open) linked to garden by paved areas. Fine views.

Spur Point, Kingsley Green ✗❀ (Mr & Mrs T D Bishop) *Marley Heights.* Plantsman's garden created by owners since 1970. 3 acres of S facing terraces containing rhododendrons, azaleas, roses, mixed borders and scree beds. Not suitable for children. *Adm £2. Private visits welcome May and June by individuals, and parties of no more than 20, please* **Tel 01428 643050**

▲ **St Mary's House, Bramber** ♿✗ (Mr Peter Thorogood) *Bramber. 10m NW of Brighton in Bramber Village off A283 or 1m E of Steyning.* Medium-sized formal gardens; amusing topiary, large example of living-fossil Gingko tree, Magnolia Grandiflora, pools and fountains, ancient ivy-clad 'Monk's Walk', all around listed Grade 1 C15 timber framed mediaeval house, once a pilgrim inn. Discover also the secret Victorian Walled and Pleasure Gardens 3½ acres, hidden for over half a century, recently rescued, now under restoration. TEAS. *Adm £2.50 Chd 50p (ACNO to Waynflete Heritage Trust). For NGS Fri, Sat Aug 4, 5 (2-5.30)*
Tel 01903 816205

▲ **Standen, East Grinstead** ✗ (The National Trust) *1½m from East Grinstead. Signed from B2110 and A22 at Felbridge.* Approx 12 acres of hillside garden, packed with surprises. Features include quarry and bamboo gardens and three summer houses. Lovely views over the Medway and Ashdown Forest. Partly suitable for wheelchairs. TEAS in aid of NT Enterprises. *Adm Garden £3 Chd £1.50. For NGS Sats May 13, Sept 9 (11.30-6 Last adm 5pm)*

Stone Cross House, Crowborough (Mr & Mrs D A Tate) *At Crowborough T-lights (A26) turn S into High St, and shortly R into Croft Rd. Straight over 2 mini roundabouts into Alice Bright Lane. Garden on L at next Xrds about 1½m from T-lights.* Created over 25yrs. 1½-acre woodland spring garden with some unusual shrubs, azaleas and rhododendrons. Herbaceous borders, lovely views. Tours to be given by garden creator. TEAS. *Adm £2 Chd 50p (ACNO to St John Ambulance, Crowborough). Fri, Sun May 5, 7 (2-6)*

Stonehurst, Ardingly ❀ (Mr & Mrs D R Strauss) *1m N of Ardingly. Entrance 800yds N of S of England showground, on B2028.* 30-acre garden set in secluded woodland valley. Many interesting and unusual landscape features; chain of man made lakes and waterfalls; natural sandstone rock outcrops and a fine collection of trees and shrubs. TEAS. *Adm £2.50 Chd £1 (ACNO to Arundel and Brighton Diocesan Pilgrimage Trust). Mons May 1, 29 (11-5)*

Three Oaks, West Broyle, Chichester ♿❀ (Mr & Mrs J C A Mudford) *From roundabout N of Chichester take B2178 (Funtington) rd NW for about 1½m. Turn L into Pine Grove and after 100yds R into West Way.* Small cottage garden with unusual plants in beds and borders that just happened. Vegetable garden. TEA. *Adm £1.50. Sun May 7, Tues May 9 (1.30-6)*

Town Place, Freshfield ♿✂❀ (Mr & Mrs A C O McGrath) *3m E Haywards Heath. From A275 turn W at Sheffield Green into Ketches Lane for Lindfield. 1¾m on L.* 3 acres with sunken rose garden, 150′ herbaceous border, walled herb and shrub rose gardens, shrubbery, ancient hollow oak, orchard and potager. C17 Sussex farmhouse (not open). TEAS. *Adm £3 Chd free (ACNO to St Peter & St James Hospice). Sat June 17, Suns June 11, July 2, 9 (2-6); Thurs June 22 (11-6). Groups welcome by appt, please* **Tel 01825 790221**

Trotton Old Rectory, Petersfield ✂ (Captain & Mrs John Pilley) *3m W of Midhurst on A272.* This typical English garden with its rose beds, designed by Hazel le Rougetel, framed in box and yew, has 2 levels with beautiful interesting trees and shrubs running down to a lake and the R Rother. Newly planted pleached limes with formal planting. *Adm £3 Chd free. Private visits and small groups welcome by appt only May-Sept, please* **TEL 01730 813612**

Udimore Gardens, Rye ✂ 3 contrasting gardens with views of unspoilt Tillingham and Brede valleys. TEAS at Beauchamps. *Combined adm 2 Chd free (ACNO to Chernobyl Children, Rye). Sun June 18 (2-6)*

> NEW **Beauchamps** ❀ (Mr & Mrs Richard Holmes) *3½m W of Rye, 3m E of Broad Oak Xrds. Turn S off B2089 down Float Lane ½m. 20mins walk from Hammonds by highly scenic public footpath.* Recently restored garden with a wide range of herbaceous plants and shrubs. Small orchard, kitchen garden and wood
>
> **The Hammonds, Rye** (Mr & Mrs P Salter) *Next door to Wick Farm.* Georgian walled rose garden, large Victorian walled kitchen garden
>
> **Wick Farm** (Mr & Mrs R Mair) *2½m W of Rye on R off B2089.* Long established terraced farm garden with old fashioned roses, herbaceous borders, 200 yr-old weeping ash tree

▲ **Uppark, South Harting** ♿✂ (The National Trust) *5m SE of Petersfield on B2146, 1½m S of S Harting.* Fine late C17 house situated high on the South Downs with magnificent views towards the Solent. Reptonian garden replanned and replanted since major fire in 1989. Woodland walk. House open (1-5). Gardener Guided Tours hourly from 11.30. Post Fire Restoration Exhibition. Restaurant and shop open. Collection for NGS. *Adm £2.50 Chd £1.25. Thurs June 8 (11.30-5.30)*

Wadhurst Park, Wadhurst ✂❀ (Dr & Mrs H Rausing) *6m SE of Tunbridge Wells. Turn R along Mayfield Lane off B2099 at NW end of Wadhurst. L by Best Beech public house, L at Riseden Rd.* This magnificent garden was re-created on C19 site with restored conservatories and is situated within an 800-acre park, stocked with 7 species of deer. Trailer rides into park at 3 and 4pm weather permitting. Partly suitable for wheelchairs. TEAS. *Adm £2 Chd 50p. Sun July 9 (2-5.30). Sorry no video or photography*

NEW **Wadhurst Village Gardens** *6m SE Tunbridge Wells. Take A267 out of Tunbridge Wells, 2½m turn L onto B2099. In Wadhurst turn R opposite church down Washwell Lane, ¼m fork R into Courthope Ave. Take R turn for Watts Close. Approaching Wadhurst from W turn L into Washwell Lane at White Hart.* TEAS. *Combined adm £2 Chd free. Sat, Sun July 1, 2 (2-5)*

> NEW **2 Courthope Avenue** ♿ (Stan Cosham) Small summer bedding plant garden with roses and a small museum at rear of house
>
> NEW **5 Courthope Avenue** ✂ (Eileen & Ray Hemsley) Small colourful village garden. Herbaceous, bedding, roses, patio tubs and hanging baskets
>
> NEW **7 Courthope Avenue** (Tony & Jean Sivyer) Small very colourful with many shrubs, hanging baskets, patio containers. Masses of roses and begonias, herbaceous and bedding. Mixed borders
>
> NEW **7 Watts Close** (Bob & Peg Pullen) Very small bungalow summer garden

Warren House, Crowborough ✂❀ (Mr & Mrs M J Hands) *Warren Rd. From Crowborough Cross towards Uckfield. 4th turning on R. 1m down Warren Rd. From S 2nd L after Blue Anchor.* Beautiful house (not open) steeped in history with 9-acre garden and views over Ashdown Forest. Series of gardens old and new, displaying a wealth of azaleas, rhododendrons, impressive variety of trees and shrubs. Sweeping lawns framed by delightful walls and terraces, woodlands, ponds and ducks. Planted and maintained solely by owner. TEAS. *Adm £2 Chd free. Suns April 23, May 14, 21, Aug 27, Mons May 1, 29 (2-5). Groups welcome by appt, please* **Tel 01892 663502**

NEW **Waterloo Farm, Burwash Common** ♿✂❀ (Claudine & Robin Cecil) *6m E of Heathfield. A265 to Burwash Common. Turn L at Shanks Nursery to Stonegate. Approx 1½m L at Kicking Donkey PH. ¼m L at triangle, ¼m L after Waterloo Barn. From N turn S off B2099 at Shovers Green to Stonegate. 3½m (passing Stonegate Station) turn R to Mayfield. 1m on L after Waterloo Barn.* Garden full of plants rescued from various sources incl unwanted shrubs and trees from old established gardens. Rustic arches, willow tunnel, brick paths weave between evergreens and interesting foliage plants. How many insects can you find? TEAS. *Adm £1 Chd 50p. Sun Aug 13 (11-4)*

93 Wayland Avenue, Brighton ✂❀ (Brian & Sylvia Jackson) *From Dyke Rd Ave into Tongdean Lane, R into*

Wayland Ave. Creatively designed small garden, with emphasis on dense, informal planting incl unusual plants, shrubs, grasses, clematis, tender perennials and climbers. Focal points provided by rose arch and water features in rockery and bog garden areas. Designed to encourage wildlife. *Adm £1.50. Suns May 21, June 18 (2-5). Private visits by appt, May to July, please* **Tel 01273 501027**

● **West Dean Gardens** (Edward James Foundation) *On A286, 5m N of Chichester.* 35-acre historic garden in tranquil downland setting. 300ft long Harold Peto pergola, mixed and herbaceous borders, rustic summer-houses, water garden and specimen trees. Restored 2½ acre walled garden contains fruit collection, 13 Victorian glass-houses, apple store, large working kitchen garden, extensive plant collection. Circuit walk (2¼m) climbs through parkland to 45-acre St Roches Arboretum. *Adm £4 OAP £3.50 Chd £2. Open daily March-April and Oct (11-5), May-Sept (10.30-5). For NGS Wed June 7* **Tel 01243 818210**

46 Westup Farm Cottages, Balcombe (Chris & Pat Cornwell) *3m N Cuckfield. ¼ m N Balcombe Station, take L off B2036 at Balcombe Primary School (signed). 3/4m.* Cottage garden in an idyllic setting designed to provide yr round interest; contains large variety of shrubs, perennials, climbers and grasses, also organic vegetable garden. Small sculptures on display add a fun element and are for sale. *Adm £1.50 Chd free. Mons, April 17, May 8, 22, June 12, 26 (2-6) Private visits incl parties welcome Feb to Nov, anytime incl evenings, please* **Tel 01444 811891**

The White Magpie, Lamberhurst (Mr Ronald J Wootton) *From Lamberhurst, on B2100 signposted Wadhurst 1m approx turn R (Hog Hole Lane) for ½m.* A small estate with some 5 acres of garden, surrounded by farmland, valley views, series of interlinking ponds, walled garden. All to the memory of Mrs J P Wootton. TEAS. *Adm £2 Chd free (ACNO to The Hodgkins Disease Association). Sat, Sun May 27, 28 (1-6)*

Whitehouse Cottage, Staplefield (Barry Gray Esq) *Staplefield Lane. 5m NW of Haywards Heath. Garden is 1m. E of A23; and 2m S of Handcross. In Staplefield at Xrds by cricket pavilion take turning marked Staplefield Lane for 1m.* 4-acre woodland garden with mixed shrubs, paths beside stream linked by ponds. TEAS. *Adm £2 Chd 50p. Open most days, please telephone first, individuals or groups welcome* **Tel 01444 461229**

Winchelsea's Secret Gardens *S of Rye.* TEAS at Five Chimneys. *Combined adm £3 Chd free. Sat June 17 (2-6)*

Alards Plat (Mr & Mrs Richard Feast) *1 High Street.* A narrow paved cottage garden

NEW **Amerique** (Mr & Mrs D O'Brien) *Castle Street.* Secluded ¼ acre town garden. Old roses and clematis of special interest

Five Chimneys (Mr & Mrs Dominic Leahy) *Mill Road.* Formal town garden

NEW **3 Hiham Green** (Mr & Mrs Robert Nicholson) Miniscule newly planted Mediterranean garden with pots

The Old Rectory (June & Denis Hyson) ½ acre of open lawn garden with views overlooking the Brede Valley

Periteau House (Dr & Mrs Lawrence Youlten) *High Street.* Old walled garden

Tower Cottage (Dr & Mrs B Chishick) *Barrack Square.* A cottage garden with views

Winchelsea Cottage (Mr & Mrs Colin Spencer) *High Street.* Small paved town garden with statuary, unusual plants, pergola and roses

NEW **Witherenden Mill, Stonegate** (Colin & Inyca Humphreys) *12m SE of Tunbridge Wells between A267 and A21. Take B2099 through Wadhurst. After 1½m turn R to Stonegate; 1½m bear R at junction. ⅓m past Stonegate station 3rd drive on R.* 3-acre formal and wild garden surrounding listed house (not open). New owners are enjoying developing the garden which incls lawns, herba-ceous borders and beds. Lovely walk down through trees to R Rother.Views. TEAS. *Adm £2.50 Chd free (ACNO to Hospice in the Weald). Sun July 16 (2-6)*

Woodstock, Chichester (Group Capt A R Gordon-Cumming) *From roundabout N of Chichester take B2178 (Funtingdon) rd NW for 1m. Turn L into Pine Grove and after 100yds R into West Way. Woodstock is at the far end.* ⅔-acre mainly woodland garden specialising in ground cover plants, camellias, and hostas. *Adm £1.50 Chd free. Sun, Mon March 26, 27 (1.30-5.30)*

Yew Tree Cottage, Crawley Down (Mrs K Hudson) *4m W of East Grinstead. 2½m E of M23 (J10). On B2028 N of Turners Hill.* 1/4 acre garden planted for yr round interest and easy management; new gravel gardens with grasses. Featured on BBC2 Gardeners World in 1997 with Gay Search. *Adm £1.50 OAPs £1 Chd free. Small Parties welcome May to Aug (10-6), please* **Tel 01342 714633**

Evening Opening (See also garden description)

Berri Court, Yapton	July 14
Cowbeech Farm, Cowbeech	June 30 & July 5
Frith Hill, Northchapel	June 11 & 18 & 25
Frith Lodge, Northchapel	June 11 & 18 & 25
72 Grand Avenue, Worthing	July 5
Neptune House, Cutmill	June 3 & 4 & July 29 & 30
Rymans, Apuldram	August 5
Sands, Warnham	June 28
Sennicotts, Chichester	July 22
Sheffield Park Garden, Sheffield Park	May 11

Parham
House & Gardens
near Pulborough, West Sussex
Open to visitors from April - October
Annual Garden Weekend: 15/16 July
Tel: 01903 742021 www: parhaminsussex.co.uk Registered Charity 276673

Warwickshire & part of West Midlands

Hon County Organiser (Warwickshire):	Mrs D L Burbidge, Cedar House, Wasperton CV35 8EB
Assistant Hon County Organisers:	Mrs Cynthia Orchard, Honington Glebe, Honington, Shipston-on-Stour CV36 5AA Mr Peter Pashley, Millstones, Mayfield Avenue, Stratford-on-Avon CV37 6XB
Hon County Organiser (West Midlands):	Mrs C R King-Farlow, 8 Vicarage Road, Edgbaston, Birmingham B15 3ES
Assistant Hon County Organiser:	Mrs M Harvey, Ashover, 25 Burnett Road, Streetly, Birmingham B74 3EL
Hon County Treasurer:	Mr Michael Pitts, Hickecroft, Mill Lane, Rowington CV35 7DQ

DATES OF OPENING

Regular openings

For details see garden description

Castle Bromwich Hall Gardens
89 Harts Green Road, Harborne
The Master's Garden, Lord Leycester Hospital, Warwick
Ryton Organic Gardens
University of Birmingham Botanic Garden at Winterbourne, Edgbaston

By appointment only

For telephone numbers and other details see garden descriptions. Private visits welcomed

Woodpeckers, nr Bidford-on-Avon

March 4 Saturday
Elm Close, Welford-on-Avon

March 5 Sunday
Elm Close, Welford-on-Avon

March 18 Saturday
Avon Cottage, Ashow nr Kenilworth

March 19 Sunday
Avon Cottage, Ashow nr Kenilworth

April 2 Sunday
Greenlands

April 9 Sunday
Ilmington Gardens, nr Shipston-on-Stour
Ilmington Manor

April 16 Sunday
The Mill Garden, Warwick
Moseley Gardens, Birmingham
52 Tenbury Road, King's Heath

April 19 Wednesday
89 Harts Green Road, Harborne

April 23 Sunday
34 The Crescent, Cradley Heath

April 26 Wednesday
The Folly Lodge, Halford

April 30 Sunday
Alveston Gardens

May 7 Sunday
Pereira Road Gardens

May 13 Saturday
Avon Cottage, Ashow nr Kenilworth

May 14 Sunday
Avon Cottage, Ashow nr Kenilworth
Ilmington Manor
University of Birmingham Botanic Garden at Winterbourne, Edgbaston

May 18 Thursday
The Mill Garden, Warwick

May 21 Sunday
Ashover, Streetly
Packington Hall, Meriden
Warwickshire Constabulary Police HQ, Leek Wootton

May 24 Wednesday
89 Harts Green Road, Harborne

May 28 Sunday
Barton House, Barton-on-the-Heath
Hunningham Village Gardens
Maxstoke Castle, nr Coleshill
Pebworth & District Gardens
219 Station Road, Sutton Coldfield

May 29 Monday
Hunningham Village Gardens
Pebworth & District Gardens

May 31 Wednesday
The Folly Lodge, Halford

June 3 Saturday
Ryton Organic Gardens

June 4 Sunday
Cedar House, Wasperton
Dorsington Gardens
6 Spring Meadow, Halesowen
172 Stonor Road, Hall Green

June 8 Thursday
Wootton Grange, Henley-in-Arden

June 11 Sunday
Idlicote Gardens
52 Tenbury Road, King's Heath

June 14 Wednesday
Packwood House

June 17 Saturday
Augusta Road & Park Hill Gardens, Moseley

June 18 Sunday
Augusta Road & Park Hill Gardens, Moseley
Avon Dassett Gardens
Compton Scorpion Farm, nr Ilmington
Greenlands
Holywell Gardens
Ilmington Manor
The Master's Garden, Lord Leycester Hospital, Warwick
The Mill Garden, Warwick
8 Vicarage Road, Edgbaston
Whichford & Ascott Gardens, Shipston-on-Stour

June 21 Wednesday
89 Harts Green Road, Harborne
52 Tenbury Road, King's Heath (evening)
8 Vicarage Road, Edgbaston (evening)

June 24 Saturday
Avon Cottage, Ashow nr Kenilworth
Clifton-upon-Dunsmore Gardens, Nr Rugby

June 25 Sunday
Avon Cottage, Ashow nr Kenilworth
Bourton Gardens, Rugby
Clifton-upon-Dunsmore Gardens, Nr Rugby
Earlsdon Gardens, Coventry
18 Grove Avenue, Moseley
Honington Village Gardens
Pereira Road Gardens
Rivendell, Newbold-on-Stour
Roseberry Cottage, Fillongley
Rowington Gardens
26 Sunnybank Road, Wylde Green
University of Birmingham Botanic Garden at Winterbourne, Edgbaston
50 Wellington Rd, Edgbaston

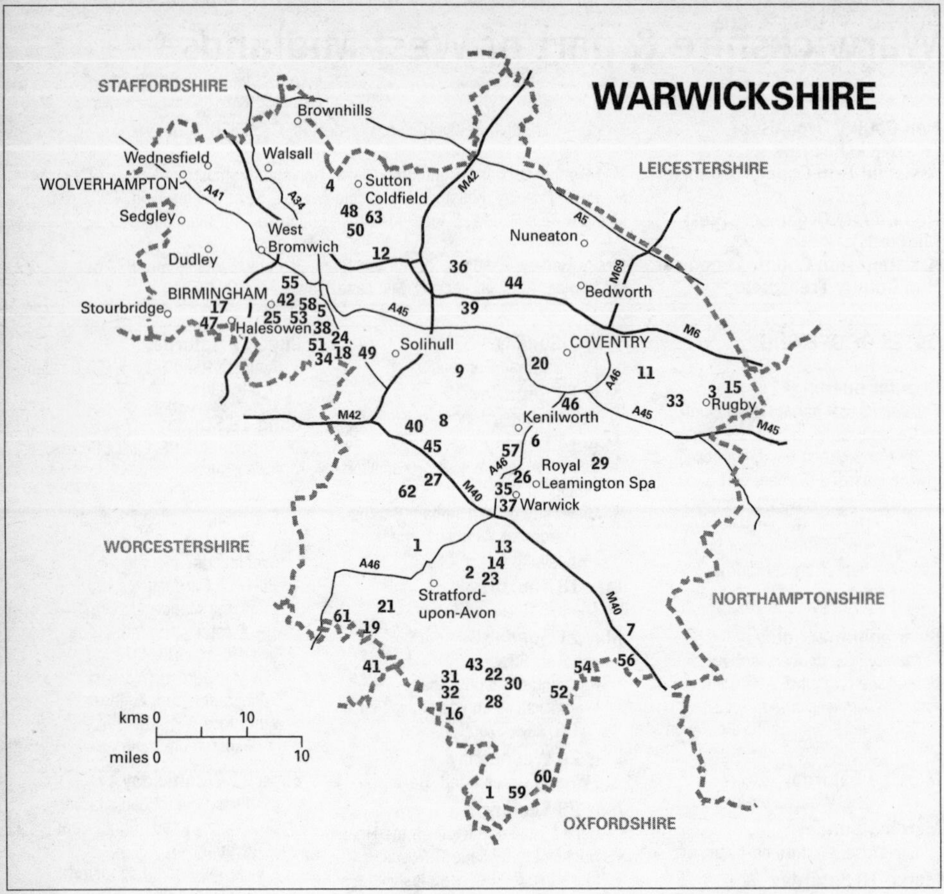

KEY

1 Alne View
2 Alveston Gardens
3 4 Arnold Villas
4 Ashover
5 Augusta Road & Park Hill Gardens
6 Avon Cottage
7 Avon Dassett Gardens
8 Baddesley Clinton Hall
9 Balsall Common Gardens
10 Barton House
11 Bourton Gardens
12 Castle Bromwich Hall Gardens
13 Cedar House
14 Charlecote Park
15 Clifton-upon-Dunsmore Gardens
16 Compton Scorpion Farm
17 34 The Crescent
18 66 Dalbury Road
19 Dorsington Gardens
20 Earlsdon Gardens
21 Elm Close
22 The Folly Lodge
23 Greenlands
24 18 Grove Avenue
25 89 Harts Green Road
26 Hill Close Gardens
27 Holywell Gardens
28 Honington Village Gardens
29 Hunningham Village Gardens
30 Idlicote Gardens
31 Ilmington Gardens
32 Ilmington Manor
33 Lawford Hill Farm
34 78 Marsham Road
35 The Master's Garden
36 Maxstoke Castle
37 The Mill Garden
38 Moseley Gardens
39 Packington Hall
40 Packwood House
41 Pebworth & District Gardens
42 Pereira Road Gardens
43 Rivendell
44 Roseberry Cottage
45 Rowington Gardens
46 Ryton Organic Gardens
47 6 Spring Meadow
48 219 Station Road
49 172 Stonor Road
50 26 Sunnybank Road
51 52 Tenbury Road
52 Tysoe Manor
53 University of Birmingham Botanic Garden at Winterbourne
54 Upton House
55 8 Vicarage Road
56 Warmington Village Gardens
57 Warwickshire Constabulary Police HQ
58 50 Wellington Rd
59 Wheelwright House
60 Whichford & Ascott Gardens
61 Woodpeckers
62 Wootton Grange
63 76 Wylde Green Road

June 28 Wednesday
The Folly Lodge, Halford (evening)
Rivendell, Newbold-on-Stour

June 30 Friday
26 Sunnybank Road, Wylde Green (evening)

July 1 Saturday
Upton House, nr Banbury

July 2 Sunday
Balsall Common Gardens

July 4 Tuesday
Charlecote Park, Warwick (evening)

July 9 Sunday
Ashover, Streetly
Ilmington Manor
Lawford Hill Farm, Long Lawford
78 Marsham Road, King's Heath
Moseley Gardens, Birmingham
Wheelwright House, Long Compton

July 13 Thursday
The Mill Garden, Warwick

July 16 Sunday
Castle Bromwich Hall Gardens
Warmington Village Gardens

July 19 Wednesday
89 Harts Green Road, Harborne

July 23 Sunday
26 Sunnybank Road, Wylde Green
76 Wylde Green Road, Sutton Coldfield

July 26 Wednesday
The Folly Lodge, Halford

July 30 Sunday
Alne View, Pathlow

August 6 Sunday
4 Arnold Villas, Rugby
Ashover, Streetly
66 Dalbury Road, Hall Green
172 Stonor Road, Hall Green

August 9 Wednesday
66 Dalbury Road, Hall Green (evening)

August 16 Wednesday
66 Dalbury Road, Hall Green

August 17 Thursday
The Mill Garden, Warwick

August 19 Saturday
Avon Cottage, Ashow nr Kenilworth

August 20 Sunday
Avon Cottage, Ashow nr Kenilworth

August 27 Sunday
18 Grove Avenue, Moseley

August 30 Wednesday
The Folly Lodge, Halford

September 2 Saturday
Hill Close Gardens, Warwick

September 3 Sunday
Hill Close Gardens, Warwick
The Mill Garden, Warwick
Tysoe Manor, Tysoe

September 8 Friday
Baddesley Clinton Hall

September 10 Sunday
6 Spring Meadow, Halesowen

October 1 Sunday
University of Birmingham Botanic Garden at Winterbourne, Edgbaston

October 8 Sunday
The Mill Garden, Warwick

October 21 Saturday
Avon Cottage, Ashow nr Kenilworth

October 22 Sunday
Avon Cottage, Ashow nr Kenilworth
Ryton Organic Gardens

DESCRIPTIONS OF GARDENS

Alne View, Pathlow ♿✂❀ (Mrs E Butterworth) *5m from Henley-in-Arden; 3m N of Stratford on A3400.* Approx ⅓ acre. Shrubs, perennials, three ponds and rockery; raised beds. Aviary, collection of fuchsia and streptocarpus; greenhouses. TEAS. *Adm £1.50 Chd free (ACNO to Wilmcote CE Primary School). Sun July 30 (2-5)*

Alveston Gardens ♿✂ *2m E of Stratford-on-Avon off B4086, Stratford to Wellesbourne rd.* TEAS in aid of Macmillan Cancer Relief. *Combined adm £2 Chd free. Sun April 30 (1-5)*

The Bower House (Mr and Mrs P S Hart) 1 acre, owner-designed; unusual trees, water garden and rockeries, pergolas, alpine sinks, choice shrubs

Court Leys (Mr & Mrs E Barnard) 1 acre. Lawns, ponds, interesting plants, trees and shrubs. New mediterranean garden and fernery

Long Acre (Dr & Mrs N A Woodward) 1 acre, owner-designed; interesting trees, shrubs, roses, rockery, barbecue area, pergola, terraces and ponds

Parham Lodge (Mr and Mrs K C Edwards) 1 acre country garden designed by owners for colour, texture and scent at all seasons. Large pond, terrace, island beds, spring and summer bulbs. Wildflower apple orchard. Old cedars, copper beech and hornbeams. Beehives, so no sprays for 20 years. *Private visits welcome, please* **Tel 01789 268955**

4 Arnold Villas, Rugby ✂❀ (Mr Patrick Pratt) *From M1 take A428 towards Rugby town centre and Rugby school. After roundabout take 1st L into Horton Crescent for parking. Follow signs to Church Walk. Arnold Villas on R.* Small town garden containing wide variety of shrubs, tender climbers and unusual plants. Mediterranean and exotic plants framed by mature palms. *Adm £1 Chd free. Sun Aug 6 (2-5.30)*

Ashover, Streetly ✂❀ (Jackie & Martin Harvey) *25 Burnett Rd. 8m N of Birmingham. Take A452 towards Streetly, then B4138 alongside Sutton Park. Turn L at shops into Burnett Rd.* ⅓ acre well-stocked, plant lovers' garden. Cottage-style mixed plantings planned for yr-round interest. Garden constantly changing. Particular emphasis in May with azaleas and other late spring colour; summer with shrubs, roses, climbers and wide range of perennials, many unusual. Attractive water feature. Cream TEAS. *Adm £1.50 Chd 50p. Suns May 21, July 9, Aug 6 (1.30-5.30). Private parties welcome, please* **Tel 0121 353 0547**

Augusta Road & Park Hill Gardens, Moseley ✂ *Approx 2½m from Birmingham city centre, just off A435 Alcester Rd, Moseley village. Car access only via Chantry Rd or Park Hill.* TEAS. *Combined adm £1.50 Chd 75p Sat, Sun June 17, 18 (2-6)*

26 Augusta Road (Derek Castle) Making the most of very small plot (84 sq yds). Secluded, terraced garden with yr-round interest. 17′ × 8′ conservatory, housing superb cactus collection. Plants for sale in aid of St Mary's Hospice. *Small groups welcome by appt, please* **Tel 0121 449 1473**

38 Augusta Road (Mr & Mrs A Barnsley) Beautifully planted and terraced small town garden in Victorian surroundings with restful feel. *Sat June 17 only*

The Coach House (Mr G Gupwell & Mr M Paton) Mature trees surround an unusual garden of interesting features, incl sunken garden, small pools, fountain courtyard, mediterranean patio and stable yard. Created from scratch over 10 yrs using original materials to complement surrounding architecture. Teas in aid of St Mary's Hospice. *Sat June 17 only*
NEW **62 Park Hill, Moseley** (Celia Feetam) Family garden reclaimed from balls, bikes and builders

Avon Cottage, Ashow nr Kenilworth ✗✿ (Neil Collett) *1½m E of Kenilworth. From A452 Kenilworth to Leamington rd take B4115 (signposted Ashow and Stoneleigh). After ¼m turn R into Ashow. Cottage at far end of village adjacent to church (driveway opp village club). Limited parking only, please park outside village and walk to avoid congestion.* Charming cottage garden surrounding picturesque C18 grade II listed building (not open). 1½ acres with extensive R Avon frontage. Diverse and interesting plantings for yr-round appeal. Orchard area with free-range domestic and waterfowl. *Adm £1.50 Chd 50p (ACNO to Ashow Parish Church). Sat, Suns March 18, 19, May 13, 14, Sats, Suns June 24, 25, Aug 19, 20, Oct 21, 22 (9-6)*

Avon Dassett Gardens & *7m N of Banbury off B4100 (use exit 12 of M40). Car parking in village and in car park at top of hill. TEAS at Old Mill Cottage. Combined adm £3 Chd free (ACNO to Myton Hamlet Hospice). Sun June 18 (2-6). Coaches welcome, please Tel 01295 690643*
Avon House (Mr & Mrs E H Dunkley) Mature garden, principally shrubs, featuring hostas.
The Coach House, Bitham Hall (Mr & Mrs G J Rice) 2-acre plantsman's garden, part of former Victorian garden overlooking Edge Hill. Walls give shelter and support for many climbers and more tender perennials and shrubs. Woodland area, orchard and fruit and vegetable garden. *Private visits by individuals or groups welcome by appt, please Tel 01295 690255*
Hill Top Farm ✿ (Mrs N and Mr D Hicks) 1 acre. Display of bedding plants, perennials, shrubs, conifers and heathers. Extensive kitchen garden. Greenhouses
4 Lower End (Mrs M J Edginton) Interesting contrasts between cottage garden, courtyard and vegetable garden
Old Mill Cottage (Mr and Mrs M J Lewis) Conservation garden of 3/4 acre with shrubs, perennial borders and rockeries. Collection of alpines and herbs. Two ponds and tropical garden. Mediterranean gravel garden under development
Old Pumphouse Cottage (Mrs W Wormell) Cottage garden with mixed borders featuring shrub roses and clematis
The Old Rectory (Mrs L Hope-Frost) 2-acre terraced garden with wide stone steps. Maturing trees, shrubs and small wood surrounding listed building (not open) mentioned in Domesday Book. Entrance to church through walled garden

▲ **Baddesley Clinton Hall** &✗ (The National Trust) *¾m W off A4141 Warwick-Birmingham rd near Chadwick End. 7½m NW of Warwick.* Mediaeval moated manor house little changed since 1633; walled garden and herbaceous borders; natural areas; lakeside walk, nature trail. Lunches and Teas.

Adm Grounds only £2.60 Chd £1.30. Shop and restaurant. Open from noon. For NGS Fri Sept 8 (12-5.30)

Balsall Common Gardens &✗ *Balsall Common. 5m S of M42/M6 intersection, 6m W of Coventry, 10m N of Warwick, junction of A452 and B4101. From t-lights of this intersection go W on B4101 towards Knowle for ¾m. Map available for each garden. TEAS at White Cottage and Silver Trees Farm Combined adm £2.50 Chd 50p (ACNO to The Helen Ley Home) Sun July 2 (1.30-6). Private visits welcome May & June, please Tel 01676 533143*
The Bungalow (Mr & Mrs G Johnson) *Table Oak Lane, Fen End.* 2 acres with mixed borders, pond and lawn. New areas developing
Fen End House (Mr & Mrs W Husselby) *Fen End.* 1 acre with lawns interspersed with borders containing formal and informal planting schemes
Firs Farm (Mr & Mrs C Ellis) *Windmill Lane.* ½-acre garden, courtyard with tubs, walled garden, formal garden with rose bed and mixed borders, grassed area with young ornamental trees
Meriglen (Mr & Mrs J Webb) *Windmill Lane, Balsall Common.* Mixed borders of shrubs and perennials
The Pines (Mr & Mrs C Davis) *Hodgetts Lane.* 1½ acre formal garden. Avenue of flowering trees; series of small gardens; vegetable garden, herb garden and rose walk
Silver Trees Farm (Mr & Mrs B Hitchens) *Balsall Street.* 1½ acres, mixed borders, orchard, bog area, woodland garden. Large formal pond
White Cottage Farm (Mr & Mrs J Edwards) *Holly Lane. Drive up lane to garden.* 1½ acre cottage garden, mixed borders, pond, sunken garden
32 Wootton Green Lane (Dr & Mrs Leeming) *Balsall Common.* Lawns, water features, greenhouse

Barton House, Barton-on-the-Heath &✗✿ (Mr & Mrs I H B Cathie) *2m W of Long Compton on A3400 Stratford-upon-Avon to Oxford rd.* 6 acres with mature trees, azaleas, species and hybrid rhododendrons, magnolias, moutan tree paeonies, Japanese garden, catalpa walk, rose garden, secret garden and many rare and exotic plants. Manor House by Inigo Jones (not open). TEAS. *Adm £2.50 Chd £1 (ACNO to St Lawrence Church). Sun May 28 (2-6). Private visits for groups by appt only, please Tel 01608 674303*

NEW **Bourton Gardens, Rugby** ✗✿ *Between Rugby and Princethorpe, 7m SE of Coventry, off B4453 signed Bourton. TEAS. Combined adm £2 Chd 50p. Sun June 25 (2-6)*
Fieldgate Cottage, Bourton ✿ (Wendy Morris & Steve Smith) Small, peaceful cottage garden alongside footpath, designed and maintained by owners. Many basket and container plantings; separate kitchen garden
Kiln Cottage, Bourton (Viv and Terry McSweeney) Small cottage garden enhanced by climbers, window boxes and hanging baskets, underplanted with shrubs and annuals. Main feature a newly constructed conifer garden
The Old Well, Bourton (Mr & Mrs H E Pughe) Created in 7 yrs. ⅔ acre, organic family garden with hot tub! Herbaceous borders with old fashioned, English roses. Interesting plantings in terracotta pots.

■ **Castle Bromwich Hall Gardens** ♿❀ (Castle Bromwich Hall Gardens Trust) *Chester Rd. 4m E of Birmingham. 1m from junction 5 of M6 (exit Northbound).* An example of C18 Formal English Garden. Restoration, started in 1985, provides visitors, academics and horticulturalists with opportunity to see unique collection of historic plants, shrubs, medicinal and culinary herbs and fascinating vegetable collection. Refreshments available; meals by arrangement. Gift shop. *Adm £3 OAPs £2 Chd £1. Open Easter to end Sept, closed Mons and Fris. Guided tours. For NGS Sun July 16 (2-6)*

Cedar House, Wasperton ♿✗ (Mr and Mrs D L Burbidge) *4m S of Warwick on A429, turn R between Barford and Wellesbourne, Cedar House near end of village on L.* 3 acres; shrubs, herbaceous borders, ornamental trees, woodland walk. Also open Gilbert Scott Church with Pugin window. TEAS. *Adm £2 Chd free (ACNO to St John's Church, Wasperton). Sun June 4 (2-6)*

▲ **Charlecote Park, Warwick** ♿✗ (The National Trust) *1m W of Wellesbourne signed from A429. 6m S of Warwick, 5m E of Stratford-upon-Avon.* Landscaped gardens featuring clipped yews and terraces with urns; C19 orangery; rustic thatched summerhouse by cedar lawn; river parterre and wilderness garden. 1m walk around park along banks of R Avon, giving fine vistas to two churches. New garden, designed by Sir Edmund Fairfax Lucy, paid for by The National Trust and The National Gardens Scheme completed in April 2000. **Evening Opening** *Adm £5. Strawberries & cream and Wine. Tues July 4 (7-dusk)*

NEW **Clifton-upon-Dunsmore Gardens, Nr Rugby** ✗❀ *2½m E of Rugby town centre. From M6 leave at junction 1(S) proceed on A426 towards Rugby, take 1st turn L, signed Clifton-upon-Dunsmore. From S leave M1 at junction 18, proceed N on A5 for 3m, take LH-turn, signed Clifton-upon-Dunsmore.* TEAS at village hall in aid of WI. Millennium wallhanging and local history exhibition. *Combined adm £2 Chd free (ACNO to St Mary's Church). Sat, Sun June 24, 25 (2-5.30)*

9 Allans Lane (Mrs M Lowden) Medium-sized front garden, small back garden, trees, climbers and plants. Paving, lawn, water feature and pergola. Interesting, pretty garden

The Manor (Christine McKimmie & Andrew Kypri) *Libourne Rd.* Large garden surrounding manor house (not open). Sunken rose garden, recently planted borders, series of pools, shade garden, mature trees and ancient wisteria

3 Orwell Close (Jennifer & Trevor Hart) Attractive small garden; colourful herbaceous borders; paving and tubs; feature archway leading to pretty front garden

26 Shuttleworth Road ❀ (Jean & Mick Foster) Medium-sized colourful garden; annuals and perennials. Lawn with arbour and climbing plants. Owner grows and exhibits chrysanthemums (national judge)

33 Shuttleworth Road (Margaret & Herbert Brockbank) Cottage-style front garden. Small colourful rear garden with paved area. Interesting plants, pond, bridge, pergola and vegetables

41 South Road ❀ (Janice & Alan Duffin) Medium-sized garden. Arbour with pots, trellis and pergola with many named rambler roses. Climbing plants, colourful herbaceous borders.

74 South Road (Miss D Allan) Small, individual feature gardens around bungalow and driveway with perennials, shrubs, climbers and alpines. Highland cattle in paddock

Compton Scorpion Farm, nr Ilmington ✗ (Mr & Mrs T M Karlsen) *8m S of Stratford-upon-Avon, 4m NW of Shipston-on-Stour. At Ilmington fork L at village hall then after 1½m turn L down steep, narrow lane, garden on L.* Garden designed and created by owners in 1989 from meadow hillside, aiming at Jekyll single colour schemes. Wild garden and cherry walk established. Dew pond created in '97. *Adm £2 Chd free. Sun June 18 (2-6)*

NEW **34 The Crescent, Cradley Heath** (Roz & Ian Goddard) *Off A459 Halesowen to Dudley Rd. 2m from junction 3 of M5 and 1.5m north from Halesowen.* Suburban spring garden 60' x 30' with auriculas, hellebores, Gold-laced and Elizabethan primroses and polyanthus. Also 3 display greenhouses with 1,000 plants in 300 varieties of Primula Auricula. *£1.50 Chd free. Easter Sun 23 April (1-5).*

66 Dalbury Road, Hall Green ✗ (Carole & Tom Herbert) *From A34 Birmingham to Stratford rd turn off at Robin Hood island. Take Baldwin Lane exit from roundabout then 2nd R followed by 1st R into Kedlestone Rd. Ist L again into Dalbury Rd.* Garden 85′ × 25′ built on three levels, has been transformed over last 5 yrs from lawns to plant persons' garden of mainly perennials. Large collection of containers. Interesting arrangements with mixtures of native and exotic plants. TEAS Aug 16 only. *Adm £1.50 Chd free. Wed Aug 16 (2-5).* **Evening Opening** *Wed Aug 9 (6-9). Also open Sun Aug 6 with* **Stonor Road Gardens**

Dorsington Gardens ♿ *6m SW of Stratford-on-Avon. On B439 from Stratford turn L to Welford-on-Avon, then R to Dorsington.* TEAS. *Combined adm £3 Chd free (ACNO to St Peter's Church, Dorsington). Sun June 4 (12-5)*

Colletts Farm (Mrs D Sawyer) Trees and shrubs. Container flowers. Highly productive kitchen garden with fan-trained fruit

9 Dorsington Manor (Melanie Pinches & Ken Holland) Being created by owners since 1993. Trees, shrubs, herbaceous borders and small vegetable garden

Glebe Cottage (Mr & Mrs A Brough) ¾ acre of land reclaimed into an uncomplicated garden, 10yrs-old, having an atmosphere and tranquility of as many decades

Knowle Thatch (Mr & Mrs P W Turner) Large garden; mature trees, shrubs and herbaceous borders

The Lodge, Dorsington Manor (Mrs P Roberts) Lawns and shrub beds graced by 3 large walnut trees

The Moat House (Mr & Mrs I Kolodotschko) 6-acre moated garden incl walled vegetable garden; conservatory with mediterranean plants. Marquee TEAS.

The Old Manor (Mr F Dennis) 3 acres with fairy walk, herb garden, fish pond; leading to **Highfield**, with Mediterranean garden and container plants. Nearby, Welshman's Track with arboretum and Udde Well. Marquee TEAS.

The Old Rectory (Mr & Mrs N Phillips) 2-acre Victorian garden with mature trees incl old espalier fruit trees, box hedges, herbaceous borders, many old roses; large pool, small wood

The Welshman's Barn (Mr F Dennis) 5 acres with Japanese garden, Oz maze, statue garden of heroes, wildflower garden and stream

Whitegates (Mrs A G Turner) Shrubs, mature trees and shrub roses

Windrush (Mrs M B Mills) Country garden with shrubs, cottage plants and roses

Earlsdon Gardens, Coventry *Turn towards Coventry at A45/A429 t-lights. Take 3rd L turn into Beechwood Ave, to St Barbara's Church.* Maps available. Plus other gardens also open and an allotments trail incl organic growers. TEAS. *Combined adm £3 Chd free. Sun June 25 (1-5)*

37 Belvedere Road (Zilpha Reed) Garden where clematis, shrubs and trees are grown for yr-round interest in form and foliage

40 Hartington Crescent (Viv and George Buss) Surprisingly large garden with interest for all ages; water feature

114 Hartington Crescent (Liz Campbell & Denis Crowley) Large, mature, pretty garden

39 Palmerston Road (Joan Miles) Secluded, pretty garden

NEW **84 Rochester Road** (Peter Harris) Interesting plantman's garden with interconnecting water feature leading to large adjoining allotment

87 Rochester Road (Edith Lewin) Peaceful, mature cottage garden

10 St Andrew's Road (Peter Turnbull Esq) Interesting evergreen and shrub garden

NEW **St Andrew's House, Coventry** (Jon Holder) Large, old communal garden being renovated to create a variety of gardens

15 Shaftsbury Road (Elaine Tierney) Plantaholic's small garden shared with young children

NEW **77 Stanway Road** (Derek & Penny Grinley) Compact town garden crammed with country garden plants

6 Stoneleigh Avenue (Ken Trewella) Traditional urban garden incl fruit trees

NEW **14 Warwick Avenue** Well established town garden aiming for low maintenance in the future

Elm Close, Welford-on-Avon ♿✂❀ (Mr & Mrs E W Dyer) *Binton Rd. 5m from Stratford off B4390. Elm Close is between Welford Garage and The Bell Inn.* ⅔ acre plantsman's garden designed and maintained by owners and stocked for yr-round effect. Bulbs, alpines; clematis and hellebores a particular speciality. Featured in Sunday Express Magazine April 1998. TEAS Sun only in aid of Red Cross. *Adm £1.50 Chd free. Sat, Sun March 4, 5 (2.30-5.30). Parties welcome by appointment, please* **Tel 01789 750793**

The Folly Lodge, Halford ✂❀ (Mike & Susan Solomon) *On A429 (Fosse Way) 9m NE Moreton in Marsh. 9m SE Stratford- upon-Avon. In Halford take turning opp PO to Idlicote. Garden is 300yds down on R.* Softly curving beds overflowing with plants enhance the fine views. Wide range of interesting plants, incl grasses, give yr-round interest. Come to sit, and enjoy the peace and beauty of our garden. TEA. *Adm £1.50 Chd free. Weds April 26, May 31, June 28, July 26, Aug 30 (2-5).* **Evening opening** *Wed June 28 (6-8). Group visits welcome by appt, please* **Tel 01789 740183**

Greenlands ❀ (Eric T Bartlett) *Leave Stratford-upon-Avon due E on B4086. Garden on Xrds at Loxley/Charlecote by airfield.* 1 acre with mature trees, shrubs, herbaceous borders and semi-wild areas. TEAS. *Adm £1.50 Chd free. Suns April 2, June 18 (11-5)*

18 Grove Avenue, Moseley ✂ (Richard & Judy Green) *3m S of Birmingham city centre, ½m E of Moseley village. From Moseley centre take B4217, Wake Green Rd, turn 3rd R into Grove Avenue. Garden 100 yds on R. Roadside parking.* Small suburban garden stocked with wide variety of unusual trees, shrubs and herbaceous, planted for colour and foliage. Cake stall. *Adm £1 Chd free (ACNO to British Diabetic Association). Suns June 25, Aug 27 (12-5).*

■ **89 Harts Green Road, Harborne** ✂❀ (Mrs Barbara Richardson) *3m Birmingham city centre [A-Z A2 p88] off Fellows Lane/War Lane.* ½ acre, split-level informal garden with troughs, rockery and mixed borders of unusual plants, shrubs and climbers. Pond and vegetable garden. Adjoining orchard contains small nursery offering wide range of plants, many propagated from garden. *Adm £1 Chd free. Open every Wed in April, May, June, July and Sept. For NGS Weds April 19, May 24, June 21, July 19 (2-5). Private visits and groups welcome, please* **Tel 0121 427 5200**

NEW **Hill Close Gardens, Warwick** (Warwick District Council) *Warwick town centre. Park in Bread and Meat Close, Friar St, or walk down Linen St.* Victorian Pleasure Gardens. 18 separate hedged gardens once enjoyed by prospeous townspeople. Derelict until 1988, now in course of restoration. Listed summerhouses, old fruit trees. Featured in Channel 4's 'Lost Gardens' Nov 99. Incl NCCPG garden of Warwickshire plants. *Adm £1 (ACNO to Hill Close Gardens Restoration Fund). Sat, Sun Sept 2, 3 (10-4)*

Holywell Gardens ♿✂ *5m E of Henley-in-Arden, nearest village Claverdon.* Coffee/TEAS in aid of Myton Hospice. *Combined adm £2 Chd free. Sun June 18 (11-6)*

Holywell Farm (Mr & Mrs Ian Harper) 2½ acres laid out in 1963 for easy maintenance, surrounding C16 half-timbered house (not open). Lawn, trees, shrubs. New Princess Diana wildflower garden

Manor Farm (Mr & Mrs Donald Hanson) Romantic garden surrounding Elizabethan farmhouse (not open), consisting of outdoor rooms walled with yew and box hedges, herb garden, white and grey borders, natural duck pond. Featured in 'Country Living'. *Visitors and groups welcome April to Sept by appt, please* **Tel 01926 842331**

Honington Village Gardens ♿✂ *1½m N of Shipston-on-Stour. Take A3400 towards Stratford then turn R signed Honington.* TEAS at Honington Hall. *Combined adm £2.50 Chd free (ACNO to All Saints Church, Honington). Sun June 25 (2.15-5.30)*

Feldon Cottage (Mr & Mrs H James)

Holts Cottage (Mr & Mrs R G Bentley)

Honington Glebe (Mr & Mrs J C Orchard) Over 2 acres of informal garden with interesting ornamental trees, shrubs and foliage. Parterre and raised lily pool laid out in old walled garden

Honington Hall (B H E Wiggin) Extensive lawns and fine trees. Carolean house (not open); parish church adjoining house

Honington Lodge (Lord & Lady Tombs)

The Old House (Mr & Mrs R S Smith)

Hunningham Village Gardens *From Leamington Spa B4453 to Rugby. Signposted Hunningham R after Weston-under-Wetherley. Or A425 to Southam at Fosseway (B4455) turn L. At Hunningham Hill turn L then follow signs to church (open).* Teas in Parish Room in church in aid of St Margaret's Church. *Adm £2.50 Chd free. Sun, Bank Hol Mon May 28, 29 (2-5)*

The Bungalow (Miss O Rouse) Cottage garden with large vegetable plot

High Cross (Mr & Mrs T Chalk) Secluded garden with small wildlife pool

Hunningham Croft (Mr & Mrs P Taylor) Interesting garden with large collection of clematis

The Old Hall (Mr & Mrs N W Horler) Large old garden with walled areas, listed building (not open)

The Olde School House (Mr & Mrs G Longstaff) 1 acre of borders, shrubs, pond and wildlife paddock area

Sandford Cottage (Mr & Mrs A Phillips) Village cottage garden

Idlicote Gardens ♿ *3m NE of Shipston-on-Stour.* TEAS. *Combined adm £3 Chd free (ACNO to Parish Church of St James the Great). Sun June 11 (2-6). Coaches by prior arrangement only* **Tel 01608 661473**

Badgers Cottage (Dr & Mrs D R N Custance)

Badgers Farm (Sir Derek & Lady Hornby)

1 Bickerstaff Cottages (Mr & Mrs C Balchin)

2 Bickerstaff Cottages (Mrs S Hopkinson)

3 Bickerstaff Cottages (Miss A Cummins)

Bickerstaff Farm (Sir John & Lady Owen)

Home Farm (Mrs & Mrs G Menzies-Kitchen)

Idlicote House (Mrs R P G Dill) About 4 acres. Fine views. Small Norman church in grounds. Grade II listed C18 house (not open)

The Old Rectory (Mr & Mrs G Thomson)

Stone Cottage (Mr and Mrs C Rosser)

Woodlands (Captain & Mrs P R Doyne)

Ilmington Gardens, nr Shipston-on-Stour *8m S of Stratford-upon-Avon, 4m NW of Shipston-on-Stour.* Ilmington traditional Morris dancers. Teas in village hall. Start anywhere, all gardens well signed and within walking distance. Free map supplied at The Manor. *Combined adm £3 Chd free (ACNO to Ilmington PCC New Bells Appeal). Sun April 9 (2-6)*

The Bevingtons (Mrs N Tustain) *Also open Sun June 18 with* **Ilmington Manor**

Crab Mill (Mr & Mrs L Hodgkin)

Foxcote Hill (Mr & Mrs M Dingley)

Foxcote Hill Cottage (Miss A Terry)

Frog Orchard (M Naish)

Ilmington Manor ♿❀ (Mr D & Lady Flower) see main entry below

NEW **Primrose Bank** (Mr & Mrs L Moore)

Ilmington Manor ♿❀ (Mr D Flower & Lady Flower) *4m NW of Shipston-on-Stour, 8m S of Stratford-upon-Avon.* Daffodils in profusion (April). Hundreds of old and new roses, ornamental trees, shrub and herbaceous borders, rock garden, pond garden, topiary, fish pond with koi. House (not open) built 1600. TEAS. *Adm £2 Chd free. Suns May 14, June 18, July 9 (2-6). Also open Sun April 9 with* **Ilmington Gardens**. *Private visits welcome, please* **Tel 01608 682230**

Lawford Hill Farm, Long Lawford ❀ (Donald & Susan Moses) *2m W of Rugby outside village of Long Lawford. Lawford Heath Lane runs between A428 and A45 ½m off A428 or 2m off A45. [OS Map Ref SP 466.747].* Gardens surround fine Grade II listed Georgian farmhouse (not open) in an acre of formal lawns, herbaceous borders, shrubberies and traditional walled vegetable and herb garden. Mature trees giving way to farm lakeside walk. Rugby's 1998 small business Green Award winner and Rugby in Bloom 1999 Hotel Category winner. TEAS. *Adm £1.50. Chd free. Sun July 9 (2-5.30)*

78 Marsham Road, King's Heath ✂❀ (Phil & Amy Harding) *Off Alcester Rd between King's Heath and Maypole. Turn into Meadfoot Ave, Marsham Rd leads off [A-Z 4A 106].* Approx 150′ leading down to Stratford canal. Specialist collection of geraniums, stone troughs, lawns, koi pool, fountain. Perennials and annuals. TEAS. *Adm £1. Sun July 9 (2-6)*

■ **The Master's Garden, Lord Leycester Hospital, Warwick** ✂ (Lord Leycester Hospital) *High Street. Town centre beside West Gate.* C14 Guildhall, Chapel, courtyard, Great Hall and Museum of the Queen's Own Hussars also open to public. Historic walled garden, incl Norman arch and ancient finial of Nilometer. Civic Trust Award 1997, visited by H M The Queen. Featured in 'The English Garden' and on BBC2 Gardeners' World. Millenium knot garden. TEAS. *Adm £1 Chd free. Open daily except Mons, March 18 to Sept 30 (10-4.30). For NGS Sun June 18 (11-5). Parties welcome, please* **Tel 01926 491422**

Maxstoke Castle, nr Coleshill ♿✂❀ (Mr & Mrs M C Fetherston-Dilke) *E of Birmingham, 2½m E of Coleshill on B4114 take R turn down Castle Lane; Castle Dr 1¼m on R.* Approx 5 acres of garden and pleasure grounds with flowers, shrubs and trees in immediate surroundings of castle (not open) and inside courtyard; water-filled moat. *Adm £2.50 OAPs/Chd £1.50 under 6 free. Sun May 28 (2-5)*

■ **The Mill Garden, Warwick** ♿✂❀ (Open in memory of Arthur Measures) *55 Mill St. Off A425 beside castle gate. Use St Nicholas car park.* 1 acre. Series of informal, partially enclosed areas, on river next to castle in superb setting. Herb garden, raised beds, small trees, shrubs, cottage plants and unusual plants. Teas in Warwick. *Adm £1 Chd free (ACNO to Lord Leycester Hospital). Open daily, Easter to Sept 30. Open for NGS Suns April 16, June 18, Sept 3, Oct 8, Thurs May 18, July 13, Aug 17 (10-5.30). Parties welcome by appt, please* **Tel 01926 492877**

Moseley Gardens, Birmingham ✂❀ *Approx 3m from Birmingham city centre halfway between King's Heath centre*

& Moseley village. TEA April 16. TEAS July 9. *Combined adm £2 Chd free. Suns April 16, July 9 (2-6)*

7 Ashfield Road (Mr & Mrs Bartlett) Small garden with secluded, cottage feel. Attractive pond with rockery, waterfall and shingle bank

14 Prospect Road (Ms Jan Birtle) Wild garden which is both low maintenance and child friendly. As featured on Channel 5's 'Instant Gardens'

16 Prospect Road ❀ (Mrs S M Londesborough) Small garden with wide range of plants. Large collection of containers. Small conservatory. Featured on several national television programmes and in various magazines *Also private visits welcome all year, please* **Tel 0121 449 8457**

19 Prospect Road (Mr A White) Well planted spring suburban garden

30 Prospect Road (Mrs J Taylor) S-facing terraced garden incorporating rockery-covered air-raid shelter. Featured on 'Garden Party' and in various magazines

33 School Rd (Ms J Warr-Arnold) Mixed garden containing plants with interesting histories. Come and spot the dragons! *Sun July 9 only*

65 School Rd (Mrs W Weston) Small shady garden with patio, pergola and pond. Featured on 'Garden Party'. *Sun July 9 only*

Packington Hall, Meriden ♿✂ (Lord & Lady Guernsey) *On A45, towards Coventry, after Stonebridge roundabout.* Packington's pleasure grounds were laid out in 1750 by Capability Brown. Lawns run down to 18 acre Hall Pool and are studded with clumps of azaleas, rhododendrons and specimen trees. Terrace has herbaceous border all around it. TEAS. *Combined adm £3.50 Chd £2 (ACNO to Assoc. for Brain Damaged Children, Coventry). Sun May 21 (2-5.30). Also open* **The Old Hall** (Earl of Aylesford) situated in grounds opp church

▲ **Packwood House** ♿✂❀ (The National Trust) *11m SE of Birmingham. 2m E of Hockley Heath.* Carolean yew garden representing the Sermon on the Mount. Tudor house with tapestries, needlework and furniture of the period. Teas at Baddesley Clinton (NT) Henley-in-Arden or Knowle. Refreshment kiosk in car park. *Adm House and garden £4.60, garden only £2.30 Chd £1.15 For NGS June 14 (1.30-5.30)*

Pebworth & District Gardens ✂❀ *9m SW of Stratford-upon-Avon. On B439 at Bidford turn L towards Honeybourne, after 3m turn L at Xrds signed Pebworth.* TEAS, toilets and parking at village hall. *Adm £3 Chd free (ACNO to St Peter's Church, Pebworth). Sun, Bank Hol Mon May 28, 29 (2-6)*

1 Elm Close, Pebworth ✂ (Mr & Mrs G Keyte) Small cottage garden, very well stocked and with many features of interest

Far View (Mr & Mrs J Carding) ⅓ acre with pond, greenhouse, vegetables, heathers, shrubs and perennial borders. Beautiful views

Ivybank (Mr & Mrs R Davis) *Fibrex Nurseries, Honeybourne Road.* ⅓ acre garden with ferns, ivies, roses and shrubs. The nursery holds the National Pelargonium collection

Martins (Mr & Mrs T Collins) ½ acre informal gardens with pond, vegetable patch and unusual plants. *Bank Hol Mon May 29 only*

Nolan Cottage (Mr & Mrs R Thomas) Cottage garden of ¾ acre with ponds, vegetable garden, ferns, mixed borders and wild garden area. TEAS.

Pereira Road Gardens ✂ *Between Gillhurst Rd and Margaret Grove, ¼m from Hagley Rd or ½m from Harborne High St. [Birmingham A-Z p88 1C]* TEAS June 25 at no 84 in aid of St Mary's Hospice. *Adm £1 each garden, combined adm £2.50 OAPs £1 Chd 30p. Suns May 7, June 25 (2-5)*

45 Pereira Road, Harborne (Mrs Alfred White) 'Alf's Garden'; on 5 levels, with spring bulbs, rhododendrons, roses, shrubs, herbaceous borders and fruit trees in formal and informal areas. Harborne Nature Reserve and Bird Sanctuary can be visited *(ACNO to Oasis Appeal, Queen Elizabeth Hospital). June 25 only*

48 Pereira Road (Liz Hurst & Rosemary Klem) Dog-friendly garden with 2 long, raised borders, rock garden with pond and koi, also patio with many pots. Plants in aid of Fireside Day Centre for the Homeless *June 25 only*

50 Pereira Road ❀ (Prof Peg Peil) ¼ acre on several levels with wide range of shrubs, perennials, alpines and herbs for all seasons, fruit and vegetables. Large bed of plants with African connections. Seen on Central TV. Unusual plants sold in aid of CAFOD

55 Pereira Road (Emma Davies & Martin Commander) Young garden with deck and gravel area; informal beds with variety of trees and shrubs *June 25 only*

84 Pereira Road (Mrs R E Barnett) Small garden with 30 degree sloping concreted bank, now extensive rockery, interesting shrubs, herbaceous borders *June 25 only*

NEW **Rivendell, Newbold-on-Stour** ✂❀ (Dr Caroline Nixon & Dr Peter Hawker) *Off A3400, 8m S of Stratford-upon-Avon. In village of Newbold-on-Stour, turn L, opp Bird in Hand public house, into Brook Lane. Garden is on R.* 1-acre, partly walled garden, redeveloped by owner over past 8yrs. Colour-themed borders incl pink and white, also 'hot' borders. Many old roses and unusual herbaceous perennials. Gravel garden, terraced ornamental vegetable garden, orchard and wild garden leading to R Stour. TEAS. *Adm £1.50 Chd free. Sun, Wed June 25, 28 (2-6)*

Roseberry Cottage, Fillongley ♿✂❀ (Mr & Mrs Richard G Bastow) *6m N of Coventry on B4098 Tamworth rd. Go under motorway bridge to top of hill, take Woodend Lane, sign on R. Turn L into Sandy Lane, opp triangle of beech trees. 1st house on R in Sandy Lane. Please use one-way system due to restricted parking.* 1¾ acres incl herbaceous border, rock garden, pool, peat and bog area, scree and small herb garden. Stone troughs, orchard with wild flowers, organically grown fruit and vegetables. Herbs for sale, thymes a speciality. TEA. *Adm £1.50 Chd 50p (ACNO to NCCPG). Sun June 25 (2-5)*

Rowington Gardens ♿✂❀ *6m NW of Warwick, 15m SE of Birmingham on B4439 between Hockley Heath and Hatton. Turn into Finwood Rd (signed Lowsonford at Rowington Xrds), then 1st L into Mill Lane.* TEAS in aid of St Laurence's & St Luke's Churches. *Combined adm £2 Chd 50p. Sun June 25 (11-5)*

Hickecroft ♿✂ (Mr & Mrs J M Pitts) 2 acres with mixed borders. Small woodland garden. Home to part of

NCCPG Digitalis collection. *Private visits welcome, please* **Tel 01564 782384**
Woodlands (Mr & Mrs M Jordan) Medium-sized informal garden with fine collection of interesting trees surrounding C16 timbered farmhouse (not open)

■ **Ryton Organic Gardens** (Ryton Organic Gardens) *5m SE of Coventry off A45 to Wolston.* HQ of Henry Doubleday Research Association, UK showcase for organic gardening. As seen on tv, 33 practical and attractive demonstration gardens incl flowers, roses, herbs, shrubs, top and soft fruit; forest garden; Heritage vegetables; composting; pest and disease control. Latest additions include herbaceous perennials in landscaping, Cook's Garden and Geoff Hamilton paradise garden! Award-winning restaurant and speciality shop. TEAS. *Adm £3 Chd free. Open daily except Christmas period. For NGS Sat June 3, Sun Oct 22 (9-5)*

6 Spring Meadow, Halesowen (Peter & Christine Bridgens) *Off B4183 ¾m from town centre. From Birmingham take A456 Manor Way W to B4183 (signposted Halesowen town centre). Turn R into Huntlands Rd, Spring Meadow is 1st L. Parking in Huntlands Rd. Bus 247 from Halesowen bus station to Hasbury, Rose and Crown [A to Z page 85 ref 4F]* S-facing, 40' garden planted for subtropical effect incl palms, cordylines, phormiums, banana. Many plants not expected to thrive in region. Exotic shrubs; herbaceous plants and bulbs for yr-round interest; water feature. Shown on Gardeners' World, in Sainsburys magazine and Garden Answers. TEAS. *Adm £1 Chd free. Suns June 4, Sept 10 (2-5)*

219 Station Road, Sutton Coldfield (Esta & Ken Johnson) *¾m S of Sutton Coldfield. Turn off A5127 towards Wylde Green Station and garden is 100yds past station.* Designed by present owners to incl conservatory; well stocked sundial garden with herbaceous plants, shrubs and bulbs; small potager and pond with bog garden. TEAS. *Adm £1.50 Chd free (ACNO to Breakthrough Trust Deaf-Hearing Group). Sun May 28 (2-6)*

172 Stonor Road, Hall Green (Mrs O Walters) *Just off Robin Hood roundabout on A34 Birmingham to Stratford Rd. Take Baldwins Lane exit from roundabout. Stonor Rd is 2nd L.* Very small, plantswoman's garden (approx 20m × 7m) wide variety of plants some not considered hardy in this area. Scree, containers, shade beds, ferns, climbers, conservatory. TEAS. *Adm £1.50 Chd free (ACNO to St Mary's Hospice). Suns June 4, Aug 6 (2-5.30). Also open 166 & 188 Stonor Road. Jointly open with* **66 Dalbury Rd** *Aug 6. Private visits by appt.*

26 Sunnybank Road, Wylde Green (Chris & Margaret Jones) *¾m S of Sutton Coldfield. Turn off A5127 towards Wylde Green Station then 2nd L.* Continuously evolving garden with cottage garden spirit. Mixed plantings of annuals, bulbs, shrubs, roses and herbaceous plants provide yr-round interest; many unusual perennials. A surprise around every corner; pond and bog area, colour-themed plantings, cool shaded areas, vibrant containers, new drought-resistant garden and water features. Seen on tv and in many magazines. July opening coinciding with **76 Wylde Green Rd** (see separate entry). TEAS in aid of St Peter's Primary, Yoxall. *Adm £1.50 OAPs £1 Chd free. Suns June 25, July 23 (2-6).* **Evening Opening** *Fri June 30, Adm £2.50. Wine (6.30-8.30).*

52 Tenbury Road, King's Heath (Mr G & Mrs V Grace Darby) *5m S of city centre off A435 (Alcester Rd). 4¾m from junction 3 off M40.* Eighth-acre suburban garden in cottage-garden style. Informal plantings of mixed beds and borders with interesting and unusual plants, shrubs, climbers. New gravel garden. Filmed for BBC and ITV. Minimum use of chemical pest control. TEAS in aid of Muscular Dystrophy. *Adm £1.50 Chd free. Suns April 16, June 11, Wed June 21(2-5).* **Evening Opening** *Wed June 21 (6-8). Private and group visits welcome by appt April to Sept, Weds preferred, please* **Tel 0121 444 6456**

Tysoe Manor, Tysoe (Mr & Mrs W A C Wield) *5m NE of Shipston-on-Stour. Take B4035 to Banbury. In Brailes turn L to Tysoe. The Manor is 1st house on L after reaching Upper Tysoe.* 4 acres; large lawns with stone walls; herbaceous and flower borders; shrubs and mature ornamental and fruit trees. TEAS in aid of Tysoe Church. *Adm £2 Chd free. Sun Sept 3 (2-6)*

University of Birmingham Botanic Garden at Winterbourne, Edgbaston *58 Edgbaston Park Rd. 3m SW from city centre via A38; turn off at Edgbaston Park Rd. Situated on R near junction with Pritchatts Rd. Buses 61, 62, 63. University Stn 10 mins.* 6 acres of themed gardens incl alpine troughs and scree garden. Woodland walk through 'giant rhubarb' Gunnera manicata. Dell garden with stepping stones. Nut walk tunnel. Rhododendrons and unusual trees. Herbaceous borders and terraces. Ornamental features. NCCPG National Rose Collection. Set around Grade II listed Winterbourne House (not open). TEAS. *Adm £2 Chd 50p (ACNO to Friends of Winterbourne Garden). Mon - Fri (11-4.30). For NGS Suns May 14, June 25 (1-5) Oct 1 (11-3)*

▲ **Upton House, nr Banbury** (The National Trust) *7m NW of Banbury on A422; 1m S of Edgehill.* Large terraced garden, herbaceous borders, roses, water garden, kitchen garden, lawns. NCCPG Collection of Asters (autumn flowering). House contains an internationally important collection of paintings, porcelain and tapestries. Partially suitable for wheelchairs. Coaches by appt. TEAS. *Adm garden only £2.70 Chd £1.30. For NGS Sat July 1 (2-6 last adm 5.30)*

8 Vicarage Road, Edgbaston (Mr & Mrs C King-Farlow) *1½m W of city centre off A456 (Hagley Rd).* ¾ acre retaining in part its Victorian layout but informally planted with mixed borders of interesting and unusual plants; shrub rose border; walled potager and conservatory. Featured in several magazines. TEAS in aid of St George's Church. *Adm £1.50 Chd free. Sun June 18 (2-5.30).* **Evening Opening** *Wed June 21 Adm £2.50. Wine (6.30-8.30). Private visits very welcome, please* **Tel 0121 455 0902**

Warmington Village Gardens *5m NW of Banbury on B4100. Car park.* Teas at village hall. *Combined adm £3 Chd free (ACNO to Warmington PCC Restoration Fund). Sun July 16 (2-6)*
Berka (Mr & Mrs B J Castle) *Chapel St*
3 Court Close (Mr & Mrs C J Crocker)

The Glebe House (Mrs J Thornton) *Village Rd*
Holly Cottage (Dr & Mrs T W Martin) *The Green*
Lilac Tree Cottage (Mr & Mrs D M Pittaway) *Chapel St*
The Manor House (Mr & Mrs G Lewis) *The Green*
The Old Rectory (Sir Wilfred & Lady Cockcroft) *The Green*
Rotherwood (Miss M R Goodison) *Soot Lane*
Sunnyside (Mr & Mrs M Borlenghi) *Chapel St*
Underedge (Mr & Mrs J Dixon) *1 Church Hill*
Woodcote (Mrs S Mellor) *School Lane*

Warwickshire Constabulary Police HQ, Leek Wootton ❀ *Mid-way between Warwick and Kenilworth, 1m N of Gaveston Island, on Kenilworth rd, off A46 Warwick to Coventry by-pass. From Warwick, turn L after Anchor public house in centre of village, signposted Police Headquarters.* Approx 6 acres of mixed garden, large and small shrubs, herbaceous borders, walk around lakes. TEAS. *Adm £1.50 Chd free (ACNO to Victim Support). Sun May 21 (1.30-5)*

50 Wellington Rd, Edgbaston ♿✂❀ (Mrs Anne Lee) *Corner of Ampton Rd and Wellington Rd.* 1-acre walled town garden. York stone paving, brick paths and summerhouse. 100-yr-old rhododendrons and mature trees with woodland walk. Two long mixed borders, shrub roses, fountain, croquet lawn. Children's quiz. TEAS. *Adm £1.50 Chd free. Sun June 25 (2-6). Private visits also welcome April to Oct, please* **Tel 0121 440 1744**

Wheelwright House, Long Compton ♿❀ (Mr & Mrs R B Shacklock) *6m S of Shipston-on-Stour on A3400; at S end of Long Compton village take rd signed to Little Compton; entrance is 300yds on L.* 1 acre surrounding C18 house (not open). Stream with attractive bridges forms centrepiece. Bog garden, shade gardens, colourful mixed borders. Formal lily pool with rose pergola. Mediterranean garden. 'Wheelwright' parterre. TEAS in aid of Long Compton Church. *Adm £2 Chd free. Sun July 9 (2-5.30). Private visits welcome, please* **Tel 01608 684478**

Whichford & Ascott Gardens, Shipston-on-Stour ✂❀ *6m SE of Shipston-on-Stour. Turn E off A3400 at Long Compton for Whichford.* Car park and picnic area. Cream TEAS in aid of St Michael's Church. *Combined adm £3 Chd free. Sun June 18 (2-6)*

Ascott Lodge ✂❀ (Charlotte Copley) Beautiful views, lawns sloping down to pond, well stocked borders, courtyard garden
Brook Hollow (Mr & Mrs J A Round) Terraced hillside garden with large variety of trees, shrubs and plants; stream and water features
Combe House (Mr & Mrs D C Seel) Hidden garden surrounding house (not open); mature fine trees
The Old House (Mr & Mrs T A Maher) Undulating garden. Natural ponds, trees and shrubs
The Old Rectory (Mr & Mrs P O'Kane) Established family garden with lawns, water garden and ponds; interesting new tree and shrub planting
Pine Tree Cottage (Mr & Mrs W Pinfold) Colourful cottage garden with unusual plants, planting and features. Bird aviary and small pool
Stone Walls (Mrs J Scott-Cockburn) Walled garden with paved garden in foundations of old stable
The Whichford Pottery (Mr & Mrs J B M Keeling) Secret walled garden, unusual plants, large vegetable garden and rambling cottage garden. Adjoining pottery

Woodpeckers, nr Bidford-on-Avon ♿✂❀ (Dr & Mrs A J Cox) *The Bank, Marlcliff, 7m SW of Stratford-upon-Avon. Off B4085 between Bidford-on-Avon and Cleeve Prior.* 2½ acre plantsman's country garden designed and maintained by owners; colour-schemed borders, old roses, meadow garden, small arboretum, alpines in troughs and gravel, pool, knot garden, potager. Featured on BBC2 'Gardeners' World' and in books and magazines. *Adm £2.50. Private visits by societies or individuals welcome at all seasons, please* **Tel 01789 773416**

Wootton Grange, Henley-in-Arden ♿❀ (Mrs Peter Tarmey) *1m E of Henley-in-Arden. Take 1st R off A4189, garden is 300yds on R.* 1-acre farm garden with yr-round interest surrounding early Victorian farmhouse (not open). Wide variety of unusual plants including bulbs, hellebores, clematis, roses and alpines. New bog garden and grass feature. TEAS. *Adm £1.50. Thurs June 8 (2-6). Groups and private visits very welcome from early spring, please* **Tel 01564 792592**

76 Wylde Green Road, Sutton Coldfield ✂❀ (Mr Brendan Lynch) *½m from Sutton Coldfield. Turn off A5127.* Large extended town garden. Remodelled 4yrs ago to become a 4-season, colour-themed garden. Characteristics: architectural plants with strong shapes; complementary plant settings; well established herbaceous beds for plant lovers and florists, and over 30 varieties of grasses. Large herb garden and extensive pond. TEAS. *Adm £1.50 Chd free. Sun July 23 (2-6). Opening coinciding with* **26 Sunnybank Rd** *see separate entry*

Evening Opening (See also garden description)

Charlecote Park, Warwick	July 4
66 Dalbury Road, Hall Green	August 9
The Folly Lodge, Halford	June 28
26 Sunnybank Road, Wylde Green	June 30
52 Tenbury Road, King's Heath	June 21
8 Vicarage Road, Edgbaston	June 21

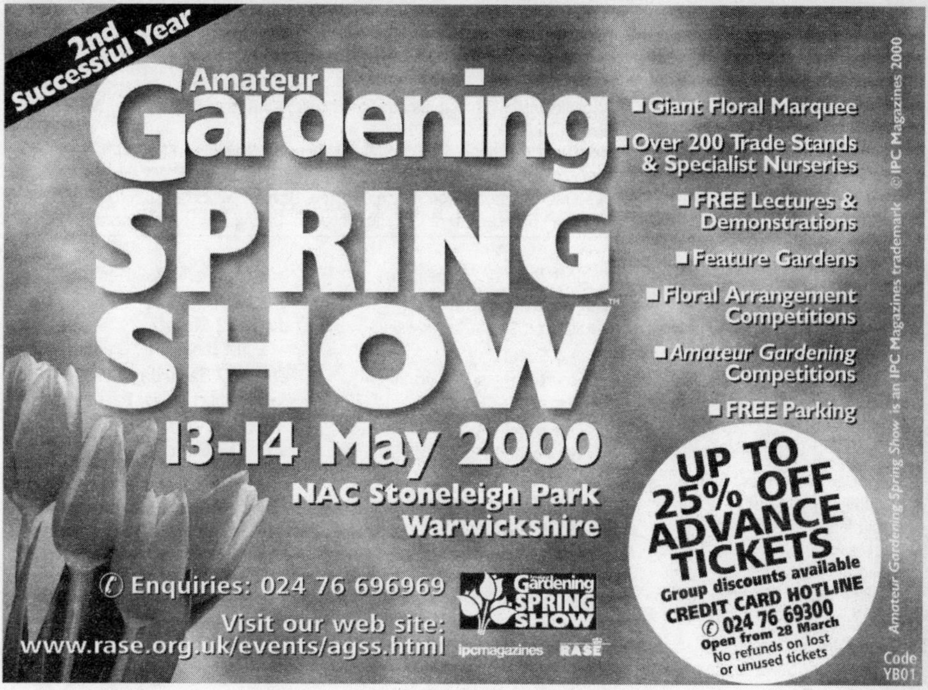

2nd Successful Year
Amateur Gardening
SPRING SHOW™
■ Giant Floral Marquee
■ Over 200 Trade Stands & Specialist Nurseries
■ FREE Lectures & Demonstrations
■ Feature Gardens
■ Floral Arrangement Competitions
■ Amateur Gardening Competitions
■ FREE Parking
13-14 May 2000
NAC Stoneleigh Park
Warwickshire
Enquiries: 024 76 696969
Visit our web site:
www.rase.org.uk/events/agss.html
Amateur Gardening SPRING SHOW
ipcmagazines RASE
UP TO 25% OFF ADVANCE TICKETS
Group discounts available
CREDIT CARD HOTLINE
024 76 69300
Open from 28 March
No refunds on lost or unused tickets
Amateur Gardening Spring Show is an IPC Magazines trademark © IPC Magazines 2000
Code YB01

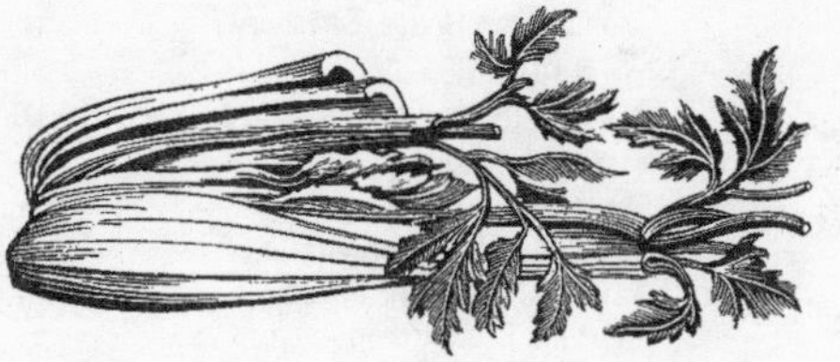

Scotland's Garden Scheme

The National Gardens Scheme has a similar but separate counterpart in Scotland. Called Scotland's Garden Scheme, it raises money for the Queen's Nursing Institute (Scotland), the Gardens Fund of the National Trust for Scotland, and over 160 registered charities nominated by Garden Owners.

The Handbook is available for £3.50 (£4.25 including p&p) from most major bookstores, from the NGS website www.ngs.org.uk or from Scotland's Gardens Scheme, 31 Castle Terrace, Edinburgh EH1 2EL.

Wiltshire

Hon County Organiser: Brigadier Arthur Gooch, Manor Farmhouse, Chitterne, Warminster, Wiltshire BA12 0LG

Assistant Hon County Organisers: Mrs David Armytage, Sharcott Manor, Pewsey, Wiltshire SN9 5PA
Mrs Anthony Heywood, Monkton House, Monkton Deverill, Wiltshire BA12 7EX
Mrs Colin Shand, Ashton House, Worton, Devizes, Wilts SN10 5RU
Mrs John Surtees, Mitre Cottage, Snowhill, Dinton, Salisbury, Wiltshire SP3 5HN

DATES OF OPENING

Regular openings

For details see garden description

The Abbey House, Malmesbury
Bowood Rhododendron Walks, nr Chippenham
Broadleas, Devizes
Cantax House, Lacock
Heale Gardens & Plant Centre, Middle Woodford
Iford Manor, nr Bradford-on-Avon
The Mead Nursery, Brokerswood
Pound Hill House, West Kington
Stourton House, Stourton

February 19 Saturday
Lacock Abbey Gardens, Chippenham

February 20 Sunday
Lacock Abbey Gardens, Chippenham

February 26 Saturday
Lacock Abbey Gardens, Chippenham

February 27 Sunday
Lacock Abbey Gardens, Chippenham
Lower House, Whiteparish

March 26 Sunday
Manor House Farm, Hanging Langford
Ridleys Cheer, Mountain Bower

April 2 Sunday
Corsham Court, nr Chippenham
Great Chalfield Manor, nr Melksham

April 5 Wednesday
Sharcott Manor, nr Pewsey

April 9 Sunday
Fonthill House, nr Tisbury
Sharcott Manor, nr Pewsey

April 16 Sunday
Broadleas, Devizes
Oare House, nr Pewsey

April 23 Sunday
The Abbey House, Malmesbury

April 30 Sunday
Iford Manor, nr Bradford-on-Avon
Little Durnford Manor, nr Salisbury
Luckington Court, Luckington
Ridleys Cheer, Mountain Bower
Spye Park, nr Chippenham

May 3 Wednesday
Sharcott Manor, nr Pewsey

May 6 Saturday
Stourton House, Stourton

May 7 Sunday
Brillscote Farm, Lea
The Pound House, Little Somerford
Stourton House, Stourton
Waterdale House, Milton

May 14 Sunday
Home Covert, Roundway
7 Norton Bavant, nr Warminster

May 21 Sunday
Conock Manor, Chirton
Dinton Gardens
Inwoods, Farleigh Wick
The Old School House, Baverstock
Pound Hill House, West Kington
Ridleys Cheer, Mountain Bower

May 27 Saturday
Mompesson House, Salisbury

June 4 Sunday
Bowood Rhododendron Walks, nr Chippenham
Brillscote Farm, Lea
Great Durnford Gardens
Landford Lodge, nr Salisbury
Martins, Bradford-on-Avon
The Pound House, Little Somerford
Stourhead Garden, Stourton

June 7 Wednesday
Sharcott Manor, nr Pewsey

June 10 Saturday
Court Lane Farm, Bratton

June 11 Sunday
Cantax House, Lacock
Chisenbury Priory, East Chisenbury
Corsham Court, nr Chippenham
The Court House, Lower Woodford
Court Lane Farm, Bratton
The Courts, Holt
Dauntsey Gardens
Edington & Coulston Gardens
Goulters Mill Farm, Burton
13 Kingsdown Road, Stratton St Margaret
Manor Farm, Monkton Deverill
Pertwood Manor, Hindon

June 12 Monday
Court Lane Farm, Bratton

June 17 Saturday
Hazelbury Manor Gardens, Wadswick, nr Box

June 18 Sunday
Avebury Manor Garden, Avebury
Benmead Cottage, Box
The Close, Pewsey
Faulstone House, Bishopstone
Goulters Mill Farm, Burton
Guyers House, Corsham
Hazelbury Manor Gardens, Wadswick, nr Box
Job's Mill, Crockerton
Ridleys Cheer, Mountain Bower

June 25 Sunday
The Abbey House, Malmesbury
Biddestone Manor, Biddestone
Bolehyde Manor, Allington
Hillbarn House, Great Bedwyn
Little Durnford Manor, nr Salisbury
Long Meadow, Winterbourne Bassett

July 2 Sunday
Sharcott Manor, nr Pewsey

July 5 Wednesday
Sharcott Manor, nr Pewsey

July 8 Saturday
Great Somerford Gardens
Yew Tree Farm, Hankerton

July 9 Sunday
Great Somerford Gardens
Hannington Hall, Hannington
Home Covert, Roundway
Lackham Gardens, Lacock
Manor Farm, Monkton Deverill
34, 38 & 40 Sherford Road, Haydon Wick, Swindon
Yew Tree Farm, Hankerton

July 16 Sunday
Benmead Cottage, Box
13 Kingsdown Road, Stratton St Margaret
Milford House Nursing Home, Salisbury

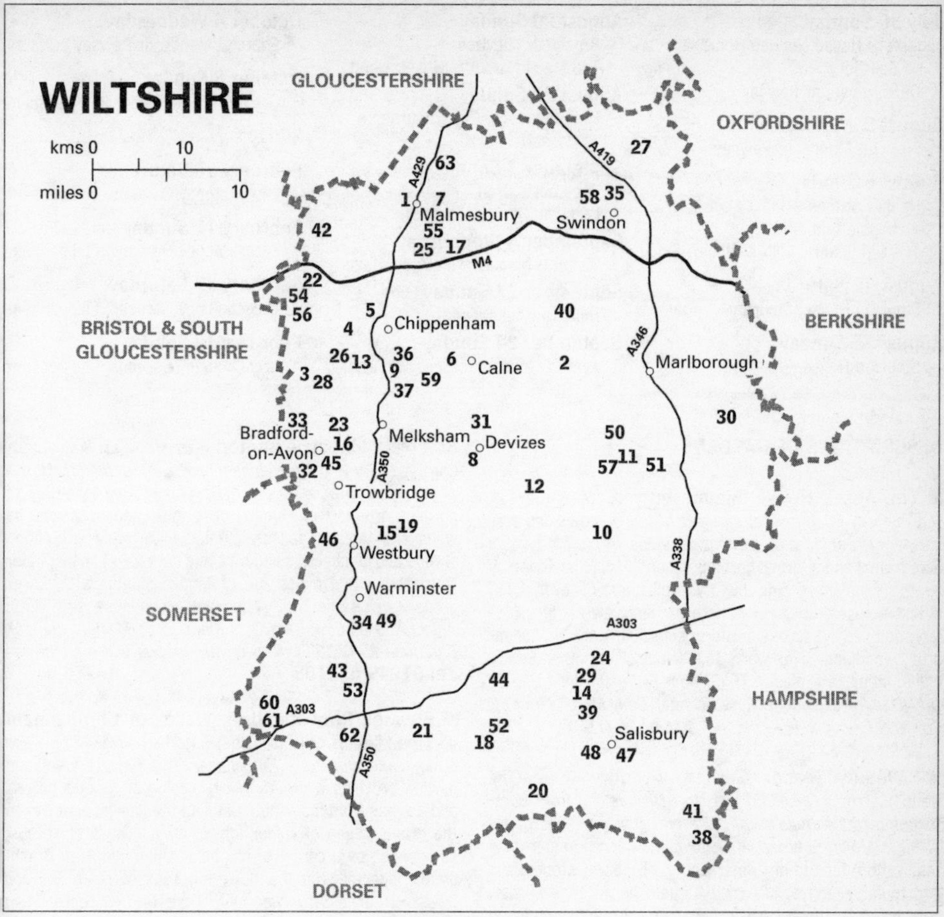

KEY

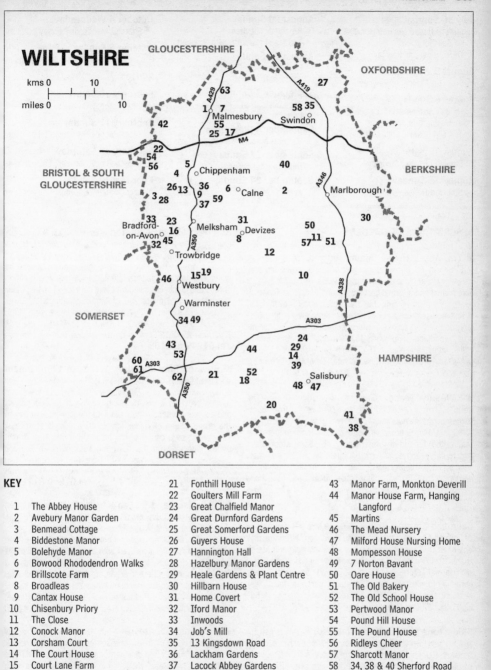

1 The Abbey House
2 Avebury Manor Garden
3 Benmead Cottage
4 Biddestone Manor
5 Bolehyde Manor
6 Bowood Rhododendron Walks
7 Brillscote Farm
8 Broadleas
9 Cantax House
10 Chisenbury Priory
11 The Close
12 Conock Manor
13 Corsham Court
14 The Court House
15 Court Lane Farm
16 The Courts
17 Dauntsey Gardens
18 Dinton Gardens
19 Edington Gardens
20 Faulstone House
21 Fonthill House
22 Goulters Mill Farm
23 Great Chalfield Manor
24 Great Durnford Gardens
25 Great Somerford Gardens
26 Guyers House
27 Hannington Hall
28 Hazelbury Manor Gardens
29 Heale Gardens & Plant Centre
30 Hillbarn House
31 Home Covert
32 Iford Manor
33 Inwoods
34 Job's Mill
35 13 Kingsdown Road
36 Lackham Gardens
37 Lacock Abbey Gardens
38 Landford Lodge
39 Little Durnford Manor
40 Long Meadow
41 Lower House
42 Luckington Court
43 Manor Farm, Monkton Deverill
44 Manor House Farm, Hanging Langford
45 Martins
46 The Mead Nursery
47 Milford House Nursing Home
48 Mompesson House
49 7 Norton Bavant
50 Oare House
51 The Old Bakery
52 The Old School House
53 Pertwood Manor
54 Pound Hill House
55 The Pound House
56 Ridleys Cheer
57 Sharcott Manor
58 34, 38 & 40 Sherford Road
59 Spye Park
60 Stourhead Garden
61 Stourton House
62 Waterdale House
63 Yew Tree Farm

July 30 Sunday
Milford House Nursing Home, Salisbury
Oare House, nr Pewsey

August 2 Wednesday
Sharcott Manor, nr Pewsey

August 6 Sunday
Heale Gardens & Plant Centre, Middle Woodford
The Old Bakery, Milton Lilbourne

August 12 Saturday
Stourton House, Stourton

August 13 Sunday
Stourton House, Stourton

August 20 Sunday
Broadleas, Devizes
The Mead Nursery, Brokerswood

August 27 Sunday
Long Meadow, Winterbourne Bassett

September 3 Sunday
The Courts, Holt
Lackham Gardens, Lacock

September 6 Wednesday
Sharcott Manor, nr Pewsey

September 17 Sunday
Hillbarn House, Great Bedwyn

September 24 Sunday
Avebury Manor Garden, Avebury

October 4 Wednesday
Sharcott Manor, nr Pewsey

October 8 Sunday
Great Chalfield Manor, nr Melksham

2001

February 10 Saturday
Lacock Abbey Gardens, Chippenham

February 11 Sunday
Lacock Abbey Gardens, Chippenham

February 17 Saturday
Lacock Abbey Gardens, Chippenham

February 18 Sunday
Lacock Abbey Gardens, Chippenham

DESCRIPTIONS OF GARDENS

■ **The Abbey House, Malmesbury** ✻❀ (Barbara & Ian Pollard) *Beautiful setting next to C12 Abbey. Long stay car park (free) close by gardens via steps, or park in town.* 5 acre formal and informal gardens around C16 house (open by appt). Horticulture and history. Collection of over 2000 different roses; 'mediaeval' herb garden; yew hedges; topiary; double herbaceous borders; laburnum walk: rhododendron, woodland, river walk. 15,000 tulips and other Spring bulbs. Many rare plants. TEAS. *Adm £4.50 OAPs £4 Chd £2 (ACNO to Royal National Rose Society). Daily March 1-Oct 31. For NGS Easter Sun, April 23; Sun June 25 (11-6)*

▲ **Avebury Manor Garden, Avebury** ✻❀ (The National Trust) *On A4361 9m N of Devizes 2m from Beckhampton roundabout on A4. Use main car park and follow signs to Manor.* 5-acres. Ancient walled garden (undergoing restoration) on site of former priory, divided by stone walls and topiary hedges, incl rose garden, herbaceous border, new orchard, topiary garden. Italian walk and half moon garden. Late mediaeval manor house (open). *Adm House and Garden £3.20 Chd £1.50; Garden only £2.25 Chd £1. For NGS Suns June 18, Sept 24 (Garden 11-5) (House 2-5)*

Benmead Cottage, Box ✻❀ (Mr & Mrs J H Hope) *6m E of Bath on A4 take N turning to Middlehill and Ditteridge at W end of Box village. Please park in adjoining field and not on roadside.* 1½-acre mature and partly walled garden with a semi-formal area; leaf garden; mixed borders; arbour garden; old pigsty garden; vegetable garden; wild flower meadow and pond. TEAS in aid of St Christopher's, Ditteridge. *Adm £2 Chd free. Suns June 18, July 16 (2-6)*

Biddestone Manor, Biddestone ♿✻❀ (Mr H Astrup) *Nr Corsham, 5m W of Chippenham, 3m N of Corsham. On A4 between Chippenham and Corsham turn N, from A420, 5m W of Chippenham, turn S.* Large garden with extensive lawns, small lake, topiary, swimming pool. Recently planted arboretum with many specimen trees. Walled kitchen garden. Orchard, herb garden and fine C17 manor house (not open) with interesting outbuildings. TEAS. *Adm £2 Chd under 16 free. Sun June 25 (2-5)*

Bolehyde Manor, Allington ♿❀ (The Earl & Countess Cairns) *1½m W of Chippenham on Bristol Rd (A420). Turn N at Allington Xrds. ½m on R. Parking in field.* A series of gardens around C16 Manor House (not open), enclosed by walls and topiary, densely planted with many interesting shrubs and climbers, mixed rose and herbaceous beds; inner courtyard with troughs full of tender plants; wild flower orchard, vegetable, fruit garden and greenhouse yard. TEAS. *Adm £2.50 Chd 50p (ACNO to Kingston St Michael Church). Sun June 25 (2.30-6). Also private groups welcome, please* **Tel 01249 652105**

■ **Bowood Rhododendron Walks, nr Chippenham** ✻ (The Marquis of Lansdowne) *Entrance off A342 between Sandy Lane and Derry Hill villages.* This 60 acre woodland garden provides a breath-taking display of rhododendrons and azaleas from the minute detail of the individual flower to the grand sweep of colour formed by hundreds of shrubs, surrounded by a carpet of bluebells. Open mid April to mid June, depending on the flowering season. *Open Bowood House & Gardens Luncheon and Teas. Garden centre. Adm £5.70 OAP £4.70 Chd £3.50. April to end Oct (11-6). For NGS Adm £3 Chd free. Sun June 4 (11-6)* **Tel 01249 812102**

NEW **Brillscote Farm, Lea** ♿ (Mr & Mrs Simon Mounsey) *1m E of Malmesbury on B 4042, turn N signposted Lea. Garden ½m on R.* A newly restored garden of 2 acres surrounding old farmhouse (not open). Attractive stables and Cotswold stone walls covered with climbing roses, clematis and other climbers. Mature and newly planted trees and hedges separate different areas of garden which incl spacious lawns; pergolas; wildflower areas; herbaceous borders; gravelled paths and pot terrace. Teas at Pound House, Little Somerford. *Adm £2 Chd Free. Suns May 7; June 4 (2-6)*

■ **Broadleas, Devizes** ❀ (Lady Anne Cowdray) *1m S of Devizes on A360 or follow tourist signs from Long Street.* 9 acre garden; sheltered dell planted with many unusual trees and shrubs. Azaleas, rhododendrons and magnolias with underplantings of trilliums erythroniums and many others. Herbaceous borders and perennial garden full of interesting plants. Home-made TEAS (on summer Sundays). *Adm £3 Chd (under 12) £1. April/Oct inclusive every Sun, Wed, Thurs (2-6). For NGS Suns April 16, Aug 20 (2-6)*

NEW Cantax House, Lacock ♿✂❀ (Andrew & Deborah van der Beek) *Off A350 between Chippenham and Melksham. Please use signed public car park. Entrance to garden in Cantax Hill.* Medium-sized garden of colour, pattern and scent; designed and maintained by artist owner; interesting and unusual plants; hornbeam spire and other topiary projects in yew; fernery; old orchard wild garden; stream; good views of village. Queen Anne former vicarage (not open). Home-made TEAS and plants for sale June 11 only. *Adm £2 Chd Free (ACNO to Amnesty International). Sun June 11 & daily with sculpture exhibition June 17 - July 1 (2-6)*

Chiffchaffs See Dorset

Chisenbury Priory, East Chisenbury ♿✂❀ (Mr & Mrs John Manser) *3m SW of Pewsey, turn E from A345 at Enford then N to E Chisenbury, main gates 1m on R.* Mediaeval Priory with Queen Anne face and early C17 rear (not open) in middle of 5-acre garden on chalk; mature garden with fine trees within clump and flint walls, herbaceous borders, shrubs, roses. Moisture loving plants along mill leat; carp pond, orchard and wild garden, many unusual plants. TEAS. *Adm £2.50 Chd free Sun June 11 (2-6)*

The Close, Pewsey ♿✂❀ (Mr & Mrs Simon Courtauld) *6m S of Marlborough, S end of Pewsey, off A345. Turn L at builders yard, then R before R Avon.* 7 acres, informal herbaceous borders, shrubs, climbers, river walk and water meadow. TEAS in aid of Pewsey Church. *Adm £2 Chd free. Sun June 18 (2-6)*

Conock Manor, Chirton ♿✂❀ (Mrs Bonar Sykes) *5m SE of Devizes, off A342.* Mixed borders, flowering shrubs; extensive replanting incl new arboretum and woodland walk; collection of eucalyptus trees. C18 house in Bath stone (not shown). TEA. *Adm £2 Chd under 16 free (ACNO to Dorothy House Foundation). Sun May 21 (2-6)*

▲ Corsham Court, nr Chippenham ♿❀ (James Methuen-Campbell Esq) *4m W of Chippenham. S of A4.* Park and gardens laid out by Capability Brown and Repton. Large lawns with fine specimens of ornamental trees; rose garden; lily pond with Indian bean trees; spring bulbs; young arboretum; C18 bath house; Elizabethan mansion with alterations (not open). TEAS. *Adm gardens £2 OAP £1.50 Chd £1. For NGS Suns April 2; June 11 (11-5.30)*

NEW The Court House, Lower Woodford (Mr & Mrs J G Studholme) *3m N of Salisbury - on Woodford Valley Rd - between A360 and A345.* 3½-acre garden on the banks of the Avon. Herbaceous borders, waterside planting, yew hedges, rambler roses and wildflowers. Ancient site of Bishop's Palace in the time of Old Sarum. TEAS in aid of Mothers Union. *Adm £2. Sun June 11 (2-6)*

Court Lane Farm, Bratton ✂❀ (Lt Col & Mrs Anthony Hyde) *2m E of Westbury on B3098.* 2 acre garden of C17/C18 thatched cottage (not open). On varied levels with mostly informal planting developed over past 24yrs. Lawns and paths lead to hidden areas, features and unusual vistas. Pots, perennials, herbs and shrubs mingle with rambling roses, fruit and vegetables. Numerous trees, wildlife areas and pond. TEAS. *Adm £2 Acc chd free. Sat, Sun, Mon June 10, 11, 12 (2-6)*

▲ The Courts, Holt ♿✂❀ (The National Trust) *2m E of Bradford-on-Avon, S of B3107 to Melksham. In Holt follow National Trust signs, park at Village Hall.* 3½-acres of formal gardens divided by yew hedges and raised terraces. Features incl conservatory, lily pond, colour-themed herbaceous borders, pleached limes, venetian gates and stone ornaments. 3½ acres wildflower and arboretum; many fine trees. NT C15 House (not shown). Plant sales in Sept in aid of Bath Cancer Research Unit. Teas in church hall in aid of Church Hall Fund. *Adm £3.10 Chd £1.55. For NGS Suns June 11, Sept 3 (1.30-5.30)*

Dauntsey Gardens ♿✂ *5m SE of Malmesbury, 8m NW of Chippenham. Approach via Dauntsey Rd from Gt Somerford, 1¼m from Volunteer Inn.* TEAS. *Combined adm £3 Chd 50p (ACNO to St James Church). Sun June 11 (2-6)*

The Coach House ♿ (Col & Mrs J Seddon-Brown) Small walled garden. New herbaceous borders and well established climbing roses, clematis and other trees and shrubs

Garden Cottage, Dauntsey Park (Miss Ann Sturgis) Continuing restoration of 5-acre garden, incl restored walled kitchen garden organically run; greenhouses; formal garden; orchard and woodland walks

Idover House (Mr & Mrs Christopher Jerram) Medium-sized mature garden in established setting with many mature trees incl two large wellingtonias; spacious lawns, herbaceous borders, formal rose garden; swimming pool garden, duck pond; yew walk to kitchen garden and woodland garden

The Pond House (Mr & Mrs Stephen Love) Informal 1½-acre new garden, currently being developed; large lily pond, lawns, wild flowers, newly planted orchard with path leading to Garden Cottage

NEW Dinton Gardens *5m W of Wilton off B3089.* Both gardens near Dinton Church. TEAS at Mitre Cottage in aid of Parish Church. *Combined adm £2.50 acc chd free. Sun May 21(2-6)*

NEW Mitre Cottage ✂❀ (Mrs John Surtees) C17 cottage with later additions (not open). Garden approx ½-acre, restored during the last 3 yrs with interesting shrubs, bulbs and herbaceous plants; small vegetable garden

NEW Wyndham Cottage ✂❀ (Mr & Mrs I M S Robertson) ½-acre garden, with stone, thatched cottage (not open). Climbing roses; herbaceous border; raised beds; pond; rock garden; alpine house and orchid house. Several unusual rock and woodland plants

Edington Gardens *4m Westbury on B3098 halfway between Westbury and West Lavington. Follow signs and park outside The Monastery Garden for the Priory or in the Church car park, and for The Old Vicarage walk up hill to B3098.* Teas in Parish Hall. *Combined adm £3.50 Chd free (ACNO to Wiltshire Garden Trust). Sun June 11 (2-6)*

Bonshommes Cottage (Michael Jones Esq) *Through Old Vicarage garden.* ¼-acre hillside garden with mixed herbaceous, roses, shrubs. Some long established Japanese knotweed has been retained as a practical feature

Edington Priory (Mr & Mrs R Cooper) 4-acre gardens with mediaeval well, walls and carp lake. Herbaceous borders, kitchen garden and extensive lawns with shrubs and roses

The Monastery Garden ♿ (Mr & Mrs Allanson-Bailey) 2½-acre garden with many varieties of spring bulbs; orchard and shrub roses; mediaeval walls of national importance

The Old Vicarage ♿✂❀ (J N d'Arcy Esq) A 2-acre garden on greensand situated on hillside with fine views; intensively planted with herbaceous borders; newly built wall borders; gravel garden; a small waterfall; shrubs; an arboretum with a growing range of unusual trees; woodland plants; bulbs; lilies and recently introduced species from abroad. NCCPG National Collection of Evening primroses, over 20 species

Faulstone House, Bishopstone ♿✂❀ (Miss Freya Watkinson) *Take minor rd W off A354 at Coombe Bissett 3m SW of Salisbury, after 2m turn S into Harvest Lane 300yds E of White Hart Inn.* Separate smaller gardens in large garden surrounding Old Manor House (not open). C14 Defence Tower converted to pigeon loft in C18. Many old-fashioned roses, herbaceous plants (some unusual), large vegetable garden. Meadow with river frontage set in rural surroundings. TEAS in aid of Bishopstone Church. *Adm £1.50 Chd free. Sun June 18 (2-6)*

Fonthill House, nr Tisbury ❀ (The Lord Margadale of Islay) *3m N of Tisbury. W of Salisbury via B3089 in Fonthill Bishop.* Large woodland garden; daffodils, rhododendrons, azaleas, shrubs, bulbs; magnificent views; formal garden, limited for wheelchairs. TEAS. *Adm £2. Sun April 9 (2-6)* www.users.globalnet.co.uk/~msw

Goulters Mill Farm, Burton ✂❀ (Mr & Mrs Michael Harvey) *On B4039 5m W of Chippenham; 2m NW of Castle Combe, through The Gibb. Park at top of 300 metre drive and walk down to garden. Elderly/Disabled car park at the premises.* Approx ¾-acre cottage garden; mixed perennials, eremurus, old-fashioned roses; water garden,walk through woodland and wild flower-meadow. Home-made cream TEAS in aid of Russian Immigrants to Israel and the Church roof. *Adm £1.50 Chd 20p. Suns June 11, 18 (2-5)*

▲ **Great Chalfield Manor, nr Melksham** ✂❀ (Mr & Mrs R Floyd) *4m from Melksham. Take B3107 from Melksham then 1st R to Broughton Gifford follow sign for Atworth, turn L for 1m to Manor. Park on grass outside.* Garden and grounds of 7 acres laid out 1905-12 by Robert Fuller and his wife to designs by Alfred Parsons, Capt Partridge and Sir Harold Brakspear: incl roses, daffodils, spring flowers; topiary houses, borders, terraces, gazebo, orchard, autumn border. C15 moated manor (not open) and adjoining Parish Church. TEAS. *Adm £2.50 Chd free (ACNO to All Saints Church). For NGS Suns April 2, Oct 8 (2-5)*

Great Durnford Gardens ♿✂❀ *Midway between Salisbury and Amesbury off the A345. Turn W at High Post Petrol Station to Woodfords. After 1m take 1st R to Great Durnford. Into village turn L and park next to Black Horse Inn (as signed).* Lunches and Teas at Black Horse. *Combined adm £2.50. Sun June 4 (2-6)*

Old Hall ❀ (Mr & Mrs M Snell) Established part cob walled 2-acre village garden with lawns, herbaceous borders, featured vegetable patch and conservatory. Staddle barn, thatched barn, chickens and Herdwick sheep

Swaynes Mead ❀ (Major & Mrs Simon Poett) An acre of intensive garden established over last 30yrs. C17 thatched cottage (not open) with climbing roses. Many unusual plants, shrubs and trees for yr-round interest

Great Somerford Gardens ♿✂❀ *2m N of M4 between junctions 17 and 18; 2m S of B4042 Malmesbury Wootton Bassett rd; 3m E of A429 Circencester-Chippenham rd.* TEAS. *Combined adm £3 Chd under 13 free (ACNO to N Wilts Holiday Club for Children with Special Needs). Sat, Sun July 8, 9 (1.30-5.30)*

The Mount House (Mr & Mrs McGrath) The complete traditional village manor house garden; 3 acres of lawns, herbaceous beds, shrubs. Large trees & fruit and vegetable garden. Approx 100 roses. Mainly creation of late Ann Phillips. The Mount area and new Coach House garden also open

Old Church School, Hollow Street (Cdr & Mrs Peter Neate) ¾-acre garden created over the last 7 yrs from school playing field. Centred around formal yew-hedged area containing flourishing pool and box garden, surrounded by herbaceous, hebe and rose beds; hostas and ferns; pergolas and arches; rockery and ground-cover garden, and a good collection of trees and shrubs. TEAS

The Old Maltings, Hollow Street (Dr & Mrs S Jevons) Front garden recently designed with extensive and interesting herbaceous and shrub borders. Behind house is walk down to and across R Avon into conservation area with plantations of young native trees and shrubs

Somerford House (Mr & Mrs Martin Jones) A 3-acre garden developed over the last 20 yrs which incorporates the original orchard and features roses, shrubs, old wisteria, perennials, rockery and pool, vegetables and soft fruit

Guyers House, Corsham ♿✂❀ (Mr & Mrs Guy Hungerford) *Pickwick. Guyers Lane directly off A4 opp B3109 Bradford-on-Avon turning.* 5-acre garden recently restored and is being extended. Herbaceous borders, new yew walks, pleached hornbeam walk. Lawns, pond, walled garden, rose hoops, climbing and shrub roses; kitchen garden. TEA. *Adm £1.50 Chd free. Sun June 18 (2-5.30)*

Hannington Hall, Hannington ♿❀ (Mrs A F Hussey-Freke) *5m N of Swindon. 2m NW of Highworth, from B4019 Highworth-Blunsdon, at Freke Arms, turn N to Hannington.* 3 acres. Interesting trees and shrubs; walled kitchen garden; new garden with small bog garden; well preserved ice house. Very interesting house built in 1653 (not open). TEAS. *Adm £2 Chd free. Sun July 9 (2-5.30)*

▲ **Hazelbury Manor Gardens, Wadswick, nr Box** ♿✂ *5m SW of Chippenham; 5m NE of Bath. From A4 at Box, A365 to Melksham, L onto B3109; 1st L; drive immed on R.* 8 acres Grade II landscaped gardens around C15 fortified manor (not open). Impressive yew topiary and clipped

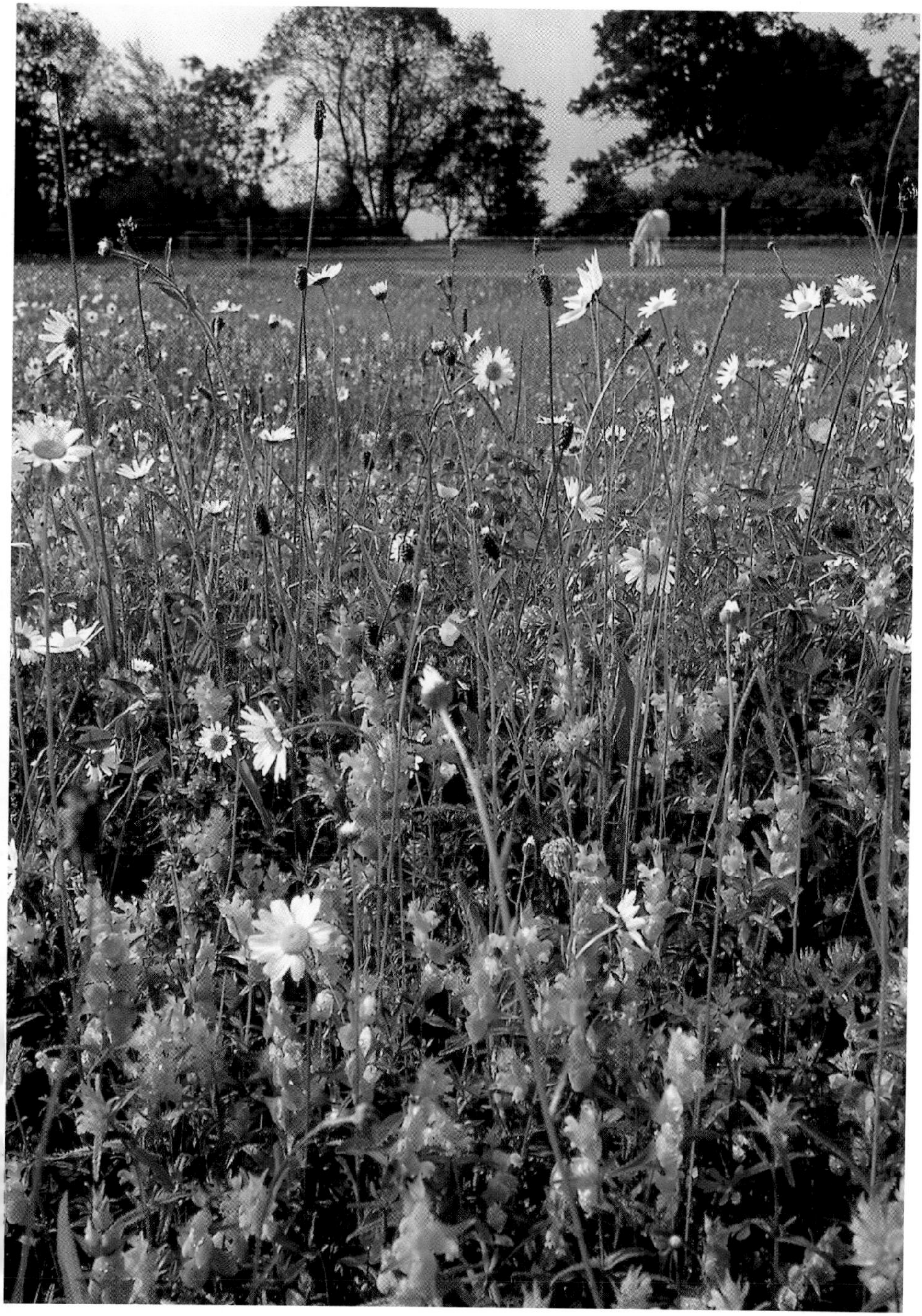

Sticky Wicket, Dorset
Planted to attract birds, butterflies and bees, this meadow is a feast for wildlife. Nearby are harmoniously coloured borders offering more food and habitat.
Photograph by Andrew Lawson

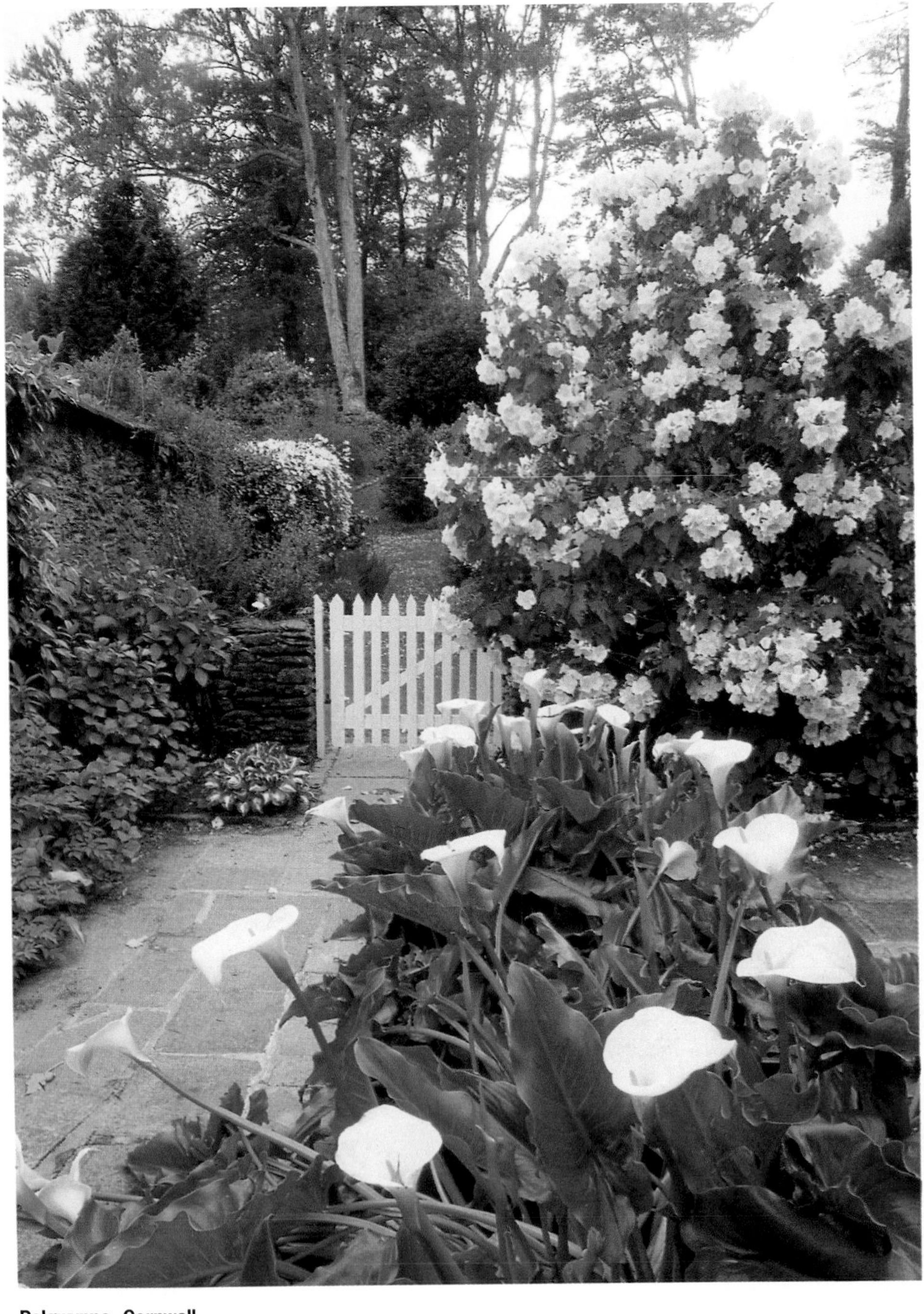

Polgwynne, Cornwall

Wall-to-wall elegance in this white garden, with *Zantedeschia aethiopica, Abutilon vitifolium* var. *album* and *Hosta undulata* var. *univittata*. Visitors will also find what is probably the largest female *Gingko biloba* in Britain, and many other rare and unusual shrubs.

Photograph by Brian Chapple

'Most people think cancer is about dying. For me, it's about living, and Macmillan's services are there to help me do that'
– a voice for life
Fiona Benham
Photograph by Roger Hutchings/Network

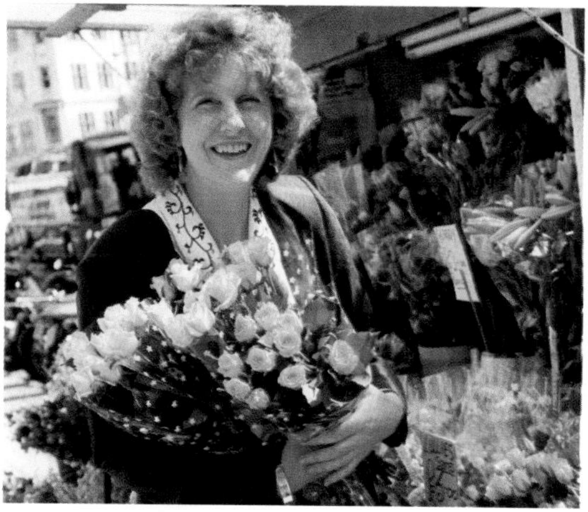

Below: **Stone House Cottage, Worcestershire**
Rare and unusual climbers, shrubs and herbaceous plants thrive within the sheltering walls of this 1-acre plantsman's garden.
Photograph by Marianne Majerus

North Court, Isle of Wight
Glorious *Eremurus* Shelford Hybrids are just one of the delights of this 15-acre garden, which also boasts a sub-tropical garden.
Photograph by Oliver Mathews

Below: **286 Handley Road, Derbyshire**
A ⅓ of an acre packed with over 1500 plants, most permanently labelled. Some of the plants surrounding the hebe in the rock garden are *Osmunda regalis* 'Purpurascens' *Acer palmatum* 'Kamagata', *Molinia caerulea* 'Variegata', *Cotoneaster congestus* 'Nanus', *Hosta* 'Shade Fanfare' and *Inula ensifolia*.
Photograph by Mike Vardy

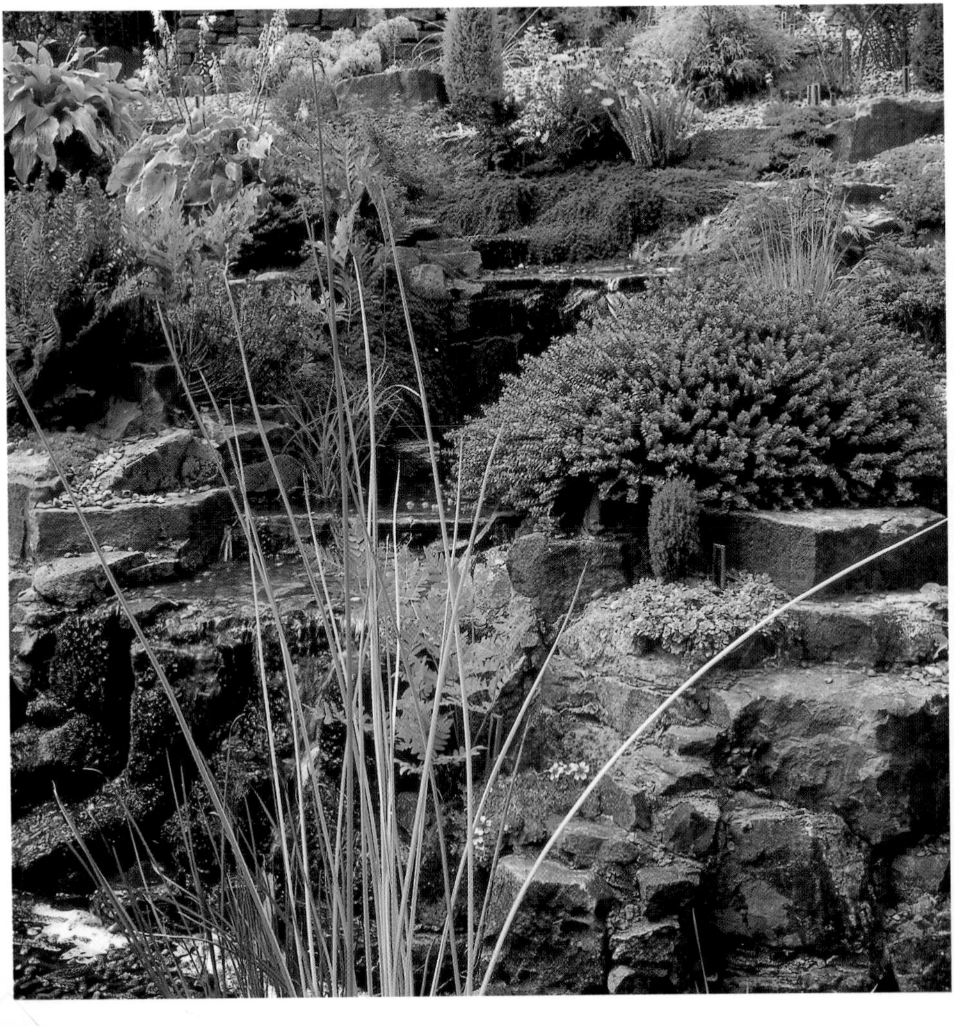

beeches around large lawn; herbaceous and mixed borders blaze in summer; laburnum and lime walkways; rose garden, stone ring and rockery. TEA. *Adm gardens only £2.80 OAP £2 Chd £1. For NGS Sat, Sun June 17, 18 (2-6). Private visits welcome by appt, please* **Tel 01225 812952/812088**

■ Heale Gardens & Plant Centre, Middle Woodford ♿❀ (Mr & Mrs Guy Rasch) *4m N of Salisbury on Woodford Valley Rd between A360 and A345.* 8 acres beside R Avon; interesting and varied collection of plants, shrubs; roses in formal setting of clipped hedges and mellow stonework surrounding C17 manor house (not open) where Charles II hid after battle of Worcester. Water garden with magnolia and acer; frames;, authentic Japanese Tea House and Nikko bridge. Well stocked plant centre. Gift shop. Open all year. TEAS. *Adm £3 Acc chd under 14 free (ACNO to Salisbury Hospice). For NGS Sun Aug 6 (10-5)* **Tel 01722 782504**

Hillbarn House, Great Bedwyn ✗❀ (Mr & Mrs A J Buchanan) *SW of Hungerford. S of A4 Hungerford-Marlborough.* Medium-sized garden on chalk with hornbeam tunnel, pleached limes, herb garden; some planting by Lanning Roper; a series of gardens within a garden. Swimming pool may be used (under 12). Topiary. TEA. *Adm £2 Chd 50p. Suns June 25, Sept 17 (2-6). Private visits of 10 and over welcome, please* **Tel 01672 870207**

Home Covert, Roundway ♿❀ (Mr & Mrs John Phillips) *1m N of Devizes on minor rd signed Roundway linking A361 to A342, 1m from each main rd.* Extensive garden on greensand created out of ancient woodland since 1960. Situated below the Downs with distant views. Formal borders around the house contrast with water gardens in the valley below. A wide range of trees, shrubs and plants grown for all-yr-round interest. TEAS on May 14 in aid of Wilts Wildlife Trust, July 9 in aid of St James Church Repair Fund. *Adm £2.50 Chd free. Suns May 14; July 9 (2-6). Open at other times by prior arrangement, groups welcome please* **Tel 01380 723407**

■ Iford Manor, nr Bradford-on-Avon (Mr & Mrs Hignett) *Off A36 7 miles S of Bath; brown tourist sign to Iford 1m. Or from Bradford-on-Avon/Trowbridge via Lower Westwood village (brown signs).* Very romantic award winning Italian-style terraced garden, listed Grade 1, home of Harold Peto 1899-1933. House not shown. TEAS May to Sept, Sats, Suns and Bank Hol Mons. *Adm £3 OAPs/Student/Chd 10+ £2.50. Open daily May to Sept (except Mons & Fris), April & Oct Suns only. Children under 10 not admitted at weekends. For NGS Sun April 30 (2-5) (Children welcome today). Private visits for groups welcome at other times, please* **Tel 01225 863146, 862364** messages and Fax

Inwoods, Farleigh Wick ♿❀ (Mr & Mrs D S Whitehead) *3m NW of Bradford-on-Avon. From Bath via A363 towards Bradford-on-Avon; at Farleigh Wick, 100yds past Fox & Hounds, R into drive.* 5 acres with lawns, borders, flowering shrubs, wild garden, wild flower wood. TEAS in aid of Home Farm Trust. *Adm £2 Chd 50p. Sun May 21 (2-6)*

Job's Mill, Crockerton ❀ (Virginia, Marchioness of Bath) *1½m S of Warminster. Bus: Salisbury-Bath, alight Warminster.* Medium-sized garden; small terraced garden, through which R Wylye flows; swimming pool; kitchen garden. TEAS. *Adm £2 Chd 50p (ACNO to CPRE). Sun June 18 (2-6)*

13 Kingsdown Road, Stratton St Margaret ✗❀ (Mr & Mrs Kenneth Tomlin) *Approach from S on A419. L at Kennedys Garden Centre (signposted Upper Stratton). ½m turn L at t-lights and park opp Kingsdown inn.* Long and narrow garden on edge of town closely planted with shrubs and herbaceous plants; vegetable garden. Unusual plants with some for sale. Example of maximum use of space available. TEA. *Adm £1.50 Chd free. Suns June 11, July 16 (2-6)*

▲ Lackham Gardens, Lacock ♿❀ (C N Gill Esq) *2m S of Chippenham on A350. Few mins S of junction 17 on M4.* Walled garden with greenhouses, lawn paths separating plots, labelled, with variety of interesting shrubs, unusual vegetables, herbaceous plants, fruit. Pleasure gardens with historical collection of roses, sensory garden, mixed borders, lawns; woodland walks down to river. Museum of Agricultural/Horticultural Equipment, animal park. Coffee shop; TEAS Bookable menu (11-4). *Adm £3 Chd £1 (ACNO to Horticultural Therapy of Frome, Somerset). For NGS Suns July 9; Sept 3 (2-5 last entry 4)*

▲ Lacock Abbey Gardens, Chippenham ♿❀ (The National Trust) *Off A350 between Melksham-Chippenham. Follow National Trust signs. Use public car park just outside Abbey.* Victorian woodland garden with a pond and exotic tree specimens. Display of early spring flowers with carpets of aconites; snowdrops; crocuses and daffodils. C13 Abbey with C18 gothic additions. (Mediaeval cloisters and Fox Talbot Museum open on NGS days, house closed until April). Teas in village. *Adm £1.80 incl NT members Chd free. For NGS Sats, Suns Feb 19, 20, 26, 27 (12-5). Sats, Suns Feb 10, 11, 17, 18, 2001 (12-5). Guided walks, please* **Tel 01249 730227/730459**

Landford Lodge, nr Salisbury ♿❀ (Mr & Mrs C Pilkington) *9m SE of Salisbury turn W off A36; garden ½m N of Landford.* C18 House (not open) in lovely parkland overlooking lake; many fine trees. Special feature 3-acre wood with rhododendrons and azaleas. Herbaceous; ornamental terrace and swimming pool (open). Tree nursery. 500 varieties of trees planted in alphabetical order in walled garden. TEAS. *Adm £1.50 Chd 50p (ACNO to Salisbury Mencap Horticultural Trust). Sun June 4 (2-5). Private parties of 10 and over welcome, please* **Tel 01794 390247**

Little Durnford Manor, nr Salisbury ♿❀ (The Earl & Countess of Chichester) *3m N of Salisbury, just beyond Stratford-sub-Castle.* Extensive lawns with cedars; walled gardens; fruit trees; large vegetable garden; small knot and herb gardens; terraces; borders; gravel garden; water garden; lake with islands; river walks; labyrinth walk. Cottage Garden also on view. Home-made TEAS. *Adm £2 Chd 50p (ACNO to Wessex Medical School Trust). Suns April 30, June 25 (2-6)*

Long Meadow, Winterbourne Bassett ♿❀ (Mike & Amanda Hopkins) *3m N of Avebury & 5m S of Wroughton off A4361. 200 yds beyond 'White Horse' turn L to Church car*

park and follow signs. ⅓-acre organic, plantspersons' garden reclaimed from field in last 2½ yrs. 2 ponds; 60' x 20' herbaceous borders; vegetables; espaliered fruit trees; arched walkways and living arbour. Combines 'soothing' and 'cool' planting with 'hot' colour schemes. Vegetables, fruit, flowers and chickens intergrated to give pleasure and food for thought. Demonstrates, however modestly, what can be achieved with enthusiasm in a short time by a family combining hobby with busy working lives. TEA. *Adm £1 Chd 50p (ACNO to Wessex Childrens Hospice Trust). Suns June 25; Aug 27 (2-6)*

Lower House, Whiteparish ♿✂❀ (Mr & Mrs D J Wood) *On A27 between Salisbury and Romsey (7m). Garden is N side of A27, Salisbury end of village, opp Newton Bungalows.* Informal garden of 1 acre containing part of National Collection of Hellebores. *Adm £1.50 Chd free. Sun Feb 27 (2-4) Private visits welcome by appt Mon to Mon Feb 28 to March 13 (10-12 and 2-4), please* **Tel 01794 884306**

Luckington Court, Luckington ♿❀ (The Hon Mrs Trevor Horn) *10m NW of Chippenham; 6m W of Malmesbury. Turn S off B4040 Malmesbury-Bristol rd.* Medium-sized garden, mainly formal, well-designed, amid exquisite group of ancient buildings; fine collection of ornamental cherries; other flowering shrubs. House much altered in Queen Anne times but ancient origins evident; Queen Anne hall and drawing-room shown. TEAS in aid of Luckington Parish Church. *Collecting box. Sun April 30 (2.30-6)*

Manor Farm, Monkton Deverill ♿❀ (W G M Wood Esq) *5m S of Warminster. Take Mere rd off A350 at Longbridge Deverill. Monkton Deverill 2m.* Garden for a C18 village farmhouse (not open). Walled kitchen garden. New orchards and hedging. Formal and informal planting. Annuals encouraged to grow where they please; grass free borders; canal garden. New herb garden by Jenny Hill-Norton. Box nursery. Picnics welcome. TEAS. *Adm £2 Chd free. Suns June 11; July 9 (12-6)*

Manor House Farm, Hanging Langford ♿✂ (Miss Anne Dixon) *9m NW of Salisbury S of A36 Salisbury-Warminster. 3m SE of A303 Wylye interchange. Follow signs from Steeple Langford.* Series of walled gardens with masses of bulbs, herbaceous plants, many shrubs, old-fashioned roses, collection of clematis, peonies and delphiniums. Ornamental pond, secret garden in walls of shearing barn, superb walnut, C14/16 Wiltshire manor house (not open). Easy access for wheelchairs. Teas Hanging Langford Village Hall in aid of Village Hall Fund. *Adm £2 Chd free. Sun March 26 (2-6)*

Martins, Bradford-on-Avon ✂❀ (Mrs Diana Young) *Bradford-on-Avon. The top of Whitehill is off New Rd (N side of town) and Martins is the 4th house down from the top. Whitehill is 200 yds from Castle Inn and Christ Church. No parking at garden. Parking in streets and town centre car parks.* Surprisingly spacious garden on several levels with magnificant S facing views. Restful but full of colour and character, incl small orchard and meadow, ancient lime and mulberry. TEAS in aid of Dorothy House Foundation. *Adm £1.50 Chd free. Sun June 4 (2-6)*

■ **The Mead Nursery, Brokerswood** ♿✂❀ (Mr & Mrs S Lewis-Dale) *Equidistant Frome and Westbury E of Rudge. Follow signs for Woodland Park. Halfway between Rudge and Woodland Park.* 1¼-acre nursery and garden giving ideas on colour and design with herbaceous borders; raised alpine beds; sink garden and bog bed. The nursery grows an extensive range of herbaceous perennials; alpines and pot grown bulbs. TEAS on NGS day only. *Adm £2 Chd £1 to incl teas. Nursery open Feb 1 to Oct 15 Wed to Sat (9-5), Sun (12-5). For NGS Sun Aug 20 (12-5)* **Tel 01373 859990**

NEW **Milford House Nursing Home, Salisbury** ♿ (Mrs A M Perry) *1m SE of Salisbury, turn L off A36 into Petersfinger Rd (signposted Laverstock), ¼m on L.* 2-acre garden with lavender edged formal terrace; wildfower meadow and woodland planting with many hardy ferns and unusual perennials. TEAS. *Adm £1.50 Chd free. Suns July 16; 30 (11-6)*

▲ **Mompesson House, Salisbury** ♿✂❀ (The National Trust) *The Close. Enter Salisbury Cathedral Close via High St Gate and Mompesson House is on the R.* The appeal of this comparatively small but attractive garden is the lovely setting in Salisbury Cathedral Close, with a well-known Queen Anne House. Planting as for an old English garden with raised rose and herbaceous beds around the lawn. Climbers on pergola and walls; shrubs and small lavender walk. TEAS. *Adm £1 Chd free. For NGS Sat May 27 (11-5)*

7 Norton Bavant, nr Warminster ♿✂❀ (Mr & Mrs J M Royds) *2m E of Warminster. From A36 turn W to Sutton Veny on Cotley Hill roundabout at Heytesbury, then 1st R to Norton Bavant. Turn 1st R in village, 1st house on R after tall conifer hedge.* Alpine plant collector's garden with numerous varieties (many rare). Spring bulbs, hebes, helebores, many troughs, borders, dwarf conifers and specialised collection of daphnes. Members of AGS especially welcome. TEAS in aid of Norton Bavant Church. *Adm £1.50 Chd free. Sun May 14 (2-5). Private visits and parties welcome March to June, please* **Tel 01985 840491**

Oare House, nr Pewsey ♿ (Henry Keswick Esq) *2m N of Pewsey on Marlborough Rd (A345).* Fine house (not open) in large garden with fine trees, hedges, spring flowers, woodlands; extensive lawns and kitchen garden. TEA. *Adm £2 Chd free (ACNO to The Order of St John). Suns April 16, July 30 (2-6)*

The Old Bakery, Milton Lilbourne ♿✂❀ (Joyce, Lady Crossley) *E of Pewsey on B3087. Turn down village st by garage at Xrds. The Old Bakery opp churchyard.* Fairly intensive 1-acre garden. Mixed shrub and herbaceous plantings. 3 small glasshouses; small rock garden; some rare plants. Home-made TEAS. *Adm £1.50 Chd free. Sun Aug 6 (2-6). Private parties welcome, please* **Tel 01672 562716**

The Old School House, Baverstock ♿❀ (Mr & Mrs Malcolm Lyell) *1m E of Dinton turn N off B3089 for Baverstock. Garden adjoins the church.* 1-acre garden created from a meadow since 1989. Ponds and rock garden. Many unusual trees and shrubs incl 9 varieties of magnolia incl a yellow one which we hope will be in flower. *Adm £2 Chd free. (ACNO to Baverstock Church). Sun May 21 (2-6)*

Pertwood Manor, Hindon ♿✂ (Mrs James Giles) *Off A350 (1m N of A303) 7m Shaftesbury, 8m Warminster. Take signs marked Pertwood Manor farm.* 1½ acre part-walled garden surrounding manor house (not open) in elevated position with lovely views. Herbaceous borders, various trees and shrubs. Sunken rose garden. Short woodland walk, small vegetable garden. Recently restored Church of St Peter. TEAS. *Adm £1.50 Chd free (ACNO to NSPCC). Sun June 11 (2-6)*

■ **Pound Hill House, West Kington** ♿❀ (Mr & Mrs Philip Stockitt) *From A420 Chippenham-Bristol rd turn R by Shoe garage, then 2nd L, 2nd R into village, entrance at nursery.* Series of small gardens, set around C15 Cotswold house (not open), to provide interest throughout yr. Old-fashioned rose garden with clipped box, small Victorian vegetable garden, old shrub roses, herbaceous borders, water garden, courtyard garden with planted pots and containers. Planted paved area, also buxus, taxus, topiary. Connoisseur plants available in retail plant area. TEAS in aid of The Muscular Dystrophy Campaign. *Adm £2. Open 7 days a week (2-5) Feb to Dec. Adm £2. For NGS Sun May 21 (2-6). Parties welcome,* **Tel 01249 782781**

The Pound House, Little Somerford ♿✂ (Mr & Mrs Michael Baines) *2m E of Malmesbury on B4042. In village turn S, leave church on R. Car park on R before railway bridge.* English vicarage garden with mature trees, old orchard, shrubberies, borders, new parterre with water, swimming pool garden, free-range ducks! TEA. *Adm £2 (ACNO to The Children's Trust). Suns May 7, June 4 (2-6)*

Marie Curie Cancer Care

Marie Curie Research Institute stands at the forefront of molecular biological research into the causes of cancer.

For more information about Marie Curie Cancer Care, ring 0800 716 146

or visit our web site at www.mariecurie.org.uk

Ridleys Cheer, Mountain Bower ♿✂❀ (Mr & Mrs A J Young) *N Wraxall. At 'The Shoe' on A420 8m W of Chippenham turn N then take 2nd L and 1st R.* 1½-acre informal garden with unusual trees and shrubs; incl acers, liriodendrons, magnolias, hellebores, hostas and euphorbias. Some 75 different shrub rose varieties incl hybrid musks, albas and species roses; planted progressively over past 30 yrs; also potager, miniature box garden and 2-acre arboretum planted 1989, and 3-acre wildflower meadow. Cream TEAS in aid of N Wraxall Church and Dorothy House Foundation. *Adm £2 Chd under 14 free. Suns March 26; April 30; May 21; June 18 (2-6). Private visits welcome, please* **Tel 01225 891204**

Sharcott Manor, nr Pewsey ♿✂❀ (Captain & Mrs D Armytage) *1m SW of Pewsey via A345.* 5-acre garden with water-planted for yr-round interest. Many young trees, bulbs, climbers and densely planted mixed borders of shrubs, roses, perennials and unusual plants, some of which are for sale in the small garden nursery. Small collection of ornamental water fowl. TEAS in aid of RSPCA and Wiltshire Air Ambulance appeal. *Adm £2 Chd free. First Weds in every month from April to Oct (11-5). Suns April 9, July 2 (2-6) all for NGS. Also private visits welcome, please* **Tel 01672 563485**

34, 38 & 40 Sherford Road, Haydon Wick, Swindon ✂❀ *From A419 Turnpike roundabout take A4311. Turn R at Moonrakers Inn B4006 and follow for 1m turning R into Thames Avenue. Turn L into Avonmead follow for 0.5m, then L into Sherford Rd.* No 34 laid primarily to kitchen; while 38 & 40 bedding and perennials. The gardens are fine examples of individual preferences, ranging from beautiful perennial borders, annual beds; pots, tubs & a large variety of vegetables.There are many permanent features, ponds, pergolas, raised beds, walkways & lawns all contained in areas of about 40' by 100' per garden. The owners believe visitors will take away ideas that will help develop their own modern urban patch, and have in the past encouraged discussion on gardening, from planting to difficulties encountered during development. TEAS. *Adm £2 Chd free. Sun July 9 (11-5)*

Snape Cottage see Dorset

Spye Park, nr Chippenham ❀ (Mr & Mrs Simon Spicer) *Take A342 Chippenham/Devizes rd, turn W at Sandy Lane opp 'The George' public house. Turn S after ½m at White Lodge. Follow signs to car park. Exit only through village of Chittoe.* 25-acre woodland walk through carpets of bluebells with paths cut through the wood. Some fine old trees mostly oak and beech, survivors of the 1989 hurricane, incl the remnants of 1000-yr-old King Oak with 900-yr-old Queen still alive. TEA. *Adm £1 Chd free (ACNO to Southmead Hospital Special Care Baby Unit). Sun April 30 (11-5). Private parties welcome when bluebells are out, please* **Tel 01249 730247**

▲ **Stourhead Garden, Stourton** ♿✂ (The National Trust) *3m NW of Mere on B3092.* One of earliest and greatest landscape gardens in the world; creation of banker Henry Hoare in 1740s on his return from the Grand Tour, inspired by paintings of Claude and Poussin; planted with rare trees, rhododendrons and azaleas over last 240yrs. Open every day of year. Lunch, tea and supper at Spread

Eagle Inn at entrance. NT shop. Teas (Buffet service Village Hall). *Adm March to Oct £4.60 Chd £2.60 parties of 15 or over £4.10 family £10. Nov to Feb £3.50 Chd 1.50 family £8. For NGS Sun June 4 (9-7)*

■ **Stourton House, Stourton** ♿✂❀ (Mrs Anthony Bullivant) *3m NW of Mere (A303) next to Stourhead. Park in NT car park.* 4½-acres informal gardens; much to attract plantsmen and idea seekers. Interesting bulbs, plants and shrubs, through all seasons. Speciality daffodils, delphiniums and hydrangeas. Well known for 'Stourton Dried Flowers' whose production interest visitors. Coffee, lunch, TEAS in Stourton House Garden. April 1 to end Nov, Sun, Wed, Thurs and Bank Hol Mons *Adm £2.50 Chd 50p (ACNO to St Peters Church, Stourton). For NGS Sats, Suns May 6, 7; Aug 12, 13 (11-6). Private visits welcome for parties of 12 and over any day, please* **Tel 01747 840417**

Waterdale House, Milton ❀ (Mr & Mrs Julian Seymour) *North of East Knoyle on A350 turn W signed Milton, garden signed from village.* 4-acre mature woodland garden with rhododendrons, azaleas, camellias, maples, magnolias, ornamental water redesigned with new terrace, bog garden; herbaceous borders. Gravelled pot garden. TEAS if fine. *Adm £2 Chd free. Sun May 7 (2-5). Private visits welcome April to July, lunches for parties up to 20 if required, please* **Tel 01747 830262**

Yew Tree Farm, Hankerton ✂❀ (E I & Mrs C H Grierson) *Off the A429 at Malmesbury take B4040 to Cricklade, turn L at E end of Charlton to Hankerton, approx 1m on L.* 1 acre developed over 11yrs, divided into smaller areas by pergolas and archways, one a walkway with over 30 clematis. Herbaceous and shrub borders, two ponds, bog garden and vegetable garden. *Adm £1.50 Chd 50p. Sat, Sun July 8, 9 (2-6)*

Crossroads

Caring For Carers

Crossroads is the leading national charity providing support to carers; giving them a regular break from their caring responsibilities.

A range of different services have been developed to meet the needs of carers, including holiday play schemes, drop-in centres and telephone helplines, but the core service remains the provision of a care worker who will take over from the carer, to give them a much needed break.

Crossroads in England and Wales now has 214 Branch Schemes, which deliver over 3 million care hours each year to 26,500 carers.

The facts:

† There are 5.7 million carers in the UK

† 1.7 million of these carers care for more than 20 hours a week

† 855,000 care for more than 50 hours

† 65% of Carers say that their health has suffered as a result of their caring responsibilities

We need to continue this vital work so carers will continue to receive the services they need.

For more information, please contact:
Crossroads **Caring For Carers**
10 Regent Place, Rugby CV21 2PN

Information is also available on the NGS website (www.ngs.org.uk)

Worcestershire

Hon County Organiser: Mrs Barbara Phillips, Cedar Lodge, Blakeshall, Wolverley, Kidderminster, Worcestershire DY11 5XR Tel 01562 850238

Assistant County Organisers:

North Mrs Jeanie Neil, Viewlands, Blakeshall, Wolverley, Kidderminster, Worcestershire DY11 5XL Tel 01562 850360

Mrs Christine Green, Lodge Farm, Gipsy Lane, Blakeshall, Wolverley, Nr Kidderminster, Worcestershire DY11 5XT Tel 01562 850287

South Mr & Mrs George Wilkinson, Upper End Lodge, Upper End, Eckington, Pershore, Worcestershire WR10 3DQ Tel 01386 750523

Hon County Treasurer: Mrs Lorraine Purcell, The Cottage, Low Hill, Torton, Hartlebury, Worcestershire DY10 4HT Tel 01299 250295

DATES OF OPENING

Regular openings

For details see garden description

- Barn House, Broadway
- Barnard's Green House, Malvern
- Bodenham Arboretum, Wolverley
- Eastgrove Cottage Garden Nursery, Sankyns Green, Shrawley
- Kyre Park, Kyre
- Little Malvern Court, Malvern
- The Manor House, Birlingham
- The Priory, Kemerton
- Spetchley Park Charitable Trust, nr Worcester
- Stone House Cottage Gardens, Stone
- The Walled Garden, Fort Royal Hill, Worcester
- White Cottage, Stock Green, nr Inkberrow

By appointment only

For telephone numbers and other details see garden descriptions. Private visits welcomed

- Conderton Manor, nr Tewkesbury
- Impney Park, Droitwich
- Keepers Cottage, Alvechurch
- Overbury Court, nr Tewkesbury

February 23 to 24 Wednesday to Thursday
Dial Park, Chaddesley Corbett

March 8 Wednesday
The Cottage, Broughton Green

March 12 Sunday
Barnard's Green House, Malvern

March 19 Sunday
Little Malvern Court, Malvern

March 22 Wednesday
The Cottage, Broughton Green
Red House Farm, Bradley Green, nr Redditch

March 23 Thursday
Dial Park, Chaddesley Corbett

March 24 Friday
The Elms, Lower Broadheath

March 26 Sunday
Kyre Park, Kyre

April 2 Sunday
Ripple Hall, nr Tewkesbury

April 6 Thursday
Barnard's Green House, Malvern

April 9 Sunday
Eastgrove Cottage Garden Nursery, Sankyns Green, Shrawley

April 16 Sunday
Shuttifield Cottage, Birchwood

April 20 Thursday
Barnard's Green House, Malvern

April 21 Friday
The Elms, Lower Broadheath
Spetchley Park Charitable Trust, nr Worcester

April 22 Saturday
The Walled Garden, Fort Royal Hill, Worcester

April 23 Sunday
24 Alexander Avenue, Droitwich Spa
Arley Arboretum, Upper Arley
Astley Towne House, Astley
Eastgrove Cottage Garden Nursery, Sankyns Green, Shrawley
1 Prickley Bungalows, Martley

April 24 Monday
Stone House Cottage Gardens, Stone
Whitlenge House Cottage, Hartlebury

April 26 Wednesday
St Egwins Cottage, Norton

April 27 Thursday
Dial Park, Chaddesley Corbett

April 29 Saturday
White Cottage, Stock Green, nr Inkberrow

April 30 Sunday
The Cockshoot, Castlemorton Common
Stone House Cottage Gardens, Stone
White Cottage, Stock Green, nr Inkberrow

May 1 Monday
The Cockshoot, Castlemorton Common
Little Malvern Court, Malvern
Stone House Cottage Gardens, Stone

May 4 Thursday
The Manor House, Birlingham

May 6 Saturday
The Walled Garden, Fort Royal Hill, Worcester

May 7 Sunday
Barn House, Broadway
Eastgrove Cottage Garden Nursery, Sankyns Green, Shrawley
The Manor House, Birlingham
1 Prickley Bungalows, Martley
Shuttifield Cottage, Birchwood
Spetchley Park Charitable Trust, nr Worcester
Windyridge, Kidderminster

May 10 Wednesday
St Egwins Cottage, Norton

May 11 Thursday
Barnard's Green House, Malvern

May 13 Saturday
White Cottage, Stock Green, nr Inkberrow

May 14 Sunday
24 Alexander Avenue, Droitwich Spa
The Cottage Herbery, Boraston, nr Tenbury Wells
Madresfield Court, nr Malvern

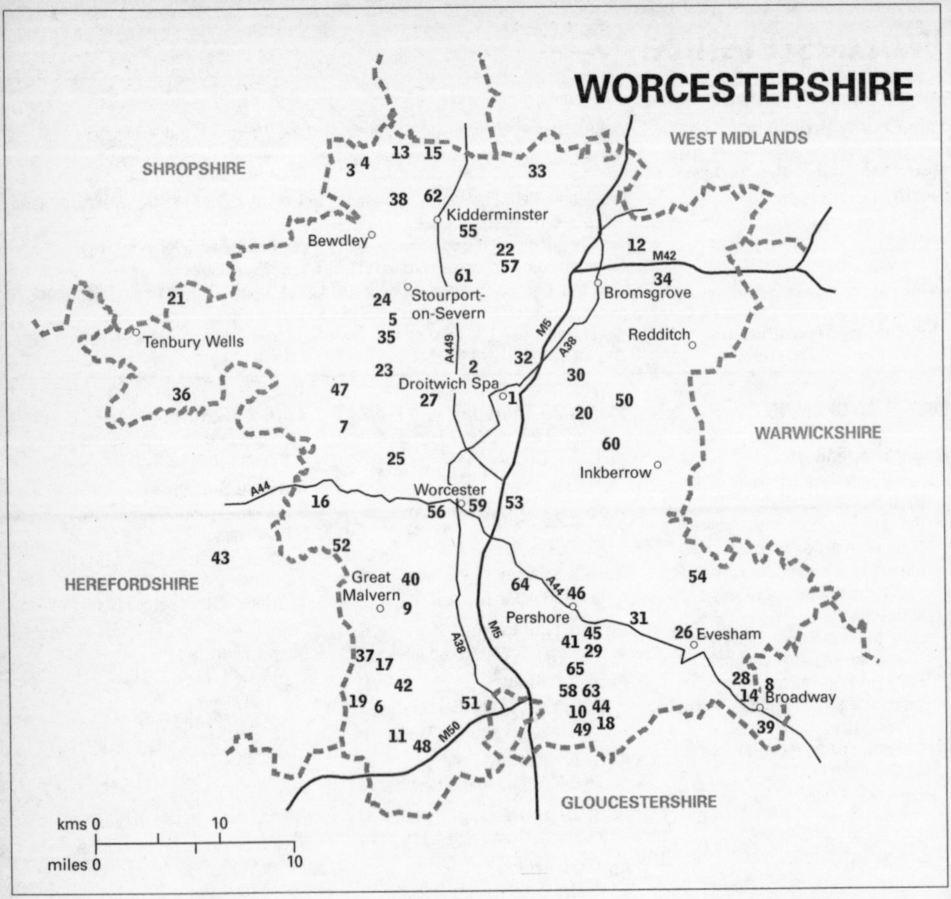

KEY

1 24 Alexander Avenue
2 The Arles
3 Arley Arboretum
4 Arley Cottage
5 Astley Towne House
6 Bannut Tree House
7 Barbers
8 Barn House
9 Barnard's Green House
10 Bell's Castle
11 Birtsmorton Court
12 21 Bittell Lane
13 Bodenham Arboretum
14 Broadway, Snowshill Road Gardens
15 Cedar Lodge
16 Charlton House
17 Chevin Cottage
18 Conderton Manor
19 The Cockshoot
20 The Cottage
21 The Cottage Herbery
22 Dial Park
23 Eastgrove Cottage Garden Nursery
24 Elm Grove and Neighbours
25 The Elms
26 94 Fairfield Road
27 Gardens at Severnbank
28 Gorsehill Abbey Farm
29 Hailey House
30 Hanbury Hall
31 Holland House
32 Impney Park
33 Ivytree House
34 Keepers Cottage
35 Koi Cottage
36 Kyre Park
37 Little Malvern Court
38 9 Low Habberley
39 Luggers Hall
40 Madresfield Court
41 The Manor House
42 Nerine Nursery
43 Orchard Bungalow
44 Overbury Court
45 Pershore College
46 Pershore Gardens
47 1 Prickley Bungalows
48 Priors Court
49 The Priory
50 Red House Farm
51 Ripple Hall
52 Shuttifield Cottage
53 Spetchley Park Charitable Trust
54 St Egwins Cottage
55 Stone House Cottage Gardens
56 21 Swinton Lane
57 Tythe Barn House
58 Upper Court
59 The Walled Garden
60 White Cottage
61 Whitlenge House Cottage
62 Windyridge
63 Wings Cottage
64 Woodmancote
65 Woollas Hall

St Egwins Cottage, Norton
White Cottage, Stock Green, nr Inkberrow

May 17 Wednesday
Red House Farm, Bradley Green, nr Redditch

May 21 Sunday
Barn House, Broadway
21 Bittell Lane, Barnt Green
The Cottage Herbery, Boraston, nr Tenbury Wells
Eastgrove Cottage Garden Nursery, Sankyns Green, Shrawley
1 Prickley Bungalows, Martley
Priors Court, Long Green
Shuttifield Cottage, Birchwood

May 24 Wednesday
St Egwins Cottage, Norton

May 25 Thursday
Barn House, Broadway
Barnard's Green House, Malvern
The Manor House, Birlingham
21 Swinton Lane, Worcester
The Walled Garden, Fort Royal Hill, Worcester

May 26 Friday
The Elms, Lower Broadheath

May 27 Saturday
White Cottage, Stock Green, nr Inkberrow

May 28 Sunday
Cedar Lodge, Blakeshall, Wolverley
The Cockshoot, Castlemorton Common
The Cottage Herbery, Boraston, nr Tenbury Wells
Luggers Hall, Broadway
Stone House Cottage Gardens, Stone
White Cottage, Stock Green, nr Inkberrow
Whitlenge House Cottage, Hartlebury
Woodmancote, Wadborough

May 29 Monday
The Cockshoot, Castlemorton Common
Stone House Cottage Gardens, Stone
Whitlenge House Cottage, Hartlebury

May 31 Wednesday
9 Low Habberley, Kidderminster

June 1 Thursday
Gorsehill Abbey Farm, Broadway
The Priory, Kemerton

June 3 Saturday
The Elms, Lower Broadheath
The Walled Garden, Fort Royal Hill, Worcester

June 4 Sunday
Barn House, Broadway
The Cottage Herbery, Boraston, nr Tenbury Wells
1 Prickley Bungalows, Martley
Shuttifield Cottage, Birchwood

June 7 Wednesday
9 Low Habberley, Kidderminster

June 8 Thursday
Gorsehill Abbey Farm, Broadway
The Manor House, Birlingham
The Walled Garden, Fort Royal Hill, Worcester

June 10 Saturday
Bannut Tree House, Castlemorton
Chevin Cottage, Upper Welland
The Elms, Lower Broadheath
Gardens at Severnbank, Shrawley
Holland House, Cropthorne
White Cottage, Stock Green, nr Inkberrow

June 11 Sunday
24 Alexander Avenue, Droitwich Spa
Bannut Tree House, Castlemorton
Barn House, Broadway
Barnard's Green House, Malvern
Chevin Cottage, Upper Welland
The Cockshoot, Castlemorton Common
Eastgrove Cottage Garden Nursery, Sankyns Green, Shrawley
94 Fairfield Road, Evesham
Gardens at Severnbank, Shrawley
Hailey House, Great Comberton
Orchard Bungalow, Bishops Frome
Pershore College, Pershore
Pershore Gardens
The Priory, Kemerton
St Egwins Cottage, Norton
White Cottage, Stock Green, nr Inkberrow
Woodmancote, Wadborough

June 14 Wednesday
9 Low Habberley, Kidderminster
St Egwins Cottage, Norton

June 15 Thursday
Gorsehill Abbey Farm, Broadway
The Manor House, Birlingham
Tythe Barn House, Chaddesley Corbett

June 17 Saturday
The Elms, Lower Broadheath

June 18 Sunday
Barbers, Martley
Barn House, Broadway
Bell's Castle, Kemerton
Birtsmorton Court, nr Malvern
Charlton House, Lulsley, Knightwick
94 Fairfield Road, Evesham
Hailey House, Great Comberton
Luggers Hall, Broadway
1 Prickley Bungalows, Martley
The Priory, Kemerton
Shuttifield Cottage, Birchwood
Stone House Cottage Gardens, Stone
21 Swinton Lane, Worcester

June 21 Wednesday
Hanbury Hall, Hanbury (evening)
9 Low Habberley, Kidderminster

June 22 Thursday
Barnard's Green House, Malvern
Gorsehill Abbey Farm, Broadway
The Priory, Kemerton
The Walled Garden, Fort Royal Hill, Worcester

June 24 Saturday
Barn House, Broadway
The Elms, Lower Broadheath
White Cottage, Stock Green, nr Inkberrow

June 25 Sunday
The Cockshoot, Castlemorton Common
The Cottage Herbery, Boraston, nr Tenbury Wells
Elm Grove and Neighbours, Astley Cross (evening)
94 Fairfield Road, Evesham
Hailey House, Great Comberton
Koi Cottage, Astley
Upper Court, Kemerton
White Cottage, Stock Green, nr Inkberrow
Woodmancote, Wadborough

June 28 Wednesday
Holland House, Cropthorne (evening)
9 Low Habberley, Kidderminster
St Egwins Cottage, Norton

June 29 Thursday
Barnard's Green House, Malvern
Gorsehill Abbey Farm, Broadway

July 1 Saturday
The Walled Garden, Fort Royal Hill, Worcester

July 2 Sunday
Barn House, Broadway
Broadway, Snowshill Road Gardens
94 Fairfield Road, Evesham
Hailey House, Great Comberton
1 Prickley Bungalows, Martley
Shuttifield Cottage, Birchwood
Spetchley Park Charitable Trust, nr Worcester

July 3 Monday
Ivytree House, Clent

July 5 Wednesday
Ivytree House, Clent

July 6 Thursday
Barnard's Green House, Malvern

Gorsehill Abbey Farm, Broadway
The Priory, Kemerton
The Walled Garden, Fort Royal Hill, Worcester

July 7 Friday
The Elms, Lower Broadheath

July 9 Sunday
Bannut Tree House, Castlemorton
Eastgrove Cottage Garden Nursery, Sankyns Green, Shrawley
94 Fairfield Road, Evesham
Orchard Bungalow, Bishops Frome
The Priory, Kemerton
Tythe Barn House, Chaddesley Corbett
Woollas Hall, Eckington

July 12 Wednesday
St Egwins Cottage, Norton

July 13 Thursday
Barnard's Green House, Malvern
Gorsehill Abbey Farm, Broadway
The Manor House, Birlingham
21 Swinton Lane, Worcester
The Walled Garden, Fort Royal Hill, Worcester

July 16 Sunday
24 Alexander Avenue, Droitwich Spa
Arley Cottage, Upper Arley
94 Fairfield Road, Evesham
Luggers Hall, Broadway
1 Prickley Bungalows, Martley
21 Swinton Lane, Worcester

July 20 Thursday
Barn House, Broadway
Barnard's Green House, Malvern
Gorsehill Abbey Farm, Broadway
The Priory, Kemerton
The Walled Garden, Fort Royal Hill, Worcester

July 22 Saturday
Charlton House, Lulsley, Knightwick

July 23 Sunday
The Arles, Haye Lane, Hadley
21 Bittell Lane, Barnt Green
94 Fairfield Road, Evesham
St Egwins Cottage, Norton
Shuttifield Cottage, Birchwood

July 25 Tuesday
Tythe Barn House, Chaddesley Corbett

July 27 Thursday
Gorsehill Abbey Farm, Broadway
The Walled Garden, Fort Royal Hill, Worcester

July 29 Saturday
Barn House, Broadway
Eastgrove Cottage Garden Nursery, Sankyns Green, Shrawley (evening)

July 30 Sunday
94 Fairfield Road, Evesham
1 Prickley Bungalows, Martley

August 2 Wednesday
St Egwins Cottage, Norton

August 3 Thursday
Gorsehill Abbey Farm, Broadway

August 6 Sunday
Barn House, Broadway
94 Fairfield Road, Evesham
Orchard Bungalow, Bishops Frome
The Priory, Kemerton
Wings Cottage, Kemerton

August 9 Wednesday
Charlton House, Lulsley, Knightwick

August 10 Thursday
Barnard's Green House, Malvern
Gorsehill Abbey Farm, Broadway
The Priory, Kemerton

August 11 Friday
The Elms, Lower Broadheath

August 12 Saturday
The Walled Garden, Fort Royal Hill, Worcester

August 13 Sunday
Barn House, Broadway
21 Swinton Lane, Worcester

August 17 Thursday
Gorsehill Abbey Farm, Broadway
The Priory, Kemerton
The Walled Garden, Fort Royal Hill, Worcester

August 20 Sunday
The Arles, Haye Lane, Hadley
St Egwins Cottage, Norton
Shuttifield Cottage, Birchwood

August 24 Thursday
Barnard's Green House, Malvern
Gorsehill Abbey Farm, Broadway
The Walled Garden, Fort Royal Hill, Worcester

August 27 Sunday
The Priory, Kemerton
Stone House Cottage Gardens, Stone
Tythe Barn House, Chaddesley Corbett
Whitlenge House Cottage, Hartlebury
Wings Cottage, Kemerton

August 28 Monday
Stone House Cottage Gardens, Stone
Whitlenge House Cottage, Hartlebury

August 31 Thursday
Gorsehill Abbey Farm, Broadway
The Walled Garden, Fort Royal Hill, Worcester

September 1 Friday
The Elms, Lower Broadheath

September 3 Sunday
Barn House, Broadway

September 7 Thursday
Barnard's Green House, Malvern
The Manor House, Birlingham
21 Swinton Lane, Worcester

September 10 Sunday
The Priory, Kemerton

September 13 Wednesday
Red House Farm, Bradley Green, nr Redditch

September 14 Thursday
The Manor House, Birlingham
The Priory, Kemerton

September 17 Sunday
Barn House, Broadway
Bodenham Arboretum, Wolverley

September 21 Thursday
Barnard's Green House, Malvern
The Priory, Kemerton

September 24 Sunday
Barn House, Broadway
Eastgrove Cottage Garden Nursery, Sankyns Green, Shrawley
The Priory, Kemerton

October 1 Sunday
Kyre Park, Kyre

October 15 Sunday
Nerine Nursery, Welland

2001

February 14 to 15 Wednesday to Thursday
Dial Park, Chaddesley Corbett

By Appointment Gardens. These owners do not have a fixed opening day, usually because they cannot accommodate large numbers or have insuffucient parking space.

DESCRIPTIONS OF GARDENS

24 Alexander Avenue, Droitwich Spa ♿✂❀ (Malley & David Terry) *South from Droitwich Spa towards Worcester A38, town centre approx 1m. Or from junction 6 M5 to Droitwich Town centre.* Garden 140′ × 40′ with yr-round interest, planted April 1996. Unusual shrubs, herbaceous perennials, ferns and shade loving plants. Collection of over 100 clematis, and pillar roses in the herbaceous borders; alpine troughs and small alpine house. Scree garden at the front with drought resistant plants. *Adm £1.50 Chd free. Suns April 23, May 14, June 11, July 16 (2-6). Private visits welcome by appt, please* **Tel 01905 774907**

NEW **The Arles, Haye Lane, Hadley** ♿✂❀ (Linda & Peter Fernyhough) *3m W of Droitwich and 1m E of Ombersley on A4133. Follow Fishery signs down Haye Lane. 7m S of Kidderminster on A449. Follow Fishery signs down Haye Lane* Approx 3/4-acre garden in a rural setting, generously planted to create an abundance of colour from both foliage and flower throughout the season. Many unusual and interesting perennials and ornamental grasses with an ever increasing collection of Hemerocallis and Kniphofia. Numerous beds and borders incl a monocot border, a long colour themed herbaceous border and an exotic island bed. TEAS. *Adm £2 Chd free. Suns July 23; Aug 20; (2-6). Private visits by welcome, please* **Tel 01905 620210**

Arley Arboretum, Upper Arley ✂ (R D Turner Charitable Trust) *and* **Arley House Garden** *(by kind permission of Mr Nigel Goodman) 5m N of Kidderminster. A442.* Arboretum containing specimen conifers and hardwoods, rhododendrons, camellias, magnolias, heathers; Italianate garden. TEA. *Adm £2 Chd free (ACNO to St Peter's Church, Upper Arley). Sun April 23 (2-7)*

Arley Cottage, Upper Arley ♿ (The Woodward Family) *nr Bewdley. 5m N of Kidderminster off A442.* The Arley Cottage garden has been in the possession of the same family for nearly 150 yrs during which time much care and attention has been given to its planting. A small country garden with lawns bordered by interesting trees and shrubs and a collection of rare and mature trees. Cream TEAS. *Adm £1.50 Chd free (ACNO to Sargent Cancer Care for Children). Sun July 16 (2-5)*

Astley Towne House, Astley ♿❀ (Tim & Lesley Smith) *3m W of Stourport on Severn on B4196 Worcester to Bewdley Road.* Approx 2½ acres; recently constructed family garden to a very ambitious design of the owners; formal kitchen garden with central fountain, grass paths winding through shrubs and herbaceous borders, children can see pets corner. TEAS. *Adm £2 Chd free. Sun April 23 (1-5.30)*

NEW **Bannut Tree House, Castlemorton** ♿✂❀ (Mr & Mrs Peter Reynolds) *7m S of Malvern on B4208 Gloucester Rd.* Grade II, Arts and Crafts house designed by CFA Voysey in 1890 (not open). The 2½-acre garden being restored and developed, incls herbaceous borders, potager, grasses, nut walk and interesting woodland area with stream. TEAS in aid of St Gregory's Church. *Adm £2 Chd free. Sat, Suns June 10, 11; July 9 (2-6)*

Barbers, Martley ♿✂❀ (Mr & the Hon Mrs Richard Webb) *7m NW of Worcester on B4204.* Medium-sized garden with lawns, trees, shrubs, pools, wild garden and walled garden. Home-made TEAS. *Adm £2 Chd free (ACNO to Martley Church). Sun June 18 (2-6)*

Barn House, Broadway ♿ (Mr & Mrs M Ricketts) *Situated in beautiful Cotswold village of Broadway in the upper High St now a cul-de-sac.* Large C17 country house (not open) set in 16 acres of garden and paddocks. The well maintained gardens contain large variety of shrubs. TEAS. *Adm £1.50 Chd free. Open daily April to Sept. By appt other times (10-6)* **Tel 01386 858633**

Barnard's Green House, Malvern ♿✂❀ (Mr & Mrs Philip Nicholls) *10 Poolbrook Rd, Malvern. On E side of Malvern at junction of B4211 and B4208.* 3-acre garden; mature trees; herbaceous border; rockery; heather beds; woodland, vegetable garden with old brick paths and box hedges. Unusual plants and shrubs for sale. Mrs Nicholls is a specialist and writer on dried flowers. 1635 half-timbered house (not open). Coach parties by appt. TEAS. *Adm £2 Acc chd free (ACNO to SCF). Suns March 12, June 11 and every Thursday April to Sept incl. (2-6). Also private visits welcome, please* **Tel 01684 574446**

Bell's Castle, Kemerton ❀ (Lady Holland-Martin DBE DL) *NE of Tewkesbury.* 3 small terraces with battlements; wild garden outside wall. The small Gothic castellated folly (not open) was built by Edmund Bell (Smuggler) c1820; very fine views. TEAS and gift stall. *Adm £1 Chd free. Sun June 18 (2-6). Parties welcome, please* **Tel 01386 725333**

Birtsmorton Court, nr Malvern ♿✂ (Mr & Mrs N G K Dawes) *7m E of Ledbury on A438.* Fortified manor house (not open) dating from C12; moat; Westminster pool, laid down in Henry V11's reign at time of consecration of Westminster Abbey; large tree under which Cardinal Wolsey reputedly slept in shadow of ragged stone; white garden. Newly planted potager; topiary. Motor Museum extra. TEAS in aid of Birtsmorton Church. *Adm £2.50 Chd 50p. Sun June 18 (2-6)*

21 Bittell Lane, Barnt Green ✂❀ (Barrie & Pauline Wild) *4m NE of Bromsgrove on B4120.* ⅓ acre 50yr old garden with ancient Bramley. Redesigned and planted by present owners; mostly colour themed borders in several rooms to incl over 1500 different species, many unusual, to provide yr-round interest from Spring rhododendrons, bulbs and hellebores to award winning late summer front cottage garden for butterflies. Pond, bog garden, mixed shrub and herbaceous borders. *Adm £1.50 Chd free (ACNO to Leukaemia Research). Suns May 21, July 23 (11-5)*

■ **Bodenham Arboretum, Wolverley** ❀ (The Binnian Family) *Situated 5m from Kidderminster, 2m N of Wolverley off the B4189. Follow brown signs from Wolverley Church Island.* Award winning arboretum landscaped in 134 acres during the last 26 yrs, contains over 500 species of trees and shrubs; 2 chains of lakes and pools; 4m of paths through woods and glades; grove of dawn redwoods and laburnum tunnel. Bring wellingtons or strong shoes. Partly suitable for wheelchairs. Refreshments in Earth Centre Restaurant. *Adm £3 Chd £1 under 5yrs free (ACNO to Kew Gardens Millennium*

Seed Bank Appeal). Open daily April 1 - Mid Nov, winter months weekends & Bank Hols only (11-5). For NGS Sun Sept 17 (2-5) **Tel 01562 852444**

Broadway, Snowshill Road Gardens *All six gardens are on Snowshill Rd. Parking available.* TEAS at Far Bunchers. *Combined adm £3 Chd free. (ACNO to Lifford Hall, Broadway). Sun July 2 (2-6)*

Far Bunchers (Mrs A Pallant) A medium size garden of mixed planting, that incl many shrub roses

Meadowside (Mrs Patricia A Bomford) A very pleasing and compact cottage garden that slopes down to a stream

The Mill (Hugh Verney Esq) A 2½-acre paddock, bounded by 2 streams has been transformed, since 1975, into an attractive garden that will support a variety of wildlife. Informal planting of trees, shrub roses and other shrubs, moisture loving plants and bulbs

Mill Hay Cottage (Dr & Mrs W Payne) The 2-acre garden is of relatively recent origin and is still being developed. A special feature is the number of unusual trees, incl many fruiting species

Mill Hay House (Mr & Mrs H Will) The large mill pond is the centre of attention in a well laid out and interesting garden

Pye Corner House (Mr & Mrs C J King) Formal, fruit and vegetable garden, with many special features

Cedar Lodge, Blakeshall, Wolverley (Malcolm & Barbara Phillips) *4m N of Kidderminster off A449 (B4189) midway between villages of Wolverley and Kinver.* Award winning garden. Designed by the owner with an eye to plant associations and the complementary textures, shapes and colours of a wide range of perennials shrubs, trees and alpines in keeping with the beautiful country setting. The 1 acre incl pools and gravel gardens. Cream TEAS. *Adm £2 Chd free. Sun May 28 (2-5.30). Private visits welcome,* **Tel 01562 850238**

Charlton House, Lulsley, Knightwick (Mr & Mrs Driver-White) *9m W of Worcester via A44, turn 1st L after Knightsford Bridge towards Alfrick, 1st L after Fox & Hounds signed Hill Rd, Lulsley; 1m at end of lane.* ⅔-acre intimate garden of shrubs and shrub roses created by owner since 1970. Fine barns; ducks & peacocks. No children. Cold drinks on request. *Adm £1.50. Sun June 18; Sat July 22; Wed Aug 9 (1.30-5.30). Coach parties and private visits by appt, please* **Tel 01886 821220**

Chevin Cottage, Upper Welland (Vivian & Simon Drake) *4m S of Great Malvern, take A449 towards Ledbury, ½m before junction with A4104, signpost to Upper Welland, garden between PO and Hawthorn Inn.* Approx ⅓ acre narrow cottage garden incorporating 6 themed informal garden rooms designed and created by owners since 1992. Containing traditional herbaceous plants and shrubs with old fashioned roses. A peaceful haven with views over surrounding countryside. Winner national garden competition and featured on ITV in 1999. TEAS in aid of Cats Protection. *Adm £1.75 Chd free. Sat, Sun June 10, 11 (12-5.30)*

The Cockshoot, Castlemorton Common (Clive & ...eth Wilkins) *2m S of Welland on B4208 turn into New Rd opp Robin Hood PH. Take 1st L ½m. After 300yds bear L at fork. Keep on narrow rd until track. Straight along track.* Paradise cottage garden set out in 'rooms' around a Georgian cottage (not open) in idyllic setting. Attractive mixed planting with perennials, roses and clematis, flowering shrubs; trees; white garden and pond. Quiet areas and vistas; over 150 varieties of hostas, many in pots in courtyard. Nursery specialising in hostas and cottage garden plants. TEAS. *Adm £1.50 Chd 50p. Bank Hols Mons May 1, 29: Suns April 30, May 28; June 11, 25 (2-6). Nursery & private visits welcome, please* **Tel 01684 833331**

Conderton Manor, nr Tewkesbury (Mr & Mrs W Carr) *5½m NE of Tewkesbury on Bredon - Beckford Rd.* 7-acre garden with magnificent views of Cotswolds. Wonderful flowering cherries and bulbs in spring, and many trees and shrubs of botantical interest; glorious autumn colour. There is a formal terrace with clipped box parterre; huge rose arch tunnel underplanted with lavender and perennials; mixed borders of roses and herbaceous plants in former kitchen garden; a new quarry garden. Best season: March to early July, Sept-Oct. Coffee and teas by arrangement for groups, PH in village. *Adm £3. Visits by appt only, yr-round. Evening visits by groups welcomed, Autumn visits recommended, please* **Tel 01386 725389**

The Cottage, Broughton Green (Mr Terry Dagley) *nr Hanbury Hall (NT). E of Droitwich, via B4090 for 3½m. Turn R at Broughton Green sign, continue for 1m. Park on side of rd. The Cottage, 250yds up farm track.* Small mature country garden designed to give yr round interest by using wide range of perennials, bulbs, shrubs and trees. The quiet situation encourages abundant wildlife, which in turn, identifies the 'wimps' from the strong growers of the plant world. *Adm £1.50 Chd free. Weds March 8, 22 (11-1 & 2-5). Private visits by individuals or groups welcome April - Oct, please* **Tel 01905 391670**

The Cottage Herbery, Boraston, nr Tenbury Wells (Mr & Mrs R E Hurst) *On A456, turn for Boraston at Peacock Inn, turn R in village, signposted to garden.* 1-acre organic true cottage garden with a mix of herbs, herbaceous perennials, old roses, vegetables and native plants; a wildlife haven. The Cornbrook runs through the garden creating areas for bog and moisture loving plants; new features for yr 2000. Featured on ITV, BBC2 'Paradise Gardens', C4 'Wild about the garden'. Gold Medal winners at major shows. TEAS weekdays by appt. *Adm £1.50 Chd free. Suns May 14, 21, 28, June 4, 25 (11-5). Groups welcome by appt, please* **Tel 01584 781575**

Dial Park, Chaddesley Corbett (Mr & Mrs David Mason) *4½m from Kidderminster, 4½m from Bromsgrove on A448. 150yds towards Kidderminster turn into Chaddesley Corbett village. Parking in village or at village hall 200yds.* Approx ¾-acre garden developed since 1990 containing interesting and unusual plants with yr-round interest; incl collections of snowdrops, sambucus and hardy ferns. Also small collection of country bygones. TEA. *Adm £1.50 Chd free. Wed, Thurs Feb 23, 24 (1-5) March 23; April 27; 20 (2-6). 2001 Feb 14, 15 (1-5). Private visits welcome, please* **Tel 01562 777451**

● **Eastgrove Cottage Garden Nursery, Sankyns Green, Shrawley** ♿✂❀ (Mr & Mrs J Malcolm Skinner) *8m NW of Worcester on rd between Shrawley (B4196) and Great Witley (A443).* Unique country cottage flower garden, though situated deep in the countryside attracts worldwide interest. A plantsman's paradise yet a joy for all; ever-changing inspired planting, meticulously maintained. Developing arboretum. Home-made ice cream. *Adm £2 Chd free. Thurs, Fri, Sat, Sun, Mon April 1 to July 31; (Aug closed) Thurs, Fri, Sat Sept 1 to Oct 14 (2-5). Special Silver Jubilee Celebratory evening Sat July 29 from 7 pm adm £4 incls coffee, flapjack and introductory talk by Malcolm and Carol. By appt Thurs in Winter, please* **Tel 01299 896389** www.hughesmedia.co.uk/eastgrove/

NEW **Elm Grove and Neighbours, Astley Cross** *A group of four gardens in and around Elm Grove, Astley Cross, Stourport-on-Severn. Take A451 westwards out of Stourport and turn onto B4196 (Worcester). At the next X-roads turn into Redhouse Rd and park.* Cream TEAS 1-5.30pm, **Evening Opening** Barbecue 5.30-8pm. *Combined adm £2 Chd free. Sun June 25 (1-8)*

NEW **86 Areley Common** ♿❀ (Mr & Mrs Caswill) Planned for all-yr colour, recent layout incl 2 pools; gazebo; greenhouses and vegetable garden. One border in shade and other in full sun giving rise to very different planting

NEW **2 Elm Grove** ♿✂ (Mr & Mrs B Petfield) A corner bungalow with well-kept lawns; flower beds and water features. Terracotta pots; window boxes and hanging baskets add extra summer colour.

6 Elm Grove ♿❀ (Michael Ecob) An old-fashioned cottage garden crammed with plants for yr-round interest, bursts into colour during June. Small vegetable patch and 2 greenhouses provide show produce. Patio area has raised pool with native wild flowers. *Private visits welcome in evening during June, please* **Tel 01299 822167**

NEW **13 Oakhampton Road** ♿✂ (Mr & Mrs R Roffe) Created in last 6 yrs, this modern estate garden shows what can be done with a small area. Water features; cosy corner; immaculate lawns & borders with mature standard fuchsias.

The Elms, Lower Broadheath ✂❀ (Marshall & Emma Stewart) *4m W of Worcester, B4204 turn opp school into Frenchlands Lane. Garden 1m.* Isolated, peaceful setting. 1½-acre surrounding late Georgian farmhouse (not open). Mixed colour-themed garden 'rooms', lily pool, rose walk, walled ornamental kitchen garden created from old fold yard; nursery specialising in unusual hardy plants; rare breed sheep. Farming bygones. TEAS. *Adm £2 Chd free. Fris March 24; April 21; May 26; July 7; Aug 11; Sept 1; Sats June 3, 10, 17, 24 (2-5). Private visits welcome, please* **Tel 01905 640841**

94 Fairfield Road, Evesham ♿ (Elsie & Wolff Wahle) *From the N, travel over the 'New Bridge' and through the t-lights towards Cheltenham, Fairfield Rd is the 1st turn to your L. From Cheltenham, it is the 1st turn R after Evesham College.* Although an ordinary garden, it is a colourful and very interesting small town garden of 14.7 × 12.1m. It contains mature trees, a variety of shrubs, ornamental grasses and many perennials: in excess of 300 kinds. It is surprising how much fits into a small garden. Featured in ITV 'Answer lies in the soil'. TEA. *Adm £1 Chd 50p. Every Sun June 11 to Aug 6 (2-6)*

NEW **Gardens at Severnbank, Shrawley** *On B4196 5m S of Stourport-on-Severn, 8m N of Worcester, ½m from Holt Heath.* TEAS. *Combined adm £3 Chd free. Sat, Sun June 10, 11 (2-6).*

NEW **The Granary, Shrawley** ♿✂❀ (Sue & Tony Russell-Jones) Natural garden planted in the last 4 yrs in 3/4 acre paddock behind barn; large colour-co-ordinated perfumed borders. Small arboretum. *Private visits welcome, please* **Tel 01905 620555**

NEW **Severnbank House, Shrawley** ✂❀ (Mary & Mark Brittain) This large, partly-walled country garden has a wealth of mature trees and some unusual plants. Features incl sweeping lawns; large mixed borders; a pond and small bog garden; potager with grass paths. A small cottage garden and pretty blue brick courtyard will also be open. *Private visits welcome, please* **Tel 01905 621205**

Gorsehill Abbey Farm, Broadway ♿✂❀ (Michael & Diane Stacey) *From Evesham; S 4m on A44 towards Broadway, L at 1st roundabout towards Willersey. Farm is on L 500m past Collin House Hotel.* A 2-acre organic garden set in open countryside with views towards Bredon and Malvern. Largely developed since 1992 and still evolving. Wide range of interesting and unusual plants giving yr-round interest. Large mixed border, pergolas, ponds and water features, wild-life areas, fruit, vegetables and permaculture. *Adm £1.50 Chd free (ACNO to Henry Doubleday Research Association). Thurs June 1, 8, 15, 22, 29; July 6, 13, 20, 27; Aug 3, 10, 17, 24, 31; (3-6).* **Tel 01386 852208**

NEW **Hailey House, Great Comberton** ♿✂❀ (Mr & Mrs David Spreckley) *3m SW of Pershore. A44 W from Pershore. Turn R after Pershore Bridge to Great Comberton. In village fork L up Church St.* Sheltered ⅔-acre garden with Bredon Hill as a backdrop. Richly planted borders show special attention to colour, texture and form. Many unusual plants and penstemons, with lavish use of grasses for a tapestry effect; themed areas offer romantic vistas and tranquil corners. Small plant nusery in productive kitchen garden; greenhouses. TEAS. *Adm £2.50 Chd free (ACNO to BASIC Birmingham Branch). Suns June 11, 18, 25: July 2 (2-6). Groups welcome, please* **Tel 01386 710 733**

▲ **Hanbury Hall, Hanbury** ♿✂❀ (The National Trust) *3m NE of Droitwich, 6m S of Bromsgrove. Signed off B4090.* Re-creation of C18 formal garden by George London incl sunken parterre, fruit garden and wilderness, grove and bowling green pavilions. The Hall is a charming brick William & Mary style house (not open), dating from 1701. Also to be found in the garden are an Orangery complete with citrus plants; a Mushroom House and Ice House. *Adm to garden & Midsummer Nights Concert £5 Chd £1. Wed June 21 bring a picnic. Gates open at 6.30pm; Music 7.30pm.*
Tickets 01527 821214 or 01562 850238

Holland House, Cropthorne (Mr Peter Middlemiss) *Main St, Pershore. Between Pershore and Evesham, off A44. Car*

park at rear of house. Gardens laid out by Lutyens in 1904; thatched house dating back to C16 (not open). TEAS. *Adm £1.50 Chd free (ACNO to USPG). Sat June 10 (2.30-5). Wed June 28 (6.30-9) Plated suppers.*

Impney Park, Droitwich (Sir Geoffrey & Lady Dear) *On A38 Droitwich/Bromsgrove Rd. 1m W of junction 5. M5 (next door to Chateau Impney).* 3-acre garden, set in 7 acre private parkland facing SW with views of Severn Vale, across to Malverns. Formal terracing sweeps down into lawns; herbaceous border and informal shrubberies massed with bulbs and hardy geraniums; formal rose garden. Surrounded by mature trees, encouraging abundant wildlife. TEA. *Adm £2 Chd free. Open by appt only for clubs, groups and societies from mid-March until October, excluding August*
Tel 01905 773309

Ivytree House, Clent ❀ (Mrs L Eggins) *[OS139 91.79] Bromsgrove Rd. 3m SE of Stourbridge and 5m NW of Bromsgrove, off A491 Stourbridge to Bromsgrove dual carriageway. Car parking next door behind the Woodman Hotel.* Over 1,000 varieties of small trees, shrubs and herbaceous plants in approx ½-acre plantsman's cottage garden; tree ivies and ivytrees, collection of aucubas, small conservatory with fuchsia trees; pond garden; fruit and vegetables; bantams and bees. *Adm £2 Chd free. Mon, Wed July 3, 5 (2-5). Also private visits welcome, please* **Tel 01562 884171**

Keepers Cottage, Alvechurch ✂❀ (Mrs Diana Scott) *Take main rd through Alvechurch towards Redditch. Turn opp sign to Cobley Hill and Bromsgrove for 1m over 2 humpback bridges.* 3-acre garden at 600ft with fine views towards the Cotswolds. Rhododendrons; camellias; old-fashioned roses; unusual trees and shrubs; rock garden; 2 alpine houses and new potager; paddock with donkeys. *Adm £2 Chd £1. Private visits welcome in May, please* **Tel 0121 445 5885**

Koi Cottage, Astley ♿❀ (Mr & Mrs M Raybold) *Astley village 3m W of Stourport-on-Severn on B4196 to Worcester 2 mins from village hall.* Small village garden converted to a classical Japanese garden with large Koi carp in a pool bridged with a Japanese bridge to the front door. *Adm £1.50 Chd free. Sun June 25 (1.30-5.30)*

■ **Kyre Park, Kyre** ♿❀ (Mr & Mrs J N Sellers) *4m S of Tenbury Wells or 7m N of Bromyard. Follow signs to Kyre Church off B4214.* Approx 29 acres. Georgian shrubbery walk under restoration; 5 lakes; waterfalls, hermitage; picturesque views; mature trees; grotto and Norman dovecote. Stout shoes advised. Ferns for sale at Rickards Hardy Fern Nursery. RHS gold medal winners since 1992 and other plant sales at Hampton Plants. TEAS, light lunches. *Adm £2 Chd 50p. Open daily 26 March to Dec. For NGS Suns March 26, Oct 1 (11-6). Coach parties by appt, please* **Tel 01885 410247**

▲ **Little Malvern Court, Malvern** ✂❀ (Mrs T M Berington) *4m S of Malvern on A4104 S of junction with A449.* 10 acres attached to former Benedictine Priory, magnificent views over Severn valley. An intriguing layout of garden rooms and terrace round house; water garden below feeding chain of lakes; wide variety of spring bulbs, flowering trees and shrubs. Notable collection of old-fashioned roses. TEAS. *Adm £3 Chd 50p (5-14). Sun March 19 (ACNO to SSAFA), Mon May 1 (ACNO to The Friends of Little Malvern Priory) (2-5). Other opening times please,*
Tel 01684 892988

9 Low Habberley, Kidderminster ✂ (Lindsay Randle) *Low Habberley is along Habberley Lane about 2m NW of Kidderminster and 3m NE of Bewdley.* A small, intimate, scented, cottage-style garden with mixed plantings of mainly old-fashioned plants, roses and herbs. Transported and replanted, mainly by hand and wheelbarrow, just over 3 years ago. Small formal pond, narrow uneven paths and steps make it unsuitable for wheelchairs and the very elderly. Featured on Gardeners World BBC and numerous publications. Teas available. Parking and food available at 'The Fountain' Inn directly opposite. *Adm £2 Chd free. Weds May 31, June 7, 14, 21, 28 (12-7)*

NEW **Luggers Hall, Broadway** ♿✂❀ (Kay & Red Haslam) *Turn off Broadway High St by Swan Hotel, bear L into Springfield Lane. Luggers Hall is on the L approx 300 yds along. Some parking but limited - if possible use village car parks which are close by.* 2½-acre formal garden was originally designed by the famous Victorian garden artist Alfred Parsons. Features incl rose garden; parterre; walled garden; white garden; Koi pool and herbaceous borders, all connected by gravel paths with seating area. An abundance of clipped box and yew hedging; plus Victorian Hazel walk. TEA. *Adm £2 Chd free (ACNO to Carmer Cat Sanctuary). Suns May 28; June 18; July 16 (2-6)*

Madresfield Court, nr Malvern ♿ (Lady Morrison) 60 acres formal and parkland garden incl rare species of mature trees, Pulhamite rock garden, maze; majestic avenues and a mass of wild flowers. TEAS. *Adm £2.50 Chd £1 (ACNO to Madresfield Primary School). Sun May 14 (2-5.30)*

● **The Manor House, Birlingham** ✂❀ (Mr & Mrs David Williams-Thomas) *nr Pershore off A4104.* Walled white and silver garden, gazebo and many herbaceous borders of special interest to the plantsman. Many plants for sale, all propagated from the garden incl plants for the dry garden. Very fine views of Bredon Hill with short walk to R Avon for picnics. Delicious home made TEAS. *Adm £2 Chd free. May every Thurs; Sun May 7; Mon 8; June & July every Thurs up to & incl July 13; Aug closed, Sept Thurs 7, 14 (11-5). Group visits welcome, please* **Tel 01386 750005**

Martins see Pebworth & District Gardens, Warwickshire

Nerine Nursery, Welland ✂❀ (Mr & Mrs I L Carmichael) *Brookend House, ½m towards Upton-on-Severn from Welland Xrds (A4104 × B4208).* Internationally famous National Collection of Nerines, 30 species and some 800 named varieties in 5 greenhouses and traditional walled garden with raised beds; hardy nerines. Coaches by appt only. TEAS. *Adm £2 Chd free. Sun Oct 15 (2-5). Private visits during Oct - Nov welcome, please* **Tel 01684 594005**

Orchard Bungalow, Bishops Frome ✂❀ (Mr & Mrs Robert Humphries) *Bishops Frome. 14m W of Worcester. A4103 turn R at bottom of Fromes Hill, through village of*

Bishops Frome on B4214. Turn R immediately after de-regulation signs along narrow track for 250yds. Park in field 200yds from garden. ½-acre garden with conifers, trees, shrubs and herbaceous borders. Over 400 roses incl many old varieties; 5 ponds; small stream; 3 aviaries and dovecote; japanese water garden and teahouse. Garden News Gardeners of the Year 1998. TEAS. *Adm £1.50 Chd 50p. Suns June 11, July 9, Aug 6 (2-6). Private visits welcome, please* **Tel 01885 490273**

Overbury Court, nr Tewkesbury ♿ (Mr & Mrs Bruce Bossom) *5m NE of Tewkesbury, village signed off A46.* Georgian house 1740 (not open); landscape garden of same date with stream and pools; daffodil bank and grotto. Plane trees, yew hedges; shrubs; cut flowers; coloured foliage; gold and silver, shrub rose borders. Norman church adjoins garden. *Adm £2 Chd free. Private visits welcome minimum charge £10 following written application or*
Fax 01386 725528

Pershore College, Pershore ♿✂❀ *1m S of Pershore on A44, 7m from M5 junction 7.* 180-acre estate; ornamental grounds; arboretum; fruit, vegetables; amenity glasshouses; wholesale hardy stock nursery. RHS Regional Centre at Pershore. Plant centre open daily for sales and gardening advice. TEA. *Adm £1.50 Chd 50p. Sun June 11 (2-4)*

Pershore Gardens ♿ A variety of gardens in Pershore ranging from small courtyard to large formal. 4 new gardens are on show this year incl The Croft in Station Rd - fine border and raised Koi pond, a lovely small bungalow garden in Whitcroft Rd and a large back garden in Broad St. Teas available at St Andrews Visitors' Centre. The Brandy Cask in Bridge St offers a lovely garden and usual fare. *Adm £2 Chd free for the tour. Sun June 11 (2-6)*

1 Prickley Bungalows, Martley ✂❀ (Megan & David Griffiths) *7m NW of Worcester to Martley on the B4204, 2m from Martley on the B4197. Turn off R into Hockhams Lane. Parking at Prickley Farm (250yds) by kind permission of Mr & Mrs Nott.* Designed by the occupants, the garden is ¼ acre in size with woodland area, wildlife pond and cottage gardens with well stocked borders. There is a large selection of 'in garden plants' for sale. *Adm £2 Chd free. Suns April 23; May 7, 21; June 4, 18; July 2, 16, 30 (2-6). All yr round by appt only, please* **TEL 01886 812523** COACHES WELCOME

Priors Court, Long Green ♿✂❀ (Robert Philipson-Stow Esq) *From Tewkesbury A438 to Ledbury. Exactly 5m pass under M50. Garden on hill on L of A438. From Ledbury, Worcester or Gloucester aim for Rye Cross (A438 and B4208) then take A438 for Tewkesbury. Priors Court is approx 3m from Rye Cross on R.* 3-acre garden established in 1920s. C15 house (not open). Rock, herb and vegetable gardens, mature trees and shrubs, herbaceous and rose borders; stunning views. Nearby Norman church open. TEAS. *Adm £2 (ACNO to Berrow & Pendock Parish Church). Sun May 21 (2-6). Private visits by appt for parties of less than 40, please* **Tel 01684 833221**

The Priory, Kemerton ♿❀ (The Hon Mrs Peter Healing) *NE of Tewkesbury B4080.* Main features of this 4-acre garden are long herbaceous borders planned in colour groups; stream, fern and sunken & knot gardens. Many unusual plants, shrubs and trees. Featured in BBC2 'Gardeners' World', 'The Garden magazine'. Small nursery. TEAS Suns only. *Adm £1.50 June, £2 July to Sept Chd free. (ACNO to Macmillan Cancer Relief, Glos) Aug 6, (St Richard's Hospice) Aug 27, (SSAFA) Sept 10. Every Thurs June 1 to Sept 28; Suns June 18; July 9; Aug 6, 27; Sept 10, 24 (2-6). (Not Saturdays) Oct by appt, private visits by appt for 20 and over, please* **Tel 01386 725258**

Red House Farm, Bradley Green, nr Redditch ✂❀ (Mrs M M Weaver) *Flying Horse Lane, Bradley Green. 7m W of Redditch on B4090 Alcester to Droitwich Spa. Ignore signpost to Bradley Green. Turn opp The Red Lion.* Approx ½-acre mature cottage garden containing wide range of interesting herbaceous perennials; roses; shrubs; alpines. Garden and small nursery open daily from 9 to 5 offering wide variety of plants mainly propagated from garden. *Adm £1.50 Chd free. Weds March 22; May 17; Sept 13 (11-5). Private visits welcome, please,* **Tel 01527 821269**

Ripple Hall, nr Tewkesbury ♿ (Sir Hugo Huntington-Whiteley Bt) *Off A38 Worcester-Tewkesbury (nr junction with motorway); Ripple Village well signed.* 6 acres; lawns and paddocks; walled vegetable garden; cork tree and orangery. TEAS. *Adm £1.50 Acc chd free (ACNO to St John Ambulance). Sun April 2 (2-5)*

St Egwins Cottage, Norton ✂❀ (Mr & Mrs Brian Dudley) *2m N of Evesham on B4088. Park in St Egwins Church car park not Church Lane. Walk through churchyard to Church Lane (50yds).* Nearly ¼-acre cottage style plantsman's garden, many unusual plants; mainly perennials incl hardy geraniums, campanulas and salvias. Featured in 'Your Garden' and 'Amateur Gardening' Magazines 1998. Small thatched cottage next to C12 church (open). TEAS Suns only. TEA Weds only. *Adm £1.50 Chd free. Suns, May 14; June 11; July 23; Aug 20 (2-5); Weds April 26; May 10, 24, June 14, 28; July 12; Aug 2 (2-5.30). Also private visits welcome May & June, please* **Tel 01386 870486**

Shuttifield Cottage, Birchwood ✂❀ (Mr & Mrs David Judge) *4½m from Malvern; 8m W of Worcester; turn R off A4103 opp Storridge Church to Birchwood. After 1¼m L down steep tarmac drive. Limited parking for those with walking difficulties, otherwise please park on rd.* Natural 2-acre garden with extensive mixed borders of unusual trees, shrubs and perennials. Large old-rose garden and rhododendrons and azaleas. 20 acre woodland walk with anemones and bluebells; small deer park with ponds, shrubs and natural wild area. (Anemonies & bluebells April 16). TEAS. *Adm £2 Chd free. Suns April 16; May 7, 21; June 4, 18; July 2, 23; Aug 20 (2-5). Also by appt* **Tel 01886 884243**

■ Spetchley Park Charitable Trust, nr Worcester ♿✂ *2m E of Worcester on A422.* 30-acre garden containing large collection of trees; shrubs and plants, many rare and unusual; new garden within kitchen garden. Red and fallow deer in nearby park. TEAS. *Adm £3.20 Chd £1.60. Open April -Sept 30 Tues-Fri (11-5), Bank Hol Mons (11-5) Suns (2-5). For NGS Fri April 21 (11-5), Suns May 7, July 2 (2-5)*

● **Stone House Cottage Gardens, Stone** (James & Louisa Arbuthnott) *Stone, 2m SE of Kidderminster via A448 towards Bromsgrove next to church, turn up drive.* 1-acre sheltered walled plantsman's garden with towers; rare wall shrubs, climbers and interesting herbaceous plants. In adjacent nursery large selection of unusual shrubs and climbers for sale. Featured in The Garden, Country Life and Hortus. Coaches by appt only. *Adm £2 Chd free. Suns April 30; May 28; June 18; Aug 27; Mons April 24; May 1, 29; Aug 28; also open March 1 to Sept 30 every Wed, Thurs, Fri, Sat (10-5.30). Private visits welcome Oct to March, please* **Tel 01562 69902**

21 Swinton Lane, Worcester (Mr A Poulton) *1½m W of city centre off B4485 from St Johns to Rushwick. Turn L between Portobello public house and golf course.* ⅓ acre 'town' garden subtly divided into colour themed areas. Unusual plants both hardy and half hardy as well as all-time favourites are used to create delightful plantings and containers. The silver and white garden and hot late border are of particular note. The expert use of colour form and texture make this garden special. *Adm £1.50. Suns June 18; July 16; Aug 13; Thurs May 25; July 13; Sept 7 (11-6). Parties and private visits welcome, please* **Tel 01905 422265**

NEW **Tythe Barn House, Chaddesley Corbett** (Judy & John Berrow) *4½m from Bromsgrove, 4½m from Kidderminster on A448. 150 yds towards Kidderminster from the turn into Chaddesley Corbett Village. Parking in village or at village hall (200 yds).* A 3/4-acre romantic garden created in an old farm rickyard; started in 1991 within an old farm building complex in a conservation area. Incl old and modern roses; herbs; heathers and herbaceous borders. Shrubs and trees together with a small vegetable plot. There is a wildlife pool with a lovely view of the church and surrounding countryside. TEA. *Adm £1.50 Chd free. Thurs June 15; Sun, Tues July 9, 25; Sun Aug 27 (2-6). Private visits welcome, please* **Tel 01562 777014**

Upper Court, Kemerton (Mr & Mrs W Herford) *NE of Tewkesbury B4080. Take turning to Parish Church from War Memorial; Manor behind church.* Approx 13 acres of garden and grounds incl a 2-acre lake where visitors would be welcome to bring picnics. The garden was mostly landscaped and planted in 1930s. TEAS. *Adm £2 Chd free. Sun June 25 (2-6)*

The Walled Garden, Fort Royal Hill, Worcester (Julia & William Scott) *6 Rose Terrace, Worcester. Close to the city centre via Fort Royal Hill, off London Rd (A44). Park on Fort Royal Hill or the first section of Rose Terrace and walk the last 20m down Rose Terrace (unmade rd). Garden entrance on the R.* Restoration in progress of ½ acre unique C19 kitchen garden to 1886 plan with vinery and astronomical observatory. A centre for the study of herbs and organic gardening. The developing areas incl herb gardens, flower gardens, potager and old and new fruit trees. Featured in The Garden & BBC 'Fresh Food'. TEA. *Adm £1.50 Chd 50p. Every Thurs May 4 - Aug 31; Sats April 22; May 6; June 3; July 1; Aug 12 (12-5). By appt for other times, coaches by prior arrangement* **Tel 01905 354629**

■ **White Cottage, Stock Green, nr Inkberrow** (Mr & Mrs S M Bates) *A422 Worcester to Alcester 2m W of Inkberrow, or 2m E of Upton Snodsbury, turn at brown sign for Cottage Garden also Stock Green, 1½m to T- junction, turn L.* 2 acres, herbaceous and shrub beds, stream and spring wild flower area, large specialist collection of hardy geraniums. Nursery, plants available. *Adm £2 OAPS £1.25 Nursery. open 10-5. Mon, Tue & Fri mid April to July 28 and Sept. Sats April 15; May 6; July 8, 22; closed May 15 - 26 For NGS April 29, 30; May 13, 14, 27, 28; June 10, 11, 24, 25 (10-5) other times by appt, please* **Tel 01386 792414**

Whitlenge House Cottage, Hartlebury (Mr & Mrs K J Southall) *Whitlenge Lane. S of Kidderminster. Take A442 (signposted Droitwich) over small island, ¼m, 1st R into Whitlenge Lane. Follow signs.* Home of Creative Landscapes, RHS medal winners. Professional landscaper's garden with over 600 varieties of trees, shrubs etc. Water features, twisted pillar pergola, gravel gardens, rockeries. 2 acres of plantsman's garden with adjacent nursery specialising in large specimen shrubs. TEAS. *Adm £2 Chd free. Mon April 24, Sun, Mon May 28, 29, Aug 27, 28 (10-5). Private visits welcome, parties of 10 and over, please* **Tel 01299 250720**

Windyridge, Kidderminster (Mr P Brazier) *Turn off Chester Rd N (A449) into Hurcott Rd, then into Imperial Avenue.* 1-acre spring garden containing azaleas, magnolias, camellias, rhododendrons, mature flowering cherries and davidia. Please wear sensible shoes. *Adm £1.50 Chd free. Sun May 7 (2-6). Private visits welcome, please* **Tel 01562 824994**

The Royal Gardeners' Orphan Fund

The RGOF has been helping the orphaned children of professional horticulturists since 1887. In 1995, the scope of the Fund was broadened. Now all the children in need, whose parents are employed in horticulture, may qualify for assistance. The RGOF gives quarterly allowances to orphaned children, and grants to those in need for school expenses, winter clothing, bedding and holidays.

For more information about the RGOF, please contact the Secretary,

Mrs Kate Wallis
14 Scholars Mews,
Welwyn Garden City,
Hertfordshire AL8 7JQ
Tel/Fax: 01707 333663

Information can also be found on the NGS website: www.ngs.org.uk

NEW **Wings Cottage, Kemerton** ♿ (Jeanette & Cecil Way) *NE of Tewkesbury, B4080. Car parking nearby; follow signs.* A delightful cottage garden set at the foot of Bredon Hill; re-designed by the present owners. The garden contains a colourful array of herbaceous planting intermingled with shrubs, dahlias, fuchsias. The cottage is framed by a beautiful old wisteria, of particular interest is the pseudo Acacia tree, which provides welcome shade in Summer, and a large brown Turkey Fig tree forming a natural corner grotto. *Adm £1.50 Chd free (ACNO to Macmillan Cancer Relief). Suns Aug 6, 27 (2-6). Group visits and teas by arrangement, please* **Tel/Fax 01386 725 273**

Woodmancote, Wadborough ♿❀ (Mr & Mrs Ian Walmsley) *1½ m S of Stoulton, which is on A44 between Worcester and Pershore.* ¾-acre with wide lawns, borders and island beds with a variety of shrubs and herbaceous plants; 2 ponds. Please park considerately at The Mason Arms (400yds). Bar meals are available. TEAS in aid of St Peter's Church, Pirton. *Adm £1.50 Chd free. Suns May 28; June 11, 25; (11-5)*

Woollas Hall, Eckington (Mr Clive Jennings) *On Bredon Hill, off B4080 Bredon to Pershore rd. From Eckington take the rd to the Combertons and Woollas Hall. Drive past farm over cattle grid, up drive marked private and park in field, before 2nd cattle grid, no cars past this point please.* The Jacobean Manor house (not open) is the setting for the 1-acre garden on several levels, created and maintained by owners, since 1984. Numerous walkways featuring separate enclosures with fine trees, shrubs, mixed and herbaceous borders. Fine views over Bredon Hill and surrounding countryside. *Adm £2 Chd 50p. Sun July 9 (2-6)*

Evening Opening (See also garden description)

Eastgrove Cottage Garden Nursery, Sankyns Green, Shrawley	July 29
Elm Grove and Neighbours, Astley Cross	June 25
Hanbury Hall, Hanbury	June 21
Holland House, Cropthorne	June 28

SPECIALIST PLANT FAIR

Spetchley Park Gardens
(2mls. E. Worcester on A422)
Sunday 16th. April
11.00am - 5.00pm.

Specialist nurseries offering interesting and unusual plants

☆ Garden Advice ☆ Garden Crafts ☆Refreshments
☆ **Plant Search:** ***looking for a particular plant? let us know, we will endeavour to find it for you.***

Entrance to Plant Fair and Gardens **£2.00**
For details telephone (01531) 650480 or (01452) 840151
http:\\www.redmarley.freeserve.co.uk

Macmillan Cancer Relief

Macmillan's nurses and doctors help to increase expertise in cancer treatment and care by sharing their knowledge and skills with other professionals across the country, a process which is aided by formal education programmes.

Macmillan nurses are specialists in cancer care, offering expert information and advice in pain and symptom management.

In recent research, Macmillan discovered that only a third of all cancer patients are offered any written information during the course of their treatment. The charity has addressed this by launching *The Cancer Guide*, a 40 page booklet which gives patients the information they need to play a full part in their treatment and care. *The Cancer Guide* is available free from the Macmillan Information Line on 0845 601 6161, a telephone information service for people with cancer and their families. *The Cancer Guide* is also being distributed via the health services in the UK.

Macmillan Cancer Relief Information Line: 0845 601 6161
Macmillan Cancer Relief Website: www.macmillan.org.uk

THE NATIONAL GARDENS SCHEME

A Millennium Midsummer Night Concert in the Gardens of Hanbury Hall

DROITWICH SPA, WORCESTERSHIRE
WEDNESDAY 21 JUNE 2000

THE WORCESTER MALE VOICE CHOIR
AND
THE HOLBORNE BRASS QUINTET

Proceeds in aid of Macmillan Cancer Relief and other charities supported by the National Gardens Scheme

Gates open 6.30 pm – concert begins 7.30 pm
Bring chairs and a picnic

Tickets £5 in advance
phone
01527 821214 or 01562 850238

By kind permission of The National Trust
and
Sponsored by Clement Keys, Chartered Accountants

Clement Keys
CHARTERED ACCOUNTANTS

Yorkshire

Hon County Organisers:
(N Yorks- Districts of Hambleton, Richmond, Ryedale, Sacarborough & Cleveland) Mrs Jane Baldwin, Riverside Farm, Sinnington, York YO62 6RY Tel/Fax 01751 431764
(West & South Yorks & North Yorks Districts of Craven, Harrogate, Selby & York) Mrs Roger Marshall, The Old Vicarage, Whixley, York YO26 8AR Tel/Fax 01423 330474 Fax 01423 331215
(E Yorks) Mrs Sally Bean, Saltmarshe Hall, Saltmarshe, Howden, Goole, Yorkshire DN14 7RX Tel 01430 430199 Fax 01430 431607

DATES OF OPENING

Regular openings

For details see garden description

- Ampleforth College Junior School, Gilling East
- Burton Agnes Hall, Driffield
- Castle Howard, nr York
- Constable Burton Hall Gardens, nr Leyburn
- Harewood House, nr Leeds
- Harlow Carr Botanical Gardens, Harrogate
- Land Farm, nr Hebden Bridge
- Newby Hall & Gardens, Ripon
- Norton Conyers, nr Ripon
- Parcevall Hall Gardens, Skyreholme
- Plants of Special Interest Nursery, Braithwell
- Shandy Hall, Coxwold
- York Gate, Leeds 16

By appointment only

For telephone numbers and other details see garden descriptions. Private visits welcomed

- Evergreens, Bilton
- Les Palmiers, Barnsley
- Maspin House, Hillam
- Tan Cottage, Cononley
- 8 Welton Old Road, Welton
- The White House, Husthwaite

March 26 Sunday
- Harlow Carr Botanical Gardens, Harrogate

April 5 Wednesday
- Acorn Cottage, Boston Spa

April 9 Sunday
- Acorn Cottage, Boston Spa

April 16 Sunday
- Bolton Percy Gardens
- Orchard House, Appleton Roebuck

April 23 Sunday
- Netherwood House, Ilkley

April 26 Wednesday
- Rye Hill, Helmsley

April 30 Sunday
- Deepdale, Boston Spa
- Hovingham Hall, Hovingham
- 54a Keldgate, Beverley
- Ling Beeches, Scarcroft
- Oxenber House, Austwick
- Shandy Hall, Coxwold

May 1 Monday
- The Chimney Place, Bilton Grange
- Old Sleningford, Mickley, nr Ripon

May 3 Wednesday
- Oxenber House, Austwick

May 7 Sunday
- Il Giardino, Bilton
- Saltmarshe Hall, Saltmarshe
- The Spaniels, Hensall
- The White Cottage, Halsham

May 10 Wednesday
- Joan Royd House, Cubley, Penistone

May 14 Sunday
- Blackbird Cottage, Scampston
- Hillbark, Bardsey
- Orchard House, Appleton Roebuck
- Stillingfleet Lodge, nr York

May 17 Wednesday
- Beacon Hill House, nr Ilkley
- Low Askew, Cropton

May 21 Sunday
- Jasmine House, Doncaster
- Sleightholme Dale Lodge, Fadmoor
- Tregonning, Ellerton
- Woodlands Cottage, Summerbridge

May 24 Wednesday
- Rye Hill, Helmsley

May 27 Saturday
- Nawton Tower Garden, Nawton
- Pennyholme, Fadmoor
- Rye Hill, Helmsley

May 28 Sunday
- Brookfield, Oxenhope
- East Wing, Thorp Arch Hall
- High Farm, Bilton
- Il Giardino, Bilton
- Loftus Hill, nr Knaresborough
- Londesborough Cross, Shiptonthorpe
- Nawton Tower Garden, Nawton
- Old Sleningford, Mickley, nr Ripon
- Shandy Hall, Coxwold
- 26 West End, Walkington

May 29 Monday
- The Chimney Place, Bilton Grange
- Nawton Tower Garden, Nawton
- Old Sleningford, Mickley, nr Ripon

May 31 Wednesday
- Brookfield, Oxenhope
- Hallgarth, Ottringham
- The Old Vicarage, Whixley

June 1 Thursday
- York Gate, Leeds 16

June 3 Saturday
- Pennyholme, Fadmoor

June 4 Sunday
- Creskeld Hall, Arthington
- Hallgarth, Ottringham
- Hunmanby Grange, Wold Newton
- Makin's Cottage, Southside, Patrington
- Park House, nr York
- 55 Rawcliffe Drive, York
- Secret Garden, York

June 5 Monday
- East Riddlesden Hall, Keighley

June 6 to 9 Tuesday to Friday
- Plants of Special Interest Nursery, Braithwell

June 10 Saturday
- Burton Agnes Hall, Driffield
- Plants of Special Interest Nursery, Braithwell

June 11 Sunday
- Burton Agnes Hall, Driffield
- The Cottage, Kellington
- Elvington Gardens, nr York
- Kelberdale, Knaresborough
- Norton Conyers, nr Ripon

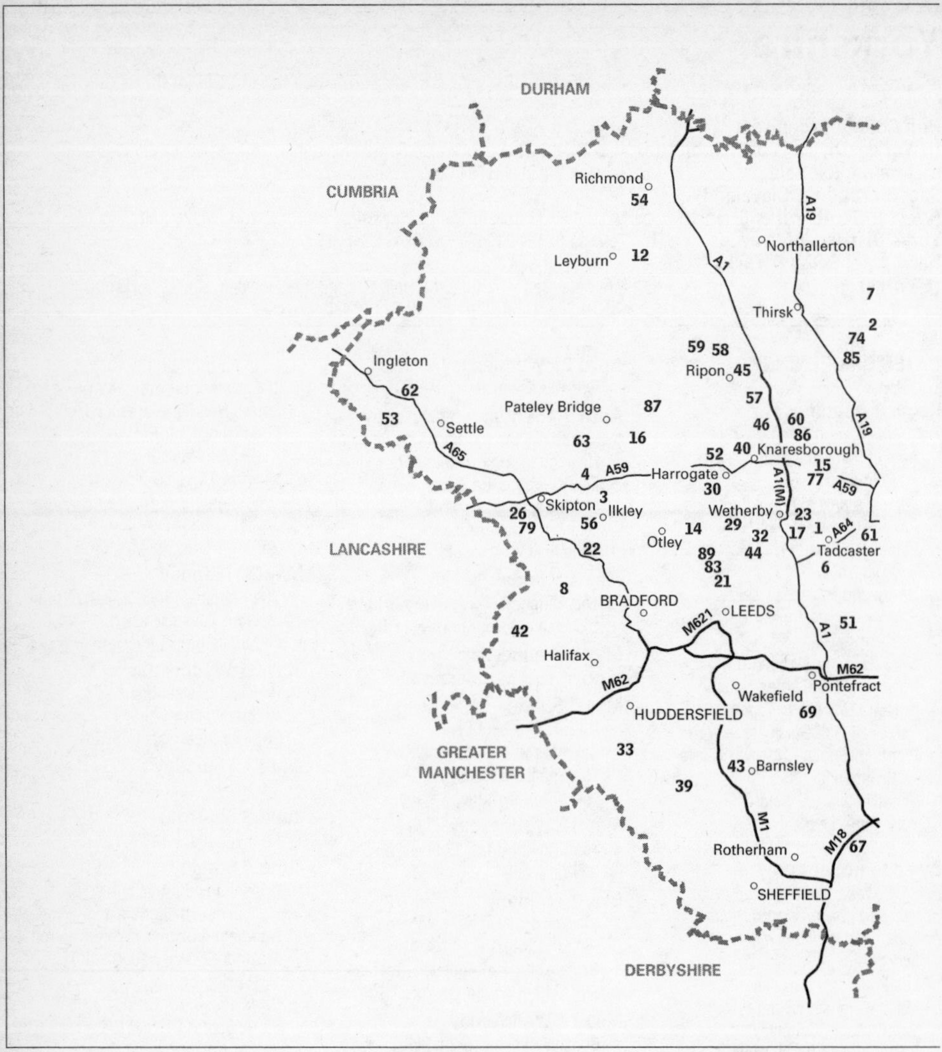

KEY

1 Acorn Cottage
2 Ampleforth College Junior School
3 Beacon Hill House
4 Beamsley Hall
5 Blackbird Cottage
6 Bolton Percy Gardens
7 Bridge Cottage
8 Brookfield
9 Burton Agnes Hall
10 Castle Howard
11 The Chimney Place
12 Constable Burton Hall Gardens
13 The Cottage
14 Creskeld Hall
15 Croft Cottage
16 Dacre Banks Gardens
17 Deepdale
18 Derwent House
19 2 Derwent Park
20 Dowthorpe Hall
21 8 Dunstarn Lane
22 East Riddlesden Hall
23 East Wing
24 Elvington Gardens
25 Evergreens
26 The Grange
27 Grimston Gardens
28 Hallgarth
29 Harewood House
30 Harlow Carr Botanical Gardens
31 High Farm
32 Hillbark
33 Holly Cottage
34 Hovingham Hall
35 Hunmanby Grange
36 Il Giardino
37 Jacksons Wold
38 Jasmine House
39 Joan Royd House
40 Kelberdale
41 54a Keldgate
42 Land Farm
43 Les Palmiers
44 Ling Beeches
45 Littlethorpe Gardens

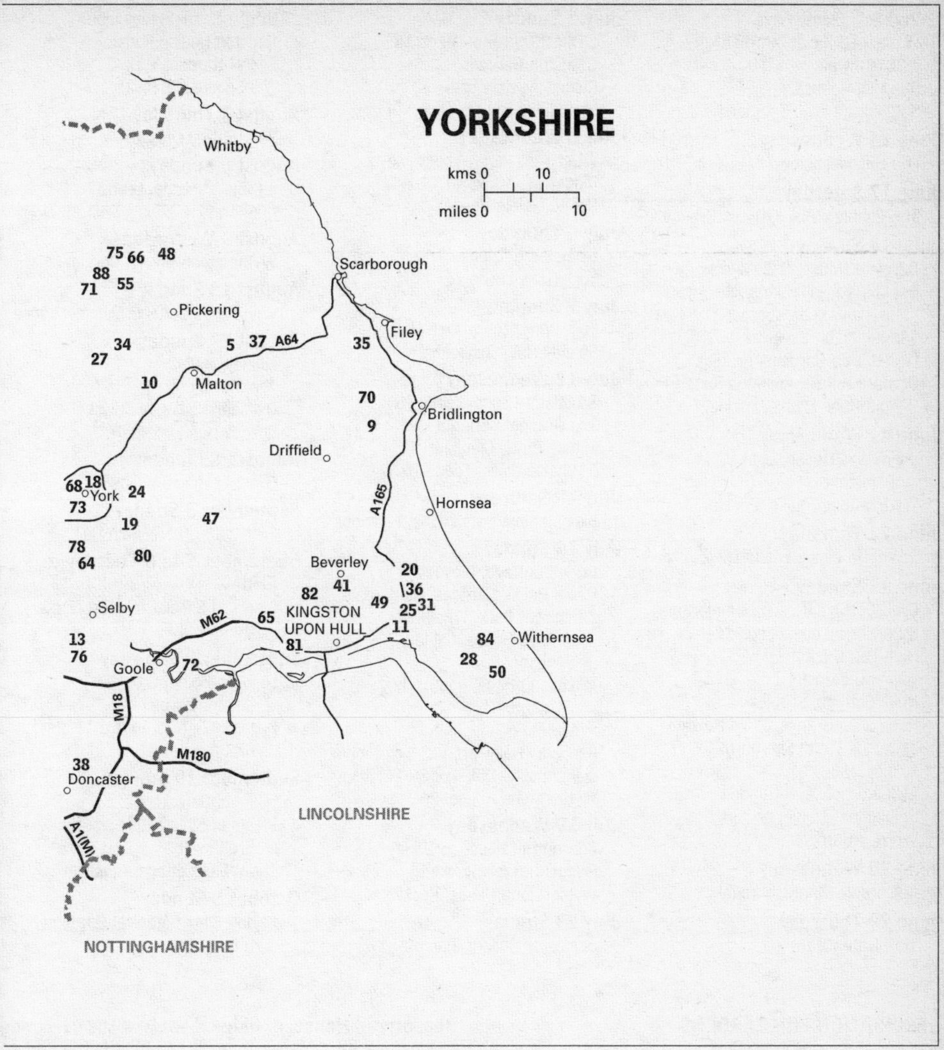

46 Loftus Hill
47 Londesborough Cross
48 Low Askew
49 Lullaby
50 Makin's Cottage
51 Maspin House
52 The Mews Cottage
53 Middle Birks
54 Millgate House
55 Nawton Tower Garden
56 Netherwood House
57 Newby Hall & Gardens
58 Norton Conyers
59 Old Sleningford
60 The Old Vicarage
61 Orchard House
62 Oxenber House
63 Parcevall Hall Gardens
64 Park House
65 Parkview
66 Pennyholme
67 Plants of Special Interest Nursery
68 55 Rawcliffe Drive
69 Ridgeway
70 Rudston House
71 Rye Hill
72 Saltmarshe Hall
73 Secret Garden
74 Shandy Hall
75 Sleightholme Dale Lodge
76 The Spaniels
77 Springfield House
78 Stillingfleet Lodge
79 Tan Cottage
80 Tregonning
81 8 Welton Old Road
82 26 West End
83 5 Wharfe Close
84 The White Cottage
85 The White House
86 Whixley Gardens
87 Woodlands Cottage
88 Wytherstone House
89 York Gate

Parkview, South Cave
Plants of Special Interest Nursery, Braithwell
Rye Hill, Helmsley
Saltmarshe Hall, Saltmarshe

June 14 Wednesday
Rye Hill, Helmsley

June 17 Saturday
The Chimney Place, Bilton Grange

June 18 Sunday
Derwent House, Osbaldwick
Dowthorpe Hall, Skirlaugh
Kelberdale, Knaresborough
54a Keldgate, Beverley
Littlethorpe Gardens, nr Ripon
Orchard House, Appleton Roebuck
Wytherstone House, Pockley

June 21 Wednesday
Joan Royd House, Cubley, Penistone
Wytherstone House, Pockley

June 22 Thursday
5 Wharfe Close, Leeds 16

June 25 Sunday
Croft Cottage, Green Hammerton
8 Dunstarn Lane, Leeds 16
High Farm, Bilton
Hillbark, Bardsey
Holly Cottage, Scholes
Hunmanby Grange, Wold Newton
Jacksons Wold, Sherburn
Lullaby, Hull
Millgate House, Richmond
Stillingfleet Lodge, nr York
Whixley Gardens

June 28 Wednesday
Kelberdale, Knaresborough

June 29 Thursday
York Gate, Leeds 16

July 2 Sunday
8 Dunstarn Lane, Leeds 16
Grimston Gardens
Ridgeway, Ackworth
Springfield House, Tockwith

July 5 Wednesday
2 Derwent Park, Wheldrake
Ridgeway, Ackworth
Rye Hill, Helmsley

July 6 Thursday
Grimston Gardens
York Gate, Leeds 16

July 9 Sunday
East Wing, Thorp Arch Hall
Shandy Hall, Coxwold

July 12 Wednesday
8 Dunstarn Lane, Leeds 16
The Grange, Carleton
Middle Birks, Clapham
5 Wharfe Close, Leeds 16

July 15 Saturday
Sleightholme Dale Lodge, Fadmoor

July 16 Sunday
Bridge Cottage, Rievaulx
Dacre Banks Gardens, Nidderdale
2 Derwent Park, Wheldrake
Joan Royd House, Cubley, Penistone
Makin's Cottage, Southside, Patrington
Middle Birks, Clapham
Parcevall Hall Gardens, Skyreholme
Sleightholme Dale Lodge, Fadmoor
Wytherstone House, Pockley

July 19 Wednesday
Beacon Hill House, nr Ilkley
Bridge Cottage, Rievaulx
Wytherstone House, Pockley

July 23 Sunday
Beamsley Hall, nr Skipton
Bridge Cottage, Rievaulx
Rudston House, Rudston
Secret Garden, York
The Spaniels, Hensall

August 3 Thursday
York Gate, Leeds 16

August 6 Sunday
8 Dunstarn Lane, Leeds 16
Wytherstone House, Pockley

August 9 Wednesday
Wytherstone House, Pockley

August 13 Sunday
Woodlands Cottage, Summerbridge

August 27 Sunday
Lullaby, Hull
The Mews Cottage, Harrogate
Oxenber House, Austwick
Shandy Hall, Coxwold

August 28 Monday
Oxenber House, Austwick

September 3 Sunday
East Wing, Thorp Arch Hall

September 5 to 8 Tuesday to Friday
Plants of Special Interest Nursery, Braithwell

September 9 Saturday
Londesborough Cross, Shiptonthorpe
Plants of Special Interest Nursery, Braithwell

September 10 Sunday
Hillbark, Bardsey
Plants of Special Interest Nursery, Braithwell
The White Cottage, Halsham

October 8 Sunday
Harlow Carr Botanical Gardens, Harrogate

DESCRIPTIONS OF GARDENS

Acorn Cottage, Boston Spa ✗ (Mr & Mrs C M Froggatt) *50 Church Street. A659 1m SE of Wetherby. Off A1 Church St opp Central Garage.* Small walled alpine garden of outstanding quality. Alpine plant collection established over 75yrs and two generations. Good range of small flowering bulbs and alpine flowers, March to May, attractively planted in local limestone formations. TEAS. *Adm £2 Chd 50p incl coffee/tea homemade biscuits and scones Wed, Sun April 5, 9 (11-4). Also by appt March to May, coaches or individuals very welcome,* **Tel 01937 842519**

Ampleforth College Junior School, Gilling East ✗ (Fr Abbot & Community) *The Castle, Gilling East, 18m N of York.* Medium-sized terraced garden with steep steps overlooking golf course. Unsuitable for handicapped or elderly. *Adm £1.50 Chd free. For NGS July & Aug daily dawn to dusk*

Beacon Hill House, nr Ilkley ✗❀ (Mr & Mrs D H Boyle) *Langbar 4m NW of Ilkley. 1¼m SE of A59 at Bolton Bridge.* Fairly large garden sheltered by woodland 900′ up, on the southern slope of Beamsley Beacon. Features of interest to garden historians survive from original Victorian garden. Early flowering rhododendrons, large shrub roses, mixed borders, unusual hardy and half-hardy shrubs and climbers, making use of south facing walls. Natural wildlife pond and greenhouse with established tender plants. TEAS. *Adm £2. Weds May 17 (2-6.30), July 19 (2-5)*

Beamsley Hall, nr Skipton ♿❀ (Marquess & Marchioness of Hartington) *Beamsley, Bolton Abbey. 5m E of Skipton.* 6-acre traditional English garden with new plantings; incl extensive herbaceous border and kitchen garden. Minor restrictions for wheelchairs. TEAS. Also at Bolton Abbey or at Devonshire Arms. *Adm £2 OAPs £1.50 Chd under 15 free. Sun July 23 (1.30-5)*

Blackbird Cottage, Scampston ♿❀ (Mrs Hazel Hoad) *5m from Malton off A64 to Scarborough through Rillington turn L signposted Scampston only. Follow signs.* ⅓ acre plantswoman's garden made from scratch since 1986. A great wealth of interesting plants, with shrub and herbaceous border. Alpines are a speciality. Please visit throughout the day to ease pressure on a small but inspirational garden. Unusual plants for sale. Morning coffee and TEAS in aid of Scampston Village Hall & Church. *Adm £2 Chd free. Sun May 14 (10-5). Private visits welcome, please* **Tel 01944 758256**

Bolton Percy Gardens ♿✂❀ *5m E of Tadcaster 10m SW of York. Follow Bolton Percy signs off A64.* Light lunches/TEAS in aid of Church. *Combined adm £3 Chd free. Sun April 16 (1-5)*

Betula (Roger Brook) Unusual plants, some alpines and the National Dicentra Collection

Bolton Percy Cemetery An acre of old village churchyard gardened by Roger Brook, in which garden plants are naturalised. Featured on TV. 1998 Cemetery of the year award winner

The White House (Mr & Mrs Nulty) *Marsh Lane.* Family garden lovingly created on a strict budget by enthusiastic plantswoman. Mixed borders of continuous interest, gravel in shade, water feature and small productive vegetable garden

Windy Ridge (Mr & Mrs J S Giles) *Marsh Lane.* Features a large collection of Barnhaven and Elizabethan primroses; Hose-in-Hose, Jack-in-the-Green etc. Also wild and unusual hardy plants, grown in a natural cottage garden style sloping down to the Ings, greatly influenced by Margery Fish. Featured on TV and in many Magazines/Journals

Bridge Cottage, Rievaulx ❀ (Mr & Mrs H Scott) *From Helmsley take the B1257 Stokesley rd then 1st turning on L to Scawton-Old Byland. Follow rd to car park on L before bridge. Early C17 cottage (not open) is over bridge on R.* 1 acre garden in picturesque setting nr Rievaulx Abbey bisected by wide clear stream crossed by 3 bridges, joining R Rye at miniature falls nr C18 stone bridge. On different levels with herbaceous borders, shrubs, trees, hostas, roses and bog garden. TEA/Coffee and biscuits 50p. Plants on sale from local nursery. *Adm £2 Chd free Suns July 16, 23 (10.30-5.30), Wed July 19 (2-5.30)*

Brookfield, Oxenhope ✂❀ (Dr & Mrs R L Belsey) *5m SW of Keighley, take A629 towards Halifax. Fork R onto A6033 towards Haworth. Follow signs to Oxenhope. Turn L at Xrds in village. 200yds after PO fork R, Jew Lane.* 1 acre, intimate garden, incl large pond with island and mallards. Many varieties of candelabra primulas and florindaes, azaleas, rhododendrons. Unusual trees and shrubs, screes, greenhouse and conservatory. TEA 50p. *Adm £2 Chd free. Sun, Wed May 28, 31 (1.30-6). Also by appt, please* **Tel 01535 643070**

● **Burton Agnes Hall, Driffield** ♿❀ (Mrs S Cunliffe-Lister) *Burton Agnes is on A614 between Driffield & Bridlington.* 8 acres. Lawns with clipped yew and fountains; woodland gardens and walled garden containing a potager; herbaceous and mixed borders; maze with thyme garden; jungle garden; campanula collection garden and coloured gardens containing giant games boards. Collections of hardy geraniums, clematis, penstemons and many unusual perennials. 'Gardeners Fair'. *Adm £2.75 Chd £1. Sat, Sun June 10, 11. Specialist nurseries, gardening advice, dried flower & herb craft. TEAS. Adm £2.25 Chd £1. April 1 to Oct 31 (11-5)*

● **Castle Howard, nr York** ♿❀ (Castle Howard Estate Ltd) *15m NE of York off the A64. 6m W of Malton.* Partially suitable for wheelchairs. Formal grounds laid out from C18 to present, incl fountains, lakes, cascades and waterfalls. The woodland garden, Ray Wood, has collection of rhododendron species and hybrids amounting to 800 varieties. A notable collection of acers, nothofagus, arbutus, styrax, magnolia and conifers. Two formal rose gardens incl old, china and bourbon roses, hybrid teas and floribunda. Plant centre by the car park. *Adm Grounds and Gardens £4.50 Chd £2.50. Every day March 17 to late Oct (10-4.30)*

The Chimney Place, Bilton Grange ✂❀ (Mrs Paddy Forsberg) *23 Parthian Road, E Hull. Take Holderness Rd, R into Marfleet Lane, R at roundabout into Staveley Rd, L into Griffin Rd. Parthian Rd 1st on R.* A small, secluded, hedge enclosed, 30-yr-old garden, designed and maintained by owner, for the welfare of birds, fish, frogs and butterflies. Chimneys with alpines and rockery plants and crockpot gardens. Allium avenue, summerhouse, rockery pool cascade and new bridge over pool. *Adm £1 Acc chd free. Mons May 1, 29, Sat June 17 (1.30-4.30). Private visits welcome, please* **Tel 01482 783804**

● **Constable Burton Hall Gardens, nr Leyburn** ♿ (Charles Wyvill Esq) *3m E of Leyburn on A684, 6m W of A1.* Large romantic garden with terraced woodland walks. Garden trails, shrubs, roses and water garden. Display of daffodils and over 5000 tulips planted annually amongst extensive borders. Fine John Carr house (not open) set in splendour of Wensleydale countryside. *Adm £2.50 OAPs £2 Chd 50p. March 25 to Oct 15 daily (9-6). Guided tours of gardens by appt, please* **Tel 01677 460225**

NEW **The Cottage, Kellington** ♿✂❀ (Barbara & Richard Ferrari) *Turn W off A19 6m S of Selby or J34 off M62 to Kellington village. Please park on Main St not in Wells Lane.* Relaxed family garden, ⅓ acre owing more to evolution than design. Wonderful plants of interest, many grown from seed by plantaholic owner, filling borders, pots and greenhouse. An excellent well-maintained vegetable garden and compost heap. TEA. *Adm £1.50 Acc chd free (ACNO to National Association for Colitus & Crohn's Disease). Sun June 11 (12-5)*

Creskeld Hall, Arthington ♿✂❀ (J & C Stoddart-Scott) *5m E of Otley on A659.* 3-4 acre Wharfedale garden with woodland plantings. Rhododendrons, azaleas, attractive water garden with canals, walled kitchen garden and flower garden. TEA. Plant & other stalls. *Adm £2 Chd free. Sun June 4 (1-5)*

Croft Cottage, Green Hammerton ♿✂ (Alistair & Angela Taylor) *Between York and Harrogate. 3m E off A1 adjacent to A59. Opp village green next to Social Club.* Secluded ½ acre cottage garden developing into a number of 'garden rooms'. Conservatory, clipped yew, old brick, cobbles and pavers used for formal areas leading to developing water feature, mixed border and orchard with wild flowers. TEAS. *Adm £1 Chd free (Combined adm with* **Whixley Gardens** *£3). Sun June 25 (12.30-5)*

NEW **Dacre Banks Gardens, Nidderdale** *4m SE of Pateley Bridge. 10m NW of Harrogate on B6451. Limited wheelchair access.* Lovely walk between gardens along Nidderdale valley or parking at each garden. Picnic area at Yorke House. TEAS. *Combined adm £3 Chd free. Sun July 16 (12- 5)*

Low Hall, Dacre (Mrs P A Holliday) Romantic walled garden on different levels around C17 family home (not open) with shrubs, climbing roses, tender plants, herbaceous borders and pond garden. Mature yews and beech hedges.

NEW **Orchard House** (Mr & Mrs J T Spain) 2-acre informal country garden with colourful mixed plantings for yr-round interest incl old orchard, vegetables and well developed wildlife pond.

NEW **Stud Cottage** (Mr & Mrs J M Kent) ½ acre planted to compliment C18 cottage (not open). Herbaceous, rockery, kitchen garden and orchard with small fish pond. *Private visits welcome by appt, please* **Tel 01423 780495**

NEW **Yorke House** (Mr Anthony & Mrs Pat Hutchinson) Flower arranger's large garden with colour-themed borders full of foliage plants and shrubs. Extensive water feature incl ornamental pond and stream. Nut walk, rose pergola, patio and children's log cabin.

Deepdale, Boston Spa (Mr & Mrs F Umpleby) *1m SE of Wetherby off A1. Take A659 turn L after ½m Deepdale Lane.* Owner made and maintained ¾ acre garden. 2 ponds, one with bridge, the other with purpose-made stream. Patio, pergola and gazebo. A restful garden in country surroundings. TEAS. *Adm £2 Chd free. Sun April 30 (11-4). Private visits and groups welcome, please* **Tel 01937 842227**

Derwent House, Osbaldwick (Dr & Mrs D G Lethem) *On village green at Osbaldwick. 2m E of York city centre off A1079.* ¾ acre attractive village garden extended in 1984 to provide a new walled garden with yew hedges and box parterres. Conservatories, terraces, rose garden and double herbaceous borders leading to meadow with plantings of eucalyptus. TEAS. *Adm £2 Chd free. Sun June 18 (1.30-5)*

NEW **2 Derwent Park, Wheldrake** (Jill & Peter Tait) *Turn off A19 at Crockley Hill (8m S of York. 10m N of Selby) into village. Derwent Park is last turning L off Church Lane (Thorganby Rd).* Mature garden created over 11 yrs by enthusiastic plant collecting owners (70 clematis). Mixed shrub and herbaceous borders, new hosta and fern border. Patio, raised beds, pots and tubs, pond with rockery, water feature and small gravel garden. TEA. *Adm £1.50 Chd free. Wed, Sun July 5, 16 (1-5). Also by appt, please* **Tel 01904 448884**

Dowthorpe Hall, Skirlaugh (Mr & Mrs J Holtby) *On the A165 Hull to Bridlington Rd ½ way between Coniston and Skirlaugh on the RH side travelling N. Signed at the bottom of drive which has white railings.* 4 acres with traditional kitchen garden, recently planted orchard, small gravel garden and main lawn area. Surrounded by shrubs and beautiful mature trees. Herbaceous borders and pond with an island. TEAS. *Adm £2 Chd free. Sun June 18 (11-4)*

8 Dunstarn Lane, Leeds 16 (Mr & Mrs R Wainwright) *Adel. From Leeds ring rd A6120 exit Adel, up Long Causeway. 4th junction R into Dunstarn Lane. 28 bus from Leeds centre stops near gate.* 2 acres of long herbaceous and rose borders of exceptional variety. 60 varieties of delphiniums and wide range of August blooming plants giving a magnificent display of summer colour. Large lawns for picnics. *Adm £2 Chd free. Suns June 25, July 2, Aug 6 (2-7), Wed July 12 (2.30-7.30)*

NEW **East Riddlesden Hall, Keighley** (National Trust) *1m NE of Keighley on B6265 between Keighley & Bingley.* The part ruined façade makes dramatic backdrop for charming enclosed garden designed by Graham Stewart Thomas with mixed perennial borders, box, roses, climbers and trained fruit trees. Over 30 herbs and large lavender hedge. New informal garden for 2000 with Yorkshire varieties of apples, honeysuckles and wild flowers to create a changing carpet of colour. TEAS. Plant stalls. *Adm £1.50 Chd free. Mon June 5 (3-7).* **Tel 01535 607075**

East Wing, Thorp Arch Hall (Fiona & Chris Royffe) *Thorp Arch 1m S of Wetherby. Take A659 into Boston Spa centre. Turn L to Thorp Arch, Thorp Arch Hall at end of main st.* ¾ acre surrounding the East Wing of an C18 John Carr house (not open), being imaginatively developed. An inspiring garden arranged to link spaces and emphasize views. Newly designed courtyards, water features, potager, earth sculpture and dry garden. Dramatic combinations of plants, unusual bamboos and climbers. Photographic exhibition and small nursery. TEAS. *Adm £2 Chd 50p. Suns May 28, July 9, Sept 3 (11-5)* **Tel 01937 843513**

Elvington Gardens, nr York *8m SE of York. From A1079, immed after leaving York's outer ring rd, turn S onto B1228 for Elvington.* Light lunches and Teas in Village Hall in aid of village hall. *Combined adm £3 Chd free. Sun June 11 (11-5)*

Brook House (Mr & Mrs C Bundy) Old established garden with fine trees. Herb garden with rustic summer house. Kitchen garden and pond garden

Elvington Hall (Mr & Mrs Pontefract) 3 acres with terrace overlooking lawns, fine trees and views. Sanctuary with fish pond

Eversfield (Helga Hopkinson) Wide variety of unusual perennials, grasses and ferns, divided by curved lawns and gravel beds. Small nursery. *Private visits welcome by appt,* **Tel 01904 608332**

Red House Farm (Prof & Mrs E Macphail) New garden created from a field 16 years ago. Fine collection of hardy perennials, shrubs and roses. Courtyard with interesting plantings and ½ acre young wood

Evergreens, Bilton (Phil & Brenda Brock) *119 Main Rd. 5m E of Hull. Leave city by A165. Exit B1238. Bungalow ¼m on L nearly opp Asda.* 1 acre with mosaics and sundials, tower, raised beds, rockeries and landscaped pond. Japanese garden, summer-house, conifer, heather and mixed beds. Collection of dwarf conifers. Photographs showing development of garden. Conifer/plant nursery open. *Adm £1 Acc chd free. Private visits and parties welcome by appt. Buffet or light refreshments may be booked mid May to mid Aug* **Tel 01482 811365**

NEW **The Grange, Carleton** (Mr & Mrs R N Wooler) *1½m SW of Skipton. Turn off A56 (Skipton-Clitheroe) into Carleton. Keep L at Swan Inn, continue through to end of village and turn R into Carla Beck Lane. From Skipton town centre follow A6131. Turn R to Carleton.* Large walled mid C19 garden with original ha ha and many mature, unusual tree specimens from different continents and developing woodland garden. Lovely sweeping herbaceous border, shrubs, ornamental pools, raised vegetable beds and greenhouse in full use, reached by a long rose and clematis walk. TEAS. *Adm £2 Acc chd free. Wed July 12 (1.30-5)*

Grimston Gardens *The hamlet of Grimston is 1m S of Gilling East, 7m S of Helmsley, 17m N of York, on B1363. Follow sign 1m S of Gilling East.* TEA and scones. *Adm £2 Chd free. Sun, Thurs July 2, 6 (1.30-5.30)*

Bankside House (Clive & Jean Sheridan) ½ acre framework of mature trees and shrubs. Different areas and planting schemes reflect different moods and styles. New ideas being tried in an attempt to add interest and improve the garden each yr. Semi-formal beds, Japanese area, "hot" bed and box parterre.

Grimston Manor Farm (Richard & Heather Kelsey) 3/4 acre garden, mostly 30 yrs old. An intricate design, profusely planted with a wide collection of herbaceous plants, trees and shrubs, incorporating fine country views and old farm buildings. A well-seated garden.

Hallgarth, Ottringham (Mr & Mrs John Hinchliffe) *Turn N in Ottringham on A1033 Hull to Withernsea rd, signed Halsham. ¾m 1st L over former railway crossing.* All-yr 1-acre informal country garden developed and maintained by owners from an initial design for part by John Brookes. Many unusual trees, shrubs and plants in rich plantings. New pond garden, flowering cherries, azaleas, dwarf rhododendrons, bush roses and flower borders. Stalls and Tea by Ottringham Church. *Adm £2 Chd free. Wed May 31, Sun June 4 (1-5). Groups visits by appt, please* **Tel 01964 622230**

● **Harewood House, nr Leeds** (Harewood House Trust) *9m N of Leeds on A61.* 80 acres of gardens within 1000 acres of Lancelot 'Capability' Brown landscaped parkland. Formal terraces restored to original Sir Charles Barry design, box edging surrounding a Victorian formal garden, enhanced by Italianate fountains and statues, charming informal walks through woodland gardens around lake to cascade and picturesque dell with an array of exotic plants, incl rhododendrons. TEAS, Cafeteria. *Adm gardens, grounds, Bird Garden and Terrace Gallery Adults £6 OAPs £5 Chd £3.50. Open daily March 1 to Oct 29 (10-6). Weekends Nov to Dec. House open from April 1. For NGS private groups by appt, please* **Tel Trevor Nicholson 0113 288 6331**

■ **Harlow Carr Botanical Gardens, Harrogate** (Northern Horticultural Society) *On B6162 (Harrogate - Otley) 1m W of town centre.* 68 acres developed to provide a showcase for northern gardeners. In 2000 the Gardens celebrate their 50th anniversary. Landscaped to incl heather, bulb, rock, scented and foliage gardens. Herbaceous borders, vegetable, fruit and flower trials and alpine houses. Extensive woodland and streamside plantings, winter garden and wildflower meadow. Five national collections. Museum. Model Village. Restaurant. Plant and Gift Shop. *Adm £4 OAPs £2 Chd under 16 free. Open all year. For NGS Suns March 26, Oct 8 (9.30-dusk)*

High Farm, Bilton (Mr & Mrs G R Cooper) *5m E of Hull City Centre, take A165 Brid Rd, turn onto B1238 to Bilton. Turn L opp Church. High Farm is at the bottom of Limetree Lane. Parking available.* A large enchanting garden with distinctive design features, displaying an extensive range of plants. Mature trees festooned with cascades of rose and clematis. Many contrasting seasonal sections unfolding with an intricate tapestry of colours, shapes and textures, provided by an outstanding collection of shrubs, ornamental grasses, succulents and rare herbaceous plants. TEAS. *Adm £2 Chd free (ACNO to RBL). Suns May 28, June 25 (1-5)*

Hillbark, Bardsey (T P Gittins & Malcolm Simm) *4m SW of Wetherby, turn W off A58 into Church Lane. The garden is on L before Church. Car parking at village hall (Woodacre Lane).* 1-acre country garden started in 1987. Past winner Sunday Express 'Large Garden of the Year'. Shrubs, perennials, and some annuals provide yr-round colour. Lively plantings across terraces, descending to ponds and stream with ducks and marginal plants. Some unusual garden ceramics. TEAS. *Adm £1.50 Chd 50p (ACNO to Cookridge Hospital Cancer Research). Suns May 14, June 25, Sept 10 (11-5). Private visits welcome by appt May to July, please* **Tel 01937 572065**

Holly Cottage, Scholes (Mr & Mrs J Dixon) *Leas Gardens, 8m S of Huddersfield on A616. Turn W at signpost to Scholes.* ½ acre sloping garden full of interest. Created from a field in 1988 now maturing into a haven for wildlife. Raised alpine bed and paved area with troughs. Pond with small bog garden. Rockery and herbaceous borders with good selection of plants. TEAS. *Adm £2 Chd free. Sun June 25 (2-6). Private visits welcome Feb to end Oct, please* **Tel 01484 684083/662614**

Hovingham Hall, Hovingham (Sir Marcus & Lady Worsley) *8m W of Malton. In Hovingham village, 20m N of York; on B1257 midway between Malton and Helmsley.* Medium-sized garden. Yew hedges, shrubs and herbaceous borders. C18 dovecote and riding school; cricket ground. TEAS in aid of Hovingham Church. *Adm £2.50 Chd free. Sun April 30 (2-5). Enquiries* **Tel 01653 628206**

Hunmanby Grange, Wold Newton (Mr & Mrs T Mellor) *Hunmanby Grange is a farm 12½m SE of Scarborough, between Wold Newton and Hunmanby on the rd from Burton Fleming to Fordon.* The garden has been created from exposed open field, on top of the Yorkshire Wolds near the coast. Foliage colour, shape and texture have been most important in forming mixed borders, a gravel garden, pond garden, orchard and laburnum tunnel. TEAS in aid of St

Cuthbert's Church, Burton Fleming. *Adm £2 Chd free. Suns June 4, 25 (11-5). Private visits welcome,* **Tel 01723 891636**

Il Giardino, Bilton ♿✂❀ (Peter & Marian Fowler) *63 Limetree Lane. 5m E of Hull City Centre. Take A165 Hull to Bridlington Rd. B1238 to Bilton Village. Turn L opp St Peter's Church.* Approx ⅓ acre redesigned since 1987 by present owners. Mixed borders and island beds of unusual plants, shrubs and trees. Beech hedge, herb garden and fruit trees entwined with clematis. Cedarwood greenhouse containing named pelargoniums, potted citrus, fig tree and other less common plants. Unusual plants for sale. TEAS. *Adm £1 Chd free. Suns May 7, 28 (12-5)*

Jacksons Wold, Sherburn ❀ (Mr & Mrs Cundall) *Malton 11m, Scarborough 10m. A64 in Sherburn. T-lights take Weatherthorpe Rd. R fork to Hesterton Wold.* 1½ acres on the Yorkshire Wolds with views over the Vale of Pickering. A walled garden with mixed borders and old shrub roses. Further shrub borders lead to an interesting ornamental vegetable garden and a wild flower meadow. TEAS. *Adm £2 Chd free. Sun June 25 (12-6)*

Jasmine House, Doncaster ✂❀ (Mr & Mrs R J Breame) *145 The Grove, Wheatley Hills. Off A18 1m E of Doncaster Royal Infirmary. Turn R into Chestnut Ave (Motor Save on corner).* A small plantsman's garden with a wealth of unusual plants, many grown by owner from seed. Garden rooms with water features, climbers, shrubs, alpine troughs and bonsai. Pots and baskets full of half hardy and tender plants, all within a typically narrow town garden. Featured on Gardeners' World, Radio 4 & finalist in Doncaster in Bloom. Some patience may be necessary due to the dense planting and narrow paths! TEA. *Adm £1.50 Chd 50p (ACNO to Talking Books for the Blind). Sun May 21 (11-5)*

Joan Royd House, Cubley, Penistone ✂❀ (Mrs M Griffiths & Dr A Owen Griffiths) *From A 628 (M1 J36A) into Penistone. At lights follow 'Town Centre' then 'Stocksbridge'. From A616 (M1J36A) to Midhopestones, follow 'Penistone'. At restriction/derestriction sign turn down Joan Royd Lane. House 3/4m on L.* 1½ acre plantsman's garden. Formal to wild and wooded incl old, single and species roses, topiary, borders and ferns. Greenhouses, garden room and small pinetum. Dell and stream. Seats and gazebos abound. TEA. *Adm £2.50 Chd under 12 £1. Weds May 10, June 21 (2-4.30), Sun July 16 (2-5)*

Kelberdale, Knaresborough ✂❀ (Stan & Chris Abbott) *1m from Knaresborough on B6164 Wetherby rd. House on L immed after new ring rd (A658) roundabout.* Owner-made and maintained, inspirational medium-sized plantsman's garden with river views. Full of yr-round interest with large herbaceous border, conifer and colour beds. Alpines and pond. Vegetable and wild gardens. Past winner of RHS and Daily Mail National Garden Competition. TEA. *Adm £2 Chd free. Suns June 11, 18 (11-5), Wed June 28 (1-8). Group visits welcome, please* **Tel 01423 862140**

54a Keldgate, Beverley ♿✂❀ (Lenore & Peter Greensides) *Half-way between the double mini roundabout at SW entrance to Beverley on the B1230 and Beverley Minster. No private parking.* ½ acre 'secret' garden. Created and maintained by present owners over 20yrs. Clematis in variety, herbaceous plantings and shrubs. An inner garden of old roses, underplanted with paeonies and geraniums. Kitchen garden, fruit trees, irises and spring bulbs in season. Plant Stall. TEAS June 18 only in aid of Shelter. *Adm £1.50 Chd free. Suns April 30, June 18 (2-5). Group visits welcome, please* **Tel 01482 866708**

● **Land Farm, nr Hebden Bridge** ✂❀ (J Williams Esq) *Colden. From Halifax at Hebden Bridge go through 2 sets T-lights. Take turning circle to Heptonstall. Follow signs to Colden. After 2¾m turn R at 'no thru' road, follow signs to garden.* 4 acres incl alpine, herbaceous, formal and newly developing woodland garden. Elevation 1000ft N-facing. Has featured on 'Gardeners' World'. C17 house (not open). Art Gallery. *Adm £2.50 Chd free. May to end Aug. Open weekends and Bank Hols (10-5). By appt parties welcome evenings during week. Adm £3.50 incl refreshments, please* **Tel 01422 842260**

Les Palmiers, Barnsley ✂❀ (Richard Darlow) *106 Vaughan Road. From M1 junction 37 take A628 towards Barnsley. Turn L at major Xrds to hospital. Turn L at hospital Xrds into Gawber Rd. After ½m turn L into Vernon Way. 1st cul-de-sac on R.* Rear Mediterranean garden permanently planted with tender and exotic palms, cordylines, yuccas, cacti, eucalyptus. Exotic plants in pots. Featured in BBC Gardeners World and journals. TEA. *Adm £2 OAPs Child £1.50. Open by appt only, weekends all yr, also evenings mid summer please* **Tel 01226 291474** Not suitable for young children due to many spiky plants!

Ling Beeches, Scarcroft ♿✂❀ (Mrs Arnold Rakusen) *Ling Lane, 7m NE of Leeds. A58 mid-way between Leeds and Wetherby. At Scarcroft turn W into Ling Lane, signed to Wike on brow of hill. Garden ⅓m on R.* 2-acre enchanting woodland garden designed by owner. Emphasis on labour-saving planting. Unusual trees and shrubs, ericaceous plants, some species roses, conifers, ferns and interesting climbers. Featured in The English Woman's Garden, other publications and TV. TEAS. *Adm £2.50 Chd free. Sun April 30 (2-5). Private visits welcome by appt, please* **Tel 01132 892450**

Littlethorpe Gardens, nr Ripon ♿✂❀ *1½m SE of Ripon off A61 Ripon bypass. ½m S of B6265 Junction.* Littlethorpe Potteries also open. Teas at Littlethorpe Village Hall (nr Church). *Combined adm £3 Chd free. Sun June 18 (1.30-5.30)*

Deanswood (Mrs J Barber) 1½ acres planted during the last 11 yrs. Herbaceous borders, shrubs, streamside garden and 3 ponds with many unusual bog and marginal plants. Adjacent nursery open. *Private visits also welcome, please* **Tel 01765 603441**

Field Cottage (Mr & Mrs Richard Tite) A maturing 1-acre plantsman's garden with walled garden and small pond, raised sleeper beds, gravel garden and interesting perennials incl new late flowering autumn bed. Vegetable plot, Victorian style greenhouse and extensive range of unusual plants in containers

NEW **Greencroft** (Mr & Mrs David Walden) *Park at Littlethorpe Pottery.* ½ acre informal garden made and built by the owners. Special ornamental features incl a gazebo, temple, pavilion, stone wall with mullions and formal pool

Littlethorpe House (Mr & Mrs James Hare) 2 acres with many beautiful varieties of old-fashioned roses. Extensive established mixed herbaceous and shrub borders

Loftus Hill, nr Knaresborough ✿❀ (C Richard Jackson Esq) *Ferrensby. 3m N of Knaresborough on A6055. Ample parking behind the house.* A walled flower garden with mixed borders, clipped box, pergola and ornamental pond leading to extensive woodlands incl spectacular water garden designed by Douglas Knight and walk through 7 acre bluebell wood, all set within 43 acres of rolling parkland. TEAS. *Adm £2 Chd free. Sun May 28 (1.30-5)*

Londesborough Cross, Shiptonthorpe ✿❀ (Mr & Mrs J W Medd) *A1079 Hull to York rd 2m from Market Weighton. 5m from Pocklington. Turn off in Shiptonthorpe down the side of church. Londesborough Cross is at bottom of Town St.* In 14 yrs a railway goods yard has been transformed by the owners into a delightful garden with ponds and other water features, bog area, island beds, large herbaceous borders, screes and rock garden. A pergola and arches planted with roses and clematis and a collection of hostas and hardy ferns. Featured in Garden News, Daily Mail Weekend magazine and BBC Garden Stories. TEAS in aid of British Diabetic Association. *Adm £2 Acc chd free. Sun May 28, Sat Sept 9 (1-5)*

Low Askew, Cropton ✿❀ (Mr & Mrs Martin Dawson-Brown) *5m NW of Pickering between the villages of Cropton and Lastingham.* Situated in the beautiful valley of the R Seven this sloping garden with moated stream merges gently into the landscape beyond. Thoughtful planting has produced impact throughout the year. Old-fashioned pelargoniums will be amongst other plants for sale. TEAS. *Adm £2 Chd free. Wed May 17 (1-6)*

Lullaby, Hull ✿❀ (Michael Whitton) *From the A165 (Holderness Rd), take Salthouse Rd towards Sutton Village. Turn R into Dunvegan Rd, R into Barra Close and R again.* As featured in video 'East Yorkshire Gardens'. A peaceful retreat with planting to attract wildlife. Architectural features incl obelisks, a summerhouse, courtyard garden, water and pergolas. Colourful herbaceous borders, shrubs and unusual plants. Cream TEAS in conservatory. *Adm £1 Acc chd free. Suns June 25, Aug 27 (2-5). Private visits welcome, please* **Tel 01482 783517**

Makin's Cottage, Southside, Patrington ✿❀ (Roy & Elaine O'Brien) *In village of Patrington 15m E of Hull. Coming E on A1033 take 1st R in Patrington (signed Patrington Haven Caravan Park). After 300yds L at T-junction, white cottage 1st on R. Ample parking signed nearby.* ⅓ acre S-facing informal garden hidden behind pretty C18 cottage (not open) with open views to the Humber Estuary, developed over last 4yrs. Interestingly planted paved/gravelled area and wide variety of plants in herbaceous borders. Sunken herb garden surrounded by densely-planted perennials, small pond and vegetable garden. TEAS. *Adm £1.50 Acc chd free. Suns June 4, July 16 (1.30-5)*

Maspin House, Hillam ♿✿❀ (Howard & Susan Ferguson) *Hillam Common Lane. 4m E of A1 on A63. Turn R in Monk Fryston after Thrust Garage. L at T junction. House 1m on R.* 1½ acres started in 1985. Created and maintained by enthusiastic plant collector and handy husband for yr-round interest. New rock garden, ponds, gravel area, 'colourful' garden and orchard planted with old roses and grasses. *Adm £2 Chd free. Visitors welcome by appt please,*
Tel 01977 684922 Email.ferguson@btinternet.com www.btinternet.com/~Maspin.House/

The Mews Cottage, Harrogate ✿❀ (Mrs Pat Clarke) *1 Brunswick Drive. W of town centre. From Cornwall Rd, N side of Valley Gardens, 1st R (Clarence Dr), 1st L (York Rd), first L (Brunswick Dr).* A small garden on a sloping site of particular interest to hardy planters. Full of unusual and familiar plants but retaining a feeling of restfulness. A courtyard with trompe l'oeil and a gravelled area enclosed by trellising, provide sites for part of a large collection of clematis. Winner Daily Mail/RHS National Garden Competition 96. TEAS. *Adm £2 Chd 50p. Sun Aug 27 (2-5.30). Private visits for groups, societies and parties welcome, please*
Tel 01423 566292

Middle Birks, Clapham ✿❀ (The Sanderson Family) *At Clapham turn S off A65 to Keasden. Pass Clapham Station, take R fork, continue for approx 2m.* Large dairy farm at 625' with wonderful panoramic views of three peaks from the drive. A 1-acre family garden developing with imagination and enthusiasm, sheltered by buildings and new plantings. Colour themed herbaceous borders, mixed beds with shrubs and old roses. Garden structures, gravelled area and small water features. TEAS by Clapham WI. *Adm £2 Chd free. Wed, Sun July 12, 16 (2-5)*

Millgate House, Richmond ✿❀ (Austin Lynch & Tim Culkin) *Market Place. House is located at bottom of Market Place opp Barclays Bank.* SE walled town garden overlooking the R Swale. Although small the garden is full of character, enchantingly secluded with plants and shrubs. Foliage plants incl ferns and hostas. Old roses, interesting selection of clematis, small trees and shrubs. RHS/Daily Mail garden competition, 1st prize. BBC Homes and Antiques, Home from Home, Weekend Telegraph and BBC out and about. Full of ideas for small gardens. *Adm £2 Chd 50p. Sun Jun 25 (8am-8pm). Parties welcome and private visits, please* **Tel 01748 823571**

Nawton Tower Garden, Nawton ♿❀ (Douglas Ward Trust) *5m NE of Helmsley. From A170, between Helmsley and Nawton village, at Beadlam turn N 2½m to Nawton Tower.* Large garden; heathers, rhododendrons, azaleas, shrubs. Tea Helmsley and Kirkbymoorside. *Adm £1.50 Chd 50p. Sat, Sun, Mon May 27, 28, 29 (2-6); private visits welcome, please*
Tel 01439 771218

Netherthorpe House See Nottinghamshire

Netherwood House, Ilkley ♿❀ (Mr & Mrs Peter Marshall) *½m W of Ilkley on A65 towards Skipton; drive on L, car parking adjacent to house.* Large natural garden with magnificent trees. Daffodils, spring flowering shrubs, duck pond, rockery, and woodland stream. Lovely views up Wharfedale. TEAS. *Adm £2 Chd free. Easter Sun April 23 (2-5.30)*

● **Newby Hall & Gardens, Ripon** ♿✂❀ (R C Compton Esq) 40-acres extensive gardens laid out in 1920s. Full of rare and beautiful plants. Winner of HHA/Christie's Garden of the Year Award 1987. Formal seasonal gardens, stunning double herbaceous borders to R. Ure and National Collection holder Genus Cornus. Miniature railway and adventure gardens for children. Lunches & TEAS in licensed Garden Restaurant. Newby shop and plant stall. *Adm Gardens only £4.70, OAPs £4, Disabled/Chd £3.20. April 1 to end Sept daily ex Mons (Open Bank Hols) (Gardens 11-5.30, House 12-5). Group bookings and further details from Administrator* **Tel 01423 322583**

▲ **Norton Conyers, nr Ripon** ♿❀ (Sir James & Lady Graham) *4m NW of Ripon. Take Melmerby and Wath sign off A61 Ripon-Thirsk.* Large C18 walled garden of interest to garden historians. Interesting borders, yew hedges and orangery. Some hardy plants for sale. House which was visited by Charlotte Brontë, and is an original of 'Thornfield Hall' in 'Jane Eyre', is also open. TEAS. *Adm £2 Chd free. For NGS Sun June 11 (2-5)*

Old Sleningford, Mickley, nr Ripon ♿❀ (Mr & Mrs James Ramsden) *5m W of Ripon, off A6108. After North Stainley take 2nd L, follow sign to Mickley for 1m.* Lovely early C19 house (not open) and garden with original layout of interest to garden historians. Many acres with magnificent trees, woodland walk and Victorian fernery. Exceptionally romantic lake with islands, watermill, walled kitchen garden, long herbaceous border, yew and huge beech hedges. Flowers and grasses grown for drying. Several plant and other stalls. Home-made TEAS. *Adm £2.50 Chd 50p (ACNO to Holyrood House Centre for Health & Pastoral Care). Bank Hol Mon May 1, Sun May 28, Mon May 29 (1-5). Groups catered for, also private visits by appt, please* **Tel 01765 635229**

The Old Vicarage, Whixley ✂❀ (Mr & Mrs R Marshall) *Between York and Harrogate. 3/4m from A59 E of A1.* A delightful 3/4 acre walled flower garden with mixed borders, unusual shrubs, climbers, roses, hardy and half-hardy perennials and bulbs. Paths and garden structures lead to new vistas and hidden areas using the garden's natural contours. Courtyard with small herb garden. Lunches and TEAS. *Adm £2 Chd free. Wed May 31 (12.30-5) Combined adm with* **Whixley Gardens** *and* **Croft Cottage** *£3. Sun June 25 (12.30-5.30). Also open by appt for groups and societies, please* **Tel 01423 330474**

Orchard House, Appleton Roebuck ♿✂❀ (David & Sylvia Watson) *9m SW of York off A64. 6m E of Tadcaster.* An interesting 1-acre garden created by the owners over the past 5 yrs, set within an old apple orchard. Extensive water feature with large pond. 'Monet' style oak bridge. Cobble lined rill leading to bog garden. Cobble and brick paths, leading to many different garden structures, meander through mixed flower beds full of unusual plants. Millennium laburnum dome. Featured on Yorkshire Television 1999. TEAS in aid of Yorkshire Cancer Research. *Adm £1.50 Chd free. Suns April 16, May 14, June 18 (11-5). Private group visits welcome, please* **Tel 01904 744460**

Oxenber House, Austwick ❀ (Mrs K Robinson & Mr P Pickford) *4m N of Settle off A65. From village main st pass public house and school on L. Town Head Lane next L.* ¾ acre plantsman's garden planted for yr-round colour and interest. Gravel garden, scree, small pond and waterfall with alpines, ornamental grasses, foliage plants, fernery, spring bulbs, herbaceous and hardy perennials. Wild flower and vegetable area. Lovely views. Plant sales all yr for NGS. TEAS. *Sun April 30, Wed May 3, Sun, Mon Aug 27, 28. Private visits welcome, please* **Tel 015242 51376**

■ **Parcevall Hall Gardens, Skyreholme** ❀ (Walsingham College (Yorkshire Properties Ltd)) *9m N of Skipton signs from B6160 Burnsall Rd or off B6265 Grassington-Pateley Bridge Rd.* 20 acres in Wharfedale. Shelter belts of mixed woodland, fine trees, terraces, fishponds, rock garden, tender shrubs incl desfontainea, crinodendron, camellia, bulbs, rhododendrons, orchard for picnics, old varieties of apples, autumn colour, birds in woodland and splendid views. TEAS. *Adm £2.50 Chd (5-12 yrs) 50p. Good Friday to Oct 31 daily (10-6), winter by appt. For NGS Sun July 16 (10-5 garden closes at 6)*

Park House, nr York ♿❀ (Mr & Mrs A T Preston) *Moreby 6m S of York. Between Naburn and Stillingfleet on B1222.* ½ acre, gardened since 1988, set within a 2-acre walled garden using some of the 16′ walls to display a wide variety of wall shrubs and climbers. Some herbaceous and mixed shrub borders. Large conservatory. TEAS. *Adm £1.50 Chd free (ACNO to Asthma Research Campaign). Sun June 4 (2-5.30)*

Parkview, South Cave ♿✂❀ (Mr & Mrs Christopher Powell) *45 Church Street. 12m W of Hull on A63 turn N to S Cave on A1034. In centre of village turn L by chemists, 250yds on L black gates under arch.* ⅓ acre sheltered garden of perennial and shrub packed beds, pond and bog bed. Rose/honeysuckle pergola underplanted with varieties of hosta. Organic fruit and vegetable garden. TEAS. *Adm £1 Chd free if on reins. Sun June 11 (2-5). Private visits welcome, please* **Tel 01430 423739**

Pennyholme, Fadmoor (Mr & Mrs P R Wilkinson) *5m NW of Kirkbymoorside. From A170 between Kirkbymoorside and Nawton, turn N, ½m before Fadmoor turn L, signed 'Sleightholmedale only' continue N up dale, across 3 cattlegrids, to garden. No Buses.* Large, wild garden on edge of moor with rhododendrons, azaleas, primulas and shrubs. Tea/Biscuits in aid of St Nicolas Bransdale. *Adm £2.50. Sats May 27 June 3 (1-5)*

■ **Plants of Special Interest Nursery, Braithwell** ♿❀ (Mr & Mrs Peter Dunstan & Jamie Dunstan) *A1(M) junction 36 (A630 to Rotherham) turn L through Old Edlington. From M18 Junction 1 take A631. Turn L in Maltby to Braithwell.* Nursery in centre of village. ¼ acre Mediterranean-style walled cottage garden with patio and water feature and raised beds. Nursery with excellent specimen trees and shrubs, unusual plants, bulbs and architectural ornaments. From August a colourful display of ornamental gourds, squashes and pumpkins. Tea-room. Lunches/TEAS. *Adm £1 Chd 50p. Nursery open Feb to Dec Tues to Suns and Bank Hol Mons (10-5). For NGS Tues to Suns June 6 to 11, Sept 5 to 10 (10-5)* **Tel 01709 790642**

55 Rawcliffe Drive, York ✇❀ (Mr & Mrs J Goodyer) *Clifton. A19 from York centre, turn R at Clifton Green traffic lights (Water Lane). Rawcliffe Drive is 1st L after new roundabout.* A 30yd by 10yd suburban garden on 2 levels. Planted for yr-round interest with excellent use of foliage and colour. Many unusual shrubs, herbaceous plants, bulbs and large number of clematis. *Adm £1.50 Chd free incl TEA. Sun June 4 (11-5). Also private visits welcome April to July, please* **Tel 01904 638489**

Ridgeway, Ackworth ✇❀ (Mr & Mrs G Billcliffe) *Mill Lane. 4m S of Pontefract off A628. 200yds before roundabout A628/A638.* ⅓ acre garden created over past 9 yrs interpreting the natural contours. Raised beds and curved borders planted for yr-round interest surrounding waterfall and stream leading to pond at centre of well kept and beautifully shaped lawn. Decorative gravel gardens with pots and sinks. Arches, obelisks, pergolas supporting climbers and over 70 varieties of clematis. TEA. *Adm £1.50 Chd free (ACNO to Prince of Wales Hospice, Pontefract) Sun, Wed, July 2, 5 (2-6), private visits welcome, please* **Tel 01977 617352**

Rudston House, Rudston (Mr & Mrs Simon Dawson) *nr Driffield. On B1253 5m W of Bridlington. S at Bosville Arms for approx 300yds.* Birthplace of authoress Winifred Holtby. Victorian farmhouse (not open) and 3 acres of garden with fine old trees, lawns, paths with clipped box hedges, interesting potager with named vegetable varieties, roses, hosta bed and short woodland walk, with a pond. Plenty of seats. Cream TEAS in aid of Rudston Church. *Adm £2 Chd free. Sun July 23 (11-5)*

Rye Hill, Helmsley ✇❀ (Dr & Mrs C Briske) *15 Station Road. In Helmsley, at the bridge on A170 (Thirsk/York) turn into Ryegate, which leads into Station Rd.* ¼ acre plantswoman's garden designed, constructed and maintained by owners. Divided into interlinking compartments, each planted in a different style: formal, woodland and cottage. Intense planting using unusual plants, aiming for yr-round colour and interest. Conservatory, well stocked with tender species and small pond. 'An inspirational garden with lots of interesting ideas and features'. Home-made TEAS. *Adm £1.50 Chd free. Weds April 26, May 24, Sat May 27, Sun June 11, Weds June 14, July 5 (2-5). Private visits welcome please write*

Saltmarshe Hall, Saltmarshe ♿✇❀ (Mr & Mrs Philip Bean) *Howden. From Howden (M62, Jct 37) follow signs to Howdendyke and Saltmarshe. House in park W of Saltmarshe village.* Large lawns, fine old trees, R Ouse and a Regency house (not open) with courtyards provide a setting for shrubs, climbers, herbaceous plants and roses. Of special interest to plantsmen and garden designers are a pond garden, a walled garden and a large herbaceous border. Approx 10 acres. TEAS in aid of Laxton Church. *Adm £2 Acc chd free. Suns May 7, June 11 (2-5.30). Private visits welcome, please* **Tel 01430 430199**

Secret Garden, York ✇❀ (Mr & Mrs A C Downes) *10 Sherwood Grove, Acomb. From York on A59, turn L into Beckfield Lane opp Manor School at mini roundabout, ¼m before Western Ring Rd. Take 1st R, 2nd L.* ¾ acre garden hidden behind suburban semi, developed and extended over 20 yrs. Features rockeries, pond, fruit cage but primarily extensive mixed plantings incl many unusual plants. 5 greenhouses with vines, cactus, succulent & tender plant collections. Small Nursery. TEA. *Adm £1.50 Chd free. Suns June 4, July 23 (10-5). Also private visits welcome, please* **Tel 01904 796360**

■ **Shandy Hall, Coxwold** ✇❀ (The Laurence Sterne Trust) *N of York. From A19, 7m from both Easingwold and Thirsk turn E signed Coxwold.* Home of C18 author Laurence Sterne. 2 walled gardens, 1 acre of unusual perennials interplanted with tulips and old roses in low walled beds. Another acre in old quarry of trees, shrubs, bulbs, climbers and wild flowers. In Country Life, Period Living and BBC TV 'Look North'. Shop. Unusual plants for sale. Wheelchairs with help. *Adm £2.50 Chd £1 (ACNO to Laurence Sterne Trust). Gardens open daily except Sats from May 1. House open Wed & Sun (2-4.30) June 1 to Sept 30. Groups by appt. For NGS Suns April 30, May 28, July 9, Aug 27 (2-5)* **Tel 01347 868465**

Sleightholme Dale Lodge, Fadmoor (Dr & Mrs O James) *3m N of Kirkbymoorside. 1m from Fadmoor.* Hillside garden, walled rose garden and herbaceous borders. Not suitable for wheelchairs. No coaches. Parking very limited in wet weather. TEAS (not available May 21). *Adm £2 Chd 50p. Sun May 21 (2-6), Sat, Sun July 15, 16 (2-6)*

The Spaniels, Hensall ♿✇❀ (Janet & Dennis Tredgett) *2m N of M62, 5m S of Selby. Turn E off A19 to Hensall. Field Lane is last turn on R in Hensall Village.* ⅔ acre planted over the last 7 yrs on previous farmland. Long mixed borders in colour themes, grasses, young conifers, trees and shrubs, divided by curved lawns with island bed, wildlife pond and bog gardens. TEAS. *Adm £1.50 Chd free. Suns May 7, July 23 (12-5). Private visits welcome, please* **Tel 01977 661858**

Springfield House, Tockwith ♿✇❀ (Mr & Mrs S B Milner) *5m E of Wetherby. 1m off B1224. Garden at W end of village.* 1½ acres. Well established walled garden, new herbaceous borders, pretty stream, water and rock gardens. Roses, conifers and shaded shrub walk. Wide variety of interesting plants. TEA. *Adm £2 Chd free. Sun July 2 (2-5)*

Stillingfleet Lodge, nr York ♿✇❀ (Mr & Mrs J Cook) *6m S of York, from A19 York-Selby take B1222 towards Sherburn in Elmet.* A plantsman's garden subdivided into smaller gardens, each one based on a colour theme with emphasis on the use of foliage plants. Wildflower meadow and natural pond. New 50 metre double herbaceous borders, holders of National Collection of Pulmonaria. Adjacent nursery will be open. Homemade Teas in village hall in aid of local church. *Adm £2 Chd over 5yrs 50p. Suns May 14, June 25 (1.30-5.30)*

Tan Cottage, Cononley ✇ (Mr & Mrs D L Shaw) *West Lane. Take A629; turn off to Cononley 2¾m S of Skipton; top of village turn R onto Skipton rd.* ¾ acre plantsman's garden, featured twice on TV, adjoining C17 house (not open). Interesting plants, many old varieties. National Collection of primroses. *Adm £2. Private visits by appt only, please* **Tel 01535 632030**

Tregonning, Ellerton ♿✂❀ (Deirdre Falcon & John Barwick) *12m S of York on B1228 to Elvington and Howden. 10m N of M62 junction 37. Next to village pond.* 1½ acres created 25 yrs ago, with fruit, vegetables and wildflower meadow with mature hedges to attract wildlife. Lawn areas planted with unusual flowering shrubs, old roses, trees, climbers and a dovecote. Large herbaceous border. Natural wild life ponds and a bog garden, Victorian wells, rockeries and terrace. Large collection of bonsai, some 25yrs old and mostly grown from seed. Unusual plants for sale. Cream TEAS. *Adm £1.50 Chd free. Sun May 21 (2-5). Private visits welcome, please* **Tel 01757 288578**

8 Welton Old Road, Welton ❀ (Dr & Mrs O G Jones) *In village of Welton 10m W of Hull off A63. Coming E turn L to village. Past church turn R along Parliament St. and up hill. House 50yds on R opp Temple Close. From E take A63 and turn off at flyover to Brough; turn R for Welton and follow above instructions. Roadside parking in village.* Informal 1-acre garden developed by owners over 30yrs. Imaginative planting with unusual shrubs, plants and less common trees. Natural pond and lily pond. *Adm £2 for NGS. Private visits welcome, please* **Tel 01482 667488**

26 West End, Walkington ✂ (Miss Jennifer Hall) *2m from Beverley on the B1230, 100yds beyond Xrds in centre of village on the R.* Interesting ½ acre cottage garden opening into an old wooded gravel pit still being developed by the owner single-handedly. Many rare plants collected over 18yrs. TEA. *Adm £2 Chd free. Sun May 28 (1.30-5)*

5 Wharfe Close, Leeds 16 ✂❀ (Mr & Mrs C V Lightman) *Adel. Signposted off Leeds ring rd A6120 (¼m E of A660 Leeds-Otley rd). Follow Long Causeway into Sir George Martin Drive. Wharfe Close adjacent to bus terminus. Please park on main rd.* Well stocked garden created from sloping site incorporating pools, rock gardens and mixed borders, small woodland walk. Unusual plants grown on predominantly acid soil. TEAS. *Adm £1.50 Chd free. Thurs June 22, Wed July 5 (2-7)*

The White Cottage, Halsham ♿✂❀ (Mr & Mrs John Oldham) *1m E of Halsham Arms on B1362. Concealed wooded entrance on R. Ample parking.* The garden created by owners 28 yrs ago. Specialised and unusual planting in island beds. Natural pond and water feature. Small woodland area, vegetable and herb garden and architect designed sunken conservatory. Traditional pergola with hosta walk and new large wildlife pond in paddock. Recently featured on BBC 'Look North'. Teas in aid of Halsham Church. *Adm £2 Chd free (ACNO to Halsham Church Restoration Fund) Sun May 7; Sun Sept 10 (1.30-5). Private group visits welcome by appt during June, July & Aug, please* **Tel 01964 612296**

The White House, Husthwaite ♿✂❀ (Dr & Mrs A H Raper) *3m N of Easingwold. Turn R off A19 signposted Husthwaite. 1½m to centre of village opp parish church.* Come and meet the gardener, an enthusiastic plantswoman. Exchange ideas and visit a 1-acre country garden with herb garden, conservatory and gardens within the garden. Herbaceous, particularly a hot summer border and shrubs and many fascinating unusual plants. New landscaping and planting in the old orchard. *Adm £2. Groups & pivate visits by appt only, please* **Tel 01347 868688**

Whixley Gardens ✂❀ *3m E of A1 off A59 York/Harrogate. Follow signs to Whixley.* Light lunches TEAS at The Old Vicarage. Several plant stalls. *Combined adm £3 Chd free (incl* **Croft Cottage, Green Hammerton***) Sun June 25 (12.30-5.30)*

Ash Tree House (Mr & Mrs E P Moffitt) A well designed unusual garden of approx 0.2 acre with extensive rockeries making full use of the sloping site. Established excellent plantings of heathers, alpines, hardy plants, climbers and shrubs

Cobble Cottage (John & Oliver Hawkridge & Barry Atkinson) An imaginatively designed, constantly changing, small cottage garden full of decorative architectural plants and old family favourites. Interesting water garden, containers and use of natural materials. New secret courtyard garden.

Croft Cottage, Green Hammerton See separate entry

The Old Vicarage See separate entry

Woodlands Cottage, Summerbridge ❀ (Mr & Mrs Stark) *½m W of Summerbridge on the B6165 (Ripley-Pateley Bridge).* 1-acre country garden constructed and developed by the owners from a sloping site incorporating part of the existing woodland edge and field and natural stone outcrops, with an attractive enclosed cottage style garden. Herbaceous, formal herb garden, unusual hardy plants, wildflower meadow and separate vegetable area. Small nursery. TEAS. *Adm £2 Chd 50p. Suns May 21, Aug 13 (1.30-5). Private visits welcome by appt* **Tel 01423 780765**

Wytherstone House, Pockley ♿✂❀ (Lady Clarissa Collin) *3m NE of Helmsley from A170 signpost.* Large garden, constantly improved, with choice and hard to find shrubs and perennials, a variety of lavenders, over 40 varieties of salvias, terracotta pots, mediterranean garden, peat terracing and raised rock garden of rare alpines. Arboretum of rare trees recently landscaped, with pond and small bog garden. Irresistable adjoining nursery. TEAS in aid of Pockley Church. *Adm £2.50 Chd 75p under 6 free. Suns, Weds June 18, 21, July 16, 19 Aug 6, 9 (1-5). Parties and individuals welcome by appt, please* **Tel 01439 770012**

▲ **York Gate, Leeds 16** ✂❀ (GRBS) *Back Church Lane, Adel. Behind Adel Church ½m from A660. Park nr Church. Public footpath through Churchyard, and a short distance beyond, passes the garden gate.* 1-acre garden created by the Spencer family and divided into a series of smaller gardens each with unique architectural features. A masterpiece of garden design. Exceptional use of evergreens. TEA. Gift Stall. *Adm £2.50 Chd free (ACNO to GRBS). For NGS Thurs June 1, 29 July 6, August 3 (2-5). For details of all other opening times* **Tel 0113 2678240**

WALES

Carmarthenshire & Pembrokeshire

Hon County Organiser: Mrs Penny Drew, Cwm-Pibau, New Moat, Haverfordwest, Pembrokeshire SA63 4RE Tel 01437 532454

Hon County Treasurer: Mr N Edmunds, Parc-y-Robert, New Moat, Clarbeston Road, Haverfordwest SA63 4RY

DATES OF OPENING

Regular openings
For details see garden description
Cilwern, Talley
Hilton Court Nurseries, Roch
Moorland Cottage Plants, Rhyd y Groes
National Botanical Gardens of Wales, Llanarthne
Picton Castle, The Rhos
Saundersfoot Bay Leisure Park

By appointment only
For telephone numbers and other details see garden descriptions. Private visits welcomed
Brynsifi, Llanelli
Cwm Pibau, New Moat
The Forge, Landshipping
Hean Castle, Saundersfoot
Le Bocage, Bryngoleu, Llannon
The Swallows, Pembroke
2 Tyfri, Burry Port

April 30 Sunday
Llysnewydd, Llangadog

May 1 Monday
Llysnewydd, Llangadog

May 13 Saturday
Colby Woodland Garden, Narberth

May 14 Sunday
Picton Castle, The Rhos

May 21 Sunday
Cilwern, Talley
Ffynone, Boncath
Great Griggs, Llanteg

June 4 Sunday
Llysnewydd, Llangadog

July 1 Saturday
Millinford, Millin Cross

July 2 Sunday
Llysnewydd, Llangadog
Millinford, Millin Cross

July 3 Monday
Cilgwyn Lodge, Llangadog

July 8 Saturday
Maesyrynn, Nantycaws

July 9 Sunday
The Grove, Tenby
Living Garden, Bryn
Maesyrynn, Nantycaws
Scotsborough House, Tenby

July 16 Sunday
Blaencilgoed House, Ludchurch
Penmeddyn, Manorowen

July 23 Sunday
Great Griggs, Llanteg
Picton Castle, The Rhos

August 5 Saturday
Maesyrynn, Nantycaws

August 6 Sunday
Llysnewydd, Llangadog
Maesyrynn, Nantycaws

October 25 Wednesday
National Botanical Gardens of Wales, Llanarthne

DESCRIPTIONS OF GARDENS

Blaencilgoed House, Ludchurch ✿❀ (Mr & Mrs Wyn Jones) *4m SE of Narberth taking B4314 to Princes Gate, or leaving A477 2m W of Llanteg.* 1 acre garden created over 30yrs. Herbaceous borders, shrubs, vegetables, conservatory. TEAS. *Adm £1.50 Chd free (ACNO to St Elidyr's Church Ludchurch). Sun July 16 (11.30-5)*

Brynsifi, Llanelli ✿❀ (A C & B Grabham) *3m W of Llanelli on B4308 Llanelli to Trimsaran rd. Signed off main rd.* Medium-sized organic garden created on shale bank with natural stone retaining walls planted to give yr-round interest. Extension to garden currently being undertaken to include wildlife pond. TEA. *Adm £1.50 Chd free (ACNO to Cats Protection League). Private visits welcome May - July, please* **Tel 01554 810294** Evenings

Cilgwyn Lodge, Llangadog ✿❀ (Keith Brown & Moira Thomas) *3m NE from the village of Llangadog. Turn off A40 into centre of Llangadog. Bear L in front of village shop then 1st R towards Myddfai. After 2½m pass Cilgwyn Manor on L then take 1st L by telephone kiosk. Garden ¼m on L.* A fascinating 1 acre garden set in glorious countryside. Profusely planted with a wide variety of shrubs, herbaceous plants featuring hostas, hardy geraniums and vegetables. 3 ponds full of fish (otters permitting) making the garden unsuitable for children. Plenty of seats to enjoy the garden and the views. Good quality plants for sale. TEAS. *Adm £1.50. Sun July 30 (1-6)*

■ **Cilwern, Talley** ♿✿❀ (Mrs A Knatchbull-Hugessen) *6m NE of Llandeilo off B4302. Turn L by large sign on main rd. Garden on L 200yds down lane.* Tranquil valley garden created from marshy wasteland over past 20 yrs. Trees, shrubs, perennials; especially hardy geraniums in variety. Pond, stream, small woodland area. Not a manicured garden but much of interest to the dedicated plant lover, and set in beautiful countryside. Adjoining nursery. TEAS. *Adm £1 Chd free. Closed Mondays except Bank Holidays. Otherwise daily (11-6) donation to NGS. For NGS Sun May 21 (2-6)*
Tel 01558 685526

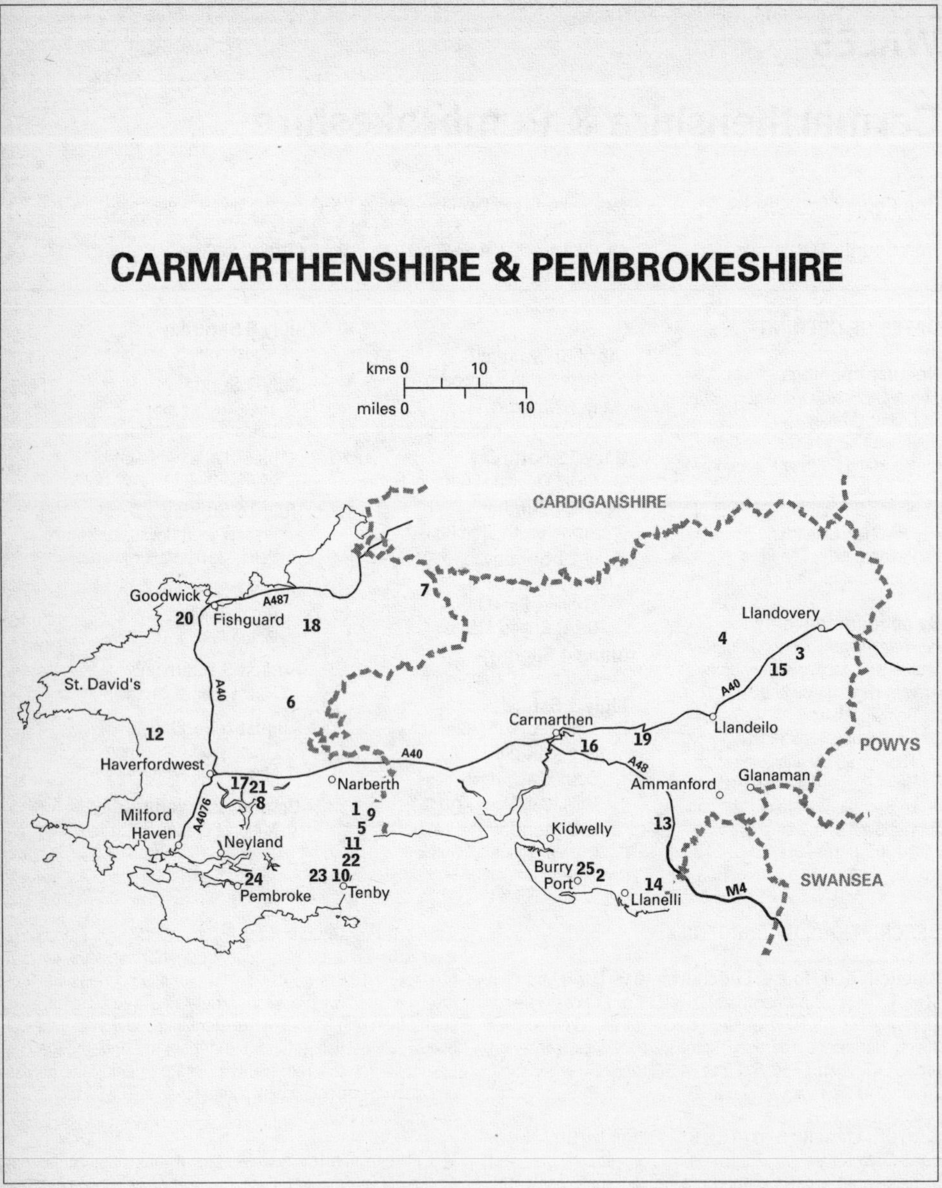

KEY

1 Blaencilgoed House
2 Brynsifi
3 Cilgwyn Lodge
4 Cilwern
5 Colby Woodland Garden
6 Cwm Pibau
7 Ffynone
8 The Forge
9 Great Griggs
10 The Grove
11 Hean Castle
12 Hilton Court Nurseries
13 Le Bocage
14 Living Garden
15 Llysnewydd
16 Maesyrynn
17 Millinford
18 Moorland Cottage Plants
19 National Botanical Gardens of Wales
20 Penmeddyn
21 Picton Castle
22 Saundersfoot Bay Leisure Park
23 Scotsborough House
24 The Swallows
25 2 Tyfri

▲ **Colby Woodland Garden, Narberth** ❀ (The National Trust) *½m inland from Amroth and 2m E of Saundersfoot. Sign-posted by brown Tourist Signs on the coast rd and the A477.* 8-acre woodland garden in a secluded and tranquil valley with a fine collection of rhododendrons and azaleas. Tea rooms and gallery. Walled garden open by kind permission of Mr & Mrs A Scourfield Lewis. TEAS. *Adm £2.80 Chd £1.40. For NGS Sat May 13 (10-5). Large parties by appt, please* **Tel 01834 811885**

Cwm Pibau, New Moat (Mrs Duncan Drew) *10m NE of Haverfordwest.* 4-acre garden bordered by streams and created since 1978; mainly young rare shrubs on a hillside. *Adm £1 Chd free. Private visits welcome, please* **Tel 01437 532 454**

Ffynone, Boncath (Earl & Countess Lloyd George of Dwyfor) *From Newcastle Emlyn take A484 to Cenarth, turn L on B4332, turn L again at Xrds just before Newchapel.* Large woodland garden in process of restoration. Lovely views, fine specimen trees, rhododendrons, azaleas, woodland walks. House by John Nash (1793), not shown. Later additions and garden terraces by F Inigo Thomas c1904. TEAS in aid of Fishguard Sea Cadets. *Adm £2 Chd under 14 free. Sun May 21 (2-6)*

The Forge, Landshipping ♿ (Mrs S McLeod-Baikie) *Nearest town Narbeth. Landshipping well sign posted. Pass New Park with pillar box; 200yds further on, gate on R.* Approx 2½ acres recently planted woodland garden with many varieties of bulbs, trees and shrub roses; pretty, very charming. *Private visits welcome mid-March to mid-April and also in June, please* **Tel 01834 891279**

Great Griggs, Llanteg ♿❀ (M A Owen & W A Owen) *A477 from St Clears through Red Roses, next village Llanteg. Signposted on L 'Colby Woodland Garden', turn L immed; 2nd entrance on R.* Approx 1-acre plantsman's organic garden created and maintained by owners, consisting of lawns bounded by borders with unusual shrubs and interspersed with scree beds full of alpines. Two ponds, and natural stonework incl seating; all leading to cottage garden with summerhouse, in turn leading to semi-wild garden with pond and shrubs. TEAS. *Adm £1.50 Chd 50p. Suns May 21, July 23 (2-6). Private visits welcome any time, please* **Tel 01834 831414**

NEW **The Grove, Tenby** ♿❀ (Mr & Mrs A Rhys Davies) *A478 Tenby N, R off A4218 (A4139) into Serpentine Rd, R into Heywood Lane. Tenby S, L off B4318.* The Grove garden lies adjacent to Scotsborough House to which there is direct garden access. 2 acres make up the original garden that surrounded the house as it stood at the turn of the century. It consists of mature trees; manicured hedging; sculptures; seating areas in a tranquil environment. TEAS. *Combined adm with* **Scotsborough House** *£2 Chd 50p. Sun July 9 (1-5)*

Hean Castle, Saundersfoot ♿✗❀ (Mr & Mrs T Lewis) *1m N of Saundersfoot. 1½m SE of Kilgetty. Take the Amroth rd from Saundersfoot or the Sardis rd from Kilgetty.* 2-acres; mixed borders with some unusual plants and shrubs; rose garden; walled garden and greenhouse; pond; pot plants and troughs. Good view. *Adm £1.50 Chd free. Private visits and groups welcome, please* **Tel 01834 812222**

Hilton Court Nurseries, Roch ♿✗❀ (Mrs Cheryl Lynch) *From Haverfordwest take the A487 to St Davids. 6m from Haverfordwest signs L to Hilton Court Nurseries.* 6 acres of garden nestling in a secluded valley. A superb setting overlooking ponds and mature woodlands. Spectacular lily ponds in July and August. Water gardens; wild flower walks and woodland walks. Great variety of interesting trees and shrubs giving colour and interest throughout the year. Nursery adjoining. Craft Shops, restaurant. TEAS. *Adm £1.50 Chd 50p. Daily March to October (10-5.30), October (10.30-3.30)*

Le Bocage, Bryngoleu, Llannon ♿❀ (Mr & Mrs Ivor Russell) *13m from Swansea, 7m from Llanelli. From junction 49 (Pont Abraham) on M4 take A48 (T) in the direction of Cross Hands. Turn L after approx 3kms towards Village of Llwyn Teg. At [map ref SN56 E on OS 159].* 1-acre garden with converted stable block, leading to extensive choice of walks each about 1/2m long in mature and newly developing woodlands and alongside natural streams. 15 acres overall incl large pond; fine views of the surrounding countryside. TEA. *Adm £1.50 Chd 50p. Open all year by appt and private parties welcome, please* **Tel 01269 842343**

Living Garden, Bryn ♿✗❀ (Alan & Justine Clarke) *4a Brynmorlais, Llanelli; 2½m NE of town on B4297. Parking in lay-by on main rd please.* Plantsman's long, slender garden subdivided for interest. Rare and attractive collection of plants, containers, water features and pools. TEAS. *Adm £1.50 Chd Free. Sun July 9 (2-5.30); also private visits welcome, please* **Tel 01554 821274** May to Sept

Llysnewydd, Llangadog ♿✗❀ (Jan Jones & Nick Voyle) *Midway between Llandeilo and Llandovery. Turn off A40 into centre of Llangadog. Bear L in front of village shop. Turn 1st R. After approx ½m turn R. Garden approx 600yds on R.* 1 acre oasis of tranquility set in scenic Towy Valley. Quiet, relaxing garden evolving from the need to prevent river erosion. Planted for yr-round interest in areas ranging from full sun to deep shade. Productive vegetable garden with greenhouses. Unsuitable for children and mobile phones. TEAS. *Adm £1. Sun, Mon April 30; May 1; Suns June 4; July 2; Aug 6 (11-5). Private visits welcome, please* **Tel 01550 777432**

Maesyrynn, Nantycaws ♿❀ (Mr & Mrs Thomas) *From Carmarthen take A48 dual carriageway E towards Swansea. After approx 3m turn L for Nantycaws. From Swansea, sign reads Police HQ and Nantycaws. Drive 300yds. Murco garage on L. Turn R into lane opp; 2nd bungalow on L.* Plantsman's cottage garden approx ½ acre. Mainly herbaceous beds and shrubs. Pond and water feature, pergolas and raised beds. Highly productive vegetable garden with greenhouses. Lovely views in rural setting. TEAS. Plants for sale. *Adm £1 Chd free (ACNO to Alzheimers Disease Soc.). Sat, Sun July 8, 9, Aug 5, 6 (10-5)*

Millinford, Millin Cross ♿✗❀ (Drs B & A Barton) *3m E of Haverfordwest, on A40 to Carmarthen turn R signposted The Rhos, take turning to Millin turn R at Millin Chapel then*

immediate L over river bridge. 4 acres on bank of Millin Creek. Varied collection of trees; shrubs; herbaceous plants and bulbs; large pond. TEAS. *Adm £2 Chd free (ACNO to NSPCC). Sat, Sun July 1, 2 (11-6)*

NEW **Moorland Cottage Plants, Rhyd y Groes** (Jennifer & Kevin Matthews) *On B4329 16m NE of Haverfordwest, 12m SW of Cardigan. Almost midway between mountain cattlegrid and signpost to Brynberian.* Small country cottage garden of approx ½ acre, situated at 720 ft on the side of the Preseli Mountains. Extensive new herbaceous plantings incl rare and unusual plants and many of our collection of 180 varieties of hardy geraniums. Nursery adjoining specialising in hardy pereinnals. *Adm £1 Chd free. June 5 to June 18 incl; July 10 to July 16 incl; Sept 4 to Sept 17 incl (10-6)*

NEW **National Botanical Gardens of Wales, Llanarthne** *7m E of Carmarthen. Signed from A48.* 568-acre estate in the hills overlooking Towy Valley, dedicated to science, education and leisure. Great Glasshouse with Mediterranean climates and interior landscape incl ravines, waterfalls and bridges. 220 metre-long herbacious broadwalk, lakes, walled gardens, a water discovery centre and woodlands walks. *Adm £6.50 Chd £3. Wed Oct 25 (10-5.30).*

NEW **Penmeddyn, Manorowen** (Mrs Alice Cleal) *2m SW of Goodwick, from Fishguard Harbour roundabout follow A487 to St Davids, pass through Manorowen and take 1st R continue ½m entrance on L.* Large country garden in a tranquil setting, deep herbaceous borders with many unusual plants, decorative vegetable garden; large pond and outdoor sculptures. Walk in 12 acres of newly planted woodland and wild meadows. TEA. *Adm £1.50 Chd free. Sun July 16 (2-6)*

■ **Picton Castle, The Rhos** (Picton Castle Trust) *3m E of Haverfordwest on A40 to Carmarthen, signposted off main rd.* Mature 40-acre woodland garden with unique collection of rhododendrons and azaleas, many bred over 35yrs producing hybrids of great merit and beauty; rare and tender shrubs and trees like magnolia, myrtle, embothrium and eucryphia. Wild flowers abound. Walled garden with roses, fernery, herbaceous and climbing plants and large clearly labelled collection of herbs. Restaurant, shop, craft shop gallery and garden nursery. *Adm £2.75 Chd £1 under 5 free. Open daily except Mons, April to Sept and Bank Hols. For NGS Suns May 14, July 23 (10.30-5)*
Tel 01437 751 326

Saundersfoot Bay Leisure Park (Gavin Steer Esq) *Broadfield, Saundersfoot. On B4316, ¾m S from centre of Saundersfoot.* Interesting layout of lawns, shrubs and herbaceous borders with many plants of botanical interest in 20-acre modern holiday leisure park. Large rock garden and water feature; laburnum walk; Japanese Garden. Holders of a National collection of Pontentilla fruticosa. Tea Saundersfoot. *Adm free, collecting box. March 28 to Oct 31 daily (10-5)*

NEW **Scotsborough House, Tenby** (John Argent) *From N (A478) bear R onto A4218, turn R into Serpentine Rd, turn R into Heywood Lane. From S (B4318) turn L into Heywood Lane.* 1-acre garden adjacent to The Grove, to which there is direct access. The garden is sheltered by mature trees (incl a Black Poplar) and includes mixed borders of shrubs; roses and herbaceous plants; former greenhouses with climbing and semi-tropical plants; a very fine old Japanese Maple; a S-facing walled area and informal lawns around a central formal lawn. TEAS. *Combined adm with* **The Grove** *£2 Chd 50p. Sun July 9 (1-5)*

The Swallows, Pembroke (Mrs Moore) *One-way system through Pembroke main st to roundabout. Keep R. Down hill. Up Grove Hill. The 'Swallows' is on the R.* A haven on the edge of the town. Garden sub-divided to give interest. Trees, shrubs, phormiums, cordylines, bamboos to give a Mediterranean feel. Hosta walk. Pergolas, ponds and water features. Wildlife haven. A plantsman's garden. Featured on TV 'Get Gardening' and voted 'Best Garden in Wales'. Home-made TEAS. *Adm £1 Chd 50p. June, July, August (10-4) Parties by arrangement (15-30). For appt*
Tel 01646 685665

NEW **2 Tyfri, Burry Port** (Mary Atkin) *4m W of Llanelli on A484 (follow signs for Pembrey Country Park) take 3rd on R after B4311 and Pemberton Arms, continue to end of lane, last cottage. Parking very limited.* 1-acre mild, sheltered garden steeply sloping down to small stream via steps, seats and banks. Plant choice dictated by the site's natural topography and microclimate, giving gravel, woodland, mediterranean bank, herbaceous beds, bog and 2 pond areas. Foliage and form is as important as flowers. 2m Country park. Some tender & unusual plants for sale. TEAS in conservatory if wet. *Adm £1.50 Chd free (ACNO to The National Botanic Garden of Wales). Open Easter - Oct everyday by appt (10-5), please* **Tel 01554 835194** after sundown

Macmillan Cancer Relief

Macmillan nurses are specialists in cancer care, offering expert information and advice in pain and symptom management.

Macmillan Cancer Relief Information Line: 0845 601 6161
Macmillan Cancer Relief Website: www.macmillan.org.uk

Ceredigion/Cardiganshire

Hon County Organiser: Mrs Joy Neal, Llwyncelyn, Glandyfi, Machynlleth SY20 8SS Tel 01654781 203
Treasurer: Mrs Sheila Latham, Garreg, Glandyfi, Machynlleth SY20 8SS

DATES OF OPENING

Regular openings
For details see garden description
Cae Hir, Cribyn
Farmyard Nursery Woodland Garden, Llandysul
The Walled Garden at Pigeonsford, nr Llangranog
Winllan, Talsarn

By appointment only
For telephone numbers and other details see garden descriptions. Private visits welcomed
Coetmor, Talybont
Felindre, Aberarth, Aberaeron
Old Cilgwyn Gardens
Winllan, Talsarn

March 26 Sunday
Farmyard Nursery Woodland Garden, Llandysul

April 16 Sunday
Farmyard Nursery Woodland Garden, Llandysul

April 23 Sunday
Pant-yr-Holiad, Rhydlewis

May 7 Sunday
Pant-yr-Holiad, Rhydlewis

May 14 Sunday
Llwyncelyn, Glandyfi
The Mill House, Glandyfi

May 27 Saturday
Dyffryn, Pennant, Llanon

May 28 Sunday
Cae Hir, Cribyn
Dyffryn, Pennant, Llanon

June 4 Sunday
Crynfryn & Tynewydd Gardens
The Walled Garden at Pigeonsford, nr Llangranog

June 11 Sunday
Glangwenffrwd, nr Tregaron

June 18 Sunday
Llanllyr, Talsarn

June 24 Saturday
Nantcellan, Clarach

June 25 Sunday
Farmyard Nursery Woodland Garden, Llandysul
The Old Vicarage, Llangeler

July 2 Sunday
Crynfryn & Tynewydd Gardens
Llanaerchaeron, Ciliau Aeron, Aberaeron
Llanllyr, Talsarn

July 9 Sunday
Cae Hir, Cribyn
Henblas, Abermad, Llanfarian

July 16 Sunday
Plas Llidiardau, Llanilar
The Walled Garden at Pigeonsford, nr Llangranog

July 23 Sunday
The Old Vicarage, Llangeler

August 13 Sunday
Plas Penglais University of Wales Aberystwyth

August 20 Sunday
Llanaerchaeron, Ciliau Aeron, Aberaeron

DESCRIPTIONS OF GARDENS

▲ Cae Hir, Cribyn ✇❀ (Mr Wil Akkermans) *W on A482 from Lampeter. After 5m turn S on B4337. Cae Hir is 2m on L.* The aim of the gardener (a Dutch plantsman) to create a balance between the natural and the cultivated, has been achieved. 6 acres of sheer delight, from colour-themed subgardens and bonsai enclosure to wild flower bog areas. As featured on radio and national and regional TV. TEA. *Adm £2.50 Chd 50p. For NGS Sun May 28, July 9 (1-6)*

Coetmor, Talybont ❀ (Dr & Mrs G Hughes) *From Aberystwyth take A487 towards Machynlleth, 7m N to Talybont. 2nd turn L after shop on village green. House visible in the trees 300yds straight up lane.* 2-acre garden extended and planted during last 10yrs with interesting trees and shrubs incl embothrium, styrax japonica, ptelea aurea, zelkova, rhododendrons, azaleas, acers and a range of sorbus. Also an increasing collection of less common conifers. *Collecting box. Private visits and parties welcome April to June and Sept to Nov, please* **Tel 01970 832365**

Crynfryn & Tynewydd Gardens ✇❀ TEAS. *Combined adm £2 Chd free. Suns June 4, July 2 (10.30-6)*

Crynfryn, Penuwch (Mr & Mrs Tom Murton) *On B4576 between Penuwch and Bwlchllan, 8m Aberaeron, 8m Tregaron.* 1-acre woodland garden with mature trees, pond, bog plants, meconopsis and primulas, herbaceous borders and collection of old shrub roses in glorious position overlooking Cambrian Mts

Tynewydd, Bwlchllan (Mr & Mrs Robin Edwards) *1m S of Crynfryn* 3-acre garden, 2 large ponds, herbaceous plantings, pergola, maturing trees and shrubs, alpine house. Extensive mountain views. Artisans' garden in memory of Geoff Hamilton

Dyffryn, Pennant, Llanon ✇❀ (Mr & Mrs O P J Richards) *SN 521, 637. From Aberarth, continue 100yds up hill, turn R, B4577 to Pennant. Xrds at centre of village turn L. Follow rd up hill past school. R fork, 250yds turn R.* ⅔-acre developed into 'rooms' ranging from wild woodland, paved walks, pergola, decorative grasses, interesting shrubs, water features and an oriental touch, local bird life. TEAS. *Adm £1.50 Chd 50p. Sat, Sun May 27, 28 (1-6)*

CEREDIGION/CARDIGANSHIRE

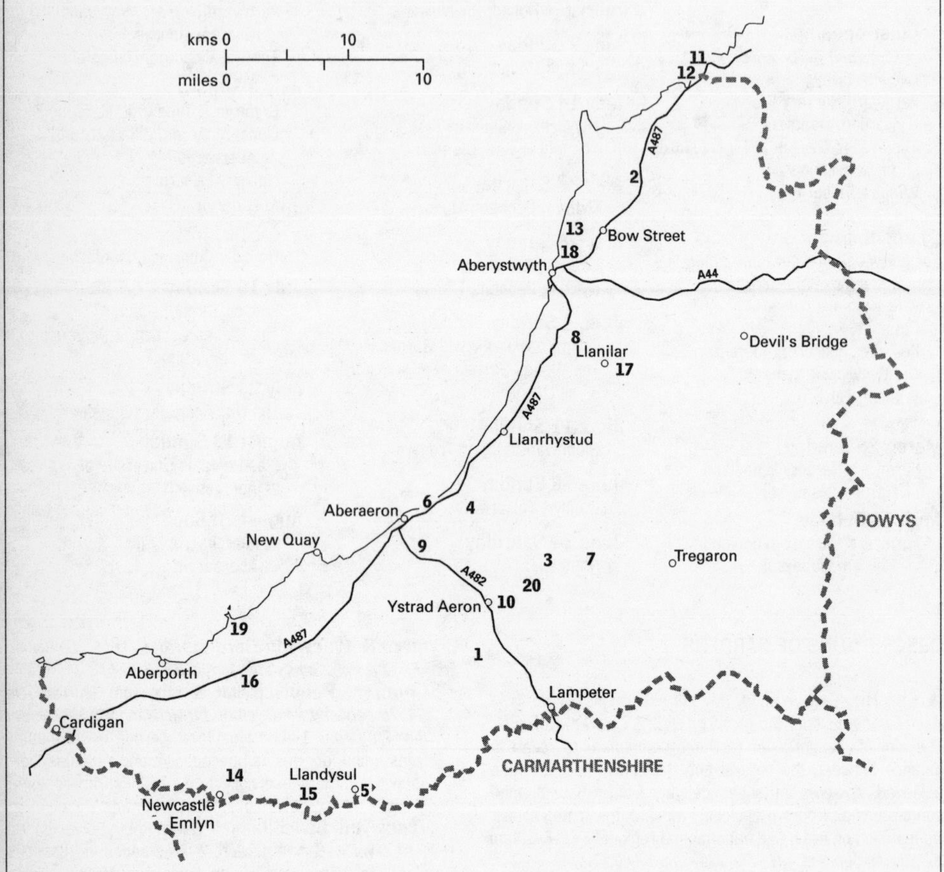

KEY

1 Cae Hir
2 Coetmor
3 Crynfryn & Tynewydd Gardens
4 Dyffryn
5 Farmyard Nursery Woodland Garden
6 Felindre
7 Glangwenffrwd
8 Henblas
9 Llanaerchaeron
10 Llanllyr
11 Llwyncelyn
12 The Mill House
13 Nantcellan
14 Old Cilgwyn Gardens
15 The Old Vicarage
16 Pant-yr-Holiad
17 Plas Llidiardau
18 Plas Penglais University of Wales
19 The Walled Garden at Pigeonsford
20 Winllan

■ **Farmyard Nursery Woodland Garden, Llandysul** (Mr Richard Bramley) *Off Carmarthen rd B4336, 2nd L opp Valley Services garage. Approx 1m following signs.* Established 1-acre shaded woodland and herbaceous garden. Peaceful walks with magnificent views, natural wildlife, friendly water features, sunken walled garden. Extensive hosta, fern and bulb planting, providing all-yr-round interest. This garden and adjoining plantsman's nursery boast the biggest collection of hand pollinated hellebores in the country. NCCPG for Tricyrtis. Coffee shop. *Adm £1 Chd free (ACNO to British Diabetic Assoc). For NGS Suns, March 26 (Hellebore Day) (9-6), April 16, June 25 (9-7). Special visits arranged for groups or horticultural societies.* **Tel 01559 363389**

Felindre, Aberarth, Aberaeron (Mr & Mrs Peter Davis) *1m N of Aberaeron on A487. Turn L towards sea after bridge.* 1-acre informal garden, 200 yds from sea, partly rough hillside. Salt-hardy coastal shrubs, pines, eucalyptus, mulberry. Wide variety of herbaceous plants, including geraniums, primulas, euphorbia and salvias, growing in sun and shade on dry stone walls and pavement, and damp pond edges. Productive vegetable garden. *Visitors welcome all yr, please* **Tel 01545 570870**

Glangwenffrwd, nr Tregaron (Mr & Mrs John Escott) *10m NNW of Lampeter on B4342 Talsarn-Llangeitho Rd.* Picturesque 5-acre garden sheltered by mature woodland. Extensive lawns, pond, stream and pretty bridge. Meadow walk. Mixed borders with range of roses, primulas, herbaceous plants and shrubs leading to woodland area and recently planted arboretum. TEAS. *Adm £2 Chd 50p. Sun June 11 (2-6). Private visits welcome May to July, please* **Tel 01974 821202**

Henblas, Abermad, Llanfarian (Professor & Mrs Ian Parrott) *2m S from Aberystwyth on A487. At Llanfarian follow A485 for just over 1m, white gate on L (before Abermad) Henblas at bottom of $\frac{1}{4}$m drive.* Garden approx $1\frac{1}{2}$ acres. 40′ wistaria. Herbaceous island beds, roses, clematis etc. Formal herb and vegetable garden, stiles to wildflower meadow. TEAS. *Adm £1.50 Chd 50p. Sun July 9 (10.30-5)*

Llanaerchaeron, Ciliau Aeron, Aberaeron (Mr Paul Boland, Property Manager) *2.5m inland from Aberaeron, N of the A482 to Lampeter.* 12-acre gardens of Nash house undergoing restoration. 2 walled gardens contain recreated rose parterre, fruit, vegetables etc. Work in the walled gardens has been carried out by dedicated volunteers. TEA. *Adm £2 Chd free. Sun Aug 20 (11-5) Also Sun July 2 (11-5) in conjunction with NGS Millennium Art Exhibition at University of Wales, Lampeter*

Llanllyr, Talsarn (Mr & Mrs Robert Gee) *6m NW of Lampeter on B4337 to Llanrhystud.* Large early C19 garden, renovated, replanted and extended since 1989. Shrub rose borders. Large pond with bog and water plants; formal water garden. Laburnum arbour; avenues of flowering trees. Formal box and herb garden. Newly planted allegorical labyrinth. Many interesting plants. TEAS. *Adm £2 Chd 50p (ACNO to Llanfihangel Church Restoration Fund). Sun June 18 (2-6). Also Sun July 2 (2-6) in conjunction with NGS Millennium Art Exhibition at University of Wales, Lampter. Private visits welcome April to Oct. Please* **Tel 01570 470900**

Llwyncelyn, Glandyfi (Mr & Mrs Stewart Neal) *Adjoining The Mill House. On A487 Machynlleth (6m). From Aberystwyth (12m) turn R just before Glandyfi sign.* 8-acre hillside garden/arboretum alongside Dyfi tributary, collections of hybrid/specie rhododendrons, azaleas, camellias, bluebells in oak woodland, hydrangeas, fernery, potager and unusual plants. TEAS. *Adm £2 Chd 50p includes entrance to The Mill House. Sun May 14 (11-6) Groups welcome by appt.* **Tel 01654 781203**

The Mill House, Glandyfi (Prof & Mrs J M Pollock) *On main A487 Machynlleth $5\frac{1}{2}$m. From Aberystwyth 12m; turn R up lane almost directly opp sign for Glandyfi (on L). 2nd house up lane, approx 150yds.* Picturesque garden of a former watermill, with millstream, millpond, and several waterfalls in woodland setting, about $1\frac{1}{2}$ acre. Azaleas, rhododendrons and Spring colour enhance waterside vistas, and new tree planting continues a programme of woodland development and rejuvenation. *Open jointly with Llwyncelyn Sun May 14 (11-6) Private visits at other times by appt.* **Tel 01654 781342**

NEW **Nantcellan, Clarach** (Peter and Celia Gardner) *3m N of Aberystwyth, in Bow St, turn W to Llangorwen and Clarach. In $1\frac{1}{2}$m turn R on B4572. Nantcellan is 300yds on L. [Map ref 599845].* 2 acres. Gently sloping, S facing, terraced garden of C17 farmhouse with views across Clarach Valley. Rose garden. Mixed borders, shrubs, recently planted indigenous woodland surrounding wildflower meadow and pond. Vegetable garden. TEA. *Adm £1.50 Chd 50p (ACNO to Abbeyfield Society Aberystwyth). Sat June 24 (11-6)*

Old Cilgwyn Gardens (Mr & Mrs E Fitzwilliams) *Situated 1m N of Newcastle Emlyn on the B4571, turn R into entrance.* A mixed garden, mainly woodland, of 14 acres set in 900 acres of parkland, 53 acres of which are Sites of Special Scientific Interest; snowdrops, daffodils, bluebells, rhododendrons, a large tulip tree, well trained fremontodendron, crinodendron and many hydrangeas make this a plantsman's garden of great interest. *Adm £1.50 Chd free. Private visits welcome all year, please* **Tel 01239 710244**

The Old Vicarage, Llangeler (Mr & Mrs J C Harcourt) *On A484 15m N of Carmarthen and 4m E of Newcastle Emlyn, from N Emlyn turn down lane on L in Llangeler before church.* A garden gem created since Sept 1993. Less than 1 acre divided into 3 areas of roses, shrubs and semi-formal pool with an interesting collection of unusual herbaceous plants. TEAS. *Adm £1.50 Chd 50p. Suns June 25, July 23 (11-8). Private visits welcome, please* **Tel 01559 371168**

Pant-yr-Holiad, Rhydlewis (Mr and Mrs G H Taylor) *12m NW Llandysul. NE Cardigan. From coast rd take B4334 at Brynhoffnant S towards Rhydlewis; after 1m turn L; driveway 2nd L.* 5-acres embracing walled garden housing tender plants, alpine beds, water features, rare trees and shrubs in woodland setting; extensive collection rhododendron species; fancy water-fowl. Collections of birch and unusual herbaceous plants. Home of 'Holiad' rhododendron hybrids. Featured on regional TV and radio. TEA. *Adm £2 Chd £1. For NGS Suns April 23, May 7 (2-5)*

Plas Llidiardau, Llanilar ♿✂❀ (Laura A Stalbow & G Taylor) *7m SE of Aberystwyth. Turn off A487 2m S of Aberystwyth onto A485 to Tregaron and Llanilar. From Llanilar take B4575 to Trawsgoed. Plas Llidiardau is $^3/_4$m on R.* 7-acre country house garden redeveloped and planted since 1985. Wide selection of unusual plants and environments. Double herbaceous borders, formal pond, gravel garden, walled garden, organic raised beds, wooded areas, stream, wildlife pond. TEAS. *Adm £1.50 Chd 50p. Sun July 16 (1-6). Private visits welcome May to July, please* **Tel 01974 241434**

Plas Penglais University of Wales Aberystwyth ✂❀ (Professor & Mrs D Llwyd Morgan) *A487 1m N of Aberystwyth on Penglais Hill.* Originally part of private mansion, sheltered from prevailing winds by broad leafed woodland. The gardens contain rockery, lawns, shrub borders and walled terrace. Extensive lawned area with specimen trees and island beds of many unusual species. Remains of old 'order beds' of Botany Dept. Large temperate and tropical greenhouse containing many exotic species still used for academic studies. TEA. *Adm £2 Chd 50p. Sun Aug 13 (2-6)*

■ **The Walled Garden at Pigeonsford, nr Llangranog** ❀ (Mr & Dr D Pritchard) *On A487 14m from Cardigan, at Pentregat turn N on B4321 for Pontgarreg. $^3/_4$m past Pontgarreg turn L at Xrds. (Ski slope is R turn). Entrance signposted R.* 1 acre of S facing early C19 walled garden rejuvenated to grow choice herbaceous, shrubs, vegetables and fruit. $1\frac{1}{2}$ acres of natural woodland and riverside and 2 acres of trees and shrubs started in 1997. Olive grove. TEAS. *Adm £2 Chd 50p. Open daily Easter to Oct 31 (10-6). For NGS Suns June 4, July 16 (10-6)*

Winllan, Talsarn (Mr and Mrs Ian Callan) *8m NNW of Lampeter on B4342, Talsarn-Llangeitho rd.* 6-acres wildlife garden owned by botanists happy to share their knowledge with visitors. The garden includes a large pond, herb-rich meadow, small woodland and 600 yds of river bank walk. Over 200 species of wildflowers with attendant butterflies, dragonflies and birds. Limited suitability for wheelchairs. *Adm £1.50 Chd 50p (under 12 free). Open May & June daily (2-6). Also private visits welcome July & Aug, please* **Tel 01570 470612**

THE GARDEN CONSERVANCY

The Garden Conservancy is a not-for-profit organisation in the United States dedicated to preserving America's exceptional private gardens and facilitating their transition from private to independent not-for-profit ownership and operation. The Garden Conservancy works in partnership with individual garden owners, and public and private organisations, and uses its legal, financial, and horticultural resources to secure each garden's future and to make it permanently accessible to the public.

In 2000, the Conservancy's Open Days Program will once again invite the public to peek behind the gates of over 400 of America's best private gardens which range from a Feng Shui-inspired Arizona desert garden to a New Hampshire parlour garden with a thyme lawn and herbaceous border. By opening these otherwise private gardens, the Conservancy brings to light the importance of preserving fine gardens for future generations and is building a constituency of committed individuals willing to act on behalf of exceptional gardens.

THE NATIONAL GARDENS SCHEME

MILLENNIUM ART EXHIBITION OF

CEREDIGION GARDENS

UNIVERSITY OF WALES, LAMPETER
1–21 JULY 2000

Paintings and engravings of 50 Wales based artists have been collected together over the past year to illustrate the National Gardens Scheme Gardens of Ceredigion. This unique exhibition will be shown in the Old Hall of St David's Building of the University in Lampeter.

All paintings will be for sale

Part of the University's collection of rare European Herbals will also be on view in the Founder's Library.

Contemporary Art Exhibition: The Old Hall 1–21 July, Monday–Saturday 11–5pm & Sunday 2–5pm

Old Herbals Exhibition: Founders Library, 1–20 July, Monday–Thursday 2–4.30pm

GALA AFTERNOON
QUADRANGLE, UNIVERSITY OF WALES, LAMPETER, CEREDIGION
SATURDAY 1 JULY 2000
2–5pm

You are invited to our Gala Afternoon to celebrate the opening of both exhibitions

Mega Plant Sale
Teas
Live Entertainment

Entrance to Gala Afternoon
£2.00 adults, 50p children under 16

Further information: County Organiser, Ceredigion.

Denbighshire & Colwyn

Hon County Organiser: Mrs Sue Rathbone, Bryn Celyn, Llanbedr, Ruthin, Denbighshire LL15 1TT Tel 01824 702077
Assistant Hon County Organiser: Miss Marion MacNicoll, Trosyffordd, Ystrad Road, Denbighshire LL16 4RL Tel 01745 812247
Hon County Treasurer: Mr A Challoner, 13 The Village, Bodelwyddan, Denbighshire LL18 5UR Tel 01745 583451

DATES OF OPENING

Regular openings
For details see garden description
Bodrhyddan, Rhuddlan

By appointment only
For telephone numbers and other details see garden descriptions. Private visits welcomed
Castanwydden, Fforddlas, Llandyrnog
Donadea Lodge, Babell
Merlyn, Moelfre, Abergele
Trosyffordd, Ystrad
Tyn Yr Odyn, Llannefydd

March 5 Sunday
Caereuni, Godre'r Gaer

April 2 Sunday
Caereuni, Godre'r Gaer
The Old Rectory, Llanfihangel Glyn Myfyr

May 7 Sunday
Caereuni, Godre'r Gaer
Plas Ffordd Ddwr, Llandyrnog

May 12 Friday
Dibleys Nurseries, Cefn-rhydd, Llanelidan

May 13 Saturday
Dibleys Nurseries, Cefn-rhydd, Llanelidan

May 14 Sunday
Dibleys Nurseries, Cefn-rhydd, Llanelidan
Gwysaney Hall, Mold

May 20 Saturday
Dolhyfryd & Lawnt Cottage, The Lawnt, Denbigh

May 21 Sunday
Dolhyfryd & Lawnt Cottage, The Lawnt, Denbigh
Rhagatt Hall, Carrog
Tyn-y-Graig, Llandrillo

June 4 Sunday
Beaver Grove House, Betws-y-Coed
33 Bryn Twr & Lynton, Abergele
Caereuni, Godre'r Gaer
Golygfa'r Llywelyn, Capel Garmon

June 11 Sunday
Glyn Arthur, Llandyrnog
Nantclwyd Hall, Ruthin

June 24 Saturday
Bryn Celyn, Llanbedr
Golf Cottage, Colwyn Bay

June 25 Sunday
Tal-y-Bryn Farm, Llannefydd
Tros-y-Parc, Ystrad, Denbigh

June 29 Thursday
Bryn Celyn, Llanbedr

July 2 Sunday
Caereuni, Godre'r Gaer
The Old Rectory, Llanfihangel Glyn Myfyr

July 9 Sunday
Gwysaney Hall, Mold
Rhyllon, St Asaph

July 15 Saturday
Cerrigllwydion Hall, Llandyrnog

July 16 Sunday
Bodrhyddan, Rhuddlan
The Coach House, Llandyrnog
Pentre Farm & Tan-y-Coed, Ruthin

August 6 Sunday
Caereuni, Godre'r Gaer
Ffridd-y-Gog, Corwen

August 20 Sunday
33 Bryn Twr & Lynton, Abergele

September 3 Sunday
Caereuni, Godre'r Gaer

October 1 Sunday
Caereuni, Godre'r Gaer

DESCRIPTIONS OF GARDENS

NEW **Beaver Grove House, Betws-y-Coed** (John Heminsley) *Opp side of R Conwy from village of Betws-y-Coed, one entrance drive on A470 200yds N of Waterloo Bridge; other entrance drive 800yds N of bridge on same rd.* Magic of a lost, old, unrestored garden; grass paths winding between wonderful, old magnolias, azaleas and rhododendrons, leading to small arboretum. Approx 5 acres. TEA. *Adm £1.50 Chd 25p. Sun June 4 (2-6)*

■ **Bodrhyddan, Rhuddlan** ✂❀ (The Lord & Lady Langford) *From Rhuddlan take A5151 to Dyserth. Garden is on L.* Parterre garden in the French style; formal garden, clipped yew hedge, water garden, woodland walk leading to St Mary's Well. TEAS. *Adm £2 Chd 50p (ACNO to St Kentigern's Hospice). House and garden open every Tues-Thurs June to end Sept (2-5.30). For NGS Sun July 16.*

Bryn Celyn, Llanbedr ♿✂❀ (Mr & Mrs S Rathbone) *From Ruthin take A494 towards Mold. After 1½m, turn L at Griffin Inn onto B5429. Proceed 1½m; garden on R [OS Ref SJ 133.603].* 1 acre; mixed borders; walled garden; old-fashioned roses. Cream TEAS. *Adm £2 Chd 25p (ACNO to St Kentigern's Hospice Garden Fund) Sat, Thurs June 24, 29 (2-6)*

33 Bryn Twr & Lynton, Abergele ✂❀ (Mr & Mrs Colin Knowlson) *From A55 heading W, take slip rd to Abergele. Turn L at roundabout then over t-lights; 1st L signed Llanfair T H. 3rd rd on L, no. 33 is on L.* Two connected gardens of approx ¾ acre in total, containing patio and pond areas; mixed herbaceous and shrub borders. Not suitable for wheelchairs. TEAS June 4 only. *Combined adm £2.50 OAPs £2 Chd free (ACNO to St Michael's, Abergele Scout Group). Suns June 4, Aug 20 (2-6). Also by appt, please* **Tel 01745 828201**

DENBIGHSHIRE & COLWYN

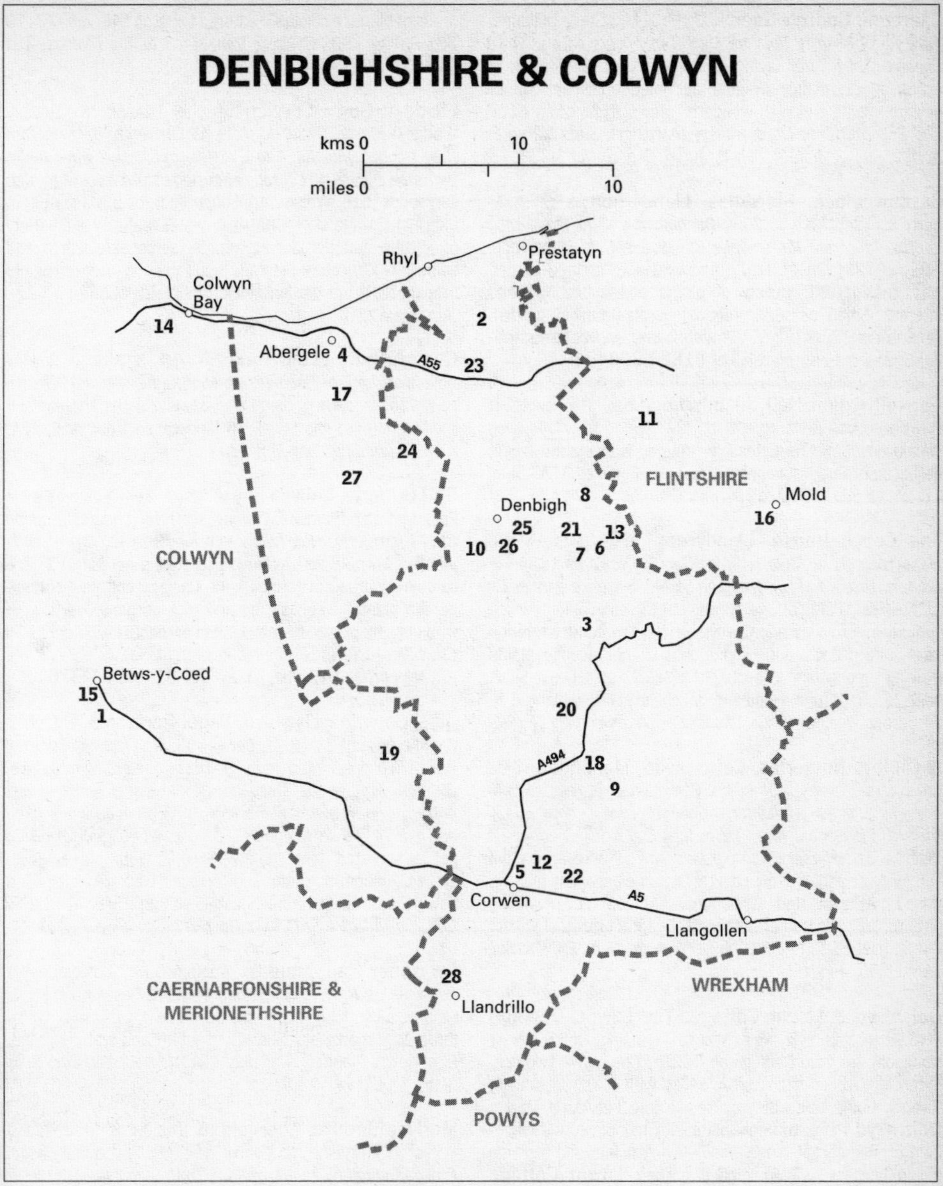

KEY

1 Beaver Grove House
2 Bodrhyddan
3 Bryn Celyn
4 33 Bryn Twr & Lynton
5 Caereuni
6 Castanwydden
7 Cerrigllwydion Hall
8 The Coach House
9 Dibleys Nurseries
10 Dolhyfryd & Lawnt Cottage
11 Donadea Lodge
12 Ffridd-y-Gog
13 Glyn Arthur
14 Golf Cottage
15 Golygfa'r Llywelyn
16 Gwysaney Hall
17 Merlyn
18 Nantclwyd Hall
19 The Old Rectory
20 Pentre Farm & Tan-y-Coed
21 Plas Ffordd Ddwr
22 Rhagatt Hall
23 Rhyllon
24 Tal-y-Bryn Farm
25 Tros-y-Parc
26 Trosyffordd
27 Tyn Yr Odyn
28 Tyn-y-Graig

Caereuni, Godre'r Gaer ♿✂ (Mr & Mrs Steve Williams) *Take A5 Corwen to Bala rd. Turn R at t-lights onto A494 to Chester. 1st R after layby; house ¼m on L.* Microcosm of exotic styles, mainly oriental and mediterranean; full of unusual plants and with wonderful views. TEAS. *Adm £1.50 Chd 25p (ACNO to Hope House, Oswestry). Suns March 5, April 2, May 7, June 4, July 2, Aug 6, Sept 3, Oct 1(2-5)*

Castanwydden, Fforddlas, Llandyrnog ♿❀ (A M Burrows Esq) *Take rd from Denbigh due E to Llandyrnog approx 4m. From Ruthin take B5429 due N to Llandyrnog. [OS ref 1264 (sheet 116)].* Approx 1-acre cottage garden with considerable variety of plants and bulbs. Yr-round interest. Small nursery propagating plants from garden. TEAS. *Adm £1.50 Chd £1. Private visits and coaches welcome, by appt only please* **Tel 01824 790404**

Cerrigllwydion Hall, Llandyrnog ✂❀ (Mr & Mrs D Howard) *E of Denbigh. On B5429 ½m from Llandyrnog village on Ruthin rd.* Extensive grounds with mature trees; herbaceous borders; vegetable and greenhouses. TEAS. *Adm £1.75 Chd 50p (ACNO to Llanynys Church). Sat July 15 (2-6)*

The Coach House, Llandyrnog ✂❀ (Mrs F Bell) *Llandyrnog. Take Mold rd from Denbigh towards village of Bodfari. Turn R to Llandyrnog on B5429. Entrance approx 1m on LH-side.* Small cottage garden set in semi-walled garden with views of valley and Clwdyian Hills. Created from rough farm land 13 yrs ago. Some unusual herbaceous plants thriving amongst an assortment of ducks and hens. Short walk to ponds and woodland which is being replanted to encourage wildlife. TEAS. *Adm £2 Chd free. Sun July 16 (2-6)*

■ **Dibleys Nurseries, Cefn-rhydd, Llanelidan** ✂❀ (Mr & Mrs R Dibley) *Ruthin 4m; Wrexham 14m. Take A525 to Xrds by Llysfasi Agricultural College. Turn L onto B5429 towards Llanelidan. After 1½m turn L at Xrds. Continue up lane for 1m. Nursery and gardens on L.* 9-acre arboretum with wide selection of unusual trees, some becoming mature, others newly planted. Glasshouses of gold-medal-winning streptocarpus and other pot plants. Beautiful views of Vale of Clwyd. *Adm £1.50 Chd 50p (ACNO to Action Aid). Fri, Sat, Sun May 12, 13, 14 (10-5)*

Dolhyfryd & Lawnt Cottage, The Lawnt, Denbigh ♿✂❀ (Captain & Mrs Michael Cunningham & Mr T Hodgson) *1m from Denbigh on B4501 to Nantglyn.* Two very different gardens set in small valley with R Ystrad running through both. Acres of crocuses in late Feb/early March. **Dolhyfryd** Paths through wildflower meadows and woodland of magnificent trees, shade-loving plants and azaleas; mixed borders; walled kitchen garden. **Lawnt Cottage** Small cottage garden filled with spring bulbs and blossom. Woodland treasure hunt. Cream TEAS and plant stall. *Combined adm £2.50 Chd 50p (ACNO to Medical Emergency Relief International-MERLIN). Sat, Sun May 20, 21 (2.30 -6.30). Private parties welcome, please* **Tel 01745 814805**

Donadea Lodge, Babell ♿✂❀ (Mr & Mrs P Beaumont) *Turn off A541 Mold to Denbigh at Afonwen, signposted Babell; T-junction turn L. A55 Chester to St Asaph take B5122 to Caerwys, 3rd turn on L.* Shady 1-acre garden with unusual plants and shrubs; climbing and shrub roses, clematis and areas of blended colours. Featured twice on S4C. *Adm £2 Chd 20p. Private visits welcome from May 1 to Aug 1, please* **Tel 01352 720204**

Ffridd-y-Gog, Corwen ♿✂❀ (David & Lindsay Watkins) *Ffordd Ty Cerrig. Take A5 Corwen to Bala rd. Turn R at t-lights onto A494 to Chester, then 1st R after layby. Entrance 200yds on L through housing estate.* ¼ acre garden surrounds C18 Welsh farmhouse (not open). Planted in informal cottage style with small water features and variety of shrubs and herbaceous plants, some established and some more recently planted. Small nursery area of plants propagated from garden stock. TEAS. *Adm £1.50 Chd 25p. Sun Aug 6 (2-5)*

Glyn Arthur, Llandyrnog ✂ (Mr & Mrs P Rowley Williams) *5m E of Denbigh, 6m N of Ruthin. From A541 take B5429 to Llandyrnog, then follow signs.* 2 acres; azaleas and rhododendrons; short walk to landscaped trout pool. TEA. *Adm £2 Chd 50p. Sun June 11 (2-6)*

Golf Cottage, Colwyn Bay ✂❀ (Mr Keith Smithies & Mr Paul Moffatt) *From A55 follow signs to mountain zoo on B5113 into King's Rd, follow into King's Drive, turn R at T-junction. Garden 200yds on L.* Fascinating garden of 1 acre containing areas of formal, wild, Chinese and new cottage garden planting. Ponds, bog and rock gardens overflowing with unusual plants. New millenium garden! TEAS. *Adm £1.50 Chd 50p (ACNO to Leukaemia Research). Sat June 24 (10-4). Private parties welcome, please* **Tel 01492 534378**

NEW **Golygfa'r Llywelyn, Capel Garmon** ♿❀ (Jeff & Wendy Tyson) *1m E of Betws-y-Coed. From junction of A5/A470 proceed N for ½m, then 1st signed rd on R to Capel Garmon. Proceed up steep hill (single track) for ½m, 1st entrance on R, over small bridge, through open white gate, down drive 100yds to arches. [OS grid ref 803.555].* Hillside garden created among natural rocks with stone walls, arches, meadering paths and terraces. Secret corners and flowing water in beautiful mountain setting. TEAS. *Adm £1.50 Chd 25p (ACNO toSt David's Hospice). Sun June 4 (2-6)*

Gwysaney Hall, Mold ❀ (Captain & Mrs Davies-Cooke) *Entrance on R, ½m from Mold on A541 Denbigh rd.* Picturesque park with many mature trees; extensive walks through gardens, shrubberies, pinetum and water garden. Fine views. Plants if available. TEA. *Adm £2 Chd 50p. Suns May 14, July 9 (2-5.30)*

Merlyn, Moelfre, Abergele ✂ (Drs J E & B E J Riding) *Leave A55 Chester to Conwy rd at Bodelwyddan Castle. Proceed uphill by castle wall for 1m to junction with B5381 (white bungalow). Turn R towards Betws yn Rhos, follow for 2m, then fork L after telephone box. Garden ⅓m on R.* 2 acres developed from a field since 1987. Long mixed border; damp and gravel garden; shrubs and old roses; rhododendrons and azaleas; spring garden. Views of sea. Yr-round interest. *Adm £1.50 Chd 25p. Private parties welcome Feb to Nov incl by prior arrangement, please* **Tel 01745 824435**

Nantclwyd Hall, Ruthin ✂❀ (Sir Philip & Lady Isabella Naylor-Leyland) *Take A494 from Ruthin to Corwen. Garden is 1½m from Pwllglas on L.* Approx 3 acres of formal gardens and further grounds. Temples and follies by Sir Clough Williams-Ellis. Grotto by Belinda Eade. Rustic bridge over R Clwyd. *Adm £2 Chd 50p. Sun June 11 (2-6). Private visits welcome following written application*

The Old Rectory, Llanfihangel Glyn Myfyr ♿✂❀ (Mr & Mrs E T Hughes) *From Ruthin take B5105 SW for 12m to Llanfihangel Glyn Myfyr. Turn R just after Crown Inn (follow The Old Rectory signs). Proceed for ⅓m, garden on L.* 9-yr-old garden of approx 1 acre set in beautiful, tranquil, sheltered valley. Abundance of spring flowers; mixed borders; water, bog, rock and gravel gardens; walled garden with old roses and bower. TEAS. *Adm £2 Chd 25p (ACNO to Imperial Cancer Research Fund - for prostate cancer only). Suns April 2, July 2 (2-6)*

Pentre Farm & Tan-y-Coed, Ruthin ✂❀ (Norma & Doug Dailey and Tania & Andrew Spink) *From Ruthin take A494 Corwen Rd for 3m to Pwllglas. Turn R after Fox and Hounds public house and follow signs for ¼m.* 2 attractive adjoining gardens with wonderful views of Clwydian Range. Created 8yrs ago, both very different. 2 lawned gardens on hillside with trees, shrubs, borders, herbaceous and island beds. Patio areas filled with pots and containers. Small stream. New features at Pentre Farm incl woodland walk and bog garden. New wildflower garden at Tan-y-Coed. TEAS. *Adm £2 Chd 50p (ACNO to Pwllglas Village Hall). Sun July 16 (2-6)*

Plas Ffordd Ddwr, Llandyrnog ♿✂❀ (Mr & Mrs D J Thomas) *2m E of Denbigh. Follow signs to Llandyrnog from roundabout at Ruthin end of Denbigh bypass A525. Entrance 2m on R.* 2½ acre country garden, elevated position in Vale of Clywd. Established shrubs, lawns and mature trees. Woodland walk to newly planted area around pond. Further conservation land recently acquired. Bring wellies if wet. TEAS. *Adm £1.50 Chd 50p (ACNO to St Kentigern Hospice Garden Project). Sun May 7 (2-5.30)*

Rhagatt Hall, Carrog ♿✂❀ (Cdr & Mrs F J C Bradshaw) *1m NE of Corwen. A5 from Llangollen, 3m short of Corwen, turn R (N) for Carrog at garage, cross R Dee and keep bearing L. 1st opening on R after Carrog and seeing river again.* 5-acre garden with azaleas, rhododendrons, trees and rare magnolias; bluebell wood; extensive views. TEAS. *Adm £2 Chd £1. Sun May 21 (2-6)*

Rhyllon, St Asaph ♿✂❀ (Mr & Mrs M Dodd & Mrs D M Dodd) *From St Asaph take A55 towards Chester then 1st L, 1st house on R.* 1 acre; herbaceous borders, wonderfully atmosheric pond area. Mature trees and shrubs. TEA. *Adm £1.50 Chd 25p. Sun July 9 (2-6)*

Tal-y-Bryn Farm, Llannefydd ♿❀ (Mr & Mrs Gareth Roberts) *From Henllan take rd signed Llannefydd. After 2½m turn R signed Bont Newydd. Garden ½m on L.* Recently designed working farmhouse garden planted to make best use of existing buildings and features, framing wonderful views. *Adm £1.50 Chd 25p. Sun June 25 (2-6). Private visits welcome by appt, please* **Tel 01745 540 256**

Tros-y-Parc, Ystrad, Denbigh ♿✂❀ (Mr & Mrs Stephen Cheshire) *A525 Ruthin to Denbigh. At roundabout follow sign to town centre. 2nd L after roundabout signed to Prion and Saron. Entrance on L after ½m.* 2 acres; established shrubs; lawns; herbaceous borders; partly walled; mature trees. Beautiful views across valley to Clwydian Hills. TEAS. *Adm £2 Chd 25p (ACNO to St Kentigern's Hospice Garden Fund). Sun June 25 (2-6)*

Trosyffordd, Ystrad ✂❀ (Miss Marion MacNicoll) *From A525 Denbigh to Ruthin rd, turn R in outskirts of Denbigh on Ystrad rd signed Prion and Saron. Follow for 1½m, Trosyffordd is 2nd drive on R after 1st hill.* Medium-sized, painter's garden of mixed herbaceous and shrub borders; full of colour. Many unusual plants, some for sale. TEA. *Adm £2 Chd 20p. Private visits welcome 1st May to 1st September, please* **Tel 01745 812247**

Tyn Yr Odyn, Llannefydd ♿✂❀ (Mr & Mrs J S Buchanan) *8m from Denbigh. From B5382 signed Henllan and Llansannan. In Bryn Rhyd yr Arian, turn sharp R signed Llannefydd and Aled Plants. Garden ½m on L.* Approx ⅔ acre cottage garden on bank of R Aled. Stream, ponds and alpine garden; conifers, heathers, roses and shrubs; greenhouses and alpine house. Featured on HTV's Get Gardening September '98. Small nursery adjacent. *Adm £1.50 Chd 50p. Private visits welcome any day April to September, please* **Tel 01745 870394**

Tyn-y-Graig, Llandrillo ✂❀ (Major & Mrs H Robertson) *1½m from Llandrillo towards Bala, turn R off B4401 Corwen to Bala rd. [Map ref SJ 008.377].* Hillside garden of approx 1½ acres developed over 25 yrs. Incorporates 6 descending, landscaped pools. TEA. *Adm £2 Chd 25p. (ACNO to Wrexham Maelor Hospital NHS Trust). Sun May 21 (2-5.30)*

Flintshire & Wrexham

Hon County Organiser Mrs J R Forbes, Pen-y-Wern, Pontblyddyn, Mold, Flintshire CH7 4HN
Tel 01978 760531

Assistant Hon County Organiser Mrs Gwen Manuel, Tir-y-Fron, Llangollen Road, Ruabon LL14 6RW
Tel 01978 821633

Hon County Treasurer Mr Peter Manuel, Tir-y-Fron, Llangollen Road, Ruabon LL14 6RW
Tel 01978 821633

DATES OF OPENING

By appointment only

For telephone numbers and other details see garden descriptions. Private visits welcomed

Cartref, Babell
Tri Thy, Pontybodkin nr Mold

March 19 Sunday
Erddig Hall, nr Wrexham

April 9 Sunday
Hawarden Castle, Hawarden

April 23 Sunday
Tir-y-Fron, Ruabon

April 24 Monday
Tir-y-Fron, Ruabon

May 14 Sunday
Hawarden Castle, Hawarden

May 21 Sunday
Argoed Cottage, Overton
Three Chimneys, Rhostyllen

May 28 Sunday
Pen-y-Bryn, Llangollen

June 4 Sunday
The Garden House, Erbistock
Pen-y-Bryn, Llangollen

June 8 Thursday
Bryn Hafod, Treuddyn, Mold
Tudor Farm, Bwlchgwyn

June 13 Tuesday
Chirk Castle, nr Wrexham

June 18 Sunday
The Garden House, Erbistock
Pen-y-Wern, Pontblyddyn

June 23 Friday
Plas-yn-Llan, Llanrhaeadr-ym-Mochnant

June 25 Sunday
The Cottage Nursing Home, Mold
Dolwen, Cefn Coch
Llangedwyn Hall, Llangedwyn

July 2 Sunday
The Bungalow, Ysceifiog
The Garden House, Erbistock

July 16 Sunday
The Garden House, Erbistock
Tudor Farm, Bwlchgwyn

August 17 Thursday
Erddig Hall, nr Wrexham

August 27 Sunday
Dolwen, Cefn Coch

September 10 Sunday
The Garden House, Erbistock

October 22 Sunday
Three Chimneys, Rhostyllen

DESCRIPTIONS OF GARDENS

Argoed Cottage, Overton ♿❀ (Mr & Mrs C J Billington) *App Overton from Wrexham on A528 cross over Overton Bridge and in about ¾m on brow of hill turn L into Argoed Lane.* 1¾-acre garden. Interesting trees and shrubs. Herbaceous beds; roses; vegetable garden and water feature. *Adm £2 Chd free. Sun May 21 (2-6)*

Bryn Hafod, Treuddyn, Mold ✂❀ (Mr & Mrs Ffoulkes Jones) *Turn S off A5104 1m W of Treuddyn into Ffordd y Blaenau (signed). Follow lane for 1¼m.* Country garden of about 1 acre in elevated position growing a wide variety of plants in mixed borders and differing situations. TEAS in aid of St Mary's Church, Treuddyn. *Adm £1.50 Chd 50p. Thurs June 8 (11-6)*

The Bungalow, Ysceifiog ✂ (Mr & Mrs H D Ponton) *Turn off the A541 Mold to Denbigh Rd on to the B5121 Lixwm Brynford Rd. 1m to sign post, turn L for Ysceifiog. A55 rd to Holywell. Turn on to B5121 at t-lights, about 4m to signpost, turn R for Ysceifiog.* Garden of approx 1 acre. Some recently landscaped, incl an old stone quarry. Terraced garden using large stone boulders. Surrounded by trees with large variety of shrubs, flowers, climbers. TEAS. *Adm £1.50 Chd free (ACNO to St Mary's Church, Ysceifiog). Sun July 2 (2-6)*

Cartref, Babell ♿✂❀ (Mrs D Jones) *Caerwys Rd. Turn off A541 Mold to Denbigh rd at Afonwen signposted Babell. At T-junction turn R, Black Lion Inn turn L, 1st L. 4th house. From Holywell old A55, turn L for Gorsedd, then R, L at Gorsedd Church for Babell, 2m down that rd turn R at Babell 'Chapel House' 4th house.* Very attractive well-stocked cottage garden; clematis, climbers, vegetables and roses. *Adm £1 Chd 25p (ACNO to Cancer Research). June and July by appt, please* **Tel 01352 720638**

▲ Chirk Castle, nr Wrexham ♿ (The National Trust) *Chirk 8m SE of Llangollen. Off A5 in Chirk by War Memorial. Entrance at New Hall.* 4½ acres of trees and flowering shrubs, rhododendrons, azaleas, rockery, yew topiary. 7 acres of woodland. TEAS. *Adm £2.80 OAP/Chd £1.40. Tues June 13 (11-4)*

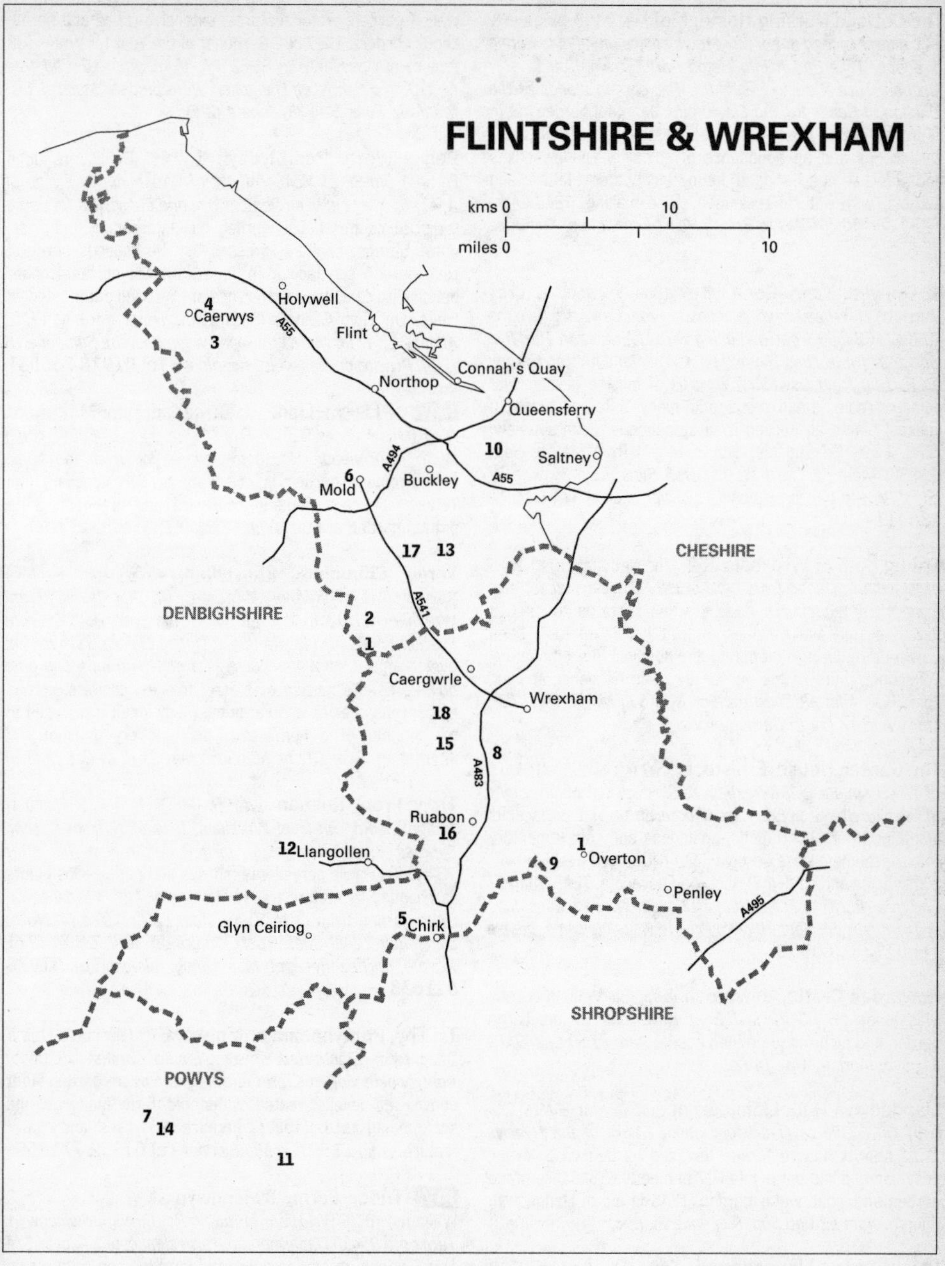

KEY

1 Argoed Cottage
2 Bryn Hafod
3 The Bungalow
4 Cartref
5 Chirk Castle
6 The Cottage Nursing Home
7 Dolwen
8 Erddig Hall
9 The Garden House
10 Hawarden Castle
11 Llangedwyn Hall
12 Pen-y-Bryn
13 Pen-y-Wern
14 Plas-yn-Llan
15 Three Chimneys
16 Tir-y-Fron
17 Tri Thy
18 Tudor Farm

The Cottage Nursing Home, Mold ♿ (Mr & Mrs A G & L I Lanini) *Proceed out of Mold town centre on A494 in Ruthin direction. Take 2nd R into Hafod Park. Straight on to a T-junction. Turn R on to Hendy Rd. The garden stands at the junction of Hendy Rd and Clayton Rd.* Beautiful garden set in approx 1 acre. There are well established shrubs, and herbaceous and an abundance of colourful window boxes and tubs. A heart-shaped patio, incl water feature and pergola, with natural reclaimed stone walling. TEAS. *Adm £1.50 Chd 50p (ACNO to British Heart Foundation) Sun June 25 (2-5)*

■ **Dolwen, Cefn Coch** (Bob Yarwood & Jeny Marriott) *Llanrhaeadr-ym-Mochnant. From Oswestry take the B4396 (or B4580 – narrow) going W to Llanrhaeadr. Turn R in village at Three Tuns Inn and up narrow lane for 1m. Garden on R. 14m from Oswestry.* 2 acres of hillside garden with pools, stream, small wood and many different types of unusual plants all backed by a stupendous mountain view. TEAS. Every Fri and last Sun in Month from May to Sept (2-4.30). *Adm £2 Chd free. For NGS Suns June 25, Aug 27 (2-5). Private parties welcome by appt, please* **Tel 01691 780411**

Erddig Hall, nr Wrexham ♿ (The National Trust) *2m S of Wrexham. Signed from A483/A5125 Oswestry Road; also from A525 Whitchurch Road.* Garden restored to its C18 formal design incl varieties of fruit known to have been grown there during that period and now incl the National Ivy Collection. Tours of the garden by Head Gardener at 1pm, 2pm. TEA. *Adm £2 Chd free. For NGS Sun March 19 (12-3), Thurs Aug 17 (12-4) Garden only*

The Garden House, Erbistock ♿ (Mr S Wingett) *5m S of Wrexham on A528 Wrexham to Shrewsbury. Follow signs at Overton Bridge to Erbistock Church.* Shrub and herbaceous plantings in monochromatic, analogous and complementary colour schemes. Rose pergolas and hydrangea avenue (over 200 species and cultivars). Victorian dovecote. TEAS. *Adm £1 Chd free (ACNO to Frank Wingett Cancer Appeal). Suns June 4, 18, July 2, 16, Sept 10 (2-6) Private visits welcome, please* **Tel 01978 780958**

Hawarden Castle, Hawarden ♿ (Sir William & Lady Gladstone) *On B5125 just E of Hawarden village.* Large garden and picturesque ruined castle. *Adm £1.50 Chd/OAPs £1. Suns April 9, May 14 (2-6)*

Llangedwyn Hall, Llangedwyn ♿ (Mr & Mrs T M Bell) *On B4396 to Llanrhaedr about 5m W of the Llynclys Xrds.* Approx 4 acre formal terraced garden on 3 levels, designed and laid out in late C17 and early C18. Sunken rose garden and small water garden. TEAS in aid of Llangedwyn Church. *Adm £2 Chd 50p. Sun June 25 (2-6)*

Pen-y-Bryn, Llangollen ♿ (Mr & Mrs R B Attenburrow) *Signs at t-lights on A5 in centre of Llangollen. Walking distance or field parking.* 3-acre garden on wooded plateau overlooking town with panoramic view. On site of old hall with established trees, shrubs and rhododendrons; walled garden; water features; extensive lawns and herbaceous borders. 1999 BBC Gardener of the Year for Wales (UK Runner-up) as seen on BBC2 TV. TEAS. *Adm £2 Chd free (ACNO to Friends of Llangollen International Musical Eisteddfod). Suns May 28, June 4 (2-6)*

Pen-y-Wern, Pontblyddyn ♿ (Dr & Mrs John Forbes) *5m SE of Mold, 7m NW of Wrexham. On E side of A541, ½ way between Pontblyddyn and Caergwrle.* 2½-acre terraced country-house garden incl interesting small gardens. Shrubs, conifers, grasses and herbaceous borders; rose garden spectacular in June/July. Magnificent copper beech with canopy circumference of 250ft and other splendid trees. On Clwb Garddio (S4C) 1998. Water garden. TEAS. *Adm £2 Chd 50p (ACNO to Hope Parish Church). Sun June 18 (2-6). Private parties welcome, please* **Tel 01978 760531**

NEW **Plas-yn-Llan, Llanrhaeadr-ym-Mochnant** ♿ (Mrs Frances Denby) *From Oswestry take B4396 going W to Llanrhaeadr. House in square 2nd from the bank.* Plantswomans garden in courtyard of C14 coaching inn. Tender climbing plants in courtyard and orangery. Slate pathed garden at rear. *Adm £2 Chd £1. Fri June 23 (1-6)*

Three Chimneys, Rhostyllen (Mr & Mrs Hollington) *3m SW of Wrexham via Rhostyllen. From Wrexham A5152 fork R at Black Lion onto B5097. From Ruabon B5605 turn L onto B5426 signed Minera. Turn R ½m over bridge, L at Water Tower. Garden ¼m on L opp post box.* Forester's garden of 1 acre; maples, conifers, cornus and sorbus species and varieties. Many small trees used in the manner of a herbaceous border. Very unusual and interesting. *Adm £2 Chd 50p Suns May 21 (2-6) Oct 22 (1-5)*

Tir-y-Fron, Ruabon ♿ (Mr & Mrs P R Manuel) *Llangollen Rd. 5m from Wrexham, take A539 from Ruabon By-Pass, signed Llangollen, turn R on brow of hill after 200yds.* 1¾-acre garden with shrubs and herbaceous plants surrounded by mature trees with quarry. Offa's Dyke separates garden from drive. TEAS. *Adm £2 Chd free (ACNO to Llangollen Canal Boat Trust). Sun, Mon April 23, 24 (2-6), Private parties by appt May - Aug, please* **Tel 01978 821633**

Tri Thy, Pontybodkin nr Mold ♿ (Norma Restall & Daughters) *Signposted off Chester to Corwen A5104 at Pontybodkin. Follow Craft Centre signs.* ⅓-acre garden 500ft above sea level. Created within old farm buildings and surrounding land. Shrubs, herbaceous, roses and water feature. *Adm £1.50 Chd 50p By appt* **Tel 01352 771359**

NEW **Tudor Farm, Bwlchgwyn** (Mr & Mrs G Williams) *A525 Wrexham to Ruthin Rd, through Bwlchgwyn. Turn onto B5430 Llanarmon Rd. Farm signposted.* Approx 3/4 acre Cottage garden on a working farm in open countryside at 1,000'. Many small gardens and borders, densely planted with perennials, many old fashioned or unusual. TEAS in aid of the RNLI. *Adm £1.50 Chd 50p. Thurs June 8, Sun July 16 (10-6)*

Glamorgan

Hon County Organiser: Mrs L H W Williams, Llanvithyn House, Llancarfan, Barry, Glamorgan CF62 3AT Tel 01446 781232

DATES OF OPENING

Regular openings
For details see garden description
The Botanical Gardens, Swansea
Clyne Gardens, Blackpill
Dyffryn Gardens, Nr Cardiff

By appointment only
For telephone numbers and other details see garden descriptions. Private visits welcomed
6 Alma Road, Penylan, Cardiff
19 Westfield Road, Glyncoch Pontrypridd

May 14 Sunday
9 Willowbrook Gardens, Mayals, Swansea

May 21 Sunday
Llanvithyn House, Llancarfan

June 4 Sunday
Cwmpennar Gardens
Nant-y-Deri, Ystradowen

June 11 Sunday
Fonmon Castle, nr Barry
Springside, Pen-y-Turnpike, Dinas Powys
St Peters Garden, Swansea

June 14 Wednesday
11 Arno Road, Little Coldbrook, Barry (evening)

June 18 Sunday
The Clock House, Llandaff

June 25 Sunday
24 Heath Park Drive, Cardiff
Nant-y-Deri, Ystradowen

July 2 Sunday
11 Eastcliff, Southgate
Old St Mellons Gardens, Cardiff

July 9 Sunday
Nant-y-Deri, Ystradowen

July 23 Sunday
The Hidden Garden, 57 Heol Bryncwils, Sarn

July 30 Sunday
Maes-y-Wertha Farm, Bryncethin

DESCRIPTIONS OF GARDENS

6 Alma Road, Penylan, Cardiff ✠ (Mr Melvyn Rees) *N from city centre, off Marlborough Rd. Take Cardiff E junction 29 from M4, Llanedeyrn exit from Eastern Avenue, then towards Cyncoed and down Penylan Rd.* Redesigned S-facing terraced house garden 30′ × 15′ with many species from the S and E hemispheres, incl Dicksonia Antarctica; new water feature. Generally Japanese look; railway sleepers used as paving material with gravel infill. *Adm £1.50 Chd 50p. Private visits welcome, please* **Tel 029 20482200**

11 Arno Road, Little Coldbrook, Barry ✠ (Mrs D Palmer) *From A4050 Cardiff to Barry, take roundabout marked Barry Docks and Sully. Then 2nd R into Coldbrook Rd, 2nd L into Langlands Rd, then 6th R into Norwood Cresc; 1st L into Arno Rd. Limited parking.* 40′ × 30′ informal plantaholic's garden with ponds, herbaceous plants, scree garden planted with low growing alpines. As featured on Gardeners World July '98, HTV Get Gardening May '98. *Adm £1.* **Evening Opening** *Wed June 14 (6-8.30). Also private visits and small groups welcome, May to Aug please* **Tel 01446 743642**

The Botanical Gardens, Swansea ♿✠❀ (City and County of Swansea) *Exit M4 from Cardiff junction 42. Follow A483 towards Swansea City. Follow coastal rd SW of City A4067, pass St Helens cricket/rugby ground and turn R into Brynmill Lane. L at top of lane into Gower Rd, A4118. Entrance to park 50yds on L (disabled badge holders parking 'only' in park). No public car park provided at present.* 20-acres in total, formal and informal. Plantings of bedding plants, trees and shrubs and specific plant collection. Glasshouses containing orchid, tropical, temperate, economic and cacti TEAS Aug only. *Adm free. Open all week Aug (9-8), Winter months (9-5), Summer months (9-6).Guided tours by booking on* **01792 298637**

The Clock House, Llandaff ♿✠❀ (Prof and Mrs Bryan Hibbard) *Cathedral Close, 2m from Cardiff city centre. Follow signs to Cathedral via A4119. Bus: Cardiff alight Maltsters Arms.* Small walled garden; fine old trees; wide variety of shrubs and plants; important collection of shrub, species and old roses. TEA. *Adm £2 Chd free. Sun June 18 (2-6)*

Clyne Gardens, Blackpill (City and County of Swansea) *3m SW of Swansea on coast rd heading towards Mumbles A4067. Turn in at Woodman Inn, and use shared car park.* 50-acre woodland garden, with four national collections. Over 200 species and hybrid rhododendrons. Extensive bog garden. Excellent collection of exotic trees. TEA in tent in May courtesy of NSPCA. *Adm free. Open all year round, open all hours*

Cwmpennar Gardens ✠ *Mountain Ash 1m. From A4059 turn R 100yds N of the traffic lights; follow sign to Cefnpennar, uphill for ¾m. Car park 100yds past bus shelter in Cwmpennar. Two of the gardens are contiguous, the third at entrance to Cwmpennar 100yds from others.* Gardens high on mountain side in one-time coal mining village in rural surroundings. Gardens with variety of features, landscapes and unusual plants. TEAS. *Combined adm £2.50 Chd £1 (Share to St Illtyd's Church Restoration Fund). Sun June 4 (2-6)*

Ivy Cottage (Mr and Mrs D H Phillips)
Tynewydd (Mr T W Scrivens)
Woodview (Miss A & Miss R Bebb)

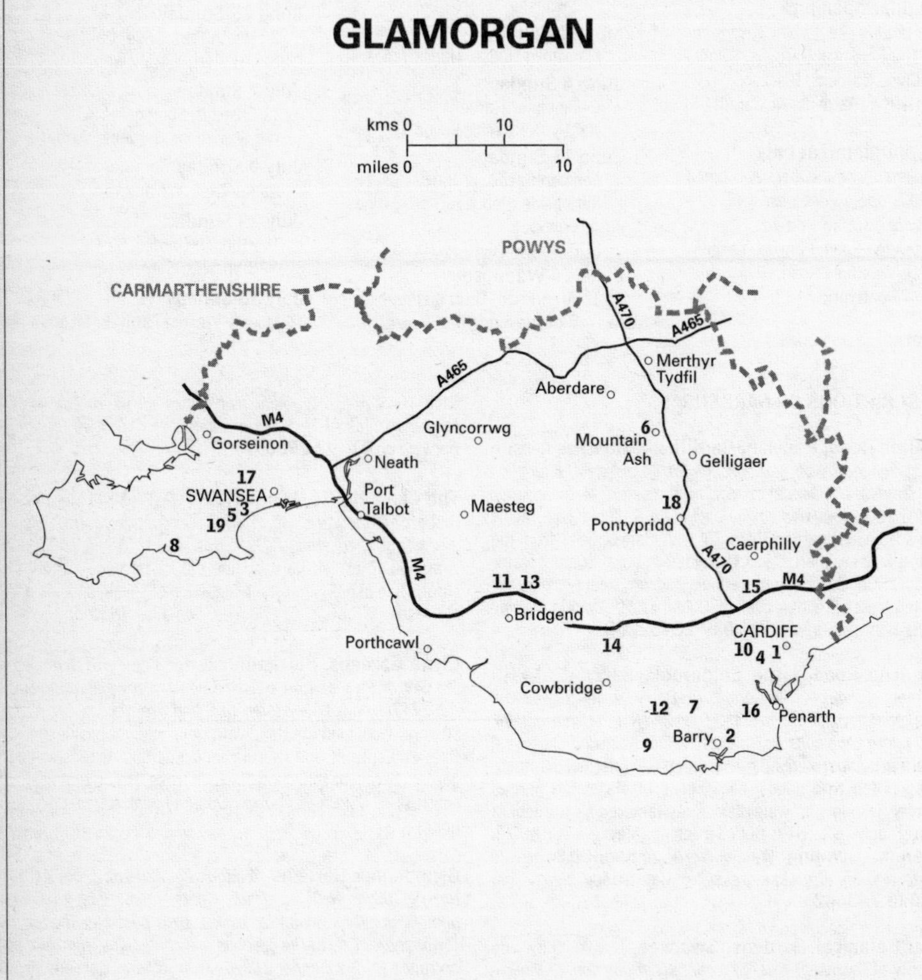

KEY

1 6 Alma Road
2 11 Arno Road
3 The Botanical Gardens
4 The Clock House
5 Clyne Gardens
6 Cwmpennar Gardens
7 Dyffryn Gardens
8 11 Eastcliff
9 Fonmon Castle
10 24 Heath Park Drive
11 The Hidden Garden
12 Llanvithyn House
13 Maes-y-Wertha Farm
14 Nant-y-Deri
15 Old Street, Mellons Gardens
16 Springside
17 St Peters Garden
18 19 Westfield Road
19 9 Willowbrook Gardens

NEW **Dyffryn Gardens, Nr Cardiff** *Exit junction 33, from the M4, on the A4232 signposted Barry, 1st interchange 4th exit A48 signposted Cowbridge. In St Nicholas village turn L Dyffryn is signposted.* An outstanding Grade 1 listed Edwardian garden. Currently undergoing restoration with the help of Heritage Lottery funding, to Thomas Mawson's original 1904 design. Formal lawns; fountains and pools; seasonal beds; trees and shrubs. Garden 'rooms'; each is unique and enclosed by yew hedge or wall, includes Pompeian, Paved Court and Theatre garden. Arboretum contains trees from all over the world incl 3 champion trees one is the original Acer griseum collected by 'Chinese Wilson'. The gardens change constantly with the seasons and are well worth a visit. TEAS. *Adm £3 Chd £2. Open daily*

11 Eastcliff, Southgate ♿✂❀ (Mrs Gill James) *Take the Swansea to Gower road and travel 6m to Pennard. Go through the village of Southgate and take the 2nd exit off the roundabout. Garden 200yds on the L.* Seaside garden approx ⅓-acre and developed in a series of island and bordered beds for spring and summer interest. A large number of white, blue-green unusual plants. Shown on HTV June 99. TEAS. *Adm £2 Chd free. Sun July 2 (2-5). Also private visits welcome, please* **Tel 01792 233310**

Fonmon Castle, nr Barry ♿✂❀ (Sir Brooke Boothby, Bt) *Take rd Cardiff-Llantwit Major, marked for Cardiff Airport. Take turning W of Penmark for Fonmon village, bear R round pond. Gate ¼m on.* Medium-sized garden. Walled kitchen garden; flowering shrubs; good trees; fuchsias. Ancient castle (shown Tues & Weds April to Sept (2-5). TEAS. *Adm £2 Chd 50p. Sun June 11 (2-6)* **Tel 01446 710206**

NEW **24 Heath Park Drive, Cardiff** ♿ (Marion Newman & Neighbours) *2m NE of city centre, 1m NE of University Hospital of Wales, ½m NW of Roath Park Lake alongside Rhumney Valley line railway near Heath Halt station. Limitd parking.* 3 small surburban neighbouring gardens created on a steep slope featuring patios, ponds, pergolas and perennials. Permament planting of shrub, palms and conifers giving yr-round interest and structure. TEAS. *Combined adm £2 Chd free (ACNO to Ty-Hafan, The Children's Hospice in Wales). Sun June 25 (2-6)*

The Hidden Garden, 57 Heol Bryncwils, Sarn ✂❀ (Mr & Mrs P J Thomas) *Approx 2½m from Bridgend. Approx 2½mins from junction 36 M4. Take rd signed Maesteg A4063, 100yds after lights turn R signed Sarn, next R then 2nd R house at centre of close.* Approx 90′ × 70′. Owners are uncontrollable plant enthusiasts. Garden is very intensively planted with huge collection of interesting and unusual plants. Herbaceous and mixed borders, shade area. Featured in HTV Get Gardening. TEAS in aid of Llansantffraid Church fund, weather permitting. No pushchairs, narrow paths. *Adm £1.50 Chd 50p. Sun July 23 (2-6). Private visits welcome Aug and Sept* **Tel 01656 720115**

Llanvithyn House, Llancarfan ✂❀ (Mr and Mrs L H W Williams) *1.8m S of A48 at Bonvilston, sign for Llancarfan 100yds W of Bonvilston Garage, 1m N of Llancarfan.* Medium-size garden on site of C6 monastery. C17 gatehouse (not open). Lawns, interesting trees, shrubs, borders. TEAS. *Adm £2 Chd 25p. Sun May 21 (2-6)*

Maes-y-Wertha Farm, Bryncethin ♿❀ (Mrs S Leyshon) *3m N of Bridgend. Follow sign for Bryncethin and turn R at Masons Arms. Follow sign for Heol-y-Cyw garden about 1m outside Bryncethin on R.* A new 3-acre garden. Informal mixed beds with large selection of perennial plants, shrubs, conifers and trees. Water garden fed by natural spring. Large grass area under new planting. TEA. *Adm £1.50 Chd 25p (ACNO to Sandville Self Help Foundation). Sun July 30 (2-6)*

NEW **Nant-y-Deri, Ystradowen** ❀ (Mrs Claire Jenkins) *Take A4222 from Cowbridge at Ytradowen postbox, then 3rd L and proceed ½m. Garden on R. Parking in road past corner.* Set within own mature oak woodland valley, areas of which are semi-tamed; other parts comprise an extensive mixed border; wild flower meadow; a multiplicity of wildlife. Some steep areas, children must be supervised. Bordervale Plants Nursery specialising in unusual herbaceous perennials and cottage garden plants. *Collection Box. Adm £1.50 Chd free. Open Fri, Sat, Sun and Bank Hol Mons April 1 to Oct 31 (10-5). For NGS Sun June 4, 25, July 9 (10-5)* **Tel 01446 774036**

NEW **Old St Mellons Gardens, Cardiff** ♿✂❀ *4m from Newport 5m from Cardiff Junction 30 M4 take Pentwyn link Rd to Eastern Ave. Turn L for Newport, take L for St Mellons at roundabout R into Old St Mellons. Straight over roundabout, R between White Hart & Bluebell public house into Tyrwinch Rd, No 4 on L ¼m ahead. Marleigh Lodge straight ahead, gates in V of the road. Parkstone Ave R. into Wern Fawr Lane (nr 4 Tyrwych Rd) straight into Parkstone Ave, garden at end of close.* TEAS. *Combined Adm £2.50 Chd free. (ACNO to Anne Atkins Memorial Fund) Sun July 2 (2-6)*

Marleigh Lodge (Mr & Mrs J C Rees) 1½ acre with garden rooms, herb garden, garden box parterre, wild sunken garden with shrubs, perennials, water features, trees, rhododendrons.

NEW **29 Parkstone Road** (Mrs M Crabtree) Garden to rear of property. Pergola, herbaceous and mixed borders, formal planting

NEW **4 Tyrwinch Road** (Mr & Mrs Tamplin) Medium size plantsman's Cottage-type garden. Mixed borders, kitchen garden, pernnials, rockery with ponds.

Springside, Pen-y-Turnpike, Dinas Powys ✂❀ (Prof & Mrs Michael Laurence) *From Cardiff take B4055 to Penarth and Dinas Powys as far as the Leckwith (Cardiff Distributor Rd) roundabout. Then take B4267 to Llandough, up Leckwith Hill past Leckwith Village, take R-hand fork in rd into Pen-y-Turnpike just past the 30mph sign. Turn R immed into Springside.* Undulating 2-acre garden recently rescued after 30yrs of wilderness. Spacious, with views: small ponds and old village water supply returned to nature, where children must be supervised; vegetable garden. It is hoped the tradition of live chamber music will be continued by generous professional musicians. TEA. *Adm £2 Chd 50p (ACNO to Dinas Powys Orchestra). Sun June 11 (2-6)*

St Peters Garden, Swansea ✂ (Mr & Mrs Tony Ridler) *4m W of Swansea behind Cockett Rd (A4216) between railway bridge and church.* ⅓-acre designer's formal garden divided by yew hedges into series of enclosed compartments.

Strong structure and box topiary. Regret no children. TEA. *Adm £1.50. Sun Jun 11 (2-6)*

19 Westfield Road, Glyncoch Pontrypridd ✂ (Mr & Mrs Brian Dockerill) *From Pontypridd travel 1.5m N along B4273. Take L turn by school. At top of hill follow rd to L. Take first R and R again into Westfield Rd.* Garden of approx 3/4 acre designed as a series of interlinked enclosures each of a different character. Varying habitats in sun and shade permit a wide range of plants to be grown extending the interest through the year. TEA. *Adm £1.50 Chd 50p. Prevented by limited parking from having specific days. We welcome visitors by appt through the yr, please* **Tel 01443 402999**

9 Willowbrook Gardens, Mayals, Swansea ✂ (Mrs G P Gallagher) *4m W of Swansea on A4067 (Mumbles) rd to Blackpill; take B4436 (Mayals) rd; 1st R along top of Clyne Park; 1st L into cul-de-sac.* ½-acre informal garden designed to give natural effect with balance of form and colour between various areas linked by lawns; unusual trees suited to small suburban garden, esp conifers and maples; rock and water garden. Open this year in honour of the late Dr K J Gallagher, whose inspiration and hard work helped create and develop this garden over the past 35 years, and which he so enthusiastically shared with visitors for the previous 18 springs. *Adm £2 Chd free. Sun May 14 (1-5.30).*

Evening Opening (See also garden description)

11 Arno Road, Little Coldbrook, Barry	June 14

The Herb Society

The Herb Society is an educational charity whose objective is to broaden the knowledge and use of herbs for the health and well-being of the individual and the community. Originally founded in 1927 as the Society of Herbalists primarily to support the practice of herbal medicine in Britain, The Herb Society is now concerned with all aspects of herbs worldwide. It provides a forum for the interchange of ideas and information and brings together all those who share an appreciation and interest in herbs, whether amateur or professional.

Members of The Herb Society receive four issues each year of Herbs, the UK's only specialist herb magazine. It features plant profiles, herb nurseries, gardening, cooking, herbal medicine, book reviews, and a diary of events at home – with special emphasis on regional group activities – and abroad. There is also a mail order service for books and products, and a list of herb suppliers offering discounts to members.

The Herb Society publishes information leaflets that are available to the public as well as members. A Schools Information Pack has been designed for teachers. It provides a simple educational approach to herb usage and the creation of herb gardens for primary schools.

The Herb Society holds workshops, garden visits, and lectures each year. For further information call the Herb Society Events hotline 01295 692001 or visit our website www.herbsociety.co.uk

The Herb Society
Deddington Hill Farm, Warmington, Banbury OX17 1XB
Tel: 01295 692000 Fax: 01295 692004
Email: email@herbsociety.co.uk

A herb is a plant used for flavouring or scenting or to improve health and vitality. Herbs include trees, annuals, perennials, even seaweeds and fungi, and their use by humans goes back millennia. 80% of the world population still rely on traditional herbal medicine for primary health care. The Holy Roman Emperor Charlemagne defined a herb as “a friend of the physician and the praise of cooks”. What's your definition of a herb? Join us. Let us know.

Gwent (Blaenau Gwent, Caerphilly, Monmouthshire, Newport and Torfaen)

Hon County Organiser: Mrs Joanna Kerr, Glebe House, Llanvair Kilgeddin, Abergavenny NP7 9BE Tel 01873 840422
Assistant Hon County Organiser: Mrs Catriona Boyle, Penpergwm Lodge, Abergavenny NP7 9AS Tel 01873 840208

DATES OF OPENING

Regular openings
For details see garden description
Penpergwm Lodge, nr Abergavenny
Plas Cwm Coed, Tredunnock
Tredegar House & Park, Newport
Veddw House, Devauden

By appointment only
For telephone numbers and other details see garden descriptions. Private visits welcomed
Croesllanfro Farm, Rogerstone
Hill Place, Llanishen
Orchard House, Coed Morgan

April 30 Sunday
The Nurtons, Tintern

May 1 Monday
Monmouth Gardens
The Nurtons, Tintern

May 14 Sunday
Great Campston, Llanfihangel Crucorney

May 21 Sunday
Glebe House, Llanvair Kilgeddin

May 28 Sunday
Barn Farm, Chepstow
Clytha Park, Abergavenny

May 29 Monday
Llan-y-Nant, Coed Morgan

June 4 Sunday
The Graig, Pen-y-Clawdd
Wyndcliffe Court, St Arvans

June 11 Sunday
Barn Farm, Chepstow
Trostrey Lodge, Bettws Newydd

June 18 Sunday
Great Killough, Llantilio Crossenny
Mulberry House, St Arvans
Veddw House, Devauden

June 24 Saturday
Castle House, Usk
Usk Gardens

June 25 Sunday
Castle House, Usk
Magor Village Gardens
Usk Gardens

July 1 Saturday
Great Campston, Llanfihangel Crucorney

July 2 Sunday
Great Campston, Llanfihangel Crucorney

July 9 Sunday
Barn Farm, Chepstow
Tredegar House & Park, Newport
The Volland, Lower Machen

July 16 Sunday
The Graig, Pen-y-Clawdd
Plas Cwm Coed, Tredunnock

July 23 Sunday
Barn Farm, Chepstow

July 30 Sunday
Llanllowell House, Usk

August 6 Sunday
Veddw House, Devauden

August 27 Sunday
Cefntilla, Usk
The Nurtons, Tintern

August 28 Monday
Cefntilla, Usk
The Nurtons, Tintern

September 3 Sunday
Castle House, Usk

September 10 Sunday
Tredegar House & Park, Newport

September 17 Sunday
Great Campston, Llanfihangel Crucorney

October 15 Sunday
Llanover, nr Abergavenny

DESCRIPTIONS OF GARDENS

Barn Farm, Chepstow ✂❀ (Stephen & Felicity Hunt) *Off B4235 Chepstow to Usk rd. 3m N of Shirenewton. Turn off at Gaerllwyd Xrds. 1m from main rd.* ¾ acre secluded garden overlooking Wentwood forest. Mainly herbaceous borders, brimming with plants and over 40 varieties of penstemons. Iris, hemerocallis and lilies provide spectacular summer colour. Vegetable garden based on raised beds. Area of soft fruit and small orchard with wild flowers, new water features. Small nursery with wide selection of perennials. TEAS in aid of Devauden Green WI. *Adm £1.50 Chd free. Suns May 28, June 11, July 9, 23 (2-6). Private visits welcome, please* **Tel 01291 650604**

Castle House, Usk ♿❀ (Mr & Mrs J H L Humphreys) *200yds from Usk centre; turn up lane opp fire station.* Medium-sized garden of orderly disorder with herb garden, topiary and vegetables. Set around ruins of Usk Castle. TEAS. *Adm £3.50 per day, £5 weekend ticket Chd free. Sat, Sun June 24, 25 (10-5) as part of Usk Gardens Open Days (donation to NGS). For NGS Sun Sept 3, Adm £2 Chd free (2-6) Teas. Private visits also welcome, please* **Tel 01291 672563**

NEW **Cefntilla, Usk** ♿ (Lord Raglan) *Take B4235 Usk to Chepstow rd to Gwernesney and follow signs N to Cefntilla, about 1m.* Rectangular Jacobean garden area extended with a circumambulatory in the 1850s. About 5 acres of trees, lawns, shrubs, flowers, topiary walk and lily pond. Dogs on leads. TEAS. *Adm £2 Chd free (ACNO to MENCAP). Sun, Bank Hol Mon Aug 27, 28 (2-6)*

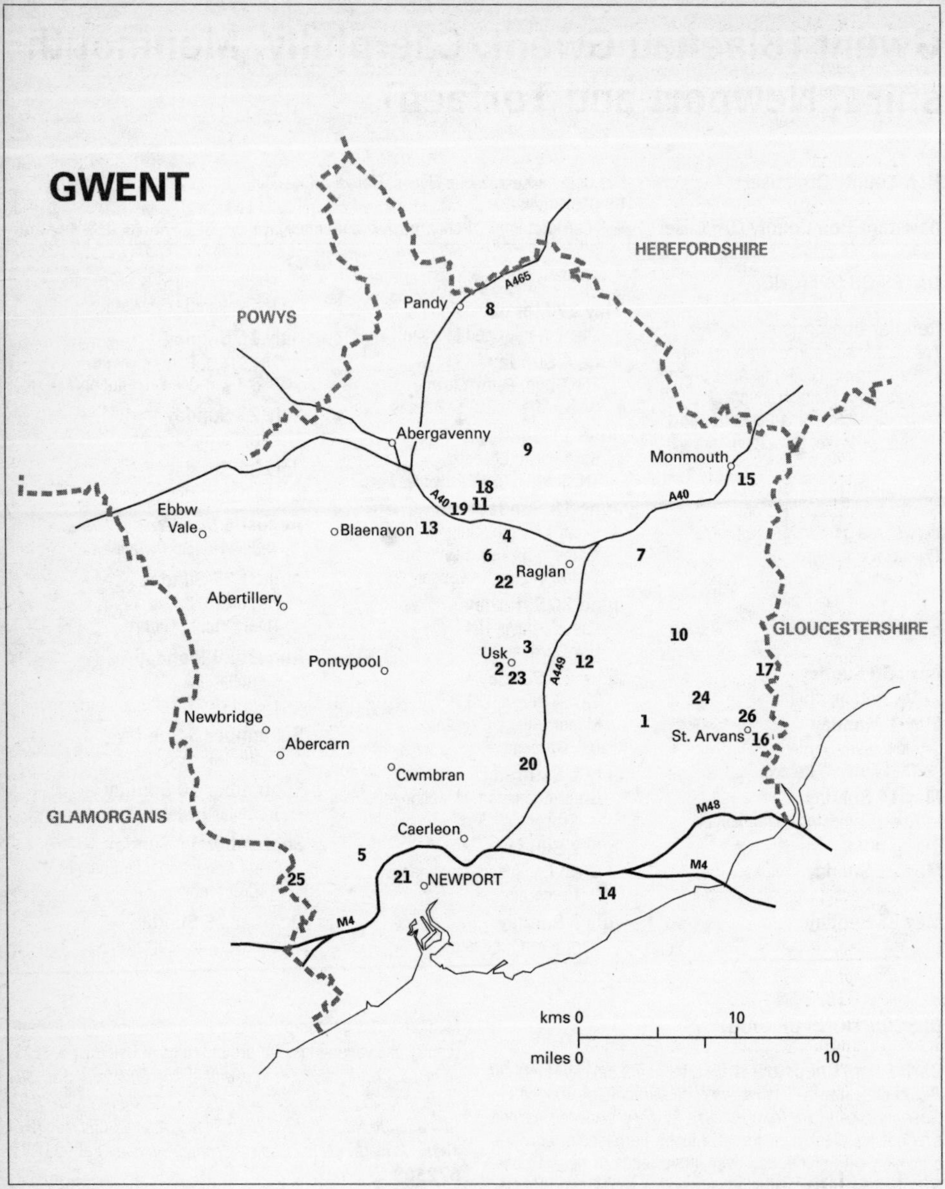

KEY

1 Barn Farm
2 Castle House
3 Cefntilla
4 Clytha Park
5 Croesllanfro Farm
6 Glebe House
7 The Graig
8 Great Campston
9 Great Killough
10 Hill Place
11 Llan-y-Nant
12 Llanllowell House
13 Llanover
14 Magor Village Gardens
15 Monmouth Gardens
16 Mulberry House
17 The Nurtons
18 Orchard House
19 Penpergwm Lodge
20 Plas Cwm Coed
21 Tredegar House & Park
22 Trostrey Lodge
23 Usk Gardens
24 Veddw House
25 The Volland
26 Wyndcliffe Court

Clytha Park, Abergavenny ♿✂ (Sir Richard Hanbury Tenison) *Half-way between Abergavenny and Raglan on B4598 (not A40).* 5 acres with C18 layout, trees, shrubs and lake. TEAS in aid of Gwent branch of National Trust. *Adm £2 Chd 50p. Sun May 28 (2-6)*

NEW **Croesllanfro Farm, Rogerstone** ✂ (Barry & Liz Davies) *From M4 junction 27 take B4591 to Risca. Take 2nd R, Cefn Walk (also signposted 14 Locks Canal Centre). Proceed over canal bridge, continue approx ½m to island in middle of lane. White farm gates opp. Limited parking.* Approx 1 acre created by Liz Davies garden designer. Wide variety of interesting plants concentrating on form and texture. Also a few surprises! *Adm £2 Chd 50p. Visitors and groups welcome by appt May to Aug, please* **Tel 01633 894343**

Glebe House, Llanvair Kilgeddin ♿✂❀ (Mr & Mrs Murray Kerr) *Midway between Abergavenny and Usk on B4598, 5m from each.* Approx 1½ acres; mixed herbaceous and shrub borders, unusual and interesting plants, orchard and vegetable garden surrounded by wonderful rural aspects of Usk Valley. TEAS. *Adm £2 Chd free. Sun May 21 (2-6)*

The Graig, Pen-y-Clawdd ♿✂❀ (Mrs Rainforth) *SW of Monmouth. Turn S from Raglan to Monmouth rd (not A40 dual carriageway) at sign to Pen-y-Clawdd. Bus: Newport-Monmouth, alight Keen's shop, ½m.* Mixed cottage garden with interesting shrubs, roses and kitchen garden. TEAS. *Adm £1.50 Chd free. Suns June 4, July 16 (2-6). Private visits welcome, please* **Tel 01600 740270**

Great Campston, Llanfihangel Crucorney ♿❀ (Mr & Mrs A D Gill) *7m NE of Abergavenny; 2m towards Grosmont off A465 at Llanfihangel Crucorney. Drive on R just before brow of hill.* Pretty 2 acres set in wonderful surroundings. Created from scratch by Mrs Gill, a garden designer. Wide variety of interesting plants and trees, lovely stone walls, paving and summerhouse with fantastic views. Set 750' above sea level on S-facing hillside with spring-fed stream feeding 2 ponds. Recently developed woodland garden. TEAS. *Adm £2.50 Chd 50p (ACNO to Hug). Sun May 14, Sat, Sun July 1, 2, Sun Sept 17 (2-6). Private visits welcome at any time, please* **Tel 01873 890465**

Great Killough, Llantilio Crossenny ♿✂❀ (Mr & Mrs J F Ingledew) *6m E of Abergavenny on B4233.* 3 acres created in 1960s to complement mediaeval house (not open). TEAS. *Adm £2 Chd free (ACNO to Barnardo's). Sun June 18 (2-6)*

Hill Place, Llanishen ✂❀ (Sean & Anne Dixon-Child) *Mid-way between Monmouth (12m) and Chepstow (12m) on B4293.* 3 acres of wildlife friendly hillside garden with lovely views. Uncultivated areas with trees and shrubs. Mixed borders, terraces with container-grown plants. *Adm £2 Chd 50p. Private visits and parties welcome by appt April to Sept, please* **Tel 01600 860 770**

Llan-y-Nant, Coed Morgan ♿❀ (Mr & Mrs Charles Pitchford) *4m from Abergavenny, 5m from Raglan on B4598 Raglan to Abergavenny rd. Turn up lane opp Chart House inn; pass Monmouthshire Hunt Kennels 500yds on R.* 3 acres of garden and woodlands. Lawn, beds, shrubs, herbs, alpines and kitchen garden. Small lake with wildlife. TEAS. *Adm £1.50 Chd 50p. Bank Hol Mon May 29 (2-6)*

NEW **Llanllowell House, Usk** ♿ (Hamish & Miskey Sandison) *2m SE of Usk on Llanllowell rd, go under dual carriageway A449, take 1st L up lane, entrance on L after 0.8m.* Informal garden around old house (not open) in secluded rural setting. Incl courtyard garden, orchard, wild-flower meadow, woodland walk, borders and large, hedged, kitchen garden with raised beds and Victorian-style green-house. Dogs on leads. TEAS. *Adm £2 Chd free (ACNO to Gwent Young People's Theatre). Sun July 30 (2-5)*

Llanover, nr Abergavenny ♿ (Mrs E Murray) *4m S of Abergavenny on A4042. Bus: Abergavenny-Pontypool, alight at drive gates.* Large water garden; many rare trees noted for their autumn colours, magnolias. TEAS. *Adm £2 Chd 50p. Sun Oct 15 (2-6)*

Magor Village Gardens ♿✂ *M4 junction 23A and follow signs to Magor Village Square on B4245, ¼m.* Group of gardens with wide appeal. Good parking in village square, limited parking at some individual gardens, map provided. TEAS. Plants for sale in aid of Save the Children Fund. *Combined adm £2.50 Chd over ten 50p. Sat June 24. For NGS Sun June 25 (2-6.30)*

15 Arlington Close, Undy (Pam & Keith Jones) An informal garden with wide variety of plants for yr-round interest

Courtney ♿ (Joyce Escott) Garden with a mediterranean touch

The Hawthorns ♿ (John & Rosemary Skinner) *Newport Rd.* Formal bedding scheme with standard fuchsias, summer bedding and conifers shaped into domes and archways

Lilac Cottage, Whitewall (Christine & Bernard Rowlands) Garden with hidden rooms, interesting water features and humorous sculptures

Merevale House (Judy & Kevin Marris) Mature garden with further developments from last year

Myrtle Cottage ♿ (Cecilia & Michael Davies) Cottage garden with broad range of plants

NEW **Monmouth Gardens** ❀ *Take A466 towards Hereford from t-lights in town.* TEAS. *Combined adm £2.50 Chd free (ACNO to Monmouth Aid). Bank Hol Mon May 1 (2-6)*

NEW **North Parade House** (Mr & Mrs T Haynes) *12 Hereford Rd.* Walled town garden of ⅔ acre incl mature specimen trees, shrubs, spring bulbs and herbaceous border

NEW **St Pega's** (Mrs Sue Carter) *47 Hereford Rd.* Large, steep ½ acre town garden, not for the faint hearted. Special features incl ducks, bog garden, dry stone walls and interesting alpine troughs. Collection of Barnhaven primulas and auriculas

Mulberry House, St Arvans ✂ (Sir Alan & Lady Cox) *2½m N of Chepstow. Turn L off A466 from Chepstow, into St Arvans, 300yds on R.* 1 acre in 2 gardens (one newly created with ha-ha). Wide variety of shrubs, roses, beds and lawns. Vegetable garden. Home-made TEAS. *Adm £2 Chd £1. Sun June 18 (2-6)*

■ **The Nurtons, Tintern** ✗❀ (Adrian & Elsa Wood) *On A466 opp Old Station, Tintern.* 2.5 acres of considerable botanical interest with notable collections of hostas, salvias, ferns, grasses, medicinal herbs and many other unusual perennials. New plantings with modern themes and good autumn colour. Nursey has extensive range of organically grown unusual perennials and herbs. TEAS on NGS days only. *Adm £1.50 Chd free (ACNO to Gwent Wildlife Trust). Wye Valley Plants Nursery and garden open daily, except Tues (10.30-5) March to mid-Oct. For NGS Suns, Bank Hol Mons April 30, May 1, Aug 27, 28 (10.30-5). Group visits also welcome, please* **Tel 01291 689253**

Orchard House, Coed Morgan ♿✗❀ (Mr & Mr B R Hood) *1½m N of old Raglan on B4598 Abergavenny rd . Approx 6m from Abergavenny. Turn opp King of Prussia or The Charthouse.* Approx 1½ acres with mixed borders of unusual herbaceous plants and shrubs, rosebeds and lawn. *Adm £1.50 Chd 50p. Private visits welcome April to Sept, please* **Tel 01873 840289**

● **Penpergwm Lodge, nr Abergavenny** ♿❀ (Mr & Mrs Simon Boyle) *3m from Abergavenny, 5m from Raglan on B4598. Turn opp King of Prussia Inn. Entrance 150yds on L.* 3 acres of formal garden with mature trees, hedges and lawns; interesting potager, mixed unusual plants and vegetables; apple and pear pergola and S-facing terraces with sun-loving plants. Nursery specialising in unusual hardy perennials. Home of Catriona Boyle's Garden School, now in its 14th yr. *Adm £2 Chd free. Thurs to Suns, March 30 to Oct 1. Private visits and groups welcome, please* **Tel 01873 840208**

■ **Plas Cwm Coed, Tredunnock** ✗❀ (John & Eliana Humphries) *N from Caerleon village towards Usk for 3m, then signed Plas Cwm Coed, L 150yds; or S from Usk for 4m, immed after Cwrt Bleddyn Hotel.* 5-acre garden in wooded valley, ponds, herbaceous borders, Victorian terrace, laburnum walk, fern and desert gardens. As featured on HTV's Get Gardening! Created by John Humphries, Gardens Correspondent, The Western Mail. TEAS and plants NGS day. *Adm £1.50 Chd over 5, 50p. Suns May 7 to Sept 17 (2-5). For NGS Sun July 16 (2-6). Other times and groups by arrangement, please* **Tel 01633 450373**

■ **Tredegar House & Park, Newport** ♿✗❀ (Newport Borough Council) *2m SW of Newport town centre. Signposted from A48 (Cardiff rd) and M4 junction 28.* Series of walled formal gardens dating from early C18 surrounding one of the most magnificent late C17 houses (also open). Orangery garden recently restored to early C18 appearance with coloured mineral parterres, espaliered fruit trees and box hedging. TEAS. *Adm £2 Chd 50p (ACNO to The Friends of Tredegar House and Park). House and gardens open Easter to end of Oct. For NGS Suns July 9, Sept 10 (11-6). For details, please* **Tel 01633 815880**

Trostrey Lodge, Bettws Newydd ❀ (Mr & Mrs R Pemberton) *Half-way between Raglan and Abergavenny on B4598. Turning to Bettws Newydd opp Clytha gates, 1m on R.* Fine views of Usk valley provide the setting for this small, walled garden in decorative orchard. High concentration of interesting plants, herbs, roses, myrtles and vines; all bordered by box, lavender and rosemary. Collection of fancy fowl. TEAS. *Adm £2 Chd free. Sun June 11 (11-6)*

Usk Gardens ♿✗❀ (Mrs Margaret Capel) *From M4 junction 24 take A449, proceed 8m to Usk exit. Good parking in town. Map of gardens provided with ticket.* More than 20 gardens from cottage to castle of enormous variety spread around town. TEAS. *Combined adm £3.50, weekend ticket £5 Chd free (donation to NGS). Sat, Sun June 24, 25 (10-5)* www.usktc.force9.co.uk

■ **Veddw House, Devauden** ✗ (Anne Wareham & Charles Hawes) *Between Chepstow and Monmouth on B4293. Signed from public house on the green.* 4 acres; emphasis on good garden pictures with colour harmonies and contrasts. Formal vegetable garden with old roses and clematis; small themed gardens; ruin; wild garden; conservatory. Wide range of herbaceous plants. Unique ornaments of wood and enamel. Lovely views, woodland walks. *Adm £2.50 Chd £1 (ACNO to Heart Research Foundation for Wales). Other times £2 Chd £1. Every Sun & Bank Hol Mon April 2 to Oct 1 incl (2-5). For NGS Suns June 18, Aug 6 (2-5). Parties welcome by appt, pm only* **Tel 01291 650836**

The Volland, Lower Machen ♿✗❀ (Mr & Mrs William Graham) *Between Newport and Caerphilly, 10mins from M4 junction 28 W of Lower Machen village, 1st R before county boundary.* 1½ acres of interesting shrubs, trees, herbaceous plants and fern rockery. TEAS. *Adm £1.50 Chd free. Sun July 9 (2-6)*

Wyndcliffe Court, St Arvans ♿❀ (H A P Clay Esq) *3m N of Chepstow off A466, turn at Wyndcliffe signpost. Bus: Chepstow-Monmouth, alight at St Arvans, Wyndcliffe stop, then ¼m.* Medium-sized garden designed by Avery Tipping; herbaceous borders; views, topiary, shrubs. Mentioned in The Historic Gardens of Wales and Country Life, July 98. TEA. *Adm £2 Chd free. Sun June 4 (2-6). Private visits welcome, please* **Tel 01291 622352**

Gwynedd

Hon County Organiser:
Anglesey, North Caernarfonshire Aberconwy Mrs B S Osborne, Foxbrush, Port Dinorwic, Felinheli, Gwynedd LL56 4JZ 01248 670463
South Gwynedd Mrs Roessa Chiesman, Bryn Glas, 26 Felindre, Pennal, Powys SY20 9DZ Tel 01654 791676
Assistant County Organiser: Mrs W N Jones, Waen Fechan, Islaw'r Dref, Dolgellau LL40 1TS 01341 423479
Hon County Treasurer Mr Michael Bishton, Bronclydwr, Rhoslefain, Tywyn, Gwynedd LL36 9LT 01654 710882

DATES OF OPENING

Regular openings

For details see garden description

Farchynys Cottage, Bontddu
Fern Hill, Trefriw
Plas Penhelig, Aberdovey
Talhenbont Hall, Pwllheli

By appointment only

For telephone numbers and other details see garden descriptions. Private visits welcomed

Cefn Bere, Cae Deintur
Gwyndy Bach, Llandrygarn
Llys-y-Gwynt, Llandegai
Pencarreg, Glyn Garth
Tyn-y-Cefn, Ffestiniog

March 12 Sunday
Bryniau, Boduan

April 9 Sunday
Bryniau, Boduan

April 12 Wednesday
Foxbrush, Felinheli

April 21 Friday
Plas Newydd, Anglesey

April 23 Sunday
Bont Fechan Farm, Llanystumdwy
Crug Farm, Griffiths Crossing
Glandderwen, Bontddu
29-30 Tan-y-Bwlch, Mynydd Llandegai

April 24 Monday
Glandderwen, Bontddu

April 26 Wednesday
Foxbrush, Felinheli

April 30 Sunday
Bryniau, Boduan
Gilfach, Rowen

May 7 Sunday
Haul-a-Gwynt, Wylfa

May 10 Wednesday
Foxbrush, Felinheli

May 13 Saturday
Talhenbont Hall, Pwllheli
Tan Dinas, Llanfairpwll

May 14 Sunday
Bont Fechan Farm, Llanystumdwy
Pen-y-Parc, Beaumaris
Talhenbont Hall, Pwllheli

May 21 Sunday
Bryniau, Boduan
Maenan Hall, Llanrwst
29-30 Tan-y-Bwlch, Mynydd Llandegai

May 24 Wednesday
Foxbrush, Felinheli

May 28 Sunday
Bryn Eisteddfod, Glan Conwy
Crug Farm, Griffiths Crossing
Felin y Ffridd, Ffriddgate
Rhyd, Trefor

May 29 Monday
Crug Farm, Griffiths Crossing

June 4 Sunday
Gilfach, Rowen

June 7 Wednesday
Foxbrush, Felinheli

June 11 Sunday
Bryniau, Boduan
Esgairweddan, Pennal

June 17 Saturday
Panteidal Garden & Nursery, Aberdovey
Penrhyn Castle, Bangor

June 18 Sunday
Blaen-y-Foel, Nebo
Bronclydwr, Rhoslefain
Henllys Lodge, Beaumaris
Marian, Talwrn
Panteidal Garden & Nursery, Aberdovey
29-30 Tan-y-Bwlch, Mynydd Llandegai

June 25 Sunday
Rhiwlas, Bala
St John the Baptist & St George, Carmel

June 28 Wednesday
Foxbrush, Felinheli
Llanidan Hall, Brynsiencyn

July 2 Sunday
Bryniau, Boduan
Trysglwyn Fawr, Rhosybol

July 9 Sunday
Braich-y-Foel, Bwlch Derwin
Felin y Ffridd, Ffriddgate
Gerddi Fron Goch, Llanfaglan

July 16 Sunday
Blaen-y-Foel, Nebo
Crug Farm, Griffiths Crossing
Henllys Lodge, Beaumaris
29-30 Tan-y-Bwlch, Mynydd Llandegai

July 23 Sunday
Haul-a-Gwynt, Wylfa
Hotel Maes-y-Neuadd, Talsarnau
Rhyd, Trefor

August 13 Sunday
Bont Fechan Farm, Llanystumdwy
Gerddi Fron Goch, Llanfaglan
Gilfach, Rowen
Pentre Bach, Llwyngwril

August 20 Sunday
Maenan Hall, Llanrwst
29-30 Tan-y-Bwlch, Mynydd Llandegai

August 27 Sunday
Bryniau, Boduan
Crug Farm, Griffiths Crossing

September 10 Sunday
Gerddi Fron Goch, Llanfaglan

September 16 Saturday
Talhenbont Hall, Pwllheli

September 17 Sunday
Hotel Maes-y-Neuadd, Talsarnau
Talhenbont Hall, Pwllheli
29-30 Tan-y-Bwlch, Mynydd Llandegai

October 1 Sunday
Bryniau, Boduan

October 15 Sunday
29-30 Tan-y-Bwlch, Mynydd Llandegai

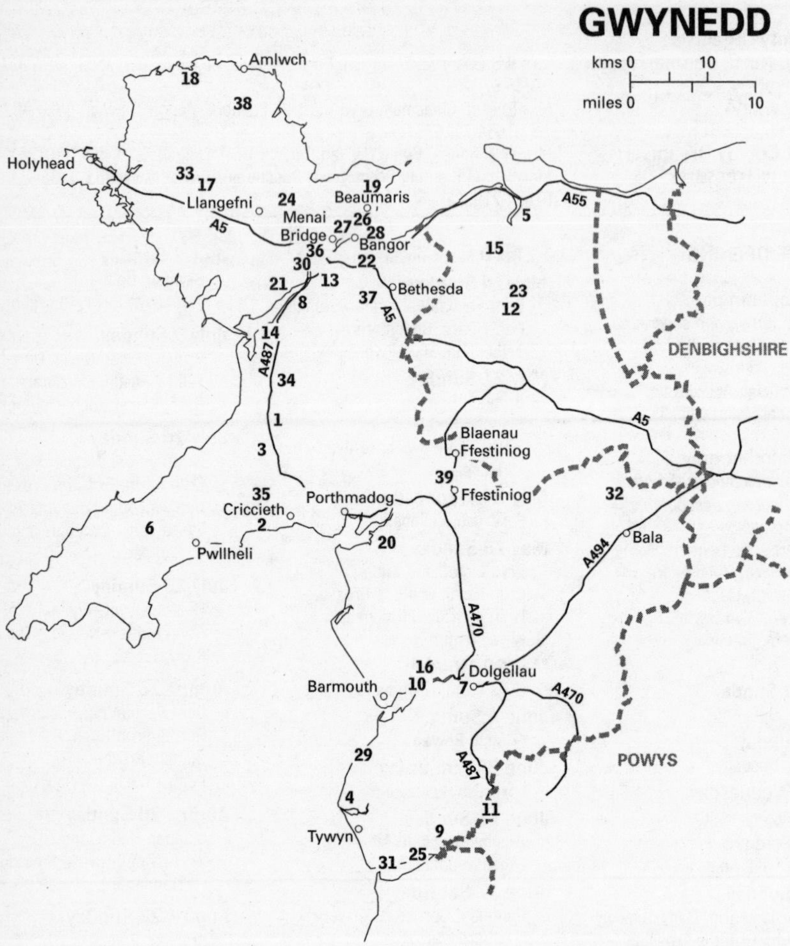

KEY

1 Blaen-y-Foel
2 Bont Fechan Farm
3 Braich-y-Foel
4 Bronclydwr
5 Bryn Eisteddfod
6 Bryniau
7 Cefn Bere
8 Crug Farm
9 Esgairweddan
10 Farchynys Cottage
11 Felin y Ffridd
12 Fern Hill
13 Foxbrush
14 Gerddi Fron Goch
15 Gilfach
16 Glandderwen
17 Gwyndy Bach
18 Haul-a-Gwynt
19 Henllys Lodge
20 Hotel Maes-y-Neuadd
21 Llanidan Hall
22 Llys-y-Gwynt
23 Maenan Hall
24 Marian
25 Panteidal Garden & Nursery
26 Pen-y-Parc
27 Pencarreg
28 Penrhyn Castle
29 Pentre Bach
30 Plas Newydd
31 Plas Penhelig
32 Rhiwlas
33 Rhyd
34 St John the Baptist & St George
35 Talhenbont Hall
36 Tan Dinas
37 29-30 Tan-y-Bwlch
38 Trysglwyn Fawr
39 Tyn-y-Cefn

DESCRIPTIONS OF GARDENS

Blaen-y-Foel, Nebo ✗❀ (Margaret & Colin Metcalfe) *A487 Caernarfon to Porthmadog. ½m out of Llanllyfni turn L at Nebo. At centre of village turn R (round back of school). 50 yds on L. 700' above sea-level in Snowdonia below the dramatic Nantlle Ridge, the cottage gardeners are turning a windy ½-acre field into a useful garden that is also peaceful, pretty and wildlife friendly. Vegetables, fruit, herbs, flowers, poultry. Also small mediaeval and Victorian gardens, wartime kitchen garden, reflecting the gardeners' interest in times past. Small greenhouses, container plants and young forest trees. Tea. Adm £1 Chd free. Suns June 18 July 16 (11-5)*

Bont Fechan Farm, Llanystumdwy ♿❀ (Mr & Mrs J D Bean) *2m from Criccieth on the A497 to Pwllheli on the L-hand side of the main rd. Small garden with rockery, pond, herbaceous border, steps to river, large variety of plants. Nicely planted tubs. TEAS. Adm £1 Chd 25p. Suns April 23, May 14, Aug 13 (11-5). Private visits welcome, please* **Tel 01766 522604**

Braich-y-Foel, Bwlch Derwin ✗❀ (Mrs E M Cooper) *Take the A487 Caernarfon/Porthmadog rd. Leave the A487 at Pant Glas and follow signs. Car park. A remote rural cottage garden on former farm. Interesting features designed for eventual 'old age' easy maintenance. ⅓-acre cared for with enthusiasm by Mrs Cooper and Sally Crookes, extra vegetable garden Mr Cooper. TEAS. Adm £1. Sun July 9 (1.30- -5.30)*

Bronclydwr, Rhoslefain ✗ (Mr & Mrs Michael Bishton) *Take the A493 Dolgellau to Tywyn rd at Rhoslefain take Tonfanau rd for about ½m. Fork L along private rd to end of tarmac rd then take unmade rd to large house on edge of wood. Peaceful garden with beautiful views of Cardigan Bay. Plantsman's garden with a wide range of camellias, shrubs and herbaceous plants. Set in informal beds with a wooded hillside backdrop. Variety of half hardy plants; cannas, echiums, embothrium, phormium, acacia, bog garden with gunnera, arums, day lillies, iris etc. Garden about 1-acre plus wild and wooded area. TEAS. Adm £2 Chd free. Sun June 18 (12-5)*

Bryn Eisteddfod, Glan Conwy ♿❀ (Dr Michael Senior) *3½m SE Llandudno 3m W Colwyn Bay; up the hill (Bryn-y-Maen direction) from Glan Conwy Corner where A470 joins A55. 8 acres of landscaped grounds incl mature shrubbery, arboretum, old walled 'Dutch' garden, large lawn with ha-ha. Extensive views over Conwy Valley, Snowdonia National Park, Conwy Castle, town and estuary. TEAS. Adm £1 Chd 50p. Sun May 28 (2-5)*

Bryniau, Boduan ❀ (P W Wright & J E Humphreys) *½m down lane opp. St Buan's Church, Boduan, which is halfway between Nefyn and Pwllheli on the A497. Bryniau is a grade II listed C18 Welsh farmstead. Garden created since 1988 on pure sand. Over 80 types of trees; hundreds of shrubs, many unusual, showing that with a little effort, one can grow virtually anything anywhere. Broadcast on BBC Gardeners World, Radio Wales, Radio Cymru, S4C Clwb Garddio and HTV's 'Get Gardening'. Plants & woodcraft for sale. TEAS. Adm £1 Chd free. Suns March 12, April 9, 30, May 21, June 11, July 2, Aug 27, Oct 1 (11-6) and private visits welcome, please Tel 01758 7213 38*

Cefn Bere, Cae Deintur ✗ (Mr & Mrs Maldwyn Thomas) *Dolgellau. Turn L at top of main bridge on Bala-Barmouth Rd (not the by-pass); turn R within 20yds; 2nd R behind school and first L half way up short hill. Small garden; extensive collection of alpines, bulbs and rare plants. Tea Dolgellau. Collecting box. Individuals and parties of up to 20 welcome, spring, summer and autumn months, please* **Tel Dolgellau 01341 422768**

Crug Farm, Griffiths Crossing ✗❀ (Mr & Mrs B Wynn-Jones) *2m NE of Caernarfon ¼m off main A487 Caernarfon to Bangor Road. Follow signs from roundabout. ⅔ acre; grounds to old country house. Gardens filled with choice, unusual collections of climbers, and herbaceous plants; over 300 species of hardy geraniums. Featured in 'The Garden' and on BBC TV Gardeners World. Only partly suitable wheelchairs. TEAS in aid NSPCC. Adm £1 Chd free. Thurs to Suns & Bank Hols Feb 26 to Sept 24 (10-6) Natural Rock garden only open Suns April 23, May 28, July 16, Aug 27, Mon May 29 (10-6). Private parties welcome, please* **Tel 01248 670232**

Esgairweddan, Pennal ♿ (Mrs Annie Parry) *Pennal is 4m from Machgulleth on the A496 towards Aberdovey; and Esgaiweddan is on the Pennal to Cwrt rd. A small garden with a 300-yr-old farm house, a ¾m drive from rd entrance leading through oak woodland with a wonderful view of the Dovey estuary. TEAS. Adm £1. Sun June 11 (2-6)*

Farchynys Cottage, Bontddu ✗ (Mrs G Townshend) *On A496 Dolgellau-Barmouth rd; well-signed W of Bontddu village. 4 acres; informal country garden on steep wooded hillside; unusual shrubs and trees; azaleas, over 75 species of rhododendron, giant Liriodendron tulipifera. Best mid-May, mid-June. Adm £1.50 Chd free. Open Sun, Mon, Tues, Wed, May 1 to Sept 14. (11-5). Parties welcome, please* **Tel 01341 430245**

NEW **Felin y Ffridd, Ffriddgate** ❀ (Mr & Mrs J W Osselton) *From the S, take A487 from Macynlleth to Dolgellau. After approx 1m turn R at the B4404 to Llanwrin. The garden is a short distance on L before the bridge. From N, take A487, turn L on B4404. The garden of approx 1-acre, borders the N Avon Dulas, and consists mainly of grassy paths and island beds of mixed plantings. Fishpond and new gravel bed. TEA. Adm £1.50 Chd 20p. Suns May 28, July 9 (2-6)*

Fern Hill, Trefriw ❀ (Annabel Senior) *10m S of the town of Conwy, on the W bank of the R Conwy; take the B5106; just before Trefriw is the Princes Arms Hotel. Fern Hill is next to it on the N side. Park in PA car park and enter garden via steps 10yds along the road. 2 acres of steep terraced hillside garden, with outstandingly beautiful views of the Conwy Valley. Herbaceous, shrubs and rose beds surrounding a circular thyme lawn. Rhododendrons and azaleas; wild flower banks; meadows; bluebell woodland, wild life encouraged. Lunches and Teas at the Princes Arms Hotel. Adm £1 Chd free. Open every day April 1 to Aug 31 (11-5)*

Foxbrush, Felinheli ♿❀ (Mr & Mrs B S Osborne) *On Bangor to Caernarfon Road, entering village opp layby with Felinheli sign post.* Fascinating 3-acre country garden created around winding river; ponds and small wooded area. Rare and interesting plant collections incl rhododendrons, ferns, primula, clematis and roses; 45ft long pergola; fan-shaped knot garden; coaches welcome. Featured BBC TV and Period Living magazine. TEAS. *Adm £1 Chd free. Weds April 12, 26, May 10, 24 (2-5) June 7, 28 (2-7). Also private visits and parties welcome, please* **Tel 01248 670463**

Gerddi Fron Goch, Llanfaglan ✂❀ (Mr & Mrs R A Williams) *1m SW of Caernarfon. ¾m off the main A487 Caernarfon to Porthmadog rd, on the outskirts of town, turning into Pant Rd. Parking in adjacent garden centre.* ¾-acre garden created from an open field in the last 12 yrs. Informal plantings of wide range of trees, shrubs and herbaceous with many unusual items. *Adm £1 Chd free. Suns July 9, Aug 13, Sept 10 (10-6)*

Gilfach, Rowen ♿✂ (James & Isoline Greenhalgh) *At Xrds 100yds E of Rowen (4m S of Conwy) S towards Llanrwst, past Rowen School on L; turn up 2nd drive on L, signposted.* 1-acre country garden on S-facing slope overlooking Conwy Valley; set in 35 acres farm and woodland; mature shrubs; herbaceous border; small pool. Partly suitable wheelchairs which are welcome. Magnificent views of River Conwy and mountains. TEAS. *Adm £1.50 Chd free. Suns April 30, June 4, Aug 13 (11-5). Private visits welcome, please* **Tel 01492 650216**

Glandderwen, Bontddu (A M Reynolds Esq) *5m W of Dolgellau. Take A496 to Bontddu. Garden is on S 100yds past Bontddu Hall Hotel.* ½-acre on N bank of Mawddach Estuary facing Cader Idris; set amid large oaks; shrubs, trees; steep and rocky nature. *Adm £1 Chd free. Sun, Mon April 23, 24 (11-6). Private visits and parties welcome any time by arrangement, please* **Tel 01341 430229**

Gwyndy Bach, Llandrygarn ♿✂❀ (Keith & Rosa Andrew) *From Llangefni take the B5109 towards Bodedern, the cottage is exactly 5m out on the L.* A ¾-acre artist's garden set amidst rugged Anglesey landscape. Romantically planted in intimate 'rooms' with interesting plants and shrubs, old roses and Japanese garden with large Koi pond. Studio attached. *Private visits welcome May to September* **Tel 01407 720651**

Haul-a-Gwynt, Wylfa ♿❀ (Mark & Wendy Markwald) *Off A5025 2m from Cemaes Bay travelling towards Holyhead. Turn R at Wylfa Power Station sign. At main gate turn R for ¼m to Nature Trail car park on R. Please park here unless disabled. Opp car park is Tyn-y-Maes and Haul-a-Gwynt House sign. Private lane 100yds to house.* ¾ acre of walled garden, sheltering 200 varieties of flowering shrubs, climbers and trees, the majority named. Fish pond and waterfall, greenhouse and alpine rockery. TEA in restored farm labourer's cottage. *Adm £1 Chd free. Suns May 7, July 23 (11-5). Private visits welcome, please* **Tel 01407 710058**

Henllys Lodge, Beaumaris ♿✂❀ (Mr K H & Mrs J Lane) *Past Beaumaris Castle, ½m turn L, 1st L again. Lodge at entrance to Henllys Hall Hotel drive.* Approx 1-acre country garden, planted in traditional cottage style using perennials, shrubs, old roses and featuring extensive collection of hardy geraniums. Small woodland area. Stunning views across Menai Straits. TEAS. *Adm £1 Chd free. Suns June 18, July 16 (12-5.30). Private visits and parties welcome, please* **Tel 01248 810106**

NEW **Hotel Maes-y-Neuadd, Talsarnau** (June & Mike Slatter & Peter & Lyn Jackson) *Take B4573 old Harlech rd at T-junction with A496 3m NW of Harlech. Hotel signed ¼m on L. Take small lane on L immed after sign, just before small bridge on bend. Follow lane ½m up hill, through small hamlet (tel box on L), hotel entrance and car park on R.* Gardens and grounds of country house hotel, parts of which C14. Views towards Snowdon, Cardigan Bay and Llyn Peninsula. 6 acres, meadows, woodland walks, 2 working walled gardens providing produce for hotel and restaurant. Unusual cultivars, cut flower borders; innovative, intensive, organic gardening methods; a fusion of productive gardening and aesthetic appeal. Vegetables, salads and cut flowers for sale. Partially suitable for wheelchairs. TEA. *Adm £1.50 Chd free. Suns July 23, Sept 17 (10-5)*

NEW **Llanidan Hall, Brynsiencyn** ✂ *From Llanfair PG (Anglesey) follow A4080 towards Brynsiencyn for 4m. Turn at/opp Groeslon PH. Continue for 1m, garden entrance on R.* Walled garden of 13/4 acres. Physic and herb gardens, ornamental vegetable garden, herbaceous borders, water features and many varities of old roses. Children must be kept under supervision. *Adm £1.50 Chd £1 (ACNO Hospice at Home). Wed June 28 (2-5) Open to groups by appt only, please* **Tel 01248 852121**

Llys-y-Gwynt, Llandegai ♿❀ (Mrs Jennifer Rickards & Mr John Evans) *3m S of Bangor and 300yds from Llandygai Roundabout at Junction of A5 and A55. Follow signs to Llanberis off A5 and 100yds from entrance to Esso Service Station, Little Chef and Travel Lodge.* 2-acre rambling garden; well established trees and shrubs and magnificent views; pond, N-facing rockery; large Bronze Age burial cairn. Planting with emphasis on wind resistance, yr-round interest and encouraging wild life. *Adm £1 Chd free. Private visits and parties welcome, please* **Tel 01248 353863**

Maenan Hall, Llanrwst ❀ (The Hon Christopher Mclaren) *Exactly 2m N of Llanrwst on E side of A470, ¼m S of Maenan Abbey Hotel.* Gardens created since 1956 by the late Christabel, Lady Aberconway and then present owners; 10 acres; lawns, shrub, rose and walled gardens; rhododendron dell; many species of beautiful and interesting plants, shrubs and trees set amongst mature oaks and other hardwoods; fine views across Conway valley. Home-made TEAS. *Adm £2 Chd £1 (ACNO to Hope House Children's Respite Hospice, Oswestery: May 21 St David's Hospice Foundation Aug 20). Suns May 21, Aug 20 (10.30-5.30). Last entry 4.30*

Marian, Talwrn ♿✂ (Dr & Mrs I R Gwynedd Jones) *Stone farmhouse situated on R, 2m from Pentraeth on Pentraeth-Talwrn Rd. Take Amlwch exit from Britannia Bridge, L-hand turn for Llangefni at Pentraeth, opp Panton Arms. Look out for church in the field on RH-side. Marian is the next* farmhouse, ¼m along the rd. Woodland garden of approx ¾ acre. Shrubs and perennials. Vegetable garden with box edging, gravel paths and pergolas. TEAS. *Adm £1 Chd free. Sun June 18 (12-5)*

Panteidal Garden & Nursery, Aberdovey ✗❀ (Mr & Mrs H G H Mathias) *3m from Aberdovey, 6½m from Dovey Bridge, Machynlleth on the A493 Machynlleth to Aberdovey coast rd.* Panteidal nestles in an enclosed wooded valley bordering the beautiful Dyfi estuary. We grow and propagate a wide range of herbaceous plants, many unusual, some exotic, courtesy of our milder climate. Visitors can stroll around the cottage garden and see many of the plants growing naturally. A 12 acre conservation area of surrounding woodland, marsh and water will be open too. Organic Cafe is licensed and offers home-made light refreshments, lunches and scrumptious TEAS. *Adm £2 Chd free. Sat, Sun June 17, 18 (10.30-5.30)*

Pen-y-Parc, Beaumaris (Mrs E E Marsh) *A545 Menai Bridge-Beaumaris rd; after Anglesey Boatyard 1st L; after Golf Club 1st drive on L.* NOT easy for wheelchairs. 6 acres; beautiful grounds, magnificent views over Menai Strait; azaleas, rhododendrons and heathers; interesting terrain with rock outcrops used to advantage for recently planted conifer and rock gardens; small lake in natural setting; 2 further enclosed gardens. We would like to share the pleasure of this garden. TEA. *Adm £1 Chd 50p. Sun May 14 (11-5)*

Pencarreg, Glyn Garth ᵫ (Miss G Jones) *1½m on A545 Menai Bridge towards Beaumaris, turn R in front of a lodge set back from the rd, Pencarreg is 100yds on R down the drive. Parking in lay-by on main rd, parking on courtyard for small cars and disabled.* Planted for all-yr interest and colour with common and unusual shrubs. Small stream. Garden terminates at cliff edge and this has been skilfully planted. Views to the Menai Straits and the Carneddi Mountains in the distance. Featured in 5 television programmes. *Collecting Box (ACNO to Snowdonia National Park Society). Private visits welcome all year, please* **Tel 01248 713545**

▲ **Penrhyn Castle, Bangor** ᵫ (The National Trust) *3m E of Bangor on A5122. Buses from Llandudno, Caernarvon. Betws-y-Coed; alight: Grand Lodge Gate.* Large grounds incl Victorian walled garden; fine trees, shrubs, wild garden, good views. Castle rebuilt in 1830 for 1st Lord Penrhyn, incorporating part of C15 building on C8 site of home of Welsh Princes. Exhibition of National Trust Countryside; museum of locomotives and quarry rolling stock. NT Shop. TEAS and light lunches. *Adm £3.50 Chd £2 (Garden and Exhibition only). For NGS Sat June 17 (11-5). Last adm ½ hr prior to closing. Private visits welcome by appt, please* **Tel 01248 353084**

Pentre Bach, Llwyngwril ✗❀ (Mr & Mrs N Smyth) *[Grid ref E591N095].* Entrance is 40yds S of stone bridge in centre of Llwyngwril, 12m from Dolgellau, on A493 coast rd. Public car park 100yds from entrance. 1-acre cultivated organically. Walled kitchen garden with glasshouse. No-dig raised bed system. Small 'woodland garden' with soft fruit and herbs, using permaculture principles, composting,

shrubs, free range hens. Magnificent sea views. TEAS. *Adm £1.50 Chd 50p. Sun Aug 13 (10-5)*

▲ **Plas Newydd, Anglesey** ᵫ✗ (The National Trust) *Isle of Anglesey. 2m SW of Llanfairpwll and A5, on A4080.* Gardens with massed shrubs, fine trees, and lawns sloping down to Menai Strait. Magnificent views to Snowdonia. Woodland walk leading to Marine Walk. Rhododendron garden April, to early June only. C18 house by James Wyatt contains Rex Whistler's largest wall painting; also Military Museum. TEAS and light lunches. *Adm garden only £2.50, Chd £1.25. For NGS special opening of the garden Fri April 21. Adm by donation (inc NT members). Guided walk with the gardener 2pm £2.50 (11-5.30) last entry 5pm*

Plas Penhelig, Aberdovey (The Richardson Family) *Between 2 railway bridges. Driveway to hotel by island and car park.* 14 acres overlooking estuary, exceptional views. Particularly lovely in spring: bulbs, daffodils, rhododendrons, azaleas; rock and water gardens, mature tree heathers, magnolias, euphorbias; herbaceous borders, rose garden; wild and woodland flowers encouraged in large orchard; formal walled garden with herbaceous borders, large range of greenhouses, peaches, herbs. TEAS. *Adm £1.50 Chd 50p. Wed to Sun incl: April 1 to mid-Oct (2.30-5.30). Collecting box*

NEW **Rhiwlas, Bala** ᵫ (Mr & Mrs Robin Price) *By the 30mph speed limit sign at the NE side of Bala on the A494, turn N up public rd where there is a small sign under an oak tree saying Rhiwlas. Do not use old drive. Turn into 1st entrance on L, opposite an archway with cottage either side.* Approx ½m from main rd. 3-acre garden and shrubbery in excess of 300yrs old which in its hey-day had 12 gardeners, now down to one part time! Fine specimen trees incl one of the largest clumps of wellingtonias in Britain. Herbaceous borders, walled kitchen garden and fine views over R Tryweryn to Berwyn Hills. TEA. *Adm £2 Chd 20p. Sun June 25 (2-5.30)*

Rhyd, Trefor ᵫ✗❀ (Ann & Jeff Hubble) *nr Holyhead. From Bodedern 2¼m along B5109 towards Llangefni, turn L.* 2½ acres of gardens and nature walks. Garden is in areas containing many unusual plants in herbaceous beds; rhododendrons, clematis and climbing roses abound; grounds contain ponds, pergolas, rockery and arboretum. Walk through the nature reserve and pause in the haven and see how many wild flowers you can identify. Garden bordered by stream. Partly suitable wheelchairs. TEAS. *Adm £1 Chd free. Suns May 28, July 23 (11-5). Private visits welcome, please* **Tel 01407 720320**

St John the Baptist & St George, Carmel (Bishop Abbot Demetrius) *On the A487 to Groeslon follow signs to Carmel. At village centre turn L and L again at Xrds.* Holy community in the making under the authority of The Orthodox Catholic Church of America. This is not a garden in the traditional sense but a spiritual retreat from the stresses and strains of modern life, surrounded on all sides by space and rural tranquillity. We are privileged to share a glimpse of a more contemplative life. TEA. *Adm £1 Chd free. Sun June 25 (2-5)*

■ **Talhenbont Hall, Pwllheli** ♿❀ (Gillian & Roger Good) *From Criccieth direction, continue along the A497 Llanystumdwy by pass and turn R towards Rhoslan. Follow brown tourist signs or take the 1st L turn and after 50yds turn L. Follow the rd inland 1m to entrance gates. [OS 123]* Hall built in 1607 is surrounded by beautiful grounds and the river Dwyfach which tumbles over a series of waterfalls; designated as a natural habitat for otters. Wild flowers in spring; flowering shrubs; trees; new terraces; many clematis; astilbes; interesting ornamental birds in 'The Quackery' and a children's play area. Light refreshments. Craft shop.TEAS. *Adm £2.50 Chd £1 under 3 free. Open daily (10-5). Off season Thurs to Suns incl (10-5). For NGS Sats, Suns May 13, 14, Sept 16, 17 (10-5)*

NEW **Tan Dinas, Llanfairpwll** ✂❀ (Charles Ellis Esq) *On main rd between Llanfairpwll and Britannia Bridge, 250yds from the Marquess of Anglesey's column. Parking in column car park, access via path through column woods.* 1½ acre cottage garden. Overlooked by the Marquess of Anglesey's column, 200yds from the Menai Straits. Carefully designed and planted on 2 levels; shrubbery, large pond garden, vegetable and fruit patch, heather garden. Careful planting ensures colour all-yr-round. Interesting specimans of Echium Pinanana, other unusual plants. TEA. *Adm £1 Chd 50p. Sat May 13 (11-4) Visits welcome by appt, please* **Tel 01248 714373**

NEW **29-30 Tan-y-Bwlch, Mynydd Llandegai** ✂ (Chas & Ilona Sewell) *From A55/A5 Llandegai roundabout take B4366 towards Caenarfon. At roundabout take B4547 for 1½m, then L towards Deiniolen, next L up hill (Marchlyn), then next L over moor. Take next R down Tan-y-Bwlch 3rd house past junction.* 2 cottages with 2 acres of land, part of the model settlement devised by the Penrhyn estate in the 1870's. Despite the land being infertile and exposed with very high rainfall a 1-acre garden has been wrested from the moorland 1000ft up on Llandegai mountain. Herbaceous beds, shrubs, ornamental grasses, roses, pond, bog areas. Woodland walk and panoramic mountain views. TEAS. *Adm £1 Chd free. Suns April 23, May 21, June 18, July 16, Aug 20, Sept 17, Oct 15 (11-5)*

Trysglwyn Fawr, Rhosybol ♿ (Lord & Lady Stanley of Alderley) *Take the road S from Amlwch to Llanerchymedd. After 2m having passed the Parys Mountain mine shaft on your R, turn L, Trysglwyn Fawr is 1,000yds down that rd on your L.* 1-acre garden overlooking farm land to fine view of Snowdonia. Mixed flower and shrub beds; vegetable garden, fruit garden and conservatory; farm walk showing amenity woodland and ponds, and wind farm. TEA. *Adm £1 Chd free. Sun July 2 (1-5)*

Tyn-y-Cefn, Ffestiniog ✂❀ (Robert & Sheila Woodier) *On the A496 3m from Maentwrog, 2m from Tanygrisiau [OS 695.439].* Set amidst the natural beauty of the mountains and wooded hillsides of Snowdonia. A large walled garden with a wealth of interesting and rare trees, plants, ferns and grasses, 35' wildlife pond, extensive herbaceous beds and borders. We work with nature in this tranquil garden and use no chemicals. Interesting plants for sale. TEA. *Adm £1. Private visits very welcome. Please* **Tel 01766 831810**

The Queen's Nursing Institute

The Queen's Nursing Institute promotes the highest standards of nursing in the community. The organisation founded in 1887, was responsible for the establishment of the district nursing service. Today, the QNI supports community nurses through its unique Innovation Award Scheme which is open to practice nurses, school nurses, nurse practitioners, health visitors, district nurses, midwives and community psychiatric nurses.

More information is available on the NGS website www.ngs.org.uk

Powys

Hon County Organiser: (North - Montgomeryshire) Capt R Watson (Ret'd), Westwinds, Common Road, Kerry, Newtown SY16 4NY
Tel 01686 670605
Assistant County Organiser: Mr J. A. Gleave, Abernant Fron, Montgomery, Powys SY15 6RZ
Hon County Organiser: (South - Brecknock & Radnor) Miss Shan Egerton, Pen-y-Maes, Hay on Wye, Hereford HR3 5PP
Tel 01497 820423
Assistant County Organiser: Lady Milford, Llanstephan House, Llanstephan, Brecon, Powys LD3 0YR
Tel 01982 560693
Hon County Treasurer: (North) Mrs Polly Smith, Crossways, Newcastle on Clun, Shropshire SY7 8QT
Hon County Treasurer: (South) Lady Milford

DATES OF OPENING

Regular openings
For details see garden description
Ashford House, Talybont-on-Usk
Bedw Hir, Gwenddwr
Tan-y-Graig, Moelfre
Woodhill, Moelfre

By appointment only
For telephone numbers and other details see garden descriptions. Private visits welcomed
Belan-yr-Argae, Cefn-Coch
Maenllwyd Isaf, Abermule
The Millers House, Welshpool

April 5 Wednesday
Diamond Cottage, Buttington, Welshpool

April 16 Sunday
Hill Crest, Brooks

April 26 Wednesday
Diamond Cottage, Buttington, Welshpool

April 30 Sunday
Baskerville Court Gardens, Clyro
Crossways, Newcastle on Clun
Hill Crest, Brooks

May 6 Saturday
Tan-y-Llyn, Meifod

May 7 Sunday
Crossways, Newcastle on Clun
Forge House, Llangrwyney
Hill Crest, Brooks
Tan-y-Llyn, Meifod

May 13 Saturday
Glansevern Hall Gardens, Berriew

May 14 Sunday
Brecon Gardens
Crossways, Newcastle on Clun
Glanwye, Builth Wells
Gliffaes Country House Hotel, Crickhowell
Hill Crest, Brooks

May 21 Sunday
Bronhyddon, Llansantffraid-ym-Mechain
Crossways, Newcastle on Clun
Ffrwdgrech House, Brecon
Ty Uchaf, nr Llanerfyl

May 24 Wednesday
Powis Castle Garden, Welshpool

May 27 Saturday
The Bushes, Pantyffridd, Berriew

May 28 Sunday
Bodynfoel Hall, Llanfechain
Crossways, Newcastle on Clun
Maesllwch Castle, Glasbury-on-Wye

May 29 Monday
The Bushes, Pantyffridd, Berriew
Llysdinam, Newbridge-on-Wye

May 31 Wednesday
Diamond Cottage, Buttington, Welshpool
Llwyn Madoc, nr Beulah

June 3 Saturday
Mill Cottage, Abbeycwmhir
Tan-y-Llyn, Meifod

June 4 Sunday
Crossways, Newcastle on Clun
Mill Cottage, Abbeycwmhir
Tan-y-Llyn, Meifod

June 5 Monday
Mill Cottage, Abbeycwmhir

June 6 to 9 Tuesday to Friday
Mill Cottage, Abbeycwmhir

June 10 Saturday
Mill Cottage, Abbeycwmhir

June 11 Sunday
Crossways, Newcastle on Clun
Llangorse Gardens, Nr Brecon
Lower House, Cusop, Hay-on-Wye
Mill Cottage, Abbeycwmhir

June 14 Wednesday
Diamond Cottage, Buttington, Welshpool

June 18 Sunday
Ashford House, Talybont-on-Usk
Crossways, Newcastle on Clun
Hill Crest, Brooks
Presteigne Gardens

June 22 Thursday
Abernant, Fron

June 25 Sunday
Baskerville Court Gardens, Clyro
Coity Gardens, Talybont-on-Usk
Crossways, Newcastle on Clun
Glanusk Park, Crickhowell
Hill Crest, Brooks
Point Farm, Newtown

June 28 Wednesday
Diamond Cottage, Buttington, Welshpool

June 29 Thursday
Abernant, Fron

July 1 Saturday
Mill Cottage, Abbeycwmhir
Tan-y-Llyn, Meifod

July 2 Sunday
Crossways, Newcastle on Clun
Mill Cottage, Abbeycwmhir
Tan-y-Llyn, Meifod
Treberfydd, Bwlch, nr Brecon

July 3 Monday
Mill Cottage, Abbeycwmhir

July 4 to 7 Tuesday to Friday
Mill Cottage, Abbeycwmhir

July 8 Saturday
Mill Cottage, Abbeycwmhir

July 9 Sunday
Hill Crest, Brooks
Mill Cottage, Abbeycwmhir
Moor Park, Llanbedr, nr Crickhowell

July 23 Sunday
Ty Uchaf, nr Llanerfyl

July 26 Wednesday
Diamond Cottage, Buttington, Welshpool

July 29 Saturday
Mill Cottage, Abbeycwmhir

July 30 Sunday
Fraithwen, Tregynon

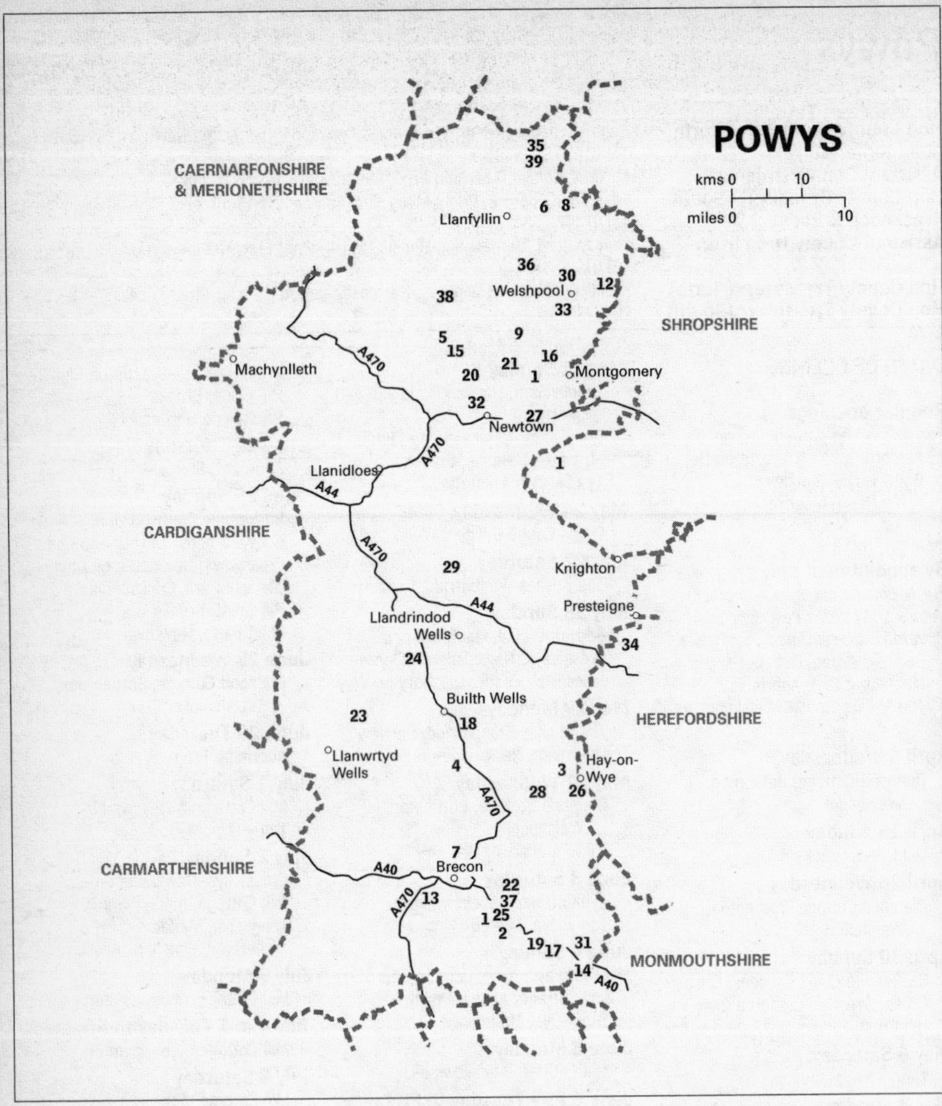

KEY

1 Abernant
2 Ashford House
3 Baskerville Court Gardens
4 Bedw Hir
5 Belan-yr-Argae
6 Bodynfoel Hall
7 Brecon Gardens
8 Bronhyddon
9 The Bushes
10 Coity Gardens
11 Crossways
12 Diamond Cottage
13 Ffrwdgrech House
14 Forge House
15 Fraithwen
16 Glansevern Hall Gardens
17 Glanusk Park
18 Glanwye
19 Gliffaes Country House Hotel
20 Gregynog
21 Hill Crest
22 Llangorse Gardens
23 Llwyn Madoc
24 Llysdinam
25 Lonicera
26 Lower House
27 Maenllwyd Isaf
28 Maesllwch Castle
29 Mill Cottage
30 The Millers House
31 Moor Park
32 Point Farm
33 Powis Castle Garden
34 Presteigne Gardens
35 Tan-y-Graig
36 Tan-y-Llyn
37 Treberfydd
38 Ty Uchaf
39 Woodhill

Mill Cottage, Abbeycwmhir

July 31 Monday
Mill Cottage, Abbeycwmhir

August 1 to 4 Tuesday to Friday
Mill Cottage, Abbeycwmhir

August 5 Saturday
Mill Cottage, Abbeycwmhir
Tan-y-Llyn, Meifod

August 6 Sunday
Lonicera, Talybont-on-Usk, Brecon
Mill Cottage, Abbeycwmhir
Tan-y-Llyn, Meifod

August 13 Sunday
Llysdinam, Newbridge-on-Wye

August 27 Sunday
The Bushes, Pantyffridd, Berriew

August 28 Monday
The Bushes, Pantyffridd, Berriew

August 30 Wednesday
Diamond Cottage, Buttington, Welshpool

September 1 Friday
The Bushes, Pantyffridd, Berriew

September 3 Sunday
Baskerville Court Gardens, Clyro

September 4 Monday
The Bushes, Pantyffridd, Berriew

September 5 to 8 Tuesday to Friday
The Bushes, Pantyffridd, Berriew

September 11 Monday
The Bushes, Pantyffridd, Berriew

September 12 to 15 Tuesday to Friday
The Bushes, Pantyffridd, Berriew

September 16 Saturday
Glansevern Hall Gardens, Berriew

September 23 Saturday
Glansevern Hall Gardens, Berriew

October 8 Sunday
Gliffaes Country House Hotel, Crickhowell

DESCRIPTIONS OF GARDENS

Abernant, Fron ✂❀ (J A & B M Gleave) *Mid-way between Welshpool and Newtown on A483. Approached over steep humpback bridge, then straight ahead through gate.* Approx 2.5 acres incl orchard. Woodland area; lawns, pond, rose garden, rockery, ornamental shrubs, trees and ferns. TEA. *Adm £1.50 OAPs £1 Chd free (ACNO to Welsh Historic Gardens Trust). Thurs June 22, 29 (2-5)*

■ **Ashford House, Talybont-on-Usk** ❀ (Mr & Mrs D A Anderson) *¾m E of Talybont-on-Usk on B4558 signed from A40 through village.* 1-acre walled garden surrounded by woodland and wild garden approx 4 acres altogether; restored and developed since 1979. Mixed shrub and herbaceous borders; small formal garden; meadow garden and pond; alpine house and beds; vegetables. Suitable in parts for wheelchairs. TEAS. *Adm £2 Chd free (ACNO to Save the Children). Open every Tues April 4 to Sept 26 (2-6). For NGS Sun June 18 (2-6). Also by appt, please* **Tel 01874 676 271**

Baskerville Court Gardens, Clyro *Nr Hay-on-Wye. Leave A438 Hereford to Brecon rd at Clyro. Baskerville Court is behind church and Baskerville Arms Hotel.* TEA. *Combined adm £2.50 Chd free. Suns April 30, June 25, Sept 3 (11-5). Also by appt, please* **Tel 01497 820 327**

8 Baskerville Court, Clyro ✂❀ (Mr & Mrs S Smith) Small, steeply terraced garden full of interesting and unusual plants imaginatively planted, incl alpines and heathers. Pergola and conservatory with magnificent views of the Black Mountains and Kilvert's Church

NEW **Tawryn, 6 Baskerville Court, Clyro** ✂ (Mr & Mrs C Young) Small, tiered garden with interesting shrubs, rose bed, fuschias and many other unusual plants. Worth a visit for view alone. Seating areas

Bedw Hir, Gwenddwr ♿✂❀ (Mrs Becky Eves) *6m S of Builth Wells. Signposted at Erwood to Gwenddwr off A470. At top of hill take L fork. After ¼m turn R uphill after Fron Farm. Bedw Hir is next L over cattle grid down drive. (Alternatively please phone for directions).* Approx 4¼ acres. S-facing cottage garden at 900′ surrounding C18 farmhouse (not open) pond, bog area, wildflower meadow; many unusual perennials, shrubs and trees. Old orchard, menagerie and stunning view of Black Mountains. *Adm £1.50 Chd free. Open Weds from April 5 to Nov 8 (11-7) and also by appt, please* **Tel 01982 560714** in advance

Belan-yr-Argae, Cefn-Coch ♿ (Ms Ivy Pritchard Evans) *14m SW of Welshpool via Llanfair Caereinion and Cefn Coch and 11m NW of Newtown via Tregynon and Adfa.* Garden attached to old-fashioned farm comprising formal and wild gardens with pools, unusual plants, shrubs and trees, all set in approx ½ acre. TEA. *Adm £1 Chd free. Mon May 29 to end Aug. Private visits welcome May 29 onwards, please* **Tel 01938 810658**

Bodynfoel Hall, Llanfechain ♿❀ (Major Bonnor-Maurice) *10m N of Welshpool. Via A490 to Llanfyllin. Take B4393 to Llanfechain, follow signs.* Approx 3½ acres; gardens and woodland; lakes; young and mature trees; heather bank. TEAS. *Adm £1.50 OAPs £1 Chd 50p. Sun May 28 (2-6)* **Tel 01691 648486**

NEW **Brecon Gardens** ❀ *From Carmarthen/Merthyr leave A40 at W roundabout. Turn L at 1st t-lights then R at next turning (Mount St). Next L, signed Nythfa Hotel. From Abergavenny/Hereford leave A40 at S roundabout. Turn R into Free St, signed Leisure Centre and Hospital. Take 2nd L into Bellevue then R and L. Combined adm £2 Chd free. Sun May 14 (2-6)*

NEW **5 Bellevue** (Mr & Mrs A Hall) Container garden full of interest and shape; many shrubs, large and small, all transportable

NEW **Deffrobani, Maescelyn** ❀ (Roland Mathias) ½ acre landscaped garden by the late Molly Mathias. Mature shrubs, very colourful rhododendrons and azaleas

NEW **Khyber Kothi, Maescelyn** ❀ (Rachel Walters) Interesting, small, informal garden full of surprises; primroses, violets and winter cyclamens growing in lawn; hellebores, erithoniums, anemones, euphorbias, rhododendrons, azaleas and early clematis

NEW **14 Maescelyn** ❀ (Mary Scutt) Plant lover's garden of seasonal variety and colour. Interesting shrubs, spring bulbs, hardy germaniums and iris. Paeonies, Dicentra spectabilis, sink garden and flowering tubs

Bronhyddon, Llansantffraid-ym-Mechain ❀ (Mr & Mrs Robert Jones-Perrott) *10m N Welshpool on A495 on E side in centre of village. Long drive.* Felled wood now planted with choice young trees & shrubs on acid soil on S-facing slope. Grass rides, mass of bluebells and foxgloves in spring; mature stand has anemones, snowdrops and primroses. Elegant Regency verandahs & balconies.. TEAS. *Adm £1 Chd free. Sun May 21 (2-6)*

The Bushes, Pantyffridd, Berriew ✂❀ (Mr & Mrs Hywel Williams) *8m from Welshpool on B4390 Berriew (3m) to Manafon rd. In picturesque Rhiew Valley.* ⅔ acres designed into terraced, colour co-ordinated 'rooms' and planted with over 700 varieties of perennials, roses, shrubs and climbers clothing old stone house (not open) and farm buildings. Imaginative use of local stone in attractive patios and water features. *Adm £1.50 Chd free. Sat, Bank Hol Mon May 27, 29, Sun, Bank Hol Mon Aug 27, 28 (2-5.30). Mon to Fri Sept 1 to 15 weekdays only (10-5). Private visits welcome, please* **Tel 01686 650338**

Coity Gardens, Talybont-on-Usk ✂❀ *Brecon 6m Crickhowell 6m. Leave village on B4558 towards Brecon. Approx ½m at pink cottages take L signed Talybont reservoir, then 1st R up to road junction turn L to Coity Mawr and Dan-y-Coity at top.* Refreshments. *Combined adm £3.50 Chd free. Sun June 25 (11-5)*

Coity Mawr (Mr & Mrs W Forwood) 4 acres at 850' created over 4 yrs, work still in progress. Terraced with spectacular view of Black Mountains across Usk valley. Mature trees, unusual plants and shrubs; rose and water gardens; parterre; willow arbour

Dan-y-Coity (P H Barker & E Dowman) 1-acre terraced, walled garden at 850' with good mountain views. Interesting variety of plants, some rare. Stream and pond feature with bog garden. Collections of sorbus, ferns, hostas and camellias, fruit trees

■ **Crossways, Newcastle on Clun** ✂❀ (Mr & Mrs R G Smith) *B4368 4m W of Newcastle turn R at Xrds signposted Crossways. 1m cottage at top of T-junction [Map ref. 205.859].* 1-acre cottage garden and nursery 1400' on Shropshire/Welsh border. Pond, rockery and woodland area, unusual and rare herbaceous plants. Small nursery. *Adm £1. Suns April 2 to Oct 1. For NGS Suns April 30, May 7, 14, 21, 28, June 4, 11, 18, 25, July 2 (2-5). Private visits welcome, please* **Tel 01686 670890**

Diamond Cottage, Buttington, Welshpool ✂❀ (Mr & Mrs D T Dorril) *From Welshpool take A458 for 3m, then turn R into Heldre Lane. From Shrewsbury, turn L past Little Chef at Trewern into Sale Lane. Then follow signs.* 1¾ acre garden on steep, N-facing slope at 700'. Unusual herbaceous plants and shrubs; wooded dingle with stream; vegetable garden, patio and pools. Extensive views to Berwyn Mountains. TEAS. *Adm £1.50 Chd free. Weds April 5, 26, May 31, June 14, 28, July 26, Aug 30 (2-6). Groups welcome April to Sept, please* **Tel 01938 570570**

Ffrwdgrech House, Brecon ♿❀ (Michael D D Evans) *Enter Brecon from A40 at W roundabout on by-pass. Take 3rd turning on R, Ffrwdgrech Rd. In ¾m oak gate and lodge on L.* 5-acre woodland garden; lake, specimen trees, rhododendrons, azaleas, stream and waterfall. Extensive views of Brecon Beacons over wide lawns. TEAS in aid of L'Arche. *Adm £2 Chd free. Sun May 21 (2-5). Also by appt, please* **Tel 01874 622519**

Forge House, Llangrwyney ♿✂ (Mr & Mrs Peter Bishop) *4m W of Abergavenny on A40, turn L at Bell Hotel in Llangrwyney. Garden on R.* 1 acre, owner maintained garden. Unusual shrubs and trees incl fine Halesia (Snowdrop tree) and Paulownia. Extensive planting around large millpond and leat. TEAS in aid of Nevill Hall Thrombosis Fund. *Adm £2 Chd free. Sun May 7 (2-5)*

Fraithwen, Tregynon ✂❀ (Mr & Mrs David and Sydney Thomas) *6m N of Newtown on B4389 mid-way between villages of Bettws Cedewain and Tregynon.* 1½-acre established garden with herbaceous borders, rockeries and ponds. Packed with interesting and rare plants for yr-round colour. Display of antique horse-drawn machinery and house implements. Partially suitable for wheelchairs. TEAS. *Adm £1.50 Chd free (ACNO to Bettws Community Centre). Sun July 30 (2-6). Private parties welcome, please* **Tel 01686 650307**

■ **Glansevern Hall Gardens, Berriew** ♿❀ (Mr & Mrs R N Thomas (Neville)) *4m SW of Powis Castle, Welshpool, on A483 at Berriew.* 18-acre mature garden situated nr banks of R Severn. Centred on Glansevern Hall, a Greek Revival house dated 1801 (not open). Noted for variety of unusual tree species; much new planting; lake with island; woodland walk; large rock garden and grotto. Walled rose garden; water features. TEAS. Free car/coach park. *Adm £2 Chd free. Fris, Sats and Bank Hol Mons, May to Sept. For NGS Sats May 13, Sept 16, 23 (12-6)*

Glanusk Park, Crickhowell ♿✂ (The Viscountess De L'Isle) *On A40 2m W of Crickhowell, 12m E of Brecon, 8m from Abergavenny.* Large garden within beautiful park edged by R Usk; formal rose garden and fountain, water garden and pool, fine trees. Original house destroyed during World War II. TEAS. *Adm £2 Chd free. Sun June 25 (2-5)*

Glanwye, Builth Wells ♿❀ (Mr & Mrs David Vaughan, G & H Kidston) *2m E Builth Wells on A470.* Large garden, rhododendrons, azaleas; herbaceous borders, extensive yew hedges, lawns, long woodland walk with bluebells and other woodland flowers. Magnificent views of upper Wye Valley. Illustrated in 'Some Borderland Gardens' by B & A Palmer. TEAS. *Adm £2 Chd free. Sun May 14 (2-5)*

■ **Gliffaes Country House Hotel, Crickhowell** ♿ (Mr & Mrs N Brabner) *3m W of Crickhowell on A40.* Large garden; spring bulbs, azaleas and rhododendrons; ornamental pond; heathers, shrubs and ornamental trees; fine maples; autumn colour; lovely position high above R Usk. Cream Teas available at hotel. *Adm £2 Chd free (collection box). April to Dec. For NGS Suns May 14, Oct 8 (2-5)*

Gregynog, Tregynon ♿ (University of Wales) *7m N of Newtown. A483 Welshpool to Newtown Rd, turn W at B4389 for Bettws Cedewain, 1m through village gates on L.* Large garden; fine banks, rhododendrons and azaleas; dell with specimen shrubs; formal garden; colour-coded walks.

Descriptive leaflet available. Early C19 black and white house (not open); site inhabited since C12. *Collection box.*

Hill Crest, Brooks ❀ (Mr J D & Mrs P Horton) *9m SW of Welshpool. Turn R to Berriew, then L by Lion Hotel, through village towards Bettws Cedewain. Turn R after 3m to Brooks then 1m up hill on L. 8m NE from Newtown. Through Bettws Cedewain. Take Brooks Rd, after 3m turn L. House at top of hill on L.* Approx 1 acre of mixed shrub borders, alpine sinks and pool; hillside arboretum with daffodils and rhododendron walk. *Adm £1.50 Chd 10p Suns April 16, 30, May 7, 14, June 18, 25, July 9, (1-5). Group visits welcome all year, please* **Tel 01686 640541**

Llangorse Gardens, Nr Brecon ♿✲❀ *On B4560 4m off A40 at Bwlch, 6½m from Brecon and 4½m from Talgarth. [Map Ref LD3 7TS]. Park in village.* Teas in aid of Llangorse Church. *Combined adm £3. Chd free. Sun June 11 (2-6)*

The Neuadd ♿✲❀ (Mr & Mrs Paul Johnson) 1-acre, informal garden; mixed borders, interesting trees incl cornus; shrubs, species roses and herbaceous plants; copse. Emphasis on good foliage and unusual forms of cottage garden and native plants. Maintained by owners on organic lines *Private visits welcome, please* **Tel 01874 658670**

The Old Vicarage ♿✲❀ (Major & Mrs J B Anderson) Small family garden maintained by owners; interesting herbaceous and shrub borders; lawns, trees and vegetables *Private visits welcome Spring to Oct, please* **Tel 01874 658639**

NEW **Llwyn Madoc, nr Beulah** ♿ (Mr & Mrs Mervyn Bourdillon) *10m W of Builth Wells. From Beulah take rd towards Abergwesyn for 1¼m.* Medium-sized terraced garden in attractive wooded valley; interesting old box hedge and newly planted pergola; rhododendrons and azaleas. TEA. *Adm £2 Chd free. Wed May 31 (2-6)*

Llysdinam, Newbridge-on-Wye ♿❀ (Lady Delia Venables-Llewelyn) *SW of Llandrindod Wells. Turn W off A470 at Newbridge-on-Wye; right immed after crossing R Wye; entrance up hill.* Large garden. Azalea, rhododendrons, water garden and herbaceous borders, shrubs, woodland garden, kitchen garden. Fine view of Wye Valley. TEAS in aid of NSPCC. *Adm £2 Chd free. Bank Hol Mon May 29, Sun Aug 13 (2-6). Private parties welcome, please* **Tel 01597 860 200**

Lonicera, Talybont-on-Usk, Brecon ♿✲❀ (Gareth & Eirona Davies) *¼m off A40, signposted Talybont-on-Usk, 6m E of Brecon and 8m W of Crickhowell. 1st bungalow on L before entering Talybont.* RHS lecturer's ¼ acre garden of varied interest incorporating several small feature gardens. Modern roses; heather garden with small conifers; herbaceous and woody perennials; colourful summer bedding displays; window boxes, hanging baskets and patio tubs forming extensive house frontage display; greenhouses. Featured in Channel 4's Real Gardens 98. Teas in village. *Adm £2 Chd free (ACNO to Arthritis and Rheumatism Council). Sun Aug 6 (2-6)*

NEW **Lower House, Cusop, Hay-on-Wye** ✲❀ (Nicky & Pete Daw) *Leave Hay-on-Wye on B4352 Bredwardine rd, take L turning, signposted Cusop Dingle (no-through rd). Drive on R 3/4m from main rd, across stone bridge. Limited parking near house, paticularly if wet. Parking available at Cusop Church. (For this turn L off Cusop Dingle rd at signpost to church. Lower House is 300yds from Church down public footpath)* Sheltered valley garden, designed and maintained by owners since 1986. Luxuriant planting around old house (not open); shady courtyard with tree fern and bamboos; new cedar conservatory and evolving terrace area with exotic planting. Ornamental vegetable garden, stream, woodland walks. TEAS. *Adm £2 Chd free. Sun June 11 (2-6)*

Maenllwyd Isaf, Abermule ♿✲ (Mrs Denise Hatchard) *5m NE of Newtown, 10m S of Welshpool. On B4368 Abermule to Craven Arms, 1½m from Abermule.* 3 acres; unusual shrubs and plants; goldfish pool; wild pool; R Mule. C16 listed house (not open). *Adm £1 Chd free (ACNO to Winged Fellowship Trust). Private visits welcome all year. Gardening clubs and groups welcome, please* **Tel 01686 630204**

Maesllwch Castle, Glasbury-on-Wye ❀ (Walter de Winton Esq) *Turn off A438 immed N of Glasbury Bridge. Through Glasbury, ½m turn R at church.* Medium-sized, owner-maintained garden. Exceptional views from terrace across R Wye to Black Mountains. Woodland walk to old walled garden now used for growing young trees. Fine trees, C18 gingko tree. TEA. *Adm £2 Chd free (ACNO to All Saints Church, Glasbury). Sun May 28 (2-5)*

Mill Cottage, Abbeycwmhir ❀ (Mr & Mrs B D Parfitt) *8m N of Llandrindod Wells. Turn L off A483, 1m N of Crossgates roundabout, then 3½m on L, signposted Abbeycwmhir.* ⅓ acre garden crammed with unusual and rare shrubs, small trees and climbers. Numerous Ericaceae. Narrow paths and steps; limited parking. TEA. *Adm £1 Chd 50p. Sat to Sun incl, June 3 to June 11, July 1 to 9, July 29 to August 6 (mid-day to dusk)*

The Millers House, Welshpool ♿❀ (Mr & Mrs Mark Kneale) *About 1¼m NW of Welshpool on rd to Guilsfield A490; turn R into Windmill Lane; 4th cottage on L.* 1½-acre country garden begun in 1988. Superb views. Mixed shrub and herbaceous borders, roses, climbers; pool. Ornamental and fruit trees incl 12 hardy eucalyptus. *Adm £1.50 Chd free. Private visits welcome, please* **Tel 01938 555432**

Moor Park, Llanbedr, nr Crickhowell ♿ (Leolin Price) *Turn off A40 at fire station in Crickhowell; continue 2m, signed Llanbedr.* 5 acres; roses, borders, trees and walled kitchen garden. Lake, water garden, woodland walk. TEAS. *Adm £2 Chd free. Sun July 9 (2-6)*

Point Farm, Newtown ♿✲❀ (Mr & Mrs F Podmore) *Bryn Lane. Head N across river from town centre. Turn R into Commercial St off roundabout. Turn L at fork into Llanfair Rd, then L at hospital for 1½m along Bryn Lane.* ¾ acre at 750' set in unspoilt views. Patio, pergola, herbaceous plants and shrub beds, wildflower area and pond. Soft fruits, raised vegetable garden with 15′ × 25′ greenhouse; peach and apricot trees, tender plants. TEAS and raffle by Aberhafesp

WI and Happy Circle. *Adm £1.50 Acc chd free. Suns June 25 (2-6). Private visits welcome, please* **Tel 01686 625709**

▲ **Powis Castle Garden, Welshpool** ✗✿ (The National Trust) *Turn off A483 ¾m out of Welshpool, up Red Lane for ¼m. Laid out in 1720 with most famous hanging terraces in the world; enormous yew hedges; lead statuary, large wild garden. Top terrace suitable for wheelchairs (available free of charge). Tea rooms. Adm (garden only) £5 Chd £2.50. For NGS Wed May 24 (11-6) last entry 5.30*

Presteigne Gardens TEAS at Broadheath House. *Combined adm £3.50 Chd free. Sun June 18 (2-5)*
 Broadheath House ᪸✿ (Mr & Mrs D McDowell) *1m E of Presteigne on B4362. 2½-acre garden designed by Sir Clough William-Ellis. Sunken rose garden, irises, ponds and enclosed yew garden, newly designed kitchen garden, orchard and recently planted nuttery. Adm £2 Chd free (ACNO to Radnor Citizens Advice Bureau).*
 The Walled Garden, Knill ᪸ (Miss C M Mills) *3m from Kington and Presteigne off B4362 Walton to Presteigne rd. In Knill village turn R over cattle grid, keep R down drive. 4 acres; walled garden; river, bog garden; primulas; shrub and climbing roses. Nr C13 church in lovely valley. Featured in Water Gardener, various books on gardens in the area and HTV's Get Gardening. Adm £2 Chd free. Also open by appt Adm £1.50. Private visits and garden clubs welcome any day (10-7), please* **Tel 01544 267411**

Tan-y-Graig, Moelfre ✗ (Pat & Don Hood) *Approx 8m from Oswestry. Take B4580 to Llansilin, follow signs for Moelfre, then 200yds on R ¾-acre garden with further 2-acre wooded area. Daffodils. Mixed herbaceous borders with conifers and many unusual shrubs. Changing colours and flowers throughout season. Adm £2 Chd free (ACNO to Born Free Foundation). Tues, Fri, Sun May to Sept incl or by appt, please* **Tel 01691 791358**

Tan-y-Llyn, Meifod ✗✿ (Callum Johnston & Brenda Moor) *From Oswestry on A495 turn L in village, cross R Vyrnwy and climb hill for ½m bearing R at Y-junction. [Map ref 167.125]. 3-acre sheltered garden and orchard in Montgomeryshire hills. Informally terraced; laid out to complement proportions of existing hillside. Thorn grove, herb garden; extensive collection of container plants. Nursery specialising in alpines, herbaceous plants and herbs. TEAS. Events, demonstrations and exhibitions. Adm £1.50 Chd free. Sats, Suns May 6, 7, June 3, 4, July 1, 2 , Aug 5, 6 (2-5)*

Treberfydd, Bwlch, nr Brecon ᪸ (Lt Col D Garnons Williams) *2¼m W of Bwlch. From A40 at Bwlch,take turning marked Llangorse, then L for Pennorth. From Brecon, leave A40 at Llanhamlach. 2¼m to sign for Llangasty Church, entrance over cattle grid. Large garden; lawns, roses, herbaceous borders, trees, rock garden. Plants for sale at commercial nursery. TEAS. Adm £2 Chd free (ACNO to Llangasty Church). Sun July 2 (2-6)*

Ty Uchaf, nr Llanerfyl ✗✿ (Mr & Mrs D Budgen) *Just off main A458 Welshpool to Dolgellau rd. 3m W of Llanfair Caereinion or 1½m E of Llanerfyl. Cottage garden with many traditional and unusual plants; water feature and vegetable garden. Further 2½-acre wild woodland walk with mature oaks, daffodils, bluebells and orchids in season. TEAS. Adm £1.50 Chd free (ACNO to Hope House). Suns May 21, July 23 (2-5)*

Woodhill, Moelfre ᪸ (Janet Randell) *Oswestry approx 9m. 6 acres. Formal garden. Footpaths designed for wheelchairs, totalling ¾m, lead to arboretum and wild area bordering stream with picnic area overlooking ponds. All-yr interest: bluebell wood in spring; rose garden in summer; arbour with picnic area and wild roses in woods, trees, shrubs and berries in autumn; scented winter shrubs. To date 1000 species of trees and shrubs planted informally. Electric wheelchairs available on request. Adm £1.50 Chd free (ACNO to Woodhill Project Trust). Open all yr. Private visits welcome, please* **Tel 01691 791486**

Marie Curie Cancer Care

Marie Curie Centres provide the largest number of hospice beds outside the NHS. Patients are supported by professional teams including consultants, nurses, physiotherapists, social workers and chaplains. For more information about Marie Curie Cancer Care, ring 0800 716 146 or visit our web site at www.mariecurie.org.uk

HELP THE HOSPICES

Help the Hospices supports hospices in ensuring that the best possible care is available for the terminally ill – people with advanced cancer, motor neurone disease, AIDS and other progressive, incurable illnesses. Hospice care is based on the simple idea that a dying patient is a living person – someone who deserves peace, love and calm until the very end of their life. Hospices seek to add life to days, even when days cannot be added to life, and restore dignity, quality and a sense of fulfilment to the closing days of a patient's life. They also work to ensure that the needs of each patient, their family and their friends, are met according to their wants and wishes.

Throughout Britain, three-quarters of this skilled and dedicated care is provided free of charge by the 190 independent voluntary hospices, nearly all with respite, home and day care services, as well as in-patient facilities. Help the Hospices, a grant-giving charity without any funding from the State, was established to serve these units, responding to their appeals for all kinds of support.

Help the Hospices provides bursary awards for the training of hospice staff, principally nurses and doctors, to help them offer even higher levels of care for patients. Other grants fund courses run by hospices for others involved in caring for the terminally ill, such as nursing home staff. Help the Hospices also organises its own training programme for hospice staff and provides major grants to purchase special equipment, to fund research and finance new posts.

Help the Hospices is a small charity, committed to fulfilling its title role to its utmost

For more information, please contact:
Help the Hospices,
34–44 Britannia Street, London WC1X 9JG

Information is also available on the NGS website (www.ngs.org.uk)

Evening openings

Bristol and South Gloucestershire

Emmaus House, Clifton Hill, Bristol	June 12 Monday
Bristol Zoo Gardens	June 27 Tuesday

Buckinghamshire

The Old Vicarage, Padbury	June 29 Thursday
The Old Vicarage, Padbury	June 30 Friday

Cambridgeshire

Fen Ditton Gardens	June 15 Thursday
Newnham College, Cambridge	June 29 Thursday
Clare College, Fellows' Garden, Cambridge	July 2 Sunday
Pampisford Gardens	July 19 Wednesday

Cheshire and Wirral

Bolesworth Castle, Tattenhall	May 12 Friday

Cumbria

Holker Hall Gardens, Cark-in-Cartmel	July 12 Wednesday

Derbyshire

Wharfedale, Duffield	June 28 Wednesday

Devon

Membland Villa, Newton Ferrers	April 21 Friday
Greenlands	June 21 Wednesday

Dorset

The Old Rectory, West Compton	June 13 Tuesday
The Old Rectory, West Compton	June 27 Tuesday
Holworth Farmhouse, Holworth	July 28 Friday

Essex

Barnards Farm, West Horndon	June 14 Wednesday

Glamorgan

11 Arno Road, Little Coldbrook, Barry	June 14 Wednesday

Gloucestershire North and Central

Mill Dene, Blockley	June 30 Friday

Hampshire

Rowans Wood, Ampfield	May 17 Wednesday
Rowans Wood, Ampfield	May 27 Saturday
The Vyne, Sherborne St John	June 28 Wednesday
South End House, Lymington	July 29 Saturday

Hertfordshire

Rustling End Cottage, Rustling End	June 30 Friday

Isle of Wight

Northcourt Gardens, Shorwell	June 21 Wednesday

Kent

Hazel Street Farmhouse, Horsmonden	May 17 Wednesday
Haydown, Great Buckland	May 31 Wednesday
Edenbridge House, Edenbridge	June 14 Wednesday
Plaxtol Gardens	June 16 Friday
Nettlestead Place, Nettlestead	June 21 Wednesday
Wyckhurst, Aldington	June 24 Saturday
Hazel Street Farmhouse, Horsmonden	June 28 Wednesday
Worth Gardens	June 28 Wednesday
Ladham House, Goudhurst	July 6 Thursday
Little Oast, Otford	July 8 Saturday

Kent *(continued)*

Haydown, Great Buckland	July 19 Wednesday
Torry Hill, Sittingbourne	July 19 Wednesday
Godinton House, Ashford	August 23 Wednesday

Leicestershire and Rutland

Gilmorton Gardens	June 21 Wednesday
The Court House, Geeston, Ketton Stamford	June 28 Wednesday

London

Flat 1, 1F Oval Road, NW1	May 11 Thursday
7 St George's Road, Twickenham	June 1 Thursday
263 Nether Street, N3	June 3 Saturday
Tewkesbury Lodge Garden Group	June 3 Saturday
5 Burbage Road, SE24	June 7 Wednesday
Fenton House, NW3	June 8 Thursday
Flat 1, 1F Oval Road, NW1	June 8 Thursday
263 Nether Street, N3	June 10 Saturday
71 Palace Road, SW2	June 14 Wednesday
Little Lodge, Thames Ditton	June 14 Wednesday
101 Cheyne Walk, SW10	June 15 Thursday
9 Montpelier Grove, NW5	June 15 Thursday
26 Kenilworth Road, SE20	June 17 Saturday
103 Thurleigh Road, SW12	June 21 Wednesday
133 Crystal Palace Road, SE22	June 21 Wednesday
5 Hillcrest Avenue, NW11	June 21 Wednesday
Seymour Buildings, W1	June 22 Thursday
Southwood Lodge, N6	June 22 Thursday
125 Honor Oak Park, SE23	June 24 Saturday
48 Rommany Road, SE27	June 24 Saturday
1 Audrey Close, Beckenham	July 5 Wednesday

London *(continued)*

8 Grafton Park Road, Worcester Park	July 5 Wednesday
48 Rommany Road, SE27	July 8 Saturday
10A Hoveden Road, NW2	July 14 Friday
24 Croom's Hill, SE10	July 16 Sunday
2 Millfield Place, N6	July 20 Thursday

Northamptonshire

The Haddonstone Show Garden, East Haddon Manor, nr Northampton	June 8 Thursday
Evenley Gardens	June 13 Tuesday
Evenley Gardens	June 20 Tuesday
Ravensthorpe Gardens	July 19 Wednesday

Shropshire

Brownhill House, Ruyton XI Towns	May 29 Monday
Brownhill House, Ruyton XI Towns	June 5 Monday

Somerset

Ilminster Gardens	May 1 Monday
Popinjays & Little Norton Mill	July 10 Monday

Staffordshire and part of West Midlands

12 Darges Lane, Great Wyrley	June 21 Wednesday

Suffolk

Washbrook Grange, Washbrook	June 3 Saturday
18 The Avenue, Ipswich	June 24 Saturday

Evening openings *(continued)*

Surrey

The Copse Lodge, Burgh Heath	June 7 Wednesday
Chilworth Manor, Guildford	June 8 Thursday
RHS Garden Wisley	June 28 Wednesday
Shepherds Lane Gardens	June 28 Wednesday
Four Aces, Pirbright	July 2 Sunday
Woodbury Cottage, Reigate	July 5 Wednesday
66 Avenue Road, Belmont	July 6 Thursday
Chilworth Manor, Guildford	July 6 Thursday
Tanyard Farmhouse, Langshott, Horley	July 8 Saturday
Culverkeys, Ewell	July 12 Wednesday
Heathfield, Albury Heath	July 12 Wednesday
Shepherds Lane Gardens	July 12 Wednesday
Tanyard Farmhouse, Langshott, Horley	July 12 Wednesday
Walnut House, Reigate	July 13 Thursday
Red Oaks, Redhill	July 14 Friday
Vale End, Albury	August 2 Wednesday
Stuart Cottage, East Clandon	August 3 Thursday
RHS Garden Wisley	August 22 Tuesday

Sussex

Sheffield Park Garden, Sheffield Park	May 11 Thursday
Neptune House, Cutmill	June 3 Saturday
Neptune House, Cutmill	June 4 Sunday
Frith Hill, Northchapel	June 11 Sunday
Frith Lodge, Northchapel	June 11 Sunday
Frith Hill, Northchapel	June 18 Sunday

Sussex *(continued)*

Frith Lodge, Northchapel	June 18 Sunday
Frith Hill, Northchapel	June 25 Sunday
Frith Lodge, Northchapel	June 25 Sunday
Sands, Warnham	June 28 Wednesday
Cowbeech Farm, Cowbeech	June 30 Friday
72 Grand Avenue, Worthing	July 5 Wednesday
Cowbeech Farm, Cowbeech	July 5 Wednesday
Berri Court, Yapton	July 14 Friday
Sennicotts, Chichester	July 22 Saturday
Neptune House, Cutmill	July 29 Saturday
Neptune House, Cutmill	July 30 Sunday
Rymans, Apuldram	August 5 Saturday

Warwickshire

52 Tenbury Road, King's Heath	June 21 Wednesday
8 Vicarage Road, Edgbaston	June 21 Wednesday
The Folly Lodge, Halford	June 28 Wednesday
26 Sunnybank Road, Wylde Green	June 30 Friday
Charlecote Park, Warwick	July 4 Tuesday
66 Dalbury Road, Hall Green	August 9 Wednesday

Worcestershire

Hanbury Hall, Hanbury	June 21 Wednesday
Elm Grove & neighbours, Astley Cross	June 25 Sunday
Holland House, Cropthorne	June 28 Wednesday
Eastgrove Cottage Garden Nursery, Sankyns Green, Shrawley	July 29 Saturday

Index to Gardens

A

B

C

D

E

F

G

H

I

J

K

L

M

P

Q

R

S

T

U

V

W

Y

The National Gardens Scheme

is pleased to invite you to two special Evening Openings
of

The Royal Horticultural Society Garden

Wisley

on

Wednesday 28th June
6:30–9:30pm

&

Tuesday August 22nd
6:00–9:00pm

Stroll through this delightful garden and enjoy an evening of musical entertainment

The Wisley Flower Show marquee will be open from 7:00–9:00pm with plant sales by Show Exhibitors between 7:00–8:00pm

Admission: £3.50 (fee also applies to RHS members)

The Terrace Restaurant and Conservatory Cafe will be open and if you wish to reserve a table for dinner in the Terrace Restaurant, please telephone (01483) 225329

Ample parking facilities

SORRY NO PICNICS

Index to Advertisers

The National Gardens Scheme Year 2001 Calendar

The perfect gift for garden-lovers, this calendar, produced by the Medici Society Ltd., is available from Medici retailers or by mail or telephone (priced £4.95 plus p&p) from the Gardeners Royal Benevolent Society, Bridge House, 139 Kingston Road, Leatherhead, Surrey KT22 7NW.

Telephone orders with debit or credit card on (44) (0) 1372 373962

Elizabeth Shaw®

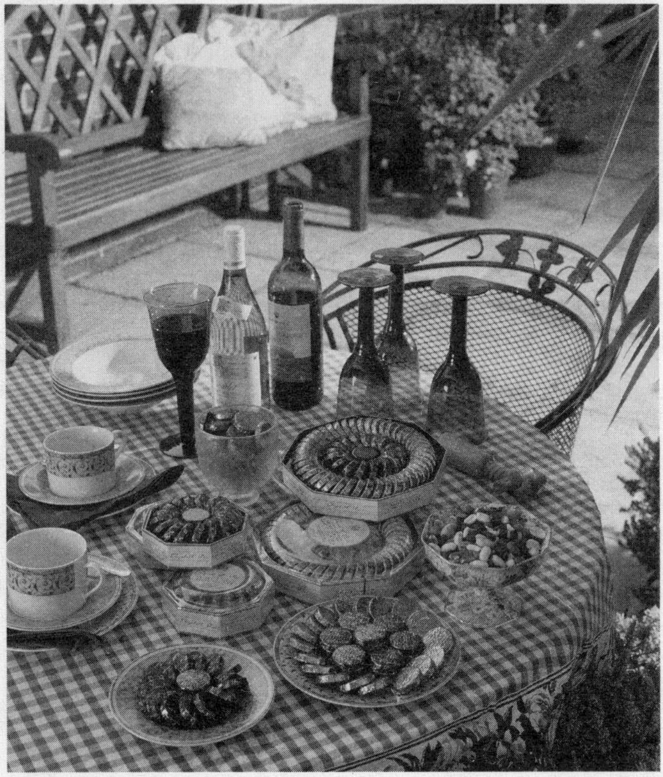

Elizabeth Shaw Chocolates are delighted to support the evening openings of the National Gardens Scheme during 2000 for the third year running.

Best known for their top quality Mint Crisps, Elizabeth Shaw has a long tradition of making fine chocolates.

What could be more appropriate than to sample an Elizabeth Shaw chocolate in a lovely British Garden?

Elizabeth Shaw looks forward to welcoming you at an evening opening soon!

FIVE ISSUES JUST £9.99!

Discover the garden of your dreams

- *Inspirational design*
- *Glorious gardens*
- *Practical advice*

less than £2.00 an issue

The ENGLISH GARDEN

HOTLINE 01858 438833 - *only £9.99!*

SPECIAL INTRODUCTORY SUBSCRIPTION OFFER

☑ **YES!** *I wish to take advantage of this special offer and receive five issues of THE ENGLISH GARDEN for just £9.99 (£14.99 overseas).*

YOUR DETAILS

Mr/Mrs/Ms ....

Address: ....

....

.... Postcode: ....

Tel No: .... (In case we have a query about your order)

☐ Please tick if you are extending an existing subscription

PAYMENT

☐ Cheque enclosed (payable to THE ENGLISH GARDEN)

☐ Please charge £.......... to my Visa/Mastercard

No: ....

Exp: .... MasterCard VISA

Signature: ....

☐ Please tick if you do NOT wish to receive mail from selected companies

RETURN WITH YOUR PAYMENT TO:
THE ENGLISH GARDEN, FREEPOST RG2509, Wokingham, RG40 1BR, UK
(no stamp required if posted in the UK)

NGB0

'We guarantee you'll be delighted ~ or your money back'

If you are not delighted with THE ENGLISH GARDEN we will refund the balance of your subscription without question and without hesitation.

The ENGLISH GARDEN

PHOTOGRAPHIC • WORKSHOPS

THE ENGLISH GARDEN magazine, in association with Pentax and the National Gardens Scheme, invites readers to take part in two one day photographic workshops with Clive Nichols

The National Gardens Scheme
Gardens open for charity

PENTAX

Sponsored by Pentax and in association with the National Gardens Scheme, THE ENGLISH GARDEN magazine has invited leading garden photographer **Clive Nichols** to pass on expert advice to readers at two one-day workshops to be held in June & September 2000 at Vale End in Surrey and Newby Hall & Gardens in Yorkshire, open under the National Gardens Scheme.

Vale End, Albury, Surrey - *Thursday 15 June 2000*
Newby Hall & Gardens, Ripon, Yorkshire - *Thursday 14 September 2000*

Photographer: Clive Nichols has three times been voted Garden Photographer of the Year; he also runs seminars on garden photography in London and Bath.

The NGS Yellow Book says of **Vale End**: *One acre walled garden in beautiful settings overlooking mill pond and woods beyond. Borders range from hot and dry to cool and shaded with wide range of roses, annuals and perennials. Clipped yew walk with rope swag, attractive courtyard, fruit, vegatable and herb garden.*

The NGS Yellow Book says of **Newby Hall & Gardens**: *40 acres extensive gardens laid out in 1920s, full of rare and beautiful plants. There are formal seasonal gardens and stunning double herbaceous borders. It holds the National Collection of cornus.*

THE WORKSHOPS

- Each workshop is limited to 22 people.
- Clive Nichols will offer instruction and supervise photography.
- The latest Pentax range will be available on loan for you to try on the day.
- In addition, the best photographs taken by participants will be featured in a future edition of THE ENGLISH GARDEN.
- Representatives from Pentax will be on hand to offer additional technical expertise.
- All film used on the day is provided free and will be developed free of charge by Pentax.
- A buffet lunch and refreshments are included in the price.
- All participants will receive an English Garden gift bag.
- The One Day Workshops cost £85 per person per day for subscribers to THE ENGLISH GARDEN and £95 for non-subscribers.
- The organisers reserve the right to cancel a workshop in the event of bad weather.

For more information on THE ENGLISH GARDEN'S PHOTOGRAPHIC WORKSHOPS, please telephone Angela Bignell on 020 7233 9191.

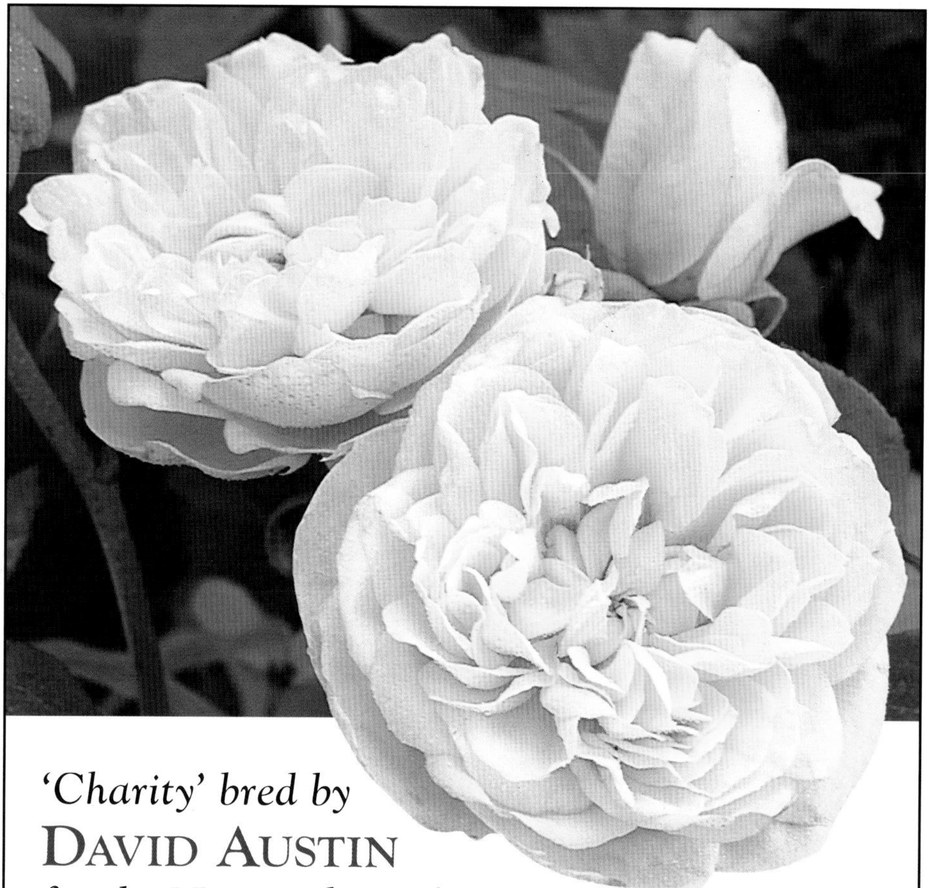

'Charity' bred by DAVID AUSTIN for the National Gardens Scheme

Charity *(Auschar)* is a magnificent soft apricot-yellow variety of true Old Rose character – and David Austin Roses is pleased to contribute a 5% royalty donation to the NGS, for each Charity rose sold by April 2001. For a full description of this rose send off now for David Austin's FREE HANDBOOK OF ROSES – 88 pages of colour photographs, rose descriptions, and many interesting and helpful rose growing tips – over 900 varieties, including all of David Austin's unique 'English Rose' introductions. Visit our superb rose gardens in Shropshire with its wonderful display of English Roses, Old Fashioned, Shrub, Climbing and Modern Roses.

To order your catalogue or reserve your roses telephone our Order Line: 01902 376377 quoting ref no. NGS 1

TM

DAVID AUSTIN® ROSES

David Austin Roses Limited
Bowling Green Lane, Albrighton, Wolverhampton WV7 3HB
Telephone: 01902 376377 www: davidaustinroses.com

Australia's Open Garden Scheme

Going to Australia?

Just as Australian gardeners visiting Britain make straight for the Yellow Book, so visitors to Australia should plan their holidays with the help of our guidebook featuring many photographs of our 700 gardens.

Gardening is a consuming passion for many Australians. From the exuberance of tropical Queensland to the cool moist woodlands of Tasmania, from inner-city Sydney to the west coast, our gardens rejoice in a huge diversity of plants and garden styles. Included in our programme are gardens composed largely of Australian plants which will challenge and surprise the European visitor, while other gardens contain a very broad range of more familiar plants in traditional settings.

Visit our finest private gardens and meet the gardeners who created them. *Australia's Open Garden Scheme Guidebook* contains descriptions , dates and directions. It is published each August by ABC Books and is available from ABC Shops, newsagents and all good bookshops throughout Australia. For further information about the Scheme, or to order copies of the guidebook, please contact our office.

an ABC BOOK

President: Mrs Malcolm Fraser

National Executive Officer: Neil Robertson, Westport, New Gisborne, Victoria 3438, Australia Tel +61 (3) 5428 4557 Fax +61 (3) 5428 4558

email: @opengarden.org.au

Australia's Open Garden Scheme Limited A.C.N. 057 467 553

A COMPREHENSIVE LISTING OF OVER 600 NATIONAL PLANT COLLECTIONS® THROUGHOUT THE UNITED KINGDOM

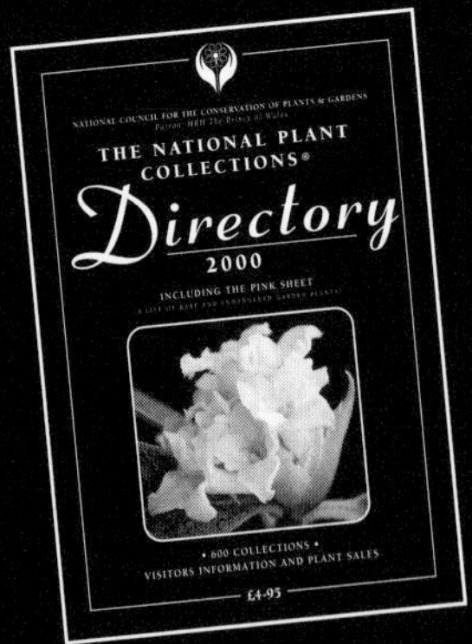

FEATURING

Millennium Edition

The Pink Sheet of Endangered Plants

NCCPG Sales of Rare and Endangered Plants

Together with articles from the Collection Holders themselves

For membership details and NCCPG publications contact NCCPG, The Stable Courtyard, Wisley Garden, Woking, Surrey GU23 6QP or Telephone: 01483 211465 with your credit card details or E-mail: ChrisC@nccpg.org.uk

£6.20 p&p incl (UK) NOW AVAILABLE

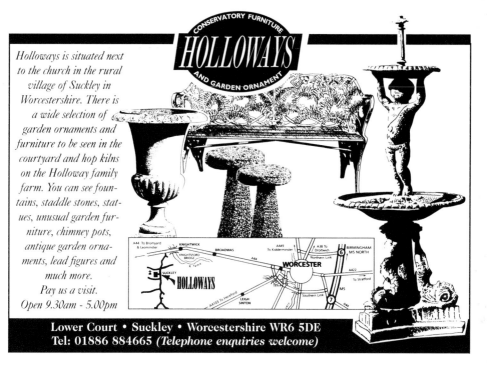

Holloways is situated next to the church in the rural village of Suckley in Worcestershire. There is a wide selection of garden ornaments and furniture to be seen in the courtyard and hop kilns on the Holloway family farm. You can see fountains, staddle stones, statues, unusual garden furniture, chimney pots, antique garden ornaments, lead figures and much more.

Pay us a visit.

Open 9.30am - 5.00pm

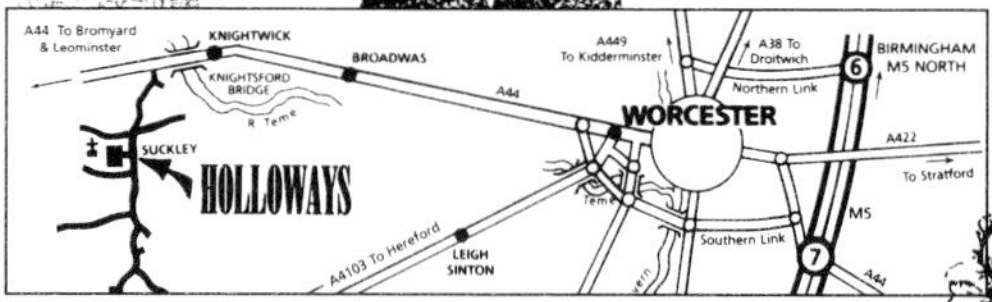

Lower Court • Suckley • Worcestershire WR6 5DE
Tel: 01886 884665 *(Telephone enquiries welcome)*

BETTER VALUE INSURANCE COVER FOR YOUR HOME...

Our specially negotiated homeplan policy gives outstanding value on your home insurance - building, contents, or both. With our discounts you could save up to 40% of your premiums.

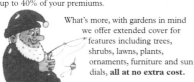

What's more, with gardens in mind we offer extended cover for features including trees, shrubs, lawns, plants, ornaments, furniture and sun dials, **all at no extra cost.**

...AND GARDEN

CALL US NOW FOR A GARDEN HOMEPLAN QUOTE AND WE WILL SEND YOU YOUR OWN GROUND COVER ***FREE!***

01443 205 410

R.V. HILLIER

Established 1978

Registered Insurance Broker, Gwynfa House, Church Village, Pontypridd, Glamorgan CF38 1RN

BAILEYS
ANTIQUE
HORTICULTURE

THE ENGINE SHED
STATION APPROACH
ROSS-ON-WYE
HEREFORDSHIRE
HR9 7BW
01989 563015

The Bay Hotel

COVERACK • CORNWALL
Never heard of it - well we would not expect you to

Quiet, comfortable hotel overlooking lovely bay in uncommercialised fishing village on England's most southerly point - The Lizard Peninsula an area of outstanding natural beauty. Real Cornwall where time has stood still, climate mild and folk friendly. If disco's are not your forte and you want a comfortable, relaxing, quiet break in breath-taking unspoilt scenery with exhilarating walks and the sound of sea live music to your ears, stay with us and let the world pass you by.

It's exclusively for adults!

Quite likely you join many guests in returning every year, there is nowhere quite like it.

SSSH! DON'T TELL EVERYONE
For Brochure:

LES ROUTIERS SILVER KEY AWARD 1998 & 1999

TEL: 01326 280464

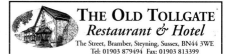

THE OLD TOLLGATE
Restaurant & Hotel

The Street, Bramber, Steyning, Sussex, BN44 3WE
Tel: 01903 879494 Fax: 01903 813399

BORDE HILL, HIGH BEECHES, NYMANS, LEONARDSLEE and PARHAM - to name but a few gardens nearby!

- Situated in a lovely old Sussex village at the foot of the South Downs.
- 31 luxuriously appointed bedrooms, all en-suite. Four posters and suites available.
- Stunning award winning carvery (booking always advisable).
- Ideally placed for garden tours.

Best Western AA ★★★ English Tourism Council ★★★ Silver Award RAC Hotel ★★★

THE LODGE
GARDEN HOTEL & RESTAURANT
TAL Y BONT, CONWY, GWYNEDD, NORTH WALES
LL32 8YX

Telephone: (01492) 660766 / 0800 917 6593
Fax: 01492-660534

Our family run hotel has ten bedrooms and four luxury suites in a rural setting, with lovely gardens - a perfect spot to visit or stay in! 5 miles from Bodnant Gardens with many 'Yellow Book' gardens close by.

Telephone for brochure and terms.
2 day breaks from £85

Curdon Mill **Hotel & Restaurant**

A delightful watermill, beneath the Quantock hills. Set in acres of gardens and farmland. A cosy family hotel where gastronomic delights are created from our garden produce. Do come and stay with us when you visit Rosemoor, Hestercombe and a host more wonderful gardens in the South West

Garden tours can be arranged

VELLOW, STOGUMBER, SOMERSET TA4 4LS
Tel: 01984 656522

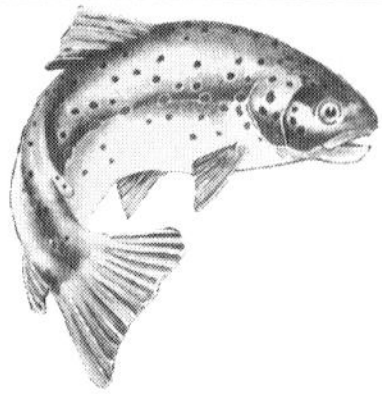

Gliffaes Country House Hotel
Tel: 0800 146719
Email: calls@gliffaeshotel.com

Thirty-three acres of grounds and gardens planted with rare trees and shrubs, many dating from the nineteenth century (see page 430).

A friendly family hotel proud of its delicious food and peaceful atmosphere, romantically situated in the lovely valley of the river Usk, midway between the Black Mountains and the Brecon Beacons.

Comfortable en suite rooms with stunning views.
A superb centre for umpteen activities. Telephone for brochure.
Web site: www.gliffaeshotel.com
We are 1 mile off the A40, 2.5 miles west of Crickhowell.

The Herb Nursery

SPECIALIST GROWERS OF HERBS • WILD FLOWERS • COTTAGE GARDEN PLANTS • SCENTED - LEAF GERANIUMS

Nursery open daily 9am - 6pm (Sorry no mail order)

THISTLETON, OAKHAM, RUTLAND LE15 7RE Tel (01572) 767658

NATIONAL FRUIT TREE SPECIALISTS

Send now for **FREE** extensive top and soft fruit catalogue.

Plant **'Deacons Millenium Apple'** - cost only £15.95 delivered.

DEACONS NURSERY (NGS)

Godshill, Isle of Wight PO38 3HW

(01983) 840750 (24 hrs), **(01983) 522243** or Fax **(01983) 523575**

SEALE NURSERIES

Est. 1948

A wide selection of hardy homegrown plants, shrubs, herbaceous and hedging.

SEALE SUPER ROSES

An extensive collection of scented roses, both classic and modern. Container grown from the start to make large fibrous roots ensuring no winter losses and rapid growth in the spring.

Seale Lane, Seale, Nr Farnham, Surrey GU10

Tel 01252 782410 Contact DAVID MAY

www.sealenurseries.demon.co.uk

TUTTS BARN NURSERY

TREES, SHRUBS, CONIFERS, ROSES, PERENNIALS, ALPINES, HEATHERS, FERNS, BULBS, SEASONAL BEDDING.

Tutts Barn Lane, Eastbourne

(01323) 734064

THE CUCKOO PEN NURSERY &PLANTING CONSULTANCY

We have one of the widest selections of hardy herbacceous perennials to be found anywhere.

We also offer a planting/garden design service.

Open 10am - 5pm daily, April 15th - Oct 31st

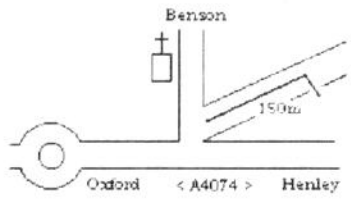

The Alottment,
St. Helens Avenue,
Benson, Oxon.
Tel: 01491 835971

FRUIT FOR THE CONNOISSEUR

IN WIDE VARIETY

Standards, espaliers, cordons, etc;
also other trees and old roses;
climbing roses and evergreens.
Free mail order catalogue from:

FAMILY TREES

Sandy Lane, Shedfield,
Hampshire SO32 2HQ
Tel: 01329 834812

TREHANE NURSERY

Camellias: Leading Specialists with large range of varieties and sizes.

Blueberries: 40 years experience. Quality plants and expert advice.

Also: EVERGREEN AZALEAS, PIERIS, MAGNOLIAS, RHODODENDRONS

Come and visit our peaceful woodland Nursery (spectacular in March and April) or send for our *'Catalogue and Grower's Guide'* with 36-photo full colour pull-out (£1.70 incl. P&P).

Open: Mon-Fri 9.00am-4.30pm. all year (excluding Christmas & New Year) Weekends-Spring only 10.00am-4.00pm

Trehane Nursery Stapehill Road, Hampreston, Wimborne, Dorset BH21 7ND Tel/Fax: 01202 873490

(Next to Knoll Gardens)

APPLE COURT

Specialising in **HOSTAS, DAYLILIES, GRASSES, FERNS,** unususal perennials and foliage plants for flower arrangers.
Good selection of plants for white gardens.
Open March to Sept. 10am-1pm & 2-5pm.
Closed Oct. to Feb. & all day Wednesday. **Mail Order.**
Send 4 x 1st class stamps for descriptive catalogue.

Tel: (01590) 642130 Fax: (01590) 644220

Hordle Lane, Hordle, Lymington, Hampshire SO41 0HU

Charity Specialist Plant Sales

All at superb venues with great plants!

Sun, 16th April (10-4) £2
Compton House, Nr Sherborne

Mon, 24th April (10-4) (BH) £2.50
Mapperton House, Nr Beaminster

Sun, 9th April (10-4) £2
Landford Lodge, Nr Salisbury

Mon, 29th May (10-4) (BH) £2
Milton Lodge, Wells

Further info & groups: 01935 421389

For up to the minute garden visiting information visit The National Gardens Scheme's website www.ngs.org.uk

ENW

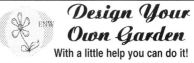

Design Your Own Garden

With a little help you can do it!

Stay with us in the Yorkshire Dales and have fun redesigning your rolling acre or small back yard with an experienced teacher and qualified Garden Designer

Elaine Newington Ward

First time designers welcome
Small groups or individuals

weekend, 3 or 5 day courses throughout the year

01729 824169 or enw@daelnet.co.uk

2 Pendle View, Giggleswick, Settle, North Yorkshire BD24 0AZ

RARE PLANTS FAIR

A feast for plant hunters... special nurseries selling unusual plants

- **Sat 8 April** **The Pavilion, Bath** 11am-4pm. **£2.50**
- **Thur 20 April** **Battersea Town Hall London.** 11am-3pm. **£3**
- **Sat 22 April** **Pittville Pump Room Cheltenham, Glos.** 11am-4pm. **£2.50**
- **Sun 30 April** **Castle Bromwich Hall Gardens.** 11am-5pm. **£3**
- **Sat 13 May** **Aylesbury Vale in Bloom Aylesbury, Bucks.** 11am-4pm. **£2**
- **Sat 20 May** **Cressing Temple, Witham Essex.** 11am-4pm. **£3**
- **Sun 28 May** **Fonmon Castle, Nr Barry Glam.** 11am-5pm. **£2**
- **Sun 4 June** **Painshill Park, Cobham Surrey.** 11am-5pm. **£2**
- **Sun 11 June** **Slimbridge Wildfowl & Wetlands Trust, Glos.** 11am-5pm. **£2**
- **Sun 18 June** **The Old Rectory Burghfield, Nr Reading Berks.** 11am-5pm. **£3**
- **Sun 25 June** **The Manor House Birlingham, Nr Pershore Worcs.** 11am-5pm. **£3**
- **Sun 3 Sept** **Borde Hill Gardens Haywards Heath, West Sussex.** 11am-5pm. **£2.50**
- **Sun 10 Sept** **Wombourne Wodehouse Nr Wolverhampton** 11am-5pm. **£3**
- **Sun 24 Sept** **Royal Free Recreation Club Hampstead.** 12-4pm. **£3**

For detailed brochure call 0117 9562566

SACRED GARDENS

Where Art, Nature & the Spirit meet in the design of beautiful gardens. From courtyard to hillside anywhere in the world.

PAMELA WOODS
(BSc Hons, Dip EGS)

AWARD WINNING LANDSCAPE DESIGNER & PLANTSWOMAN

Tel: 01453 885903
Fax: 01453 885253
www.sacredgardens.co.uk

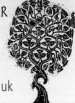

THE HISTORIC HOUSES ASSOCIATION

Become a friend of the HHA

and visit nearly 300 privately-owned houses and gardens for FREE

Benefits of Friends membership

- Visit around 300 privately owned houses and gardens for free.
- Enjoy over 70 glorious gardens, including the winners of the annual HHA / Christie's Garden of the Year Award.
- Receive the HHA quarterly magazine.
- Take advantage of tours in the UK and overseas.
- Join specially arranged visits to houses and gardens, some of which are not usually open to the public.

The HHA Friends Scheme provides amazing value for the interested visitor
Two thirds of Britain's built heritage remains in private ownership - more houses and gardens than The National Trust and English Heritage put together. The HHA helps these owners by representing their interests in Government, and providing practical and technical advice.

For just £28 for an individual or £40 for two people at the same address you can become a Friend of the HHA by calling our membership department on **(01462) 896688.**

THE GARDENERS' ROYAL BENEVOLENT SOCIETY

Each time you visit any of the delightful gardens noted in this book, you are helping the Gardeners' Royal Benevolent Society, a charity devoted to the care of retired and disabled professional gardeners and their partners. As one of the beneficiaries of the National Gardens Scheme, a percentage of the profits come to us for the care of our gardeners.

We also open our own gardens – the Seven Houses in Barton near Cambridge (said to have been modelled on Versailles) and the inimitable York Gate, one of Britain's most celebrated small gardens.

More details of both gardens appear in this book, and we are always delighted to welcome visitors from horticultural societies, gardening clubs or individuals.

The **GRBS** provides its beneficiaries with pensions and grants, and can also provide holidays, accommodation, advice and support. We are always in need of volunteers, donations and legacies to help us continue our work.

The Gardeners' Royal Benevolent Society
Bridge House, 139 Kingston Road,
Leatherhead, Surrey, KT22 7NT
Tel: 01372 373962 Fax: 01372 362575

The GRBS is an exempt charity registered No. 15408R

The Hardy Plant Society

Explores, encourages *and* conserves *all that is best in gardens*

- local groups
- specialist groups
- gardening by post
- conservation
- plant sales
- social & educational events
- shows
- seed distribution scheme
- new plants
- slide library

Membership: £10 single £12.00 two members

The Administrator, Mrs Pam Adams,
Little Orchard, Great Comberton,
Pershore, Worcs WR10 3DP.
Tel: 01386 710317 www.hardy-plant.org.uk

"Since a friend introduced me to Rukba my life has been much less of a worry"

Rukba is unique among charities for the elderly. Our financial help assists people to stay in their own homes, and our beneficiaries do appreciate visits from members of our 1,000 strong force of volunteers. They listen to the problems and offer friendship. If you would like more information about our work, complete the coupon below or telephone

0345 58 56 80

local call rates apply

Please send me more information

Name ______

Address ______

______

postcode ______

Please send to: William Rathbone, Dept NGS, Rukba, FREEPOST, 6 Avonmore Road, London W14 8BR.

The Royal United Kingdom Beneficent Association. Reg. Charity No. 210729

THE ROYAL GARDENERS' ORPHAN FUND

Established 1887

Patron: H.M. Queen Elizabeth the Queen Mother

Allowances or grants of money are made to aid the maintenance and education of children in need, particularly orphans, of professional horticulturists. The allied Constance Spry Fund assists those children whose abilities qualify them for education beyond the normal school leaving age.

The Fund is supported by donations and subscriptions from whatever source we can find - and people who are interested in gardens are our mainstay in this respect.

Please send a donation or subscription now to:

The Secretary, 14 Scholars Mews, Welwyn Garden City, Herts AL8 7JQ
Tel/Fax: 01707 333663

(Registered Charity No 248746)

Are you interested in the history of PARKS, GARDENS AND GARDENING?

Come and join the

GARDEN HISTORY SOCIETY

and discover more about our historic parks and gardens and the latest developments in the conservation of these designed landscapes.

Members receive two journals and three newsletters a year packed with information on garden history, garden restorations, current conservation issues and full details of our membership programme of garden tour at home and abroad, lectures and conferences.

Please contact:
The Director, The Garden History Society
70 Cowcross Street, London EC1M 6EJ.
TEL 0171 608 2409 FAX 0171 490 2974
EMAIL gardenhistorysociety@compuserve.com

GARDENERS' GARDEN TOURS

For The Knowledgeable Gardener

Join us on one of our exclusive tours, exploring some wonderful gardens in the south west of England. Accompanied at all times by a gardening expert you will also be joined by many of the owners, who will happy to answer questions and explain the planning behind the displays.

Each tour includes accommodation in handpicked hotels, chosen for their comfort and atmosphere. All gardens are less than 50 miles from the hotel, so that your time is spent seeing gardens and not travelling.

For more information contact:
Gardeners' Garden Tours, South Knowle, Limers Lane, Northam, Bideford, Devon EX39 2RQ.
Tel: 01237 472891 Fax: 01237 422975
Email: sales@gardenerstours.co.uk
Web site: www.gardenerstours.co.uk

MUSEUM OF GARDEN HISTORY

Fascinating permanent exhibition of the history of gardens, collection of ancient tools, re-creation of 17th century garden displaying flowers and shrubs of the period - the seeds of which may be purchased in the Garden Shop. Also tombs of the Tradescants and Captain Bligh of the 'Bounty'. Lectures, courses, concerts, fairs and art exhibitions held regularly throughout the year.

Knowledgeable staff, a shop selling books and gifts and a cafe offering light refreshments all combine to make a visit both pleasurable and worthwhile.

Open: Mon-Fri 10.30 - 5.00; Sun: 10.30 - 5.00. Closed Sat. Closed from 2nd Sun in Dec to 1st Sun in Mar.

Further information available upon application with sae to:
Dept GEW, **THE MUSEUM OF GARDEN HISTORY**
Lambeth Palace Road, London SE1 7LB
Enquiry telephone line: 0171 401 8865
Internet: http//www.compulink.co.uk/-museumgh

WOMEN'S FARM AND GARDEN ASSOCIATION

YOU
supply the garden
WE
supply the trainee Woman Gardener under our Wrag scheme

Ring for details (01285) 658339

175 Gloucester Street, Cirencester, Glos. GL7 2DP
Registered Charity 212527

H E R B G A R D E N

Foliage, Scented and Herb Plants

Specialist Grower of Herbs, Scented Geraniums.
Display Gardens. Garden talks with lunches and teas can be arranged.
Ranmore Common, Dorking, Surrey Tel & Fax: 01483 282273
Open by appointment Wed. - Sun., April - Sept. 10.00-17.00

Spains Hall, Finchingfield, Essex

Gardens open during 2000
on 21st May, 9th July, 16th July, 23rd July and 30th July
2pm - 5pm

ROUSHAM HOUSE

Rousham, Steeple Aston, Oxfordshire OX6 3QX
Tel: 01869 347110 0r 0860 360407
(C. Cottrell-Dormer Esq.)

Rousham House was built by Sir Robert Dormer in 1635 and the shooting holes were put in the doors while it was a Royalist garrison in the Civil War. Sir Robert's successors were Masters of Ceremonies at Court during eight reigns and employed Court artists and architects to embellish Rousham. The house stands above the River Cherwell one mile from Hopcroft's Holt, near the road from Chipping Norton to Bicester. It contains 150 portraits and other pictures and much fine contemporary furniture. Rooms were decorated by William Kent (1738) and Roberts of Oxford (1765). The garden is Kent's only surviving landscape design with classic buildings, cascades, statues and vistas in thirty acres of hanging woods above the Cherwell. Wonderful herbaceous borders, pigeon house and small parterre. Fine herd of rare Long-Horn cattle in the park. Wear sensible shoes and bring a picnic, and Rousham is yours for the day.

Location: 12m N of Oxford; E of A4260; S of B4030.

Station: Heyford (1m).

Open: Apr-Sept inclusive Wed Sun & Bank Hols 2-4.30pm. Gardens Only every day all year 10-4.30. No children under 15. No dogs. Groups by arrangement on other days.

Admission: House: Adults £3. Garden £3.

IT'S SOMEWHERE YOU'VE DREAMED OF

Come and discover Exbury Gardens, where natural beauty is found at every corner. The world famous displays of rhododendrons, azaleas and camellias form a riot of colour and many rare specimens can be found within the 200 acre grounds. With an excellent plant centre, gift shop and catering facilities to help you enjoy your visit, Exbury is truly a memorable day out!

Open daily 10 am - 5.30 pm (Spring, Summer & Autumn)
Near Beaulieu, 20 minutes from M27 Junction 2
Telephone enquiries: (023) 8089 1203/8089 9422
Website: http://www.exbury.co.uk

EXBURY
GARDENS

Discover *the* beauty

See the ornamental lakes, cascades walled garden, English flower garden or venture further into the surrounding ancient woodlands.

Peace and tranquillity on your doorstep. Why not bring a picnic and relax on this beautiful estate.

- Visitor Centre - Teas, Home-made Fare and Gift Shop open Easter to 31st Oct, 10.30am - 4.30pm weekdays. 10.30 - 6.00pm weekends/Bank holidays. Closed Mondays except Bank holidays
- Winter Walks
- Admission Cars £3

MARKS HALL is just off the A120 (follow the brown signs), north of the picturesque village of Coggeshall

Tel: 01376 563796

The Thomas Phillips Price Trust is a Registered Charity No. 256700

MARKS HALL ESTATE
COGGESHALL ESSEX

FORDE ABBEY AND GARDENS

Alan Titchmarsh described Forde Abbey's 30 acre garden as 'One of the greatest gardens in the West Country'.

Gardens open daily throughout the year 10.00 am to 4.30 pm.
House 1st April - 31st October Sun, Tues, Wed, Thurs and Bank Holidays 1.00 - 4.30 pm.

Signposted from A358 Chard-Axminster and A30 Chard-Crewkerne.

Forde Abbey, Chard, Somerset TA20 4LU
Tel: 01460 221 290
Groups 20+ tel 01460 220 231

A blooming good education starts here

ISIS
Independent Schools Information Service

For the best results of all consider an **Independent fee paying school** offering

- **Nurseries (& Kindergartens) for early development**
- **Tender care throughout**
- **Disciplined growth**
- **Healthy, nurturing environment**
- **all leading to a mature product!**

The Independent Schools Information Service (ISIS) is an important first step in providing you with up to date information about Independent fee paying schools throughout England and Wales.

For a regional ISIS Handbook giving details and information on schools throughout your chosen area call the number below.

London and the Home Counties -
ISIS London & SE on 020 7798 1560

Hampshire, Bristol and the South West -
ISIS S&W on 01736 799250

East Anglia - ISIS East on 01263 741333

The English Midlands -
ISIS Central on 01993 813006

Cheshire and northern English counties -
ISIS North on 01524 735977

Wales - on 01348 874460

The regional handbooks give details of all the ISIS schools in the area. ISIS London & SE has a consultancy service for which there is a fee; consultations with the other regions are free.

Find the artist inside...

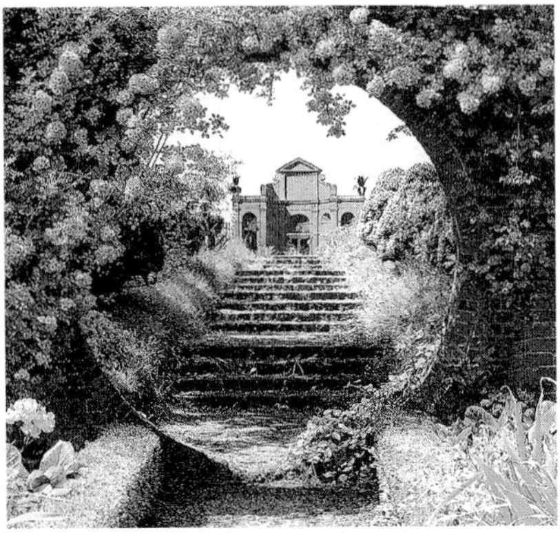

'The Art of Garden Design', is a course for several kinds of people. You may be a keen gardener or a qualified horticulturist well–acquainted with plantmanship and want to know more about the aesthetics and history of garden. You may have a particular wish to develop your ability to design and to communicate your designs to others, or you may be starting from scratch.

Some students see the course as offering Continuing Professional Development (CPD) for them. While the course is primarily intended for amateurs, many have found it valuable as a way of testing their potential for a career in the subject, and some students have achieved exemptions when applying for degree courses. The optional CATS points awarded to first and second levels combined are equivalent to 0.75 of a year of a full-time degree course.

Phone now for your free 'Guide to Courses': Freephone 0800 731 2116 (24hrs).

Open College of the Arts, Houndhill, Worsbrough, Barnsley, South Yorkshire, S70 6TU
Fax: 01226 730 838
Minicom: 01226 205 255
Email: open.arts@ukonline.co.uk
Registered Charity No. 327446
Affiliated to The Open University

OCA – Adventure in the Arts

Open College of the Arts

www.oca-uk.com

A Garden Lover's Paradise in the Heart of Kent

The elegant spa town of Royal Tunbridge Wells is the perfect base for exploring the countless beautiful gardens of Kent.

For further information on gardens and accommodation in the area contact the Royal Tunbridge Wells Tourist Information Centre, Dept GNS2K, The Old Fish Market, The Pantiles, Royal Tunbridge Wells, Kent TN2 5TN or call FREE on 0800 393686
www.tunbridgewells.gov.uk/tourism

GREYCOAT
PLACEMENTS
We have excellent and highly experienced

GARDENERS - ESTATE MANAGERS
BUTLERS - COUPLES - HOUSEKEEPERS
CHAUFFEURS - CLEANERS
COOKS/CHEFS - NANNIES
MATERNITY NURSES
LADY'S MAIDS - MOTHER'S HELP
SECRETARIES - PAs - RECEPTIONISTS

We are pleased to hear from clients looking for a tailor made quality service, in the UK or overseas

GREYCOAT PLACEMENTS
020 7233 9950

33-37 Grosvenor Gardens
London SW1W 0BS
(member of FRES)
www.greycoatsplacements.co.uk
E-mail:
info@greycoatsplacements.co.uk

Take a fresh look at
BLOOMS
• Friendly advice and service
• Huge range of nursery-fresh plants
• Display gardens and inspirational ideas
• Complementary range of garden sundries and gifts
• Full garden design service from border to complete make-over
• Delicious home-made fare
Spring 2000 brings with it stunning new looks and exciting fresh features at all of our Plant Centres. An experience not to be missed.
Planting ideas
Bressingham, Diss, Norfolk IP22 2AB tel 01379 688133
Borde Hill, Haywards Heath, West Sussex RH16 1XP tel 01444 414151
Clandon Park, West Clandon, Nr. Guildford, Surrey GU4 7RQ tel 01483 222925
Dorney Court, Dorney, Windsor SL4 6QP tel 01628 669999
Elton Hall, Elton, Peterborough PE8 6SH tel 01832 280058

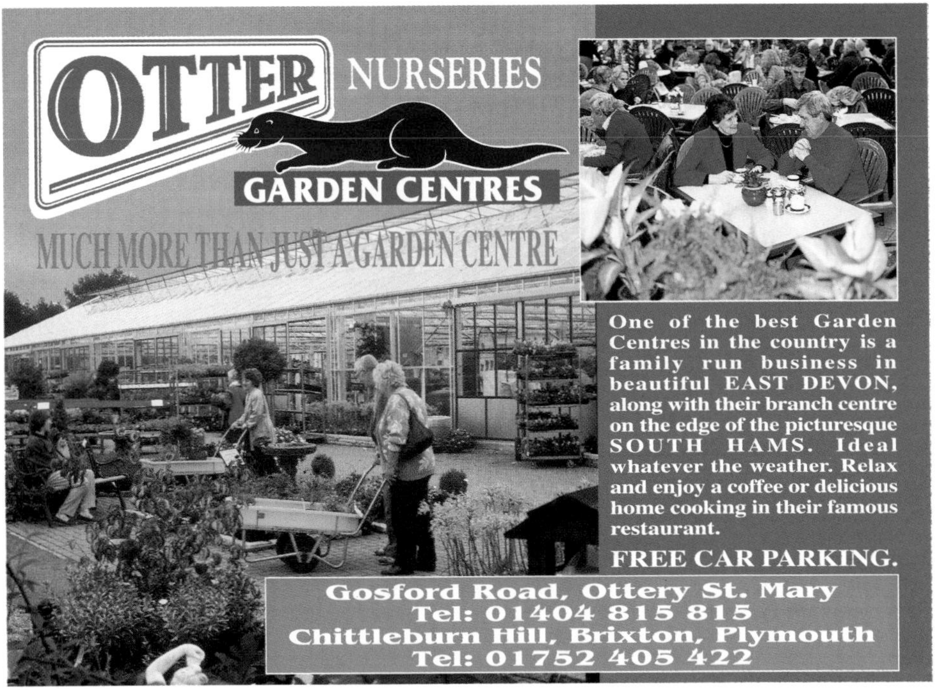

Professionally Designed Garden-Watering Systems

Precise Irrigation UK Ltd

- Full design, supply and installation service. More than 35 NGS gardens have one of our systems.
- We also design systems for DIY from your plans.
- Efficient use of water.
- Automatic/manual control.
- Micro-sprinklers and drippers.
- Night watering.
- Pumps, filters and boreholes.
- Pop-up lawn sprinklers.

Free DIY CATALOGUE AND BROCHURE

(Please send SAE)

Precise Irrigation UK Ltd
Unit 1, The Warehouse, Reading Road, Wantage, Oxon OX12 8HP
Tel 01235 763760 Fax 01235 765467
Technical Helpline Tel 01235 772723

Visit our Website at http://www.preciseirrigation.co.uk/ email: diy@preciseirrigation.co.uk

"Gardened naturally, free from the restrictions of institute, experimenting continuously, and always permitting nature to have its say."

MERRIMENTS GARDENS

HAWKHURST ROAD,
HURST GREEN,
EAST SUSSEX TN19 7RA

**Telephone:
01580 860666**

SITUATED ON THE A229
JUST OFF THE A21 AT
HURST GREEN

ENGLISH COUNTRY GARDENERS

We specialise in the confidential recruitment of full-time professional gardeners for private gardens and estates

Please write or telephone for details to:
English Country Gardeners, Petworth,
West Sussex, GU28 0JP
Tel: 01798 865850 Fax: 01798 865920
e-mail: info@englishcountrygardeners.co.uk
www.englishcountrygardeners.co.uk

FRUIT PRESSES AND CRUSHERS

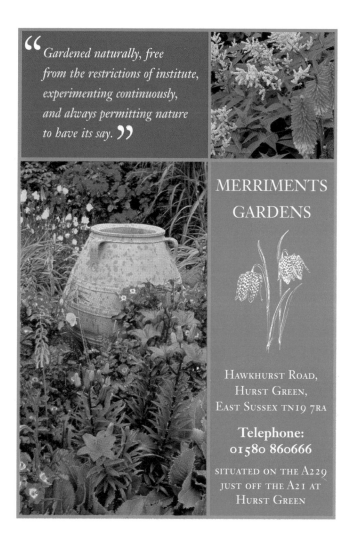

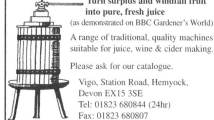

Turn surplus and windfall fruit into pure, fresh juice
(as demonstrated on BBC Gardener's World).

A range of traditional, quality machines suitable for juice, wine & cider making.

Please ask for our catalogue.

Vigo, Station Road, Hemyock,
Devon EX15 3SE
Tel: 01823 680844 (24hr)
Fax: 01823 680807

THE BURFORD GARDEN COMPANY

A unique and beautiful

Garden Department Store

Many plants and trees including 460 different roses and 75 species of Clematis. Expert staff to advise.

Unparalleled choice of fine garden leisure buildings, pergolas, non-slip decking and other wood structures.

Elegant furniture, plants, planters and statuary for conservatories and terraces.

Inspired gift ideas for adults and many other exclusive items.
Fresh flowers and arrangements.

Acclaimed Planters Restaurant for English country cooking.

Open daily throughout the year except on Christmas Day, Boxing Day and Easter Sunday.

Shilton Road, (off the A40) Burford, Oxfordshire. OX18 4PA

BURFORD GARDEN COMPANY

Telephone: 01993 823117/ 823285/ 822502 e.mail: www.bgc.co.uk

– Ask for Hudson's –
The best and most comprehensive annual guide to heritage property in Great Britain and Ireland

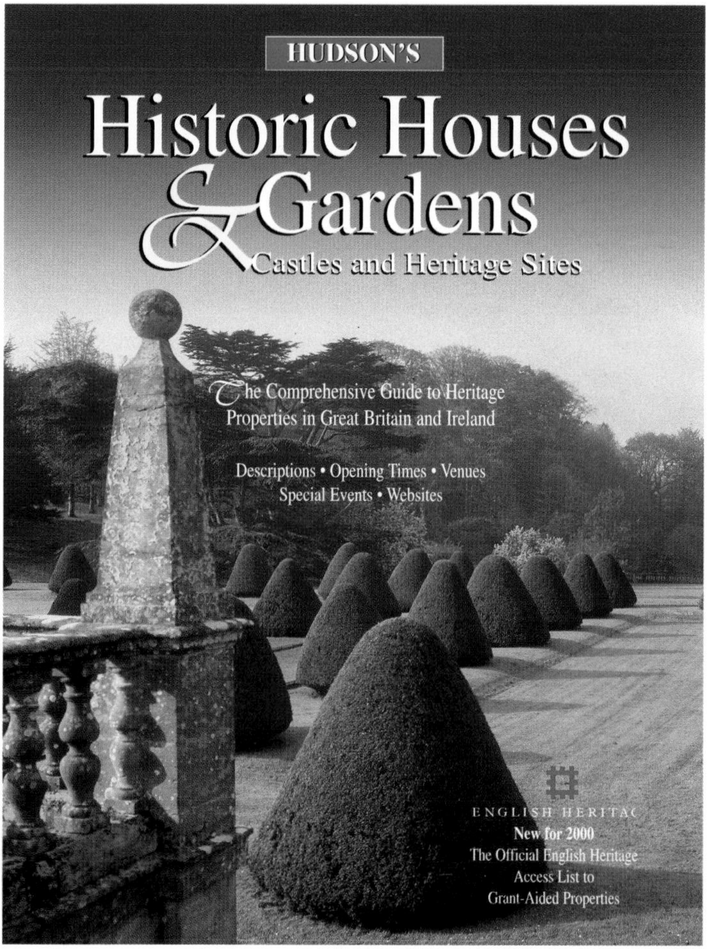

The new 2000 edition has:

- Over 1,000 colour photographs that capture the magic of classic houses and gardens, on over 500 pages.
- National Trust, English Heritage, private, National Trust for Scotland, Historic Scotland and Cadw properties included.

"The 'bible' of the stately house visitor to Britain" – the British Tourist Authority

"Superlative – the best" – Historic Houses Association

Available from good bookshops, at National Trust shops and other properties.

Price: £7.99 • ISBN: 0 9531426 4 7

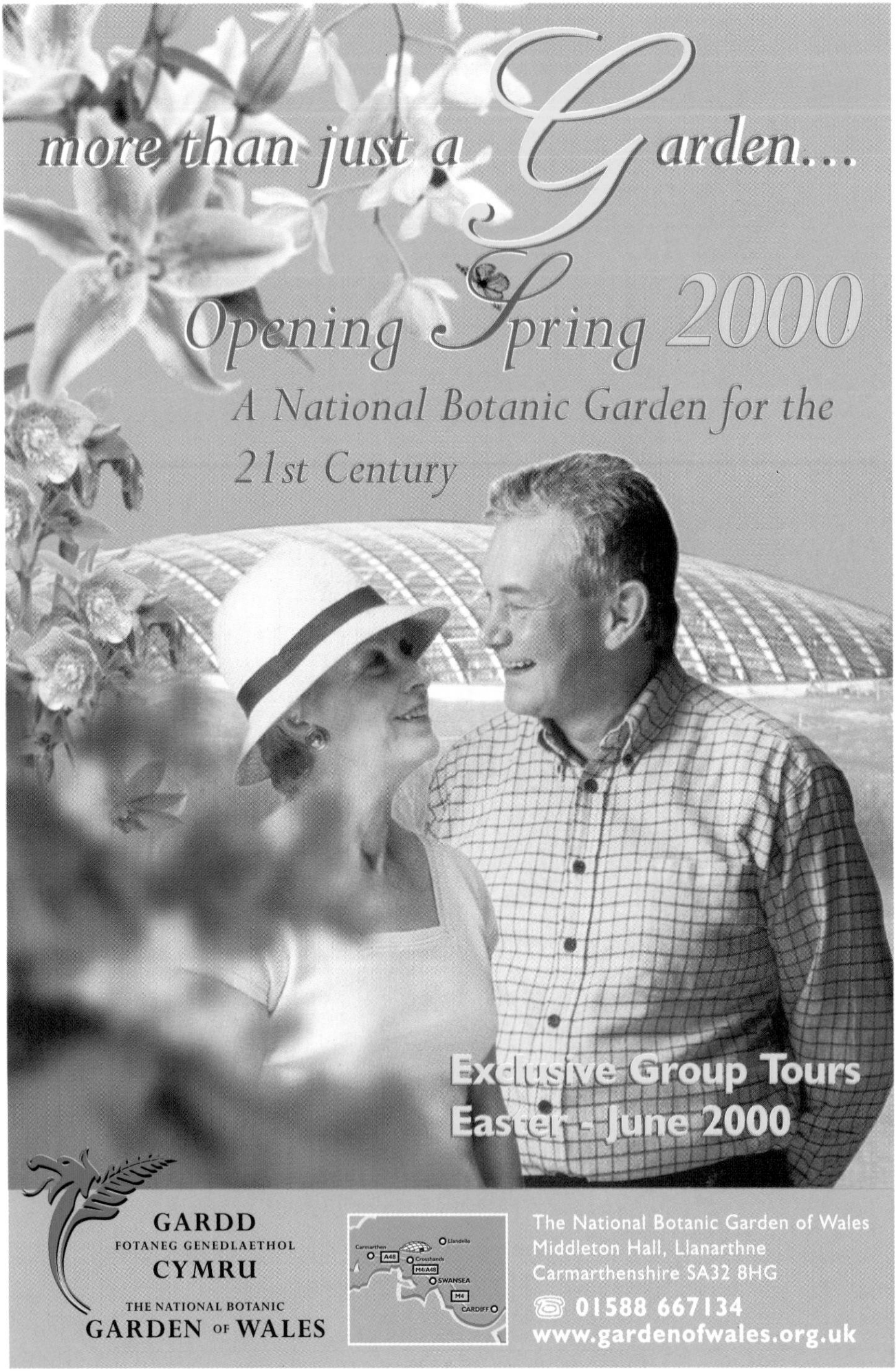
more than just a Garden...
Opening Spring 2000
A National Botanic Garden for the 21st Century
Exclusive Group Tours
Easter - June 2000
GARDD
FOTANEG GENEDLAETHOL
CYMRU
THE NATIONAL BOTANIC
GARDEN OF WALES
Carmarthen
Llandeilo
A48
Crosshands
M4/A48
SWANSEA
M4
CARDIFF
The National Botanic Garden of Wales
Middleton Hall, Llanarthne
Carmarthenshire SA32 8HG
01588 667134
www.gardenofwales.org.uk

Quality Garden Tours 2000

Brightwater Holidays is Britain's leading specialist Garden Tour Operator. Our fully inclusive itineraries combine the famous and grand gardens with the small and private - most tours also visit specialist nurseries.

Tours for 2000 include:

*Tresco and The Abbey Gardens • South Africa's Garden Route • Dutch Bulbfields Cruise • Madeira • **Rome and the Gardens of Ninfa** • Gardens of New Zealand • Gardens of Australia • Italian Lakeland Gardens • West Cork's Garden Trail • **Monet's Garden Château Weekend** • **Springtime in Crete** • Gardens of Andalucia • Princess Sturdza's Le Vasterival • Arts and Gardens of Tuscany • Private Gardens of Dublin • **The Flowers of Argentina** • Wild Flowers of the Alps • **Gardens of California** • Highland and Island Gardens • Arts and Gardens of Cornwall • Gardens of Cheshire & the Tatton Park Flower Show • Autumn Tints of the Cotswolds **plus many, many more***

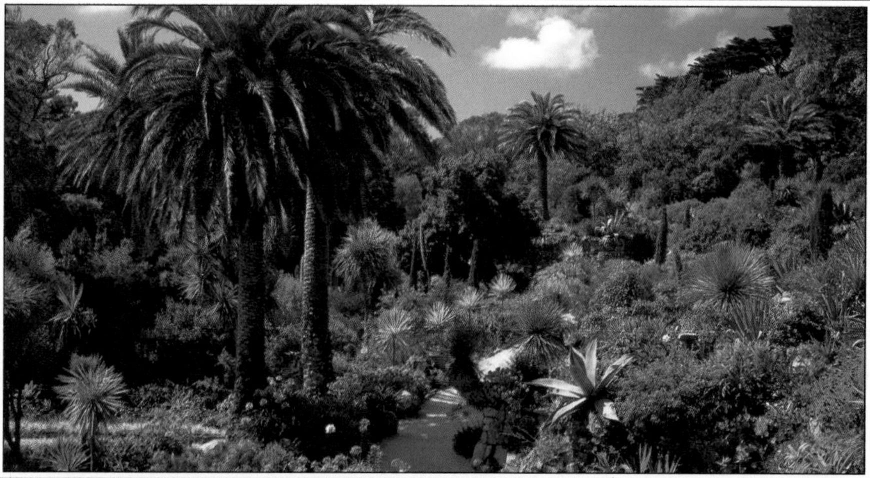

If you have your own group and are looking for a tailor made itinerary we are happy to work to suit your interests and budget.

To obtain full details of these and other garden tours please telephone for a copy of our 2000 brochure: 01334 657 155

BRIGHTWATER HOLIDAYS, Eden Park House, Cupar, Fife KY15 4HS.

Tel: 01334 657155 Fax: 01334 657144

Email: BrightwaterHolidays@ compuserve.com Website: www.brightwaterhols.demon.co.uk

BRIGHTWATER HOLIDAYS

ABTO TRUST ABTOT No. 5001 A fully bonded tour operator

ATOL 4498

HISTORIC HOUSES CASTLES & GARDENS 2000

THE ESSENTIAL REFERENCE GUIDE FOR VISITORS SINCE 1954

Over 2000 places to visit and stay in Great Britain & Ireland including Belgium, France, Germany & The Netherlands

OPENING TIMES • ADMISSION CHARGES • CALENDAR OF EVENTS

ONLY £4.99

a JOHANSENS publication

On sale at all good bookshops or order direct on 0800 269 397

Classical Stone

Classical Stone

Brochure available from:
Classical Stone Ltd
Dobell Barn Swan Street
Wittersham
Kent TN30 6PR

tel: 01797 270152
fax: 01797 270153

Why spend every weekend in the same garden? We have over 200 to choose from.

Discover over 200 different gardens with the National Trust. From rose gardens to kitchen gardens, landscape to water gardens, woodland and orchards, every season holds its own surprises. For a free copy of the National Trust's gardens map guide, please call 020 8315 1111, Monday-Friday 9.30 am-5.30 pm.

The National Trust,
36 Queen Anne's Gate, London SW1H 9AS.
E-mail: traveltrade@ntrust.org.uk
Web Site: www.nationaltrust.org.uk

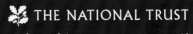

THE NATIONAL TRUST

Where history *never* repeats itsel